Organic Chemistry

Organic Chemistry

NORMAN L. ALLINGER
University of Georgia

MICHAEL P. CAVA
University of Pennsylvania

DON C. DE JONGH
University of Montreal

CARL R. JOHNSON
Wayne State University

NORMAN A. LEBEL
Wayne State University

CALVIN L. STEVENS
Wayne State University

WORTH PUBLISHERS, INC.

Organic Chemistry

Copyright © 1971 by Worth Publishers, Inc.

All rights reserved. No part of this publication
may be reproduced, stored in a retrieval system,
or transmitted in any form or by any means,
electronic, mechanical, photocopying, recording,
or otherwise, without the prior written permission
of the publisher.

Printed in the United States of America

Library of Congress Catalog Card No. 70-143550

ISBN 0-87901-015-0

Designed by Malcolm Grear Designers, Inc.

This book is printed on recycled (60–70 percent
post-consumer waste) paper.

Third printing May 1973

Worth Publishers, Inc.

444 Park Avenue South

New York, New York 10016

PREFACE

As organic chemistry becomes increasingly complex, it is more and more difficult for a single chemist to write authoritatively on all the topics that must be covered in a basic textbook. This book is the result of an effort to solve that problem in a new way. Six chemists currently active in both research and teaching have each written about the areas that they know best. The results have been edited to form a unified presentation, and any remaining differences in emphasis and viewpoint are typical of differences among members of the profession as a whole.

The book is intended for use in a one-year course in organic chemistry. It has been tested in preliminary editions for four years at Wayne State University, and also at Arizona State University and the University of Louisville. The level has been found to be suitable for both chemistry majors and nonmajors at such universities.

In order not to overwhelm the student with material, careful consideration has been given to choosing topics that are of primary importance in organic chemistry now and for the forseeable future. Some traditional subjects have been eliminated; much chemistry, while interesting, is now mainly of historical value. There should be time in a year's course to cover topics such as the chemistry of terpenes, proteins, and sugars, which are important to many students and yet are so far back in most textbooks that they are never reached. Our aim has been to produce a textbook, not an encyclopedia.

The subjects covered fall into three general parts: The first (Chapters 1-13) deals with the structures of organic molecules. The second part (Chapters 14-23) discusses the reactions these structures undergo. The third part (Chapters 24-36) covers the determination of the structures of more complicated compounds, the synthesis of such structures, and the chemistry of natural products.

One reason for dividing organic chemistry in this way is that structures and physical properties can be determined and studied independently of the chemical reactions of molecules. Once the student has mastered the ideas involved in structure, especially electron distribution, he can see why molecules show the chemical behavior they do. When the connections between chemical behavior and structure are clear, the student can realistically attack the synthesis of a complicated structure, as well as the determination of the structure of a complex molecule, employing both physical and chemical methods.

A few additional features require comment:

☐ The reactions of alkanes come late (Chapter 25), in keeping with the relative importance of such reactions in the laboratory.

☐ Compounds are covered first with respect to structure, again with respect to reactions, and once again with respect to synthesis (Chapter 24). In most current texts the topic of synthesis is given a cursory treatment. When synthesis is mentioned only in passing in chapters on reactions of classes of compounds, it is easy for the student to forget about one class while studying another. By studying synthesis repeatedly in increasing detail, most students find it easier to retain what they have learned.

☐ Most of the reaction chapters contain summaries of synthetic methods arranged for easy reference (for example, see page 339).

☐ A more advanced chapter on synthesis is given (Chapter 34) for the instructor who wishes to orient his class that way, and for reference.

☐ Finally, we have included a chapter on industrial chemistry (Chapter 35), because we feel the usual practice of mixing together laboratory and industrial chemistry confuses many students. The industrial chapter will be important to some students (engineers for example) and not to others (such as pre-medical students), and the instructor may use it as he sees fit.

Advanced material that may be of interest to the inquisitive student but is *not* intended to be covered in lecture is set off by a slightly smaller type face and a vertical rule to the left. None of this advanced material is used as a basis for later discussion, except in other sections of advanced material. Interesting sidelights and historical notes are set off from the regular text by italic type. Students may read these in passing but need not study them.

It is important throughout the course to study models of the compounds under discussion. We have pointed out in the text where models will be most useful to a student. Photographs and perspective drawings are included, but this is no substitute for actually handling a model.

Short exercises, to emphasize particular points, are interspersed throughout the text. It is recommended that these be answered by the student when he comes upon them. Answers to most of these exercises are included at the end of the book. Many longer problems are given at the ends of chapters. These problems come in approximately the same order as the corresponding topics within the chapter.

It has been our experience that if the lecture course begins one quarter or semester before the laboratory course, the students are able to utilize their laboratory time with high efficiency right from the start. Whether this is done or not, the instructor will find that the method of presentation used here has some pronounced advantages as far as coordination with the laboratory is concerned. Traditionally, the structures and reactions of the compounds being studied are covered concurrently, one class at a time. This means that those functional groups that come near the end in the sequence (usually amines, carbonyl compounds, or other important classes as far as laboratory work is concerned) are unknown to the student. He is thus faced with the problem of running reactions on these unfamiliar compounds to convert them to other compounds that are unknown to him, by reactions that are also unknown. The casual introduction of so much new material in the laboratory invariably has an unsettling effect on the student.

Our approach, on the other hand, covers the nomenclature, structural features, and electron distributions of the common kinds of functional groups in the first one-fourth of the book. Thus, when the student sees a reaction, say of hydroxylamine with cyclohexanone to form an oxime, it does not surprise him that the reaction proceeds as it does, since he already knows that hydroxylamine is a Lewis base, cyclohexanone is a Lewis acid, and water is a very stable molecule. Experience has shown that it is far easier for the student to grasp material presented in this way, than when neither the starting material, nor the product, nor the nomenclature, nor the reaction itself have been part of his previous experience.

The authors are greatly indebted to many reviewers for their contributions and counsel. We particularly would like to thank Professors K. Grant Taylor, John L. Wong, and Harold Klingele at the University of Louisville, and Professors Morton Munk and George Yuen at Arizona State University, for their extensive class testing of the preliminary manuscript, and Professors Peter A. S. Smith and Clayton Heathcock for critically reading the entire manuscript. We very much appreciate the contributions of Professor Harmon McAllister to the chapter on amino acids and proteins, and of Dr. Arthur Ashe and Dr. Leonard Miller to the chapter on industrial chemistry. We thank Professors K. Andersen, D. Applequist, R. Bach, W. Bailey, W. Barnett, H. Baumgarten, O. T. Benfey, R. E. Dickerson, J. T. Edsall, R. A. Ford, P. G. Gassman, M. Goodman, G. Handler, G. K. Helmkamp, E. T. Kaiser, J. Keiser, A. J. Kresge, N. J. Leonard, A. Liberles, J. Meinwald, B. Rickborn, P. von R. Schleyer, E. N. Trachtenberg, N. J. Turro, and many other friends for their constructive criticism. And, finally, our thanks to the many secretaries who typed, to the teaching assistants who taught, and to the students who learned, or at least studied, from the preliminary versions of the manuscript. We also would like to acknowledge the kindness of Varian Associates and of Merck and Company for some of the spectra used in text.

April, 1971

NORMAN L. ALLINGER
MICHAEL P. CAVA
DON C. DE JONGH
CARL R. JOHNSON
NORMAN A. LEBEL
CALVIN L. STEVENS

TO THE STUDENT

When you undertake the study of an unfamiliar subject, there are a number of questions you inevitably ask. What is this subject all about? How does it relate to things I already know? How useful will it be to me in my future studies? How useful will it be in my chosen profession?

We will try to give some brief answers to these questions.

Organic chemistry is that portion of chemistry which deals with the compounds of carbon. The chemistry of living systems is largely organic chemistry. The relationship between organic chemistry and some of the other physical and biological sciences is shown by their order in the following list:

Mathematics
Physics
Physical chemistry and chemical physics
Organic chemistry
Biochemistry
Biology
Medicine

Organic chemistry is in the middle of the range from mathematics, which is highly abstract, to medicine, which is practical and applied. Although organic chemistry is based on a very large body of sound theory, there is still much we do not know, and current advances in the subject are often made by the empirical approach (the "let's try and see" method), based on educated guesses.

Each area of science in the list above is important as a basis for the one below it. Thus the basis of organic chemistry lies largely in the fields of mathematics, physics, and physical chemistry. We will have to make some use of these subjects in developing the theory of organic chemistry. However, we will explore them only to show how some of their principles are applied in organic chemistry. Just as some knowledge of physical chemistry is important for understanding organic chemistry, so is organic chemistry a basis for biochemistry, and, although more distantly related, a basis for biology and medicine.

Is this going to be a difficult course? Organic chemistry is usually regarded by students as a challenging course. A considerable amount of reading and study are required. It will be necessary to memorize quite a lot of material, and above all, to apply your ability to reason in order to solve problems of widely varying types.

Organic chemistry is like a pyramid turned upside down and standing on its point. There are a few basic facts at the bottom; once these are understood, more facts may be piled on top of them. This gives us a broader base to work with, on which we may build still more, and so on. Thus, as our study of the subject proceeds, we will refer constantly to material previously discussed. It is not possible to learn the material in one chapter, take an examination, and forget it. This would amount to chopping away the point on which the pyramid stands. Rather, everything new builds on what has gone before. Anything left unlearned at the beginning of the course is a hole into which something on top is later going to collapse. Therefore, it is vital that you keep up with the progress of the course and understand all of the essential material as you proceed through the text.

We have presented in the main text material which the authors collectively believe is important. Material which the authors feel is interesting, but not of fundamental importance, is included in italics and set off from the main text. Intriguing sidelights and historical notes are presented in this manner. These are things which we hope you will enjoy reading, but they need not be studied and learned. In addition, advanced material is contained in small-print sections marked with a vertical line at the left. These advanced sections are for the inquisitive student and for reference, but they can be skipped unless your instructor specifically designates otherwise.

Organic chemistry as it is covered in this book can be divided into three general categories: (1) structure (Chapters 1-13); (2) reactions (Chapters 14-23); and (3) applications (Chapters 24-36).

By *structure*, we mean the three-dimensional geometries of molecules; the way the atoms are put together; the physical properties, including spectra, which depend upon the structure and give us information about it; and the electron distribution in molecules. There are only about a dozen important classes of organic compounds, depending on how one counts, and perhaps another dozen less important classes. We will study the structures of all of these types in more or less detail as their importance warrants.

The chemical *reactions* which organic molecules undergo are in large part predictable, or at least reasonable, once the electronic structures of the molecules are understood. Reagents carrying a positive charge tend to attack a molecule at the point of high electron density, while reagents carrying a negative charge tend to attack a molecule at a point where the electron density is low. The transformation of one compound into another depends in part on thermodynamics—the ability of the reacting system to reach a more stable configuration—and in part upon kinetics—the rate at which the process takes place. Again, depending upon how one classifies, there are perhaps a dozen principal types of organic reactions and a whole host of subtypes that are rather easy to rationalize once the basic types are understood.

The third part of the text we have called *applications*. This is a discussion of the things most organic chemists are doing or thinking about as they go about their work. This section can be divided into three broad categories: (1) structure determination; (2) synthesis; and (3) topics largely concerned with the organic compounds found in nature. The material in this part of the text presupposes a good working knowledge of the first two parts.

The work of most organic chemists is concerned directly or indirectly with two principal activities: structure determination and synthesis. Approximately three million organic compounds have been isolated and characterized; their structures are now accurately known. New ones are being isolated daily, many from studies of natural sources and living things, some from industrial processes, and others from laboratory studies. Some of these compounds have properties which make them desirable for a particular use; others are toxic or otherwise harmful, and still others just intellectually intriguing. To understand why a compound has a certain physiological or chemical effect, one first must know what the compound is—one must know its *structure*.

Of the three million known organic compounds, only about two thousand are available commercially in pure form. If the chemist wants any one of the other three million, or any of the infinite number of possible compounds so far unknown, he is going to have to make it from something that is available—in other words, he must *synthesize* it.

To determine the structures of compounds and to synthesize compounds, the organic chemist has to utilize all his knowledge of the elements of structure and reactions that are discussed in the first two parts of this text. The last third of the book is primarily concerned with applications of the material covered in the first two parts.

Hundreds of items that pass through everyone's hands every day have been improved and changed by organic chemistry. To pursue the improvement of our environment, the interaction of organic chemicals in the air and water must be understood. We believe you will find that organic chemistry will aid you not only in your profession, but in living intelligently in the modern world.

NORMAN L. ALLINGER
MICHAEL P. CAVA
DON C. DE JONGH
CARL R. JOHNSON
NORMAN A. LEBEL
CALVIN L. STEVENS

CONTENTS

CHAPTER 8   **Functional Groups Containing Oxygen Multiply Bonded to Carbon: The Carbonyl Group**

CHAPTER 9   **Infrared Spectroscopy**

CHAPTER 10   **Other Functional Groups Containing Multiply Bonded Heteroatoms**

CHAPTER 1

INTRODUCTION

1.1   The First Organic Molecules

If we wish to begin at the beginning, we must go back about three billion years to the time when life first took hold on earth. The young earth had all the right conditions for life as we know it: a stable temperature, neither too hot nor too cold; abundant energy from the sun; sufficient mass to hold an atmosphere; and the few ingredients from which all living things are formed—carbon, hydrogen, oxygen, and nitrogen. These four elements make up 98 percent of all living tissue. This is rather curious, since the most abundant elements in the earth's crust are oxygen, silicon, and a number of light metals. The elements which make up the bulk of the known organic compounds, with the exception of oxygen, are trace elements which occur to the extent of 1 % or less in the earth's crust.

How did life get started? How did complex carbon compounds develop from those simple atoms and molecules available when our planet was just one and a half billion years old? In 1923, A. I. Oparin,† a Russian chemist,†† suggested that the first organic molecules, the "precursors" of life, arose in a world that contained little or no free oxygen. Water vapor was in the atmosphere, as well as carbon dioxide, nitrogen, ammonia (NH_3), and methane (CH_4). The sun beat down, clouds formed, lightning flashed, the rains fell. Radioactive substances within the earth decayed, adding their energy to the crucible. According to Oparin, it was out of this chaos that the first complex organic molecules were formed and life got its chance. The simple gases broke apart and their components reformed in more complex ways.

During the 1950s, Stanley Miller††† ran some experiments that tested Oparin's ideas. In his laboratory apparatus at the University of Chicago, Miller arranged methane, ammonia, water, and hydrogen to form an atmosphere similar to that which, according to Oparin, must have surrounded the primitive earth. When Miller discharged a spark into these gases to simulate lightning, he found that, among other organic molecules, amino acids were formed. This result is striking because all proteins, major components of living things, are made by the linking together of amino acids.††††

The simple organic compounds which formed over a long period of time would have dissolved in the primitive ocean, which gradually became enriched with a large variety of organic materials. It is not yet known just how these first organic molecules evolved to form living cells. With the passage of time the intricate system somehow developed by which molecular aggregates could grow and divide into two identical parts in an

---

† Aleksandr I. Oparin. Born 1894. USSR Academy of Science, Moscow.
†† Short biographies will be presented at appropriate places in the text to give the student a little historical and geographic perspective. The authors have tried to select for this purpose biographies of those chemists whose contributions are of particular importance in the specific area under discussion.
††† Stanley L. Miller. Born 1930, Oakland, California. University of California, San Diego.
†††† Proteins are complicated molecules which have a variety of functions in living systems. Some of them are *enzymes*, which are catalysts for various reactions which take place in living systems. Without enzymes life as we know it would not be possible.

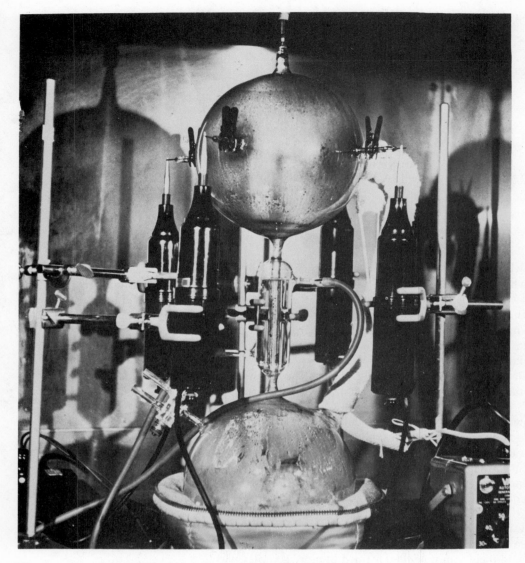

The apparatus which Miller used to simulate the conditions believed to exist on the primeval earth. Methane and ammonia are continuously circulated between the heated lower flask (the "ocean") and the upper flask (the "atmosphere") through which an electric discharge is transmitted. (From Cyril Ponnamperuma.)

orderly way, thus reproducing themselves. One thing is clear: throughout this process of evolution, in collaboration with water and sunlight and a few other elements, the carbon atom has played, and still plays, a central role.

1.2   Why Carbon?

Carbon is the core element around which the chemistry of life has evolved. For example, proteins, just one kind of carbon compound, have developed an astonishing diversity of shapes and function in the course of evolution. These are very complicated molecules with molecular weights that run from many thousands up into the millions. Complete structures are known for only about 50 proteins, and only recently has it been possible to synthesize a simple one by chemical methods. The variety of proteins now at work in living systems is staggering. Using the same 20 amino acids as building blocks, each species on earth has developed its own special set of proteins. Even the physiologically simple bacterium, *Escherichia coli*, contains about 5000 different chemical compounds, about 3000 of which are proteins, each different from the others. Man contains about 5 million separate kinds of proteins, all of which are different from those found in *E. coli* or in any other organism. When you consider the multitude of species now on earth, the variety of proteins is truly amazing. Biologists set the number of living species at about 1,200,000. This means something like 10^{12} different kinds of proteins must be taking a part in life processes on the surface of the earth today. And carbon provides the backbone for this fantastic molecular diversity.

Why is carbon so well suited to life processes? Why not one of the other 100-odd elements? The answers are to be found through an examination of the atomic structure of carbon, for it is this structure that allows carbon to form a greater variety of compounds than any other element. Carbon has four electrons in its outer shell. Each of these can be shared with those other elements that are able to complete their electronic shells

The earth, as photographed from the moon. (From National Aeronautics and Space Administration.)

by sharing electrons to form covalent bonds. (In Chapter 2, we shall discuss covalent bonding in greater detail.) Nitrogen, hydrogen, and oxygen are among the elements that can bond to carbon in this way. A single carbon atom can share a maximum of four electron pairs to yield such compounds as methane:

$$
\begin{array}{c}
\mathrm{H} \\
| \\
\mathrm{H-C-H} \\
| \\
\mathrm{H}
\end{array}
$$

But the carbon atom's most distinctive feature, the feature that separates it from all other elements (except silicon) and that accounts for its fundamental role in the origin and evolution of life, is its ability to share electron pairs with other carbon atoms to form covalent carbon–carbon bonds. This single phenomenon provides the foundation for organic chemistry. It allows formation of vast arrays of linear, branched, cyclic, and cagelike carbon–carbon structures studded with hydrogen, oxygen, nitrogen, and other atoms capable of covalent bonding. Only those few elements containing four electrons in their outer shell are able to form strong repetitive covalent bonds with atoms of the same element. Of these, silicon is the only element, besides carbon, that can form such bonds with itself in a relatively stable way. But silicon–silicon compounds do not stand up in the oxygen-laden atmosphere on earth. They oxidize to form silica (SiO_2), the main ingredient in sand and quartz, but not the sort of material capable of sustaining life. So, at least on earth, carbon alone is able to provide a backbone for the molecular components of living things.

The eagle is a victim of DDT poisoning for a complicated reason. DDT causes the bird's liver to produce enzymes that break down the female hormones which are used to mobilize calcium at the time of egg production. The birds therefore very often produce thin-shelled eggs which crack or break easily, like the egg shown here. The eaglet and the egg (which never hatched) were photographed in a nest near the Muskegon River in Michigan. It is estimated that more than a million pounds of DDT are circulating in the ecosystem at the present time. Even if the use of chlorinated hydrocarbons were discontinued immediately, their effects would be felt for many years to come. (From Michigan Department of Natural Resources.)

1.3   Carbon Chemistry and the Planet Earth

It has taken about 4.5 billion years of sunlight and carbon compounds to form all present life on earth. Man, a newcomer, has walked this small planet for only a few million years; and in the space of just 100 years he has learned to turn carbon compounds into medicines, fuels, and fabrics on a massive scale.

Until recently, our ability to work these industrial transformations with organic molecules was thought to be an undiluted virtue that gave man and his machines power over the environment. We have wonder drugs, fantastic fibers, miracle detergents, super fuels. We have aspirin, birth-control pills, plastic toys, Pepsi's, and enough food for most people most of the time.

And now we have foul air. Fish are dying in lakes and streams that we no longer dare to swim in. The seas' beaches, even the seas themselves, are threatened by a killing combination of crude oil and industrial waste. The U.S. Food and Drug Administration reports that over 500,000 kinds of new synthetic molecules, carried by the great rivers of the world, find their way to the sea each year. The lead from gasoline is now found amid the distant snows of polar regions. The body fat of antarctic seals and penguins is contaminated by DDT.

The DDT problem is worthy of further comment. This single chemical has controlled the world's insect population to the point where the earth now produces enough food to feed its human population. We have not gotten off scot-free, however, as the DDT levels have now reached harmful proportions. While we could cease using DDT (and let a large fraction of the human population starve), better long-range solutions are clearly needed.

Obviously the organic chemical industry has changed our world for better *and* for worse. Pollution and overpopulation are serious problems, and they are getting more serious. These problems are both scientific and political. The scientific part is soluble, but it will be expensive. The political part is less clear. It is a question of how to utilize our resources—a question of priorities. As beginning students of organic chemistry you might do well to keep these problems in mind. Many of you will probably become

("Air Pollution," Pack, D. H., *Science*, Vol. 146, Cover Photo, 27 November 1964. Copyright 1964 by the American Association for the Advancement of Science.)

biologists, physicians, teachers, or research chemists. From these, and other such positions, you may have a chance to solve some of the problems that others before you have helped create. The quality of life, perhaps life itself, depends upon our tidying up the earth. Those who have some knowledge of organic chemistry will have an opportunity and an obligation to work at this task. We hope you will take part.

CHAPTER 2

THE STRUCTURAL THEORY

2.1   The Early Days of Organic Chemistry

Prehistoric peoples made use of the properties of some organic compounds, and they carried out a few organic chemical reactions. The ancient Egyptians, Romans, and Phoenicians employed a number of dyes which were pure chemical compounds: indigo, alizarin, and the legendary Tyrian purple. The first two dyes were isolated from plants, and the latter was obtained in minute quantities from a rare species of mollusk.

The conversion of animal fat into soap by treatment with lye has been known since ancient times. Only as recently as 1948 were organic chemists finally able to synthesize products (detergents) which could compete commercially with soap.

The fermentation of starch and sugars to yield alcohol has also been known since prehistoric times, and it is used almost without change today.

Organic chemistry as we know it today had its beginnings in the latter part of the eighteenth century, when a determined effort was first made to isolate pure organic compounds, as opposed to extracts. During the period from 1769 to 1786, the German-born Carl Scheele, who lived and worked in Sweden as an apothecary, isolated a number of pure organic compounds from natural sources, and he carried out some studies of their chemistry.

In 1784 Antoine Lavoisier† devised a method (discussed in Section 2.2) for burning a sample of an organic compound and of collecting and analyzing the combustion products. Although his procedures were of limited accuracy, he was able to deduce that the great bulk of organic compounds were made up of various combinations of the same small group of elements: C, H, O, and N.

In 1807, the Swedish chemist Berzelius,†† was the first to describe substances derived from once living materials as *organic compounds*; compounds derived from *organized* systems. Berzelius and other chemists of his time felt that organic compounds contained a "vital force" in addition to their chemical elements, and that it would no more be possible to synthesize an organic compound from the elements than it would be to convert inorganic material into a living creature. However, the popularity of this "vital force" theory of organic compounds declined as it became increasingly clear from accumulating analytical evidence that the usual chemical laws which governed the behavior of inorganic materials, such as the law of multiple proportions, held also for organic compounds. The vital force theory was dealt a severe blow in 1828 when Wöhler††† discovered that evaporation of an aqueous solution of the inorganic salt *ammonium cyanate* results in the production of *urea* identical with the natural product. This was the synthesis of a typical organic compound from a typical inorganic salt without the intervention of a living organism.

---

† Antoine Lavoisier. Born Paris, 1743. Guillotined during the French Revolution in 1794.
†† Joens J. F. von Berzelius. 1779–1848. Stockholm.
††† Friedrich Wöhler, 1800–1882; born Strasbourg; University of Göttingen.

In 1837, Liebig† wrote, "the extraordinary and to some extent inexplicable production of urea without the assistance of vital functions, for which we are indebted to Wöhler, must be considered one of the discoveries with which a new era in science has commenced." The following year, Wöhler and Liebig in a joint paper on uric acid drew the conclusion that all organic compounds would be capable of preparation: "...the philosophy of chemistry will draw the conclusion that the production of all organic compounds, as long as they are not a part of an organism, must be seen not as merely probable but as certain."

During the years 1811–1831 better methods of analysis were developed, mainly by Gay-Lussac, Thenard, and Dumas in Paris; Berzelius in Stockholm; and Liebig in Giessen, Germany. Chemists learned how to determine not only which elements a compound contained, but in what proportions the elements were present. Analytical methods and their application are discussed further in Section 2.2.

By the middle of the nineteenth century both the analytical methods for the determination of the elements and radicals present in an organic compound and the synthetic methods for preparing a compound from simpler materials were moderately well developed, but there was one aspect of organic chemistry which had resisted the efforts of many able minds. This aspect concerned the *structures* of organic compounds. It was known, for example, that ethyl alcohol and dimethyl ether both have the same formula (C_2H_6O), but the former is a beverage constituent, a liquid boiling at 78°C, and the latter is a gas. Since each of these two compounds contains the same number and the same kinds of atoms, the difference between them, and between many other similar sets of compounds then known, was clearly due to the way in which the atoms were put together, that is, the structures of the molecules. The dilemma can be appreciated by looking at the correct structures for these two compounds.

Ethyl alcohol
C_2H_6O

Dimethyl ether
C_2H_6O

The chemists at that time faced an exceedingly difficult problem. They wished to understand the structures of organic molecules, but the only means they had for investigating these structures were chemical reactions which led to changes in structure which were themselves unknown. The paths that were followed were tortuous indeed. A considerable amount of effort was expended by a number of brilliant men: Frankland at Manchester, Berzelius, Dumas, and several others contributed significantly to the concepts of molecular structure. Finally, in 1858 two men, Kekulé†† at Heidelberg, and Couper at the Sorbonne in Paris, independently introduced the general rules of valence bonds and the pictorial representation of a molecule as a group of connected atoms. They also specified rules describing how the connections occur; these are discussed in Section 2.3.

2.2   Chemical Analysis and Molecular Formulas

The combustion method developed by Lavoisier was capable of telling whether or not carbon and hydrogen were present, and of giving a rough idea of the amount of each, but it was not accurate enough for more detailed studies on organic compounds. A method for bringing about the combustion in a controlled way was devised by Liebig in 1831. It made use of the already known fact that organic vapors are efficiently and smoothly

---

† Justus von Liebig. 1803–1873. Born Darmstadt, Germany. Universities of Giessen and Munich.
†† Friedrich August Kekulé. 1829–1896. Born Darmstadt, Germany. Universities of Ghent (Belgium), Heidelberg, and Bonn.

burned upon contact with red-hot copper oxide, as the following equations illustrate:

$$CH_4 + 4CuO \rightarrow CO_2 + 2H_2O + 4Cu$$
$$C_2H_6O + 6CuO \rightarrow 2CO_2 + 3H_2O + 6Cu$$

By this method chemists could determine accurately the percentage of each element present in an organic compound.

Figure 2.1
A schematic representation of the apparatus used for carbon–hydrogen analysis.

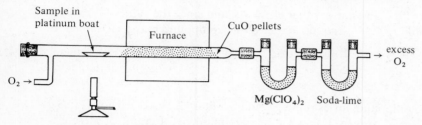

Liebig's Method. Figure 2.1 is a diagram of the combustion apparatus for Liebig's method. The sample to be burned is vaporized, and the vapor is passed through a tube packed with hot copper oxide, using a stream of oxygen as a carrier gas. The organic material is oxidized by the copper oxide, and the oxygen stream reoxidizes the copper to copper oxide. The carrier gas sweeps the water and carbon dioxide that are formed out of the system. This gas stream is passed first through a tube containing a drying agent (usually magnesium perchlorate) and then through a soda-lime tube. The initial sample, the drying tube, and the soda-lime tube are each weighed before the combustion. As the gas sweeps through the drying tube, the water produced in the reaction is absorbed by the drying agent. The gas then sweeps through the soda-lime tube, in which the carbon dioxide is absorbed and converted to carbonate. After the combustion is complete, the absorption tubes are again weighed. From the increase in weight of the drying tube, the amount of water produced in the combustion is found. From the increase in weight in the soda-lime tube, the amount of carbon dioxide produced is similarly found.

On the basis of the known amount of carbon dioxide and water produced by the combustion, and the known amount of sample which was initially burned, one can calculate the percentage of carbon and hydrogen present in the original sample. The calculation is carried out as in the following example. Using the atomic weights $H = 1.008$, $C = 12.01$, and $O = 16.000$, the weight of hydrogen in the sample is equal to the weight of water produced times the fraction of the water that is hydrogen:

$$g \text{ of } H = g \text{ of } H_2O \times \frac{2.016}{18.016} \frac{g (H)}{\text{mole } (H_2O)}$$

$$\text{percent } H = \frac{gH}{g \text{ sample}} \times 100$$

$$gC = g \, CO_2 \times \frac{12.01}{44.01} \frac{g (C)}{\text{mole } (CO_2)}$$

$$\text{percent } C = \frac{g \, C}{g \text{ sample}} \times 100$$

The analysis does not give directly the percentage of oxygen in the compound. But we can assume that any percentage of the sample which is not carbon or hydrogen, and which is known (from other preliminary tests) not to be any other element, is oxygen.

In the time of Liebig, organic chemists did their own combustion analyses, and it was most important for them to understand the exact experimental details of the combustion because the accuracy obtained from the analysis is reflected in the amount of care taken in the experiment. At the present time an organic chemist hardly ever carries out his own analyses. This area of work has now been taken over by a group of specialists. Given a sample of an organic compound, they will furnish the chemist with the percentage of each element in the sample. What is still important to the average chemist is that he be able to deduce the formula for the compound being studied from the percentage composition.

How do we calculate the formula of a compound once the percentage composition is known?

As an example we will take a combustion analysis of methyl ether (a gas). Let us assume that the following experimental values were found:

> 52.24% carbon
> 13.05% hydrogen

Qualitative tests showed the absence of other elements, and since the values for carbon and hydrogen do not add to 100%, the remainder of the compound may be assumed to be oxygen:

> 34.71% oxygen

A 100 g sample of the compound, for example, would contain 52.24 g of carbon, 13.05 g of hydrogen, and 34.71 g of oxygen. Using the relative numbers of grams of these elements, we want to find the relative number of moles. The atomic weights are for carbon, 12.01; hydrogen, 1.008; and oxygen, 16.00.

In 100 g of the compound there are

> 52.24/12.01 = 4.36 moles of carbon
> 13.05/1.008 = 12.93 moles of hydrogen
> 34.71/16.00 = 2.16 moles of oxygen

Our initial attempt gives the formula as $C_{4.36}H_{12.93}O_{2.16}$. This formula shows us the correct ratios for the elements. It is clear that the molecule contains fewer atoms of oxygen than it does of carbon and hydrogen. Atoms come only in whole numbers, so the molecule must contain at least one atom of oxygen, or it may contain two or three or some larger whole number. If we take the subscripts of this formula and divide them all by the subscript of the lowest value (2.16) we will obtain the ratios of the elements on the basis of the presence of just one oxygen atom. The formula that we obtain is $C_{2.02}H_{5.98}O$. There is some experimental error in the analysis (not more than 0.3% for each element if the analysis is carefully done), and hence the formula that we have obtained so far does not have exactly whole numbers, but almost certainly corresponds to a formula of C_2H_6O. This formula is called the *empirical formula* for the compound. It is the formula with the correct ratio of elements described by the *smallest possible set of whole numbers*. The actual formula could be a multiple of this; it could be $C_4H_{12}O_2$, for example, which contains exactly the same ratio of elements as does the formula C_2H_6O. It could also be $C_6H_{18}O_3$, or any other multiple of the empirical formula. To find which of these possible formulas represents the actual *molecular formula* of the compound, we need to know the molecular weight. For a gas, this can be found conveniently from pressure, volume, and temperature measurements; for a liquid or solid, from the freezing-point depression of a suitable solvent, or in various other ways. For our compound, which is a gas, let us say that the weight of a sample of known volume, temperature, and pressure indicated a molecular weight of 44.5. For the empirical formula C_2H_6O the molecular weight would be a multiple of 46.1 or a multiple of this number. The experimental number is close to 46.1 and far from 92.2 or from 138.3 or from any higher multiple, and the molecular formula of the compound is therefore C_2H_6O.

The desirability of obtaining accurate analyses can be seen from the following example. Cyclohexane has the molecular formula C_6H_{12}, while a different compound, called cyclohexene, has the formula C_6H_{10}. The percentage of the two elements present in these compounds is as follows: for C_6H_{12}, C, 85.6; H, 14.4; and for C_6H_{10}, C, 87.7; H, 12.3. The analytical method developed by Liebig was sufficiently good that one could obtain an accuracy of 0.3% for each element. Thus, the method would easily distinguish the two compounds mentioned.

The disadvantage of Liebig's method as he used it was that it required 0.5–1.0 g of material for an analysis. The isolation of an organic compound in pure form from nature is often very difficult, and many of the compounds that have been studied in recent years have been available only in amounts far smaller than this. A procedure of microanalysis was introduced in 1911 by Pregl†, utilizing the basic method of Liebig, but greatly refining all of the different instruments and accessories, and especially the sensitivity of the balance used for the weighing. Pregl was able to develop the method sufficiently so that the analysis could be carried out on 3–4 mg of material. Pregl received the Nobel Prize for the development of this procedure.

It may be mentioned at this point that while molecular formulas are today for the most part still determined by the method of Pregl as just described, another method for carrying out such a determination makes use of an instrument called a mass spectrometer. *This device bombards molecules in the gas phase with a beam of electrons. Positive ions, corresponding to the original molecule minus an electron and to assorted molecular fragments, are formed and separated on the basis of their mass. From the masses of these ions it is possible to deduce the exact molecular formula. The high cost of the mass spectrometer (in the $30,000–$100,000 range) has so far prevented this method of determining molecular formulas from becoming the standard method, but it will probably become so in the future. The mass spectrometer will be discussed in some detail in Chapter 32.*

2.3   The Kekulé Theory of Structure

In the field of inorganic chemistry, once the formula of a substance is known, the structural formula for the molecule can often be written down immediately. There is only one compound with the formula Na_2SO_4, for example. The same situation does not persist in the field of organic chemistry. For example, there are 2 compounds with the formula C_4H_{10} and 14 different known compounds which have the formula $C_5H_{12}O$. Each of these 14 compounds has different physical properties, such as melting points and solubilities, and they consequently correspond to different molecules. Since they have the same formula, there must be something about the way in which the atoms are connected to one another which differentiates each compound from the others. The importance of understanding how the atoms are joined together in a molecule was recognized during the early part of the nineteenth century, but the chemists of that time saw no way of solving the problem. The simple solution was put forth independently by Kekulé and by Couper in 1858. They proposed that the carbon atom has the same normal valence of 4 in complicated organic molecules as it does in simple compounds such as carbon tetrachloride (CCl_4) or carbon dioxide (CO_2). Hydrogen and chlorine each have a valence of 1, while the valence of oxygen is 2, and that of trivalent nitrogen is 3. Carbon can thus join with four hydrogen atoms to form the methane molecule, or with four chlorine atoms to form carbon tetrachloride. Using these valences, carbon dioxide, hydrogen cyanide, methylamine, and ethane can be written as shown.

† Fritz Pregl. 1869–1930. Born Laibach, Austria. Universities of Innsbruck, and Graz. Nobel Prize 1923.

When two different molecules have the same molecular formula, they are called *isomers*. Ethyl alcohol and dimethyl ether are isomers with the formula C_2H_6O.

$$H-\underset{\underset{H}{|}}{\overset{\overset{H}{|}}{C}}-\underset{\underset{H}{|}}{\overset{\overset{H}{|}}{C}}-OH = CH_3CH_2OH \qquad\qquad H-\underset{\underset{H}{|}}{\overset{\overset{H}{|}}{C}}-O-\underset{\underset{H}{|}}{\overset{\overset{H}{|}}{C}}-H = CH_3OCH_3$$

Ethyl alcohol   Dimethyl ether

It should be clear to the student that from Kekulé's rules of valence, these are the only two ways that these particular atoms can be put together.

How to tell experimentally which compound has which structure is a more difficult problem which we will take up in subsequent chapters.

2.4   The Covalent Bond

Kekulé used a simple line to represent the attachment or bond between two atoms, but it was not clear at that time just what this attachment was all about. The possibility for the development of what we now consider to be a reasonable theory concerning the bonds and structures of organic molecules came into existence after J. J. Thompson's discovery of the electron in 1897 and Lord Rutherford's subsequent description in 1911 of an atom as a system consisting of a small positive nucleus surrounded by relatively distant electrons.

In 1916, G. N. Lewis† in Berkeley and W. Kossel in Munich independently utilized Rutherford's model as a basis for explaining many of the chemical properties of atoms and their ions. Lewis further extended his concepts to include covalent bonds, and thus the earlier theories could finally be expressed in terms of the fundamental particles involved. The Lewis theory forms a basis for understanding the structures and properties of organic molecules in classical terms, and, because of its simplicity, it is widely used for qualitative purposes today in organic chemistry.

Since the beginnings of their science, organic chemists have devised theories in attempts to interpret their observations. A good theory explains all the known facts in its province, and can be used to predict new facts which in turn can be verified by experiment. Because of a lack of understanding during the nineteenth century as to what constituted an atom, theories concerned with the structures and reactions of organic molecules did not develop rapidly enough to be of much predictive value. Rather, they were mainly concerned with explaining facts that were already known experimentally. The ideas of Kekulé and his contemporaries were correct in their essentials, however, and modern chemists have the greatest admiration for these early chemists who did a remarkable job of deducing the structures of molecules long before the corresponding facts about atoms were understood.

Many of the more complicated structural situations could not be understood, however; until during and after the 1930s with the availability of the quantum mechanical theory. Rather than pursue the subject of structural organic chemistry from the historical viewpoint, which would reveal an extremely laborious and difficult, although highly successful, approach to the problem, we will proceed differently from this point on. On the basis of the elementary ideas of the theory, it is now possible to deduce essentially all of the facts concerning the structures of organic molecules in which we will be interested. It is therefore convenient to pursue the applications of quantum theory to organic molecules, and to show how the theoretical predictions are in accord with the experimental facts. This approach is advantageous at the present time, because it relieves the student of the necessity of grappling with unmanageable masses of experimental facts and shows how all of the facts will follow once the theory is understood. It should be remembered, however, that this is not the way the subject developed historically.

---

† Gilbert Newton Lewis. 1875–1946. Born Weymouth, Massachusetts. University of California at Berkeley.

There are three kinds of bonds which we may differentiate: ionic, metallic, and covalent. The *ionic bond* (e.g., NaCl) was rather well described by Lewis and also by Kossel; it is really not a bond at all, but rather a nondirectional electrostatic attraction. The *metallic bond* is peculiar to metals in the solid or liquid phase and will not concern us here. Organic molecules are held together by *covalent bonds*, and such bonds form the basis of organic chemistry. The Lewis theory was the first step in understanding the covalent bond, and qualitatively the ideas were correct as they applied to a majority of cases. The covalent bond will exist between those atom pairs which can complete their electronic shells by sharing electrons, and it is generally stronger when one or both of the atoms belongs to one of the groups near the middle of the periodic table. A carbon atom is hard-pressed to form a stable closed shell of electrons by ionization, as this would require a charge of either $+4$ or -4 to be present on a very small atom—a highly unfavorable energetic situation.

$$C: 1s^2 2s^2 2p^2 \rightarrow C^{4+}: 1s^2 2s^0 2p^0$$

$$\text{or}$$

$$\rightarrow C^{4-}: 1s^2 2s^2 2p^6$$

Rather than lose or gain electrons permanently, therefore, a carbon atom tends to share electrons in the form of covalent bonds. Many inorganic molecules are also held together with covalent bonds, the molecules N_2, $AsCl_3$, and H_2O being familiar examples.

REVIEW OF LEWIS STRUCTURES. *The student will need to recall what Lewis structures are, and how they are represented, and also what* formal charge *is. These paragraphs are added by way of review.*

Lewis noted that the electronic systems of the rare gases can be considered as composed of shells of electrons, containing in the outer shell 2 electrons (helium), 8 electrons (neon), 8 electrons (argon), and so on. Not only are the rare gases themselves very stable and inert, but so are other similar electronic systems. Thus we have F^-, *with the electronic configuration of neon, or* K^+, *with the argon configuration. Methane, ammonia, water, and hydrogen fluoride all have an octet of electrons in the outer shell of the first-row element (counting shared electrons too), while each hydrogen has a duet. Hence these molecules are all electronically analogous to the rare gases, and they are very stable covalent substances. Their structures can be represented as follows:*

H H:C:H H	H:N:H H	H:O: H	H:F:	He:	:Ne:
Methane	Ammonia	Water	Hydrogen fluoride	Helium	Neon

To determine the formal charge on an atom, one counts all the electrons which in the Lewis formula belong exclusively to the atom, plus one-half of the electrons shared in covalent bonds. If this number is equal to the number of valence electrons in the free atom, the formal charge on the atom in the Lewis structure is zero. If the number of electrons counted in this way for the Lewis structure exceeds the number of valence electrons of the free atom by 1, 2, 3 . . ., then the formal charge of the atom in the Lewis structure is $-1, -2, -3$ . . . . *On the other hand, if the number of electrons counted for the Lewis structure are less than those of the free atom by 1, 2, 3 . . ., then the formal charge of the atom in the Lewis structure is* $+1, +2, +3$ . . . .

Some examples of formal charge calculation may be helpful. In the methane molecule above, each atom has a formal charge of zero, since for the carbon we count one-half of the number of electrons in covalent bonds $(\frac{1}{2} \times 8 = 4)$, *and the number obtained is just equal to the number of valence electrons of a carbon atom (formal charge = 4 − 4 = 0).*

Similarly, the hydrogens in methane each have $\frac{1}{2} \times 2 = 1$ electrons, formally, which equals the number of valence electrons of a hydrogen atom. It can likewise be seen that all of the atoms in NH_3, H_2O, and HF have formal charges of zero.

Next, consider the structures below.

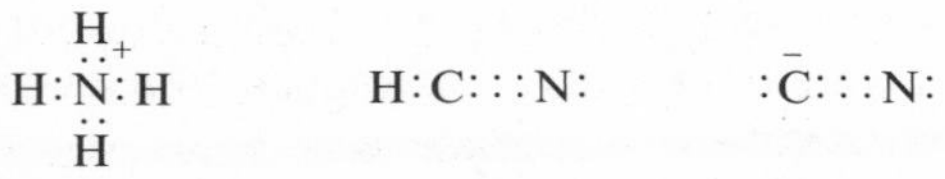

$$\begin{array}{c} \overset{+}{\underset{\cdot\cdot}{H}} \\ H\!:\!\overset{\cdot\cdot}{\underset{\cdot\cdot}{N}}\!:\!H \\ \overset{\cdot\cdot}{H} \end{array} \qquad\qquad H\!:\!C\!:\!:\!:\!N\!: \qquad\qquad \overset{-}{:}\!C\!:\!:\!:\!N\!:$$

Ammonium ion	Hydrogen cyanide	Cyanide ion

Note that all of the atoms have complete octets (duets for hydrogen). The ammonium ion has $\frac{1}{2} \times 8 = 4$ electrons belonging to nitrogen. Since the free nitrogen atom has 5 electrons, there is a formal charge of $+1$ on the nitrogen of an ammonium ion.

For the HCN molecule, H has a formal charge of zero ($1 - 2/2$), as do carbon ($4 - 8/2$) and nitrogen ($5 - 2 - 6/2$). In the case of CN^-, the nitrogen formally has 5 electrons, and zero formal charge, while the carbon has 5 electrons, and hence a formal charge of -1.

The student may recall that an exact description of the hydrogen atom can be obtained by solving the Schroedinger equation† which can be written

$$H\psi = E\psi$$

where an infinite set of wave functions called *orbitals* (ψ) exist. Each orbital is a mathematical function which describes a possible distribution of the electron in space.

The remainder of this section and some subsequent material will be concerned with results obtained by solution of the Schroedinger equation. The mathematics actually used in obtaining such solutions is rather complicated and beyond the scope of this course. We will want to make use of some of these results here and later, but we are now interested only in the results themselves and not in the details of how they were obtained.

Each of these orbitals has an energy (E) associated with it. The electron has any one of these distributions, and the atom has the corresponding energy.

The complicated part of the equation is **H**, the Hamiltonian operator. (An operator is a mathematical symbol which tells us to carry out a manipulation on the quantity which follows it.) This operator contains the second derivatives (of ψ) with respect to the coordinates. To solve the equation, it must be integrated. Unfortunately, this can be done exactly in only a few special cases, such as for the hydrogen atom. Approximate solutions to the equation (to several significant figures) have been carried out now for small atoms and for a few small molecules. Even the helium atom is too complicated for an *exact* solution, but the energy has been correctly calculated to eight significant figures. There is no question but that the equation applies equally well to larger molecules, but for these, only approximate solutions to the Schroedinger equation have so far been possible because of the mathematical complexities.

The simplest system which contains an ordinary (electron pair) covalent bond is the hydrogen molecule (H_2). This molecule has been studied theoretically with great care. It is somewhat more complicated than the helium atom, but similar to it in many ways. If we call the two hydrogen nuclei in the molecule H_A and H_B, we can use the hydrogen $1s$ atomic orbitals for each atom (ψ_A and ψ_B) and write a *molecular orbital*, $\psi_A + \psi_B$. Here the molecular orbital is formed from a linear combination of atomic orbitals. Just as an atomic orbital tells us where an electron is likely to be found around an atom,

† Erwin Schroedinger. 1887–1961. Born Austria. Universities of Vienna, Jena, Stuttgart (Technische Hochschule), Breslau, Zurich, Berlin, Graz, Dublin, Trinity College, National University of Ireland, and Glasgow. Formulated his famous equation in 1926, for which he received the Nobel Prize in 1933.

so a molecular orbital tells where an electron is likely to be found around a molecule. (Recall that the value of ψ^2 at any point is the electron density, or the probability of finding the electron, at that point.) The shape of the molecular orbital, or the probability function for finding an electron in different regions of space about the molecule, is usually much more complicated than that of an atomic orbital. As with the helium atom, the more refined the calculations, the better the agreement between the calculated and experimental values for the bond length and energy. The idea of a molecular orbital formed by a combination of atomic orbitals is a most important one. It permits us to interpret the structure of molecules in terms of the structures of atoms, which in turn we know quite a lot about by analogy with the hydrogen atom, the case where the Schroedinger equation can be exactly solved. *The mathematics of the formation of molecular orbitals works out in such a way that, in general, if we start with n atomic orbitals and combine them, we will always obtain n molecular orbitals.* The energies of the molecular orbitals will differ from the energies of the atomic orbitals from which they were formed, some being lower and some higher than those of the original atomic orbitals. The molecular orbitals of lower energy are referred to as *bonding orbitals*, while those of higher energy are referred to as *antibonding orbitals*. It may happen that one (or more) of the molecular orbitals has the same energy as that of one of the atomic orbitals, and such an orbital is said to be *nonbonding*. For the hydrogen molecule, solution of the Schroedinger equation gives two molecular orbitals, which can be called ψ_σ and $\psi_{\sigma*}$, and which are the following combinations of the atomic orbitals:

$$\psi_\sigma = \psi_A + \psi_B \quad \text{and} \quad \psi_{\sigma*} = \psi_A - \psi_B$$

It is found that the first orbital (ψ_σ) is a bonding orbital, whereas the second is anti-bonding (see Figure 2.2). Molecular orbitals are like atomic orbitals in that they will hold at most two electrons, and then only if the electron spins are paired (Pauli exclusion principle). In the hydrogen molecule in the ground state there are just two electrons, and they have paired spins. Clearly they will both occupy the bonding orbital, and for this arrangement the energy of the system is at a minimum when the separation between the nuclei is 0.74 Å. These bonding electrons are more stable under these circumstances than they would be in the isolated hydrogen atoms, and they tend to hold the nuclei together and form a bond. Specifically, they form a bond with a bond length of 0.74 Å, and the strength of the bond corresponds to the depth of the potential well in which the electrons are located. Conversely, electrons in the antibonding orbital avoid the region between the nuclei, which then tend to push one another apart.

Figure 2.2
The energy of two hydrogen atoms as a function of the distance (*d*) between nuclei when the electrons are in bonding and antibonding orbitals.

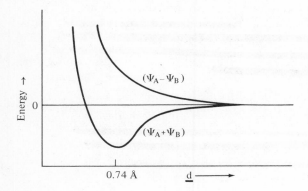

A simple line has been used by organic chemists since the time of Kekulé to represent a covalent bond, and it is still used to mean the same thing, although the meaning attached to this line has now been greatly expanded by our increased understanding of bonding phenomena. Various ways of representing the bonding orbital of the hydrogen molecule are illustrated in Figure 2.3. The most simple way of representing the $1s$ orbitals is by a circle, as shown. One might think of this circle as representing a sphere, which contains some amount, say 90%, of the electron density of the orbital inside of its boundaries. The shaded figure represents the probability distribution of the electrons, the darker the shading, the higher the probability of finding the electron at that position. Often a contour map of electron density is useful.

Figure 2.3
The bonding orbital of the hydrogen molecule.

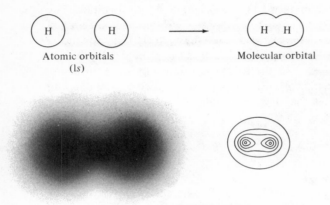

The bond in the H_2 molecule is a typical covalent bond, similar to those found in organic molecules. In a complicated molecule, it is usually a good approximation to consider the atoms as being joined together in pairs by covalent bonds.

A covalent bond between any two atoms is described by a wave function which has a certain resemblance to the one used for the hydrogen molecule. For a molecule like HF, the wave function for the bonding orbital is such that there is greater electron density on the electronegative atom (fluorine), as one would expect.

The bonding wave function for HF is $\psi_\sigma = \psi_{H_{1s}} + \lambda\psi_{F_{2p}}$ where $\lambda > 1$, corresponding to a greater electron density in the F_{2p} part of the bonding orbital than in the H_{1s} part.

Conversely, an electron in the antibonding orbital spends most of its time nearer to the electropositive element. The electron densities corresponding to the bonding and antibonding orbitals of the hydrogen fluoride molecule are shown in Figure 2.4. (The fluorine has many nonbonding electrons in addition, which are not shown. Note that the fluorine atom uses a $2p$ orbital for bond formation.) If the electrons are in the bonding orbital, they tend to concentrate between the nuclei, but the antibonding orbital has a node (surface of zero electron density) in between the nuclei—the electrons in such an orbital do not concentrate there, but rather avoid this region.

The student may well ask, How does the electron get across the node? The most direct answer is that the nodes are predicted on the basis of nonrelativistic mathematics, and textbooks usually fail to mention that when the effects of relativity are taken into account, the surface of zero electron density now has a finite (but very small) electron density. The node is therefore just an approximation and doesn't really exist, and the electron can cross it without dire consequences.

The state of lowest energy for the molecule is ordinarily the one of the most interest, and it is referred to as the *ground state*. If energy is supplied to the molecule in the proper way, it is possible to excite an electron from a bonding orbital to an antibonding orbital. This absorption of energy occurs at one or more selected wavelengths, which depend upon the energy differences between the orbitals occupied by the electron in the ground and excited states. This electronic excitation can be made to yield the absorption spectrum of the molecule. An *absorption spectrum* is measured by shining light through a substance and measuring the radiation that comes through. The amount of radiation absorbed by the substance is used to excite the atoms or molecules to higher energy states. Such absorption spectra often give much useful information concerning molecular structures and will be discussed in later chapters.

Figure 2.4
The bonding and antibonding orbitals of hydrogen fluoride.

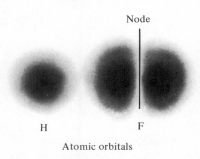

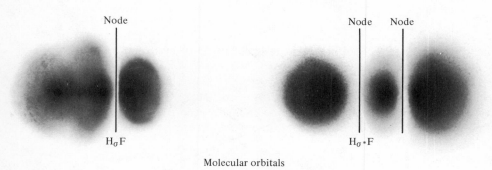

The yellow color which is imparted to a flame by sodium is a familiar example of an *emission spectrum*. The sodium acquires thermal energy from the flame, which excites the electrons to higher orbitals. When the electrons fall back to lower energy levels, various wavelengths are emitted. One of these happens to be in the visible spectrum, and we see the characteristic yellow color. An emission spectrum is measured as radiation given off when the electrons fall from excited states down to the ground state.

2.5   The Structure of Methane

Methane is the principal constituent of the natural gas widely used at the present time for heating. It is sometimes referred to as *marsh gas* because it is a product of vegetation decaying in damp places in the absence of air. Methane has the formula CH_4. It is the simplest hydrocarbon, or molecule containing only carbon and hydrogen. During the last century, it was established that the geometry of this molecule is that of a regular tetrahedron (Figure 2.5), with hydrogens at the four corners, the carbon at the center, and angles of 109.5° between any two bonds. The proof of structure rested upon the fact that all four hydrogens could, by various sequences of reactions, be shown to be geometrically identical. Thus, there is only one kind of methylene chloride: CH_2Cl_2.

Figure 2.5
The regular tetrahedron structure of methane. (The dashed lines are imaginary, and are included here only to outline the tetrahedron.)

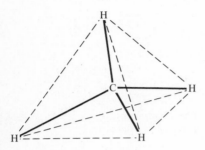

Since the four corners of a tetrahedron are equivalent, it would not matter which two hydrogens of the tetrahedron were replaced by chlorine; the same unique structure would result. On the other hand, if the structure of the molecule were a square-planar one, for example, then the chlorines could be either on adjacent or opposite corners of the square, and there would be two compounds with the formula CH_2Cl_2 (Figure 2.6).

Figure 2.6
The isomers that would be possible for methylene chloride if it were square-coplanar.

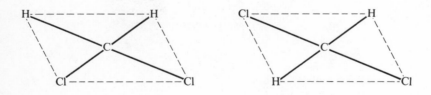

Studies on a great many substituted methanes have invariably shown that the total number of isomers is consistent with a regular tetrahedral structure for methane itself, and all other conceivable geometries for the methane molecule were eliminated by such considerations. The tetrahedral carbon was proposed independently by van't Hoff[†] and LeBel[††] in 1874, on the basis of experimental facts to be discussed in Chapter 3. This structure has since been fully substantiated by numerous types of physical and chemical experiments. Just why methane has this structure as opposed to some other alternative could not be understood until the advent of the quantum mechanical theory and was just accepted as an experimental fact.

As the quantum mechanical theory developed during the late 1920s and 1930s, the structure of methane was studied from the theoretical point of view. The hydrogen atoms attached to carbon utilize their $1s$ orbitals for bonding, just as in H_2 or in HF. In its

[†] Jacobus Hendricus van't Hoff. 1852–1911. Born Rotterdam. University of Amsterdam. Nobel Prize 1901.
[††] Joseph Achille LeBel. 1847–1930. Born Péchelbronn, France. Chemist in Paris.

ground state, a carbon atom has two unpaired electrons (Figure 2.7).†

Figure 2.7
The electronic ground state of carbon.

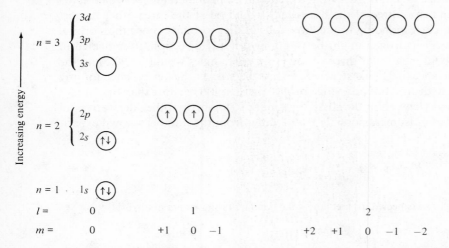

It might therefore be expected that instead of forming CH_4 the carbon would bond to just two hydrogen atoms and form CH_2, leaving one $2p$ orbital empty. CH_2 is a known chemical species (called carbene) but it is a highly reactive substance and has only a momentary existence.

The answer to this puzzle was quickly found. By the addition of 96 kcal/mole of energy to a carbon atom, one of the $2s$ electrons can be excited to the empty $2p$ orbital, giving the configuration shown in Figure 2.8.

Figure 2.8
The lowest electronic state of tetracovalent carbon.

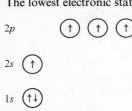

Now the carbon atom has available four electrons with which to form bonds, and by forming four covalent bonds the rare gas configuration can be obtained, if we count as belonging to the outer shell of each atom all of the electrons in it, whether they are owned outright by the atom or shared by it with another atom. The formation of a covalent bond results in a decrease in the energy of the pairs of atoms involved, as was noted for the reaction $2H \cdot \rightarrow H_2$ (Section 2.4). From the reaction $CH_2 + 2H \cdot$, two C—H bonds are formed, which gives an energy decrease of 174 kcal/mole. This decrease more than outweighs the 96 kcal/mole increase in energy that we required to promote the carbon atom from the ground state to the excited state shown in Figure 2.8, and it shows why carbon tends to be tetravalent. Carbon monoxide (C=O) is the only common stable divalent carbon compound.

† The student may recall that four quantum numbers are required to specify an electron. Three of these characterize the orbital the electron occupies, the fourth (s, spin) can be looked upon as a property of the electron itself, and it can take either of two values ($\pm\frac{1}{2}$). The quantum numbers n, l, and m, specify, respectively, the size of the orbital ($n = 1, 2, 3, \ldots$), the shape of the orbital ($l = 0, 1, 2, \ldots, n - 1$), and the spatial orientation of the orbital ($m = 0, \pm 1, \pm 2, \ldots, \pm l$). For historical reasons the values $l = 0, 1, 2, 3 \ldots$ are usually represented by the letters s, p, $d \ldots$.

While it was not difficult to see why carbon tends to be tetravalent, it was not so obvious why carbon tends to be tetrahedral. The four orbitals from which the bonds are formed consist of three p orbitals at right angles to one another and a nondirectional s orbital. A bond between two atoms is strongest when the atoms lie along the line of greatest electron density; hence, we might guess that the carbon atom in methane would be at the corner of a cube and that three of the hydrogens would be at the three other nearest corners of the cube, corresponding to the directions of the p orbitals. Since the s orbital is spherical, the fourth hydrogen might be positioned in any direction, as indicated in Figure 2.9. This would mean that three of the H—C—H angles would be 90°, and the others could not be specified. This structure cannot be correct, however, since for any arrangement of the hydrogen bound to the s orbital there would be more than one isomer of, for example, methylene chloride possible; similarly, for many other derivatives of methane, the number of isomers possible would differ from the number known experimentally to exist.

Figure 2.9
The structure that might be expected for methane if the bonding orbitals were not hybridized.

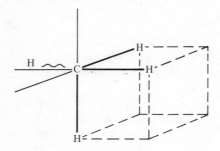

The difficulty here is a theoretical one, since the experimental evidence is quite clear. The error must result from the bonds not being formed in the simple way envisioned in the preceding paragraph. The orbitals used to describe the molecule must not be proper, or in other words, the carbon atom must undergo some sort of change in its orbital description upon bond formation. The system of one $2s$ and three mutually perpendicular $2p$ orbitals is a satisfactory approximate solution to the Schroedinger equation for the shell with $n = 2$, but linear combinations of these four orbitals can be formulated which are also equally satisfactory solutions to the Schroedinger equation. How might we construct such *hybrid orbitals*? It is mathematically legitimate to mix these $2s$ and $2p$ orbitals together in any way, as long as in constructing the four new orbitals we use up exactly one s and three p orbitals. Such a mixing yields hybrid orbitals which are part s and part p. One way in which to carry out the mixing is to generate four new orbitals, each of which is $\frac{1}{4}s$ and $\frac{3}{4}p$ in character. The four hybrid orbitals are then equivalent to one another and, since they contain three times as much p character as s, they are referred to as sp^3 hybrids.

The Energetics of Hybridization. As a specific illustration, consider the neon atom. The $n = 2$ shell is filled, and the resultant total electron cloud for the shell is therefore spherical in shape. (The total electron density which results from the presence of two electrons in each $2p$ orbital is spherical, although this is not apparent from inspection of the shapes of the p orbitals.) We can consider that two electrons are in the $2s$ orbital with energies of E_s, and six electrons are in the $2p$ orbitals with energies E_p, and the total electronic energy of the shell is therefore $2E_s + 6E_p$.

If we consider four sp^3 orbitals each containing two electrons, the total energy is 8 electrons × $(\frac{1}{4}E_s + \frac{3}{4}E_p) = 2E_s + 6E_p$, just as before, and the eight electrons altogether describe the same spherical electron distribution as previously. Thus, the description of the outer shell of the neon atom can be given in terms of one s and three p orbitals, or it can be given in terms of four sp^3 orbitals. These descriptions are equivalent. It is like saying that 12 can be considered to be 3×4 or 6×2. Both are correct, but one may be more convenient for a particular purpose.

The hybridization of the orbitals does not affect the energy, electron distribution, or any other property of the ground state of neon, and therefore we can use hybrid orbitals to describe the atom or not, as we choose. (This is not true, however, for excited states. Why not?)

In a fluorine atom, the electron distribution and energy depend on the hybridization, and this can be conveniently seen by using seven electrons and following the type of energy calculation used with neon.

EXERCISE 2.1

Carry out the energy calculation for the fluorine atom as described.

A moment's thought will show that hybridization will not change the total energy if the shell is completely full or empty, or if there is exactly one electron in each orbital. The latter case is the one in which we are really interested, because this is the electronic configuration of the carbon atom in organic compounds (Figure 2.8). Hence, we can use hybrid orbitals to describe the carbon atom if there are special reasons for doing so, which there are.

If we examine a contour plot of the electron density of an sp^3 orbital, we find that it has two lobes as does a p orbital, but that in this case, the lobes are rather unequal in size (Figure 2.10).

Figure 2.10
Contour map of the electron density corresponding to an sp^3 orbital.

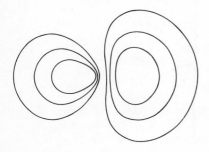

We know that to form a strong bond it is necessary to have the electrons doing the bonding in between the nuclei of the atoms bound together. An sp^3 orbital, by virtue of its shape, can put much more electron density in a specific direction from the carbon atom than can either an s or a p orbital, and we might guess that an sp^3 orbital would form a considerably stronger bond than would either of the other types. It is found experimentally that the strength of an sp^3 hybrid bond from carbon to hydrogen is 103 kcal/mole, while the corresponding s and p bonds have strengths of only 60 and 80 kcal/mole, respectively.

Now, all of the above discussion would be only of minor interest were it not for the fact that the four sp^3 hybrid orbitals that can be formed by the valence shell of carbon turn out to be directed away from one another at angles of 109.5°; that is, they point directly at the corners of a regular tetrahedron (Figure 2.11).

The sp^3 hybrid orbitals furnish the best description of the carbon atom in methane, because the carbon atom itself (before bond formation) has the same energy whether hybridized or not, but the hybridized configuration can form stronger bonds. There is an additional advantage to a tetrahedral geometry for the methane molecule. Such an arrangement allows the hydrogen nuclei to be as far apart from one another as possible for a given C—H bond length, and since these nuclei are all positively charged, the further apart they are the lower the energy of the system, other things being equal.

In summary, methane is tetrahedral, and this structure can be considered to result from hybridization of the four atomic orbitals ($2s, 2p_x, 2p_y, 2p_z$), each containing one

Figure 2.11

The electron density about an sp^3 hybridized carbon atom. Only the larger lobe is shown for each orbital. Note that the total electron density is spherical.

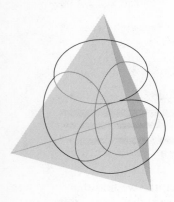

electron, to four equivalent sp^3 orbitals, which simultaneously allows for both the formation of stronger bonds and the best placement of the hydrogen nuclei for minimization of their mutual repulsions. Thus, we can describe mathematically the bonding in the methane molecule, and we can understand why it has the geometry that it does. Furthermore, we can use the concept of hybrid bonds for understanding more complicated molecules (Section 4.2).

Figure 2.12

The electronic description of tetracovalent carbon.

SOLVING THE SCHROEDINGER EQUATION. *While it is not possible to solve the Schroedinger equation in an analytical way for molecules containing several atoms, it is in principle possible to carry the solution out to any desired accuracy, and it has in principle been possible for over 30 years. Reducing the principle to practice has been quite another matter, however, for the reason that the solution must be carried out using approximation methods. It turns out that we can express the properties of an atom in terms of an infinite series of orbitals, and for molecules we need combinations of these infinite series.*

In practice, one truncates the series to some small or large number of terms, depending on what sort of accuracy is desired. In solving the Schroedinger equation for a molecule, it becomes necessary to multiply together many of these truncated series, where each term in a series may be an integral which is difficult to evaluate, and for a reasonable degree of accuracy, the sheer mathematics becomes overwhelming. Great strides have been made since 1950, however, in dealing with this type of problem, and this progress stems from the development of electronic computers. The IBM 360/50 computer, a typical medium-size computer of a type widely available today, can perform 150,000 additions or subtractions with seven-digit numbers, or it can perform 50,000 multiplications or

*divisions, or about 5000 more complex operations (powers, roots, trigonometric functions)
per second, with perfect accuracy. A relatively simple quantum mechanics problem may
require an hour of computer time, and obviously such problems are completely out of
reach of the man with a slide rule. The undertaking of problems which would have been
unthinkable in 1950 is now routine. Nevertheless, really accurate solutions to
ordinary polyatomic problems by the methods of the present time are apparently going
to require computers faster than the 360/50 by roughly the amount by which the
360/50 is faster than the slide rule. Thus for the present, quantum theory is very useful
in giving approximate answers to all sorts of problems in chemistry, but except for
small molecules, accurate determinations must almost always be made by experiment.*

PROBLEMS

1. What is the empirical formula of an organic compound whose percentage
    composition is:

    (a) 85.6% C, 14.4% H   (d) 39.4% C, 11.6% H, 23.0% N
    (b) 40.0% C, 6.7% H   (e) 60.0% C, 13.4% H
    (c) 40.7% C, 8.5% H, 23.8% N (f) 12.6% C, 3.2% H, 84.1% Br

2. Combustion of 6.51 mg of a compound gave 20.47 mg of carbon dioxide and 8.36 mg
    of water. At 100°C and 760 mm pressure, 0.284 g of the compound occupied 100 cc.
    Calculate (a) percentage composition; (b) empirical formula; and (c) molecular formula
    of the compound.

3. The hormone insulin contains 3.4% sulfur. (a) What is the minimum molecular weight
    of insulin? (b) The actual molecular weight is 5734; how many sulfur atoms are
    probably present per molecule?

4. Cantharidin, the active ingredient of "Spanish fly," gives an elemental analysis of
    61.2% carbon and 6.2% hydrogen. Qualitative tests show nitrogen, sulfur, phosphorus,
    halogens and metals are absent. A molecular weight was determined in camphor by
    freezing point measurements, and was 201 ± 20. What is the molecular formula of
    cantharidin?

5. Taking the valences of the atoms as below, how many isomers do you predict for the
    molecular formulas given. (H = 1, C = 4, O = 2, N = 3).

    (a) C_2H_7N (b) C_3H_8O (c) C_2H_7NO

6. Look at Figure 2.7. Draw a similar diagram for the following:
    (a) Lithium in the ground state
    (b) Fluorine in the ground state
    (c) Neon in the *lowest* excited state

7. Draw a contour map of an sp^3 orbital.

8. Explain why methane has bond angles of $109\frac{1}{2}°$, rather than having some bond angles
    of 90° and others variable.

9. Analysis of the blood of a suicide victim showed the presence of a compound not
    normally present. This compound contained carbon and hydrogen, but no halogen,
    nitrogen, or sulfur. No test was made for oxygen. Combustion of 33.0 mg gave 63.0 mg
    of carbon dioxide and 39.1 mg of water. (a) What is the empirical formula of the com-
    pound? (b) Molecular weight determination indicated that the molecular formula was
    the same as the empirical formula. Write all possible isomers of the substance and name
    them. (c) The compound reacts vigorously with sodium. What is the structure of the
    unknown compound in the victim's blood?

10. What is the formal charge on each atom (except hydrogen) in the following structures?

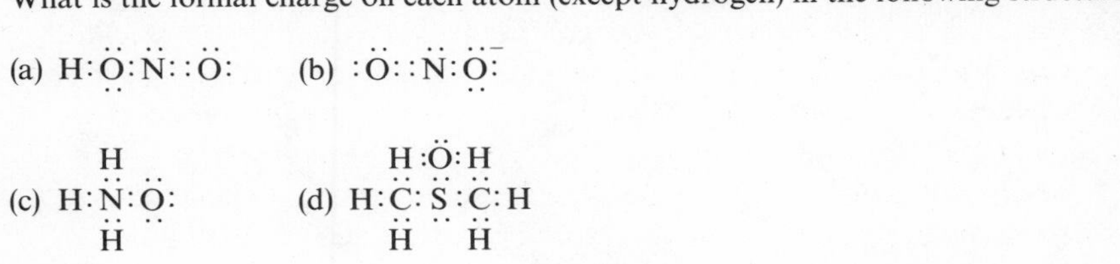

    (a) $H : \overset{\cdot\cdot}{\underset{\cdot\cdot}{O}} : N : : \overset{\cdot\cdot}{\underset{\cdot\cdot}{O}} :$ (b) $: \overset{\cdot\cdot}{\underset{\cdot\cdot}{O}} : : N : \overset{\cdot\cdot}{\underset{\cdot\cdot}{O}} :$

    (c) $H : \overset{\displaystyle H}{\underset{\displaystyle H}{N}} : \overset{\cdot\cdot}{\underset{\cdot\cdot}{O}} :$ (d) $H : \overset{\displaystyle H : \overset{\cdot\cdot}{\underset{\cdot\cdot}{O}} : H}{\underset{\displaystyle H \quad\quad H}{C : S : C}} : H$

11. Write Lewis structures (similar to those in problem 10) for the following:
    (a) HNO_3 (b) H_2SO_4 (c) HCl   (d) NH_2F
    (e) CH_3F (f) CH_3CN (g) HOCl   (h) H_2CO_3

12. (a) With a desk calculator, a man can multiply large numbers together at the rate of about one every 10 seconds. How many per hour can he do? How many in a 40-hour week? How many in a 50-week year? How many in a 50-year life?
    (b) The 360/50 computer will multiply numbers at the rate of 50,000/second. If we call the amount of arithmetic in part (a) one man-life, how long does it take the 360/50 to do a man-life of work?

CHAPTER 3

THE ALKANES

3.1 Structure and Nomenclature

There exist a large number of hydrocarbons with the formula C_nH_{2n+2}. These compounds are called *alkanes* or *paraffins*, and methane, CH_4 (Section 2.5), is the simplest one. By increasing n, we obtain the formulas of a family of compounds—a *homologous series*. The first four members of this family are as follows:

Methane   Ethane   Propane   Butane

The compounds shown are all gases, and the latter two are widely used as fuels. The next higher homologs—pentane, hexane, heptane, octane, nonane, and so on—are liquids (Table 3.1).

Table 3.1   The Normal Hydrocarbons

No. of carbons	Formula	Name	Total isomers possible	b.p. °C	m.p. °C
1	CH_4	Methane	1	−162	−183
2	C_2H_6	Ethane	1	−89	−172
3	C_3H_8	Propane	1	−42	−187
4	C_4H_{10}	Butane	2	0	−138
5	C_5H_{12}	Pentane	3	36	−130
6	C_6H_{14}	Hexane	5	69	−95
7	C_7H_{16}	Heptane	9	98	−91
8	C_8H_{18}	Octane	18	126	−57
9	C_9H_{20}	Nonane	35	151	−54
10	$C_{10}H_{22}$	Decane	75	174	−30
11	$C_{11}H_{24}$	Undecane	—	196	26
12	$C_{12}H_{26}$	Dodecane	—	216	−10
20	$C_{20}H_{42}$	Eicosane	366,319	334	+36
30	$C_{30}H_{62}$	Tricontane	4.11×10^9	446	+66

TRIVIAL NOMENCLATURE. *The nomenclature of simple organic molecules is not completely systematic, because the compounds were known and named long before their structures were understood. For example, the name* butane *was derived from a related compound (*butyric acid*), which was first isolated from rancid butter. The higher homologs have a more systematic nomenclature based on Greek numbers.*

Straight-chain homologs containing 18 or more carbons are low-melting waxy solids, mixtures of which are commercially known as *paraffin wax*, a material once widely used for sealing jars of jelly, but now perhaps better known as a moderator for atomic reactors.

The bonding in all alkanes is fundamentally the same as that in methane, the atoms are joined together by electron-pair bonds which are made up of sp^3 hybrid orbitals from carbon and $1s$ orbitals from hydrogen. Each carbon atom has its *substituents* (attached atoms or groups) located about it in a tetrahedral arrangement. For example, ethane could be represented as shown in Figure 3.1, using a perspective formula. The orbital representation is also shown.

Figure 3.1
Various representations of ethane.

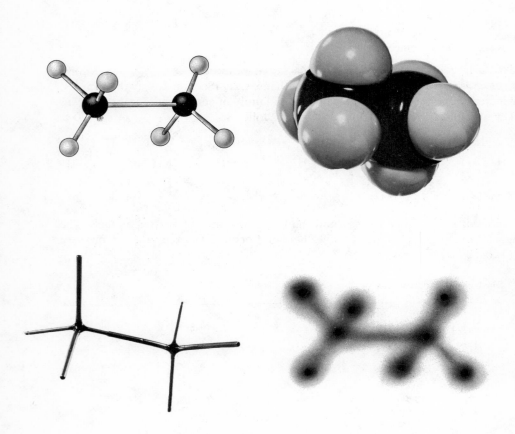

Often it is difficult to visualize the three-dimensional structure of a molecule. It is very useful to have "molecular models" to help us understand structures. There are three principal types of models—"ball-and-stick" models which are the simplest, "framework" models, which are useful for seeing outlines of structures, and "space-filling" models, which attempt to give some idea of the physical sizes of the different atoms (see Figure 3.1). Each type of model is a mechanical approximation to a molecule. While none is completely accurate, each has a certain usefulness, depending on which molecular properties are under examination. The student should become familiar with each type of model. We will use pictures of each type in this text, depending on what is appropriate for the case under discussion.

There is in principle no limit to the number of carbon atoms which may be connected together in a hydrocarbon chain, and hydrocarbons containing more than 100 carbons are known. One of the reasons for the existence of so many organic compounds is that there is really no limit to the size of a molecule which can be formed. The principal reason, however, for the existence of so many different types of organic compounds stems from the phenomenon known as *isomerism*. Two different compounds are said to be *isomers* if they have the same molecular formula. While propane and the smaller homologs do not have structural isomers, there are two compounds with the formula C_4H_{10}, three with the formula C_5H_{12}, and five with the formula C_6H_{14}. The number of isomers continues to increase with increasing molecular size, as indicated in Table 3.1.

If we write propane, C_3H_8, with a carbon valence of 4 and a hydrogen valence of 1, it can have only one possible structure. The two formulas

$$
\begin{array}{ccc}
& H & & CH_3 \\
& | & & | \\
CH_3-C-CH_3 & \text{and} & H-C-H \\
& | & & | \\
& H & & CH_3
\end{array}
$$

correspond to the same molecule viewed from two different positions, and they represent the same structure. The formula

$$
\begin{array}{c}
H \\
| \\
CH_3-C-H \\
| \\
CH_3
\end{array}
$$

is also equivalent to the others, although it may not look it in a two-dimensional representation, since the four corners of a tetrahedron are equivalent. Three different views of a model of propane are shown, corresponding to the three orientations above.

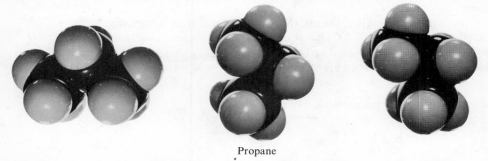

Propane

The formula C_4H_{10} corresponds to two different molecular structures, which can be written as

$$
\begin{array}{cccc}
H & H & H & H \\
| & | & | & | \\
H-C-C-C-C-H \\
| & | & | & | \\
H & H & H & H
\end{array}
\qquad
\begin{array}{ccc}
H & H & H \\
| & | & | \\
H-C-C-C-H \\
| & | & | \\
H & | & H \\
& H-C-H \\
& | \\
& H
\end{array}
$$

n-Butane   Isobutane

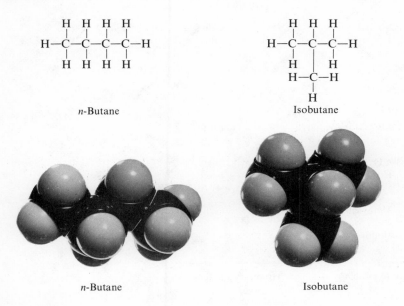

n-Butane   Isobutane

These structures are clearly different. One isomer, isobutane, has one carbon atom which is bound to three other carbons, and there is no such carbon atom in the other isomer, n-butane.

A compound with its carbon atoms arranged in a straight chain is always referred to as a normal (n-) isomer, and a second one is referred to as an iso- (meaning branched) structure. There are three isomers of the C_5 homolog: a *normal* pentane, isopentane, and one which is called neopentane.

$$CH_3-CH_2-CH_2-CH_2-CH_3 \qquad CH_3-\underset{\underset{CH_3}{|}}{CH}-CH_2-CH_3 \qquad CH_3-\overset{\overset{CH_3}{|}}{\underset{\underset{CH_3}{|}}{C}}-CH_3$$

n-Pentane   Isopentane   Neopentane

It became clear many years ago that since the number of possible isomers for a large molecule was so enormous, simply designating each isomer with an arbitrary name would not be adequate. A more systematic nomenclature was therefore adopted by the International Union of Pure and Applied Chemistry (IUPAC), an organization formed by international agreement for the purpose of dealing with such problems.

In IUPAC nomenclature the longest chain in the molecule is named as the parent hydrocarbon. The atoms in this longest chain are numbered consecutively from one end so that the substituents on the chain will have the lowest possible numbers. When one portion of a hydrocarbon is considered as a substituent on another portion, the substituent is referred to as an *alkyl group*, and the general name of the compound is an *alkylalkane*.

To obtain the name of the alkyl group, the -*ane* of the alkane is replaced with -*yl*. Thus, CH_3CH_3 is eth*ane*, and CH_3CH_2- is eth*yl*. The names and shorthand symbols for the common alkyl groups are given in Table 3.2. A carbon is sometimes referred to as *primary, secondary, tertiary*, or *quaternary*, depending on whether it is attached to

Table 3.2   Common Alkyl Groups (R−) and Related Fragments[a]

Group	Name	Shorthand
CH_3-	Methyl	Me
CH_3CH_2-	Ethyl	Et
$CH_3CH_2CH_2-$	n-Propyl	n-Pr
$CH_3\underset{\underset{CH_3}{\|}}{CH}-$	Isopropyl	i-Pr
$CH_3CH_2CH_2CH_2-$	n-Butyl	n-Bu
$CH_3\underset{\underset{CH_3}{\|}}{CH}CH_2-$	Isobutyl	i-Bu
$CH_3CH_2\underset{\underset{CH_3}{\|}}{CH}-$	*sec*-Butyl	*s*-Bu
$CH_3\overset{\overset{CH_3}{\|}}{\underset{\underset{CH_3}{\|}}{C}}-$	*t*-Butyl (or *tert*-butyl)	*t*-Bu
$CH_3CH_2CH_2CH_2CH_2-$	n-Pentyl (Alternate name: n-Amyl)	n-Am
$CH_3\underset{\underset{CH_3}{\|}}{CH}CH_2CH_2-$	Isoamyl	i-Am
$-CH_2-$	Methylene	
$-\overset{\|}{\underset{\|}{C}}-H$	Methine	

[a] Often the symbol R− is used to mean any alkyl group (radical), and then R—H is any alkane.

one, two, three, or four other carbons. The names *sec*-butyl and *tert*-butyl in Table 3.2 indicate that in these alkyl groups the points of attachment are at carbon atoms connected, respectively, to two and three other carbon atoms.

Let us now consider how one would name the following compound by the IUPAC system.

$$\overset{1}{C}H_3\overset{2}{C}H\overset{3}{C}H_2\overset{4}{C}H_2\overset{5}{C}H_3$$
$$\underset{CH_3}{|}$$

2-Methylpentane

The longest straight chain contains five carbon atoms, so the compound will be an alkyl-pentane. The alkyl group is a methyl, and we must number the pentane chain consecutively from one end in such a way as to give the carbon to which the methyl is attached as low a number as possible. If we number from the left, the methyl is on carbon 2, whereas if we number from the right, it is on carbon 4, so the first choice is the correct one. The compound is therefore *2-methylpentane*. Application of the IUPAC rules to the following compounds shows that they have the indicated names.

$$\begin{array}{lll}
CH_3 & CH_3\ CH_3 & CH_3CH_2CHCH_2CH_3 \\
| & |\quad | & | \\
CH_3CCH_2CH_3 & CH_3CH\ CHCH_3 & CH_2 \\
| & & | \\
CH_3 & & CH_3
\end{array}$$

2,2-Dimethylbutane   2,3-Dimethylbutane   3-Ethylpentane

EXERCISE 3.1

Write the IUPAC names for the following compounds:

(a) $CH_3CH_2CHCH_2CH_2CH_2CH_3$
$\qquad\qquad\ \ |$
$\qquad\qquad\ CH_3$

(b) $CH_3CHCH_2CHCH_2CH_2CH_3$
$\qquad\quad\ |\qquad |$
$\qquad\ CH_3\quad CH_3$

It should be remembered that the longest chain in the molecule is the parent hydrocarbon, even though the longest chain may not always be written in a straight line. Thus the compound

$$CH_3CH_2CHCH_2CH_2CH_3$$
$$\qquad\quad |$$
$$\qquad CH_2CH_2CH_3$$

is not named as a derivative of hexane, but rather as a derivative of heptane. The longest chain starts with the methyl group in the upper right-hand corner, proceeds to the branch, and then goes down and around the corner. The correct name for the compound is *4-ethylheptane*.

If there are two or more different kinds of alkyl groups present, their names are usually placed in alphabetical order, without regard to hyphenated prefixes (*t*-, *sec*-) or prefixes indicating the number of such groups (di-, tri-, tetra-), but prefixes like iso and neo (which are not hyphenated) *are* used in alphabetizing. Thus we have the following:

$$\begin{array}{ll}
CH_3 & CH_3 \\
| & | \\
CH_3CCH_2CH_2CHCH_2CH_3 & CH_3-CCH_2CH_2CHCH_2CH_2CH_3 \\
|\qquad\qquad\ | & |\qquad\qquad\ | \\
CH_3\qquad CH_2CH_3 & CH_3\qquad CHCH_3 \\
& \qquad\qquad\ | \\
& \qquad\qquad CH_3
\end{array}$$

5-Ethyl-2,2-dimethylheptane
(not 2,2-dimethyl-5-
ethylheptane)

5-Isopropyl-2,2-dimethyloctane
(not 2,2-dimethyl-5-isopropyloctane)

The rules for naming hydrocarbons may be summarized as follows:

Rule 1: Find the longest continuous chain of carbon atoms. This gives the name of the parent hydrocarbon.

Rule 2: Identify the substituent groups attached to the parent hydrocarbons.

Rule 3: Name each substituent group and place these names in alphabetical order before the name of the parent hydrocarbon. Hyphenated prefixes (*t-*, *sec-*) and prefixes denoting the number of each group (di, tri, tetra) are not regarded in alphabetizing substituent groups. Nonhyphenated prefixes such as iso and neo are used in alphabetizing.

Rule 4: Number the parent hydrocarbon chain in such a way as to use the *smallest* numbers for the carbons to which substituent groups are attached. Prefix each substituent by a number denoting its position of attachment.

Using these rules, even a complicated molecule can be named in a clear and unambiguous manner. For example, the formidable structure

$$
\begin{array}{cc}
CH_3 & CH_3 \\
| & | \\
CH_3CHCH_2CHCH_2CCH_3 \\
| & | \\
CH_3CH & CH_2 \\
| & | \\
CH_3 & CH_2CH_3
\end{array}
$$

is correctly named 4-isopropyl-2,6,6-trimethylnonane.

With a very complicated structure, it may be difficult to decide which of several names is preferable; most chemists feel that in such a case any reasonable name that unambiguously defines the structure will do. Any *useful* name must lead to a unique structure, but sometimes a structure may lead to more than one useful name.

3.2   Petroleum

The major source of organic compounds in the world today is petroleum. Crude oil is a mixture of a great many compounds, and most of them are hydrocarbons. The alkanes from methane to those containing over 30 carbon atoms are the principal components of the hydrocarbon fraction. Straight-chain alkanes predominate.

REFINING. *The processing of crude oil, called* refining, *is an exceedingly complex operation. Refining begins with the separation of crude oil into various fractions by the process of* fractional distillation. *The material to be distilled is placed in a suitable vessel, and the temperature is gradually raised. The lowest-boiling constituents distill off first, followed by progressively higher boiling materials. The fractions which are separated in the ordinary refining process are indicated in Table 3.3.*

The petroleum ether and ligroin fractions are used largely as solvents. The lubricating oil fraction is distilled under reduced pressure to give light, medium, and

Table 3.3   Fractions from distillation of Crude Oil

Name of fraction	Carbon content	Approximate boiling range, °C
Natural gas	C_1-C_4	Below room temperature
Petroleum ether	C_5-C_6	20–60
Ligroin (light naphtha)	C_6-C_7	60–100
Gasoline	C_6-C_{12}	50–200
Kerosene	$C_{12}-C_{18}$	175–275
Gas oil (furnace oil, diesel oils)	Above C_{18}	Above 275
Lubricating oils		Not distilled at atmospheric pressure
Waxes		Not distilled at atmospheric pressure
Asphalt		Residue

heavy lubricating oils. The kerosene fraction furnishes the fuel necessary for gas turbine and jet engines. The demands of our civilization for these products have greatly changed during the last 50 years. Before automobiles became common, kerosene was much in demand for lighting, and gasoline was nearly worthless. By 1950, the situation was just about reversed. More recently, kerosene has been in increasing demand for aircraft fuel. A very important operation in the petroleum industry has therefore been the conversion of those fractions which are not in demand into those which are. Such conversions involve a good deal of complicated chemistry, some of which will be discussed in later chapters.

3.3   Acyclic Compounds. Conformational Analysis

Up to this point we have tacitly assumed that the rotation about a single bond was completely free, so that, for example, one of the methyl groups in ethane may rotate with respect to the other without any change in the energy of the molecule. If rotation about the central bond in butane were not free, then one might expect to find rotational isomers, perhaps like these:

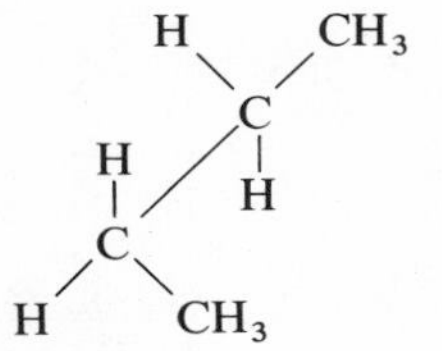

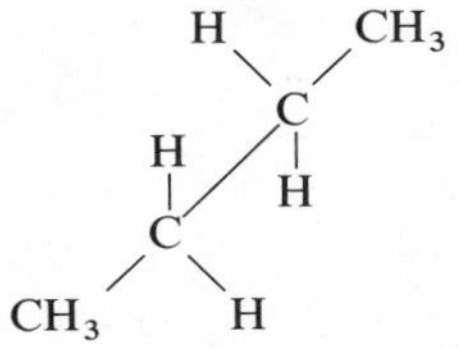

Because no such isomers were ever found by the early chemists, "free rotation about single bonds" was erroneously assumed to be the case.

In 1935, E. Teller and B. Topley suggested that this assumption of free rotation might not, in fact, be correct. They had been studying the heat capacity of ethane and noticed that it was significantly lower than theory indicated that it should be, if free rotation was assumed. They suggested that if the rotation about the C—C bond were not free, but was hindered by an energy barrier, theory and experiment could be brought into agreement.

Subsequent studies have shown that energy barriers to rotation do exist for C—C bonds in general, as well as for C—N, C—O, and most other single bonds. Thus the possibility of the existence of isomers that differ only in their internal rotational arrangements had to be considered. This kind of isomerization was given some attention by a few chemists from 1935 to 1950. Many of the basic principles involved were worked out during that period by physical chemists, the most notable contributions being made by Pitzer[†] and by Mizushima.[††]

The energy barriers to rotation about a single bond are known to be low (a few kilocalories per mole) in most cases, so that at room temperature the molecules have sufficient thermal energy to easily surmount them. It is therefore not surprising that isomers corresponding to different rotational arrangements were never isolated by the early chemists. Such isomers exist, but they interconvert too rapidly to permit easy separation. In 1950, Barton[†††] (then at Glasgow) showed that many of the relative chemical and physical properties of complicated molecules could be interpreted in terms of their specific or preferred rotational arrangements. Even though we cannot isolate rotational isomers, the properties of a molecule depend on the proportions of the different rotational isomers present.

[†] Kenneth S. Pitzer. Born Pomona, California, 1914. University of California (Berkeley), Rice and Stanford Universities.

[††] San-ichiro Mizushima. Born Tokyo, 1899. Tokyo University.

[†††] Derek H. R. Barton. Born Gravesend, England, 1918. University of Glasgow, Imperial College, London. Nobel Prize, 1969.

Molecules which differ from one another only by rotation about single bonds (rotational isomers) are usually called *conformational isomers* or *conformers*. The interpretation of the properties of compounds in terms of their conformations is referred to as *conformational analysis*. This is a branch of organic chemistry that is currently being explored by a number of chemists, but the fundamental principles are now quite clear.

In ethane, we can imagine two extremes in the arrangement of one methyl group with respect to the other caused by rotation about the C—C bond. These are referred to as *eclipsed* and *staggered* arrangements. Both the perspective formulas and the *Newman†* projections (which are end-on views looking down the C—C bond) are shown.

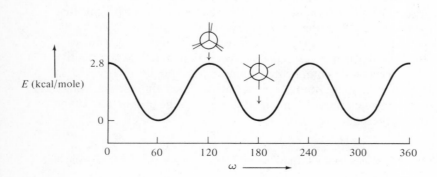

Newman projections

In a Newman projection, the angle in the plane of the paper between the front C—H bond and the rear C—H bond (the dihedral angle ω) varies from $0°$ to $360°$ as one methyl rotates. If we define $0°$ as the arrangement in which the hydrogens on the rear carbon are directly behind those on the front carbon (although in the drawing they are offset a little for clarity) as the *eclipsed conformation*, then $60°$ corresponds to a *staggered conformation*, $120°$ is another eclipsed conformation, and so on. The energy of the ethane molecule varies with ω in an approximately sinusoidal way, with three maxima and three minima. The height of this rotational barrier in ethane is known (from heat capacity measurements) to be 2.8 kcal/mole. These data are summarized pictorially in Figure 3.2.

Figure 3.2
The rotational or torsional energy of ethane.

† Melvin S. Newman. Born 1908, New York. Ohio State University.

The barrier height is such that at room temperature the molecules spend most of the time just rocking back and forth in the potential energy trough, and only occasionally does a molecule acquire enough energy to go over the top. Since events occur very rapidly on a molecular scale, however, "only occasionally" still means many times per second.

WHAT CAUSES ROTATIONAL BARRIERS? *The existence of rotational barriers has been recognized since 1936, but in spite of a considerable amount of work since that time, we are still not completely sure what causes them, in terms of a simple mechanical or electrostatic model. A variety of reasons have alternately been put forth and disproven. One simple picture was that the hydrogens are too close together in the eclipsed form, and a van der Waals repulsion (see Section 4.20) exists between them; however, the repulsion was calculated to be only a tenth of that which would be required to cause a barrier as large as that observed. Since the other explanations put forth have also been disproven, one is led to ask whether a simple physical picture of the barrier can, in fact, be given. If the Schroedinger equation is solved (by approximation methods) for ethane in the eclipsed form, and for ethane in the staggered form, it is found that the energy is lower in the staggered form by about 3 kcal. This is as it should be, and is really all that the Schroedinger equation can tell us. Nonetheless, chemists will continue to look for a simple physical picture for this phenomenon, as it would be of some help to know whether or not to expect barriers in new and novel situations, and direct solution of the Schroedinger equation is usually prohibitively difficult. In any event, as incomplete as our understanding of the cause of such barriers may be, we know now for ordinary situations just where such barriers will occur and how large they are, and this is sufficient for us to make effective use of them in conformational analysis.*

If we consider the rotation about the central bond in butane, we may expect a sinusoidal barrier similar to that in ethane. When $\omega = 0°$, the two methyl groups are eclipsed, and this arrangement should have a maximum energy. At $\omega = 60°$, there is a staggered arrangement which corresponds to an energy minimum. Another eclipsed arrangement is found at $\omega = 120°$ and a staggered arrangement at 180°. Butane differs from ethane, however, in that the 60° and 180° conformations are not identical. The 60° arrangement is given the name *gauche conformation*, while the 180° arrangement is called the *anti conformation*. Because the methyl groups are close enough together in the gauche conformation to exert a van der Waals repulsion on one another, the energy of the gauche form is 0.8 kcal/mole higher than that of the anti form.

eclipsed 0°   gauche 60°   eclipsed 120°   anti 180°   gauche 300°

anti   gauche   gauche

gauche *n*-Butane   anti *n*-Butane

EXERCISE 3.2

Draw perspective formulas and Newman projections for the eclipsed and staggered forms of propane.

Pitzer Strain. The full curve showing the energy of *n*-butane as a function of ω about the 2,3 bond is indicated by the heavy line in Figure 3.3. This *rotational energy* (sometimes called *torsional*

Figure 3.3
The rotational energy of butane : total energy, ——; CH_3/CH_3 repulsion, – – –; CH_3/H repulsion, ····; ethane barrier, –·–·.

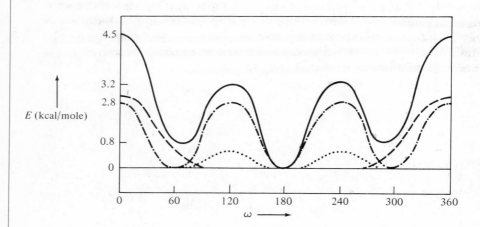

energy or *Pitzer strain*) is made up from three components. The first is the ethane barrier contribution, which accounts for 2.8 kcal/mole at 0°, 120°, and 240°. To this must be added the repulsion between the two methyl groups, which is a maximum of 1.7 kcal at $\omega = 0°$, but is negligible when the methyls are far apart. The third arises when a methyl group eclipses a hydrogen ($\omega = 120°$, 240°), for they exert a small unfavorable van der Waals repulsion on one another. These quantities are shown individually in Figure 3.3, together with their sum.

EXERCISE 3.3

Draw a qualitative curve similar to the one in Figure 3.3 for propane.

The *n*-alkanes exist as completely *anti* chains in crystals:

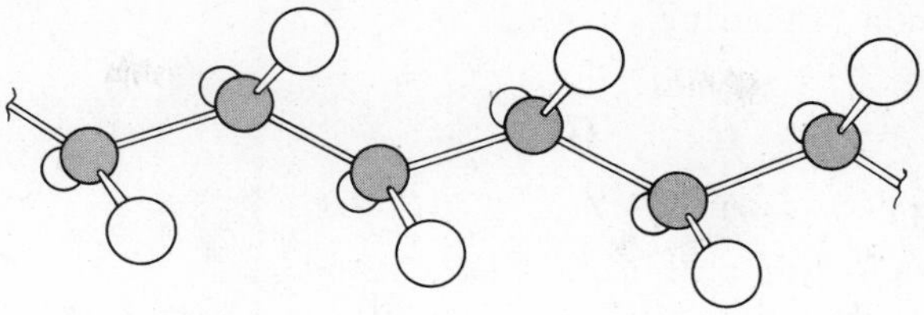

In the liquid phase, however, there are a significant number of molecules which are *gauche* at any one bond at a given instant, fewer which are *gauche* at two bonds (in different conformational arrangements), and fewer yet which are *gauche* at three bonds, and so on. An alkane, then, if it is very large, is usually a mixture of a great number of conformers, and its conformational properties are consequently mathematically awkward to study. (The term *conformer* is usually restricted to a conformational arrangement that corresponds to an energy minimum.)

3.4   Cyclohexane. Conformational Analysis

The alkanes which we have so far discussed have the general formula C_nH_{2n+2}, and they may be referred to as *acyclic* (without rings). The *cyclic*, or *alicyclic* (meaning aliphatic cyclic) compounds with the formula C_nH_{2n} form another major class of hydrocarbons. Cyclic hydrocarbons can be pictured as alkanes which have the chain looped around, so that hydrogens can be removed from the two end carbons and the carbons joined together. For example, *n*-hexane and its cyclic relative *cyclohexane*. (The latter is often abbreviated as a hexagon.)

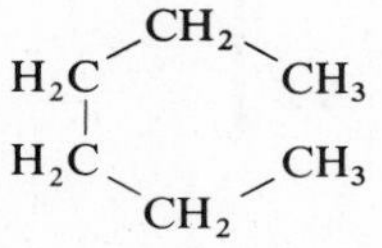

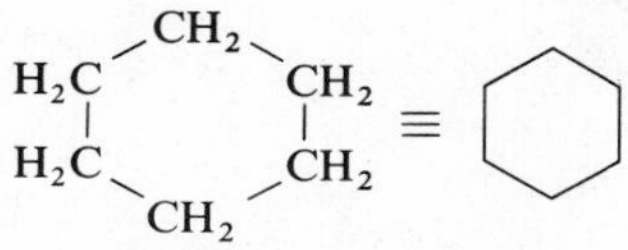

In the representations above the molecule looks flat, in reality the carbons of cyclohexane do not all lie in the same plane. If they did, the C—C—C bond angles would have to be 120° (the value of the interior angle of a regular hexagon). However, a C—C—C angle prefers to be close to tetrahedral (actually it is 112° in propane), and to force the bond angles to 120°, would require energy. Therefore in the ground state— the lowest energy state—cyclohexane is puckered.

This section will deal with cyclohexane. Other alicyclic hydrocarbons will be discussed in the next section.

We usually tend to think of the normal alkanes as "simple cases," but as far as conformational properties are concerned, the simplest system is cyclohexane. The stable conformer of this molecule is the so-called *chair form*. This conformer is rigid, in the sense that to change the dihedral angle about any bond or bonds requires a simultaneous change in one or more of the bond angles in the molecule. Cyclohexane therefore has only one important conformation, in contrast to the normal alkanes, which are mixtures of *anti* and *gauche* arrangements.

The student should examine a model of the cyclohexane ring as an aid to understanding the following discussion, preferably a framework or ball-and-stick model.

The cyclohexane ring presents a particularly simple conformational system for two reasons: first, because it exists in a single conformation (less than 1% of other conformations at room temperature); and second, because the molecule has a very high degree of symmetry. The symmetry is such that all of the carbon atoms are equivalent, and the hydrogens can be divided into only two equivalent classes, which are referred to as *axial* (a) and *equatorial* (e). The axial C—H bonds are all parallel to one another and to the symmetry axis of the molecule, which in the figure is shown as a dotted line passing vertically through the center of the ring.

Framework models will show these facts clearly, while space-filling models are less informative, as the photographs show. The same view is presented in each case. As we proceed around the ring, one axial hydrogen (H_a) points up, the next one points down, the next points up, and so on. The equatorial hydrogens (H_e) all lie roughly in the general plane of the ring, and they also alternate in their up–down directions. If the axial hydrogen attached to a given carbon atom points straight up, the equatorial hydrogen attached to the same carbon points slightly down, and vice versa.

Cyclohexane

There is another possible conformation for the cyclohexane ring which has normal bond angles and is commonly referred to as the *boat form.* It is energetically unfavorable because of the eclipsed butanelike arrangements it possesses. (Note in the figure below, and with models, that the heavy-lined portion of the ring corresponds to a *gauche* butane in the chair form, but to an eclipsed butane in the boat form.) Nevertheless, a tiny amount of the boat form is in equilibrium with the chair form at room temperature, and the equilibrium is rapidly established. If we consider the chair form A, and focus our attention

A
Chair

B
Boat

C
Chair

on the axial hydrogens, we see that we can lift up the corner of the molecule on the far left, and thereby convert the chair form into the boat form B (in which only the same hydrogens are shown for sake of clarity). It is possible to push that same carbon back down again, and to go from B back to chair A. It is also possible instead, to push down the carbon in the upper right-hand corner of B, in which case the molecule goes over to another chair form, C. These two chair forms, A and C, are indistinguishable in cyclohexane itself, but note that as one goes from the chair on the left to the chair on the right, the axial hydrogens on the left have become equatorial hydrogens on the right. (The equatorial hydrogens on the left have conversely become the axial hydrogens on the right.)

The possibility of the existence of a boat form for cyclohexane was recognized as long ago as 1890 by the German chemist Sachse. The boat form has natural (approximately tetrahedral) bond angles, as does the chair, and these are the only two forms which do. While the chair form is quite rigid, the boat form is not, and it can flex into what are referred to as *twisted* or *stretched conformations* (T) without any bond angle deformation:

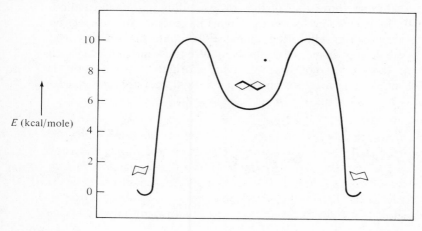

By a continuous flexing motion, the prow (or stern) of the boat moves around the ring from C-1 to C-2 to C-3, and so on. This motion has led to the boat form being referred to as the *flexible form*. It is necessary that the student examine models to understand this phenomenon.

Since rigid mechanical models indicate separate chair and flexible forms for cyclohexane, both of which appear to be strainless, Sachse thought that they should be separately isolable. Only one kind of cyclohexane was ever found experimentally, however, leading most chemists at the turn of the century to the incorrect belief that cyclohexane was planar.

We now know that our rigid mechanical models of cyclohexane are misleading in two respects. First, the reason that the chair and flexible forms are not separable by gross techniques such as distillation is that they interconvert too rapidly. The barrier which separates the two interconvertible chair forms A and C from one another is approximately 10 kcal/mole. A barrier of this size is low enough that the molecules pass over it many times per second at room temperature. This low barrier to interconversion was the reason why the early chemists were not able to isolate the two separate conformations of cyclohexane. In addition, however, the models are further misleading in that they show no difference in energy between the chair and flexible forms. Because of the rotational barrier about the C—C bond, the chair form proves to be about 5 kcal/mole more stable than the flexible form.

The energetics of the interconversion of the two chair forms of cyclohexane through the flexible form can be conveniently summarized with the aid of a *reaction coordinate diagram*, Figure 3.4.

Figure 3.4
The reaction coordinate diagram for the conformers of cyclohexane.

An inspection of the drawings and an examination of models will show that the regular boat form B contains two eclipsed and four staggered butane units, while in the chair form, all of the butane units are staggered. The twist conformation T of the flexible form proves to be more stable than that of the regular boat, however. In the twist conformation, none of the butane units are exactly eclipsed, but none are exactly staggered either. From the actual dihedral angles and Figure 3.3, it is estimated that the energy of the twist conformation is about 5 kcal/mole above that of the chair. This energy difference is sufficient that there will be only about 0.01 % of the flexible form in equilibrium with the chair form. Thus it is not only impossible to isolate the flexible form of cyclohexane, it is not even possible to detect it in any direct way. Simple derivatives of cyclohexane are also found to be in the chair conformation, essentially exclusively. Flexible forms are sometimes isolable in more complicated molecules, however.

In a monosubstituted cyclohexane, such as methylcyclohexane, there exists an equilibrium in which only two conformations are present to a significant extent. These are two chair forms, one with the methyl group axial, and the other with it equatorial.

Axial methyl   Equatorial methyl

Equatorial methylcyclohexane

The equilibrium again is established via a flexible form. Since methylcyclohexane is a mixture of two conformers in rapid equilibrium, we might ask, Which conformer is the more stable, and by how much?

In our discussion of the *n*-butane molecule (Section 3.3), it was pointed out that the *anti* form is more stable than the *gauche* because of a van der Waals repulsion between the two methyl groups in the latter. We can also analyze the conformations of methylcyclohexane in terms of these *anti* and *gauche* butane-type arrangements. As with *n*-butane itself, each *gauche* conformation may be expected to increase the energy of the molecule by about 0.8 kcal/mole above that of the corresponding *anti* conformation. Experiment shows this to be true for cyclohexane systems in general. Any interaction which involves only atoms of the ring will be the same in either conformation, and need not be considered. For methylcyclohexane, we need look only at those interactions which involve the methyl group; there are two of these for each conformation. If the methyl is equatorial, both of these interactions are *anti*, whereas if it is axial, they are both *gauche*.

gauche interactions
(axial methyl)

anti interactions
(equatorial methyl)

Newman projections looking from C-1 toward C-2

EXERCISE 3.4

Draw Newman projections like those in the figure which correspond to looking from C-6 down the C—C bond toward C-1. *Hint:* Use models.

This means that the equatorial conformer is more stable than the axial by $2 \times 0.8 = 1.6$ kcal/mole, and at room temperature it should and does comprise about 93% of the equilibrium mixture. (The connection between the energy difference and the equilibrium constant will be discussed in Chapter 13.)

EXERCISE 3.5

Draw a reaction coordinate diagram similar to Figure 3.4 which shows the interconversion of axial and equatorial methylcyclohexane.

3.5   Other Alicyclic Hydrocarbons

The cycloalkanes form a homologous series, of which cyclopropane is the smallest member, and higher members of which are cyclobutane, cyclopentane, cyclohexane, and so on.

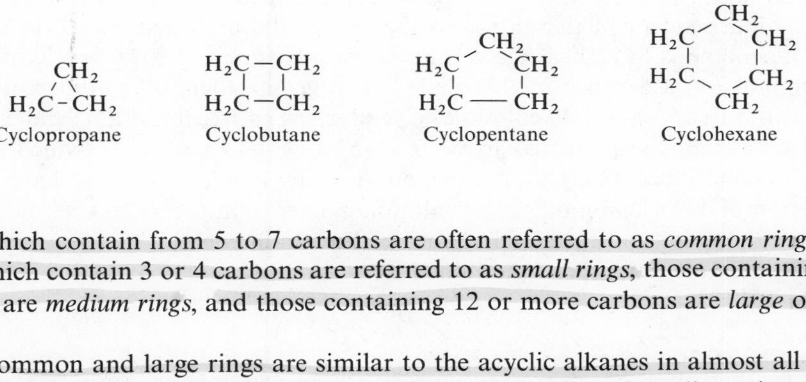

Cyclopropane	Cyclobutane	Cyclopentane	Cyclohexane

Rings which contain from 5 to 7 carbons are often referred to as *common rings*, while those which contain 3 or 4 carbons are referred to as *small rings*, those containing 8–11 carbons are *medium rings*, and those containing 12 or more carbons are *large* or *macro rings*.

The common and large rings are similar to the acyclic alkanes in almost all of their physical and chemical properties, whereas both the small and medium rings behave rather differently. The unusual characteristics of small rings arise because the sp^3 carbon tends to have bond angles near the tetrahedral value ($109\frac{1}{2}°$), while the geometric requirements of the small rings reduce these angles to much smaller values.

Two p orbitals on the same carbon have an angle between them of 90°. If these orbitals are hybridized by adding s character to them, the angle between them increases steadily, reaching a value of 180° when the amount of s character reaches 50%. There is no hybrid combination of s and p orbitals possible which will yield an interorbital angle of less than 90°. This means that in cyclopropane the carbons do not have their bonding orbitals pointing directly at one another, and the carbon–carbon bonds are best described as bent. Such bonds are not as strong as ordinary bonds, and such a molecule has a higher energy than usual. High-energy molecules of this type are said to be *strained*.

While the C—C—C interorbital angles in cyclobutane could be 90°, the resulting bonds would have to be pure p and very weak. The addition of some s character makes them stronger, even though they are no longer quite colinear. Cyclobutane, and especially cyclopropane, are said to have *bent bonds*, and they are highly strained.

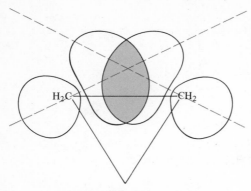

"Bent bond" in cyclopropane

The expression steric strain (*from the Greek* stereos = *space*) *is sometimes used to indicate the strain in a molecule imposed by its three-dimensional (spatial) geometry. Cyclopropane is said to possess* angular strain, *while* gauche-*butane and eclipsed ethane possess* van der Waals strain *and* torsional strain, *respectively.*

A chemical reaction which leads to the rupture of the strained system releases this strain; such a reaction tends to be much more exothermic, and to proceed more readily, than the same kind of reaction involving a cyclohexane ring or an acyclic system.

Strain in a molecule can be most easily detected from its heat of combustion, which is obtained by burning the compound in a calorimeter and measuring the heat evolved. For an alkane the reaction is

$$C_nH_{2n+2} + \frac{3n+1}{2}O_2 \rightarrow nCO_2 + (n+1)H_2O + \text{Heat}$$

The bond between any two atoms, say a C—H bond, has an energy which to a first approximation is independent of the nature of the rest of the molecule. The heat of combustion of *n*-pentane is 845.2 kcal/mole and that of *n*-hexane is 1,002.6 kcal/mole. The heat of combustion of a single methylene (–CH$_2$–) group, then, is the difference between these two values, or 157.4 kcal/mole. Cyclohexane is free of strain, and its heat of combustion might be predicted to be $6 \times 157.4 = 944.4$ kcal/mole, which is exactly what is found (Table 3.4). Cyclopropane, on the other hand, is, found to have a heat of combustion of 499.8 kcal/mole, 27.6 kcal/mole higher than the 472.2 kcal/mole that would be predicted for an unstrained structure. The strain energies for the cyclo-alkanes up to cyclodecane have been determined from their heats of combustion, and they are listed in Table 3.4.

Table 3.4   Strain and Heats of Combustion of Cycloalkanes

Cycloalkane, (CH$_2$)$_n$	n	Heat of combustion,[a] H, kcal/mole	Total strain,[b] kcal/mole
Cyclopropane	3	499.83	27.6
Cyclobutane	4	655.86	26.3
Cyclopentane	5	793.52	6.5
Cyclohexane	6	944.48	0.0
Cycloheptane	7	1108.2	6.4
Cyclooctane	8	1269.2	10.0
Cyclononane	9	1429.5	12.9
Cyclodecane	10	1586.0	12.0
Cyclopentadecane	15	2362.5	1.5
Open-chain, *n*-alkane	n	$157.4n + 58.2$	0.0

[a] For gaseous hydrocarbons to give liquid water at 25°C.
[b] Calculated by subtracting ($n \times 157.4$) from the observed heat of combustion.

The conformations and strain energies of these cycloalkane rings will now be considered briefly. The carbon atoms in cyclopropane are necessarily in a single plane (because three points determine a plane). This molecule has a fairly high degree of symmetry, and all of its hydrogens are equivalent.

It has been found that cyclobutane is not planar, but is puckered into the shape shown.

Cyclobutane

Cyclopentane

Puckering decreases the interior C—C—C bond angle from what would have been 90° in the planar form, to approximately 88°. This deformation of the angle even further from the tetrahedral value requires energy, but by puckering in this way, the molecule can reduce the torsional energy. As can be seen from the figure, the hydrogens are no longer eclipsed in this puckered form. The total energy is a minimum when the ring is puckered, and of course, the molecule adopts the conformation which leads to a minimum total energy.

Cyclopentane is puckered for the same reason. It has the conformation shown above. In cyclopentane, one or two carbon atoms are out of the plane of the others, but the ones out of the plane are successively changing. One atom pushes down into the plane and forces another out. Thus the nonplanarity moves about the ring. Such a motion is called a *pseudo-rotation*, and it is the same type of motion which the flexible form of cyclohexane undergoes. Note that the bending strain is less per angle for cyclobutane than for cyclopropane, but because more angles are bent, the total strain energies of the molecules are similar (Table 3.4).

The C—C—C bond angles in cyclopentane average around 105°, so the bending strain is much less serious than in cyclobutane, whereas the eclipsing strain is similar. The total strain energy in the molecule is consequently much less than that in cyclobutane.

The lowest-energy conformations of cycloheptane and cyclooctane are not yet definitely known, but they are thought to be as shown.

Cycloheptane

Cyclooctane

The strain energy of cycloheptane is due mainly to unfavorable torsional angles. It is not possible to have a perfectly staggered arrangement about each C—C bond, as it is in cyclohexane. Instead of dihedral angles of 60°, as in cyclohexane, these average about 75°, and as can be seen from Figure 3.3, this leads to torsional strain.

Cyclooctane

Cyclooctane and cyclononane also contain considerable torsional strain. In addition, there exist in these molecules serious transannular hydrogen–hydrogen repulsions, which occur because hydrogens on opposite sides of the rings are brought close enough to one another to experience van der Waals repulsion.

Cyclodecane has quite an unusual conformation, as revealed by X-ray crystallography. If the molecule had a crown conformation it would have very serious torsional and van der Waals strain. By adopting the conformation shown, the molecule achieves a much more stable (but still appreciably strained) geometry. The C—C—C bond angles in cyclodecane are considerably larger than usual, averaging 117°. These larger angles allow the molecule to expand and reduce the transannular repulsions between the hydrogens in the interior of the ring.

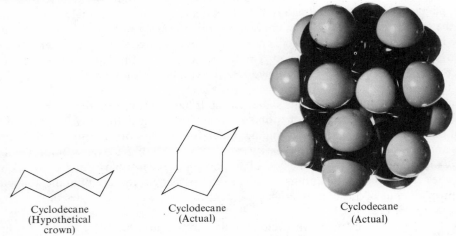

Cyclodecane
(Hypothetical
crown)

Cyclodecane
(Actual)

Cyclodecane
(Actual)

In each of the medium rings, there is a compromise between angular, torsional, and van der Waals strain, and each of these molecules adopts the conformation of lowest overall strain, or lowest total energy. Because of their strained nature, medium-sized rings are rather difficult to synthesize, and they are relatively scarce (see Section 34.2).

Each medium ring is found to have some hydrogens which are approximately equatorial, and others which are approximately axial, but there are different kinds of each. The conformational problems are much more formidable here than in cyclohexane, and so far very little progress has been made in their solution.

The still-larger rings usually have a preferred conformation which consists of two long parallel chains, which look like two normal alkanes side by side with all *anti* arrangements, joined together by two short end segments. They are essentially strainless.

Molecules containing two or more rings are well known. Cyclopentylcyclohexane is a representative of this type of molecule.

Cyclopentylcyclohexane

More novel are systems in which one or more carbons are common to two rings, such as the *spiran systems*, in which there is just one carbon common to two rings,

$$CH_2 \qquad CH_2$$
$$\diagdown C \diagup$$
$$CH_2 \qquad CH_2$$
Spiropentane

$$CH_2 \qquad CH_2$$
$$CH_2 \qquad C \qquad CH_2$$
$$CH_2 \qquad CH_2$$
Spirohexane

and the *bicyclo systems*, in which two or more carbons are common to two rings.

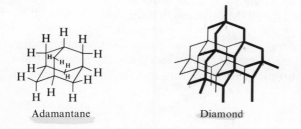

Bicyclo[2.2.1]heptane (Norbornane)   Decalin   Hydrindane

The decalin ring system, being composed of six-membered rings, is very stable and has been found to occur widely in nature. Even more complicated systems, such as perhydrophenanthrene and perhydroanthracene, are quite common among naturally occurring compounds.

Perhydrophenanthrene   Perhydroanthracene

Adamantane contains a three-dimensional arrangement of cyclohexane rings and corresponds to a building block from which the structure of a diamond is built up. A portion of the diamond structure is also shown for comparison. The great strength and hardness of a diamond is largely due to the fact that the whole crystal is really one giant molecule, held together with covalent bonds.

Adamantane   Diamond

3.6   Optical Isomerism

The French physicist Biot† discovered during the early nineteenth century that a number of naturally occurring organic compounds rotate the plane of polarization of an incident beam of polarized light. Because this "optical rotation" occurs even when the compounds are in the liquid phase it must be a molecular phenomenon. Some crystals, such as quartz, also rotate polarized light, but the rotation is obviously a property of the crystal and not the molecule, for the rotation disappears when the crystal is melted or dissolved. Such cases will not interest us.

In the latter part of the nineteenth century, it was found that in many instances there exist a pair of compounds which have identical physical properties such as melting point or solubility, and seem to have identical structures, but which have equal and opposite effects on polarized light. Such compounds are called *optical isomers*. Before we discuss the geometry of the tetrahedral carbon atom, which explains the existence of optical isomers, we will describe the polarimeter, a key instrument in the study of optical activity, and discuss the principles upon which it is based.

A light ray has an electromagnetic vibration associated with it; this vibration occurs in a plane perpendicular to the line of propagation of the ray. A beam of ordinary light consists of a bundle of rays, and each ray has an associated electromagnetic vibration.

† Jean Baptiste Biot, 1774–1862. Born Paris. Physicist, College de France.

The vibrations are always perpendicular to the line of transmission, but otherwise unrestricted. The vibrations of the whole beam thus occur in all of the perpendicular directions simultaneously, so that if we look at the beam end on, we see the vibrations in various directions as indicated in Figure 3.5. These vibrations have the properties of

Figure 3.5
The electric vectors of a beam of ordinary light, on the left, and polarized light, on the right.

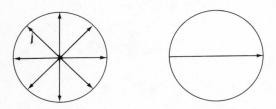

vectors, so that any single vibration can be considered to be made up from components in two mutually perpendicular directions only. All of the vibrations of the entire beam can therefore be considered as the sum of two separate sets of vibrations that are mutually perpendicular.

Polarized light (or more properly, plane-polarized light) is light from which one of the two vector components has been removed. The resulting electromagnetic vibration of the light is therefore entirely in a single plane. There are a number of ways of accomplishing the plane polarization of a light beam, one of which makes use of a *Nicol prism.* This type of prism divides ordinary incoming light into two beams polarized in perpendicular planes. One beam is diverted out of the prism, so that the light transmitted by the prism is plane-polarized.

In a polarimeter, illustrated in Figure 3.6, ordinary light (usually monochromatic sodium light) enters through a polarizing prism (polarizer) and is converted into plane-polarized light, which then proceeds through the sample tube and strikes another Nicol

Figure 3.6
Schematic representation of a polarimeter.

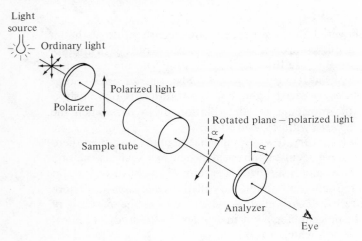

prism, called the *analyzer.* If there is no sample in the sample tube, the light remains polarized in the same plane as when it emerged from the polarizing Nicol prism, which is rigidly attached to the mounting of the instrument. The analyzer prism may be rotated, and when properly oriented, all of the light striking it will pass through. If the analyzer prism is rotated 90° from this orientation, then it will pass only light which is polarized at right angles to that coming through the polarizing prism, so that in fact no light will be transmitted and the field will be dark. At a rotation between 0° and 90°, a fraction of the light will be transmitted, that component of the vector which is vibrating in the proper plane. As the analyzer prism rotates, the angle of rotation can be read on a device which looks like a large protractor.

When the sample tube is empty, a maximum amount of light is transmitted through the analyzer at a rotational angle of 0°. If various common substances such as water or a solution of salt are placed in the sample tube, a maximum amount of light is still transmitted when the rotational angle of the analyzer is 0°. For some substances, this is no longer true. For a solution of sugar, for example, the analyzer prism must be rotated away from 0° for a maximum of light to be transmitted. How much it must be rotated depends on the size of the sample and its concentration, the length of the sample tube, the temperature, the wavelength of the light, and the solvent.

In order to accurately compare measurements of polarization on one sample with measurements on another, all of the variables must be specified when the measurement is reported. To put the results on a more systematic basis, a quantity referred to as the *specific rotation*, [α], is defined as the rotation in degrees brought about by a solution containing 1 gram of a substance in 1 milliliter of solution, examined in a polarimeter tube having a length of 1 decimeter. The rotation value, which may be clockwise (positive) or counterclockwise (negative), is then a characteristic of the compound examined, as long as the other variables are kept constant.

$$[\alpha] = \frac{\text{Observed rotation}}{\text{Tube length (dm)} \times \text{Concentration (g/ml)}}$$

The D line of sodium (the line at 5893 Å which imparts the yellow color to a sodium flame) is the most commonly used light source and the temperature most often used is 25°C. The symbol $[\alpha]_D^{25}$ denotes this information. Since the rotation sometimes depends on the solvent and concentration, it is also customary to write the solvent and the concentration (in this case in grams per 100 ml) after the value. For example,

$$[\alpha]_D^{25} = -32.2° \ CHCl_3(c2.05)$$

The correct interpretation of the phenomenon of optical isomerism was finally given independently in 1874 by van't Hoff in the Netherlands and LeBel in Paris. The experimental facts both require and are explained by a tetrahedral carbon atom. Prior to this time, chemists did not consider it possible to know anything about the three-dimensional spatial arrangement of molecules—a knowledge of structure meant simply a knowledge of the order in which the atoms of the molecule were joined together.

The geometric properties of a tetrahedron are such that if there are four *different* substituents attached to a carbon atom, the molecule does not contain a plane of symmetry, and there are two kinds of geometrical arrangements which the molecule can have. These two arrangements (*configurations*) are different in that it is not possible to simultaneously superimpose all of the atoms of one figure on the like atoms of the other. The two configurations are, in fact, *nonsuperimposable mirror images.* Such molecules result when the four groups attached to the carbon atom are all different, and a molecule of this kind is said to be *asymmetric*, or to contain an asymmetric carbon. If two or more of the groups attached to the carbon are the same, the mirror images are superimposable and both correspond to the identical substance. (This is best seen with the aid of models.)

Nonsuperimposable mirror images

In this text a heavy line will be used to mean a bond which protrudes forward out of the plane of the paper, and a dashed line of the kind shown (ⅢⅢⅢ) will be used to indicate a bond which points back away from the plane of the paper. Another kind of dashed line (---) will be used for other purposes, such as to indicate a bond which is partially broken.

Two nonsuperimposable mirror image structures for the same molecule are called *enantiomers*. It is found experimentally that enantiomers possess identical physical properties, as we might expect, *except* that they rotate polarized light in opposite directions (by equal amounts). If a molecule is superimposable on its mirror image, then that substance cannot exist as a pair of enantiomers, but will exist only as a single compound which will not rotate polarized light.

If two enantiomers are mixed together in equal amounts, a *racemic mixture* results, which also does not rotate polarized light. The left- and right-handed rotations cancel out.

We meet a number of enantiomeric items in daily life. The left hand, for example, is the mirror image of the right hand, and they are not superimposable. This becomes obvious if we try to put a right glove on a left hand. Similarly, shoes have an enantiomeric relationship, while the stock in a shoe store constitutes a racemic mixture.

Molecular Rotation. Often one wishes to compare compounds of different molecular weights, for which it is convenient to have a *molecular*, rather than a *specific rotation*, i.e., based on moles rather than on grams. Since such a number would tend to be excessively large if one simply multiplied the specific rotation by the molecular weight, the number obtained thereby is divided by 100 to obtain the molecular rotation (M_D).

$$M_D = \frac{[\alpha]_D \times MW}{100}$$

Figure 3.7
Typical rotatory dispersion curves.

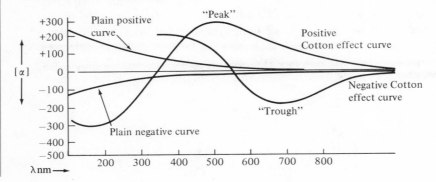

Rotatory Dispersion. The rotation of a compound varies with the wavelength of light at which the measurement is made. For many simple compounds, the rotation simply increases in absolute value as we proceed from visible light farther and farther into the ultraviolet region. The function which describes the variation of the rotation of a compound with wavelength is called the *rotatory dispersion curve.* The type of curve described above is referred to as a *plain curve,* and it may be either positive or negative, as shown in Figure 3.7.

Sometimes a compound will give a characteristically shaped optical rotatory dispersion curve referred to as a *Cotton effect curve,* (see Figure 3.7). Such curves are called positive if, when going from long toward short wavelength the curve first increases in the positive direction, and then becomes more negative. A Cotton effect curve is called negative if the signs of the segments are reversed. Obviously, more information can be obtained from such a curve than from a single point at the D line. The usefulness of such curves in determining organic structures will be discussed later (Section 6.8).

We might ask at this point if the existence of optical isomers is an academic curiosity, or if it plays a significant part in the real world. As will become apparent in later chapters, many, indeed most, of the compounds which occur in living systems contain one or more asymmetric carbon atoms. Biological systems are usually quite particular as to which mirror image they require, and it thus becomes *very important* to understand this phenomenon if we are going to understand any kind of living system.

We might also ask "Why do enantiomers behave as they do toward polarized light?" If we look at a solution of a compound, or a pure liquid or gas, say methane, we find that it contains a very large number of molecules oriented in all possible ways. A given molecule in a fixed arbitrary orientation would rotate the plane of polarization a small amount, say to the left. If the molecule is superimposable on its mirror image, as is methane, it is equally probable that another molecule will have the mirror image orientation of the first one at any particular instant; the rotational contributions of the two molecules will thus be equal and opposite, and they will cancel out. If one works with a macroscopic sample, the various possible orientations will each rotate the light by varying amounts in different directions, but the compensations will always cause the total rotation to average to zero.

If now we have a solution composed of identical molecules which are not superimposable on their mirror images, and if all the molecules are of the same enantiomer, then different molecules will have different orientations which will all contribute to the optical rotation of the whole solution. But for any given orientation, the mirror image is not present, as it would correspond to the other enantiomer. Therefore, the rotations do not cancel out and will add up to give some resultant (nonzero) value. The other enantiomer would give a solution of mirror image orientations, hence an equal and opposite total resultant rotation. A mixture of equal amounts of the two enantiomers (racemic mixture) would give a solution in which for any orientation there would be an equal probability of a mirror-image orientation, and the resultant rotation of such a mixture is zero.

Unfortunately, it is somewhat difficult to represent a tetrahedron with a drawing or formula. The two chief representations are *perspective* (Section 3.1) and *projection* formulas. Both types of formulas will be used in this text. Projection formulas show two dimensions only, the other dimension being imagined as perpendicular to the

Figure 3.8
Four equivalent representations of a tetrahedral carbon.

Perspective formulas   Projection formula   Fisher projection

plane of the paper; heavy lines indicate bonds above the plane, and dotted lines indicate bonds below the plane. *Fischer projections* (Figure 3.8) are widely used because of their simplicity. By convention, bonds drawn horizontally are above the plane of the page and those drawn vertically are below it. In a Fischer projection then, while

$$
\begin{array}{c}
c \\
a\!\!-\!\!\!\!\begin{array}{|c}\;\end{array}\!\!\!\!-\!\!b \\
d
\end{array}
\quad\text{and}\quad
\begin{array}{c}
d \\
b\!\!-\!\!\!\!\begin{array}{|c}\;\end{array}\!\!\!\!-\!\!a \\
c
\end{array}
$$

refer to the same molecule,

$$
\begin{array}{c}
c \\
a\!\!-\!\!\!\!\begin{array}{|c}\;\end{array}\!\!\!\!-\!\!b \\
d
\end{array}
\quad\text{and}\quad
\begin{array}{c}
a \\
d\!\!-\!\!\!\!\begin{array}{|c}\;\end{array}\!\!\!\!-\!\!c \\
b
\end{array}
$$

are not identical but are enantiomers. (The student should study models of the above until the meaning of a Fischer projection is quite clear.)

To tell whether or not two Fischer projections refer to the identical molecule or to a pair of enantiomers, the following method may be found useful. If we want to show that the following two compounds are identical

$$
\begin{array}{c}
c \\
a\!\!-\!\!\!\!\begin{array}{|c}\;\end{array}\!\!\!\!-\!\!b \\
d
\end{array}
\qquad
\begin{array}{c}
d \\
b\!\!-\!\!\!\!\begin{array}{|c}\;\end{array}\!\!\!\!-\!\!a \\
c
\end{array}
$$

we can interchange any two groups, a pair at a time. Each such interchange corresponds to converting the molecule to its enantiomer. If two interchanges are made, the original molecule is again obtained. Three interchanges give the enantiomer of the original molecule, while four give back the original. Thus we can take

$$
\begin{array}{c}
c \\
a\!\!-\!\!\!\!\begin{array}{|c}\;\end{array}\!\!\!\!-\!\!b \\
d
\end{array}
$$

and interchange c and d to give

$$
\begin{array}{c}
d \\
a\!\!-\!\!\!\!\begin{array}{|c}\;\end{array}\!\!\!\!-\!\!b \\
c
\end{array}
$$

which is the enantiomer of the original molecule. If we make a second interchange of a and b, we have

$$
\begin{array}{c}
d \\
b\!\!-\!\!\!\!\begin{array}{|c}\;\end{array}\!\!\!\!-\!\!a \\
c
\end{array}
$$

Since *two* interchanges were required to convert the first structure to the second we conclude that they both have the same configuration. There are many different ways in which the interchanges could have been made to interconvert the two molecules but no matter what the order of the interchanges or how many were required, an *even number* of interchanges would always be necessary. An *even number* of interchanges will always give back the original molecule, while an odd number will always give the enantiomer.

EXERCISE 3.6

Show that

$$\text{a}\!-\!\!\!\overset{\text{c}}{\underset{\text{d}}{\vert}}\!\!\!-\!\text{b} \quad \text{and} \quad \text{d}\!-\!\!\!\overset{\text{a}}{\underset{\text{b}}{\vert}}\!\!\!-\!\text{c}$$

are enantiomers by showing that an odd number of interchanges is required to interconvert them.

A system of nomenclature had to be devised in order to conveniently discuss optical isomers—isomers which differ in configuration.

The difference between conformation *and* configuration *is most easily seen by recognizing that to change conformation only a rotation about a single bond is required, while a change in configuration requires the breaking of a bond, and reforming it in a different way.*

The original system of nomenclature had as the starting point the enantiomers of a standard compound, glyceraldehyde,

$$HOCH_2\!-\!\!\overset{\vert}{\underset{\underset{\textstyle OH}{\vert}}{CH}}\!\!-\!CHO$$

One enantiomer rotated polarized light to the right or clockwise, and it was referred to as (+)-glyceraldehyde, while the other enantiomer rotated polarized light to the left or counterclockwise and was referred to as (−)-glyceraldehyde.

The two enantiomers of glyceraldehyde can be represented with Fischer projections. The two projections shown were called D and L, from the Latin words *dexter* and *laevus*, meaning right and left, respectively. The problem is to decide which of the formulas (D or L) corresponds to which actual compound (+ or −). The *absolute configurations*

CHO
H——OH
CH₂OH
D-Glyceraldehyde

CHO
HO——H
CH₂OH
L-Glyceraldehyde

of the glyceraldehydes could not be established by the early chemists because they could devise no method for determining which actual compound corresponded to which Fischer projection. What they could do was to determine *relative configurations*. For example, there are two enantiomers of glyceric acid, one of which is obtained upon oxidation of (−)-glyceraldehyde. Since the asymmetric carbons are not involved in the oxidation, they must be the same in the glyceric acids as they were in the glyceraldehydes.

CHO
H——OH   [O]→
CH₂OH
D-Glyceraldehyde

COOH
H——OH
CH₂OH
D-Glyceric acid

CHO
HO——H   [O]→
CH₂OH
L-Glyceraldehyde

COOH
HO——H
CH₂OH
L-Glyceric acid

Thus while the absolute configurations of these compounds were all unknown, the configurations of the glyceric acids relative to the glyceraldehydes were easily determined.

The decision was therefore made to *arbitrarily* assign the D configuration to (+)-glyceraldehyde, and the L configuration to (−)-glyceraldehyde. All other compounds containing asymmetric carbons could (in principle at least) be related to one or the other of the glyceraldehydes, and therefore all relative configurations could be determined. Either they would all be right, or all reversed, depending on whether or not the arbitrary assignment for D-glyceraldehyde was correct. This was done, and happily, when the absolute configurations of the glyceraldehydes were finally determined in 1951 (Section 6.8), it was found that the arbitrary assignment was indeed correct. D-(+)-glyceraldehyde and L-(−)-glyceraldehyde do have the formulas shown earlier.

Finally then, the absolute configurations for many compounds which had already been related to glyceraldehyde became known. Compounds related to D-glyceraldehyde were said to have a D configuration, while those related to L-glyceraldehyde were said to have an L configuration. A difficulty arose, however, because it was not always clear to which glyceraldehyde a given compound was "related." For example, it is clear enough that the compounds

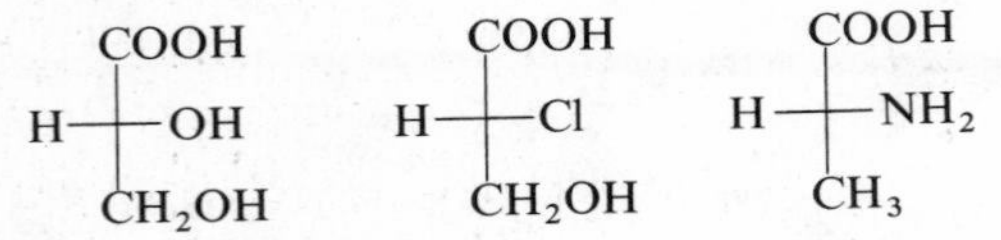

$$
\begin{array}{ccc}
\text{COOH} & \text{COOH} & \text{COOH} \\
\text{H}\!-\!\!-\!\text{OH} & \text{H}\!-\!\!-\!\text{Cl} & \text{H}\!-\!\!-\!\text{NH}_2 \\
\text{CH}_2\text{OH} & \text{CH}_2\text{OH} & \text{CH}_3
\end{array}
$$

are D rather than L but it is not at all clear whether

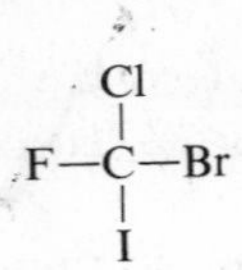

$$
\begin{array}{c}
\text{Cl} \\
\text{F}\!-\!\text{C}\!-\!\text{Br} \\
\text{I}
\end{array}
$$

is D or L.

Because of the somewhat ambiguous definitions of D and L, another system of nomenclature was devised for asymmetric compounds, and it has been used increasingly since the early 1960s. The symbols used in this system for the two enantiomers are R (from the Latin *rectus*, meaning right) and S (from the Latin *sinister*, meaning left). What was D in the old system in most cases becomes R in the new system, and what was L in most cases becomes S. The definitions of R and S are more precise and quite different from those of D and L, however.

Assignment of R *and* S. We will consider how to assign configuration (R or S) to the enantiomer of 3-methylhexane shown. If the student will examine a model of this enantiomer, the following discussion will be clearer.

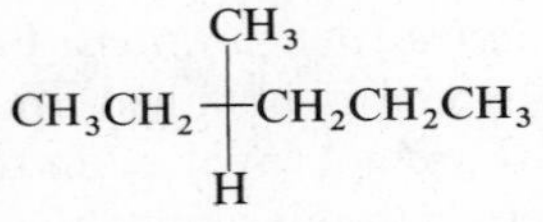

$$
\begin{array}{c}
\text{CH}_3 \\
\text{CH}_3\text{CH}_2\!-\!\!-\!\text{CH}_2\text{CH}_2\text{CH}_3 \\
\text{H}
\end{array}
$$

First we decide which of the atoms attached to the asymmetric carbon has the lowest atomic weight (hydrogen in this case) and then orient the molecule so that atom is away from us. The other three groups are now protruding toward us, in a manner analogous to a steering wheel facing a driver—as pictured in Figure 3.9.

Figure 3.9
Determination of the configuration of 3-methylhexane.

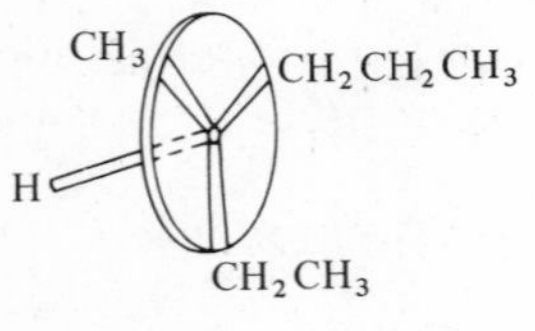

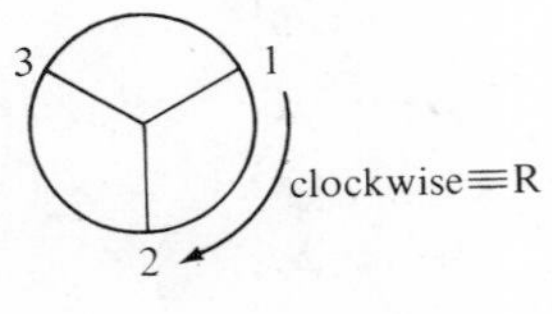

It is now necessary to assign *priority numbers* 1, 2, and 3 to the three groups facing us (the hydrogen is number 4). Priority numbers are determined as follows. First note the atom of each group which is attached directly to the asymmetric center. If one has a larger atomic weight than the others, it is assigned priority number 1, the next heaviest is 2. In this case, however, all three are carbons; they have the same atomic weight, and no priority assignment is possible on this basis. (Hydrogen has the smallest atomic weight, however, so it is number 4.)

When there are two or more groups which cannot be assigned priority numbers on the basis of the atoms directly attached to the asymmetric center, we look at the atoms attached to the atoms attached to the asymmetric center. If one is heavier than the others, it receives priority number 1. In the present case, the methyl carbon has only hydrogens attached to it, while the ethyl carbon attached to the asymmetric center has a carbon attached to it. The ethyl group therefore will have a higher priority than will the methyl. Next, looking at the carbon of the propyl group attached to the asymmetric center, we see that it has in turn one carbon attached to it, so at this level it is of the same priority as the ethyl group. Hence we go still one atom further away from the asymmetric center, and now consider the methyl carbon of the ethyl group, and the middle carbon of the propyl group. The former has only hydrogens attached to it, while the latter has a carbon, and the latter thus has a higher priority. The propyl, ethyl, and methyl groups, therefore, have priorities 1, 2, and 3, respectively. Then looking at our steering wheel (Figure 3.9) again, we start with the group having priority number 1, and draw an arrow toward 2. If the arrow goes clockwise, as it does in this case, the molecule has the R configuration, while if it had gone counterclockwise, the molecule would have been S.

EXERCISE 3.7

Show that

$$
\begin{array}{cc}
\begin{array}{c} F \\ H\!-\!\!\!\begin{array}{c}|\\|\end{array}\!\!\!-Cl \\ Br \end{array}
& \text{and} &
\begin{array}{c} COOH \\ H\!-\!\!\!\begin{array}{c}|\\|\end{array}\!\!\!-NH_2 \\ CH_3 \end{array}
\end{array}
$$

each have the R configuration.

There are additional rules for more complicated cases, of which we will take up but one more here. If there are two heavy atoms attached to the atom next to the asymmetric center, the priority is higher than if there is but one heavy atom. Thus isopropyl has a higher priority than *n*-propyl,

$$
\begin{array}{c}
CH_3 \\
| \\
CH_3\!-\!C\!- \\
| \\
H
\end{array}
\qquad CH_3CH_2CH_2\!-
$$

since the former has the atom in question bound to two carbons, compared to one for the latter. Isopropyl is, in fact, of higher priority than neopentyl; because the attached carbon in the former case is bound to two other carbons,

$$
\begin{array}{c}
CH_3 \\
| \\
CH_3\!-\!C\!- \\
| \\
H
\end{array}
\qquad
\begin{array}{c}
CH_3\ H \\
|\ \ \ | \\
CH_3\!-\!C\!-\!C\!- \\
|\ \ \ | \\
CH_3\ H
\end{array}
$$

the latter only to one. Similarly, a fluorine atom has a higher priority number than a butyl group, because the atomic weight of fluorine is larger than that of carbon, and what is subsequently attached to the carbon is therefore irrelevant. It might be pointed out that a heavier isotope has priority over a light one, and for deuterium-containing compounds, D has priority over H.

Unfortunately, there is no simple relationship between the sign of rotation (+ or −) and the configuration (D or L). If we have a group of assorted compounds, all with the D configuration, it will be found that some are dextrorotatory and others are levorotatory. If the configuration of a compound is unknown, therefore, a determination of the sign of rotation of the compound is not sufficient to permit an assignment of configuration. Such assignments of configuration usually have been made by relating the compounds to glyceraldehyde (or to other compounds previously related to glyceraldehyde) by reactions which either do not involve the asymmetric center, or by reactions which do involve the asymmetric center but lead to a configurational result that is precisely known. In some cases it is possible to assign the absolute configuration from the optical rotatory dispersion curve.

The symbols d and l have been used extensively in the older literature by some people to mean the same thing as $(+)$ and $(-)$, and by other people to mean the same thing as D and L. Therefore, the symbols d and l are somewhat ambiguous. However, a racemic mixture is spoken of as a dl mixture without ambiguity. The symbols D and L are now seldom used, except in certain specialized areas (for example, for carbohydrates and amino acids), where they are used extensively. The recommended symbolism is $(+)$ or $(-)$ for the sign of rotation, and, except in a few specialized areas, R or S for configuration.

PROBLEMS

Hint: Use models to help you see the following.

1. Write the structures of all of the isomeric hexanes.

2. Give names for the following:

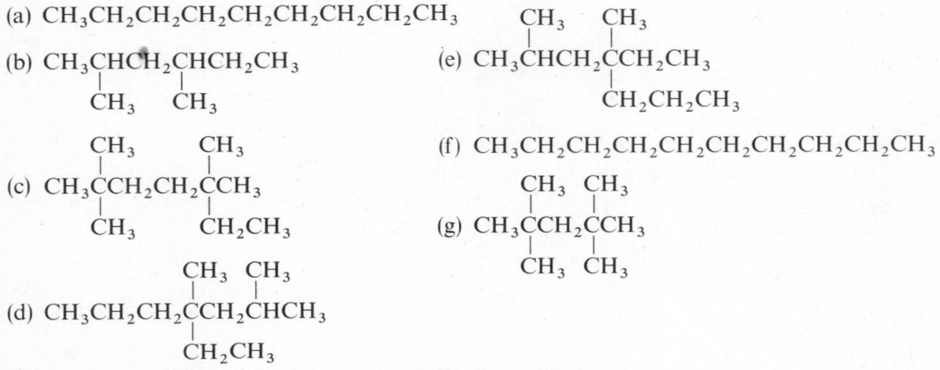

    (a) $CH_3CH_2CH_2CH_2CH_2CH_2CH_2CH_2CH_3$

    (b) $CH_3CHCH_2CHCH_2CH_3$
          | |
         CH_3 CH_3

    (c) $CH_3CCH_2CH_2CCH_3$
    with CH_3 substituents and CH_2CH_3

    (d) $CH_3CH_2CH_2CCH_2CHCH_3$
    with CH_3 CH_3 and CH_2CH_3

    (e) $CH_3CHCH_2CCH_2CH_3$
    with CH_3 CH_3 and $CH_2CH_2CH_3$

    (f) $CH_3CH_2CH_2CH_2CH_2CH_2CH_2CH_2CH_2CH_3$

    (g) $CH_3CCH_2CCH_3$
    with CH_3 CH_3 and CH_3 CH_3

3. Draw perspective views and Newman projections for:
    (a) Ethane, staggered form
    (b) Ethane, eclipsed
    (c) Propane, staggered form
    (d) *n*-Butane, staggered form (i) *anti*; (ii) *gauche*.

4. *Optional Problem.* As rotation about the central bond in butane occurs, the energy of the molecule varies. Draw a graph which shows the energy as a function of dihedral angle (ω).

5. Sketch a perspective drawing of the chair form of cyclohexane. Indicate (a) the axial hydrogens; (b) the equatorial hydrogens.

6. Which is more stable, axial-methyl, or equatorial-methyl cyclohexane? By how much? Why?

7. Which of the following have (or are capable of having) enantiomeric forms?

    (a) Shoe   (e) Nail   (i) Wood screw
    (b) Stocking   (f) Screw driver   (j) Automobile
    (c) Baseball cap   (g) Hammer   (k) Ear
    (d) Cup   (h) Drill (bit)   (l) Ear muff

8. Is cyclobutane planar? Why?

9. (a) A compound (0.3 g) is dissolved in chloroform to give a total volume of 10 ml. When this solution is placed in a 20 centimeter tube, it shows an optical rotation of $+7.52°$ at the sodium D line at 25°C. What is the specific rotation, and how is it symbolized? (b) The molecular weight of the compound is 146. Calculate the molar rotation and indicate the symbolism.

10. The homogeneous compound (+)-4-methyldodecanoic acid shows a rotation of +0.175° in a 1 dm tube at the sodium D line at 25°C. The density of the compound is 0.888 g/ml. Calculate the specific rotation, and indicate how the data are to be summarized.

11. *Optional Problem.* (+)-3-Methylcyclohexanol shows a plain positive optical rotatory dispersion curve, while the closely related compound (+)-3-methylcyclohexanone shows a positive Cotton effect. Draw qualitative sketches of these curves.

12. For each of the following pairs of compounds, indicate which are enantiomers.

    (a)

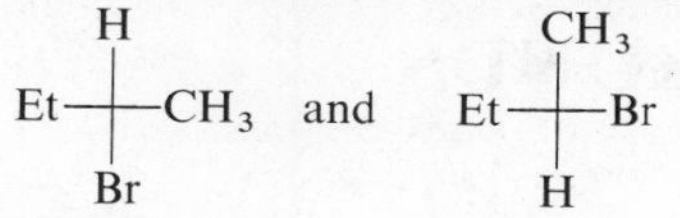

$$\underset{Br}{\overset{H}{Et-\!\!\!\!\!-CH_3}} \quad and \quad \underset{H}{\overset{CH_3}{Et-\!\!\!\!\!-Br}}$$

    (b)

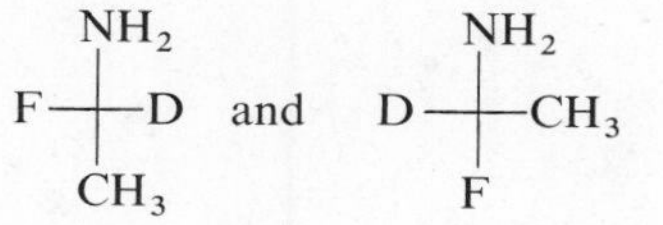

$$\underset{CH_3}{\overset{NH_2}{F-\!\!\!\!\!-D}} \quad and \quad \underset{F}{\overset{NH_2}{D-\!\!\!\!\!-CH_3}}$$

    (c)

$$\underset{HO\quad CH_2OH}{\overset{CH_3}{\bigwedge^{\text{\tiny{IIIIIII}}CH_2CH_3}}} \quad and \quad \underset{CH_3\quad OH}{\overset{CH_2OH}{\bigwedge^{\text{\tiny{IIIIIII}}CH_2CH_3}}}$$

    (d)

$$\underset{HO\quad CH_2CH_3}{\overset{CH_2CH_3}{Cl^{\text{\tiny{IIIIIII}}\!\bigwedge}}} \quad and \quad \underset{CH_3CH_2\quad OH}{\overset{CH_2CH_3}{\bigwedge^{\text{\tiny{IIIIIII}}Cl}}}$$

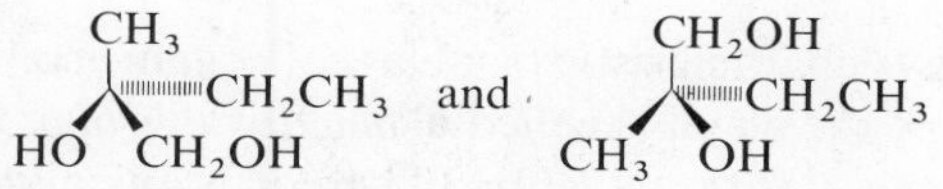

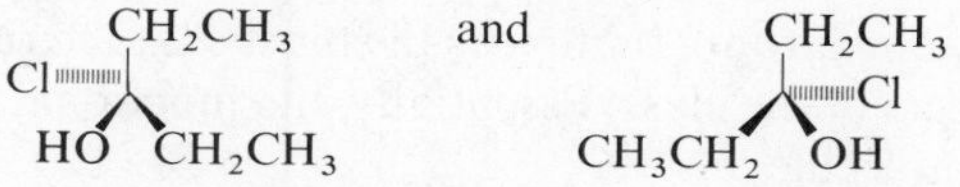

13. Draw structures for the following compounds:
    (a) 2,3-dimethylhexane; (b) 3-ethyl-4-methyloctane; (c) 4,5-diisopropyloctane.

    Optional Problems

1. Do the following compounds have R or S configuration?

    (a)

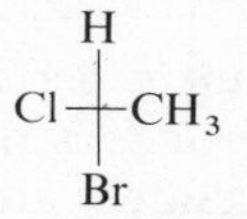

$$\underset{Br}{\overset{H}{Cl-\!\!\!\!\!-CH_3}}$$

    (b)

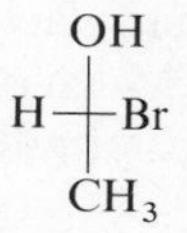

$$\underset{CH_3}{\overset{OH}{H-\!\!\!\!\!-Br}}$$

    (c)

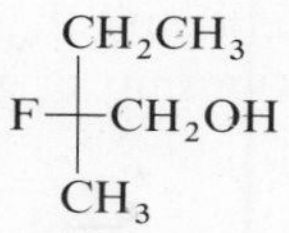

$$\underset{CH_3}{\overset{CH_2CH_3}{F-\!\!\!\!\!-CH_2OH}}$$

    (d)

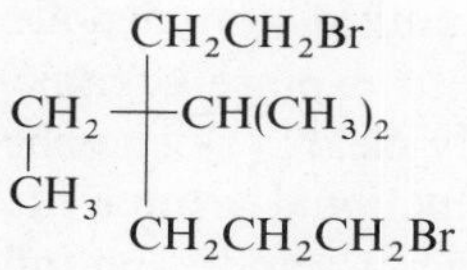

$$\overset{CH_2CH_2Br}{\underset{\overset{|}{CH_3}}{CH_2-\!\!\!\!\!-CH(CH_3)_2}} \\ CH_2CH_2CH_2Br$$

    (e)

$$\overset{CH_3}{\underset{CH_3}{\overset{H-\!\!\!\!\!-OH}{H-\!\!\!\!\!-OH}}}$$

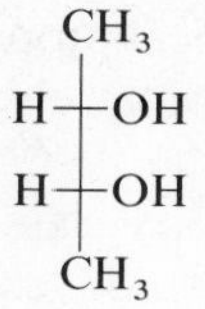

2. Build a model of ethylcyclohexane, and decide which of the possible conformations is the most stable. Explain.

CHAPTER 4

FUNCTIONAL GROUPS
CONTAINING SINGLE BONDS

4.1   Functional Groups

An atom or group of atoms which is characteristic of a class of organic compounds, and which determines the properties of the class, is called a *functional group*. For example, in the alcohols, which have the general formula ROH (where R is any alkyl group), the hydroxyl group, –OH, is the functional group. It imparts the most characteristic physical and chemical properties to members of the class. Essentially, the functional group is the nonhydrocarbon portion of the molecule.

Simple functional groups are formed by the attachment of a *heteroatom* (halogen, oxygen, sulfur, nitrogen, etc.) to the carbon of an alkyl group by a single bond. In this chapter we shall be concerned with the structure, nomenclature, and properties of the common classes of organic compounds whose functional groups contain only single (sigma) bonds. At the end of this chapter (Section 4.20) we will be able to make some generalizations about the properties of these compounds as they are affected by the intermolecular forces acting on the functional groups. In subsequent chapters functional groups containing multiply bonded atoms will be considered.

As we continue to explore organic chemistry, two important generalizations will become increasingly clear: (1) The chemistry of organic compounds is the composite chemistry of the functional groups present; the hydrocarbon residues attached to the functional groups act as modifying influences rather than as primary factors, in determining the physical and chemical properties of the compounds. (2) Much of chemistry is quite understandable in light of the electronic structure of the atoms or groups of atoms involved.

Before we discuss the individual classes of compounds, there is a topic that is important for all classes, which we must now explore further: the relationship of geometry and hybridization.

4.2   Geometry and Hybridization

In Chapter 2, the hybridization of carbon orbitals by combination of the s with the three p orbitals to form four identical sp^3 orbitals was discussed. This orbital configuration allowed simultaneously for the formation of stronger bonds, and for the best placement of the substituent nuclei so as to minimize their repulsions. We now wish to consider in a more general way the bonding and geometry that may be expected for carbon and other elements occurring as single-bonded constituents in organic molecules.

The geometry of a molecule can usually best be understood in terms of the hybridization of the bonds which hold it together. The hybridization will depend upon a number of factors. The bonds should be strong; the nuclei should be as far apart as possible; and most important, the s orbital should be used efficiently. Since the energy of an s orbital is lower than that of the corresponding p orbitals, the molecule will be more stable, the more fully occupied the s orbital is. These different factors often work against one another, and some kind of compromise is reached by the molecule in the hybridization of the various orbitals. We want to look into this matter in detail at this point, and, by examining a number of examples, deduce some general rules which will enable us to predict hybridization and geometry. (We will confine ourselves here to an examination of atoms of the first two rows of the periodic table only, since these are the atoms commonly found in organic compounds.)

The bonds which are formed determine the geometry of the molecule, and the bonds are formed from orbitals of the valence shell. These valence shell orbitals are either s or p, or some hybrid of s and p. For each orbital, there are three possibilities: Either the orbital is doubly occupied (such as the lone-pair orbitals in water or ammonia), or unoccupied (such as the empty orbital on the boron atom of trimethylboron), or singly occupied. In the case of covalent bond formation, as in methane, for example, the atomic orbitals which are contributed by carbon for bond formation are each singly occupied, since the hydrogen atom contributes the other electron used for bonding. In a fluorine atom the best arrangement is to have two electrons occupying the s orbital; two of the p orbitals are then filled, and one is half-filled. When the fluorine atom forms a bond, as in methyl fluoride, the orbital used by the fluorine for bonding will be essentially p, as this allows the s orbital to remain doubly occupied. Similarly, it might be deduced that the phosphine molecule should have the lone pair of electrons in an s orbital, and p orbitals should be used for the three bonds. In each case it is found that these rationalizations are approximately true. We can summarize them with the aid of three rules for the prediction of geometry and hybridization. In the order of their importance they are as follows:

1. Use the s orbital as efficiently as possible.
2. Form bonds which are as strong as possible.
3. Place the substituent atomic nuclei in positions (consistent with bond lengths and other constraints such as ring size) so as to minimize repulsions.

While Rule 1 is the most important of the rules given above, it is sometimes forced into a compromise by Rules 2 and 3, and a number of examples in the following sections will illustrate this situation in detail. Keep in mind that the molecule in question will always be trying to achieve as low an energy state as possible. These rules will be found to be very helpful in predicting what a molecule will do in an unknown case.

Up to this point we have considered only sp^3 hybrid orbitals. Many other kinds of hybrid orbitals can be formed, an infinite number, in fact. It is only necessary that the components of the hybrid orbitals add up to the total of the unhybridized components with which we began. For example, one p orbital can be left alone (say p_z) and the other two p orbitals (p_x and p_y) can be combined with the s orbital to yield three equivalent sp^2 orbitals. The shape of an sp^2 orbital is similar to that of an sp^3 orbital: there is a large electron density on one side of the nucleus and a small density on the other side. The three sp^2 orbitals lie with their axes at $120°$ to one another in the xy plane. The remaining p_z orbital is perpendicular to that plane (Figure 4.1).

Figure 4.1
Hybrid sp^2 orbitals.

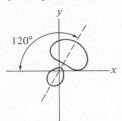

sp^2 atomic orbital

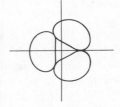

Three sp^2 atomic orbitals
with a common origin
(only the larger lobe
is shown for each)

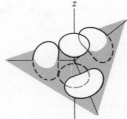

Three sp^2 atomic
orbitals and p_x
orbital

As another example—hybridization may occur by a combination of the *s* orbital with a single *p* orbital to yield two *sp* orbitals, leaving the other two *p* orbitals alone. The two *sp* orbitals formed lie along an axis at 180° from one another (Figure 4.2).

Figure 4.2
Hybrid *sp* orbitals.

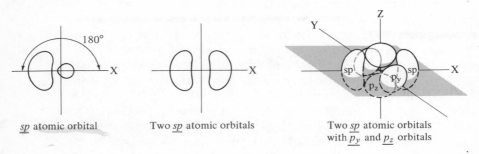

sp atomic orbital   Two *sp* atomic orbitals   Two *sp* atomic orbitals
                                                              with $\underline{p_y}$ and $\underline{p_z}$ orbitals

In a particular atom within a molecule, the state of hybridization which obtains is that which leads to the lowest overall energy for the molecule, and usually this means the hybridization which yields the strongest bonds. Hybrid orbitals can form strong single bonds (σ bonds) because the electron density is mainly directed between the bonding atoms. This leads to highly efficient overlap at the proper internuclear distances (Figure 4.3).

Figure 4.3
Comparison of atomic orbital overlaps between *p* and hybrid orbitals at the same internuclear distance.

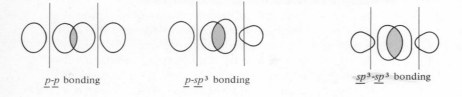

p-p bonding   *p-sp*³ bonding   *sp*³*-sp*³ bonding

Since the overlap possible with another orbital at a given distance increases as *s* character is added to a *p* orbital, and since the *s* orbital is of lower energy than the *p* in the first place, it is clear that bonds become increasingly strong in the order

$$p < sp^3 < sp^2 < sp$$

Rule 2 indicates that bonds will tend to form as far along this series as possible (as long as this causes no conflict with Rule 1).

From the above discussion, one might conclude that hybridization always yields an appropriate number of identical hybrid orbitals. Actually, there is no necessity for all of the hybrid orbitals to be exactly the same. For example, with an sp^2-hybridized atom, there is no necessity for the three hybrid orbitals each to be exactly sp^2; one or two of them can contain slightly more *p* character, as long as the others contain a correspondingly smaller amount. Small changes in hybridization are accompanied by changes in bond angles and bond lengths. An increase in the *s* character of a hybrid orbital tends to decrease the bond length. An increase in the *s* character of two orbitals of the same atom tends to increase the bond angle between them (Table 4.1).

Table 4.1 Carbon Single-Bond Properties as a Function of Hybridization[a]

Bond type	s Character, %	Bond angle	Average covalent radius, Å
$C_p - C_p$	0	90°	—
$C_{sp^3} - C_{sp^3}$	25	109° 28′	0.763
$C_{sp^2} - C_{sp^2}$	33.3	120°	0.743
$C_{sp} - C_{sp}$	50	180°	0.691

[a] An average $C_{sp^3} - C_{sp^3}$ bond is $0.763 + 0.763 = 1.526$ Å in length; an average $C_{sp^3} - C_{sp^2}$ bond is $0.763 + 0.743 = 1.506$ Å; and so on.

Bond Angles. To understand why certain bond or interorbital angles are characteristically associated with a given degree of hybridization (Section 2.5), consider the substituent nuclei bonded to a central atom as point charges on a more or less spherical surface. The most favorable arrangement will be the one where each substituent nucleus exerts the minimum repulsion on the others. This occurs when these nuclei are as far apart from one another as possible within the constraint of our spherical surface (Rule 3). Application of Coulomb's law indicates that two equivalent point charges will move to opposite positions on a sphere (at an angle of 180° to one another). Three equivalent point charges will move into a plane (at 120° from each other), while four equivalent charges will move to form the apexes of a regular tetrahedron, and so on (Figure 4.4).

Figure 4.4
Geometry and hybridization for minimum of repulsion.

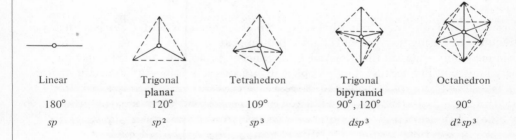

Linear	Trigonal planar	Tetrahedron	Trigonal bipyramid	Octahedron
180°	120°	109°	90°, 120°	90°
sp	sp^2	sp^3	dsp^3	d^2sp^3

The above treatment of repulsions is oversimplified. We must consider not only repulsions between nuclei, but also repulsions between the electron pairs forming the various bonds, and repulsions between bonded electrons and nonbonded electron pairs. A lone pair might be expected to have a higher charge density close to the atom on which it resides than will a bonding pair, because the former lacks the outward pull of the second nucleus. Lone pairs therefore repel one another more strongly than do bonding pairs. Because of such repulsions, it is often found that bond angles about a central atom bearing a lone pair or pairs are compressed somewhat over what might be expected based upon hybridization.

Strengths of pair–pair repulsions:

lone pair–lone pair > lone pair–bonding pair > bonding pair–bonding pair

Even when we consider all of the various repulsive and attractive interactions among the various substituent nuclei, bonded electrons, and nonbonded electrons, we still come to the same qualitative results illustrated in Figure 4.4. The idealized geometries are modified (1) by unsymmetrical substitution about the central atom which is often accompanied by slight changes in the distribution of s and p character among the various hybrid orbitals in order to achieve stronger bonds and minimize repulsions; (2) by ring strain; and (3) by steric strain (Figure 4.5).

Figure 4.5
Modification of idealized geometries for sp^3-hybridized atoms.

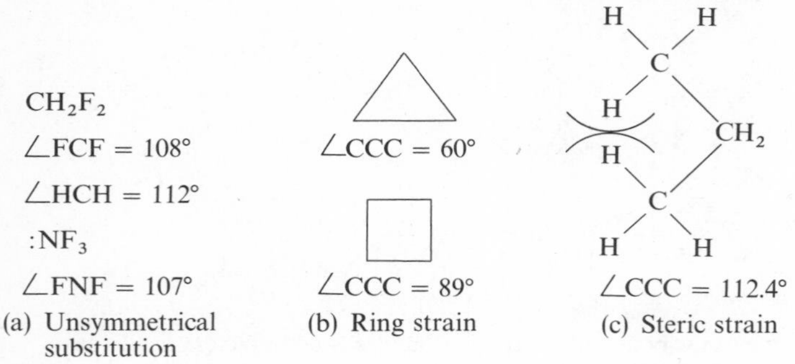

CH_2F_2	$\angle CCC = 60°$	
$\angle FCF = 108°$		$\angle CCC = 112.4°$
$\angle HCH = 112°$		
$:NF_3$	$\angle CCC = 89°$	
$\angle FNF = 107°$		
(a) Unsymmetrical substitution	(b) Ring strain	(c) Steric strain

4.3   Acids and Bases

In 1887 the Swedish chemist Arrhenius† proposed that an acid was a substance whose water solution contained an excess of hydrogen ions, H^+; a base correspondingly was a substance whose water solution contained an excess of hydroxyl ions, OH^-. Today we realize that the driving force for most chemical reactions is the formation of a stable electronic configuration. The hydrogen atom of a proton acid is not likely to part with its share of the bonding electron pair to form a bare proton; the fraction of protons that would remain unhydrated in water is approximately 1 in 10^{190} (less than one in a pool of water larger than our known universe). The reaction that occurs upon the solution of hydrogen chloride in water can be represented as follows:

$$HCl + H_2O \rightarrow H_3O^+, H_5O_2^+, H_7O_3^+, H_9O_4^+, \text{etc.} + Cl^-$$

The formulation H_3O^+ is customarily used to represent aqueous acid. Chemists often take the liberty of using the symbol H^+ for a proton acid.

It is immediately apparent that the Arrhenius concept, profound as it was for its time, is of very limited utility because it only applies to aqueous solutions. An important and greatly broadened concept of acids and bases was suggested independently in 1923 by Brønsted and by Lowry. They proposed that any substance which can donate a proton to any other substance (a proton donor) be called an acid, and that any substance which can accept a proton from another substance (a proton acceptor) be called a base.

Consider the reaction of hydrogen chloride with water from the Brønsted–Lowry viewpoint.

$$HCl + H_2O \rightleftharpoons H_3O^+ + Cl^-$$

In the forward reaction, hydrogen chloride (an acid) donates a proton to water (a base); in the reverse reaction, H_3O^+ (an acid) donates a proton to Cl^- (a base). An acid and base which can be formed from one another by the loss or gain of a proton are called a *conjugate acid–base pair*.

$$HA \underset{H^+}{\overset{-H^+}{\rightleftharpoons}} A^-$$

Conjugate acid   Conjugate base

The stronger an acid, the weaker its conjugate base, and vice versa.

An important corollary of the Brønsted–Lowry concept is that the equilibrium in any proton transfer reaction will favor the formation of the weaker acid and the weaker base from the stronger acid and stronger base.

† Svante Arrhenius, 1859–1927. Born Wijk, Sweden. Technical High School, Stockholm. Nobel Institute. Nobel Prize, 1903.

Stronger acid + Stronger base $\rightleftharpoons$ *Weaker acid + Weaker base*

$$\text{HCl} \quad + \quad \text{H}_2\text{O} \quad \rightleftharpoons \quad \text{H}_3\text{O}^+ + \text{Cl}^-$$
$$\text{H}_2\text{O} \quad + \quad \text{NH}_2^- \quad \rightleftharpoons \quad \text{NH}_3 \quad + \text{OH}^-$$
$$\text{CH}_3\text{OH} \quad + \quad \text{CH}_3^- \quad \rightleftharpoons \quad \text{CH}_4 \quad + \text{CH}_3\text{O}^-$$

The order of the acidities and basicities of some simple common compounds is as follows:

	Weak acids		*Strong acids*	

Acidity $\text{CH}_4 < \text{NH}_3 < \text{H}_2\text{O} < \text{NH}_4^+ < \text{H}_2\text{S} < \text{HF}$

	Strong bases		*Weak bases*	

Basicity $\text{CH}_3^- > \text{NH}_2^- > \text{HO}^- > \text{NH}_3 > \text{HS}^- > \text{F}^-$

As broad as this new concept was, a severe limitation was still imposed by the word "proton." It remained for G. N. Lewis to strike at what he called "the cult of the proton" and to remove this limitation from the earlier concepts of acids and bases. In 1923 Lewis proposed that an acid be defined as *an electron-pair acceptor* and a base as *an electron-pair donor*. In the Lewis concept, an acid–base reaction is the sharing of an electron pair from a base with an acid. Often the result is the formation of a coordinate covalent bond between the acid and the base. The transfer of a proton is only a special case. The Lewis concept of acids and bases, as logical as it may seem today revolutionized our understanding of chemistry, especially of organic chemistry.

Bases are much the same in the Lewis or Brønsted–Lowry sense. Species which share their electrons with any electron-pair acceptor (Lewis acid) will generally do so with a proton (Brønsted acid). On the other hand, the range of acids is greatly expanded by the Lewis definition to include the following:

1. *Positive ions*

Acid   Base   Coordinated complex

$$\text{Ag}^+ + 2\,\text{NH}_3 \quad \rightarrow \quad [\text{NH}_3-\text{Ag}-\text{NH}_3]^+$$
$$\text{NO}_2^+ + \text{CH}_2{=}\text{CH}_2 \quad \rightarrow \quad {}^+\text{CH}_2-\text{CH}_2\text{NO}_2$$
$$\text{CH}_3^+ + \text{CH}_3\text{OCH}_3 \quad \rightarrow \quad (\text{CH}_3)_3\text{O}^+$$

2. *Compounds containing an atom which has an unfilled octet*. These are among the most important Lewis acids; many are especially useful as catalysts for chemical reactions.

Acid   Base   Coordinated complex

$$\begin{array}{c} \text{Cl} \\ \overset{..}{} \\ \text{Cl}{:}\text{Fe} + \text{Cl}_2 \\ \overset{..}{} \\ \text{Cl} \end{array} \quad \rightarrow \quad \left[\begin{array}{c} \text{Cl} \\ \overset{..}{} \\ \text{Cl}{:}\text{Fe}{:}\text{Cl} \\ \overset{..}{} \\ \text{Cl} \end{array} \right]^- + \text{Cl}^+$$

$$\text{AlCl}_3 + (\text{CH}_3)_3\text{CCl} \quad \rightarrow \text{AlCl}_4^- + (\text{CH}_3)_3\text{C}^+$$
$$\text{BF}_3 \quad + (\text{CH}_3\text{CH}_2)_2\text{O} \rightarrow (\text{CH}_3\text{CH}_2)_2^+\text{O}-{}^-\text{BF}_3$$

Two other important classes of Lewis acids will be discussed in Section 10.6.

Some discussion will now be given which the student should find familiar, but may wish to review.

Acid strength in water solution is defined in terms of the equilibrium constant K_a, for the reaction

$$\text{HA} + \text{H}_2\text{O} \rightleftharpoons \text{H}_3\text{O}^+ + \text{A}^-$$

If activity coefficients are assumed to be equal to unity

$$K_a = \frac{[\text{H}_3\text{O}^+][\text{A}^-]}{[\text{HA}]}$$

(where square brackets indicate concentration) and $\text{p}K_a = -\log K_a$. The greater the value of K_a and the smaller the value of $\text{p}K_a$, the stronger the acid. The $\text{p}K_a$ is directly proportional to the standard free energy change ($\Delta G°$) involved in the ionization

$$pK_a = \frac{\Delta G°}{2.303RT}$$

where R is the gas constant and T is the absolute temperature.

Base strength can be defined in a similar way for the reaction

$$B + H_2O \rightleftharpoons BH^+ + OH^-$$

and

$$K_b = \frac{[BH^+][OH^-]}{[B]}$$

Alternatively, the strength of a base B can be expressed in terms of the acidity of BH^+; the weaker the base B, the stronger its conjugate acid BH^+. Thus for the reaction

$$BH^+ + H_2O \rightleftharpoons B + H_3O^+$$

the acidity of BH^+ is measured by K_a:

$$K_a = \frac{[H_3O^+][B]}{[BH^+]}$$

It follows that K_a for BH^+ and K_b for B are related by

$$K_a K_b = K_w$$

where K_w is the ionic product for water, and at 25°C, $K_w = 1.0 \times 10^{-14}$; or, in more convenient form

$$pK_a + pK_b = 14.00$$

In this text K_a and pK_a will be used throughout. Thus, instead of discussing pK_b for NH_3 (4.76), we will talk about pK_a for NH_4^+ (9.24).

As a little algebra will show, the pK_a of an acid is the pH in aqueous solution at which it is just half-neutralized, and $[HA] = [A^-]$.

The pK_a values express the relative acidities of compounds toward a single reference base—water; the larger the value of pK_a, the weaker the acid. Outside the 1 to 13 range, the values are not related to the degree of ionization. The very strong acids (pK_a's less than 1) are completely ionized in water and their acidities are "leveled," in that H_3O^+ is the strongest acid present in such solutions. Acids with pK_a's greater than 13 do not show any readily detectable acidity toward water; their acidities must be related to water by indirect methods. Quantitative values for the pK_a's of acids will be discussed in Section 12.4.

4.4   The Structures of the Alkyl Halides

Alkyl halides are derivatives of hydrocarbons in which one or more of the hydrogens have been replaced by halogen. Almost any hydrogen in any hydrocarbon can be replaced by halogen; in fact, all of the hydrogens may be replaced. Completely fluorinated compounds are known as *fluorocarbons*; these materials are of particular interest because of their high thermal stability.

Chemists often use RX as a general notation for alkyl halides; R stands for any alkyl group and X for any halogen, unless otherwise specified. To begin our study of the bonding in such molecules, let us first examine the ground-state configurations of the halogens.

Note that in each case the highly electronegative halogens are only one electron short of attaining rare gas configurations. We may therefore expect halogens to form stable molecules by formation of a single covalent or ionic bond with another atom.

$$
\begin{aligned}
&\text{F} && 1s^2\,2s^2\,2p^5 \\
&\text{Cl} && 1s^2\,2s^2\,2p^6\,3s^2\,3p^5 \\
&\text{Br} && 1s^2\,2s^2\,2p^6\,3s^2\,3p^6\,3d^{10}\,4s^2\,4p^5 \\
&\text{I} && 1s^2\,2s^2\,2p^6\,3s^2\,3p^6\,3d^{10}\,4s^2\,4p^6\,4d^{10}\,5s^2\,5p^5
\end{aligned}
$$

Furthermore, such halogens will have nonbonding outer orbitals containing lone pairs, so we may anticipate that covalent (and ionic) halogens will act as Lewis bases.

In methyl fluoride, CH_3F, the C—F bond is formed, to a first approximation, by the overlap of an sp^3 orbital of carbon with a $2p$ orbital of fluorine (Figure 4.6).

Figure 4.6

Hybridization and bonding in methyl fluoride.

$(2sp^3-1s)\sigma$ bond $1s$ $(2sp^3-2p)\sigma$ bond

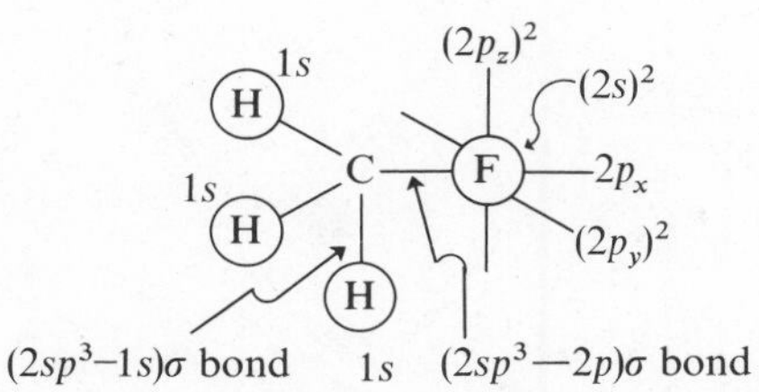

$\angle$HCH   and $\angle$HCF $= 109°$

A Better Approximation for the Bonding in Methyl Fluoride. The fluorine orbital used for the formation of the covalent C—F bond should, according to Rule 1, be a p orbital. However, adding a little s character can increase the bond strength considerably, and a compromise is reached, with the bonding orbital being almost pure p. The s orbitals hold onto their electrons more strongly than p orbitals because of their lower energy; accordingly, the more s character hybrid orbitals contain, the more strongly electron-attracting they will be. The highly electronegative fluorine atom attracts the electrons of the C—F bond. The methyl group can release additional electron density to the fluorine by using a hybrid orbital with less than 25% s character for bonding the fluorine, provided the extra s character shows up in the three C—H bonds. That this is the case is shown by the fact that the C—H bond distances in methyl fluoride are shorter than those of methane.

Methyl chloride, bromide, and iodide are formed by similar overlaps of an sp^3 carbon orbital with the $3p$, $4p$, and $5p$ orbitals of chlorine, bromine, and iodine, respectively. The C—X bond strengths fall off as we go down the periodic table. This is a reflection of the general principle that orbital overlap is most efficient between orbitals of the same principal quantum level (i.e., in the same row of the periodic table), and the efficiency decreases as the difference in principal quantum numbers increases. One can appreciate the reason for this situation from a consideration of the relative sizes of the orbitals involved (Figure 4.7). The relatively small $2sp^3$ orbital cannot penetrate the larger p orbitals sufficiently to form a strong bond.

4.5   Nomenclature of the Alkyl Halides

The simple alkyl halides are commonly named as alkyl derivatives of the hydrogen halides. The IUPAC system names halides as halo derivatives of hydrocarbons. In the examples throughout this chapter, common names will be given in parentheses under

Figure 4.7
Carbon–halogen bonds. For clarity, the inner nodes of the $3p$, $4p$, and $5p$ orbitals are not shown.

Bond	Bond energy, kcal/mole	Bond length, Å
$-\overset{\displaystyle |}{\underset{\displaystyle |}{C}}\!\!-\!\!F$ $2sp^3$ $2p$	105.4	1.42
$-\overset{\displaystyle |}{\underset{\displaystyle |}{C}}\!\!-\!\!Cl$ $2sp^3$ $3p$	78.5	1.77
$-\overset{\displaystyle |}{\underset{\displaystyle |}{C}}\!\!-\!\!Br$ $2sp^3$ $4p$	65.9	1.91
$-\overset{\displaystyle |}{\underset{\displaystyle |}{C}}\!\!-\!\!I$ $2sp^3$ $5p$	57.4	2.12

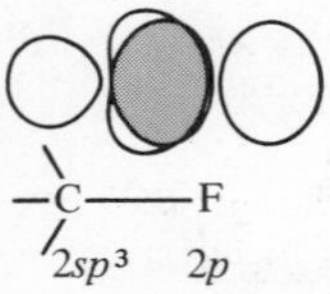

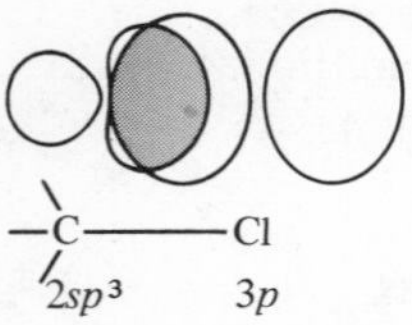

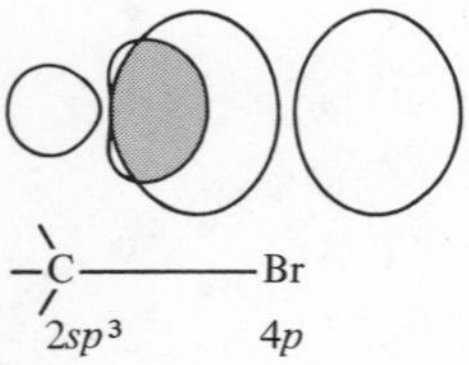

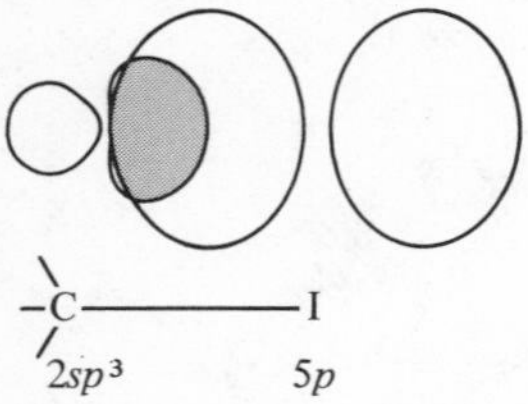

the IUPAC names. In common names, the prefixes *n*-, *sec*- (*s*-), and *tert*- (*t*-) indicate normal, secondary, and tertiary, respectively (see Section 3.1).

CH_3F

Fluoromethane
(Methyl fluoride)

CH_3CH_2Cl

Chloroethane
(Ethyl chloride)

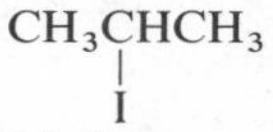

$CH_3\overset{\displaystyle |}{\underset{\displaystyle I}{C}}HCH_3$

2-Iodopropane
(Isopropyl iodide)

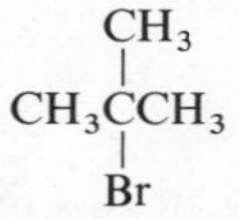

$CH_3\overset{\displaystyle CH_3}{\underset{\displaystyle Br}{C}}CH_3$

2-Bromo-2-methylpropane
(*t*-Butyl bromide)

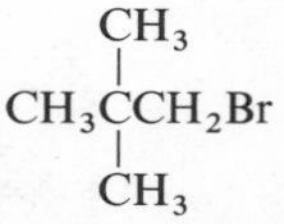

$CH_3\overset{\displaystyle CH_3}{\underset{\displaystyle CH_3}{C}}CH_2Br$

1-Bromo-2,2-dimethylpropane
(Neopentyl bromide)

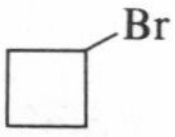

Br

Bromocyclobutane
(Cyclobutyl bromide)

With the IUPAC system, the naming of all compounds containing only univalent functions [simple functions attached to carbon by a single bond such as –Cl (chloro-), –OH (hydroxy-), –NO$_2$ (nitro-), etc.] which can be expressed by prefixes alone follows easily after the naming of the parent hydrocarbons; the principle of lowest possible numbers is always followed. *Chemical Abstracts*, the most important abstracting and

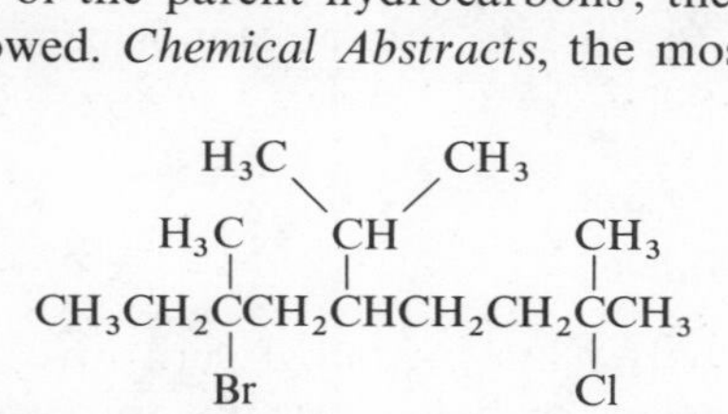

$$\underset{\underset{\displaystyle Br}{\displaystyle |}}{CH_3CH_2\overset{\displaystyle |}{C}}CH_2\overset{\overset{\displaystyle H_3C\diagdown\quad\diagup CH_3}{\displaystyle CH}}{C}HCH_2CH_2\underset{\underset{\displaystyle Cl}{\displaystyle |}}{\overset{\overset{\displaystyle CH_3}{\displaystyle |}}{C}}CH_3$$

IUPAC: 2-Chloro-5-isopropyl-7-bromo-
2,7-dimethylnonane

Chem. Abstr.: 7-Bromo-2-chloro-5-
isopropyl-2,7-dimethylnonane

indexing journal in chemistry, writes the substituent names in alphabetical order regardless of the number of each (Section 3.1). The order in which a name is written does not have great importance in understanding what compound is meant.

Chemical Abstracts *is published weekly by the American Chemical Society. It summarizes the chemical patents and all original articles on chemistry which appear in journals from all countries of the world. Each six months, complete author, subject, and formula indexes appear for that period. Every five years a cumulative index is published. Use of* Chemical Abstracts *is the only practical way to conduct a thorough search for literature that is pertinent to any subject in chemistry. Without* Chemical Abstracts, *chemistry as we know it today would be impossible. To get an idea of how rapidly chemical knowledge is growing, consider that for a typical recent six-months period,* Chemical Abstracts *amounted to 11,500 pages containing 122,000 abstracts, in addition to an index for the same period of 6300 pages.*

Frequently occurring hydrocarbon groupings that have more than one site for the attachment of substituents are also given common or trivial names.

$$CH_2Cl_2$$
Dichloromethane
(Methylene chloride)

$$ICH_2CH_2CH_2CH_2I$$
1,4-Diiodobutane
(Tetramethylene iodide)

The terms *geminal* (*gem-*) (from the Latin *geminus*, meaning twin) and *vicinal* (*vic-*) (from the Latin *vicinus*, meaning neighbor) are sometimes used to show the relative positions of substituents as being 1, 1 and 1, 2 respectively.

$$CH_3CHBr_2$$
1,1-Dibromoethane
(*gem*-Dibromoethane)

$$BrCH_2CH_2Br$$
1,2-Dibromoethane
(*vic*-Dibromoethane)

4.6 Properties of Alkyl Halides

The physical properties of some representative alkyl halides are given in Table 4.2. Most halides are liquids; the bromides, iodides, and polyhalides in general, have specific gravities greater than 1. The alkyl halides are insoluble in water, but they are miscible in all proportions with liquid hydrocarbons.

Table 4.2 Alkyl Halides

Name	Formula	$Mp, °C$	$Bp, °C$	$Sp. Gr. (liq)$
Methyl fluoride	CH_3F	−79	−142	0.877
Methyl chloride	CH_3Cl	−97	−23.7	0.920
Methyl bromide	CH_3Br	−93	4.6	1.732
Methyl iodide	CH_3I	−64	42.3	2.279
Ethyl chloride	CH_3CH_2Cl	−139	13.1	0.910
Ethyl bromide	CH_3CH_2Br	−119	38.4	1.430
n-Propyl chloride	$CH_3CH_2CH_2Cl$	−123	46.4	0.890
Isopropyl chloride	$(CH_3)_2CHCl$	−117	36.5	0.860
n-Butyl bromide	$CH_3(CH_2)_3Br$	−112	101.6	1.275
Isobutyl bromide	$(CH_3)_2CHCH_2Br$	−120	91.3	1.250
s-Butyl bromide	$CH_3CH_2CHBrCH_3$		68	0.871
t-Butyl bromide	$(CH_3)_3CBr$	−20	73.3	1.222
n-Octadecyl bromide	$CH_3(CH_2)_{17}Br$	34	170/0.5 mm	

USES OF ALKYL HALIDES. *Alkyl chlorides are good solvents for many organic materials. Many stable, readily available polychloro solvents are used for general chemical and industrial purposes; among the most important are methylene chloride, chloroform, and carbon tetrachloride. Increasing the halogen content of organic materials decreases flammability. Carbon tetrachloride has been used in fire extinguishers, but it is not recommended because at high temperatures it may react with oxygen in the air to produce the highly toxic* phosgene ($COCl_2$). *Teflon* [$F(CF_2)_nF$, *where n is a very large indefinite number] is a useful material of extreme chemical and thermal stability. It has a slippery feel and is sometimes used for bearing surfaces as it requires no lubrication. It is also used as a coating for the insides of frying pans because foods show little tendency to adhere to it. Many fluoro chloro compounds, known as* Freons, *are used as nontoxic stable refrigerants.*

4.7   The Structures of Oxygen Compounds

The electronic configuration of the oxygen atom is $1s^2 2s^2 2p^4$. When an oxygen atom in an organic compound is connected by two single bonds to other groups, it is generally found that the bond angle between the groups is close to the tetrahedral value. It is therefore a useful approximation to think of these compounds as sp^3-hybridized at oxygen.

Oxygen Hybridization. If we look at the hybridization at oxygen a little more closely, it becomes clear that the sp^3 hybridization mentioned above is only an approximation. We may consider the water molecule as a simple, typical example of what is found with organic oxygen compounds. In water, the observed bond angle H—O—H does not have exactly the tetrahedral value, but is 105°. There are two approaches to explaining this bond angle. The more simple supposes that one of the lone pairs in the valence shell occupies the *s* orbital, and the second a *p* orbital. This would leave two *p* orbitals available for bonding to the hydrogens. If *p* bonds were formed, one would expect an H—O—H angle of 90°. Because of the electronegativity difference between hydrogen and oxygen, each hydrogen atom bears a partial positive charge. Repulsion between these charges would be expected to cause the bond angle to widen beyond 90° (Figure 4.8a). As the angle opens, the efficiency of the orbital overlap, and hence the O—H bond strength, would decrease; the optimum balance between bond strengths and internuclear repulsion is reached for water at 105°.

Recent calculations indicate, however, that electrostatic repulsion alone cannot account for the expansion of the bond angle in water from 90 to 105°, and they suggest that the observed angle is best accounted for by the use of hybrid orbitals. Four equivalent sp^3 orbitals would yield angles between the bonds and also between the lone pairs of 109.5°. This situation would not be entirely satisfactory, because the *s* orbital has not been utilized effectively. However, to put a pair of electrons into the *s* orbital, we would have to reduce the bond angle to 90°, which would lead to weak *p* bonds and a substantial electrostatic repulsion between the protons. A compromise is therefore reached in which the bond angle is reduced from 109.5 to 105°, with a corresponding reduction of *s* character in the bonding orbitals. The lone-pair orbitals have their *s* character increased, and the angle between them expands to 114° (Figure 4.8b).

Figure 4.8
The water molecule.

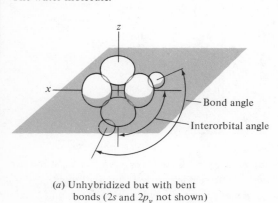

(a) Unhybridized but with bent bonds ($2s$ and $2p_y$ not shown)

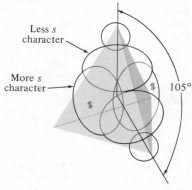

(b) Approximately sp^3-hybridized

To reemphasize a point made earlier, there is no reason for a central atom—oxygen, nitrogen, carbon, or whatever it might be—to form all equivalent hybrid orbitals if all orbitals are not to be used in identical ways. In general, we will find that single-bonded oxygen, as well as sulfur, nitrogen, phosphorus, carbon, and silicon compounds, have bond angles that are best accounted for by slightly unsymmetrical sp^3 hybridization, rather than by p^2 or p^3 bonding.

Organic derivatives of water may be formed by replacing one or both of the hydrogens by alkyl groups. When one hydrogen is replaced, an alcohol (ROH) is formed. The hybridization of the oxygen atom in an alcohol is approximately the same as that in water.

Since the oxygen is very electronegative, it will support a negative charge nicely; the hydrogen of an alcohol ($pK_a = 15.5–19$) is therefore weakly acidic, similar to the hydrogen in water ($pK_a = 15.3$).

$$ROH + Na \rightarrow RO^-Na^+ + \tfrac{1}{2}H_2$$

Alcohol   Sodium alkoxide

When both hydrogens of water have been replaced by alkyl groups, ethers (ROR) result. Ethers are geometrically similar to water and the alcohols, and do not present any special bonding considerations. One would anticipate that the bond angle involving oxygen as the central atom might increase slightly as the size of the substituents increase, and this is what is found experimentally.

Organic derivatives of hydrogen peroxide also exist. Both *peroxides* (ROOR) and *hydroperoxides* (ROOH) are quite unstable, sometimes even highly explosive compounds. They are seldom isolated, but are important intermediates in oxidation and combustion of organic materials.

Since divalent oxygen derivatives have lone pairs available, they act as Lewis bases. Accordingly, a number of tricovalent oxygen ions analogous to the hydronium ion (H_3O^+) are well known. Cations of the type ROH_2^+, formed by protonation of an alcohol, and R_2OH^+, formed by protonation of an ether, are not usually isolated, but occur frequently in solution and are often transient intermediates in reactions. The trisubstituted oxonium salts, $R_3O^+Y^-$, although less stable than ammonium or sulfonium salts, may be isolated from inert media provided the anion is unreactive and stable, such as fluoborate (BF_4^-). Ethers often form stable complexes with Lewis acids; boron trifluoride diethyl etherate $[(CH_3CH_2)_2O^+\!-\!^-BF_3]$ is a stable liquid boiling at 126°. The oxygen atom in such derivatives is sp^3-hybridized, with bond angles near 109°.

4.8   Nomenclature of Alcohols

The common names of the simple alcohols include the name of the alkyl group followed by the word *alcohol*. In the IUPAC system of nomenclature the final *-e* of the hydrocarbon name is replaced by *-ol*, and the position of the hydroxyl group (–OH) is indicated by the lowest possible number. Note that the longest chain containing the hydroxyl group (which may not be the longest chain in the molecule) is used to determine the name .

$$CH_3OH \qquad CH_3CH_2OH \qquad \underset{\underset{\displaystyle OH}{|}}{CH_3CHCH_3} \qquad \underset{\underset{\displaystyle CH_2OH}{|}}{CH_3CH_2CH_2CHCH_2CH_3}$$

Methanol   Ethanol   2-Propanol   2-Ethyl-1-pentanol
(Methyl alcohol)   (Ethyl alcohol)   (Isopropyl alcohol)

It is often convenient to classify alcohols as *primary*, *secondary*, or *tertiary* according to the number of carbons attached to the carbon bearing the hydroxyl. Of the alcohols shown below, *n*-butyl and isobutyl alcohol are primary alcohols, *sec*-butyl alcohol is a secondary alcohol, and *t*-butyl alcohol is tertiary.

$$CH_3CH_2CH_2CH_2OH$$

1-Butanol
(*n*-Butyl alcohol)

$$\underset{\displaystyle\overset{|}{CH_3}}{CH_3CHCH_2OH}$$

2-Methyl-1-propanol
(Isobutyl alcohol)

$$\underset{\displaystyle\overset{|}{OH}}{CH_3CH_2CHCH_3}$$

2-Butanol
(*sec*-Butyl alcohol)

$$\underset{\displaystyle\overset{|}{OH}}{\overset{\displaystyle\overset{CH_3}{|}}{CH_3CCH_3}}$$

2-Methyl-2-propanol
(*t*-Butyl alcohol)

Many compounds contain more than one hydroxyl group; the general name for this class of compounds is *polyhydric alcohols*. Compounds containing two hydroxyls are referred to as *glycols* or *diols*, those containing three hydroxyls, as *triols*. (Note that when a suffix is attached to a hydrocarbon name, the final -*e* is not dropped if the suffix begins with a consonant. Thus *ethane* gives *ethanol*, but the diol is *ethanediol*.)

$$HOCH_2CH_2OH \qquad HOCH_2CH_2CH_2OH \qquad \underset{\displaystyle\overset{|}{OH}}{HOCH_2CHCH_2OH}$$

1,2-Ethanediol
(Ethylene glycol)

1,3-Propanediol
(Trimethylene glycol)

1,2,3-Propanetriol
(Glycerin, glycerol)

Sometimes it is convenient to name alcohols as derivatives of methanol. The term *carbinol* is used in place of methanol in such names, and the name is written as one word. The system has the advantage that formulas for rather complex alcohols may be easily visualized from the name.

$$CH_3OH \qquad \triangleright\!\!-\!\!\underset{\displaystyle\overset{|}{OH}}{CHCH_2CH_3} \qquad (CH_3CH_2)_3COH$$

Methanol
(Carbinol)

1-Cyclopropyl-1-propanol
(Cyclopropylethylcarbinol)

3-Ethyl-3-pentanol
(Triethylcarbinol)

When compounds contain a hydroxyl group as well as other functions, it is often convenient to use the prefix *hydroxy*- rather than the suffix -*ol* for the -OH groups present.

$$\underset{}{\overset{\displaystyle\overset{OH}{|}}{CH_3CHCH_2CO_2H}}$$

3-Hydroxybutanoic Acid

EXERCISE 4.1

Name the following compounds:

(a) $\underset{\displaystyle\overset{|}{CH_3}\quad\overset{|}{CH_2CH_3}}{\overset{\displaystyle\overset{Br}{|}}{CH_3CHCHCH_2CHCH_2CH_2OH}}$

(b) $\underset{\displaystyle\overset{|}{CH_3}}{\overset{\displaystyle\overset{OH\quad OH}{|\quad\ \ |}}{CH_3CH_2CHCHCH_2CHCH_2OH}}$

4.9 Properties of Alcohols

Table 4.3 summarizes the physical properties of representative common alcohols. Methyl, ethyl, *n*-propyl, isopropyl, *t*-butyl, and many polyhydric alcohols are completely miscible with water. Other alcohols are fairly soluble to insoluble, depending on the number of carbon atoms per hydroxyl group. In general, one hydroxyl group can "solubilize" three to four carbon atoms. The alcohols have much higher boiling points

Table 4.3   Alcohols

Name	Formula	Mp, °C	Bp, °C	Sp. Gr.
Methyl alcohol	CH_3OH	−97	64.7	0.792
Ethyl alcohol	CH_3CH_2OH	−114	78.3	0.789
n-Propyl alcohol	$CH_3CH_2CH_2OH$	−126	97.2	0.804
Isopropyl alcohol	$CH_3CHOHCH_3$	−88	82.3	0.786
n-Butyl alcohol	$CH_3(CH_2)_3OH$	−90	117.7	0.810
Isobutyl alcohol	$(CH_3)_2CHCH_2OH$	−108	107.9	0.802
sec-Butyl alcohol	$CH_3CH_2CHOHCH_3$		99.5	0.808
t-Butyl alcohol	$(CH_3)_3COH$	25	82.5	0.789
n-Hexyl alcohol	$CH_3(CH_2)_5OH$	−52	155.8	0.820
Cyclohexyl alcohol	$C_6H_{11}OH$	24	161.5	0.962
Lauryl alcohol	$n\text{-}C_{12}H_{25}OH$	24	259	0.831
Ethylene glycol	$HOCH_2CH_2OH$	−12	198	1.12
Trimethylene glycol	$HOCH_2CH_2CH_2OH$		212	1.06
Glycerin	$HOCH_2CHOHCH_2OH$	18	290	1.26

than do hydrocarbons or most other compounds of similar molecular weight (Table 4.4). The high solubility in water and the unexpectedly high boiling points can be attributed to intermolecular *hydrogen bonding* (Section 4.20).

Table 4.4   Structure and Boiling Point

Compound	Formula	MW	bp °C
n-Pentane	CH_3—CH_2—CH_2—CH_2—CH_3	72	36
Diethyl ether	CH_3—CH_2—O—CH_2—CH_3	74	35
n-Propyl chloride	CH_3—CH_2—CH_2—Cl	78	46
n-Butyl alcohol	CH_3—CH_2—CH_2—CH_2—OH	74	118

USES OF ALCOHOLS. *All of the alcohols listed in Table 4.3 have commercial importance as solvents and/or chemical intermediates. As we shall see in later chapters, alcohols are very versatile chemical entities; they may be converted to nearly every other kind of aliphatic compound. The most important of the alcohols is ethyl alcohol, known simply as "alcohol" to the layman. It is important as an industrial and pharmaceutical solvent, as a reaction medium, and as the active ingredient in a host of delightful beverages. Ethylene glycol is the principal ingredient in antifreezes.*

In 1961, alcoholic beverages produced $1,225,029,369 in revenue for the fifty states and the District of Columbia. Fermentation, the term given to the biochemical reactions that are used to produce alcohol, generally involves two distinct steps, each of which is catalyzed by enzymes. The first step involves the conversion of polysaccharides (carbohydrates, Chapter 27) from any of several natural products into monosaccharides (simple sugars), and the second involves the conversion of the sugar to ethyl alcohol. The sources of the carbohydrate are quite varied; the best are generally considered to include corn, wheat, and rye. Potatoes are used in some countries, and the use of dandelions in emergencies has been recorded. In man, small doses of ethanol produce a state of euphoria; larger doses severely depress the central nervous system. In rats the lethal dose is 13.7 g/kilo, or about 2/5 gallon (two "fifths") for each 180 pounds of rats.

4.10   Nomenclature of Ethers

Ethers are named by first naming the two hydrocarbon groups attached to the oxygen, and then adding the word *ether*. If the two hydrocarbon groups are identical, it is common practice to omit the prefix *di-*.

$$CH_3OCH_3 \qquad CH_3CH_2OCH_2CH_3 \qquad CH_3OCH_2CH_2CH_3$$

Dimethyl ether   Diethyl ether   Methyl *n*-propyl ether
(Methyl ether)   (Ethyl ether)

Ethers containing one simple and one complex hydrocarbon group can be named as alkoxy (RO-) derivatives of the more complex group.

$$\begin{array}{c} CH_2CH_3 \\ | \\ CH_3CH_2CHCHCH_3 \\ | \\ OCH_3 \end{array} \qquad CH_3CH_2OCH_2CH_2OCH_2CH_3$$

3-Ethyl-2-methoxypentane   1,2-Diethoxyethane
                                   (Ethylene glycol diethyl ether)

EXERCISE 4.2

Name the following compounds:

(a) $CH_3CHCH_2CH_2CHOCH_2CH_2CH_3$
        | |
        CH_3 CH_3

(b) $CH_3\overset{\displaystyle OH}{\underset{\displaystyle CH_3}{\overset{|}{\underset{|}{C}}}}CH_2CH_2OCH_3$

Ether linkages in rings are well known. Cyclic systems containing ring members other than carbon are known under the general name of *heterocycles*. The commonly occurring heterocyclic ethers have trivial names which are ordinarily used.

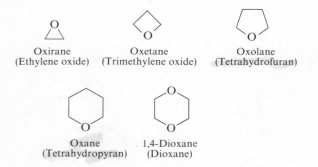

Oxirane   Oxetane   Oxolane
(Ethylene oxide)   (Trimethylene oxide)   (Tetrahydrofuran)

Oxane   1,4-Dioxane
(Tetrahydropyran)   (Dioxane)

4.11   Properties of Ethers

The melting and boiling points of ethers (Table 4.5) are comparable to those of hydrocarbons of similar molecular weight. Most ethers are immiscible with water; however, dioxane and tetrahydrofuran, which are often used as reaction solvents, are miscible in all proportions with water. At room temperature, ethyl ether dissolves 1.5% of water and water dissolves 7.5% of ether. Ethers are indifferent to most chemical reagents. They have high solvent power for most organic substances, but they dissolve few inorganic materials. These properties, along with their low boiling points and water immiscibility, make them excellent solvents for commercial and laboratory use, especially in extraction procedures.

Ethyl ether, known simply as ether, is by far the most important member of this class. It is highly volatile and quite flammable; its vapor is heavier than air and tends to settle and catch on fire. When exposed to air for long periods of time, ethyl ether (as well as

Table 4.5   Ethers

Name	Mp, °C	Bp, °C
Methyl ether	−140	−24
Ethyl ether	−116	34.6
n-Propyl ether	−122	91
Isopropyl ether	−60	69
Ethylene oxide	−113	10.7
Tetrahydrofuran	−108	66
Dioxane	11	101

other ethers) forms nonvolatile peroxides which are left as highly explosive residues upon evaporation of the ether. To prevent the formation of such peroxides, commercial ether contains a little ethyl alcohol and traces of water, and is shipped in specially treated containers. Commercial absolute ether (alcohol- and water-free) contains 0.05 ppm of sodium diethyldithiocarbamate $[(CH_3CH_2)_2NCS_2^- Na^+]$ as an antioxidant.

ANESTHETICS. *Ethyl ether has been one of the most generally used anesthetics for prolonged surgical operations. Ethyl ether and other volatile ethers, along with chloroform, ethylene, and cyclopropane, are physiologically active as inhalation anesthetics, not by any chemical action, for they are excreted unchanged, but by promoting physical changes in the lipoids (fatty materials) of the nerve tissue when they are dissolved in the fats. For compounds of this type the anesthetic activity is related to the oil–water solubility ratio.*

Practical general anesthesia by inhalation techniques began around 1850. As early as 1799 Sir Humphrey Davy had discovered the anesthetic properties of nitrous oxide (laughing gas). In December 1844 Horace Well, a dentist in Hartford, Connecticut, witnessed a demonstration by Colton on the effects of nitrous oxide. The next day the dentist himself had a tooth extracted while under the influence of the gas. The operation was a success and laughing gas was introduced into general dental practice.

In the early 1840s, Charles W. Jackson, a Boston chemist, became unconscious from the inhalation of ether and, independent of Well, conceived the idea of its use as an anesthetic. In September 1846, a Boston dentist, William G. T. Morton, at the suggestion of Jackson, successfully used ether as an anesthetic. [The term anesthesia (Greek, without sensitivity) was suggested to Morton by Oliver Wendell Holmes.] Shortly thereafter, the use of ether in major surgery was introduced by J. C. Warren at the Massachusetts General Hospital. Earlier, in 1842, C. W. Long of Jefferson, Georgia, had administered ether as a surgical anesthetic, but the results were not published.

Common in the early nineteenth century in England were "chloroform parties" at which guests would sit around a bowl of chloroform and whiff until they toppled to the floor. Simpson, the Queen's physician, first used chloroform on man in a surgical procedure in 1847. Victoria took chloroform during the delivery of the royal children, causing some public consternation based upon the biblical passage "In sorrow thou shalt bring forth thy children" (Genesis 3 : 16); Simpson rebutted, noting that the first surgical operation of record was performed under surgical anesthesia (after "the Lord caused a deep sleep to fall upon Adam"). Chloroform produces significant liver damage and is now seldom used in anesthesia.

Cyclopropane, introduced at the University of Wisconsin General Hospital in 1934, is the most potent of the inhalation anesthetics, producing deep unconsciousness in a matter of seconds.

4.12   The Structures of Sulfur Compounds

Oxygen and sulfur are both members of Group VI of the periodic table: Therefore they have similar outer shell configurations

O $1s^2$ $2s^2$ $2p^4$
S $1s^2$ $2s^2$ $2p^6$ $3s^2$ $3p^4$ $3d^0$

and their chemistry is similar in part. Any differences in chemical behavior may usually be attributed to the facts that sulfur is larger, less electronegative, and has unoccupied *d* orbitals which are only slightly higher in energy than the occupied 3*p* orbitals. (By contrast, the lowest unoccupied oxygen orbital in simple compounds is the 3*s*, which is energetically much higher than the occupied orbitals.)

The structures of many organic derivatives containing sulfur more or less parallel those containing oxygen. In addition, as we shall see in forthcoming chapters, sulfur is often found in higher oxidation states.

> Arguments on the exact nature of the bonding in hydrogen sulfide and its organic derivatives follow the same lines as those previously discussed for water, and other oxygen compounds (Section 4.7).
>
> The HSH bond angle is 92°, very close to that expected in the absence of hybridization. The S—H bond distance is significantly longer than the corresponding O—H distance, and sulfur is less electronegative than oxygen. The combination of these two factors results in considerably less electrostatic repulsion between the hydrogens of hydrogen sulfide than between those of water (HOH angle 105°). On the other hand, it is interesting to note that the bond angle at the sulfur atom approaches that expected for *sp*[3] hybridization as the number of alkyl substituents on sulfur increases.

The *thiols* (RSH), also called *mercaptans*, are more acidic than the corresponding alcohols, because the larger sulfur atom can better accommodate the charge of the anion; ethanethiol (CH_3CH_2SH) has $pK_a = 10.5$, compared to ethanol (CH_3CH_2OH) at 15.9. Sodium *mercaptides* are readily formed from thiols by reaction with sodium hydroxide.

$$RSH + \overset{+}{Na}OH^- \longrightarrow RS^-Na^+ + H_2O$$

Sulfur can also better accommodate a positive charge, and in general, sulfur compounds are better Lewis bases than the analogous oxygen compounds. Trimethylsulfonium chloride $[(CH_3)_3S^+Cl^-]$ is a very stable salt, whereas trimethyloxonium chloride $[(CH_3)_3O^+Cl^-]$ cannot be isolated. Sulfonium salts are tetrahedral, the lone pair being considered as the fourth substituent. When appropriately substituted, they may be resolved into stable optically active forms.

R- and S-Ethylisopropylmethylsulfonium bromide

Sulfur compounds analogous to the peroxides also exist. In contrast to the oxygen–oxygen bond (35 kcal/mole), the sulfur–sulfur bond (65 kcal/mole) is quite strong. *Disulfides* (RSSR) are very stable compounds, many of which play key roles in the chemistry of living systems. A number of higher sulfides [R—(S)$_n$—R] are known, but they are seldom encountered.

4.13   Nomenclature of Sulfur Compounds

The prefix *thio-* indicates that sulfur has replaced oxygen in an organic compound. The IUPAC names of the sulfur analogs of alcohols are formed by adding the suffixes

-thiol, *-dithiol*, and so on, to the name of the parent hydrocarbon. Common names are formed by first naming the alkyl group, followed by the word *mercaptan*. When other functions are present, the thiol function is sometimes denoted by the prefix *mercapto-*.

CH_3OH	CH_3SH	$HOCH_2CH_2OH$	$HSCH_2CH_2SH$
Methanol	Methanethiol	1,2-Ethanediol	1,2-Ethanedithiol
(Methyl alcohol)	(Methyl mercaptan)	(Ethylene glycol)	

Cyclohexanol
(Cyclohexyl alcohol)   —OH

Cyclohexanethiol
(Cyclohexyl mercaptan)   —SH

$HSCH_2CH_2OH$
2-Mercaptoethanol

The nomenclature of sulfides (thioethers) and disulfides is similar to that of ethers. Sulfonium salt nomenclature follows the standard form for the naming of salts.

$$CH_3CH_2SCH_2CH_3$$
Diethyl sulfide
(Ethyl sulfide)

$$\overset{\displaystyle SCH_3}{\underset{\displaystyle}{CH_3CHCH_2OH}}$$
2-Methylthio-1-propanol

$$(CH_3)_3CSSCH_3$$
t-Butyl methyl disulfide

$$\overset{+}{\underset{CH_3}{S}} \quad I^-$$
$$CH_3 \diagup \ \diagdown CH_3$$

Trimethylsulfonium
iodide

The prefix *thia-* is sometimes used to indicate that sulfur has replaced carbon in an organic compound.

HO—⟨ ⟩—S
4-Thiacyclohexanol

⟨ ⟩S
Thiacyclopentane
(Thiolane)

$$HOCH_2CH_2-S-CH_2CH_2-S-CH_2CH_2OH$$
3,6-Dithia-1,8-octanediol

4.14 The Structures of Nitrogen and Phosphorus Compounds

Amines are organic derivatives of ammonia formed by replacing one, two, or all three hydrogens with alkyl groups. The nitrogen of ammonia may be considered as sp^3-hybridized; the molecule is nearly tetrahedral with hydrogens at three corners and a lone pair at the fourth corner. The HNH angle is 107°. If nitrogen were to adopt a planar geometry in which the bonding orbitals were sp^2 and the remaining p orbital contained a lone pair, the energy of the molecule would be higher because of the somewhat less efficient use of the s orbital. The energy difference between the pyramidal and planar geometries is only about 10% of that of a normal chemical bond. The nitrogen in ammonia and amines can therefore invert quite easily, via the planar configuration, like an umbrella in a windstorm (Figure 4.9). No simple amine which is asymmetric at

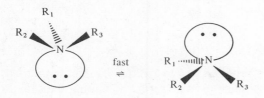

Figure 4.9
Energy diagram for inversion of an amine.

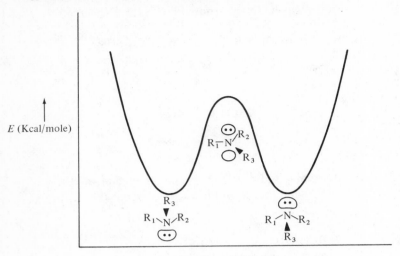

nitrogen has ever been separated into enantiomers, because racemization (interconversion of enantiomers) is very rapid at room temperature. Recall that the racemization of an asymmetric carbon requires the breaking of a bond to a substituent, and the reattachment of the substituent to the other side of the carbon atom, that is, a chemical reaction.

Ammonia and amines are Lewis bases, and they will share their lone pairs with Lewis acids to form ammonium compounds. (Lone pairs of electrons will not ordinarily be indicated in formulas unless they are important to the discussion.)

$$CH_3 \overset{..}{N}H_2 + HCl \longrightarrow CH_3^+ NH_3 \ Cl^-$$

$$(CH_3)_3 N\colon\ + AlCl_3 \longrightarrow (CH_3)_3^+ N\text{—}^- AlCl_3$$

The ammonium ion, NH_4^+, is geometrically and electronically analogous to methane; such species are said to be *isoelectronic* with each other. Ammonium ions having four different groups attached to nitrogen $(R_1 R_2 R_3 R_4 N^+)$ exist in two enantiomeric forms. These are not spontaneously racemized, as are the amines, but are configurationally stable like the asymmetric carbon compounds. (Why?)

A number of other types of singly bonded nitrogen compounds are structurally related to amines or to ammonium salts. Among the more important of these are the tertiary amine oxides $(R_3 N^+ \text{—} O^-)$ and the organic derivatives of hydrazine $(NH_2 NH_2)$, hydroxylamine $(NH_2 OH)$, and chloramine $(NH_2 Cl)$.

Phosphorus lies just below nitrogen in the periodic chart, and the configuration of its outer electronic shell is similar to that of nitrogen. There are, of course, many similarities in the organic chemistry of the two elements. However, nitrogen forms stable compounds having only three (amines, etc.) or four (ammonium compounds) covalent bonds, whereas phosphorus compounds are known having three, four, five, or six covalent bonds to phosphorus. The existence of the latter compounds means that phosphorus can accommodate 10 to 12 electrons in its outer shell by utilizing its empty *d* orbitals (Section 10.5).

$$
\begin{array}{cc}
\underset{\text{Ethylisopropylmethylphosphine}}{\overset{\displaystyle CH_3CH_2}{\underset{\displaystyle CH_3}{(CH_3)_2 CH\text{—}P\colon}}}
&
\underset{\text{Ethylmethylphosphonium iodide}}{\overset{\displaystyle CH_3}{\underset{\displaystyle CH_3CH_2}{\overset{+}{P}H_2 \ I^-}}}
\end{array}
$$

Inversion in Phosphines. The typical bond angle for trivalent phosphorus compounds is 100°, while for tetravalent phosphorus the angles are very near 109°. In each case the phosphorus can be considered to be approximately sp^3-hybridized, with deviations from the regular tetrahedral values resulting from unsymmetrical substitution. In contrast to amines, the inversion rates for phosphines are very low, and phosphines as well as phosphonium salts, may be resolved into optically active forms.

4.15 Nomenclature of Amines and Ammonium Salts

Amines are divided into subclasses according to the number of alkyl groups attached to the nitrogen,

$$RNH_2 \qquad R_2NH \qquad R_3N$$

Primary amine   Secondary amine   Tertiary amine

and they are named by specifying these groups and adding the suffix *-amine*. The name is written as one continuous word. Note the differences in the nomenclature of amines and alcohols (see Section 4.8): $(CH_3)_3COH$ is a *tertiary* alcohol and $(CH_3)_3CNH_2$ is a *primary* amine; the names of amines are run together, but the word "alcohol" stands apart (ethylamine, ethyl alcohol). These differences are based on the chemical properties of the compounds, as will be discussed later (Chapters 18 and 21).

$$CH_3NH_2 \qquad (CH_3)_2NH \qquad (CH_3)_3N$$

Methylamine   Dimethylamine   Trimethylamine

$(CH_3)_3CNH_2$ Methylpropylamine   Ethylmethylpropylamine

t-Butylamine

The parent ring systems of a number of important nitrogen heterocycles are known by trivial names.

Ethylenimine   Pyrrolidine   Piperidine   Morpholine
(Aziridine)

In forming a derived name when the name of a nitrogen compound is chosen as the parent, an italic capital *N* is placed before the name of the substituent to show that it is attached to nitrogen. *Chemical Abstracts* and a number of other indexes use this nomenclature system for indexing purposes. The name is formed by choosing the largest or most important hydrocarbon grouping present and naming the amine from that, then indicating the other substituents attached to nitrogen by the *N* followed by the group names. Some examples will illustrate this system.

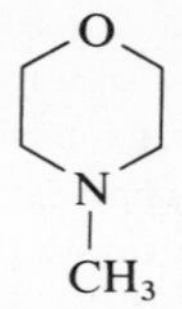

N-Methylmorpholine 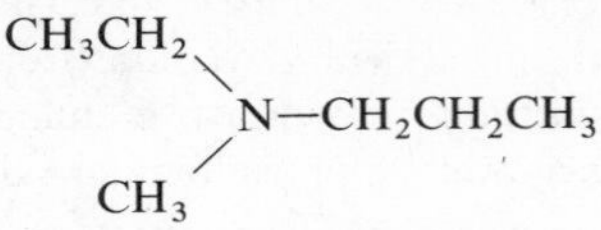   N-Ethyl-N-methylpropylamine

Many times it is necessary to identify the amine function by means of the prefix *amino-*.

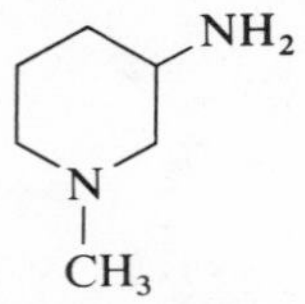

$(CH_3)_2NCH_2CH_2OH$

1-Methyl-3-aminopiperidine   2-Dimethylaminoethanol

Salts of amines are simply named as derivatives of the ammonium ion, NH_4^+. Ammonium compounds in which all of the hydrogens have been substituted by alkyl groups are called *quaternary ammonium salts*.

$CH_3 \overset{+}{-} NH_3 \; Cl^-$

ClO_4^-

Methylammonium chloride   Ethyldimethylpropylammonium
(Methylamine hydrochloride)   perchlorate

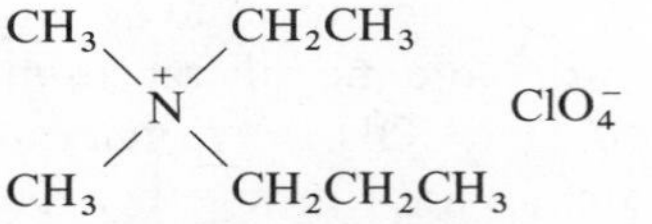

Frequently amine salts are indicated by adding names such as *hydrochloride, hydrobromide, methiodide*, to the name of the amine. This is a holdover from older days when the structures of such "adducts" of amines were not understood.

The ammonium ions derived from amines with common names are usually named by adding the ending *-ium* to the name of the amine (dropping an *e* if it is present).

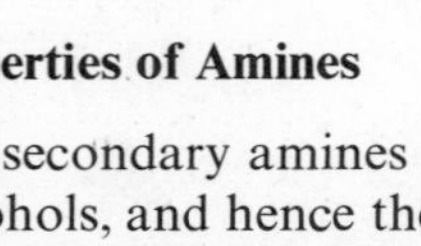

I^-

N,N-Dimethylpiperidinium iodide
(N-Methylpiperidine methiodide)

4.16   Properties of Amines

Primary and secondary amines do not form as strong intermolecular hydrogen bonds as do the alcohols, and hence their boiling points are intermediate between those of the alcohols and the hydrocarbons of similar molecular weight (Section 4.20). Tertiary amines have boiling points which are just slightly higher than those of the corresponding hydrocarbons (Table 4.6). Simple amines have a pronounced and characteristic odor, sometimes described as fishy (more descriptive terms are often applicable). Amines having five or fewer carbons are miscible with or very soluble in water. Their aqueous solutions are basic to litmus. Almost all amines are soluble in dilute acid, owing to the formation of soluble ammonium salts.

$$RNH_2 + H_3O^+ \longrightarrow RNH_3^+ + H_2O$$

Table 4.6   Amines

Name	Mp, °C	Bp, °C	Name	Mp, °C	Bp, °C
Methylamine	−92	−7.5	*n*-Butylamine	−50	78
Dimethylamine	−96	7.5	*t*-Butylamine	−67	46
Trimethylamine	−117	3	Cyclohexylamine		134
Ethylamine	−80	17	Pyrrolidine		88.5
Triethylamine	−115	89	Piperidine	−9	106
n-Propylamine	−83	49	Morpholine	−5	129

EXERCISE 4.3

The pK_a of NH_4^+ is 9.24 while that of $CH_3NH_3^+$ is 10.64. Is methylamine a stronger or a weaker base than ammonia? How many times stronger or weaker? What do you think this difference is due to?

USES OF AMINES. *Amines constitute one of the most important classes of organic compounds. The lone pair on the amine nitrogen enables it to participate in a large variety of reactions. Amines play very prominent roles in biochemical systems; they are widely distributed in nature in the form of amino acids, proteins, alkaloids, and vitamins. Many complex amine derivatives have pronounced physiological activity, for example, penicillin, LSD, the poison of the hemlock, novocaine. The odor of decaying fish is due to simple amines. They are used to manufacture many medicinal chemicals such as sulfa drugs and local anesthetics. The synthetic fiber* nylon *is made from two raw materials, one of which is a simple diamine.*

4.17   Organosilicon Compounds

Since both silicon and carbon are members of Group IV of the periodic table, a resemblance between the chemistry of these two elements is to be expected. Silicon, like carbon, prefers to use sp^3 σ bonding in most of its compounds (Table 4.7). There is a wide range of structural similarity between the compounds of silicon and carbon with regard to σ bonding and molecular geometry. Tetravalent silicon derivatives are configurationally stable, and examples of optical and geometrical isomerism attributable to the silicon atom are commonplace. A striking difference in the fundamental chemistry of the two elements is seen in their bond strengths: The carbon–carbon bond is quite strong (82.6 kcal/mole), the silicon–silicon bond is relatively weak (53 kcal/mole). The silicon–hydrogen bond is also weaker than the carbon–hydrogen bond. Consequently the silanes of the formula Si_nH_{2n+2} are much less stable than are the analogous alkanes; silane (SiH_4) and disilane (SiH_3SiH_3) are spontaneously flammable in air. Silanes not containing Si—H bonds, such as tetramethylsilane (Me_4Si), are stable in air. On the other hand, certain bonds such as Si—O are even more stable than the analogous carbon bonds. As we shall see in Section 10.6, this is in large part an effect due to the availability of empty $3d$ orbitals on silicon. The "silicones" contain chains of Si—O—Si bonds and have a high thermal stability; they are used as lubricants, hydraulic fluids, and synthetic rubbers.

A linear silicone polymer

Table 4.7   Organosilicon Compounds

Silanes (analogous to alkanes)
SiH_3SiH_3	$CH_3CH_2SiH_3$	$(CH_3)_4Si$
Disilane	Ethylsilane	Tetramethylsilane

Silyl halides (analogous to alkyl halides)
H_3SiCl	$(CH_3)_2SiCl_2$	$(CH_3)_3SiCl$
Silyl chloride	Dimethylsilyl dichloride	Trimethylsilyl chloride

Silanols (analogous to alcohols)
H_3SiOH	$(CH_3)_3SiOH$	$(CH_3)_2Si(OH)_2$	$CH_3Si(OH)_3$
Silanol	Trimethylsilanol	Dimethylsilanediol	Methylsilanetriol

Siloxanes and alkoxysilanes (analogous to ethers)
$(CH_3)_3SiOCH_3$	$(CH_3)_2Si(OCH_3)_2$	$(CH_3)_3SiOSi(CH_3)_3$
Trimethylmethoxysilane	Dimethyldimethoxysilane	Hexamethyldisiloxane

Silazanes (silylamines) (analogous to amines)
H_3SiNH_2	$(CH_3)_3SiNH_2$	$[(CH_3)_3Si]_2NH$
Silazane	Trimethylsilazane	Hexamethyldisilazane
	(Trimethylsilylamine)	[Bis(trimethylsilyl)amine]

There has been considerable speculation over the years as to whether or not living systems based on silicon rather than carbon might be possible. Because of the great tendency for silicon compounds to form Si—O bonds rather than Si—H (compared to carbon), it would be more difficult to construct functional metabolic systems based on silicon. The corresponding carbon systems function because the oxidized compounds (especially CO_2) can be reduced again using the energy of sunlight in the process of photosynthesis (Section 31.11). To reduce SiO_2 is much more difficult, especially when the planet's atmosphere contains so much oxygen. But on other planets?

4.18   Organoboron Compounds

Up to this point we have considered the structures and bonding arrangements of carbon and silicon compounds containing electronegative elements to the right of carbon in the periodic table. All of these electronegative elements have one characteristic in common: when they are in their lowest stable coordination state, there remains on each of them at least one lone pair of valence electrons. Thus, methyl halides, methyl ether, methyl sulfide, methylamine, and methylphosphine are all Lewis bases. As has already been implied in earlier discussions, many covalent derivatives of the elements to the left of carbon in the periodic table (electropositive elements) act as Lewis acids by virtue of their low-lying unoccupied orbitals. We shall begin our discussion of organic derivatives of the electropositive elements by a consideration of the structures and bonding of organoboron compounds.

Boron has the ground electronic state $1s^2 2s^2 2p^1$, but in its neutral compounds is always trivalent and never univalent. The decrease in energy upon the formation of three bonds to boron exceeds the decrease in energy for the formation of one bond in a univalent boron compound by more than enough to provide for promotion of a $2s$ electron into the $2p$ level. (The situation is analogous to that discussed for carbon in Section 2.5, which the student might like to review.) Boron utilizes the three outer-shell electrons to form three coplanar sp^2 bonds in compounds of the type BY_3, and one $2p$ orbital on the boron remains empty. Such molecules are often referred to as *electron-deficient*. There is a considerable tendency for the boron to acquire an additional electron pair to fill the unoccupied orbital and thus complete the octet of electrons. The boron trihalides (BX_3) and organoboranes (BR_3) are strong Lewis acids, and they readily accept electron pairs from a variety of Lewis bases to form tetracovalent boron compounds in which the boron atom is sp^3-hybridized.

$$sp^2 \quad \underset{\substack{\text{F} \\ }}{\overset{\substack{\text{F} \quad \text{F} \\ \text{B}}}{}} 120° \quad + \quad \text{F}^- \quad \longrightarrow \quad 109° \quad \underset{\substack{\text{F} \\ sp^3}}{\overset{\substack{\text{F} \quad \text{F} \\ \bar{\text{B}}}}{}} \text{F}$$

Boron trifluoride   Fluoborate
(planar)   (tetrahedral)

$$B(CH_3)_3 + :N(CH_3)_3 \longrightarrow (CH_3)_3^+N-B^-(CH_3)_3$$

Large numbers of boron compounds are known in which carbon is bonded to boron, either directly, or indirectly via oxygen or nitrogen (Table 4.8). The nitrogen and oxygen derivatives of boron are much weaker Lewis acids than the trialkylboranes or boron trihalides.

Table 4.8   Organoboron Compounds

Borane ("BH_3") derivatives

$B(CH_3)_3$	$Na[B(CH_3)_4]$	$(CH_3)_3^+N-^-B(CH_3)_3$
Trimethylborane	Sodium tetramethylborate	Trimethylamine-
	(Sodium tetramethylboron)	trimethylborane

Boric acid [$B(OH)_3$] derivatives

$B(OCH_3)_3$ $Na[HB(OCH_3)_3]$
Methyl borate   Sodium trimethoxyborohydride
(Trimethoxyborane)

Boronic acid [$HB(OH)_2$] derivatives

$CH_3B(OH)_2$ $CH_3B(OCH_3)_2$
Methylboronic   Dimethyl methylboronate
acid   (Methyldimethoxyborane)   Trimethylboroxine   Borazine

Borinic acid [H_2BOH] derivatives

$(CH_3)_2BOH$ $(CH_3)_2BOCH_3$
Dimethylborinic acid   Methyl dimethylborinate
(Dimethylmethoxyborane)

Multicenter Bonding. The most striking feature of the chemistry of boron is provided by the boron hydrides. The simple hydride, BH_3, is not stable but dimerizes to form diborane (B_2H_6). A number of higher hydrides also exist, for example, B_4H_{10} and $B_{10}H_{14}$.

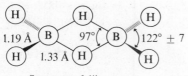

Structure of diborane

The student will recognize that it is impossible to write conventional Lewis structures for such compounds, because they would require divalent hydrogen atoms. The solution to this dilemma lies in multicenter bonding. In diborane, for example, each boron is approximately sp^3-hybridized. Two of the orbitals on each boron, along with two of the boron's electrons, are used to form two normal (two-center) bonds to the terminal hydrogens. Two of the hybrid orbitals and one electron from each boron are free for further bonding. Each bridged hydrogen has one electron in a $1s$ orbital. A hydrogen $1s$ orbital and one orbital from each of the borons overlap to form a three-center bonding orbital, which is occupied by two electrons.

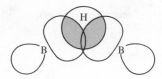

The atomic orbitals used to form the three-center bond. The lowest resulting molecular orbital contains two electrons. The remaining two molecular orbitals are empty.

Multicenter bonding of this type may be expected only in molecules where there are more usable atomic valence orbitals than the electrons are able to utilize by the formation of ordinary two-center bonds [e.g., $(Me_3Al)_2$, Section 4.19]

4.19   Organometallic Compounds

Substances possessing carbon–metal bonds are called *organometallic compounds*. The nature of the carbon–metal bond depends on the metal and to some extent on the nature of the alkyl group involved. Such bonds vary from substantially ionic to essentially covalent. In the figure the structure on the left is covalent, while that on the right is ionic. If the structure on the right alone describes the bond in question, that bond is said to be 100% ionic, while if the structure on the left describes it, it is 0% ionic.

$$-\overset{|}{\underset{|}{C}}-M \leftrightarrow -\overset{|}{\underset{|}{C}}{}^{-} \quad M^{+}$$

When the actual charge distributions are studied it is usually found that the true situation is somewhere in between. Such in-between cases are described with the aid of a two-headed arrow, as shown. (Note the two-headed arrow does *not* represent an equilibrium, but rather an intermediate between the extremes.) In general, the more electropositive the metal, the more ionic the carbon–metal bond. Estimates of the percent ionic character of some carbon–metal bonds are given in Table 4.9.

Table 4.9   Percent Ionic Character of Carbon–Metal Bonds

C—K	51	C—Mg	35	C—Sn	12
C—Na	47	C—Al	22	C—Pb	12
C—Li	43	C—Zn	18	C—Hg	9
C—Ca	43	C—Cd	15		

As might be expected, the reactivity of organometallic compounds increases with the ionic character of the carbon–metal bond. Highly ionic compounds, such as alkylsodiums and alkylpotassiums, inflame in air, react explosively with water, are nonvolatile, and are insoluble in nonpolar solvents.

$$CH_3Na + H_2O \rightarrow CH_4 + NaOH$$

They are among the strongest bases known. These compounds are too reactive for most practical purposes. Alkyllithium reagents, on the other hand, can be prepared and used in hydrocarbon or ether solvents, and they are very useful in synthetic procedures. In contrast to highly ionic compounds such as alkylsodium, more covalent compounds are for the most part relatively stable in air, react slowly or not at all with water, may be distilled, and are quite soluble in solvents such as hydrocarbons and ethers. Organometallic compounds of intermediate ionic character are usually of more interest to the organic chemist. They are relatively easy to make and to handle. The most important of these are the magnesium compounds. Many organomagnesium halides (or *Grignard reagents* as they are called) can readily be prepared by reaction of the corresponding alkyl halides with magnesium metal in ether or a similar solvent.

$$CH_3CH_2I + Mg \qquad\qquad CH_3CH_2MgI$$
A Grignard reagent

The Grignard reagent is usually represented as $RMgX$, although in ether solution more complex solvated structures apparently exist.

Group I (Alkali).

$$CH_3CH_2CH_2CH_2Li \qquad CH_3CH_2Na \qquad CH_3K$$
n-Butyllithium   Ethylsodium   Methylpotassium

Lithium has a single $2s$ electron which may be used for bond formation. From Rule 1 (Section 4.2) we know that this $2s$ orbital should be used for bonding, since the orbital is thereby half-utilized. To a first approximation, a compound such as methyllithium is formed by the overlap of a carbon sp^3 orbital with the lithium $2s$ orbital, and the $2p$ orbitals of the lithium remain empty. (In a more thorough analysis, it is found that the addition of a few percent of p character to the bonding orbital of lithium strengthens the bond sufficiently to outweigh the small decrease in the utilization of the s orbital.)

Similarly, alkylsodium and alkylpotassium compounds are formed by overlap of their $3s$ and $4s$ orbitals, respectively, with the carbon orbital. Again the p orbitals remain empty. Unoccupied orbitals always tend to be p, which can be understood in terms of Rule 1, Section 4.2.

Group II (Alkaline Earth)

$$[(CH_3)_2Be]_n \qquad (CH_3CH_2)_2Mg \qquad CH_3MgBr \qquad (CH_3)_2Ca$$
Dimethylberyllium   Diethylmagnesium   Methylmagnesium   Dimethylcalcium
bromide

The use of two sp orbitals (at 180° from one another) on beryllium, magnesium, or calcium for overlapping with the carbon orbitals makes efficient use of the s orbitals, forms strong bonds, and places the substituent nuclei as far apart as possible. There are remaining to the beryllium two empty $2p$ orbitals, and similarly there are two empty $3p$ orbitals on the magnesium. Dialkylberyllium and dialkylmagnesium compounds are therefore Lewis acids. In contrast to the very important magnesium compounds, the organoberyllium compounds are seldom encountered. Dimethylberyllium will react with methyllithium to produce the trimethylberyllium anion in which the beryllium atom is sp^2-hybridized.

Group III

$$[(CH_3)_3Al]_2 \qquad [(CH_3)_2AlCl]_2 \qquad (CH_3)_3Ga$$
Trimethylaluminum   Dimethylaluminum   Trimethylgallium
                              chloride

Aluminum, like boron, is tricovalent, and forms compounds such as trimethylaluminum in which the sp^2-hybridized metal atom is two electrons short of having a complete octet. Aluminum chloride, aluminum bromide, and the aluminum alkyls are strong Lewis acids, and they are excellent catalysts for a number of organic reactions.

The lower aluminum alkyls exist as dimers in which the bridging atom is involved in a three-center bond, such as was discussed for diborane in the previous section.

$$CH_3 \qquad CH_3 \qquad CH_3 \qquad CH_3 \qquad Cl \qquad CH_3$$
$$Al \qquad \qquad Al \qquad \qquad Al \qquad \qquad Al$$
$$CH_3 \qquad CH_3 \qquad CH_3 \qquad CH_3 \qquad Cl \qquad CH_3$$

In the presence of Lewis bases, such as coordinating solvents, the dimers are broken down as a result of coordination of the metal with the base.

$$[(CH_3)_3Al]_2 + 2(CH_3CH_2)_2O \longrightarrow 2(CH_3)_3^-Al-{}^+O(CH_2CH_3)_2$$

Group IV

$$(CH_3CH_2CH_2CH_2)_2SnCl_2 \qquad (CH_3CH_2)_4Pb$$
Di-*n*-butyltin dichloride   Tetraethyllead

The organometallic derivatives of the Group IV elements are largely covalent in character, and they exhibit the expected properties, such as solubility in nonpolar solvents. The hybridization of the metal atom in the derivatives shown is sp^3. The most important organic compound of Group IV elements is tetraethyllead, which has been made on a large scale for use as an antiknock agent in gasoline.

Sub-Group II

$$(CH_3CH_2)_2Zn \qquad (CH_3)_2Cd \qquad CH_3CH_2HgCl$$
Diethylzinc   Dimethylcadmium   Ethylmercuric chloride

Divalent zinc, cadmium, and mercury compounds have linear geometries with the metal atom sp-hybridized. All of these compounds can exist in higher coordination states by combination with Lewis bases.

The organozinc compounds made by Frankland in 1848 were the first organometallic compounds to be prepared. Organozinc and cadmium compounds are particularly useful in organic synthesis when organometallic reagents of mild reactivity are desired. Apparently species such as RZnX and RCdX do not exist as such but rather as $R_2Zn \cdot ZnX_2$ and $R_2Cd \cdot CdX_2$. Organozinc and cadmium compounds are nonpolar liquids, or low melting solids, soluble in most organic solvents. The lower zinc compounds are spontaneously flammable in air; the cadmium compounds are less sensitive to oxygen.

The RHgX compounds exist as such, and are usually stable crystalline solids, many of which may be recrystallized from aqueous solutions. The dialkylmercury compounds are volatile and extremely toxic.

4.20   Intermolecular Forces

It is reasonable to expect the boiling and melting points of compounds to increase with increasing molecular weight and with increasing strength of the intermolecular forces. We have already noted significant differences in the boiling and melting points of compounds having approximately the same molecular weights. These differences can be accounted for in large part by three types of intermolecular forces: (1) van der Waals forces, (2) dipole association, and (3) hydrogen bonds.

van der Waals Forces

The van der Waals force is of the widest importance, as it affects every type of atom and molecule, without exception. It is of major importance in determining the properties of liquids (bp, density, viscosity, etc.), and of some importance in solids and gases. The van der Waals force is responsible for the energy difference between *anti* and *gauche* butane, and it has a far-reaching effect on the conformations of molecules, and hence upon their physical and chemical properties.

Perhaps the easiest way to understand the van der Waals type of force is to study a plot of the energy of two helium atoms as a function of the distance which separates them (Figure 4.10). If we take the energy of the system to be zero when the atoms are far

Figure 4.10
The energy of two helium atoms as a function of the distance between them.

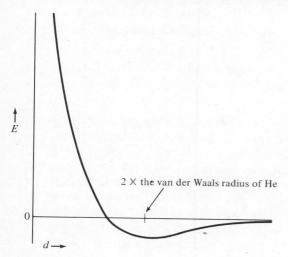

apart, we note that as they come together the energy first decreases, and then increases abruptly. The energy decrease at relatively long distances is called *van der Waals attraction*. It is a result of the *correlation* of the motions of the electrons of one atom with those of the other atom, as shown in Figure 4.11. If the electrons of the atom on the left, for example, are between the two atoms as shown, then the electrons of the atom on the right will tend to be to the right of the nucleus (Case A). When the electrons of the left atom are to the left of the nucleus, the electrons of the right atom tend to be between the nuclei (Case B). The electrons are, of course, in constant movement, and the pictures shown are oversimplifications, but the basic idea is that the motions of the electrons of one atom are

Figure 4.11
Schematic diagram showing the correlation of electron motions which leads to van der Waals attraction.

Case A

Case B

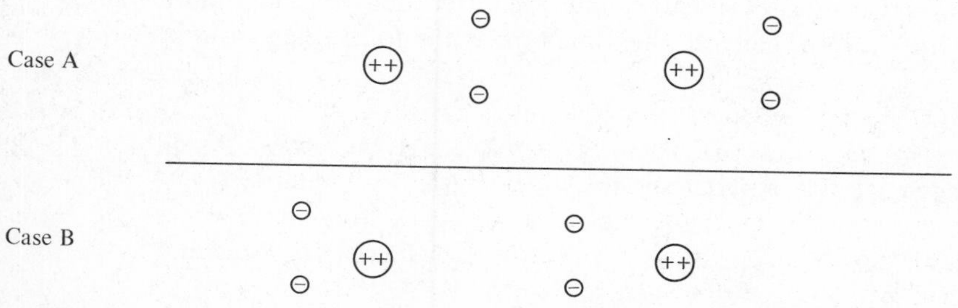

not independent of the motions of the electrons of the other atom. The motions are correlated so that the electrons of one atom are nearer to the nucleus of the second atom than they are to the electrons of the second atom, on the average. The attractions of the electrons for the nuclei are thus greater than the repulsions (nuclei for nuclei, and electrons for electrons), and the atoms tend to stick together at a distance corresponding to the energy minimum. This distance is called the *sum of the van der Waals radii of the atoms*.

If the two helium atoms are pushed closer together than the distance of the energy minimum, their electron clouds seriously interpenetrate one another. The two clouds are trying to be in the same place at the same time, and a serious electrostatic repulsion, called *van der Waals repulsion*, results.

The completely general nature of these van der Waals forces can be appreciated by realizing that they result from interactions between nuclei and electrons, even when the latter are in filled shells, and thus they will occur between all atoms and molecules.

For atoms such as the rare gases and for nonpolar molecules such as hydrocarbons, the only intermolecular forces are van der Waals forces. These determine the boiling points of such substances in a straightforward way. The more electrons a molecule has, the more *polarizable* it is, and the more important the van der Waals attraction.

The ease of deformation of an electron cloud by an electric field is called its polarizability. *In Figure 4.10, the polarizability is related to the energy lowering at the minimum of the curve. The more polarizable the molecule, the deeper the energy minimum.*

Thus the larger a hydrocarbon is, the more polarizable it is, the more the molecules stick together, and the higher its boiling point. Large atoms are more polarizable than small ones, because there are more electrons, and the outer electrons are not very tightly held. Bonding electrons are more tightly held (and less polarizable) than lone pairs. Hence molecules containing oxygen or nitrogen are more polarizable than those containing just carbon and hydrogen. Molecules containing still larger atoms such as sulfur or bromine are much more polarizable.

For hydrocarbons, boiling points increase roughly with increasing molecular weight. However, substantial differences in boiling points are found among isomers, as a direct result of molecular shape. For the van der Waals attraction to be most effective, the molecules must be able to "touch" large portions of their surfaces together. Two molecules of *n*-pentane can touch better than two molecules of neopentane, as the figures show.

Two molecules of *n*-pentane   Two molecules of neopentane

Spheres have the minimum surface area for their volume of any geometrical figures. Consequently, the more spherical molecules become, the lower their boiling points (other things being equal). This is a very general phenomenon, as the following examples will illustrate:

$$CH_3CH_2CH_2CH_2CH_3 \qquad CH_3CH_2\underset{\underset{CH_3}{|}}{C}HCH_3 \qquad CH_3\underset{\underset{CH_3}{|}}{\overset{\overset{CH_3}{|}}{C}}CH_3$$

| *n*-Pentane | Isopentane | Neopentane |
| bp 36°C | bp 28°C | bp 9.5° |

$$CH_3CH_2CH_2CH_2OH \qquad CH_3CHCH_2OH \qquad CH_3CH_2CHCH_3 \qquad CH_3COH$$

| | CH₃ | OH | CH₃ |

| *n*-Butyl alcohol | Isobutyl alcohol | *s*-Butyl alcohol | *t*-Butyl alcohol |
| bp 117°C | bp 107°C | bp 100°C | bp 85°C |

Van der Waals forces are also important in determining the structure and melting point of a crystal. A crystal, however, has its component molecules perfectly ordered, in contrast to the rather random structure of a fluid. The melting point of a crystal is therefore greatly influenced by the rigidity and symmetry of its component molecules, since these properties affect the increase in disorder upon melting. In general, it is much more complicated to estimate melting points of crystals than to estimate boiling points of liquids.

Dipole Association

When two atoms of different electronegativity are covalently bound together, there is an unequal sharing of electrons, with the atom of higher electronegativity assuming a greater share of the electron density (Chapter 2). This unequal sharing gives rise to bond dipoles. A molecule with lone pairs of electrons, such as ammonia or water, also has a lone-pair dipole moment. Such bond and lone-pair moments are simply referred to as *dipole moments* (μ). (Sometimes these are called *permanent dipoles*, to differentiate them from the momentary *induced dipoles* responsible for van der Waals attractions.) In the liquid phase, molecules tend to orient themselves so that dipole moments in different molecules attract one another. Thermal motions of the molecules tend to upset this order, however, and a liquid is only partially ordered (Figure 4.12).

Figure 4.12
Ordered structure of liquid resulting from dipole–dipole interactions.

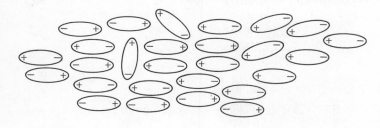

Since this attraction has to be overcome in order to vaporize the liquid, polar molecules tend to have higher boiling points than do their nonpolar relatives.

CH₃CH₂N⟨CH₃/CH₃⟩	CH₃CH₂CH⟨CH₃/CH₃⟩	CH₃OCH₃	CH₃CH₂CH₃
Ethyldimethylamine	Isopentane	Methyl ether	Propane
MW 73; bp 37.5°C	MW 72; bp 28°C	MW 46; bp −25°C	MW 44; bp −45°C

Dipoles are often represented by arrows, the negative end being the point.

$$H_3C{\rightarrow}Br \quad \text{or} \quad CH_3CH_2{\leftarrow}Mg{\rightarrow}CH_2CH_3$$

Sometimes partial ionic charges are represented by the Greek δ, meaning not a full charge (ion) but a partial charge or dipole.

$$\overset{\delta+}{C}H_3\mathrel{\text{——}}\overset{\delta-}{F} \qquad \overset{\delta+}{C}H_3{-}\overset{\delta-}{O}{-}\overset{\delta+}{C}H_3$$

Hydrogen Bonds

When a hydrogen is covalently bound to a highly electronegative atom, it has an affinity for a second electronegative atom. For example, a hydrogen atom may act as a bridge between two oxygen atoms, holding one by a covalent bond and the other by electrostatic forces. This kind of electrostatic attraction is a special case of dipole–dipole association and is of great practical importance. It is called a *hydrogen bond*. Usually a hydrogen bond is represented by a dashed line rather than by the solid line used for a covalent bond.

Intermolecular hydrogen bonds   Intramolecular
                                             hydrogen bond

The strengths of such bonds (approx. 5 kcal/mole) are much less than the strengths of ordinary covalent bonds (50–100 kcal/mole), but much greater than the van der Waals attraction between atoms (0.05–0.5 kcal/mole for the rare gases). The strongest hydrogen bonds, and the most important, are those in which both of the electronegative atoms involved come from the group O, N, or F (small atoms with concentrated electron density).

Strong hydrogen bonds

$$F—H\cdots F \qquad O—H\cdots N \qquad O—H\cdots O \qquad F—H\cdots N$$

Weak hydrogen bonds

$$N—H\cdots O \qquad N—H\cdots N \qquad O—H\cdots \pi \text{ electrons} \qquad S—H\cdots S$$

$$S—H\cdots O \qquad S—H\cdots N \qquad C—H\cdots O$$

EXERCISE 4.4

Ethanolamine, $HOCH_2CH_2NH_2$, can in principle hydrogen-bond to itself in two different ways:

Actually, one of these arrangements is much more important than the other. Explain.

The hydrogen bond plays a very prominent role throughout chemistry, especially in biological systems. Essentially all physical properties, including spectra, are substantially altered by hydrogen bonds. We will briefly examine a few of these effects here.

Intermolecular hydrogen bonds cause dramatic increases in the boiling points of alcohols over those of most other compounds of similar molecular weight.

$$CH_3CH_2CH_2OH \qquad CH_3OCH_2CH_3 \qquad CH_3CH_2OH \qquad CH_3OCH_3 \qquad CH_3CH_2CH_3$$
MW 60; bp 98°C   MW 60; bp 8°C   MW 46; bp 78°C   MW 46; bp −25°C   MW 44; bp −45°C

The effect is noticeable with amines, but it is not as dramatic.

2-Methylpyrrolidine   *N*-Methylpyrrolidine
bp 100°C   bp 79°C

The —SH group forms very weak hydrogen bonds. Water boils higher than does hydrogen sulfide, and alcohols boil higher than the corresponding thiols. Note, however, that dialkyl sulfides have higher boiling points than do the corresponding ethers. Since hydrogen bonding is not a factor here, the boiling point is primarily determined by the atomic numbers (polarizability) of sulfur versus that of oxygen.

Boiling points, °C

HOH	100°	HSH	−62°
CH_3OH	66°	CH_3SH	6°
CH_3OCH_3	−24°	CH_3SCH_3	38°

Intramolecular hydrogen bonds which form five- or six-membered rings are stronger than the corresponding intermolecular bonds, and they are formed at the expense of the latter. They cut down on intermolecular association, and hence have effects opposite to those of intermolecular hydrogen bonding on boiling point and many other physical properties.

Intramolecular hydrogen bond   *Intermolecular hydrogen bond*

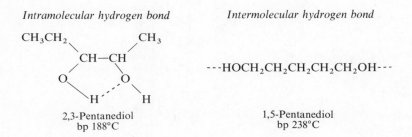

2,3-Pentanediol   1,5-Pentanediol
bp 188°C   bp 238°C

The formation of hydrogen bonds between water and organic compounds containing oxygen or nitrogen markedly affects the water solubility of the organic compounds.

Hydrogen bonding and solubility

Compound	Solubility in water (g per 100 ml) near room temperature	Comment
$CH_3CH_2CH_2CH_2CH_3$	0.04	No H bonding
$CH_3CH_2OCH_2CH_3$	7.5	Water to ether oxygen H bonding
$CH_3CH_2CH_2CH_2OH$	7.9	Reciprocal H bonding with water
$CH_3CH_2CH_2CH_2NH_2$	∞	Reciprocal H bonding with water

PROBLEMS

1. What advantage is gained by the use of hybrid orbitals in the formation of a bond?

2. Define, and illustrate by a picture of a specific example, the following:
    (a) Lewis acid   (e) Conjugate acid
    (b) s–sp^3 σ bond   (f) Hydrogen bond
    (c) p–sp^3 σ bond   (g) Multicenter bonding
    (d) sp^2–sp^3 σ bond

3. Make drawings of atomic orbital models for each of the following (show only valence shell electrons). Label the orbitals as to type (s, p, sp^2, etc.) and indicate the expected bond angles.
    (a) HCl   (f) $LiNH_2$
    (b) CH_3OH (g) CH_3MgCl
    (c) H_3O^+ (h) CH_3^+
    (d) CH_3SF (i) NH_3—BF_3
    (e) $(CH_3)_4N^+$ (j) SiF_4

4. Account for the observation that diethyl ether (MW 74) is readily soluble in cold concentrated sulfuric acid; whereas pentane (MW 72) is quite insoluble.

5. Write systematic names for the following compounds:

    (a) $CH_3CHCH_2CHCH_2CH_3$
    $\qquad\;\; |\qquad\;\; |$
    $\qquad\;\, CH_3\quad Cl$

    (b)
    —CH_2CH_3
    Br

    (c) $CH_3OCH_2CH_2CH_2OH$

    (d)
    OH
    CH_3
    CH_3

    (e) $CH_3\overset{\displaystyle CH_3}{\underset{\displaystyle CH_3}{C}}CH_2CH_2CH_2\overset{\displaystyle CH_2CH_3}{\underset{\displaystyle CH_3\;CH}{C}}CH_3$
    $\qquad\qquad\qquad\qquad\qquad\qquad\;\; OH$

    (f) $CH_3OCH(CH_3)_2$

    (g) $(CH_3CH_2)_3P$

    (h) $HSCH_2CH_2CH_2OH$

    (i) CH_3CHCH_2Li
    $\qquad\; |$
    $\qquad CH_3$

    (j)
    B

    (k) $CH_3SCH_2CH_2OH$

    (l)
    CH_3CH_2
    $\qquad\qquad\diagdown$
    $\qquad\qquad\quad N$—CH_3
    $\qquad\qquad\diagup$
    $CH_3(CH_2)_{10}$

    (m)$(CH_3)_3S^+OH^-$

    (n)
    N
    CH_2CH_3

    (o) $NH_2CH_2CH_2CH_2NH_2$

6. Write IUPAC names for the following compounds:
    (a) t-Butyl alcohol   (e) Ethyldimethylamine hydrochloride
    (b) Cycloheptyl bromide   (f) Isopropyl mercaptan
    (c) Tetramethylene glycol   (g) Neopentyl alcohol
    (d) Tri-n-butylcarbinol   (h) Isohexyl chloride

7. Write structures for the following compounds:
    (a) 3-Bromo-2,5-dimethylhexane   (h) 4-Methoxypiperidine
    (b) 4,5-Dibromo-2-chloro-2-methylheptane (i) 4-Dimethylaminobutanol
    (c) 2-Methyl-2-butanol   (j) Isopropylammonium sulfate
    (d) 3-Ethyl-1,3-hexanediol   (k) Triethylammonium hydroxide
    (e) 3-Hydroxymethyl-1,6-hexanediol   (l) t-Butylmercuric iodide
    (f) Isobutylisopropylmethylsulfonium iodide (m) Potassium t-butoxide
    (g) Diisopropyl disulfide

8. Discuss the possibility of optical activity in a compound such as

$$CH_3CH_2CH_2 \overset{+}{\underset{\underset{CH_3}{|}}{O}} CH_2CH_3$$
$$ClO_4^-$$

9. Give an example of a compound whose optical activity depends on asymmetry at:
   (a) A nitrogen atom   (d) A phosphorus atom
   (b) A sulfur atom   (e) A boron atom
   (c) A silicon atom

10. Which compound would have the higher boiling point and why?

   (a) $CH_3\underset{\underset{CH_3}{|}}{\overset{\overset{CH_3}{|}}{C}}Cl$ or $CH_3CH_2CH_2CH_2Cl$

   (b) $(CH_3)_2CHOCH_3$ or $(CH_3)_3COH$

   (c) $CH_3CH_2CH_2NH_2$ or $(CH_3)_3N$

   (d) CH_3SSCH_3 or CH_3OOCH_3

   (e) CH_3CH_2SH or CH_3CH_2OH

   (f) $CH_3(CH_2)_7CH_3$ or $CH_3(CH_2)_8CH_3$

   (g) [cyclohexane ring with NH₂ and OH on adjacent carbons]   or   [cyclohexane ring with NH₂ and OH on 1,3-carbons]

11. There are 14 isomers with the formula $C_5H_{12}O$. Draw their structures and name them.

12. Is $(CH_3)_3N$ a stronger or a weaker base than $(CF_3)_3N$? Explain.

13. Write the structures of all the isomeric primary hexyl alcohols $(C_6H_{13}OH)$, and give the IUPAC name of each. Which one is isohexyl alcohol?

Optional Problems

1. Rationalize the fact that the C—O—C bond angle observed in dimethyl ether is 107°.

2. Discuss the geometry and hybridization in diborane.

CHAPTER 5

NUCLEAR MAGNETIC RESONANCE SPECTROSCOPY

5.1   Identification of Organic Compounds

When a student approaches organic chemistry in the laboratory, his view is much different than it is when he studies the subject in a textbook such as this one. The physical appearance of organic compounds has little relationship to the lines, symbols, and theories with which they have been described in the book. When a chemist must identify a compound, his task can be very difficult and time consuming. It is of utmost importance that he know what tools are available to aid in identification, as well as how and when to apply these tools, and how to interpret the information they provide.

If two samples are alike in *all* physical and chemical properties, they are the same compound. Therefore, the first step in the identification of a compound of unknown structure is to gather as much information as possible about the compound. Its physical state is examined and data such as boiling or melting points, solubility characteristics, the presence or absence of acidic or basic properties, index of refraction, and specific rotation are collected.

Any or all of several spectral techniques may also be used in obtaining information about an unidentified compound. An *infrared spectrum* can be interpreted in terms of the presence or absence of *functional groups*. From a *nuclear magnetic resonance spectrum*, the number, nature, and environment of the *hydrogens* in a molecule can be determined. From this information, the structure of the molecular skeleton can frequently be deduced. A *mass spectrum* yields data on molecular weight and formula, and on the arrangements of specific groups within the molecule. *Ultraviolet spectra*, resulting from electronic excitations, are obtained from compounds which contain multiple bonds. These tools give different types of data which are most effectively used in conjunction with each other and with additional physical and chemical facts. The organic chemist has available a wide range of spectroscopic, chemical, and physical techniques which he can use to identify and characterize compounds, and to determine structures. By the time he has obtained and studied the accumulated physical, chemical, and spectroscopic data, he knows a lot about the unknown compound and the functional group class to which it belongs, and he may be able to suggest a structure for it.

The second step in identification of an unknown is a literature search. The properties of the unknown compound can be compared with existing compilations of data reported for all previously described compounds. Also, derivatives can be prepared by well-characterized reactions, and their physical and chemical properties can be compared with corresponding published values. The spectral data can be compared with reference spectra obtained from known compounds; if the two samples are the same compound, their spectra will be superimposable. If computer facilities and programs are available, much of the search of published data can be done rapidly.

If, at the end of a search of the chemical literature, a compound cannot be identified, the chemist must assume that he has a new compound and he is faced with the tasks of characterizing it, elucidating its structure, and reporting his findings. To confirm the postulated structure, the chemist may choose to synthesize the compound from starting materials of known structure by well understood reactions and then to test whether the synthetic material and the unknown compound are identical. Another approach to identifying an unknown compound is to chemically degrade it to smaller compounds which can be unequivocally identified. One can often arrive at the structure of the unknown from the structures of the smaller compounds, if the reactions used in the degradation steps are well understood.

It is important to remember that an assigned structure is acceptable only as long as it is consistent with *all* the data known about the compound.

Infrared spectroscopy (ir), nuclear magnetic resonance spectroscopy (nmr), ultraviolet spectroscopy (uv), and mass spectrometry have had great impact on chemistry and are now widely used by organic chemists. These techniques will be discussed in this textbook with emphasis on their use as tools for the identification of organic compounds. Nuclear magnetic resonance spectroscopy, which proves to be the most informative and widely used technique the organic chemist has available today for studying molecular structure, will be introduced in this chapter. Chapter 9 is devoted to infrared spectroscopy; ultraviolet spectroscopy is discussed in Chapter 31 and mass spectrometry in Chapter 32 (Section 32.3). Also in Chapter 32, nmr is discussed in further detail and illustrations are given of how the data from different spectral techniques are brought together in solving identification problems.

5.2   Orientation of a Nucleus in an External Magnetic Field

All nuclei have *charge* and *mass*. Those with either an odd mass number or an odd atomic number also possess a spin; that is, they have angular momentum. For example, $_1^1H$, $_1^2H$, $_6^{13}C$, $_7^{14}N$, and $_8^{17}O$ possess spins, whereas $_6^{12}C$ and $_8^{16}O$ do not. Any nucleus which has a spin can be studied by nmr, but this chapter will be limited to a discussion of the $_1^1H$ nucleus (the proton), which in practice has given the most useful information.

A spinning charge, such as the $_1^1H$ nucleus, generates a magnetic field which has a magnetic moment (μ) associated with it. *Such a nucleus can be considered as analogous to a bar magnet.* When an external magnetic field (H_0) is applied, the bar magnet attempts to align its magnetic moment along the field direction, just as the bar magnet of a compass aligns itself with the earth's magnetic field. The spin quantum number of the nucleus is designated I; there are $2I + 1$ possible orientations and corresponding energy levels for a magnetic nucleus with respect to the external field.

A proton, $_1^1H$, has a spin quantum number of $\frac{1}{2}$; thus, it has $2 \times \frac{1}{2} + 1 = 2$ possible orientations: parallel ($\uparrow$) and antiparallel ($\downarrow$) to the external magnetic field. In the absence of a magnetic field, each proton has the same nuclear spin energy and the spins are oriented in random directions. In the presence of a magnetic field, the proton spins are aligned either parallel or antiparallel to the field, and the energy difference between these two orientations is proportional to the strength of the external magnetic field:

$$\Delta E = kH_0 \tag{1}$$

where $k = (h\gamma/2\pi)$ and ΔE is the energy difference between orientations; γ, the gyromagnetic ratio (a constant for a given nucleus); H_0, the strength of the external magnetic field; and h, Planck's constant. This variation in the spacing between energy levels (ΔE) as a function of the applied field strength (H_0) is shown in Figure 5.1 for the $_1^1H$ nucleus. The lower energy level in Figure 5.1 corresponds to alignment parallel ($\uparrow$) to the applied field, and the higher energy level corresponds to antiparallel ($\downarrow$) alignment.

For a given field strength the proton can go from one energy level to the other by absorbing or emitting a discrete amount of energy

$$\Delta E = h\nu \tag{2}$$

Figure 5.1
Spin energy level separation for a hydrogen nucleus as a function of an external magnetic field (H_0).

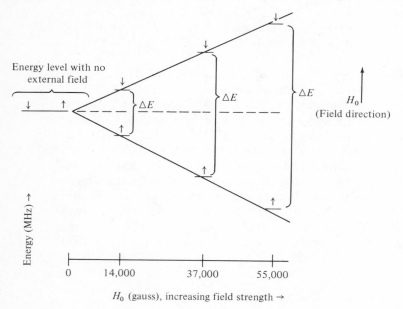

where v is the frequency of the radiation being absorbed or emitted. Combining Equations (1) and (2), we find

$$v = (\gamma/2\pi)H_0 \tag{3}$$

As can be seen from these equations, when protons are placed in a magnetic field having a fixed strength, there will be a definite frequency separating the two energy levels. In practice, a field of about 14,100 gauss requires a frequency of 60 MHz of energy (from the radiofrequency region of the electromagnetic spectrum) for the transition between orientations.† In a 23,500 gauss field, 100 MHz is required; for a 47,000 gauss field, 200 MHz is required (Figure 5.1). It is important to note that 60 MHz corresponds to a very small amount of energy (6×10^{-3} cal/mole). This means that the number of molecules in the ground state is only slightly greater than the number in the excited state.

Figure 5.2
The basic elements of a nuclear magnetic resonance spectrometer.

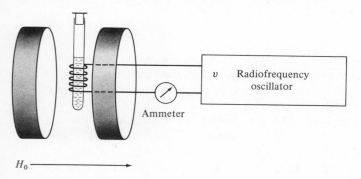

† The unit Hz ("hertz") is equal to cycles per second. Thus, MHz (megahertz) is 10^6 cycles per second.

In a nuclear magnetic resonance spectrometer, the sample is placed in the field of an electromagnet and a radiofrequency field is applied by passing a current through a coil which is wound around the sample (Figure 5.2). The magnetic field (H_0) is slowly increased, and the excitation or "flipping" of the nuclei from one orientation to another is detected as an induced voltage, resulting from the absorption of energy from the radiofrequency field. An *nmr spectrum* (Figure 5.3) is a plot of the induced voltage against the sweep of the magnetic field. The area under a "peak" depends on the total number of nuclei which are "flipping."

Figure 5.3
The nmr spectrum of ethane.

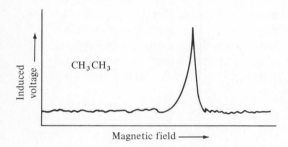

Energy absorbed by a nucleus can be released by "spin–spin relaxation," in which spin energy is transferred to a neighboring nucleus, or by "spin–lattice relaxation," in which spin energy is converted to thermal energy. The nuclei are thus excited from the lower spin state to the higher one by the radiofrequency field. They spontaneously fall back to the lower energy state to be excited again, and so on.

5.3   Shielding of Hydrogen Nuclei

If all hydrogen nuclei absorbed energy at the same field strength at a given frequency, nmr spectroscopy would be only a method for the quantitative analysis of protons. Actually, it is considerably more than this. The field strength required for absorption by a given proton depends on its immediate environment, that is, upon molecular structure. By observing the field at which a proton absorbs, it is possible to deduce something about the local molecular structure.

The external field induces a circulation of electrons around the proton in a plane perpendicular to the external field; this circulating charge in turn generates an induced magnetic field in the region of the nucleus which usually opposes the external field (Figure 5.4). The electrons surrounding the proton are said to *shield* the proton if the induced field opposes the external field, as in Figure 5.4. In such a case, the electrons

Figure 5.4
Shielding ($H_{induced}$) caused by electrons circulating around a nucleus in a plane perpendicular to the external field (H_0).

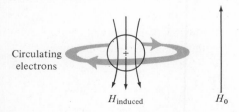

shield the proton from the effects of the external field. Conversely, the electrons are said to *deshield* the nucleus if the induced field augments the external field. Hydrogen nuclei in different environments are shielded or deshielded to different extents by circulating electrons. The result is that the proton is subjected to an "effective" or net magnetic field (Equation 4).

$$H_{net} = H_{external} - H_{induced} \qquad (4)$$

When the magnetic field sweep occurs, all protons do not flip at the same field strength. The field strength at which they do flip depends on how much they are shielded, which in turn depends on their chemical environments.

From Figure 5.4 it can be seen that the extent of shielding will depend on the electron density surrounding the hydrogen nucleus. For example, the protons in methyl iodide (CH_3I) are more shielded than the methyl protons in methanol (CH_3OH)† because the electronegativity of oxygen is higher than that of iodine. The electron-withdrawing effect of the oxygen is greater, and it reduces the electron density around the methyl more than does iodine. From the nmr spectrum of a compound, therefore, we are able to tell not only the relative numbers of the different kinds of protons present, but also something about the environment of each proton.

5.4   The Chemical Shift

To be of maximum use, the shielding phenomenon discussed in the previous section must be put on a quantitative basis. Because shielding is dependent on chemical environment, the field strengths required for energy absorption by different protons are said to be *chemically shifted*, relative to some standard. Tetramethylsilane [TMS, $(CH_3)_4Si$] is the usual standard; it is dissolved in a solution of the sample to be studied and used as an *internal reference*. Since all the protons in TMS are chemically equivalent, it has only one absorption frequency, and since silicon is more electropositive than the atoms usually found in organic compounds (C, N, O, P, S, halogen), very few hydrogen nuclei absorb at a frequency as high as those in TMS. The TMS peak is therefore found at one side of the spectrum and not mixed into the middle of the spectrum, which makes it a convenient reference compound.

The *chemical shift* of a particular hydrogen nucleus is the difference between the field strength at which that proton absorbs and the field strength at which the protons of the TMS standard absorb. The *delta* (δ) scale has been widely used as a means of reporting chemical shifts. The observed chemical shift (in hertz units, Hz) is divided by the frequency (in Hz) of the spectrometer used giving δ in parts per million (ppm) [Equation (5)].

$$\delta = \frac{\text{Observed shift (Hz)} \times 10^6}{\text{Spectrometer frequency (Hz)}} \text{(ppm)}. \qquad (5)$$

The tau (τ) scale was fairly widely used at one time; τ units may be converted to δ units by use of the following equation: $\delta = 10 - \tau$.

EXERCISE 5.1

If the observed chemical shift of a proton is 200 Hz from TMS, and the spectrometer frequency is 60 MHz, what is the chemical shift in terms of δ?

The chemical shift of a given proton under the same conditions (same solvent, temperature, etc.) is a constant and does not depend on the frequency of the particular nmr

---

† In writing about nmr spectra it is customary to designate the particular protons under observation by printing them in boldface type.

spectrometer used for the measurement. The TMS peak is assigned a δ value of 0.000, and peaks of the sample under study are related to it and reported in parts per million.

It was mentioned earlier that the nmr peak of a methyl group does not always occur at the same place. This is illustrated in Figure 5.5 for methyl groups attached to oxygen,

Figure 5.5
Chemical shifts of protons on methyl groups attached to different heteroatoms. Note that *downfield* is in the direction of *increasing* δ values.

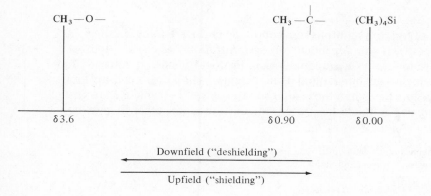

carbon, and silicon. Although all hydrogen nuclei having a chemical shift higher than δ 0.000 are less shielded than the protons of TMS, in common practice, the terms "shielded" and "deshielded" are used to denote that one nucleus absorbs at a lower δ value or a higher δ value, respectively, than another nucleus. For example, the methyl protons of CH_3O- are said to be more "deshielded" than those of CH_3-C- (see Figure 5.5). By definition, the downfield region of the nmr spectrum is toward higher δ values and the upfield region toward lower δ values. Most hydrogen nuclei absorb between δ 0.5 and δ 12.

Table 5.1 Examples of Chemical Shift Data for Protons Attached to Carbon[a]

Proton	Chemical shift range δ
$Si(CH_3)_4$	0.000
CH_4	0.22
$CH_3-\overset{\mid}{\underset{\mid}{C}}-$	0.95–0.85
$-CH_2-$	1.35–1.20
$-\overset{\mid}{\underset{\mid}{C}H}-$	1.6–1.4
$CH_3-\overset{\mid}{\underset{\mid}{C}}-X$[b]	1.9–1.2
CH_3-X[b]	5.0–2.8

[a] A more complete table is given in the Appendix.
[b] X = F, Cl, Br, I, OH, OR, OAr, N.

If a methyl group is attached to carbon, the shift is δ 0.95–0.85, the exact value depending on various other structural features. If the methyl is attached to oxygen, however, the more electronegative oxygen attracts the electrons away from the protons and shifts the absorption to δ 3.8–3.5. In Table 5.1 are given a few examples of chemical shift data for hydrogen nuclei attached to carbon, but in different chemical environments.

EXERCISE 5.2

Estimate the δ value for the protons in a structure $-O-CH_2-O-$, and explain your reasoning.

The chemical shifts of hydroxyl protons in alcohols generally are found in the δ 5.0–0.5 region. The position is quite dependent on concentration because of hydrogen bonding, and it shifts to lower δ values upon dilution. Protons attached to nitrogen and sulfur can also form hydrogen bonds, and their chemical shifts are concentration-dependent, but to a lesser extent than those attached to oxygen. In Table 5.2 are given some examples of chemical shift data for protons attached to atoms other than carbon.

Table 5.2   Examples of Chemical Shift Data of Protons
Attached to Oxygen, Nitrogen, and Sulfur

Proton	*Chemical shift range, δ*
Aliphatic alcohols	
$-O-H$	0.5 (monomeric; "infinite" dilution[a])
	5.0–0.5 (hydrogen-bonded; concentration-dependent)
Alkylamines	
$\overset{\text{H}}{\underset{\vert}{-N-H}}$	1.6–0.6 (infinite dilution[a])
$\overset{\vert}{-N-H}$	0.5–0.3 (infinite dilution[a])
Aliphatic thiols	
$-S-H$	1.7–1.3 (infinite dilution[a])

[a] *Infinite dilution* refers to a solution, usually in an inert solvent, in which the concentration approaches zero. The type of spectra discussed here cannot be obtained on solids, but can be obtained on liquids, gases, or solutions.

The nmr spectrum (Figure 5.6) of 2,2-dimethylpropanol illustrates the effect of structure on absorption frequency. The methyl protons ($-CH_3$) are found at δ 0.92. The methylene protons ($-CH_2-$), which are adjacent to an electronegative oxygen atom, are more "deshielded" and absorb at δ 3.20. The frequency at which the hydroxyl proton ($-O-H$) absorbs is concentration-dependent and is here seen at δ 4.20.

The areas under the peaks are difficult to measure accurately graphically when the peaks are such sharp spikes as these. As the nmr spectrum is being obtained, a device called an *integrator* is usually attached to the recorder; this device measures the area under the curve (the integral of the function), and furnishes this information in the form of a series of steps which can be seen across the spectrum. The total height of a step is proportional to the area of the peak scanned through during a step. In Figure 5.6 the steps from left to right have heights in the ratio 1:2:9, corresponding to the *relative* numbers of protons from one step to the next. These areas tell us the ratios of the numbers of protons contributing to each peak.

In comparison with Figure 5.6, the nmr spectrum of *t*-butyl methyl ether (Figure 5.7), an isomer of 2,2-dimethylpropanol, shows only two types of equivalent protons, giving by integration a ratio of 1:3. The protons of the methyl group attached to oxygen

Figure 5.6
NMR spectrum of 2,2-dimethylpropanol.

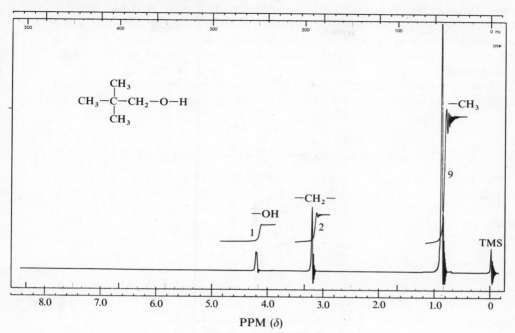

account for the peak at δ 3.12 and those of the *t*-butyl group account for the peak at δ 1.12. Figures 5.6 and 5.7 illustrate how nmr spectra are characteristic of the structures of the compounds from which they were obtained, in terms of both chemical shift and relative areas under peaks.

Figure 5.7
NMR spectrum of *t*-butyl methyl ether.

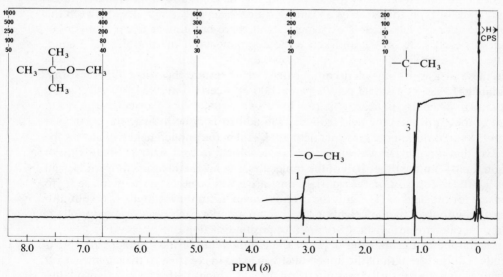

5.5   Spin–Spin Coupling

When protons attempt to align themselves with respect to an external magnetic field, an interaction between them called *spin–spin coupling* may occur. The effect of the spin of one nucleus (H_a) is transferred to adjacent chemically different nuclei (H_b), generally through the bonding electrons. This causes the adjacent nuclei (H_b) to experience different effective, or net, magnetic fields than they would have felt in the absence of H_a. The influence of H_a on the strength of the net magnetic field experienced by $\mathbf{H_b}$ depends on the orientation of the spin of H_a relative to the external magnetic field. One effect of spin–spin coupling is to complicate the spectrum and make interpretation much more difficult. However, such coupling also provides very valuable information about the numbers and types of protons on carbon atoms *adjacent* to the one bearing the proton under observation.

Suppose we consider a single proton $\mathbf{H_b}$, which is undergoing resonance at a certain applied field strength and shows a single peak at a certain δ value (Figure 5.8a). Then

Figure 5.8
Spin–spin coupling of $\mathbf{H_b}$: (a) with no neighbor protons, and (b) with one neighbor, H_a.

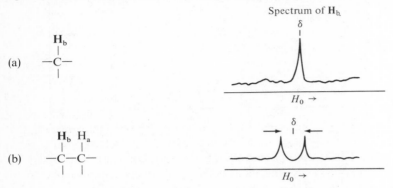

consider what happens to $\mathbf{H_b}$ when another proton (H_a) is brought into the vicinity (Figure 5.8b). $\mathbf{H_b}$ will feel not only the applied field, but also the field from H_a. The nucleus H_a can have either of two orientations with respect to the applied field, parallel ($\uparrow$) or antiparallel ($\downarrow$). The small field generated by H_a can either augment or decrease the total field felt by $\mathbf{H_b}$. To maintain resonance, then, it will be necessary to reduce or increase the applied field correspondingly to compensate for the field of H_a. The signal from $\mathbf{H_b}$ in the presence of H_a is thus seen as a doublet. Since the energy differences between the parallel and antiparallel states is extremely small there are almost equal numbers of molecules in each state (p. 90) and hence the components of the doublet have equal intensity.

Since these ideas are somewhat complicated, let us restate them in a different way. The isolated $\mathbf{H_b}$ shows a single peak of area 1.00 at a certain applied field strength δ (Figure 5.8a). When H_a is nearby, it can have two equally likely orientations, so in one-half of the molecules, the field from H_a will add to H_0 (the little arrow on the left of Figure 5.8b). To obtain the same net field at $\mathbf{H_b}$, then, the applied field will have to be reduced by that amount, so we will see a peak downfield from δ, with an area $\frac{1}{2}$ that of the original peak. In the other half of the molecules, the magnetic moment from H_a will oppose H_0 (the little arrow on the right). In this case it will be necessary to increase H_0 to compensate for the field of H_a. Thus the original signal from the isolated $\mathbf{H_b}$ is split into a symmetrical doublet by the neighbor H_a. The area under each peak in the doublet is 0.5, and the peaks are equidistant from δ in opposite directions.

The magnitude of the splitting between the components of the doublet from $\mathbf{H_b}$ is independent of the strength of the applied field. [This is in contrast to the chemical shift in Hz, which has to be converted to δ units (Equation 5), which are then field-independent.] The separation between the components of the doublet depends only on the distance of H_a and the environment. The separation between the components of the doublet is called the *coupling constant*, J, which is expressed in hertz (Hz). Coupling is essentially zero if $\mathbf{H_b}$ and H_a are separated by more than three bonds, except in special cases. In the spectra discussed in this chapter, the magnitude of J is approximately 5 Hz. The significance of J values will be considered in subsequent chapters.

Next, let us consider the more complicated case where two chemically equivalent protons (H$_a$) are adjacent to a chemically different proton (H$_b$), and the latter is under observation. Four spin arrangements of the two adjacent H$_a$ protons are possible and can be transmitted to H$_b$: (1) both spins parallel to H_0($\uparrow\uparrow$); (2) one spin parallel, one antiparallel ($\uparrow\downarrow$); (3) one antiparallel and one parallel ($\downarrow\uparrow$); (4) both antiparallel ($\downarrow\downarrow$) (see Figure 5.9). Both of the H$_a$ nuclei may augment the applied field, which means that

Figure 5.9
Spin–spin coupling of **H$_b$** with 2H$_a$'s.

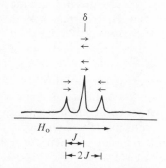

the applied H_0 has to be reduced. Similarly, both H$_a$ nuclei may oppose the applied field (two arrows to right), which means that the applied H_0 has to be increased. Finally, one H$_a$ nucleus may oppose H_0, while one augments it, and there are two possible ways for this to happen [arrangements (2) and (3)]. In this case there is no net effect from the two H$_a$ nuclei on H$_b$, and the H_0 required is the same as if the H$_a$ nuclei were not present. The **H$_b$** proton is therefore seen as a triplet, with the center peak twice as large (since the corresponding arrangement of nuclei is twice as probable) as the end peaks. The areas will thus be in the ratios 1:2:1. The coupling constant J corresponds to changing the orientation of one nucleus and is given by the distance between adjacent peaks.

Continuing with the next case, suppose that there are three equivalent protons H$_a$ adjacent to H$_b$. What will the splitting pattern be for **H$_b$**? There are eight different spin arrangements possible for H$_a$'s, $\uparrow\uparrow\uparrow$, $\uparrow\uparrow\downarrow$, $\uparrow\downarrow\uparrow$, $\downarrow\uparrow\uparrow$, $\uparrow\downarrow\downarrow$, $\downarrow\uparrow\downarrow$, $\downarrow\downarrow\uparrow$, $\downarrow\downarrow\downarrow$, and these will lead to four observed peaks, with areas 1:3:3:1 (Figure 5.10).

Figure 5.10
Spin–spin coupling of **H$_b$** with three H$_a$'s.

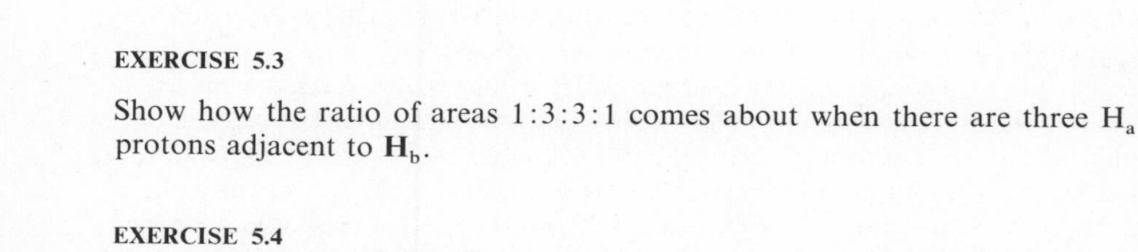

EXERCISE 5.3

Show how the ratio of areas 1:3:3:1 comes about when there are three H$_a$ protons adjacent to **H$_b$**.

EXERCISE 5.4

If there are four equivalent protons H$_a$ coupled to **H$_b$**, what will the observed spectrum of **H$_b$** look like? How many peaks are there in the multiplet, and what are their relative areas?

From the cases discussed, a general rule can be deduced as follows: *if a proton* (H_b) *has n equivalent protons* (H_a) *on adjacent carbons, its absorption will be split into* (n + 1) *peaks.* The value of (n + 1) is called the *multiplicity.* This way of determining the multiplicity holds if the chemical shift difference between the protons is considerably larger than the coupling constant. As the values of the chemical shift difference and the coupling constant approach one another, this pattern goes over into one that is more complex.

We have used the expression *equivalent protons* without really defining it. Two protons are said to be equivalent if they occupy identical environments *as viewed with the nmr spectrometer.* From this standpoint, the protons in methane are certainly all equivalent, since they have identical intramolecular environments. As the molecules tumble around, the intermolecular environments also average. To decide if protons are equivalent, we need only decide if by internal and external rotations of the molecule, the protons *on the average* occupy the same environment.

The protons in ethane are equivalent to one another (but different from those in methane). In propane there are two sets of nonequivalent protons: the two secondary protons are equivalent to each other and different from the six methyl protons, while the methyl protons are all equivalent to one another. Looking at a model, it might seem that two protons on a methyl have a different environment from the third one, since two are gauche to the other methyl while one is trans. This is true at a given instant; however, the nmr spectrometer operates at a certain frequency, and it takes a finite time to make the measurement. The methyl protons lose their individuality and become equivalent when the methyl rotates, and since the frequency of rotation is very fast with respect to the frequency of the measurement, the nmr spectrometer does not see separate methyl protons, but only their average. The methyl groups in propane therefore contain six equivalent protons. The peaks from equivalent protons occur at the same δ value, and they are not split due to coupling with one another. Thus ethane, with six equivalent protons, shows only a single unsplit peak.

It is important to be able to decide when protons are equivalent, because equivalent protons show the same chemical shift and their peaks will not exhibit splitting from their coupling with one another. In the following examples, protons are divided into sets by letters a, b, . . . etc. Those with the same letter are equivalent to each other.

$$CH_3^a-CH_2^b-Br \qquad Br-CH_2^a-CH_2^a-Br \qquad CH_3^a-\overset{\overset{\displaystyle H_b}{|}}{\underset{\underset{\displaystyle Br}{|}}{C}}-CH_3^a$$

EXERCISE 5.5

For the following compounds, label equivalent sets of protons a, b, c, ...

$$CH_3CH_2-\overset{\overset{\displaystyle Br}{|}}{\underset{\underset{\displaystyle \overset{\displaystyle |}{CH_3}}{CH_2}}{C}}-CH_2CH_3 \qquad BrCH_2CH_2\underset{\underset{\displaystyle CH_3}{|}}{CH}CH_3 \qquad BrCH_2CH_2\underset{\underset{\displaystyle CH_3}{|}}{CH}CH_2CH_2Br$$

With this rather abstract introduction to the principles of spin–spin coupling in hand, let us now look at the nmr spectrum of an actual compound, ethyl alcohol, in Figure 5.11.

Figure 5.11
NMR spectrum of ethanol.

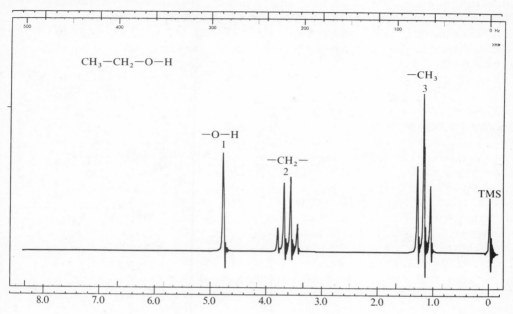

Beginning at the right-hand side of the spectrum, we see the standard peak for TMS at δ 0.00. The triplet at δ 1.20 is from the methyl protons, and the relative total area under it is 3. The singlet at δ 4.80 is the hydroxyl proton, area = 1, and finally, the quartet at δ 3.63 is from the methylene protons, area = 2. If we look first at the methyl group (δ 1.20), we see that these three protons are equivalent and do not couple with one another. They have two neighboring protons on the methylene group. The multiplicity of the methyl is thus $2 + 1 = 3$, so the methyl is observed as a triplet. Next, we see that the methylene protons do not couple with one another, but couple with the methyl protons, of which there are three. The multiplicity of the methylene is therefore $3 + 1 = 4$, a quartet. Note that coupling is a reciprocal affair: if H_a is coupled to H_b, then H_b is likewise coupled to H_a. The coupling constants J_{ab} and J_{ba} must always be equal. The spacings between the components of the triplet are therefore equal to the spacings between the components of the quartet, in this case 7.5 Hz.

One might expect the $-OH$ to couple with the $-CH_2-$, and vice versa. Ordinarily such coupling is not seen, because the proton on oxygen is rapidly *exchanging*, or being passed back and forth from one molecule to another. It does not stay in the same environment long enough for its coupling with the methylene protons to be detected, and is therefore seen as a singlet. The methylene protons are seen as a quartet from coupling with CH_3- only.

Finally, we should point out that in actual spectra, the multiplets are less symmetrical than in Figures 5.8–5.10. Symmetrical multiplets are the limiting case when the chemical shift is very large compared to J. If the chemical shift differences between protons are of average size, the multiplets become unsymmetrical in such a way as to "grow" toward one another, as in Figure 5.11. In this case, note that the right-hand peaks in the quartet are taller than the corresponding left-hand ones. Correspondingly, in the triplet, the left peak is taller than the right one. In complicated spectra it sometimes takes some effort to decide what is coupled to what. In interpreting such spectra it is helpful to remember that if two sets of peaks correspond to protons coupled to one another, the J's have to be the same in both sets, and the peaks usually grow toward one another as in Figure 5.11.

Nmr spectra can be very useful for identifying unknown compounds. Figures 5.6 and 5.7 easily identify two isomers of $C_5H_{12}O$. The nmr spectrum of dimethyl ether contains a single peak at δ 3.47, from the six protons, all of which are chemically equivalent. Compare this spectrum with the other isomer of C_2H_6O, namely ethanol, Figure 5.11.

The most effective way to differentiate simple molecules from one another is usually by means of their nmr spectra. In order to see this more fully, let us consider the formula C_3H_7Cl. There are two isomers of this formula. Will their nmr spectra permit us to decide which is which? The two spectra are shown in Figures 5.12 and 5.13. They are clearly quite different, and we should easily be able to determine which spectrum represents which isomer.

Figure 5.12
NMR spectrum of a chloropropane.

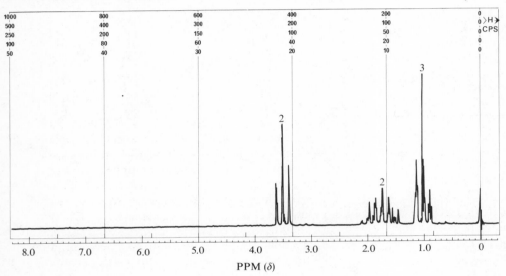

Figure 5.13
NMR spectrum of the other chloropropane.

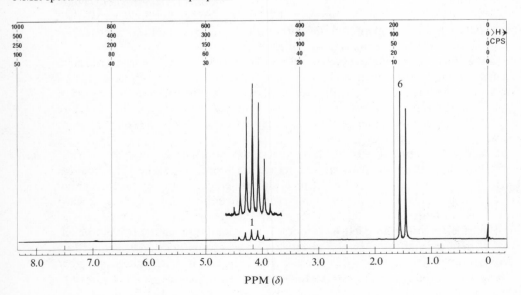

Let us begin with 2-chloropropane and predict what the nmr spectrum should look like. The structural formula

$$CH_3-\underset{\underset{Cl}{\overset{|}{C}}}{\overset{\overset{H}{|}}{C}}-CH_3$$

shows us that the six hydrogens on the methyls are all equivalent and different from the hydrogen on C-2. The spectrum will consist of two groups of peaks: the methyl protons with an area of 6 at about δ 1.5 (from Table 5.1) and the C-2 proton at about δ 4.0 with an area of 1. The methyl protons have just one adjacent proton, so they will show a multiplicity of $1 + 1 = 2$. The C-2 proton has six adjacent protons and will show a multiplicity of $6 + 1 = 7$. If we look at Figures 5.12 and 5.13, we see that Figure 5.13 corresponds quite well to what is predicted, whereas Figure 5.12 does not.

Next, let us predict the spectrum of 1-chloropropane.

$$CH_3CH_2CH_2Cl$$

There are three different sets of protons. The protons on C-1 should give a peak at about δ 3.5 (Table 5.1) with an area of 2 and a multiplicity of $2 + 1 = 3$; while the protons on C-2 should show a peak at about δ 1.5, with an area of 2 and a multiplicity of $(3 + 2) + 1 = 6$. This multiplicity assumes that the protons on C-1 have coupling with those on C-2 which is equivalent to the coupling of the protons on C-3 with those on C-2. While not exactly true, this is a satisfactory approximation. Finally, the methyl protons are expected to give resonance at about δ 0.9, with an area of 3 and a multiplicity of $2 + 1 = 3$. Looking again at Figures 5.12 and 5.13, we find that the spectrum in 5.12 fits these data, and that in 5.13 does not. We may therefore assign the structures to these two isomers in an unequivocal manner from the nmr spectra.

To summarize—the nmr spectrum of a compound gives us three kinds of information. The *chemical shift* of a multiplet tells us something about the environment of the proton involved, the *area* under the peak tells us how many protons are involved, and the *multiplicity* tells us how many neighboring protons there are. For simple molecules, this information is often enough to deduce the total structure. With complicated molecules, often many of the multiplets overlap one another and cannot be resolved. Usually, however, a number of structural features can be picked out, and portions of the structure can be deduced from the nmr spectrum.

This chapter is an introduction to nmr. Much more will be said about applications of nmr to chemical problems in succeeding chapters.

PROBLEMS

1. The hydrogen nucleus is a proton. When samples of organic compounds are placed in the field of an electromagnet and a radiofrequency field is applied, not all protons absorb energy at the same field strength at a given frequency. Why not?

2. Why is an internal standard used in obtaining an nmr spectrum? Why is tetramethylsilane a good standard?

3. If methane is used as the internal reference, *ie*, CH_4: δ 0.00, what is the chemical shift of TMS? What would be the chemical shifts of the peaks in Figure 5.6?

4. Why is the absorption of the hydroxyl proton found within a large chemical-shift range? Why does the chemical shift become larger (in terms of δ) as the concentration increases?

5.   Is the nmr spectrum given here the spectrum of *t*-butyl alcohol, *t*-butyl bromide, or *t*-butylamine? Assign the peaks to specific protons in your answer. How would the nmr spectra of the other two differ from the spectrum of your choice?

NMR spectrum of unknown, Problem 5.

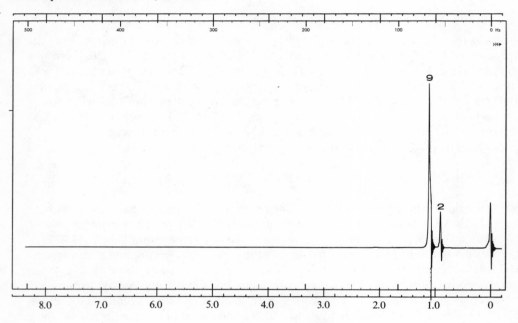

6.   In a preparation of 1-butanol a small amount of an isomeric by-product was produced. The by-product and 1-butanol exhibited similar solubility in water, but the by-product had a lower boiling point than 1-butanol. The nmr spectrum of the by-product is given. What is the structure of the by-product? Assign all peaks in the spectrum.

NMR spectrum of unknown, Problem 6.

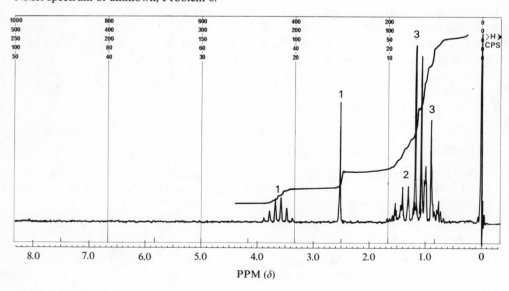

PPM (δ)

7.   The spectrum shown here was obtained from a compound with the formula $C_2H_3Cl_3$. Interpret fully the spectrum of the compound and deduce its structure.

NMR spectrum of unknown, Problem 7.

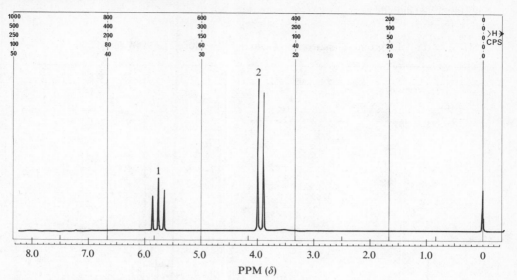

8. How many spin arrangements are transmitted by five adjacent equivalent protons? Show the energy levels and spin states of five H_a's in an external field, and the appearance of H_b coupled to them.

9. What is the multiplicity of each proton in:
   (a) Isobutyl bromide
   (b) *sec*-Butyl bromide
   (c) *t*-Butyl bromide
   Predict the nmr spectra of (a), (b), and (c).

10. An unknown compound gave an elemental analysis of: 62.1 % C; 10.35 % H. Its nmr spectrum consisted of a quintet centered at δ 2.72 and a triplet centered at δ 4.73. Suggest a structure for the unknown.

11. Gasoline fuels obtained from petroleum are rated on knocking characteristics on the basis of *n*-heptane (octane number 0) and isooctane (2,2,4-trimethylpentane, octane number 100) as standards. The following nmr spectrum was obtained from one of these standards. Which one? Support your choice by discussing the spectrum in terms of your answer.

NMR spectrum of unknown, Problem 11.

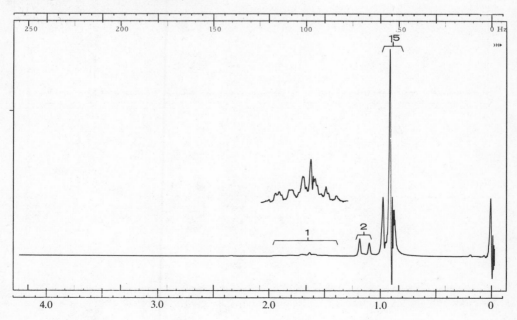

12.   The nmr spectrum of 1-bromo-3-chloropropane is given. Discuss the chemical shifts and spin–spin coupling.

NMR spectrum of 1-bromo-3-chloropropane in deuterochloroform, Problem 12.

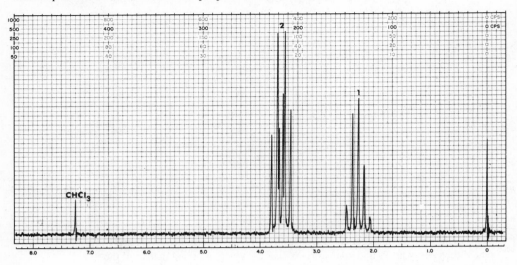

13.   A compound sometimes prescribed as a hypnotic has the formula $C_6H_{12}O_3$ and contains a 1,3,5-trioxane ring system. Its nmr spectrum is given. Interpret the spectrum and deduce the structure of the compound.

NMR spectrum of unknown, Problem 13.

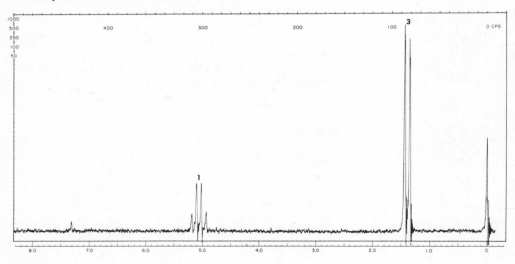

CHAPTER 6

STEREOCHEMISTRY

6.1   Structural Isomers, Stereoisomers, and Some Definitions

The word "isomer" is used as a general term for compounds related to each other in one of two ways: as structural isomers or as stereoisomers.

Many examples of structural isomerism have been cited in Chapters 3 and 4. *Structural isomers* have identical molecular formulas, but differ from one another because their atoms are joined in a different order. Methylcyclopropane (I) and cyclobutane (II) are examples of structural isomers.

$$
\begin{array}{cc}
\text{CH}_2 & \text{CH}_2-\text{CH}_2 \\
| \quad \text{CHCH}_3 & | \qquad | \\
\text{CH}_2 & \text{CH}_2-\text{CH}_2 \\
\text{I} & \text{II}
\end{array}
$$

Stereoisomers also have identical molecular formulas. However, their atoms are linked together in the *same* order. *Stereoisomers* differ from one another because their atoms are arranged differently in space. For example, there are two different *configurations* (spatial arrangements) possible for 2-chlorobutane, $CH_3CH_2CHClCH_3$.

From the discussion of optical isomerism in Section 3.6 it should be apparent that carbon atom 2 in 2-chlorobutane is an asymmetric carbon atom, and that III and IV should rotate plane-polarized light in equal and opposite directions. Configurations III and IV are related as object and mirror image. They are called *enantiomers* and bear an enantiomeric relationship to one another. Optical isomerism is one type of stereoisomerism.

If stereoisomers are not related as object and mirror image, they are called *diastereomers*; their relationship is a diastereomeric one. Consider the three possible spatial arrangements of the 1,2-dibromocyclopropanes:

The words cis (*Latin: on this side*) *and* trans (*Latin: across*) *are used as prefixes to specify isomers of this type. V is called* cis-1,2-dibromocyclopropane, *and both VIa and VIb are called* trans-1,2-dibromocyclopropane. (*The difference between VIa and VIb is discussed below*).

It is quite clear from these three-dimensional representations that V bears a stereoisomeric relationship to both VIa and VIb. In V (the cis isomer) both bromine atoms lie on the same side of the plane of the three-membered ring, whereas in VIa and VIb (the trans isomers) the bromine atoms are on opposite sides of the ring plane. The trans isomers VIa and VIb are enantiomers. The cis compound V, which is superimposable on its mirror image, is diastereomerically related to both VIa and VIb. In other words, V and VIa are diastereomers and so are V and VIb. Two stereoisomers cannot be both enantiomers and diastereomers—a molecule can have only one enantiomer, but it may (if valences, etc., permit) have several diastereomers.

NOMENCLATURE. *There has been a tendency for chemists to be much more restrictive in the use of the term diastereomer (or diastereoisomer) than is implied by the definition given in this text. For example,* cis-*1,2-dibromocyclopropane (V) is often referred to as a* geometrical isomer *of the enantiomeric trans forms VIa and VIb—in fact, the prefixes cis and trans demand a different geometry. In some texts, diastereomer is only used to describe the non-mirror-image relationship between optically active stereoisomers. It will become clear in later sections that a complete set of stereoisomers for a given structure may contain* both *optically active and optically inactive members, and that diastereomer is the most general term to use to relate the non-mirror-image stereoisomers.*

6.2   The Barrier to Interconversion of Stereoisomers

The individual stereoisomers which we have discussed so far are unique, separable, and characterizable species. There is no way of interconverting these isomers without using the large amount of energy necessary to break a bond. The enantiomers III and IV of 2-chlorobutane cannot be interconverted unless we break the C—Cl bond (or the C—H or C—C bond) and reform it on the other side. Similarly, bond cleavage is the only way to interconvert the diastereomers of 1,2-dibromocyclopropane, V and VIa, V and VIb, or the enantiomers of the trans isomer VIa and VIb.

Conformational isomers are the other extreme. To take the example of *n*-butane—the three most important arrangements, or *conformations*, are the anti and the two gauche forms (Figure 6.1). The anti conformation is a diastereomer of the two gauche forms;

Figure 6.1
Conformations of *n*-butane.

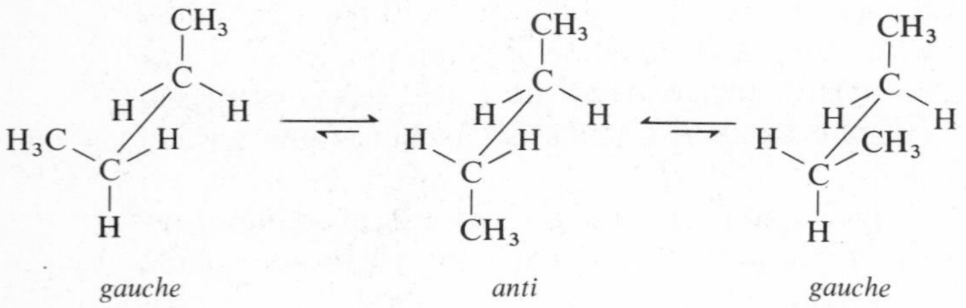

the two gauche conformations are enantiomers. These three arrangements in space differ from each other only by rotation about a single bond, a process which requires relatively little energy. Even at very low temperatures the three conformations are rapidly interconverting, preventing the isolation of any individual conformation.

Chemists generally use the term configuration *to refer to the arrangement in space of molecules which are separable species (they may be enantiomers or diastereomers). The term* conformation *is reserved for forms which differ only by rotation about a single bond and are not usually isolable; they are called* conformers.

Conformational isomerization is important in considerations of the stereochemistry of cyclohexanes (Section 3.4). Two diastereomeric chair forms are possible for mono-substituted cyclohexanes. The forms differ as to whether the substituent is in the axial or equatorial position, as shown for chlorocyclohexane. These stereoisomers are not

separable at normal temperatures because they are a rapidly interconverting equilibrium mixture (which, of course, contains mostly the equatorial conformer).

ISOLATION OF A PURE CONFORMER IN SOLUTION. *In 1966, the equatorial conformer of chlorocyclohexane was separated from the axial conformer, and studied at low temperature in solution by F. R. Jensen and C. H. Bushweller at Berkeley. The method by which this was done is quite interesting, and should prove to be general. A crystal is almost always a pure conformation. A crystal of* n-butane, *for example, contains all of the molecules in the* anti *conformation while a crystal of chlorocyclohexane contains only the equatorial conformation. When a crystal of equatorial chlorocyclohexane was allowed to melt and dissolve at* −150°C, *the nmr spectrum was determined, and it was found that the solution contained only the equatorial conformer. Furthermore, this conformer was stable at that temperature, as expected from the known height of the inversion barrier for cyclohexane.*

Let us next examine *cis*-1,2-dimethylcyclohexane, which exists as a 50:50 mixture of two equivalent conformations, each having an axial and an equatorial methyl group. These two conformations are enantiomers. We cannot separate these enantiomers at room temperature, and thus there is no such thing as an optically active *cis*-1,2-dimethyl-cyclohexane (as of this writing). The enantiomers are, in principle, separable at very low temperature, however.

We have now considered two extremes—structures which may lead to unique stereo-isomers because the barrier to interconversion is very high, namely, the breaking of single bonds; and structures which may have nonseparable stereoisomers (conformers) because the barrier to interconversion by rotation is very low. It is conceivable that we could have a certain molecular arrangement in which the barrier to rotation would be sufficiently high to permit the separation of conformational isomers by ordinary physical methods. Examples of this situation are known, and some will be discussed in later chapters.

6.3   Classification of Stereoisomers

Stereoisomers may be organized into distinct classes based on two independent but complementary characteristics, the *symmetry properties* of the various stereoisomeric molecules, and the *processes by which the stereoisomers may be interconverted.*

The symmetry classification involves one simple criterion which we have already discussed: a molecule and its stereoisomer are either related as an object and its non-superimposable mirror image, or they are not. Stereoisomers are either enantiomers or diastereomers.

For a molecule to exist in enantiomeric forms, the molecule must be *chiral* (not superimposable on its mirror image). How do we establish whether or not a molecule (or a molecular conformation) is chiral? The most direct approach would be to construct reasonably accurate molecular models of the isomer and its mirror image, and to determine by inspection whether or not the two are superimposable. For simple molecules, we can draw pictures to simulate the models and mentally try to superimpose them. It is easy for us to see from the representations of 2-chlorobutane (III and IV) that III is not superimposable on its mirror image IV. We conclude, therefore, that 2-chlorobutane is chiral, and that it should occur as two enantiomeric stereoisomers.

Representations of 3-pentanol and of its mirror image are given as VII and VIII, respectively. These are superimposable, the molecule is not chiral, and 3-pentanol *cannot* exist in enantiomeric forms. 3-Pentanol does not have an asymmetric carbon

$$CH_3CH_2 \overset{\displaystyle OH}{\underset{\underset{\displaystyle H}{|}}{\underset{\displaystyle C}{}}} CH_2CH_3 \qquad CH_3CH_2 \overset{\displaystyle HO}{\underset{\underset{\displaystyle H}{|}}{\underset{\displaystyle C}{}}} CH_2CH_3$$

VII   VIII

3-Pentanol
Superimposable—no enantiomers

atom. It must always be kept in mind, however, that the absolute criterion for whether or not a molecule can exist in enantiomeric forms is molecular chirality. The presence of an asymmetric carbon atom suggests the *possibility* that a molecule will be chiral. Many—*but not all*—molecules containing an asymmetric carbon (or other atom) are chiral; and many—*but not all*—chiral molecules contain an asymmetric atom. *cis*-1,2-Dibromocyclopropane (V) contains two asymmetric carbon atoms, but it is not chiral. We shall later see several examples of molecules which are chiral and do not contain asymmetric atoms.

In many situations, it is not practical to construct models to aid in the detection of molecular chirality. Furthermore, when structures are complex it is difficult (even for experts) to transpose mentally a picture of a molecule to determine whether it is superimposable on its mirror image. Fortunately, there are techniques available which can be used to simplify matters.

Every molecule (or more accurately every molecular conformation) may be classified according to its symmetry. Each *symmetry class* is characterized by the number and type of *symmetry elements* present. For each symmetry element there corresponds a *symmetry operation* which, if performed, returns the molecule to an arrangement indistinguishable from the original. There are three important symmetry elements with which we should be familiar: a *plane of symmetry*, designated as sigma (σ); a *simple* or *proper axis of rotation of order n* (*n-fold axis of symmetry*), designated as C_n; and a *rotation–reflection axis of order n* (*n-fold alternating axis of symmetry*), designated S_n.

A *sigma plane* (σ plane) is defined as a *mirror plane* which bisects a rigid object so that one-half of the object coincides with the reflection in the mirror of the other half. Examples from everyday life of objects that contain only one plane of symmetry are idealized chairs, cups, spoons, toothbrushes, and file cabinets.

An object is said to have a C_n *axis of symmetry* if it contains an axis such that a rotation of $360°/n$ around this axis will result in a geometrical arrangement which is indistinguishable from the original object. The triangular block of wood with pegs at two corners pointing in opposite directions in Figure 6.2 has only a twofold simple axis (C_2).

Many molecules will contain *both* planes of symmetry *and* simple axes of symmetry. An extreme example of this kind of molecule is the highly symmetrical methane, CH_4,

Figure 6.2
Illustration of a C_2 axis.

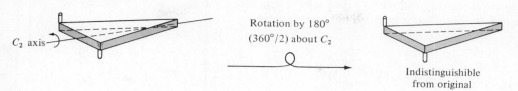

C_2 axis

Rotation by 180°
(360°/2) about C_2

Indistinguishible
from original

which we know as a perfect tetrahedral shape. Methane contains four C_3 axes, three C_2 axes, and six σ planes (the student should verify this with the aid of a model).

Now let us consider the elements of symmetry present in some of the molecules discussed earlier in this chapter. It is very easy to recognize that the two enantiomers of 2-chlorobutane (III and IV) *do not have any* elements of symmetry—they are *asymmetric* (without any symmetry) as well as chiral molecules.

ASYMMETRY, DISSYMMETRY, AND CHIRALITY. *The distinction between asymmetric and dissymmetric can be stated as follows: an asymmetric molecule lacks all symmetry elements (and must be dissymmetric as well). A dissymmetric molecule may contain axes (but not planes) of symmetry; the criterion for dissymmetry is whether or not a molecule is superimposable on its mirror image. The word* nondissymmetric *means superimposable upon the mirror image (containing reflection symmetry) and this is a more restrictive category than* symmetric. *The words* chiral *and* achiral *mean dissymmetric and nondissymmetric, respectively.*

The two enantiomers of *trans*-1,2-dibromocyclopropane (VIa and VIb) each possess a C_2 axis, contained in the plane of the ring bisecting the bond between carbon atoms 1 and 2 and intersecting carbon atom 3. They are analogous to the triangular board in Figure 6.2; these molecules are not asymmetric, but they *are* chiral.

C_2 axis

Br

Br

trans

Br

Br

σ plane

cis

3-Pentanol (VII) and *cis*-1,2-dibromocyclopropane (V) each have one σ plane, and are therefore achiral. If we consider cyclobutane to be planar as indicated by structure II (it is actually not planar; see Section 3.5), we can recognize five planes of symmetry. One is the plane of the ring (σ_1); two pass through diagonal corners of the ring and are perpendicular to the plane of the ring and to each other (σ_2 and σ_3); and the remaining two bisect C—C bonds on opposite sides of the ring and are also perpendicular to each other and to the plane of the ring (σ_4 and σ_5). There are four C_2 axes (all in

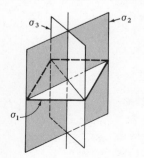

σ_3

σ_2

σ_1

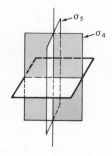

σ_5

σ_4

the plane of the ring, two bisecting the molecule through opposite bonds, and two bisecting the molecule through opposite carbon atoms), and one C_4 axis (perpendicular to the plane of the ring and passing through the center of the ring). The latter is of higher degree and is unique, so it is called the *principal axis*.

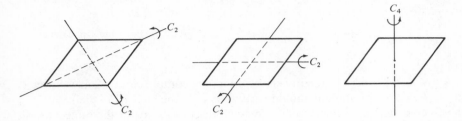

In Figure 6.3 are illustrated the elements of symmetry possessed by several molecules. The student should verify the symmetry elements for each molecule in Figure 6.3 by studying models.

Figure 6.3
Elements of symmetry contained by some simple molecules.

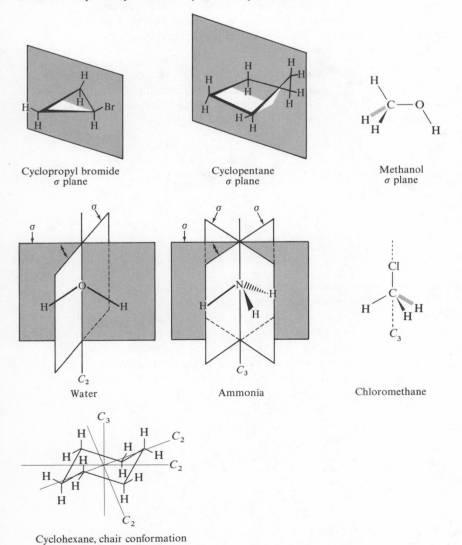

The Alternating Axis of Symmetry. The most difficult element of symmetry to visualize in an object is an *n-fold alternating axis* of symmetry. An object will have such an axis if a rotation of 360°/n about the axis followed by reflection in a plane perpendicular to that axis leaves a geometrical arrangement indistinguishable from the original.

A simple illustration is given in Figure 6.4. The rectangular board, with two pegs in opposite corners pointing in opposite directions, has a two-fold alternating axis (S_2).

Figure 6.4
Object with a twofold alternating axis.

rotation by 180°

(360°/2) about S_2

S_2

Reflection in plane ⊥ to S_2

Indistinguishable from original

An alternating axis of symmetry of order 2 (S_2) corresponds to a *center of symmetry* and is often recognizable as such. A molecule has a center of symmetry (sometimes called a *center of inversion*) if, proceeding from that center in any direction, the atoms encountered are the same as those encountered when proceeding in the opposite direction (180° from the original direction).

There are relatively few molecules with *n*-fold alternating axes as the only symmetry element present. One example will suffice—the staggered conformation of *meso*-2,3-butanediol (Figure 6.5) (see Section 6.4 for definition of *meso*). *In general, it is found that an object having an n-fold alternating axis of symmetry cannot be chiral.*

Figure 6.5
S_2 axis in *meso*-2,3-butanediol, anti conformation.

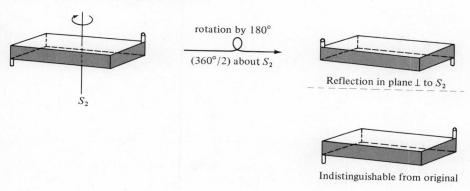

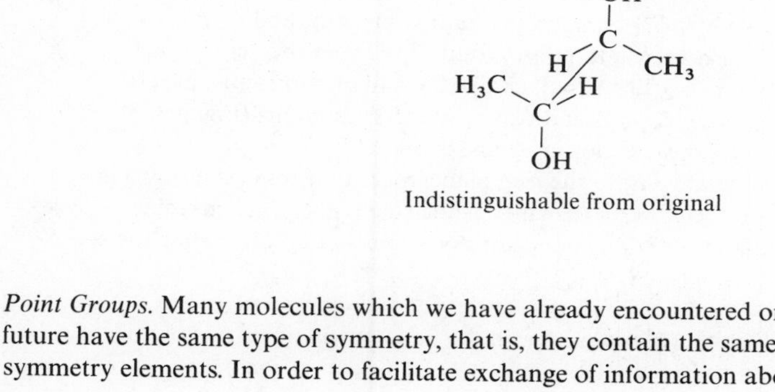

Center of symmetry

Rotation

Reflection

Indistinguishable from original

Point Groups. Many molecules which we have already encountered or will encounter in the future have the same type of symmetry, that is, they contain the same type and number of symmetry elements. In order to facilitate exchange of information about symmetry a shorthand notation system has been devised. The *point group* defines the symmetry class to which a molecule belongs. In our present treatment, to assign a point group to a molecule we count up the number and types of symmetry elements present in that molecule and employ the summation given in Table 6.1. To do this effectively, we must further differentiate between types of planes of symmetry in molecules that contain several planes and axes of symmetry. The symbol σ_v is used to designate a plane of symmetry containing the principal proper axis of symmetry; σ_h is used to designate a plane of symmetry perpendicular to the principal proper axis of symmetry. The symbols σ_v and σ_h stand for vertical and horizontal planes, respectively, when the principle axis is located as shown.

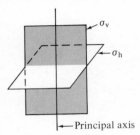

An obvious advantage of the point group notation system in discussions of stereoisomerism is that only molecules belonging to certain point groups are chiral, and molecules in other point groups cannot be. The symmetry of a molecule is extremely important in structure elucidation by spectroscopic methods.

Table 6.1   Point Group Notation

Chiral molecules	Achiral molecules[a]
C_n: C_n only	C_s: σ only
D_n: $C_n + nC_2$ only	S_n: no σ
	C_{nv}: $C_n + n\sigma_v$ only
	C_{nh}: $C_n + \sigma_h$ only
	D_{nd}: $C_n + nC_2 + n\sigma_v$, but no σ_h
	D_{nh}: $C_n + nC_2 + n\sigma_v + \sigma_h$

[a] There are a few other rare classes which will not concern us here.

Now let us practice by assigning point groups to the molecules discussed earlier, beginning with chiral molecules. 2-Chlorobutane (III) has no elements of symmetry; it is asymmetric and is in point group C_1. In other words, rotation about any axis must go through 360° before we return to an arrangement indistinguishable from the original. All asymmetric molecules belong to point group C_1.

trans-1,2-Dibromocyclopropane (VIa, VIb) contains only a C_2 axis and is therefore in point group C_2.

An example of a molecule which is not chiral is *cis*-1,2-dibromocyclopropane (V), which belongs to point group C_s (only one σ plane). Cyclopropyl bromide and methanol in Figure 6.3 and 3-pentanol (VII) also belong to point group C_s, as does the "envelope" form of cyclopentane shown in Figure 6.3. (The "half-chair" form of cyclopentane, page 41, is C_2.) Water (Figure 6.3) is C_{2v} (it has a C_2 axis and two σ_v planes); ammonia (Figure 6.3) is C_{3v} (it has a C_3 axis and three σ_v planes). Chloromethane is also C_{3v}.

Cyclopropane has a C_3 axis perpendicular to the ring plane, three C_2 axes in the ring plane, three σ_v planes each containing a C_2 axis, and a σ_h which is the ring plane. This molecule belongs to point group D_{3h}. Planar cyclobutane (II) belongs to point group D_{4h}, while the chair form of cyclohexane (Figure 6.3) belongs to D_{3d}.

Note in Table 6.1 that only C_n and D_n point groups correspond to chiral molecules. For molecules which belong to the other point groups in the table, it will never be possible to find enantiomeric compounds or optical activity.

6.4   Nomenclature for Diastereomers Containing Two Asymmetric Atoms

If two (or more) asymmetric atoms are present in a structure, several diastereomeric forms are possible. Consider an acyclic molecule having two asymmetric carbon atoms. If the two asymmetric carbons are identically substituted, as in the example

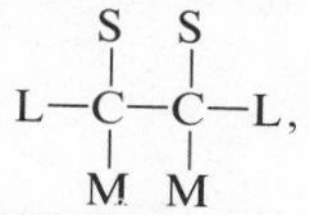

$$
\begin{array}{c}
\quad\; \overset{\displaystyle S}{|} \;\; \overset{\displaystyle S}{|} \\
L-C-C-L, \\
\quad\; \underset{\displaystyle M}{|} \;\; \underset{\displaystyle M}{|}
\end{array}
$$

the diastereomers shown in Figure 6.6 are possible (only one of several possible conformations is shown for each stereoisomer).

Figure 6.6
Stereoisomers of CLMS–CLMS.

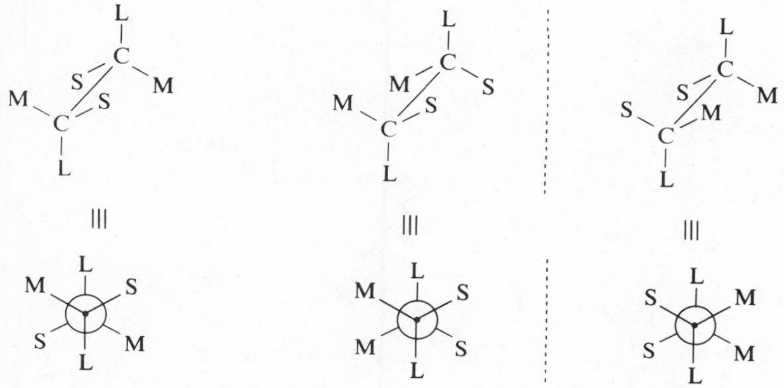

(A)   (B)   (C)

meso   *dl* or racemate

EXERCISE 6.1

Draw Fischer projections for the meso and dl molecules shown in Figure 6.6 (the student may wish to review pp. 47–48).

Answer: If a rotation about the single bond is first carried out to get two end groups down, then meso, for example, becomes

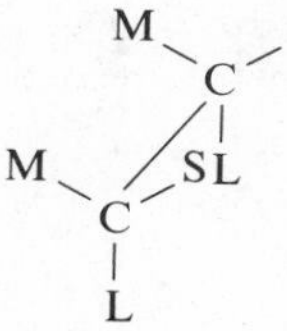

and in a Fischer projection this is

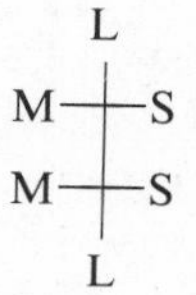

$$
\begin{array}{c}
L \\
M-\!\!\!\!-\!\!\!\!-S \\
M-\!\!\!\!-\!\!\!\!-S \\
L
\end{array}
$$

The diastereomer A is achiral. It has a superimposable mirror image, and hence cannot exist in optically active forms. This kind of diastereomer is referred to as a *meso* compound. A meso form is *not optically active* because it has certain elements of symmetry which make it achiral, in this case, 2 asymmetric carbons of *opposite configuration*. We recognize A as a meso compound because it has a center of symmetry in the conformation shown. (We can also recognize this as a meso form by rotation about the carbon–carbon bond to an eclipsed conformation which would have a plane of symmetry.)

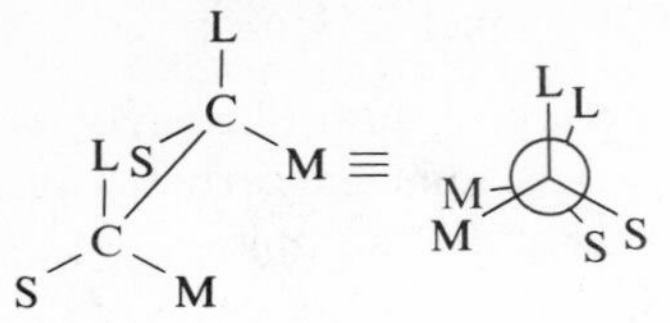

(A) *meso*

The remaining possible stereoisomers are B and C, which are enantiomeric. These are truly diastereomeric with A. In other words, simple rotation about bonds cannot interconvert A, B, and C with each other. The pair of enantiomers B and C is designated as the *dl diastereomer* or the *racemate*.

A specific example of a structure which has meso and *dl* diastereomers is 2,3-butane-diol. The meso compound is shown in Figure 6.5 and the two enantiomers which make up the *dl* diastereomer are shown as structures IX and X.

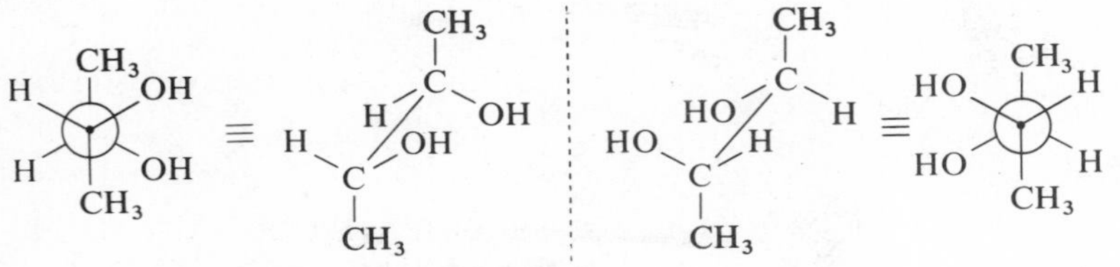

IX   X

dl-2,3-Butanediol

The total number of stereoisomers possible for compounds containing two or more asymmetric atoms that are not identically substituted is 2^n, where n equals the number of asymmetric atoms. All of these diastereomers would be optically active. Thus, a structure containing two differently substituted asymmetric carbon atoms, for example,

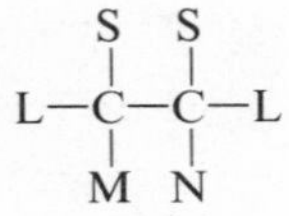

in which M and N are similar but not identical, would have four stereoisomers, occurring as two pairs of enantiomers. The top row of structures in Figure 6.7 depicts a staggered conformation of each stereoisomer, and the bottom row shows projection formulas of

Figure 6.7
Stereoisomers of CLMS–CLNS.

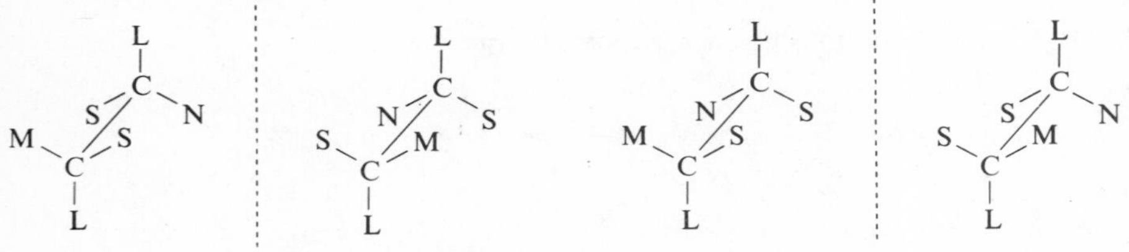

(A)   (B)   (C)   (D)

dl-erythro   *dl-threo*

one of the three possible eclipsed conformations of this same stereoisomer. If at least two of the substituents attached to each asymmetric carbon atom are similar or identical, the following terminology will apply. The *erythro* diastereomer (a pair of enantiomers) corresponds to that *diastereomer in which the sets of similar or identical substituents are superimposed on each other in the projection of one of the three eclipsed conformations*. If this is not true, then one is dealing with the *threo* diastereomer (a pair of enantiomers). According to this definition, A and B in Figure 6.7 are the pair of enantiomers of the erythro compound; C and D correspond to the threo compound.

The names erythro *and* threo *are derived from the names of two simple sugars. To decide whether a compound has the erythro or threo configuration, it is necessary to decide if it has a configuration more like erythrose, or more like threose, Fischer projections for which are shown.*

CHO
H—OH
H—OH
CH₂OH
Erythrose

CHO
HO—H
H—OH
CH₂OH
Threose

An example of erythro and threo compounds is furnished by the 3-bromo-2-butanols: structures XIa and XIb are the erythro racemate and structures XIIa and XIIb are the threo enantiomers.

XIa XIb
dl-erythro

XIIa XIIb
dl-threo

EXERCISE 6.2

Draw Fischer projections for XIa and XIIa, and deduce which is erythro and which is threo by comparing your structures with the projections of erythrose and threose given above.

A different terminology is employed with cyclic compounds. The diastereomers are differentiated by *cis* if the substituents lie on the same side of the average ring plane, and *trans* if the substituents are on opposite sides of the ring (Section 6.1).

As we shall see in Section 7.4, a double bond may be formally treated as a two-atom ring. Diastereomers resulting from different arrangements of substituents attached to a double bond are also called cis, trans isomers.

1,2-Dibromocyclopropane is an example of a cyclic compound with two identically substituted asymmetric carbon atoms. The cis isomer V is achiral—it is meso (*usually all achiral diastereomers are called* meso *compounds*). The trans isomer VIa, VIb exists as a pair of enantiomers. In this case we have a situation similar to that with the butanediols in that the actual number of stereoisomers (the *theoretical* maximum is 2^n) is lowered because of achirality. On the other hand, 2-methylcyclopropyl chloride has two asymmetric carbon atoms which are substituted differently. Four stereoisomers are possible; the cis isomer as a pair of enantiomers (XIIIa, XIIIb), and the trans isomer also as a pair of enantiomers (XIVa, XIVb).

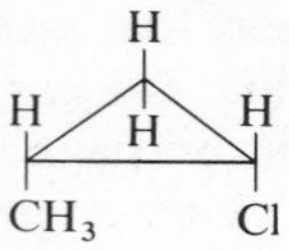

XIIIa   XIIIb   XIVa   XIVb

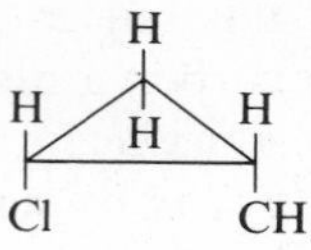

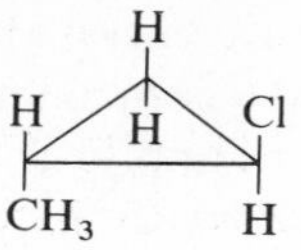

dl-cis   dl-trans

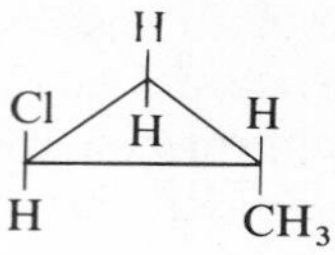

6.5   Prediction of the Total Number of Stereoisomers

Let us now try to predict the total number of stereoisomers (excluding conformational isomers) that are theoretically possible for some real cases, and then try to decide the actual number that more complex structures should have. For the structures shown below we shall ask ourselves: How many stereoisomers are possible? Which of these are capable of showing optical activity (are chiral)? Which of these are meso diastereomers (are achiral)?

Example: $CH_3CHCHCHCH_3$
                        | | |
                        F Cl Br

There are three asymmetric carbon atoms, each substituted differently.

Answer: Eight stereoisomers are theoretically possible. These are found to occur as four *dl* pairs. All eight stereoisomers are optically active.

EXERCISE 6.3

Draw Fischer projections for the eight stereoisomers of the preceding example. For these projections, indicate which are enantiomers and which are diastereomers.

Example: $CH_3CH—CH—CHCH_3$
                         | | |
                         OH   OH   OH

Two carbon atoms are asymmetric but identically substituted. The central carbon atom may or may not be asymmetric. We know that at most there can be $2^3 = 8$ stereoisomers, but since the ends of the molecule are the same there will be fewer than this, because there will be some meso forms. To arrive at our answer we use projection formulas for aid.

Answer: We can begin by writing the eight possible Fischer projections a–h.

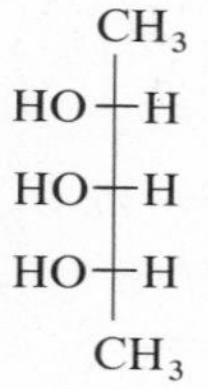

                (a) 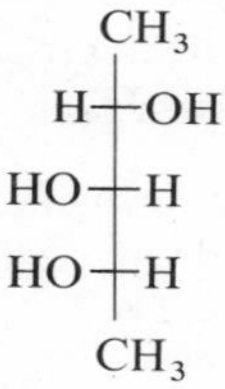   (b) 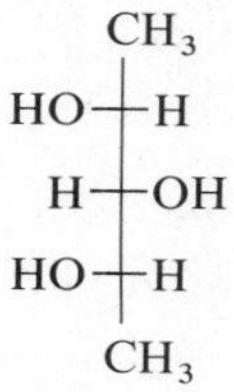   (c) 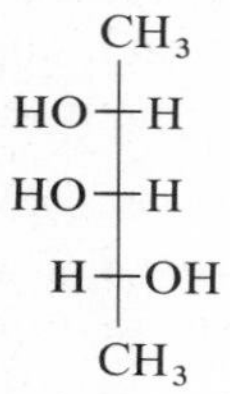   (d)

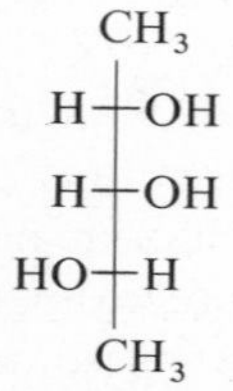

(e) (same as b) 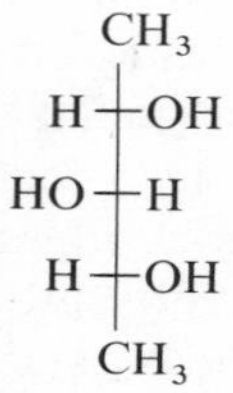   (f) (same as c) 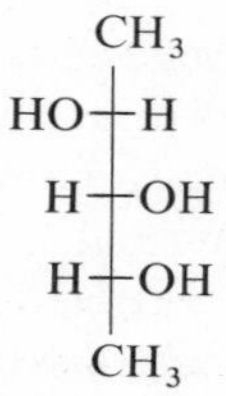   (g) (same as d) 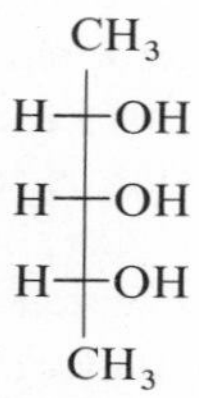   (h) (same as a)

Recall that if a Fischer projection is rotated 180° in the plane of the paper, it is not changed (Section 3.6). Thus *a* and *h* can be interconverted by such a rotation. They are mirror images which are identical, and thus they correspond to the same compound, which is meso. Similarly, *c* and *f* correspond to a second (meso) compound. Structures *b* and *e* are the same compound but not mirror images. Similarly *d* and *g* are the same compound, but not mirror images. Thus we find that there are actually only four stereoisomers for this compound, two meso forms (*a* and *c*) and a *dl* pair (*b* and *d*).

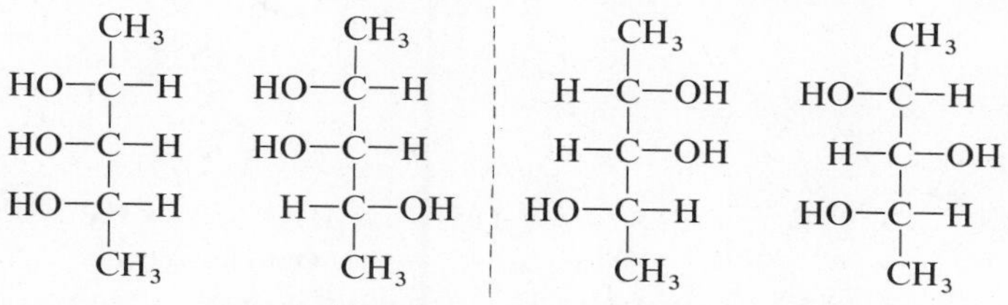

meso   Optically active   Optically active   *meso*

dl pair

Example:

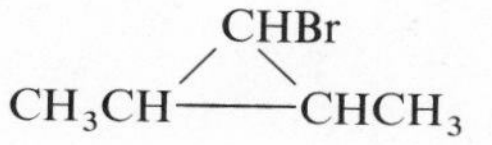

$$CH_3CH{-}{-}CHCH_3$$ with CHBr bridge

Again, we should use pictures to get our answer. This time we employ a projection formula in which a heavy dot indicates that the hydrogen attached to that carbon lies above the plane of the ring. If there is no heavy dot, the hydrogen is below the plane of the ring.

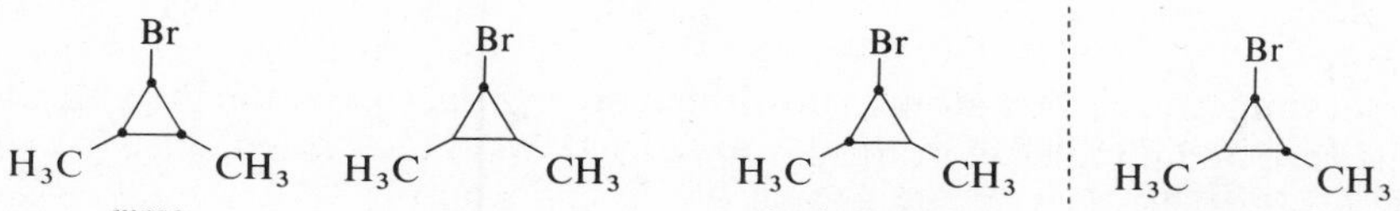

meso   *meso*   Optically active   Optically active

dl pair

Answer: $2^3 = 8$ is the theoretical maximum; there are actually four stereoisomers, of which two are meso and two are optically active (a *dl* pair).

EXERCISE 6.4

Write out all eight of the possible structures for the above problem and show that only four of these are different.

Example:

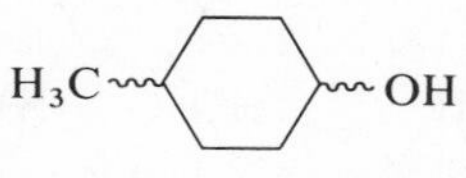

Use projection formulas first.

Answer:

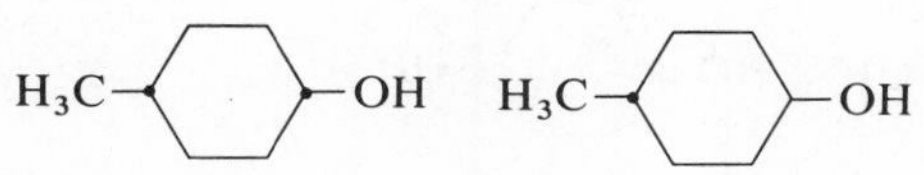

Optically inactive, *cis*   Optically inactive, *trans*

Two optically inactive stereoisomers, cis and trans.

EXERCISE 6.5

Draw out the four possible isomers of the above, showing the cyclohexane rings as chair forms (use models). Why does it turn out that there are only two stereoisomers instead of four?

Example:

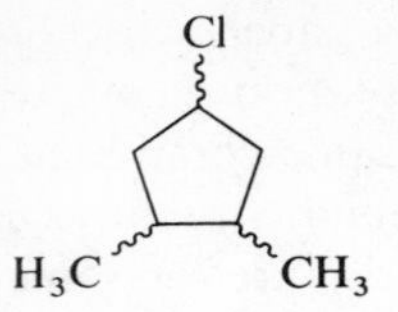

In systematic fashion we draw all eight projection formulas. After discarding duplications we find:

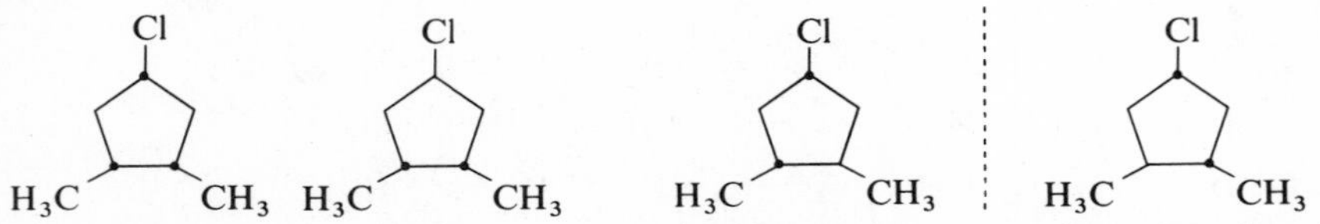

meso	*meso*	Optically active	Optically active

dl pair

Answer: Four stereoisomers: two are meso and two are optically active (a *dl* pair).

EXERCISE 6.6

Verify the above.

Example:

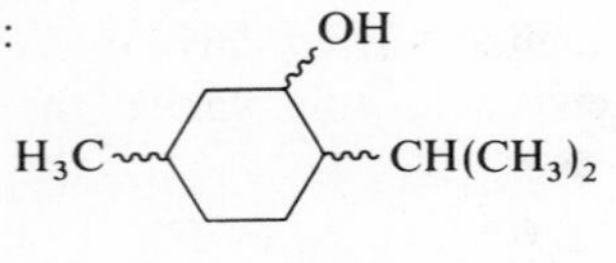

There are three asymmetric carbon atoms, substituted differently, so that the theoretical maximum is the expected number of isomers.

Answer: Eight stereoisomers, occurring as four *dl* pairs. All are optically active.

Example:

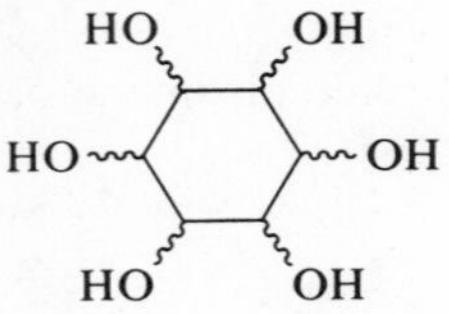

Use projection formulas.

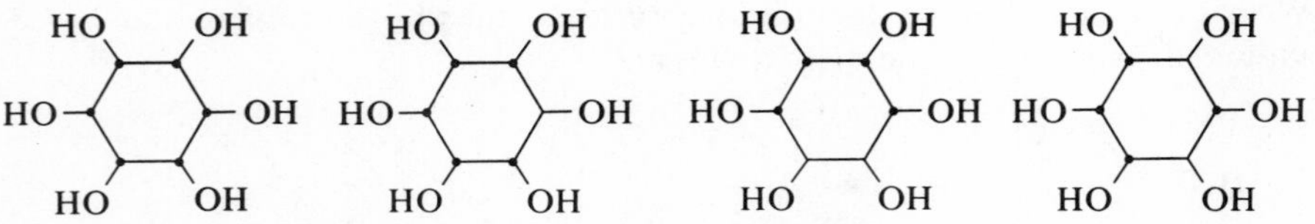

meso	*meso*	*meso*	*meso*

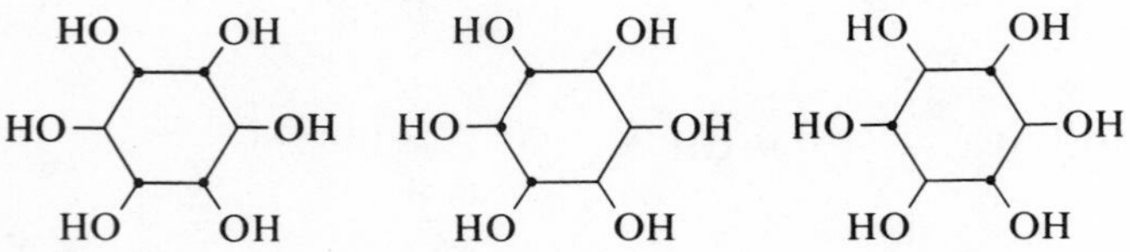

meso	*meso*	*meso*

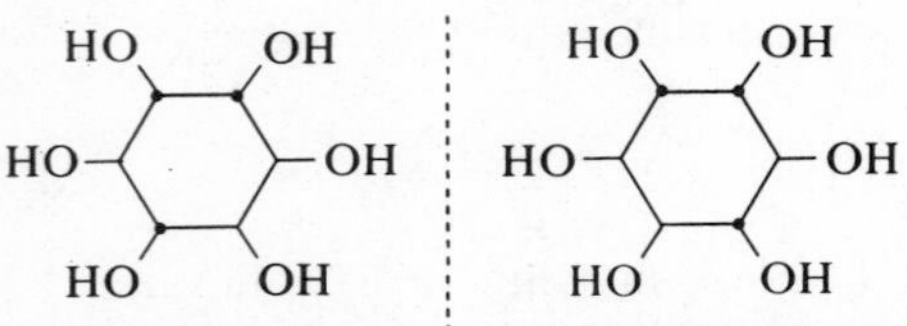

Optically active	Optically active

dl pair

Answer: Because of the high symmetry, only nine of the 64 theoretically possible stereo-isomers exist. Seven are meso and two are optically active (a *dl* pair).

EXERCISE 6.7

A small protein may contain 100 asymmetric carbon atoms. What is the theoretical number of stereoisomers possible for such a molecule?

6.6 Racemic Forms, Racemization, and Resolution

Diastereomers, like structural isomers, differ in every physical property. Moreover, although diastereomers contain the same functional groups and undergo the same kinds of chemical reactions, the rates at which these reactions occur differ significantly from one diastereomer to another.

As mentioned earlier in this chapter, a mixture containing equimolar parts of two enantiomers is called a *racemic form* or a *dl pair*. Consider briefly how racemic forms differ from the pure enantiomers, both in the solid state and in solution. A pure dextro-rotatory enantiomer forms crystals that are the exact mirror image of the crystals formed from the levorotatory enantiomer. These crystals have the same melting point and show the same solubility properties. The racemate, however, must form a different crystal, and the melting point, the solubility, and so on, of the racemate *will be different* from those of the pure enantiomers. An analogy that illustrates this principle is the difference in packing arrangement of a box filled with *pairs* of gloves from that of a box filled with only right-handed gloves.

Racemates and Conglomerates. Most commonly, racemic forms are either simple 1:1 eutectic mixtures (called *conglomerates*) in which each individual crystal is a single enantiomer, or distinct 1:1 *association compounds* of the two enantiomers (called *racemates*), in which both enantiomers are present in equal amounts in each individual crystal. The diagrams of melting point versus composition (binary phase diagrams) given in Figure 6.8 show the different melting behavior of pure enantiomers and racemates. Conglomerates are eutectic mixtures, and as with other mixtures, they must melt lower than a pure enantiomer. Racemates are

Figure 6.8
Binary phase diagrams for R and S enantiomers.

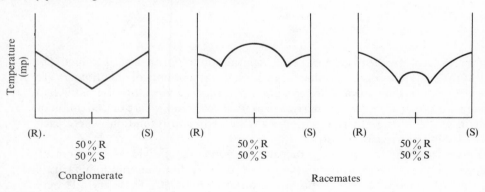

association compounds whose melting points may lie either below or above those of the enantiomers. In order to determine whether a racemic form is a conglomerate or a racemate, all we need to do is add a very small amount of a pure enantiomer to the *dl* pair, and measure the melting point of the resulting mixture. The melting point of a conglomerate will be raised slightly, while that of a racemic compound will be lowered.

In dilute solutions the distinction between racemic forms and the individual enantiomeric components disappears. Thus, the spectra and other properties will be the same. The only difference will be the optical rotation—one enantiomer will be dextrorotatory, the other will be levorotatory by exactly the same amount, and the racemic form will show no rotation.

Racemic forms are generated in one of three ways: (1) chemical reactions of achiral compounds with achiral reagents; (2) mixing of equal amounts of the two enantiomers; and (3) racemization.

Racemization refers to the conversion of an optical isomer into a *dl* mixture containing equal amounts of it and its enantiomer. This process can be followed by observing the complete loss of optical activity with time. The position of equilibrium in racemization is *always* an equimolar mixture of the enantiomers. *Epimerization* is the changing of configuration at a single asymmetric center in a molecule containing more than one asymmetric center; or, in other words, it is the interconversion of diastereomers. Because diastereomers may or may not be optically active, epimerization cannot always be followed by measuring the *change* in optical rotation with time. Both racemization and epimerization usually involve bond-breaking reagents and chemical reactions. These will be discussed in detail in later chapters.

The conversion of (+)-2-iodobutane or the (−) isomer into an equimolar mixture of (+)- and (−)-2-iodobutane (*dl* pair) when it is treated with iodide ion is an example of racemization.

(+)-2-Iodobutane   (−)-2-Iodobutane

Racemization—optical activity lost.

The equilibration of one enantiomer of *trans*-3-*t*-butylcyclohexanol with one enantiomer of *cis*-3-*t*-butylcyclohexanol is an epimerization.

trans-(1S,3S)-3-*t*-Butyl-   *cis*-(1R,3S)-3-*t*-Butyl-
cyclohexanol   cyclohexanol

Epimerization—optical activity not
lost in this case, but it is
changed from the value characteristic
of the trans isomer to that of
the mixture of isomers.

Whenever reactions are carried out under achiral conditions, achiral products are obtained. If the molecules of the product are chiral, equal amounts of enantiomers are obtained, that is, a racemic form. The separation of a racemic form into the individual enantiomers is termed *resolution*. We may have partial resolution, where one enantiomer is present in excess of the other, and we may have complete resolution, where each enantiomer is obtained free of the other.

Pasteur† was the first to separate a racemic form into the individual enantiomers. He examined under a microscope crystals of racemic sodium ammonium tartrate that had been obtained by crystallization from water below 27°C. These crystals were of two different chiral forms, one the nonsuperimposable mirror image of the other. Pasteur separated the crystals with the aid of a magnifying glass and a pair of tweezers. One type of crystal dissolved in water to give a dextrorotatory solution; the other type gave a levorotatory solution which had a rotation equal in magnitude to that of the first. This laborious technique of resolution can, in principle, be applied whenever the solid racemic form is a conglomerate composed of observably different crystals. However,

† Louis Pasteur, 1822–95. Born Dole, France; Universities of Dijon, Strasbourg, Lille, Sorbonne.

cases of successful resolution by this means are rare, because observably different crystals in a conglomerate are uncommon, and the labor involved in such a separation is very great.

The most generally applicable way to effect the resolution of a *dl* pair, also developed by Pasteur, is to allow it to react with a chiral reagent (*a resolving agent*). This will convert the two *enantiomers* into two *diastereomers*, which can then be separated by techniques such as fractional crystallization, or chromatography. The separated diastereomers are then decomposed by appropriate chemical reagents to liberate the individual enantiomers. The following equations illustrate the general sequence:

$$(+)\text{-B-}(+)\text{-A} \longrightarrow (+)\text{-B}$$

$$(+)\text{-B} + (-)\text{-B} \quad + \quad 2(+)\text{-A} \longrightarrow$$

$$(-)\text{-B-}(+)\text{-A} \longrightarrow (-)\text{-B}$$

| *dl* pair | Resolving agent | A mixture of diastereomers— different physical properties, can be separated | Separated enantiomers |

A judicious choice of resolving agent must be made. It must react in high yield with the *dl* pair, the resulting diastereomers must be separable in some practical way, and the resulting separated diastereomers must be easily and cleanly decomposed to give back the pure enantiomers. Salts from simple acid–base reactions make excellent diastereomers for resolution purposes.

An illustrative case is the resolution of *dl*-α-phenylethylamine (**B**) by diastereomer formation using (+)-tartaric acid (**A**) as the resolving agent.

An optically active substance cannot be formed in a reaction in which all reagents are inactive and all experimental conditions are achiral. However, an optically active product can be generated in a reaction that employs chiral reagents and/or conditions.

In the so-called *asymmetric* ("dissymmetric" would be a better word) *decomposition method* of *resolution*, one enantiomer of a *dl* pair is selectively destroyed by treatment with an optically active reagent. In biological systems, many reactions are catalyzed by enzymes which are optically active; and, consequently, asymmetric decompositions can be carried out by using enzymes. Again, Pasteur pioneered in this area, for he found that the mold *Penicillium glaucum*, when allowed to grow in the presence of racemic tartaric acid, preferentially destroyed the (+) enantiomer, and (−)-tartaric acid could be recovered from the medium.

6.7   Configurations and Their Correlation by Physical Methods

The *configuration* of a stereoisomer (either an enantiomer or a diastereomer) describes the specific geometrical arrangement of the atoms. The enantiomers III and IV of 2-chlorobutane are said to have *opposite configurations*. The enantiomers of *erythro*-3-bromo-2-butanol (XIa and XIb) have opposite configurations at *both* asymmetric carbon atoms.

> In Section 3.6 the specification of configuration at an asymmetric atom by use of the R and S convention was discussed. III is R-2-chlorobutane and its enantiomer IV is S-2-chlorobutane. Structure XIa represents 2R, 3S-3-bromo-2-butanol, whereas XIb is 2S, 3R-3-bromo-2-butanol. Diastereomers also have different configurations. For example, *cis*-1,2-dibromocyclopropane (V) has the configuration 1R, 2S, and the two enantiomers (VIa and VIb) of the trans isomer are 1R, 2R and 1S, 2S.

It now becomes appropriate for us to ask, How can the configurations of stereoisomers be established and correlated in practice? There are really two separate aspects to this question. The first is concerned with the different possible arrangements of the atoms in diastereomers—the configuration of one chiral grouping within a diastereomer as compared with other groupings in the same molecule. This is an internal comparison concerned with *relative configuration*. We wish to know, for example, which diastereomer is meso and which is *dl*; or which is erythro and which is threo; or which is cis and which is trans. The second aspect of the question involves our desire to know the *absolute configuration* of a chiral molecule. Does the (−)-enantiomer (the one that is levorotatory) of 2-chlorobutane actually have the R configuration III or does it have the S configuration IV? Which is the (+)-enantiomer of *threo*-3-bromo-2-butanol, XIIa (2R, 3R) or XIIb (2S, 3S)? Note that if the absolute configuration of one chiral grouping in a diastereomer and the relative configurations of all the groupings are known, then the absolute configuration of the whole molecule may be specified.

As mentioned earlier, the absolute configurations of molecules were not known to the early chemists. They assumed the absolute configuration of D-glyceraldehyde and determined the relative configurations of all other molecules with respect to it. The elucidation of the absolute configurations of several molecules by physical methods has been successful in recent years, and the configurations of many more compounds can be determined by correlation with those already known. Both chemical and physical methods for configurational correlation have been developed. In this section we will discuss only the physical approaches.

The relative configurations of diastereomers are often easily established because differences in gross physical properties (and in chemical reactivities) serve to distinguish and characterize the isomers. Typical of these physical differences are the following: (1) *cis*-1,2-Dibromocyclopropane (V) has a much higher dipole moment than the trans *dl* pair (VI). (2) *dl*-2,3-Butanediol (IX, X) can be resolved into enantiomers, whereas the achiral meso isomer (Figure 6.5) is not resolvable. (3) When equilibrium is established between *cis*- and *trans*-4-methylcyclohexanol, the trans isomer predominates. (4) The nuclear magnetic resonance spectrum of *erythro*-3-bromo-2-butanol (XIa, XIb) is characteristic and different from that of the threo diastereomer (XIIa, XIIb).

Relative configuration within a molecule can be established unequivocally by diffraction analysis. X-ray crystallography provides detailed structural parameters (such as bond lengths, bond angles, and dihedral angles) and usually allows definite assignment of the relative three-dimensional arrangement of the atoms. If a structure has several possible diastereomers, X-ray analysis can tell us which diastereomer we have. It is not possible to distinguish enantiomers (e.g., assign absolute configuration) by ordinary X-ray crystallography because the intensities of the diffracted waves are identical from crystals of both forms. However, when certain types of atoms (whose nonbonding electrons can be excited by X-rays of proper frequencies) are present in a chiral molecule, special interference patterns in the diffracted waves can be detected and measured. Complex calculations will allow exact assignment of the spatial distribution of all atoms. This method is referred to as *anomalous X-ray scattering*, and the principle was recognized by J. M. Bijvoet† in 1951. He successfully applied the technique to the assignment of the absolute configurations of (+)-tartaric acid (the sodium rubidium salt was used) and (−)-isoleucine as XV and XVI, respectively, (the configurations of these compounds relative to D-glyceraldehyde were already known). Fortunately, these were exactly the configurations assigned to these compounds by convention many years earlier, and this meant that the absolute configurations of all other compounds that had been related to glyceraldehyde were correctly known.

$$
\begin{array}{cc}
\text{COOH} & \text{COOH} \\
| & | \\
\text{H}-\text{C}-\text{OH} & \text{H}-\text{C}-\text{NH}_2 \\
| & | \\
\text{HO}-\text{C}-\text{H} & \text{H}-\text{C}-\text{CH}_3 \\
| & | \\
\text{COOH} & \text{CH}_2\text{CH}_3 \\
\text{XV} & \text{XVI} \\
(+)\text{-Tartaric acid (R, R)} & (-)\text{-Isoleucine (R, R)}
\end{array}
$$

Optical rotation measurements or rotatory dispersion curves (Section 3.6) are often used for correlation of configuration. Unlike X-ray crystallography, this is an indirect approach, and it requires a comparison of the data for the molecule whose configuration is to be established with those of a molecule whose configuration is already known. Measurements at a single wavelength are usually taken at the sodium D line, 5893 Å. (We can learn the same type of thing from ORD curves that we can learn from simple optical activity measurements, but we can sometimes learn more, and with a deeper understanding and higher degree of reliability.) One approach is to assign a rotational contribution of specific sign and magnitude (estimated from molecules of known configuration) to each chiral grouping. Summation of these contributions gives a calculated molecular rotation for each of the various possible configurations, and the correct configuration of the molecule is considered to be that for which the calculated value is closest to the measured molecular rotation. Another approach is based on the assumption that when two similarly constituted chiral molecules are chemically altered in the same way, and these changes are accompanied by a significant shift in optical rotation in the same direction, the two compounds have the same configuration. Despite the empirical nature of this approach, optical rotation comparisons have been applied with remarkable success for correlation of configuration of many types of compounds.

Optical Rotatory Dispersion. ORD curves are of two types: "plain curves" and "Cotton effect curves" (Section 3.6). An ORD curve reflects the difference of the dispersion (refractive index) curves of plane-polarized light caused by a chiral medium. Rotatory dispersion curves are usually more reliable for correlations than are optical rotation measurements at a single wavelength because the configuration of a chiral grouping will affect the actual shape of the curve. The sign and magnitude of rotational values at one wavelength can sometimes mislead us, whereas the shape of an ORD curve is much less ambiguous to interpret and compare. Enantiomers always give mirror-image ORD curves. If the ORD curve of an optically active compound of known configuration and that of a chemically similar molecule

† J. M. Bijvoet. Born Amsterdam, 1892. Municipal University of Amsterdam. State University, Utrecht.

of unknown configuration are very similar in shape, the two molecules probably have the same configurations. Conversely, when the shape of the ORD curve of a compound of known absolute configuration is very nearly the mirror image of that of a chemically similar, optically active species, the two most likely have opposite configurations.

Because of experimental difficulties, few ORD curves were determined prior to 1956. With the advent of reliable instrumentation, ORD has become quite useful, and it is an important tool in the kit of the stereochemist.

The use of ORD for the solution of stereochemical problems has mainly been developed by C. Djerassi† and his collaborators.

6.8   Stereoisomerism and Nuclear Magnetic Resonance Spectroscopy

The proton nmr spectra of organic molecules are often considerably simplified because several of the protons are magnetically (or chemically) equivalent. For example, all of the protons of ethane are equivalent, and only one resonance line is seen for the compound. Similarly, the two protons in bromochloromethane (XVII) show only one resonance line. However, in this case the two protons are not in identical environments; rather, they occupy mirror-image environments. Such protons are called *enantiotopic protons*. The only way in which they can be distinguished is under chiral conditions (such as when dissolved in an optically active solvent), and ordinary nmr measurements cannot differentiate between them.

XVII

The plane of the page is a mirror
plane, and the environment of one
proton is the mirror image of the
environment of the other.

The nmr spectrum of an ethyl derivative is also simplified because some of the protons lose their identity. For example, ethyl chloride shows a triplet centered at δ 1.48 corresponding to the three methyl protons split by the adjacent pair of methylene protons, and a quartet centered at δ 3.57 for the two methylene protons split by the three methyl protons. The perspective formula of ethyl chloride in the staggered conformation (XVIII) shows that the protons labeled H_b and H_b' are enantiotopic and should be equivalent in the nmr, but that the anti proton H_a should have a slightly different chemical shift. (H_c and H_c' are also enantiotopic and would have the same chemical shift.) However, rotation about the carbon–carbon single bond is very rapid (about

XVIII   XIX   XX

10^{-6} second), and this is sufficient to average out the difference between the methyl protons. What is seen is an average line position corresponding to the three protons H_a, H_b, and H_b'—on the nmr time scale the protons appear equivalent.

The chair conformation of cyclohexane contains two chemically different types of protons—the six equatorial and the six axial protons (Section 3.4). Therefore, we might

---

† Carl Djerassi. Born 1923, Vienna. Ciba, New Jersey; Syntex, Mexico City. Wayne State and Stanford Universities.

expect to see two lines in the nmr spectrum (probably further split by spin–spin coupling). In fact, only a single sharp line appears when the spectrum is determined at room temperature. This is because chair–chair interconversion (Figure 3.4) is occurring very rapidly. Each hydrogen is equatorial 50% of the time and axial 50% of the time. All hydrogens have the same average position and must therefore give the same signal. Since the protons are all equivalent, they do not couple, and only a single line is seen. If the temperature is lowered, the rate of chair–chair interconversion will be slowed down, and fewer and fewer molecules will have sufficient thermal energy to surmount the inversion barrier. At $-100°C$, the nmr spectrum of cyclohexane shows two families of bands corresponding to the equatorial and axial protons. As cyclohexane is warmed from $-100°C$, the two bands gradually come together, and they coalesce at $-66.7°C$.

A similar situation is encountered with monosubstituted cyclohexanes. The two chair arrangements for cyclohexyl bromide are in rapid equilibrium; however, the conformation with equatorial bromine (XIX) is preferred. Even though the methine hydrogens (labelled H_a and H_e) are chemically different, only one multiplet from the methine hydrogen is seen in the nmr spectrum at $+22°C$; it is centered at δ 4.06. (Protons such as H_a and H_e that differ in spatial environment are called *diastereotopic* protons.) The proton resonances are averaged by the rapid chair inversion. However, at $-84°C$ two distinct multiplets are observed, one at δ 3.87 for H_a in the equatorial bromo conformation XIX, with a peak area corresponding to about 70%, and one at δ 4.59 for H_e in conformation XX (30%).

When chair inversions are prevented, averaging of the proton positions cannot occur and diastereotopic protons will show different resonances. An illustration of this is shown by the diastereomeric 4-*t*-butylcyclohexyl bromides XXI and XXII. The bulky *t*-butyl group would have such a large energy in the axial position that it effectively "freezes" the molecule in a conformation in which it is equatorial.

It is important to note that while enantiotopic protons (protons in enantiomeric environments) are not distinguished by nmr, diastereotopic protons are, as long as they remain diastereotopic and do not become equivalent because of some internal motion of the molecule.

Let us further note that while the three protons of a methyl group are equivalent because of the very low barrier to rotation of the group, the two protons of a methylene group are not always equivalent. Consider structure XXI as an example. The two protons H_e are enantiotopic, and hence equivalent in the nmr. The two protons H_a are similarly equivalent. But H_a and H_e are not enantiotopic: they are diastereotopic and thus nonequivalent. The ring is prevented from inverting by the *t*-butyl group, and H_a can never become equivalent to H_e. Since H_a and H_e on the same carbon are nonequivalent, they can couple with each other. Structure XXIII will show four lines for the protons H_a and H_b in the general case (when there is no further coupling with Y or Z); H_a and H_e are nonequivalent, and each one splits the other into a doublet. The cases we have previously examined, such as ethyl chloride, have the methylene protons equivalent, because they are enantiotopic. In more complicated molecules, methylene protons may be diastereotopic and nonequivalent, and hence may give more complicated coupling patterns. We will postpone a detailed discussion of these complicated cases to Chapter 32, and for now will want only to be able to recognize when protons are enantiotopic or diastereotopic, as this recognition can frequently be put to good use.

Example: The two diastereomers of 1,3-dimethyl-1,3-dibromocyclobutane were obtained in a reaction. The nmr spectrum of diastereomer A consisted of a sharp singlet at δ 2.13 (rel. area = 3) and a sharp singlet at δ 3.21 (rel. area = 2). Diastereomer B showed a sharp singlet at δ 1.88 (rel. area = 3) and a symmetrically arranged complex multiplet centered at δ 3.17 (rel. area = 2). Which corresponds to *trans*-1,3-dimethyl-1,3-dibromocyclobutane, diastereomer A or diastereomer B? The possibilities are

Answer: In both compounds the methyl groups are equivalent. Rotation of the cis isomer about an axis perpendicular to the plane of the ring passing through its center exchanges the methyl groups. Similarly, for the trans isomer, rotation about an axis in the plane of the ring passing through carbons 2 and 4 exchanges the methyl groups. The tumbling motions of these molecules in solution therefore brings about the equivalence of the methyls within each molecule, so in each case the methyls are seen as sharp singlets at δ 2.13 and δ 1.88 (the relative areas of 3:2 are equivalent to 6:4; e.g., six methyl protons and four methylene protons). However, the four methylene hydrogens in the trans diastereomer are equivalent because of the symmetry, and only a single line would be expected (δ 3.21). For the cis compound, the methylene hydrogens are equivalent in pairs, the pair cis to the bromines is equivalent, but they are different from the pair cis to the methyl groups. This should lead to a more complex pattern. Therefore, diastereomer A is the trans compound.

AN APOLOGY TO THE STUDENT. *Most students find that stereochemistry is the most difficult topic covered in this course. No way is known to make this topic "easy." Nature has chosen the tetrahedron as the basic geometric element of organic chemistry, and the complications that follow are an unavoidable result of the geometric properties of a tetrahedron. On the encouraging side, if you are able to master the material in this chapter, things are not likely to get any worse.*

PROBLEMS

1. Locate all of the planes and simple axes of symmetry in the following (use models):
    (a) Methyl chloride   (b) Methyl mercaptan
    (c) Isobutane   (d) Equatorial methylcyclohexane
    (e) Norbornane   (f) Spiropentane
    (g) Diborane   (h) Piperidine
    (i) *trans*-Decalin

2. Define and give an example of:
    (a) Enantiomer   (b) Diastereomer
    (c) Racemization   (d) Epimerization

3. Listed below are several pairs of molecules (or molecular conformations). Pick from the following list the word that best describes each pair: *enantiomers, diastereomers, conformational isomers,* or *identical.*

(a)

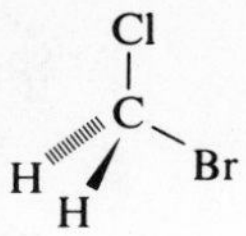

and

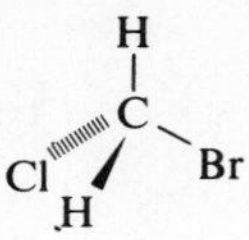

(b)

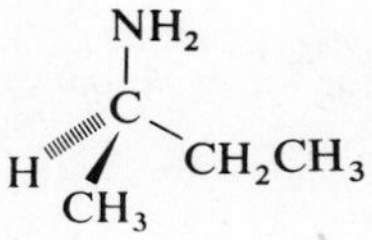

and

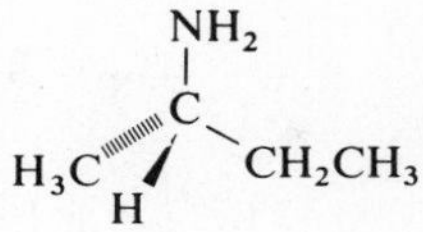

(c)

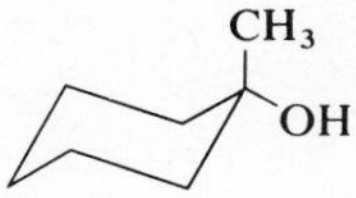

and

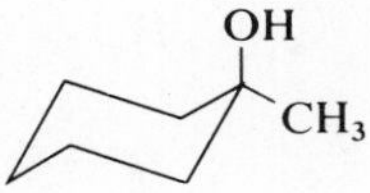

(d)

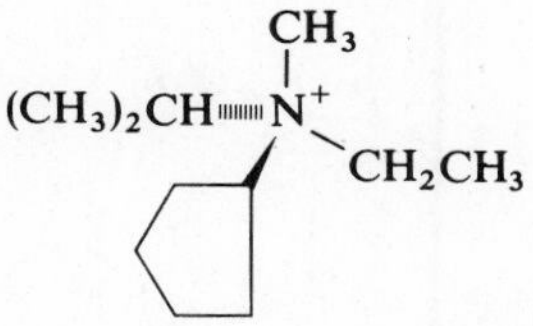

and

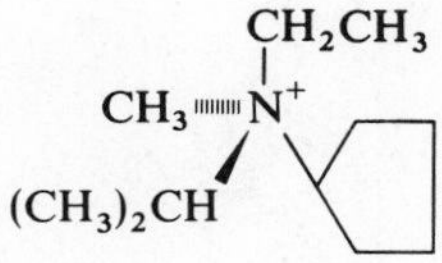

(e)

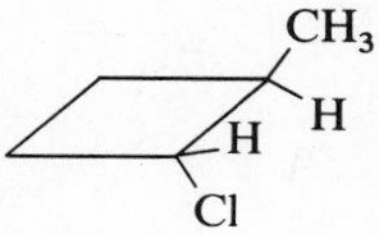

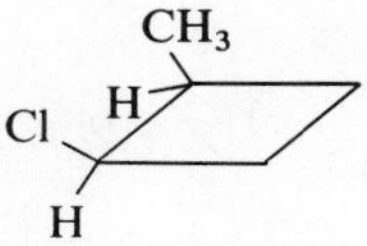

(f)

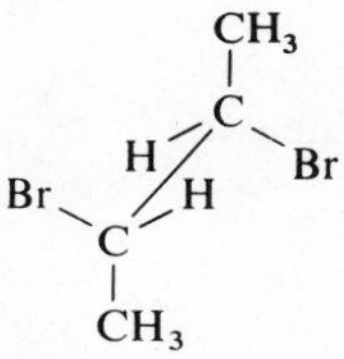

and

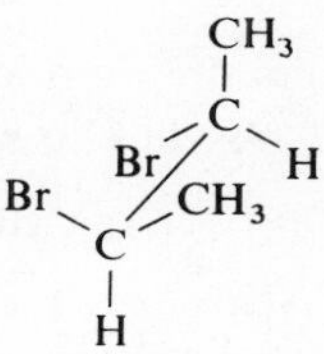

(g)

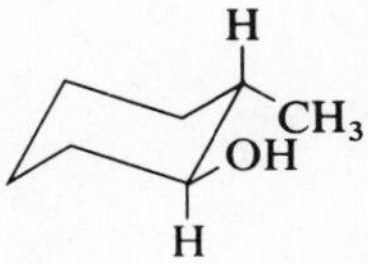

and

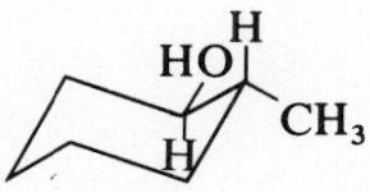

(h)

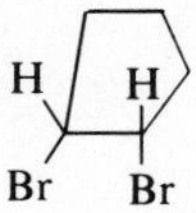

and

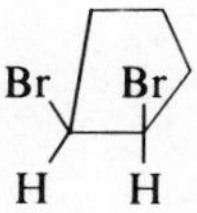

4. Which of the structures of problem 3 are capable of showing optical activity?

5. For each of the compounds shown, draw a comparable structure for the *epimer*.

(a)

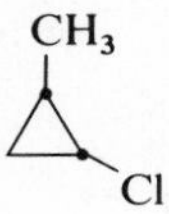

(b)

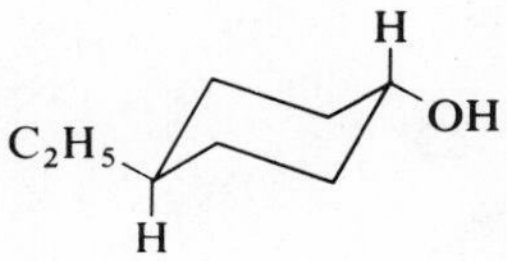

(c)

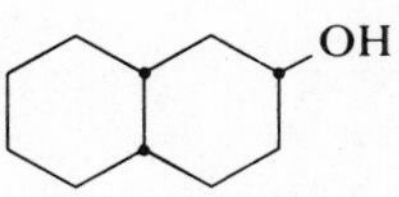

(d)

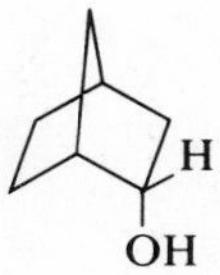

(e)

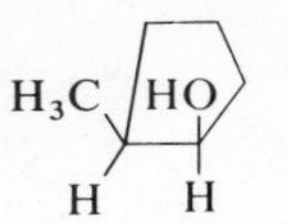

(f) 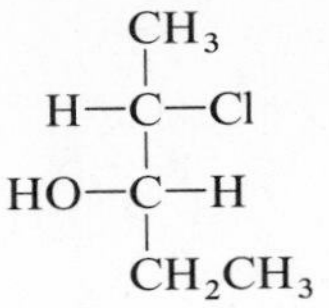
$$CH_3$$
$$H-C-Cl$$
$$HO-C-H$$
$$CH_2CH_3$$

6.   For each of the compounds shown, draw a comparable structure for the *enantiomer*.

(a) 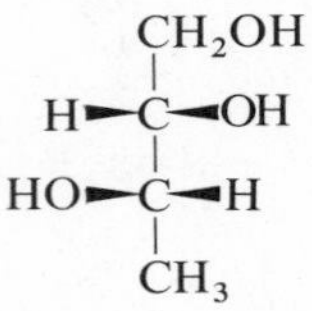
$$CH_2OH$$
$$H-C-OH$$
$$HO-C-H$$
$$CH_3$$

(b)

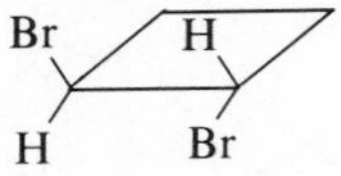

(c)

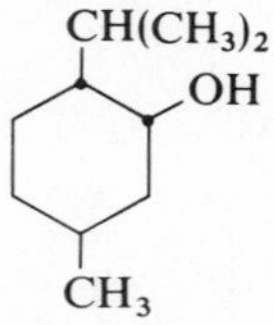

(d)

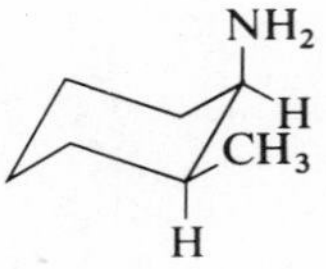

(e)

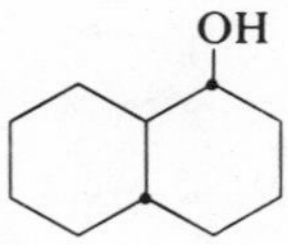

(f)

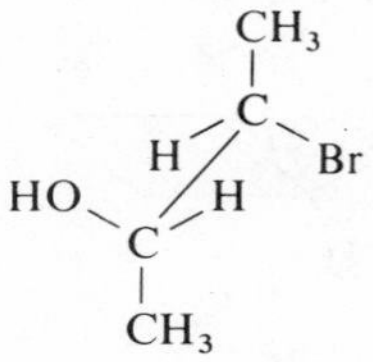

7.   For each of the following molecules, draw projection formulas for all of the stereoisomers, and indicate which are optically active and which are meso.

(a) $CH_3CHBrCHBrCH_3$

(b) $CH_3CHOHCHOHCHClCH_3$

(c)

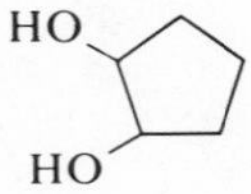

(d)

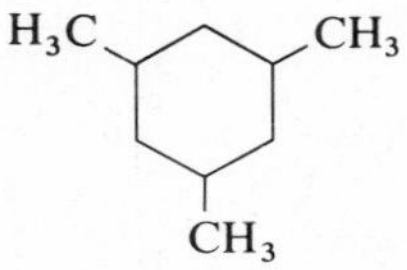

(e)

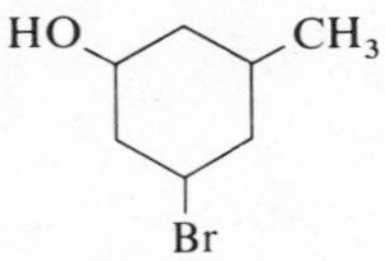

(f)

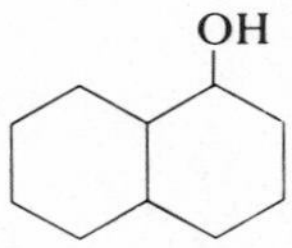

8.   Define and give two examples of each:
     (a) A pair of enantiotopic protons
     (b) A pair of diastereotopic protons

9.   How many magnetically different kinds of protons are there in each of the following compounds?

(a) 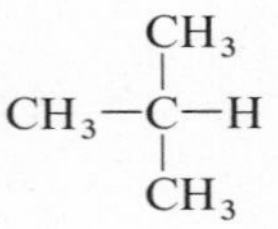
$$CH_3$$
$$CH_3-C-H$$
$$CH_3$$

(b)

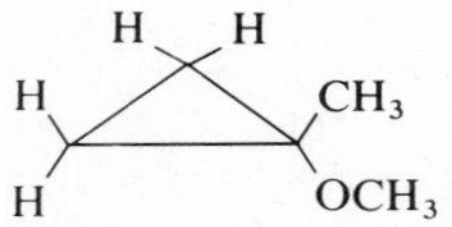

(c)

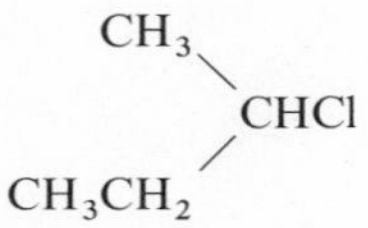

(d)

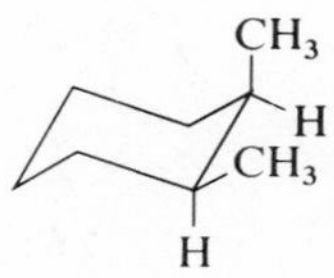

(e) $CH_3OCH_2CH_2CH_2OCH_3$

(f) Br   H
     H   Br

(g) H_2N H NH_2
          H

(h) Br
     H
     Br
     H

10. One diastereomer of 1,3-dichlorocyclopentane shows five types of magnetically different protons in the relative ratios 2:2:1:1:2. Write the structure.

11. Only one of the nine stereoisomers of 1,2,3,4,5,6-hexachlorocyclohexane shows a single proton resonance upon cooling to $-100°C$. Write the structure.

12. Describe step by step the laboratory operations you would carry out in order to resolve a synthetic sample of malic acid ($HOOCCH_2CHCOOH$) by chemical methods.
    |
    OH

13. A compound having the molecular formula C_4H_9NO gave the following nmr spectrum. What is the structure of the compound?

NMR spectrum of unknown, Problem 13.

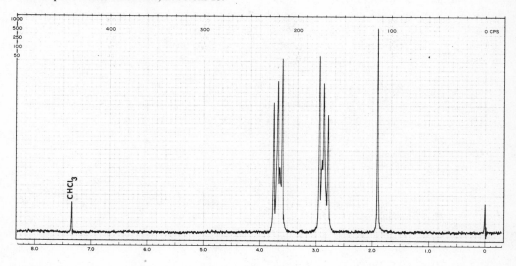

14. Rewrite each of the following Fischer projections in comparable form with the hydroxyl at the top. Are they the same, or are they enantiomers, or diastereomers?

CH_3 H
H—OH CH_3—OH
H—NH_2 CH_3—NH_2
CH_3 H

Optional Problems

Using Table 6.1 on page 112, show that the molecules below belong to the point groups indicated:

cis-1,2-Difluorocyclopropane	C_s
Methanol	C_s
Cyclopropane	D_{3h}
Methyl bromide	C_{3v}
1,4-Diequatorial dichlorocyclohexane	C_{2h}
gauche-vicinal-Dichloroethane	C_2

CHAPTER 7

ALKENES AND ALKYNES

7.1 Unsaturated Hydrocarbons

Alkenes and alkynes are families of acyclic (open-chain) hydrocarbons which contain less hydrogen per carbon atom than alkanes, and which can be converted to alkanes by the addition of hydrogen. *Alkenes*, often called *olefins*, have the formula C_nH_{2n}, and *alkynes* have the formula C_nH_{2n-2}. These and all other hydrocarbons which contain fewer than the maximum number of hydrogen atoms are called *unsaturated hydrocarbons*. Hydrocarbons such as the alkanes which contain the maximum number of hydrogen atoms are called *saturated hydrocarbons*. Acyclic saturated hydrocarbons have the formula C_nH_{2n+2} (Section 3.1). An alkene reacts with one molar equivalent of hydrogen to give an alkane; an alkyne requires two moles of hydrogen to give an alkane (Figure 7.1).

Figure 7.1
Reactions of unsaturated hydrocarbons with hydrogen to give alkanes.

$$C_nH_{2n} + H_2 \rightarrow C_nH_{2n+2}$$
Alkene   Alkane

Example

$$C_2H_4 + H_2 \xrightarrow{\text{catalyst}} C_2H_6$$
Ethylene   Ethane

$$C_nH_{2n-2} + 2H_2 \rightarrow C_nH_{2n+2}$$
Alkyne   Alkane

Example

$$C_2H_2 + 2H_2 \xrightarrow{\text{catalyst}} C_2H_6$$
Acetylene   Ethane

The physical properties of the alkenes and alkynes are much like those of the alkanes. Compounds containing fewer than about five carbon atoms are colorless gases, and those with about five or more carbon atoms are colorless liquids, except for very large or unusual ones, which may be solids. Unsaturated acyclic hydrocarbons generally have sharp, somewhat unpleasant odors. They and their reaction products are responsible for some of the air pollution caused by automobile exhaust gases.

7.2 The Carbon–Carbon Double Bond

The simplest alkene has the formula C_2H_4 and is named *ethylene*. In assigning a structure to ethylene on the basis of only elementary chemical facts, we would take into account the following: (1) It is a stable compound. (2) The normal rules of valency (four valences to carbon and one valence to hydrogen) must be met. (3) Ethylene reacts with hydrogen to give ethane, C_2H_6, whose structure we know. It would seem that ethylene must contain a carbon–carbon bond. By attaching two hydrogens to each carbon atom with covalent bonds, and by forming two covalent bonds between the two carbon atoms, we arrive at a satisfactory picture of ethylene. This structure satisfies the requirements that each carbon atom must have an octet of electrons in its valence shell and that each hydrogen atom must have two electrons in its valence shell.

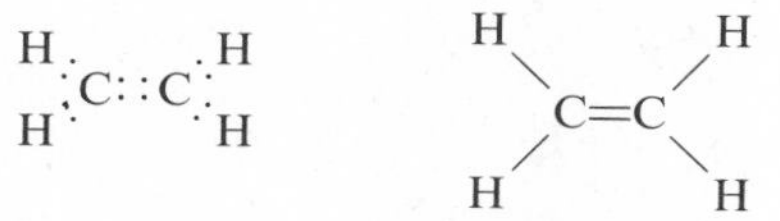

Ethylene

When two atoms form *two* covalent bonds with each other (i.e., share two pairs of electrons) the atoms are said to be joined by a *double bond*. Ethylene has a carbon–carbon double bond. It is this double bond which represents the characteristic feature of alkenes, C_nH_{2n}. Cycloalkanes have the same formula but contain only single bonds.

By the quantum mechanical approach we can derive a more detailed picture of the carbon–carbon double bond in ethylene and its homologs. We will find that the double bond is not composed of two equivalent covalent bonds.

A carbon atom in ethylene is bound to three other atoms, and the rules given in Section 4.2 tell us that the best hybridization of the four atomic orbitals is that which will provide the maximum overlap so that the resulting bonds will be as strong as possible. This may be done by mixing the $2s$ orbital with two of the $2p$ orbitals (say the $2p_x$ and $2p_y$ orbitals) to provide three sp^2 hybrid orbitals. These sp^2 hybrid orbitals are equivalent in energy and have the properties described in Table 4.1. They lie in the same plane (the x, y plane because we have chosen the $2p_x$ and $2p_y$ orbitals for mixing), and they are directed as far apart as possible—toward the corners of an equilateral triangle, providing angles of 120° between each pair (Figure 4.1, Table 4.1).

Each carbon atom forms two C—H bonds by overlap of a carbon sp^2 orbital with a hydrogen $1s$ orbital, and the two units are joined by a carbon sp^2–carbon sp^2 bond. A picture of the σ-bond framework of ethylene is given in Figure 7.2. All of the bonds are σ bonds (remember there are also five σ^* molecular orbitals which do not contain electrons). All of the C—C—H and H—C—H bond angles are 120°.

Figure 7.2
Predicted σ-bond framework of ethylene.

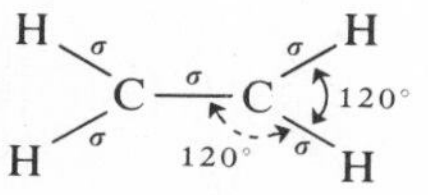

To complete the molecule, we recognize that each carbon atom has a $2p_z$ atomic orbital which has not yet been utilized for bonding and which contains one electron. One of these carbon $2p$ orbitals is shown separately in Figure 7.3a. It has two lobes, and signs are given to each lobe to represent the algebraic signs of the wave functions in the different regions.

THE SIGNIFICANCE OF THE SIGNS ASSOCIATED WITH ORBITALS. *Note that the* $(+)$ *and* $(-)$ *signs associated with the orbitals in Figures 7.3 and 7.4 do* not *represent charges. These indicate that the numerical values of* ψ_1 *and* ψ_2 *are either positive or negative as*

Figure 7.3
(a) Carbon $2p_z$ orbital showing signs and node. (b) Two $2p_z$ orbitals on the carbon atoms of ethylene.

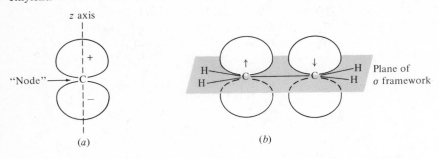

shown. These signs have no simple physical meaning. The value of ψ^2 at a point gives the electron density at that point. Note, however, that ψ^2 is always positive; whether ψ is positive or negative makes no difference. The sign of ψ becomes important, however, when we add it to another ψ to form a bond or molecular orbital.

The wave function for this $2p$ orbital has the value zero at the carbon atom. This is called a *node*. The nodes are points that mark a change in sign of the wave function (actually when we speak of atomic orbitals we are dealing with three-dimensional wave functions, and the nodes occur as nodal surfaces). In order for the two $2p_z$ orbitals to overlap effectively, they must be oriented parallel to one another and perpendicular to the σ-bond framework (Figure 7.3b). This requires that the entire σ framework be coplanar and that all six atomic nuclei lie in the same plane. The two parallel $2p_z$ orbitals are close enough to overlap in a side-by-side fashion, and we can combine them in two ways as shown schematically in Figure 7.4. When lobes of the same sign overlap (Figure 7.4, top) a bond is formed. If the signs do not match (or in other words if we subtract the ψ's instead of adding them) an antibonding orbital is generated (Figure 7.4 bottom).

Figure 7.4
Ethylene carbon–carbon double bond. Overlap of p orbitals gives a π bond. The other combination of p orbitals leads to a π^* orbital.

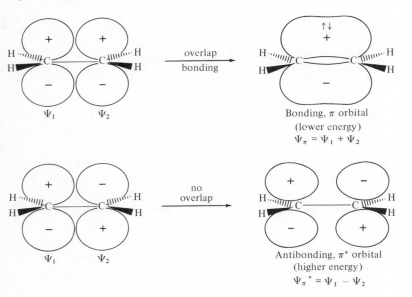

Since only two p electrons are available, both may be placed in the bonding orbital (ψ_π). This bond, formed by parallel (or sideways) overlap of p orbitals, has symmetry properties different from a σ bond; it is called a π *bond*. It consists of two lobes with opposite signs (just like the original p atomic orbitals), and there is a node along the axis of the carbon–carbon σ bond. The overlap of p orbitals in this manner (p–p π bonding) is less efficient than the end-on overlap by which σ bonds are formed; therefore, a π bond is weaker than a σ bond. *It is the parallel overlap of p orbitals which forces the atoms in ethylene to lie in a single plane, resulting in a flat molecule.*

The carbon–carbon double bond is composed of a strong σ bond (about 100 kcal/mole bond energy) and a weaker π bond (about 45 kcal/mole).

The bond energy of the double bond in ethylene is known by experiment to be 145 kcal/mole. The σ and π components are estimated to have the stated values from theoretical calculations. The σ component of the double bond is stronger than the single C—C bond of an alkane because of differences in hybridization and bond length.

The total bond strength of a carbon–carbon double bond is therefore about 145 kcal/mole, stronger than a carbon–carbon single bond (about 83 kcal/mole). Because of the stronger double bond, the carbon–carbon bond length in ethylene is shorter than that in ethane, for at least two different reasons: First, the σ bond in ethylene is formed from the overlap of two carbon sp^2 hybrid orbitals, whereas in ethane the σ bond arises from overlap of the sp^3 orbitals. This leads to a reduction in the bond length from 1.53 to 1.49 Å (Table 4.1). Second, and more important, the overlap of the p orbitals which make up the π bond increases if the atoms come closer together.

The molecule of ethylene derived from the above reasoning should have three σ planes (the major plane of symmetry being the one that contains the six atoms, the other two planes are mutually perpendicular and also perpendicular to the major plane), and three C_2 axes (each of the planes would contain a C_2 axis). [The symmetry class would be D_{2h}.]

All of these deductions for the geometry of ethylene derived from molecular orbital theory have been verified by electron diffraction and spectroscopic measurements. The molecule is planar; the C—C—H bond angles are 121° and the H—C—H bond angles are 118° (all very close to 120°); the C—C bond length is 1.34 (in ethane the C—C bond length is 1.54 Å); and the C—H bond length is 1.09 Å (the C—H bond length in ethane is 1.10 Å).

7.3   Propylene

The next homolog in the alkene family after ethylene is *propylene* (propene), C_3H_6. The properties of propylene are very similar to those of ethylene, and propylene obviously contains a double bond. Straightforward considerations provide us with the following structure:

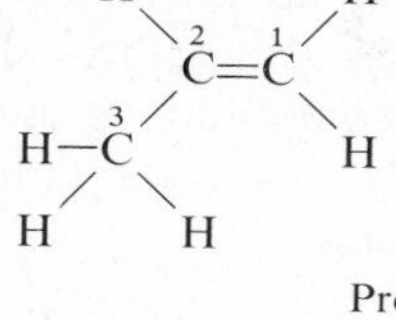

Propylene

What can we say about the C-2—C-3 bond of propylene? Because it results from overlap of the C-2 sp^2 hybrid orbital and the C-3 sp^3 hybrid orbital, it should be shorter than the carbon–carbon bond of ethane (sp^3–sp^3, 1.54 Å), and longer than the carbon–carbon bond of ethylene (sp^2–sp^2, 1.34 Å), The value predicted from Table 4.1 is 0.763 Å + 0.743 Å = 1.506 Å. (The experimental value is 1.501 ± 0.004 Å.)

7.4   The Butenes. Cis–Trans Isomerism

The formula C_4H_8 describes the *butenes*, the next homologs in the series. Several isomeric structures are possible. We can have the carbon atoms in a straight-chain or in a branched-chain arrangement. In the straight-chain array, the double bond could be located between the first and second carbon atoms in the chain, or between the second and the third carbons. Only one branched-chain butene isomer is possible. Our predictions to this point suggest that there would be three isomeric butenes; but experimentally, *four* C_4H_8 alkenes have been characterized. Where does the fourth come from? Let us first examine the structures of the three isomers that we are sure of:

$$CH_3CH_2CH=CH_2 \qquad CH_3CH=CHCH_3 \qquad \begin{matrix} CH_3 \\ \diagdown \\ \diagup \quad C=CH_2 \\ CH_3 \end{matrix}$$

1-Butene   2-Butene   Isobutylene
                                        (2-Methylpropene)

From our detailed description of ethylene and the carbon–carbon double bond, we know that the carbon atoms involved in double-bond formation and *all* the atoms attached to these doubly bonded carbon atoms must lie in the same plane. This is a consequence of the necessity of parallel overlap of p orbitals to form a π bond. With the double bond located as it is in 2-butene, we find that there are actually two possible arrangements for the atoms about the double bond. In one, the two methyl groups are on the same side of the double bond; in the other, the two methyl groups are on opposite sides. These are unique structures, and the two compounds have different physical properties. The first is called *cis*-2-butene, the second *trans*-2-butene.

$$\begin{matrix} H & & H \\ \diagdown & & \diagup \\ & C=C & \\ \diagup & & \diagdown \\ CH_3 & & CH_3 \end{matrix}$$

cis-2-Butene

$$\begin{matrix} CH_3 & & H \\ \diagdown & & \diagup \\ & C=C & \\ \diagup & & \diagdown \\ H & & CH_3 \end{matrix}$$

trans-2-Butene

The two 2-butenes are stereoisomers; in more specific terms, they are diastereomers, because they are non-mirror-image stereoisomers (Section 6.3). Just as with diastereomers of cyclic compounds (Section 6.4), diastereomers resulting from different arrangements of atoms about a double bond (the double bond may be thought of as a hypothetical two-membered ring) are often called *geometrical isomers*. The diastereomer having the methyl groups on the same side of the double bond is called the cis isomer; that with methyl groups on opposite sides of the double bond is the trans isomer.

cis-2-Butene and *trans*-2-butene are not optically active. In the absence of other dissymmetric groupings, every alkene will have at least one plane of symmetry (the plane of the atoms attached to the double bond), and no molecule containing a plane of symmetry can be optically active.

It was mentioned above that *cis*-2-butene and *trans*-2-butene are distinct, isolable compounds. The only way that they could be interconverted would be to rotate about the carbon–carbon double bond. Such rotation requires that the π bond be broken, because when the rotation is half complete, the *p* orbitals forming the original π bond are seen to have their axes in perpendicular planes, rather than in the same plane (Figure 7.5.). When at right angles, the *p* orbitals do not overlap, and are said to be *orthogonal* to one another. It would require about 45 kcal/mole of energy to break this π bond. We

Figure 7.5
Rotation about a double bond. Overlap of *p*-orbitals impossible; π bond is broken.

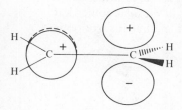

may state, therefore, that there is *restricted rotation about a double bond*; and that geometrical isomers of alkenes are configurationally quite stable. This may be contrasted to *conformational isomerism* (Sections 3.3, 3.4) which occurs because of relatively non-hindered rotation about single bonds.

7.5   The NMR Spectra of Alkenes

The nmr chemical shifts of protons attached to doubly bonded carbon atoms occur at much lower field than those of protons attached to sp^3-hybridized carbons, indicating that the protons experience less magnetic shielding. Typically, such vinyl protons resonate at approximately δ 4.8–6.2. Since the resonance of these protons is shifted about 3–4 δ units higher than that of the protons of simple alkanes or cycloalkanes, qualitative analysis for the presence of vinyl protons is easily accomplished by nmr.

The CH_2=CH– *group is called the vinyl group. Any protons attached to the carbon of a carbon–carbon double bond may be called* vinyl protons.

Why do vinyl protons show resonance at such low field? The sp^2 carbon is more electronegative than the sp^3 carbon (Section 7.9), but the difference in electronegativity is not sufficient to account for the large difference in chemical shift. Most of the down-field shifts results from the fact that the π electrons are rather loosely held, and the applied magnetic field causes them to circulate as shown in Figure 7.6. These circulating π

Figure 7.6
The effect of the circulating π electrons on the chemical shift of vinyl protons.

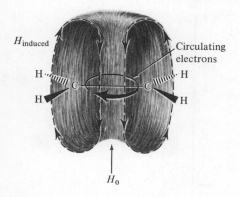

electrons induce a field which *opposes* the applied field at the center of the molecule, but *augments* the applied field along the outer edges of the molecular plane where the protons are located. The magnitude of the applied field required to flip the protons is therefore reduced, and resonance occurs at lower field than it would in the absence of these π electrons.

The four vinyl protons of ethylene are magnetically equivalent, and the compound shows a single nmr line at δ 5.64.

Propylene has three vinyl protons (shown as H_a, H_b, and H_c) and three methyl protons. The methyl protons are magnetically equivalent. Because it is attached to sp^2-hybridized carbon, the methyl group will absorb in the nmr at δ 1.6, at somewhat lower field than if it were part of an alkane carbon skeleton. The methyl absorption is split into a doublet by the vicinal vinyl hydrogen H_c

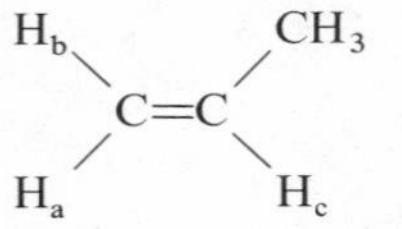

The three vinyl hydrogens H_a, H_b, and H_c are magnetically nonequivalent (H_a and H_b are diastereotopic vinyl protons). Since they have very similar chemical shifts, and since they are mutually spin-coupled as well as spin-coupled to the methyl protons, the vinyl protons of propylene appear as a complex multiplet at δ 4.9–5.3.

This complex pattern for the vinyl protons occurs with all monosubstituted ethylenes ($CH_2{=}CHX$). The chemical shifts of the vinyl protons are dependent on the nature of the substituent X, and thus the vinyl resonances are more spread out and more amenable to analysis when X is an electronegative atom or group.

Next we examine the coupling constants of larger alkenes. For two vinyl protons H_a and H_b (which must be nonequivalent, or else they will show one single unsplit peak in the nmr and then coupling will not be observable), the usual range of coupling constants is as shown:

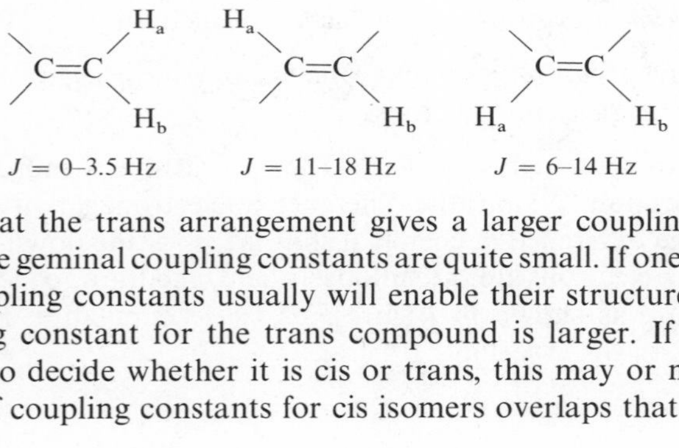

$J = 0$–3.5 Hz $J = 11$–18 Hz $J = 6$–14 Hz

Note that the trans arrangement gives a larger coupling constant than does the cis, while the geminal coupling constants are quite small. If one has a cis–trans pair of isomers, the coupling constants usually will enable their structures to be assigned, because the coupling constant for the trans compound is larger. If one has a single isomer and wishes to decide whether it is cis or trans, this may or may not be possible, since the range of coupling constants for cis isomers overlaps that for trans isomers.

EXERCISE 7.1

Estimate the expected splitting (Hz) for the lettered protons (a, b, . . . , etc.) in the following structures:

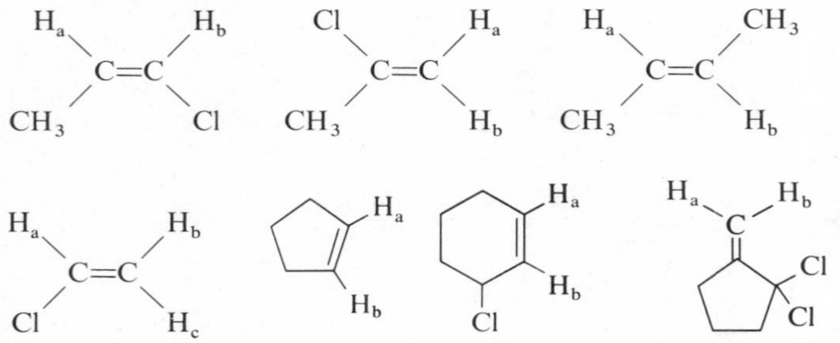

MAGNITUDES OF COUPLING CONSTANTS. *Vicinal protons in saturated systems which are anti to one another also have larger coupling constants than protons which are gauche (about 5–12 Hz for anti and 1–4 Hz for gauche), while geminal coupling constants are quite large (12–15 Hz). However, the easy interconversion of conformers usually makes many of the protons equivalent in simple molecules, and so their apparent coupling constants become zero, as discussed in Chapter 5.*

7.6   Structural Requirements for Cis–Trans Isomerism in Alkenes

The substitution pattern at the double bond determines whether or not cis and trans diastereomeric forms can exist. Geometric isomerism will not be possible if one of the two carbon atoms forming the double bond carries two identical groups. Some specific examples of alkenes in this category are illustrated.

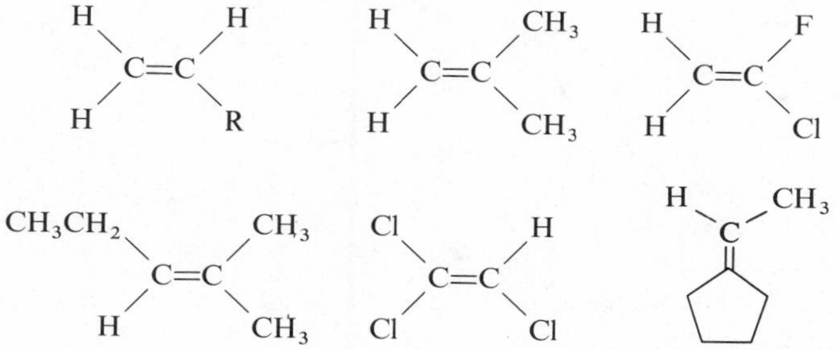

Combinations of substituents which will lead to stereoisomerism, and a few specific examples are shown in Figure 7.7.

Figure 7.7

Geometrical isomers of alkenes.

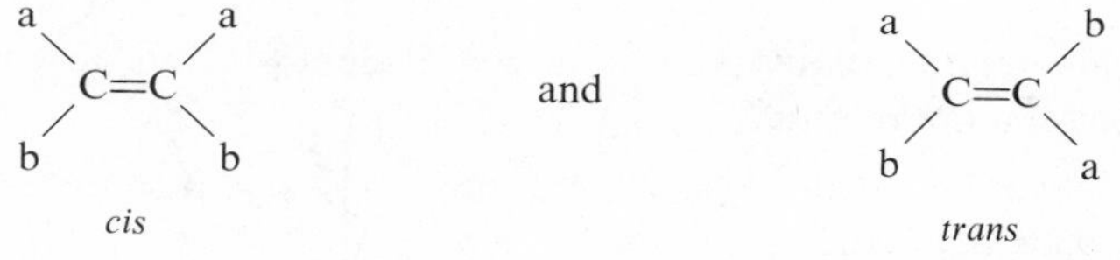

Examples:

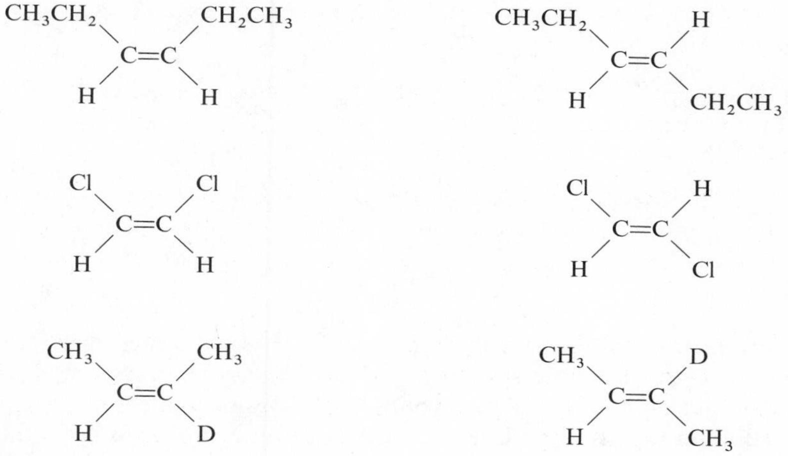

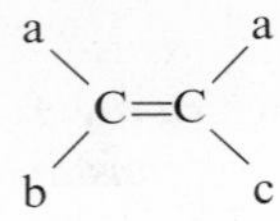

cis 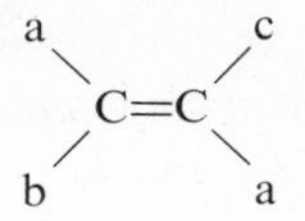   trans

Examples :

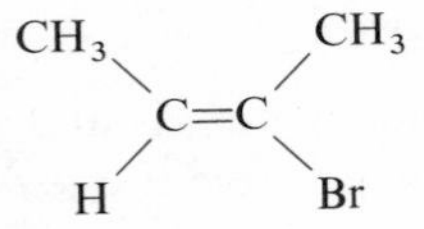

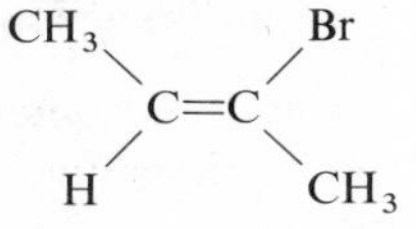

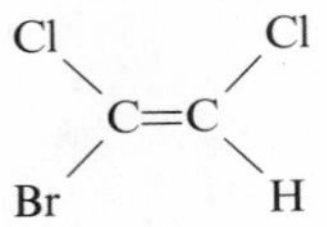

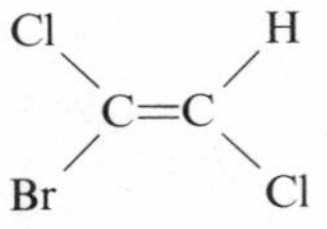

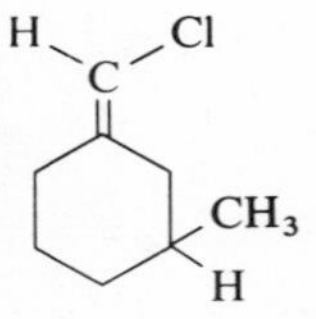

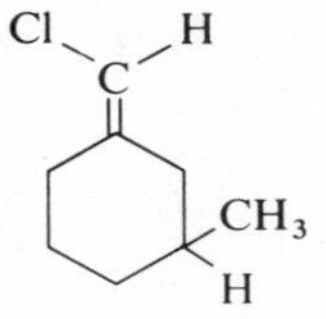

This is a case where we have geometrical isomerism and also an asymmetric carbon atom. Each structure has a nonsuperimposable mirror image.

EXERCISE 7.2

How many stereoisomers are there for each of the following?

(a) 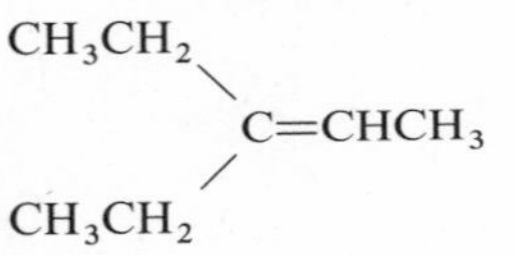   (b) 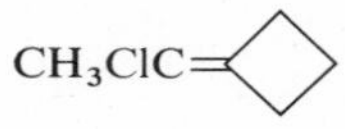 $CH_3ClC=$ ⬦   (c) $CH_3HC=C$

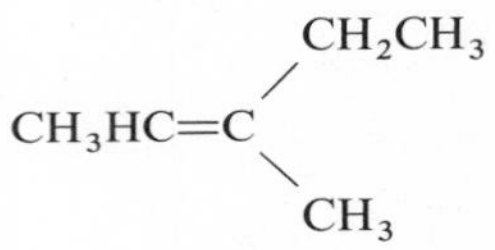

For each of the above, how many types of nonequivalent protons do you anticipate will be seen in the nmr?

7.7   Higher Alkenes and Cycloalkenes

The structures of the six isomeric alkenes of formula C_5H_{10} are shown:

Straight chain $CH_3CH_2CH_2CH=CH_2$

1-Pentene   trans-2-Pentene 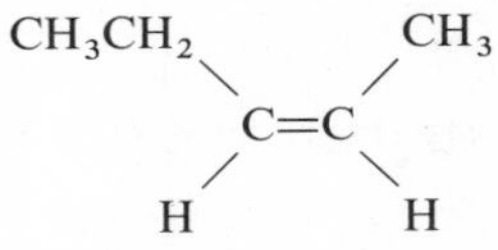   cis-2-Pentene

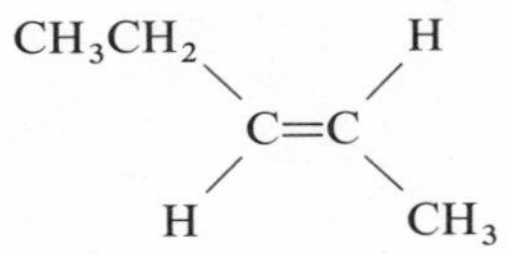

Branched chain

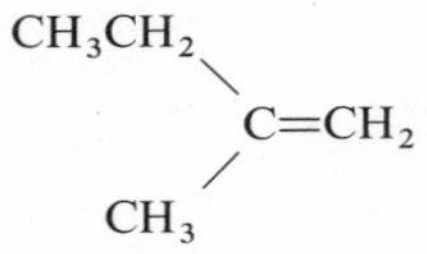

2-Methyl-1-butene 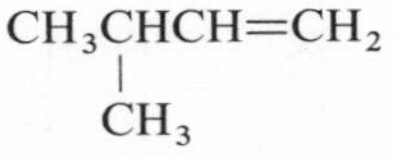   3-Methyl-1-butene 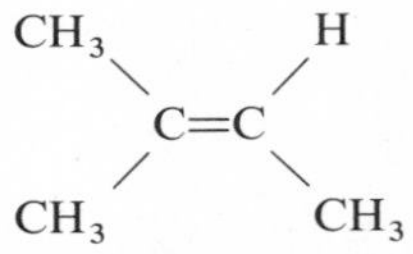   2-Methyl-2-butene

For each successive member of the homologous series (C_nH_{2n}) of alkenes, there is a big increase in the number of isomeric structures possible. There is always a greater number of isomers for alkenes than for alkanes containing the same number of carbon atoms because, in addition to variations in the carbon skeleton common to both, the alkenes have several possibilities for the position of the double bond, and in addition, geometrical isomerism can occur.

A double bond can also be contained in a ring structure, and there is a homologous series of *cycloalkenes* with the formula C_nH_{2n-2}. The first five members of this family are *cyclopropene, cyclobutene, cyclopentene, cyclohexene,* and *cycloheptene.*

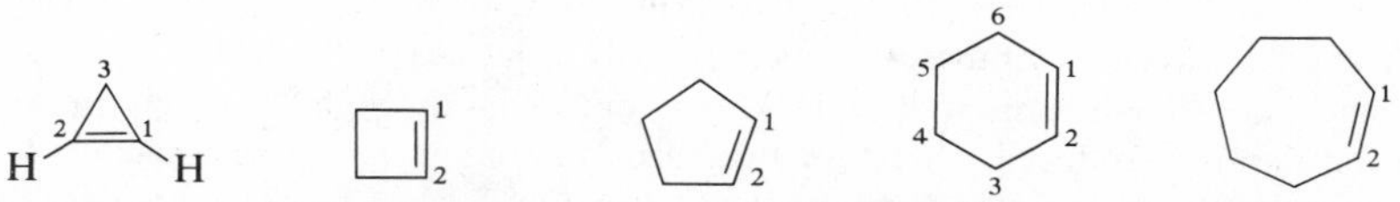

| Cyclopropene | Cyclobutene | Cyclopentene | Cyclohexene | Cycloheptene |

For the first two, all of the ring carbon atoms lie in one plane. Cyclopentene is thought to be approximately planar. In contrast with these smaller molecules, cyclohexene is clearly nonplanar. Cycloheptene and the larger cycloalkenes are also nonplanar.

Geometry of Cyclohexene. Carbon atoms 1, 2, 3, and 6 in cyclohexene must lie in a plane because of the sp^2 hybridization of carbons 1 and 2; but, in order to maintain proper bond angles, carbons 4 and 5 must be above or below this plane. The chair conformation of cyclohexene (a rapid equilibrium between two chair forms occurs just as with cyclohexane) is shown in Figure 7.8.

Figure 7.8

Chair conformation of cyclohexene. Positions for attachment of substituents are labeled a, axial; e, equatorial; a′, pseudo-axial; e′, pseudo-equatorial.

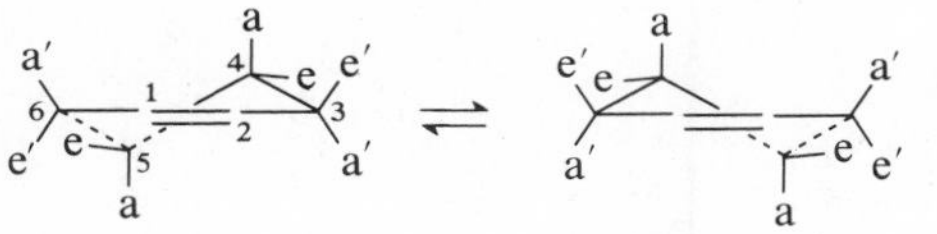

Cyclopropene is one of the most highly strained alkenes that has been isolated. Our discussion in Section 3.5 pointed out why cyclopropane has so much strain energy, and it should be reviewed. The strain is even greater in cyclopropene because the two un-saturated carbon atoms would normally prefer 120° bond angles (sp^2 hybridization). However, the ring size forces these angles to have values of near 60°. The difference (60°) is even greater than the difference of 49.5° (109.5° − 60°) predicted for cyclopropane. Thus cyclopropene is even more strained than is cyclopropane. "Bent" bonds, utilizing orbitals having a large amount of p character, comprise the ring bonds of cyclopropene, and the C—H bonds attached to the olefinic carbons are formed from carbon hybrid orbitals with nearly 40% s character. Cyclobutene is also quite strained.

The cyclic alkenes having three-membered through seven-membered rings do not exist in stereoisomeric forms. Only the cis isomers have been isolated. This is obviously because there is no reasonable way in which the ring carbons can be attached trans at the double bond and still be connected to form a ring without introducing prohibitive strain in the molecules (Figure 7.9). The lowest member of the series for which both cis and trans isomers have been isolated and characterized is the eight-membered ring

Figure 7.9

cis- and *trans-*Cycloalkenes.

cis-Cycloalkene	*trans*-Cycloalkene
Isolable for all values of n	Unstable for $n < 6$
	Isolable for $n \geqslant 6$

(Figure 7.9, $n = 6$). Naturally, we would expect *trans*-cyclooctene to be somewhat less stable than *cis*-cyclooctene, because some strain is introduced in the former by bridging the trans positions of the double bond with a chain of only six carbon atoms. This has been experimentally verified and will be discussed in Section 7.10.

> *Interconversion of Enantiomers and Diastereomers. trans*-Cyclooctene shows the interesting feature of being capable of existing in optically active forms. The two enantiomers are shown in Figure 7.10. The interconversion of these enantiomers only requires rotation about carbon–carbon single bonds. However, to do this the ring must pass through a geometry in which much more strain is introduced. Therefore, racemization does not occur very fast at room temperature or below, though it is quite rapid at about 120°C. Here we encounter our first example of optical activity (the existence of enantiomers) due to *restricted rotation about*

Figure 7.10
Enantiomers of *trans*-cyclooctene.

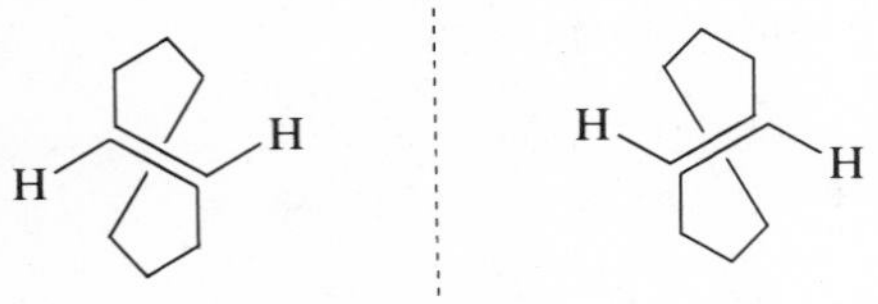

single bonds. A summary of the processes required for the interconversion of enantiomers or diastereomers is given in Table 7.1 in order of *decreasing energy* requirement.

Table 7.1   Interconversions of Enantiomers or Diastereomers

Process required to interconvert enantiomers or diastereomers	Energy barrier, kcal/mole	Rate of interconversion at 25°C
Breaking σ bonds	50–100	None
Breaking π bonds (Restricted rotation about double bonds)	30–50	None–very slow
Restricted rotation about single bonds (Steric hindrance)	15–30	Very slow–slow
Conformational isomerism (Unhindered rotation about single bonds)	0–12	Fast–extremely fast

To summarize: If the barrier is less than about 10 kcal/mole, it can be detected only by rather sophisticated studies. A barrier of about 10–30 kcal/mole can be detected by nmr measurements, but the molecule will surmount the barrier too quickly to permit us to physically isolate the separate compounds. A barrier of about 20–30 kcal/mole means that the compounds are isolable if the proper technique can be found, but they will interconvert upon heating. If the barrier is greater than about 30 kcal/mole, the compounds are stable in the ordinary sense.

Bridged bicyclic alkenes are exceedingly important from both a theoretical and a practical standpoint. The structures of several are shown here.

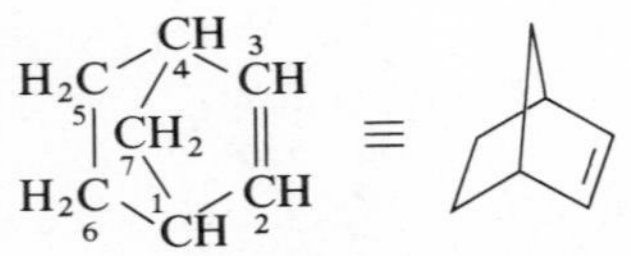

Bicyclo[2.2.1]hept-2-ene
(Norbornene)

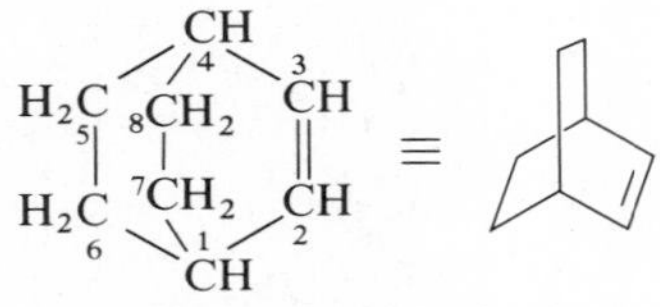

Bicyclo[2.2.2]oct-2-ene

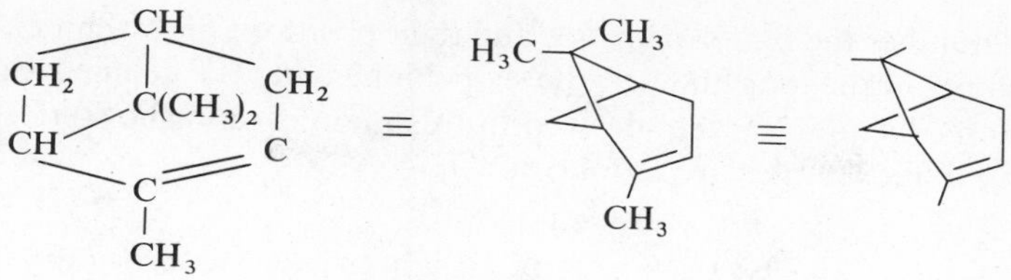

α-Pinene
(Oil of turpentine)

Note that in complex structures, methyl groups are often represented by simple lines.

7.8 Nomenclature of Alkenes

For the simplest alkenes the common names *ethylene*, *propylene*, and *isobutylene* are almost always used. Monofunctionally substituted ethylenes are named as *vinyl compounds* (the correct, but rarely used IUPAC name is shown in parentheses):

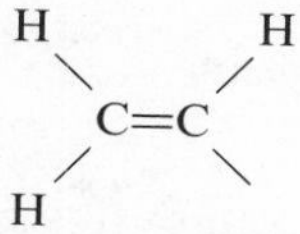

The vinyl group

Examples

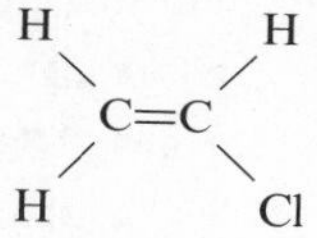

Vinyl chloride
(Chloroethene)

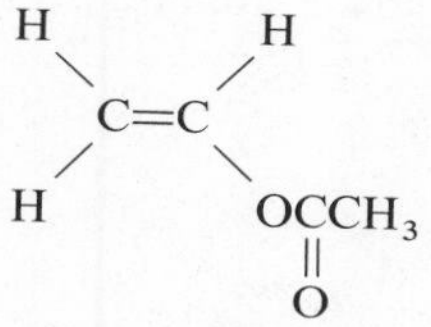

Vinyl acetate
(Ethenyl acetate)

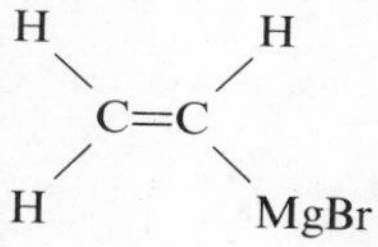

Vinylmagnesium
bromide

Functional derivatives at the saturated carbon atom of propylene are called *allyl compounds*.

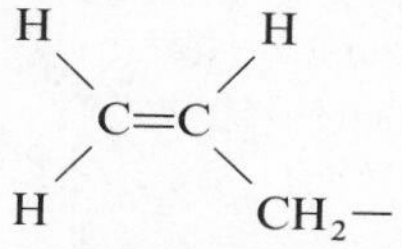

The allyl group

Examples

$CH_2{=}CHCH_2Br$
Allyl bromide
(3-Bromopropene)

$CH_2 {=} CHCH_2OH$
Allyl alcohol
(2-Propen-1-ol)

$(CH_2{=}CHCH_2)_2NH$
Diallylamine

The IUPAC system is the best way to name most higher alkenes. A stepwise approach allows us to build up the name of the compound from the functional end to the front:

1. Select the longest carbon chain *containing the double bond* and assign this a parent name derived by changing the ending -*ane* of the alkane having the same number of carbons to -*ene* (prop*ene*, but*ene*, oct*ene*, cyclohex*ene*, etc.)

2. Number the carbon chain starting from the end nearest the double bond, and indicate the position of the double bond by the number of the first doubly bonded carbon encountered (1-pentene, 2-pentene, etc.).

3. Indicate by name and number the kinds of groups and their positions of attachment to the parent chain. The names of the four butenes, the six pentenes, and the geometrical isomers discussed in Sections 7.4 and 7.7 were derived in this manner, and the student should review these. Additional examples are as follows:

$$CH_3CCH=CH_2$$

3,3-Dimethyl-1-butene

cis-2,2,5-Trimethyl-3-hexene

1-Methylcyclopentene

3-Ethylcyclopentene

trans-2-Bromo-2-butene

The nomenclature for unsymmetrical tri- and tetrasubstituted alkenes requires special comment. The word cis is used to indicate that the "most similar" groups are on the same side of the double bond. Thus the 3-methyl-2-pentene shown is trans, not cis, because the methyl group is the *small* group on the right end, and the large group on the left end. The methyl on the right is therefore "most similar" to the hydrogen (not the methyl) on the left.

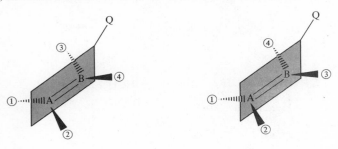

no⟶ trans-3-Methyl-2-pentene
cis

The E–Z Nomenclature. Recently, a new pair of descriptors has been proposed to replace the common terms cis, and trans for describing double-bond stereoisomerism. With these descriptors go a set of rules based on the priority rules of Cahn, Ingold, and Prelog (Section 3.6), which allow unambiguous designation of the configuration about all double bonds. In the general case, we consider a pair of doubly bonded atoms A and B to which substituents 1, 2, 3, and 4 are attached. If $1 \neq 2$ and $3 \neq 4$, two isomers are possible, shown as

All atoms lie in a single plane, and we now consider a reference plane (Q), perpendicular to the plane of the double bond and bisecting the angles 1—A—2 and 3—B—4. The isomer on the left has atoms 1 and 3 on the same side of Q, whereas in the stereoisomer on the right, 1 and 3 are on opposite sides of Q. The rules go as follows: (1) For each double bond to be described configurationally, determine which of the two groups attached to each doubly bonded atom has the higher priority according to the Cahn, Ingold, Prelog convention. (2) That configuration in which the two groups of higher priority are on the *same side* of the

reference plane is assigned the stereochemical descriptor *Z* (from the German *zusammen*).
(3) That configuration in which these groups are on *opposite* sides is assigned the descriptor *E*
(from the German *entgegen*).

Some examples are as follows:

Cl   I
   C=C
H   Br
(Z)-1-Bromo-2-
chloro-1-iodoethylene

CH_3 CH_3
   C=C
H   Br
(E)-2-Bromo-2-butene

CH_3CH_2 CH_3
   C=C
CH_3 H
(Z)-3-Methyl-2-pentene

(E)-3,3-Dimethylethyl-
idenecyclohexane

CH_3 H
   C=C CH_2CH_3
H   C=C
H   H
(E, Z)-2,4-Heptadiene

Sometimes alkenes are named as derivatives of ethylene by naming the groups or
atoms (other than hydrogen) that are attached to the carbon–carbon double bond.

CH_3 H
   C=C
CH_3 CH_3
Trimethylethylene
(2-Methyl-2-butene)

$(CH_3)_3C$ H
   C=C
H $C(CH_3)_3$
trans-1,2-Di-*t*-butylethylene
(*trans*-2,2,5,5-Tetramethyl-3-hexene)

F   F
   C=C
F   F
Tetrafluoroethylene

No matter which system of nomenclature is used, cis and trans always designate the
stereoisomers.

If a *methylene group* (=CH_2) is attached to a ring carbon, the compound is named as a
methylene derivative of the cycloalkane:

=CH_2
The methylene group

Examples

Methylenecyclobutane

4,4-Dimethylmethylenecyclohexane

EXERCISE 7.3

Name the following compounds by the IUPAC system:

(a) $CH_3CH=CHCH_2CHCH_3$
                 |
                 CH_3

(b)

(c)

(d)

7.9   Properties of Alkenes

A survey of the physical properties of some representative alkenes and substituted alkenes is given in Table 7.2. The properties and solubility characteristics of these

Table 7.2   Alkenes

Name	Formula	Bp, °C	Sp. Gr.
Ethylene (ethene)	$CH_2{=}CH_2$	-102	
Propylene (propene)	$CH_3CH{=}CH_2$	-48	
1-Butene	$CH_3CH_2CH{=}CH_2$	-6.5	
1-Pentene	$CH_3(CH_2)_2CH{=}CH_2$	30	0.643
1-Decene	$CH_3(CH_2)_7CH{=}CH_2$	171	0.743
cis-2-Butene	cis-$CH_3CH{=}CHCH_3$	4	
trans-2-Butene	trans-$CH_3CH{=}CHCH_3$	1	
Isobutylene	$(CH_3)_2C{=}CH_2$	-7	
cis-2-Pentene	cis-$CH_3CH_2CH{=}CHCH_3$	37	0.655
trans-2-Pentene	trans-$CH_3CH_2CH{=}CHCH_3$	36	0.647
3-Methyl-1-butene	$(CH_3)_2CHCH{=}CH_2$	25	0.648
2-Methyl-2-butene	$(CH_3)_2C{=}CHCH_3$	39	0.660
2,3-Dimethyl-2-butene	$(CH_3)_2C{=}C(CH_3)_2$	73	0.705
Cyclopentene	$\overline{}CH{=}CH(CH_2)_3\overline{}$	44	0.772
Cyclohexene	$\overline{}CH{=}CH(CH_2)_4\overline{}$	83	0.810
Bicyclo[2.2.1]hept-2-ene	$\overline{}(CH_2)_2CHCH{=}CHCH(CH_2)_2\overline{}$	96	
Vinyl chloride	$CH_2{=}CHCl$	-14	
Allyl chloride	$CH_2{=}CHCH_2Cl$	45	0.938
2-Chloropropene	$CH_2{=}C(Cl)CH_3$	23	0.918
Tetrafluoroethylene	$F_2C{=}CF_2$	-78	
Tetrachloroethylene	$Cl_2C{=}CCl_2$	121	1.623
Trichloroethylene	$Cl_2C{=}CHCl$	87	1.464
Allyl alcohol	$CH_2{=}CHCH_2OH$	97	0.855

compounds are very similar to those of the analogous (same carbon skeleton) alkanes (Chapter 3), and haloalkanes (Chapter 4). The nmr spectra of alkenes were discussed in Section 7.5.

Unlike alkanes, which are nonpolar, certain alkenes show weakly polar properties. These alkenes are, however, much less polar than compounds such as alkyl halides and alcohols. The polar properties of alkenes result because an sp^2-hybridized carbon atom is somewhat more electronegative than an sp^3 carbon atom. In general, an orbital which is hybridized sp^n has more s character the smaller the value of n. Since s electrons are closer to the nucleus and more tightly held than p electrons, the smaller the value of n, the more electronegative the orbital. Thus electronegativity increases: $p < sp^3 < sp^2 < sp < s$.

In a compound such as propene, the bond joining the methyl group to the double bond is slightly polar, and the electrons of that bond are held closer to the doubly bonded carbon atom. This influence creates a small dipole which has the negative end toward the double bond and the positive end toward the alkyl group. Alkyl groups thus show an electron-donating *inductive effect* when attached to an unsaturated carbon. If the bond polarity is not offset by polarity in the opposite direction, the molecule will have a net dipole moment. The dipole moment of propylene is 0.35 D; this value appears to be common to all 1-alkenes, $RCH{=}CH_2$, in which R is an unstrained alkyl group.

CH₃ structures with dipole moments:

$$\mu = 0.35 \text{ D} \qquad \mu = 0.35\text{--}0.40 \text{ D}$$

When two alkyl groups are attached to the same side of a double bond as in *cis*-2-butene, the combined inductive effects are additive (in a vector sense), and the molecule will have a net dipole moment. With *trans*-2-butene, where one methyl group and one hydrogen are on each side of the double bond, the bond moments cancel and no dipole moment is expected or observed. As a consequence of the higher polarity of the cis isomer, it has a higher boiling point than its trans counterpart, because intermolecular

$$\mu = 0.4 \text{ D} \rightarrow \qquad \mu = 0 \text{ (no dipole moment expected)}$$
$$(\text{bp} + 4°\text{C}) \qquad\qquad (\text{bp} + 1°\text{C})$$
cis   *trans*

(dipole–dipole) interactions are greater. In fact, for any alkene of the type abC=Cba, where a and b can be almost any substituents, the cis isomer will have the greater dipole moment and the higher boiling point. These differences in dipole moments and boiling points between cis and trans isomers are larger for alkenes that have strongly electro-negative atoms attached directly to the double bond.

cis   *trans*
$$\mu = 1.85 \text{ D} \qquad \mu = 0$$
$$(\text{bp } 60°\text{C}) \qquad (\text{bp } 48°\text{C})$$

EXERCISE 7.4

There are two isomers of 1-chloropropene:

and

The dipole moments of the two isomers have been found experimentally to have the values 1.97 and 1.71 D. Which isomer has the larger moment, the cis or the trans? Why?

INDUSTRIAL SOURCES AND USES OF ALKENES. *Alkenes are obtained in industrial quantities chiefly by the* cracking (*high-temperature degradation*) *of petroleum* (*Section 3.2*). *The lower molecular weight alkenes* (*ethylene, propylene*) *can be obtained in pure form by fractional distillation. The higher alkenes generated by cracking cannot be separated economically, and the mixture is utilized as an important component of gasoline. A major source for 1-alkenes containing an even number of carbon atoms* (C_8–C_{18}) *is their preparation from ethylene.*

The most important uses for alkenes are as chemical intermediates: ethylene for ethyl alcohol, ethylene oxide, higher 1-alkenes; propylene for propylene oxide, 1,2-dichloropropane; the C_8–C_{12} 1-alkenes for detergents. Trichloroethylene (Triclene) and tetrachloroethylene (Perclene) are used in large quantities as cleaning solvents. A number of olefins and olefinic derivatives are converted to useful plastics (polyethylene, Teflon, polystyrene, etc.) and to fibers for synthetic fabrics (Acrilan, Orlon, etc.), as will be discussed in Chapter 25.

7.10   Relative Stabilities of Alkenes

We learned earlier (Section 3.5) that strain in a molecule can be estimated from heat of combustion data. There is an even more accurate physical method that can be employed to correlate the relative strain energies of alkenes. The quantity of heat evolved when one mole of an unsaturated compound is hydrogenated is called the *heat of hydrogenation* (ΔH_H), as defined by the equation:

$$\ce{>C=C<} + H_2 \rightarrow \ce{-\underset{H}{\overset{|}{C}}-\underset{H}{\overset{|}{C}}-} + \text{Heat}$$

The heat of hydrogenation is always a negative number (the reaction is exothermic) because the difference in strength of a C=C bond (145 kcal/mole) and a C—C bond (83 kcal/mole) is 62 kcal/mole, and the H—H bond energy is 104 kcal/mole. The strengths of the bonds that are broken are therefore less than the sum of the bond energies of the newly formed C—H bonds (about 98 kcal/mole each).

If one alkene is *less stable* than an isomeric unsaturated compound, the internal energy of the former *will be higher*. Therefore, *more heat* will be evolved on hydrogenation of the less stable alkene, and the heat of hydrogenation will have a *larger negative value*. Consider as an example the hydrogenation of the isomeric butenes.

$$\underset{H}{\overset{CH_3}{\diagdown}}C=C\underset{H}{\overset{CH_3}{\diagup}} + H_2 \rightarrow CH_3CH_2CH_2CH_3 + 28.6\ \text{kcal/mole}$$

$$\underset{H}{\overset{CH_3}{\diagdown}}C=C\underset{CH_3}{\overset{H}{\diagup}} + H_2 \rightarrow CH_3CH_2CH_2CH_3 + 27.6\ \text{kcal/mole}$$

The differences in heats of hydrogenation for isomeric alkenes are a quantitative measure of their relative stabilities. Figure 7.11 shows the relative energies of the *cis*- and *trans*-2-butenes. The cis compound is less stable, and it gives off 1 kcal more heat upon hydro-

Figure 7.11
The relative heat contents of the *cis*- and *trans*-2-butenes.

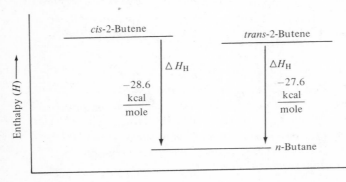

Figure 7.12
Relative steric strain energies in *cis*- and *trans*-alkenes.

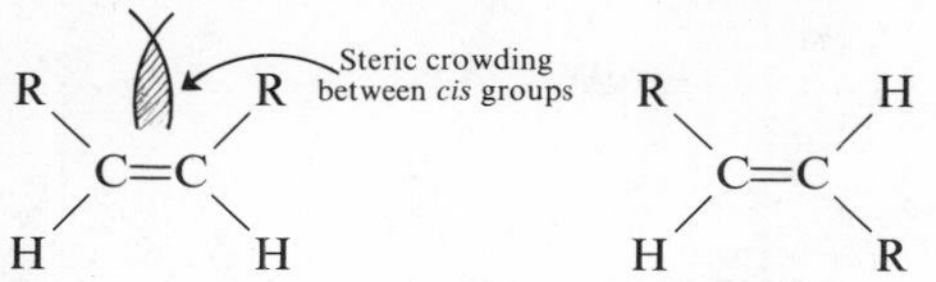

genation. From these data we may conclude that trans acyclic alkenes are usually more stable than their cis isomers, and by an amount that depends on the substituents attached to the double bond. This difference in stabilities can readily be accounted for by inspection of the diagram shown in Figure 7.12. In the cis isomers, the two bulky substituents on the double bond crowd each other, creating steric compression in the molecule and raising the van der Waals strain energy. The larger the substituents, the greater the strain. In the trans isomers the two substituents are far apart and steric crowding is less severe. Thus, *trans*-2-butene and *trans*-2-pentene are about 1.0 kcal/mole more stable than their cis counterparts; but *trans*-1,2-di-*t*-butylethylene is 9.3 kcal/mole more stable than the cis isomer.

Each molecule of a set in the following comparisons produces the same alkane on hydrogenation, and the differences in heats of hydrogenation must be due to differences in relative stabilities of the olefins:

$CH_3CH_2CH{=}CH_2$ vs $CH_3CH{=}CHCH_3$
−30.3 kcal/mole   cis, −28.6; trans, −27.6 kcal/mole

$CH_3CH_2CH_2CH{=}CH_2$ vs $CH_3CH_2CH{=}CHCH_3$
−30.1 kcal/mole   cis, −28.6; trans, −27.6 kcal/mole

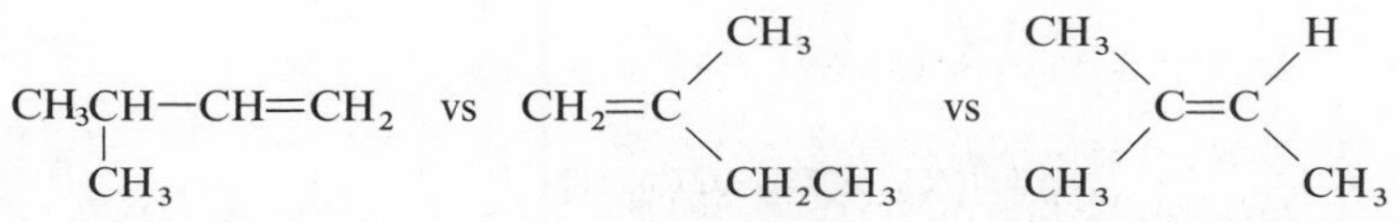

$CH_3CH{-}CH{=}CH_2$ vs $CH_2{=}C$
　　　CH_3
−30.3 kcal/mole   −28.5 kcal/mole   −26.9 kcal/mole

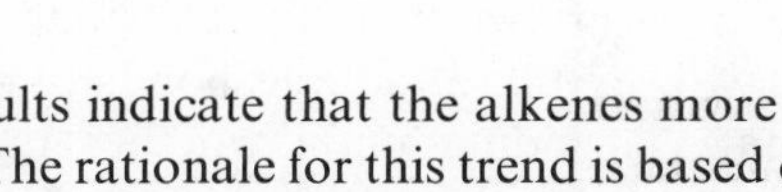

−27.8 kcal/mole   −25.4 kcal/mole

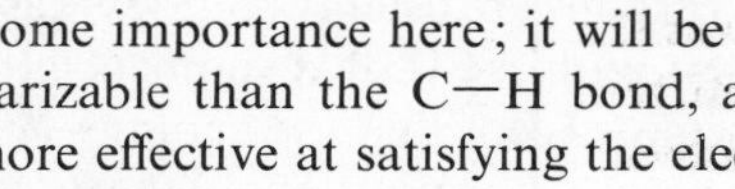

−26.9 kcal/mole   −23.0 kcal/mole

The results indicate that the alkenes more highly substituted by alkyl groups are more stable. The rationale for this trend is based on the inductive effects of alkyl groups, which were discussed in Section 7.9. (An effect called *hyperconjugation* is also suspected of being of some importance here; it will be disussed in Section 12.3.) The C—C bond is more polarizable than the C—H bond, and the alkyl group attached to the double bond is more effective at satisfying the electron-withdrawing characteristics of the sp^2-hybridized carbon.

The following order of stability of (unstrained) alkenes has been derived from heat of hydrogenation data:

$R_2C{=}CR_2 > R_2C{=}CHR > R_2C{=}CH_2 \approx$

trans-$RCH{=}CHR > $ *cis*-$RCH{=}CHR > RCH{=}CH_2 > CH_2{=}CH_2$

Other kinds of information can be obtained from heats of hydrogenation. For example, *cis*-cyclooctene is 9.2 kcal/mole more stable than the trans isomer:

cis-Cyclooctene   *trans*-Cyclooctene

vs

−23.0 kcal/mole   −32.2 kcal/mole

These results provide experimental justification of our earlier prediction (Section 7.7) that connecting the trans positions of a double bond by a chain of only six methylene groups should result in a strained alkene. This energy difference between isomers becomes less with increasing ring size, and for C_{11} rings and larger, the trans isomer is more stable.

That angle strain is present in the bicyclic alkene norbornene is reflected by the high heat of hydrogenation as compared to that of the relatively unstrained cyclohexene.

−33.1 kcal/mole   −27.1 kcal/mole

Note this last comparison differs from the others given so far, in that norbornene and cyclohexene do not hydrogenate to give the same product. Norbornane is much more strained than is cyclohexane, but the difference in strain is even greater with the corresponding unsaturated derivatives.

EXERCISE 7.5

For each of the pairs of compounds shown, which one do you expect will show the more positive heat of hydrogenation? Explain in each case.

(a) $CH_3CH_2-\underset{\underset{H}{|}}{\overset{\overset{H}{|}}{C}}=C-CH_3$ and $(CH_3)_2CH_2-\underset{\underset{H}{|}}{C}=CH_2$

(b) $CH_3CH_2-\underset{\underset{H}{|}}{\overset{\overset{H}{|}}{C}}=C-CH_3$ and $CH_3CH_2-\underset{\underset{H}{|}}{C}=\underset{\underset{H}{|}}{C}-CH_3$

7.11 Classification of Dienes

Dienes are *bifunctional* compounds that contain two carbon–carbon double bonds. The chemical properties of compounds containing two (or more) double bonds in a carbon chain (polyenes) may be strikingly different, depending upon whether the double bonds are *cumulated*, *conjugated*, or *isolated* (see Table 7.3). As far as physical properties, the compounds containing fewer than five carbons are usually colorless gases, the larger ones colorless liquids, except in special cases. With the IUPAC nomenclature system, dienes are named in the same manner as alkenes, except that the ending -*ene* is replaced by -*adiene*, and two numbers must be used to indicate the positions of the double bonds. A simple extension of this approach will allow the designation of -*trienes*, -*tetraenes*, and so on.

The straight-chain *pentadienes* are named below as examples.

$CH_3CH_2CH=C=CH_2$ $CH_3CH=C=CHCH_3$
1,2-Pentadiene   2,3-Pentadiene

$$CH_3CH=CH-CH=CH_2 \qquad CH_2=CH-CH_2-CH=CH_2$$

1,3-Pentadiene

(cis–trans isomers exist
about the internal
double bond)

1,4-Pentadiene

Dienes, in which the two double bonds occur successively in a carbon chain, that is, one carbon is double-bonded to both of the adjacent carbons, are said to have *cumulated* double bonds (Table 7.3). Both 1,2-pentadiene and 2,3-pentadiene are cumulated dienes. Structures having two cumulated carbon-carbon double bonds are known collectively as *allenes* after the simplest member of the series.

Table 7.3 Classification of Dienes

$\begin{matrix} \diagdown \\ \diagup \end{matrix} C=C=C \begin{matrix} \diagup \\ \diagdown \end{matrix}$	Cumulated double bonds; allenes
$\begin{matrix} \diagdown \\ \diagup \end{matrix} C=C-C=C \begin{matrix} \diagup \\ \diagdown \end{matrix}$	Conjugated double bonds
$\begin{matrix} \diagdown \\ \diagup \end{matrix} C=C-(CH_2)_n-C=C \begin{matrix} \diagup \\ \diagdown \end{matrix}$	Isolated double bonds, $n \geqq 1$

Whenever the carbon chain has *alternating* single and double bonds, the compounds are said to have *conjugated* double bonds (Table 7.3). We recognize *1,3-pentadiene* as a *conjugated diene.*

If the double bonds are neither conjugated nor cumulated, the unsaturated compound contains *isolated* double-bond systems (Table 7.3). The lowest possible homolog of an isolated diene is 1,4-pentadiene. The properties of a compound containing isolated double bonds are generally similar to those of the simple alkenes, because the double bonds are effectively insulated from each other by the intervening $-CH_2-$ groups. On the other hand, the properties of conjugated dienes and allenes are sufficiently different from the simple alkenes as to warrant a more detailed examination of their structures.

7.12   Allenes

The parent compound of the series of *cumulated dienes* is *allene* (1,2-propadiene), $CH_2=C=CH_2$. The formula suggests that the two double bonds, and therefore the two

$$\begin{matrix} H \\ H \end{matrix} \diagdown C=C=C \diagup \begin{matrix} H \\ H \end{matrix}$$

Allene
(Propadiene)

terminal methylene groups, should lie in two different planes which are at right angles to each other. An atomic orbital representation will point out the reasons for this. Let us consider first the σ-bond system of allene. The two terminal carbon atoms are attached to three other atoms (two hydrogens and a carbon) and should utilize sp^2 hybrid orbitals for σ bonding as in ethylene. The central carbon atom attached (with double bonds) to the other two carbons will form the σ bonds with sp hybrid orbitals (directed 180° apart, review Table 4.1 and Figures 4.1 and 4.2).

The central carbon atom has two p orbitals available for π bonding ($2p_y$ and $2p_z$). One of these can overlap to form a π bond with the $2p_y$ orbital of one of the methylene groups, and the other will overlap in a perpendicular plane with the $2p_z$ orbital of the other methylene group. This leads to the π bond framework of allene shown in Figure 7.13b.

Figure 7.13
(a) σ-Bond framework of allene; (b) π-bonds of allene.

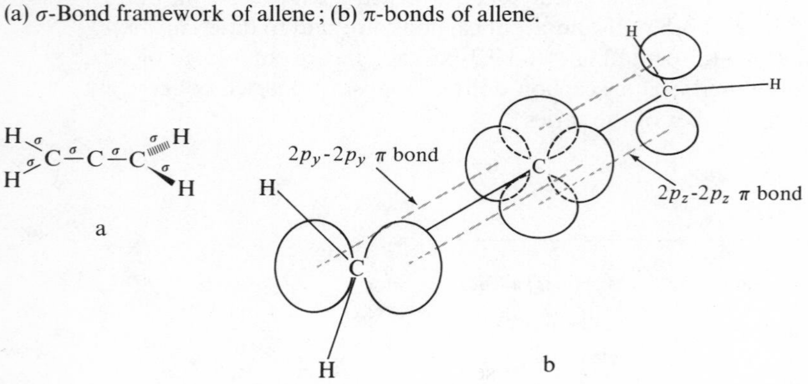

There is a very important consequence of this special geometry of allenes. Any allene with the substitution pattern abC=C=Cba will exist in two enantiomeric forms and is capable of showing optical activity. The two enantiomers are depicted in Figure 7.14

Figure 7.14
Enantiomers of substituted allenes, abC=C=Cba.

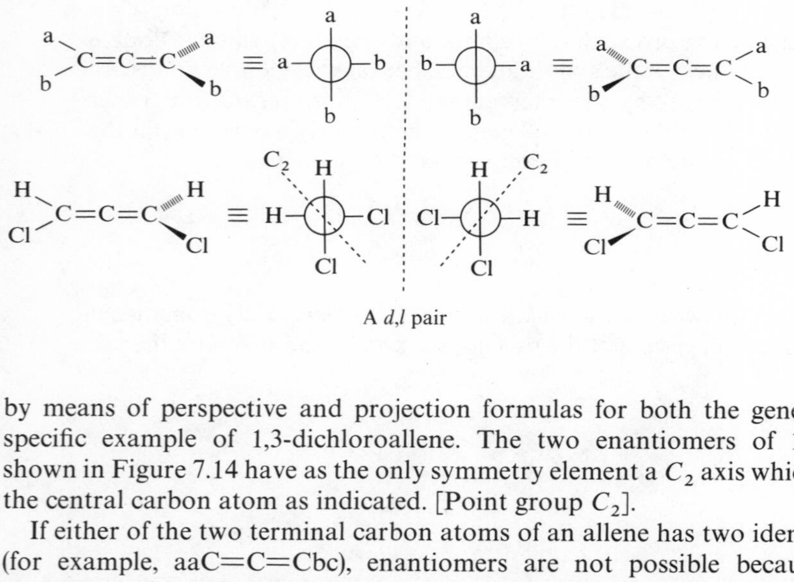

A d,l pair

by means of perspective and projection formulas for both the general case and the specific example of 1,3-dichloroallene. The two enantiomers of 1,3-dichloroallene shown in Figure 7.14 have as the only symmetry element a C_2 axis which passes through the central carbon atom as indicated. [Point group C_2].

If either of the two terminal carbon atoms of an allene has two identical substituents (for example, aaC=C=Cbc), enantiomers are not possible because the molecule possesses a plane of symmetry. Stereoisomerism of the cis–trans type does not exist with allenes.

EXERCISE 7.6

Show by means of an atomic orbital picture that a cumulated triene, abC=C=C=Cab, will not show optical isomerism, but will show cis–trans isomerism.

7.13 Conjugated Dienes. The Resonance Approach

Typical conjugated dienes are illustrated.

$$CH_2{=}CH{-}CH{=}CH_2 \qquad \underset{\underset{CH_3}{|}}{CH_2{=}C{-}CH{=}CH_2} \qquad \underset{\underset{Cl}{|}}{CH_2{=}C{-}CH{=}CH_2}$$

1,3-Butadiene   2-Methyl-1,3-butadiene   2-Chloro-1,3-butadiene
                            (Isoprene)   (Chloroprene)

Cyclopentadiene   1,3-Cyclohexadiene

The chemical properties of conjugated dienes are unusual compared to those of simple alkenes and dienes containing isolated double bonds. Chemical reactions often occur faster with conjugated dienes, and reactions unavailable to simple alkenes may take place. Although conjugated dienes are more reactive than isolated olefins, they are more stable than nonconjugated dienes in the sense that they have lower heats of hydrogenation and lower heats of combustion. These and other varied observations suggest that a single valence-bond structure does not adequately picture the actual electron distribution present in a conjugated diene. The double bonds interact in some way, and this conspicuously alters the properties of the molecule.

Before we examine the structure of conjugated dienes in more detail, it will profit us to look again at the electron-dot representation of ethylene. In addition to the electronic structure given for ethylene in Section 7.2 (conventional structure) in which all atoms are shown with a rare gas configuration, other structures can be considered:

Conventional structure   Other possible electronic structures

or, to simplify,

$$H_2C{=}CH_2 \qquad H_2\overset{-}{C}{-}\overset{+}{C}H_2 \qquad H_2\overset{+}{C}{-}\overset{-}{C}H_2 \qquad H_2\dot{C}{-}\dot{C}H_2$$

Conventional   Other possible structures
structure

Each of the other electronic configurations has the same number of spin-paired electrons and the identical atom locations as the conventional structure. The differences are that the pair of electrons comprising the π bond is localized on one carbon or the other (resulting in the charge-separated structures); or one electron is localized on each carbon. Quite obviously the conventional structure is the best representation for ethylene, because in the other three structures, one or both carbon atoms do not have the stable octet electronic configuration. In a symmetrical and simple alkene such as ethylene, the conventional structure is adequate to account for all of the properties.

Let us reconsider the structure of butadiene in the same sense by writing other valence-bond structures which could be expected to reflect the electron distribution in the molecule. It becomes apparent that if structures II, III, and IV (which show a double bond between carbon atoms 2 and 3 of butadiene) *contribute* in any way to the structure of butadiene, the π electrons are not confined to the space between carbon atoms 1, 2 and 3, 4 as indicated by the normal structure I. No single one of these structures is adequate to describe the properties of butadiene; the *actual butadiene* is a structure which may be said to be a *weighted average* of the *contributing forms* I, II, III, and IV plus six structures similar to V. This approach is called the *resonance method*, and butadiene is

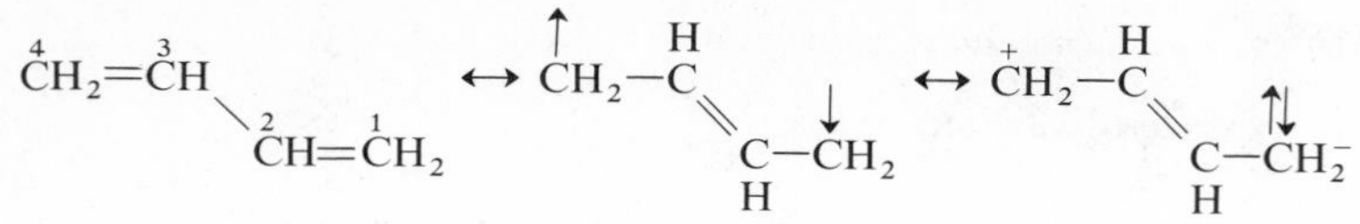

$$\overset{4}{C}H_2=\overset{3}{C}H \quad\underset{\overset{2}{C}H=\overset{1}{C}H_2}{} \quad \longleftrightarrow \quad CH_2-C\overset{H}{\underset{C-CH_2}{}} \quad \longleftrightarrow \quad \overset{+}{C}H_2-C\overset{H}{\underset{C-CH_2^-}{}}$$

I   II   III

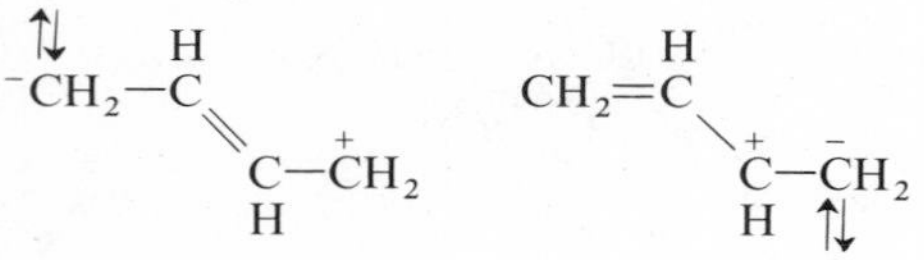

$$\overset{-}{C}H_2-C\overset{H}{\underset{\overset{+}{C}-CH_2}{}} \qquad CH_2=C\overset{H}{\underset{\overset{+}{C}-\overset{-}{C}H_2}{}}$$

IV   V

said to be a "*resonance hybrid*" of structures I–V. The resonance forms I, II, III, ... do not separately have physical reality or independent existence; and we use a double-headed arrow to indicate that the structures represent only different electron-pairing schemes and not different species in equilibrium. Butadiene is not a *mixture* of structures I, II, III, ... Butadiene is a real molecule, one that cannot be completely and adequately represented by any single valence structure. Remember, it is only our inability to accurately describe the electron distribution of a compound that forces us to depict it by several contributing forms. The fault is ours, not the compound's.

EXERCISE 7.7

Draw the six resonance forms similar to V (different from I–IV) which would have to be considered here to make the set complete.

If we return to ethylene for a moment (page 151), we can see now that the best description of the molecule is the conventional structure, but that the other three structures shown each contribute a little bit to the overall molecular properties.

Ionic structures can become much more important in more complicated cases. For example, methyl vinyl ether has the following resonance forms, by analogy with ethylene:

$$CH_3-\ddot{O}-CH=CH_2 \longleftrightarrow CH_3-\ddot{O}-\overset{-}{C}H-\overset{+}{C}H_2 \longleftrightarrow CH_3-\ddot{O}-\overset{+}{C}H-\overset{-}{C}H_2$$

The form on the left is most important, as usual. The next one is also fairly important, because the electrons have been pulled over next to the electronegative oxygen atom. Conversely, the form on the right is quite unimportant. (Why?) Still another form is found to be the second most important one, however,

$$CH_3-\overset{+}{\underset{..}{O}}=CH-\overset{-}{C}H_2$$

In this form, each atom has a full octet, but the charge separation prevents it from being as important as the conventional structure.

Resonance is still more important with other kinds of unsaturated compounds. Ideally, we should hope to be able to predict when and to what extent resonance is important in affecting the properties of unsaturated systems. The following *rules for the use of the resonance method* can be applied:

1. All resonance structures must have *the same number of electrons* with their spins paired, and they must have all atoms in the same location in space.

   Example

$$\overset{\uparrow}{C}H_2-CH=CH-\overset{\downarrow}{C}H_2 \text{ and } CH_2=CH-\overset{\uparrow}{C}H-\overset{\downarrow}{C}H_2$$

are resonance forms, but

$$CH_2{=}CH{-}\overset{\uparrow}{C}H{-}\overset{\uparrow}{C}H_2$$

is not a resonance form of either of these, but corresponds to an electronically excited state.

2. The relative energies of the various structures may be estimated by considering:
a. *Bond energies.* (The greater the number of formal covalent bonds, the greater the contribution of that structure.)

Example

$CH_2{=}CH{-}CH{=}CH_2$ is of lower energy than $CH_2{=}CH{-}\overset{+}{C}H{-}\overset{-}{C}H_2$
because it possesses one additional covalent bond. (In addition, the latter is of higher energy because of the separation of charge.)

b. *Electron-attracting power* of the atoms involved in ionic structures. (Ionic structures with charge separation are usually less important than covalent structures; but ionic structures can contribute, especially when atoms of different electronegativities are involved, and that structure which places a negative charge on the most electronegative atom would be more important.

Example

$CH_2{=}CHCl$; $\overset{+}{C}H_2{-}\overset{-}{C}H{-}Cl$ is more important than $\overset{-}{C}H_2{-}\overset{+}{C}H{-}Cl$

3. Resonance, or electron stabilization, will be greatest when there are at least *two equivalent structures* of lowest energy. If there is only a *single contributing structure* of lowest energy, *the resonance hybrid may be assigned the properties expected for that structure.*

Example

Ethylene is well represented by the structure $CH_2{=}CH_2$, but carbonate ion is not adequately represented by

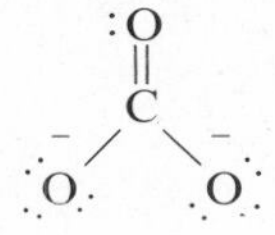

which implies that one oxygen is not equivalent to the other two. The carbonate ion must be represented as follows:

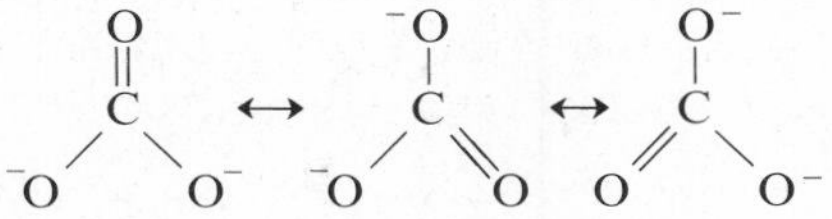

In the case of butadiene, resonance is not very important because structure I has the greatest number of covalent bonds (Rule 2a), ionic structures are not of major importance because no strongly electronegative or electropositive atoms are present (Rule 2b), and no other low-energy structure is possible (Rule 3). However, with aromatic compounds (Chapter 11), with other unsaturated groups such as nitro groups and carboxylates (Chapter 8), and with reaction intermediates (Chapter 12), the effects of resonance on bond lengths, chemical reactivity, and other properties can often be quite dramatic.

EXERCISE 7.8

Draw the four principal resonance forms of $CH_2=CH\ddot{F}:$, and explain which are more important and why.

7.14   Conjugated Dienes. The Molecular Orbital Approach

The molecular orbital approach is the alternative to the resonance method as a means of explanation and prediction of the properties of conjugated systems. The molecular orbital and resonance methods are two different approximate methods for solving the Schroedinger equation. If refined sufficiently, they both converge to the same solution; however, at the pictorial level, they offer alternative viewpoints. Which of them is more informative depends upon the particular case, and both methods are commonly used.

As with the molecular orbital treatment of ethylene, we consider that the σ bonds of conjugated dienes represent localized pairs of electrons. A linear combination of the p atomic orbitals (LCAO) centered on the various atoms will provide us with a set of molecular orbitals of varying energy to describe the π-electron system (recall that the number of molecular orbitals always equals the number of atomic orbitals that were combined; Section 2.4). The available π electrons are then assigned in pairs (compare ethylene, Section 7.2) to these molecular orbitals in order of increasing energy. For butadiene, the four atomic $2p$ orbitals (one from each carbon atom) are combined to give four molecular π orbitals, and the four available π electrons are then placed in the two molecular orbitals of lowest energy.

In Figure 7.15, an orbital energy diagram is used to compare the π-electron energies of ethylene and butadiene. As indicated earlier (Figure 7.4), each carbon atom in ethylene contributes one $2p_z$ orbital and one electron. The energy of the electron in the $2p_z$ orbital of the isolated atom will be taken as zero. The two $2p_z$ orbitals are combined to give a π orbital (bonding) of energy 1β (β is called a *resonance integral*, and is a negative number) if the corresponding lobes of like sign are allowed to overlap, and a π^* orbital (antibonding) of energy -1β if the lobes of opposite sign are combined. Both electrons

Figure 7.15
Orbital energy diagram for ethylene and 1,3-butadiene.

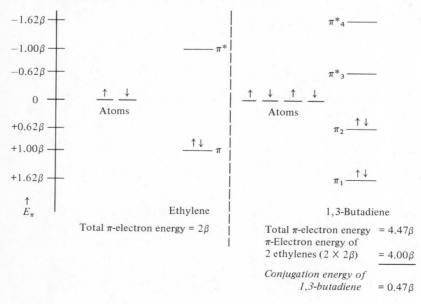

may be placed (with spins paired) into the bonding π orbital (the orbital of lowest energy), resulting in a total π electron energy of 2 (electrons) $\times$ 1β (orbital energy) = 2β. Note that if any electrons were available to be placed in the antibonding orbital (π^*), the π-electron energy would become higher. This is because the antibonding orbitals are above the $E_\pi = 0$ line, and electrons in these orbitals do not contribute to bonding the nuclei together, but rather tend to force them apart. (See Section 2.4 for the discussion of the H_2 molecule, most of which is applicable here also.)

For butadiene, when the Schroedinger equation for the π system is solved (approximately) using the LCAO approach, four molecular orbitals are obtained which have the relative energies shown in Figure 7.15. Four π electrons are to be placed in the two bonding π orbitals, and the total π-electron energy may be calculated as $2 \times 1.618\beta + 2 \times 0.618\beta = 4.472\beta$. From the diagram it is clear that the total π-electron energy of butadiene is *less than* that of two isolated ethylenes by an amount of energy equal to 0.472β. This extra stability is called the *conjugation energy*. From experimental measurements, it corresponds to about 3.5 kcal/mole.

This quantity has also been called resonance energy, delocalization energy, *or* stabilization energy, *but these terms are less explicit. The relationship between β (a theoretical quantity) and the conjugation energy from experimental measurements is, unfortunately, quite complex. It will be discussed further in Chapter 11.*

Conjugation, or resonance, lowers the energy of a system relative to that of a comparable system containing noninteracting groups.

Obviously if the number of conjugated double bonds is increased, the possibility of delocalization of π electrons is greater, and the conjugation energy becomes larger. 1,3,5-Hexatriene has three conjugated double bonds in a chain and has more conjugation energy (0.99β, 7.7 kcal/mole) than does butadiene.

7.15   Experimental Determination of Conjugation Energies

Resonance is said to stabilize an unsaturated system because the overall energy of the system is lower than that predicted for a single valence structure. For butadiene, we were able to conclude by the resonance method (Section 7.13) that electron delocalization was present, but not very significant. Molecular orbital calculations (Section 7.14) gave a theoretical value for the conjugation energy of butadiene of 0.472β. There are two general methods of quantitatively measuring conjugation energies of dienes in the laboratory: by heats of combustion, and by heats of hydrogenation. The latter is much more accurate, and several values are listed in Table 7.4.

Table 7.4   Heats of Hydrogenation of Dienes

Compound	ΔH_H, *kcal/mole*	Conjugation energy, *kcal/mole*
1-Butene	−30.3	—
1,4-Pentadiene	−60.8	—
1,5-Hexadiene	−60.5	—
1,3-Butadiene	−57.1	3.5
1,3-Pentadiene	−54.1	3.6
2-Methyl-1,3-butadiene (Isoprene)	−53.4	5.3
2,3-Dimethyl-1,3-butadiene	−53.9	3.0
Cyclohexene	−28.6	—
1,3-Cyclohexadiene	−55.4	1.8

All 1-alkenes, such as 1-butene, have heats of hydrogenation close to −30 kcal/mole. For dienes with isolated double bonds, the heat of hydrogenation should be very close to twice that of a simple 1-alkene ($2 \times -30 = -60$ kcal/mole). This conclusion is obviously supported by the experimental measurements on 1,4-pentadiene and 1,5-hexadiene (Table 7.4).

On the other hand, if conjugation lowers the energy of a compound, the heat of hydrogenation of a conjugated diene should be *less than twice* that of a simple alkene. For butadiene, the value $\Delta H_H = -57.1$ kcal/mole is 3.5 kcal/mole less than twice that of 1-butene ($2 \times 30.3 = -60.6$ kcal/mole). We may thus conclude that the conjugation energy of butadiene is 3.5 kcal/mole. For a localized 1,3-pentadiene we would predict the heat of hydrogenation to be the sum of that for *trans*-2-butene (-27.6 kcal/mole) and 1-pentene (-30.1 kcal/mole), or -57.7 kcal/mole. The observed value is -54.1 kcal/mole, indicating a conjugation energy of 3.6 kcal/mole. The conjugation energies of the dienes listed in Table 7.4 were evaluated in this manner.

EXERCISE 7.9

Draw an energy diagram analogous to Figure 7.11 which shows the relative heat contents of 1-butene, 1,3-butadiene, and butane. Show on the diagram the heats of hydrogenation and the conjugation energy of the diene.

7.16   Bond Orders

Resonance in butadiene, as evaluated from the valence structures I, II, III, and IV (Section 7.13), should result in making the C-1—C-2 and C-3—C-4 bonds less than full double bonds, and the C-2—C-3 bond more than a simple single bond. The π-*bond order* is an index of the amount of double-bond character between two atoms. It has the value zero for a single bond and unity for a double bond. If we could estimate the proper weighting that should be given to structures I–IV to arrive at the electron distribution of the resonance hybrid butadiene, we could calculate each of the C—C bond orders. The molecular orbital method does allow a calculation of bond orders. Such calculations show that the C-1—C-2 and C-3—C-4 bonds have about three times as much double-bond character as does the C-2—C-3 bond.

> *Bond Lengths.* Bond lengths are often cited as evidence for, or against, conjugation stabilization in unsaturated molecules. Using butadiene as an example, and remembering that single bonds are longer than double bonds, the bond orders evaluated above lead us to predict that the C-1—C-2 and C-3—C-4 bonds of butadiene should be somewhat longer than a double bond, and the C-2—C-3 bond should be slightly shorter than a single C—C bond. The double-bond lengthening in butadiene is too small to detect experimentally; however, the single bond has a length of 1.47 Å. It is a fallacy to attribute this shortening entirely to resonance, however. Bond lengths should be used with caution in estimating the importance of resonance (and bond orders) because bond lengths also depend upon hybridization. As the hybridization at carbon changes from sp^3 to sp the bonds to this carbon become progressively shorter (Table 4.1). We would, therefore, expect that the C-2—C-3 (sp^2–sp^2) bond in butadiene should, simply as a result of hybridization, be shorter than the C—C single bond in ethane (sp^3–sp^3) or the C-2—C-3 bond in propylene (sp^3–sp^2). (The latter has a length of 1.50 Å.) Some, but not much, of the C-2—C-3 bond shortening in butadiene is attributed to resonance.

7.17   Electron-Donor Properties of π Bonds

The electrons involved with π bonding in alkenes and dienes may be considered to be weakly shared by the bonded atoms. In addition, the special geometry of π molecular orbitals makes these electrons quite accessible to electron-deficient reagents. Double bonds can, therefore, function as electron-pair donors (Lewis bases), and they will undergo acid–base reactions with Lewis acids (Section 4.3). Many coordinated complexes between alkenes and electrophilic species are known; some are quite stable and have been isolated in pure form, whereas others are thought to function as the first intermediates in a large number of reactions that occur with alkenes.

These complexes are generally loosely bound and are designated *π-complexes*. The name results from the fact that one component of the complex has an intact π-electron system. It is not possible to depict such π complexes with simple valence structures, and they are commonly represented in the following manner (A$^+$ refers to a Lewis acid):

$$
\begin{array}{c}
\overset{\displaystyle A^+}{\underset{\displaystyle \uparrow}{}} \\[-2pt]
\diagdown \ \diagup \\
C\!=\!C \\
\diagup \ \diagdown
\end{array}
$$

The arrow denotes that the π electrons of the double bond are associated in coordinate bonding with the acid. The term *charge-transfer complex* is also used to describe these species; the designation has its derivation from considerations of the various possible resonance structures that could contribute to the complex.

When iodine is dissolved in a saturated and indifferent solvent, the solution is purple. A solution of iodine in cyclohexene, on the other hand, is brown. This color is attributed to the formation of the iodine–cyclohexene π complex.

Iodine–cyclohexene
π complex

Silver–alkene
π complex

Silver ion (Ag$^+$) forms π complexes with many alkenes, and especially with conjugated dienes. This can sometimes be used to great advantage as a convenient means of separation of saturated from unsaturated compounds. A mixture in a solvent such as pentane is shaken with a saturated aqueous alcoholic solution of silver nitrate; the π complex, being a saltlike compound, is extracted into the aqueous layer. Often these complexes can be obtained in crystalline form. Treatment with ammonium hydroxide regenerates the purified alkene or diene, since silver ion forms a more stable complex with ammonia than with the diene.

Other Olefin–Metal Complexes. The electron-donor properties of alkenes allow them to function as *ligands* (groups attached to a metal) in coordination with many transition metals. These π complexes have important applications in catalysis, as reaction intermediates, and as a means of stabilization of unstable dienes (for example, cyclobutadiene).

Palladium dichloride ethylene

Cyclobutadiene iron tricarbonyl

Palladium chloride butadiene

7.18   The Carbon–Carbon Triple Bond. Alkynes

Alkynes are also unsaturated hydrocarbons. They have the general formula C_nH_{2n-2} and contain a smaller proportion of hydrogen (are more unsaturated) than do alkenes. Although alkynes have the same general formula as dienes, the bonding situation and hence the properties of these two classes of compounds are quite different—they contain *different functional groups.*

The parent member of the alkyne family is the colorless gas acetylene, C_2H_2. The only reasonble way to construct a suitable valence structure for acetylene is to join the carbon atoms by a *triple bond.*

$$H:C:::C:H \quad \text{or} \quad H—C≡C—H$$
Acetylene

The carbon–carbon triple bond is the distinguishing functional group of alkynes.

Quantum mechanics provides much more detail about the triple bond in acetylene. Each carbon atom is bonded to only two other atoms, and according to our rules of hybridization (Section 4.2) the σ bonds will be formed by utilizing *sp* hybrid orbitals. The *sp* hybrid orbitals lie along a straight line that passes through the carbon nuclei (Table 4.1, Figure 4.2). The σ framework of acetylene, derived in the usual way by maximum overlap of orbitals, is shown in Figure 7.16a. It is quite obvious that acetylene is a *linear molecule*; all four atoms lie on a single molecular axis.

Each carbon atom of acetylene (like the central carbon atom of an allene) has two unhybridized *2p* atomic orbitals available for π bonding. One pair (the $2p_y$ orbitals of each carbon) will overlap to give a π bond having one lobe in front and one in back of the molecular axis. The pair of adjacent $2p_z$ atomic orbitals will combine to give a second π bond, whose lobes are above and below the σ-bond axis (Figure 7.16b). The result is a cylindrical molecule in which the carbon atoms of the triple bond are "buried" by two π-electron systems.

Figure 7.16
(a) σ framework of acetylene;
(b) atomic orbital representation of the two π bonds of acetylene;
(c) the total π-electron density of acetylene.

$$H\underset{s\text{-}sp}{\overset{\sigma}{—}}C\underset{sp\text{-}sp}{\overset{\sigma}{—}}C\underset{sp\text{-}s}{\overset{\sigma}{—}}H$$
σ Framework

$(a$

$2p_z\text{-}2p_z$ π bond

H

$2p_y\text{-}2p_y$ π bond

H

(b)

H ———— H

(c)

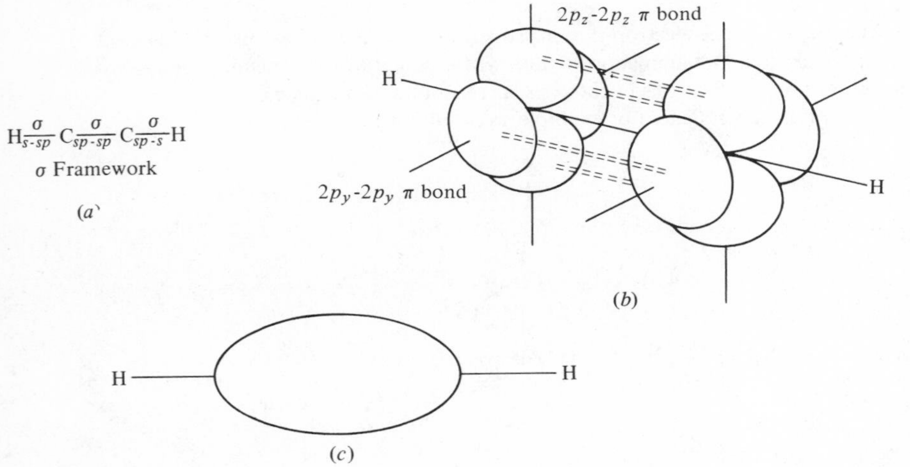

SHAPE OF THE ELECTRON CLOUD IN ACETYLENE. *It is perhaps not apparent from Figure 7.16b that the π-electron density of acetylene yields a cylindrical cross section. Just as three equally occupied 2p orbitals on an atom give an electron density which is spherical (a hollow sphere—see Section 2.5), so do two p orbitals on an atom give an oblate spheroid (flattened sphere). The electron density from the four p orbitals of acetylene is approximately represented by a prolate spheroid, Figure 7.16c. A cross section of this figure, perpendicular to the principal axis, gives a (hollow) cylinder. The σ-bonding electrons are concentrated in the hollow part of the cylinder*

where the π-electron density is rather low, but the σ and π electrons do occupy some space in common.

The carbon–carbon triple bond is composed of one strong σ bond and two weaker π bonds. The total bond strength is 196 kcal/mole, and the bond length is 1.20 Å. The triple bond is shorter and stronger than the double bond. The carbon–hydrogen bond length (*sp–s*) is also quite short (1.06 Å). The predictions concerning the structure and geometry of acetylene as derived from simple hybridization theory have been well substantiated experimentally.

7.19   Higher Alkynes. Nomenclature

The naming of alkynes follows easily if the nomenclature for alkenes has been mastered. The IUPAC rules tell us to use the ending *-yne* and to designate the position of the triple bond by number. Acetylene has the systematic name ethyne; and the next homolog is propyne, $CH_3C{\equiv}CH$. There are two *butynes*

$$CH_3CH_2C{\equiv}CH \qquad\qquad CH_3C{\equiv}CCH_3$$
$$\text{1-Butyne} \qquad\qquad\qquad \text{2-butyne}$$

and three pentynes

$$CH_3CH_2CH_2C{\equiv}CH \qquad CH_3CH_2C{\equiv}CCH_3 \qquad (CH_3)_2CHC{\equiv}CH$$
$$\text{1-Pentyne} \qquad\qquad \text{2-Pentyne} \qquad\qquad \text{3-Methyl-1-butyne}$$

Alkynes are sometimes named as alkylacetylenes: propyne can be named as methylacetylene, and so on.

Because of the linear geometry of the triple bond, cis–trans isomerism is not possible for simple alkynes.

The smallest ring size that can accommodate a triple bond to give a reasonably stable cycloalkyne is the eight-membered ring. *Cyclooctyne* has a high degree of ring strain, but it is isolable in a pure state. *Cycloheptyne and cyclohexyne* have been reported

$$CH_2{-}C{\equiv}C{-}CH_2$$
$$\text{(CH}_2)_4$$
$$\text{Cyclooctyne}$$

as transient intermediates which were "trapped" by a fast reaction with another molecule. It has not been possible to isolate them, because of their high reactivity. These molecules cannot contain a linear triple-bond system, and are examples of "bent" alkynes.

Some examples of important alkynes which contain other functional groups are

$$HC{\equiv}CCH_2OH \qquad\qquad HOCH_2C{\equiv}CCH_2OH \qquad\qquad HC{\equiv}CBr$$
Propargyl alcohol   2-Butyne-1,4-diol   Bromoacetylene
(2-Propyn-1-ol)   (Bromoethyne)

Alkynes occur in nature, including some rather complicated ones, as exemplified by the highly unsaturated hydrocarbon,

$$CH_2{=}CH{-}C{\equiv}C{-}C{\equiv}C{-}C{\equiv}C{-}C{\equiv}C{-}C{\equiv}C{-}CH_3,$$

one of many acetylenic compounds isolated from the essential oils of the *Compositae*.

7.20   Properties of Alkynes

The boiling points, melting points, and specific gravities of simple alkynes are normally slightly higher than those of the alkanes and alkenes with the corresponding carbon skeleton. This probably results from the fact that alkynes, because they contain a triple bond, are compact, rodlike molecules. They can pack closer together in the solid and liquid phases, which allows stronger van der Waals attractions between molecules. Alkynes have low polarity and are insoluble in water, but they are quite soluble in solvents of low polarity such as ligroin, ether, benzene, and carbon tetrachloride.

COMMERCIAL PRODUCTION AND USES OF ACETYLENE. *Acetylene is produced on a commercial scale by either of two processes: the hydrolysis of calcium carbide (CaC_2) or the partial oxidation of methane. Calcium carbide is readily obtainable from the reaction of calcium oxide with carbon at 2000° C, so this route makes a simple useful organic compound available from elemental carbon, which is in turn readily available from coal. Acetylene will decompose explosively when compressed to a few hundred pounds per inch and even liquid acetylene (bp −83° C) must be handled with extreme care. When acetylene is burned with pure oxygen, a high flame temperature (2800° C) can be obtained. Large quantities of acetylene are used as fuel for oxyacetylene torches. Acetylene supplied for this use is dissolved in acetone under pressure in a cylinder packed with an inert porous solid material to cut down on the free volume.*

Acetylene is the starting material for large-scale syntheses of many important organic compounds, among which are acetic acid and several unsaturated compounds for polymerization to plastics and rubber. Other alkynes are important laboratory-scale synthetic intermediates.

Acetylene is less acidic than water, but more acidic than ammonia. The acidities of 1-alkynes relative to those of other proton acids are given in Table 7.5. The explanation

Table 7.5   Relative Acidities

Compound	Approximate pK_a	
CH_4	40	
NH_3	34	
$CH_3C{\equiv}CH$	25	Increasing acidity
CH_3OH	16	
H_2O	16	

for the enhanced acidity of acetylene and other 1-alkynes, relative to other hydrocarbons, is based on hybridization theory. The more s and the less p character is an sp^n-hybridized carbon atomic orbital, the greater the relative electronegativity of the hybridized carbon orbital (Section 7.9). When the electrons of a C—H bond are more tightly held by the carbon nucleus, the hydrogen is more easily lost as a proton—the compound is more acidic. The s character of the C—H bond of a 1-alkyne (sp–s σ bond) is greater than that of an alkene C—H bond (sp^2–s σ bond) or an alkane C—H bond (sp^3–s). The relative order of acidities is

$$R_3C{-}H \quad < \quad R_2C{=}C{\overset{R}{\underset{H}{\diagup\!\!\diagdown}}} \quad < \quad RC{\equiv}C{-}H$$

Alkane   Alkene   Alkyne

Another way of saying essentially the same thing requires that we reexamine the treatment of electron-pair repulsions of Section 4.2. In a 1-alkyne the six electrons making up the triple bond are largely localized between the two carbon atoms. The average positions of these electrons are further away from the electron pair of the C—H bond than are the corresponding six electrons of a saturated carbon atom. The C—H bonding electrons in the 1-alkyne suffer less repulsion from the other bonding electrons and will be able to move closer to the carbon nucleus. The hydrogen thus becomes more positive and more easily removed as a proton.

Acid–base reactions between 1-alkynes and bases lead to salts. Alkali and alkaline earth salts of 1-alkynes are valuable chemical reagents.

$$H-C\equiv C-Li \qquad H-C\equiv C-Na \qquad H-C\equiv C-MgBr$$

Lithium acetylide   Sodium acetylide   Ethynylmagnesium bromide

1-Alkynes react with heavy metal ions (Ag^+, Cu^+), and the insoluble (and often unstable) salts precipitate. The formation of such precipitates is a qualitative test for 1-alkynes.

$$R-C\equiv C-Ag \qquad CaC_2, [:C\equiv C:]^{2-}Ca^{2+}$$

A silver acetylide   Calcium carbide
(often explosive)

7.21   The NMR Spectra of Alkynes

The protons of acetylene are found at δ 2.35 in the nmr spectrum. This chemical shift value appears anomalous, because it means that acetylenic protons are more shielded than vinyl protons, rather than less shielded. This is so in spite of the fact that the sp carbon in acetylene is more electronegative than the sp^2 carbon in ethylene. In fact, acetylenic protons have chemical shifts approaching those of alkyl protons. The anomalous high-field resonance for acetylenic protons is accounted for in terms of an unusually large polarizability for the π electrons, which circulate in the magnetic field. Consider acetylene itself, a linear molecule with cylindrical symmetry. The triple bond is symmetrical about the linear axis; if this axis is aligned with the applied magnetic field (H_0), the π electrons circulate at right angles to the applied field (Figure 7.17). This

Figure 7.17

Shielding of acetylenic protons.

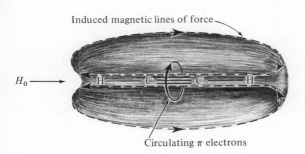

Induced magnetic lines of force

$H_0 \longrightarrow$

Circulating π electrons

results in an induced magnetic field with magnetic lines of force opposed to the applied field. The acetylenic protons lie along the magnetic axis, and they experience an overall field resulting from the applied field minus the induced field. Compare the situation here with that in ethylene, Section 7.5. In each case the electrons circulate primarily in the direction of their highest polarizability, which is different in olefins and acetylenes; in the olefin, the vinyl proton lies in the deshielding region of these circulating electrons, while in the 1-alkyne, the proton is in the shielding region. The nmr spectrum of 3-methyl-1-butyn-3-ol (Figure 7.18) shows this feature of a shielded acetylenic proton.

Figure 7.18
NMR spectrum of 3-methyl-1-butyn-3-ol.

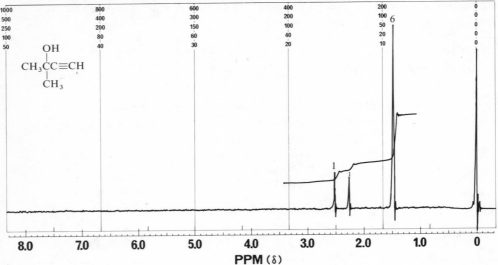

7.22   Sites of Unsaturation

In any approach directed toward the identification of an organic molecule of unknown structure, a knowledge of whether or not the compound is unsaturated is extremely useful. The number of *sites of unsaturation* present in any molecule may be calculated by determining how many molecules of hydrogen (H_2) would be required to transform the compound into the completely saturated compound containing the same number of carbon atoms. From our earlier discussion, we know that an alkene has one site of unsaturation and an alkyne has two. Suppose we desired to know the number of sites of unsaturation present in the unknown hydrocarbon C_6H_8. The saturated molecule has the formula C_nH_{2n+2}, or in this case C_6H_{14}. Six hydrogen atoms would be required to convert C_6H_8 to the formula C_6H_{14}; this corresponds to 3 moles of hydrogen, and the compound therefore contains three sites of unsaturation.

Sites of unsaturation *is a commonly used, but not completely accurate term. It is hard to think of cyclohexane as unsaturated, for example, but it is in this sense. The expression* rings and/or double bonds *is sometimes used (accurate only if a triple bond is considered as two double bonds), and is equivalent to* sites of unsaturation.

Even if a molecule is composed of other atoms in addition to carbon and hydrogen, it is still easy to determine the number of sites of unsaturation. When the formula of the unknown compound contains an oxygen (or sulfur) atom, we simply take out the oxygen leaving the basic hydrocarbon formula, and then proceed as above. For example, consider C_4H_8O—removing the oxygen atom gives C_4H_8, which requires two hydrogen atoms to be transformed to C_4H_{10}. Therefore C_4H_8O has one site of unsaturation.

EXERCISE 7.10

How many sites of unsaturation does a compound with the formula $C_8H_{12}O_2$ contain?

With atoms that have an odd number of valences, slight modifications of the approach are necessary. If the formula of the unknown contains a trivalent atom such as nitrogen (or phosphorus), we remove one N and one H and proceed as before. If the formula contains a halogen atom (F, Cl, Br, I), we remove the halogen and add one H and then continue as usual. Two simple illustrations are $C_5H_{13}N$ and C_5H_5Cl. For the first $(C_5H_{13}N)$, remove N and H to give C_5H_{12}, which is the formula of an alkane. Thus $C_5H_{13}N$ has no sites of unsaturation. For C_5H_5Cl we remove Cl and add H to obtain C_5H_6, which requires six hydrogen atoms to give C_5H_{12}, implying three sites of unsaturation.

Let us apply all of these principles to determine in systematic fashion the number of sites of unsaturation contained by $C_7H_{12}NO_2SCl$: Remove S and 2O, giving $C_7H_{12}NCl$; remove N and H, giving $C_7H_{11}Cl$; remove Cl and add H, giving C_7H_{12}; add four H, giving C_7H_{16}; therefore, the compound has two sites of unsaturation.

EXERCISE 7.11

A compound has the formula C_4H_6OBrCl. How many sites of unsaturation does it contain? Draw a structural formula that fits the empirical formula and point out the sites of unsaturation.

PROBLEMS

1. What type of molecular orbitals are formed by atomic orbitals overlapping along their axes? Perpendicular to their axes? Which forms the stronger bond and why?

2. There are 13 isomeric C_6H_{12} alkenes (the hexenes) if we disregard cis–trans isomerism:
   (a) Draw the structure and give the IUPAC name for each.
   (b) Indicate which four show geometrical isomerism and draw the isomeric structures.
   (c) One of these isomeric C_6H_{12} alkenes is dissymmetric. Which is it?

3. Draw structures for the four chloro-2-methyl-2-butenes.

4. What experimental evidence is there against the structural formula CH_3CH for ethylene?

5. Write structural formulas for each of the following compounds:
   (a) 2,3-Dimethyl-2-butene   (b) 2,4,4-Trimethyl-1-pentene
   (c) 1-Chlorocyclohexene   (d) 2,3-Dibromopropene
   (e) *cis*-4-Octene   (f) Allylcyclopentane
   (g) 1,5-Hexadiene   (h) 3-Methylcycloheptene
   (i) *trans*-2-Bromo-2-butene   (j) *cis,cis*-1,4-Cyclooctadiene
   (k) 1,1-Dichloroallene   (l) *trans*-1,3-Pentadiene

6. Name the following by the IUPAC system.

   (a) $(CH_3CH_2)_2C{=}CH_2$

   (b)

   (c)

   (d) $CH_2{=}CH-CHCH_3$ with Cl below the CH

   (e)

   (f)

   (g)

7. Show the cis and trans diastereomers for whichever of the following compounds are capable of exhibiting such isomerism.
   (a) 2-Butene
   (b) Allyl chloride
   (c) 1,2-Dibromopropene
   (d) 3-Hexyne
   (e) Cyclodecene
   (f) 2-Pentyne
   (g) 2,4-Hexadiene
   (h) 1,4-Dibromo-2-butene

8. Draw structures for all possible compounds having the formula C_5H_8 and which contain a double bond and a ring (note: the double bond may be in the ring, it may join a side chain to the ring, or it may be in the side chain). Are any of these compounds capable of showing cis–trans isomerism? Are any of the structures dissymmetric?

9. Predict the approximate values for all key bond angles in the compound

   $$H-C\equiv C-CH_2-CH_2-CH=CH-CH_2OH$$

10. Alkynes are often named as derivatives of acetylene. Name the pentynes (see page 159) as derivatives of acetylene.

11. List the following in order of increasing acidity: propene, water, methylamine, t-butyl alcohol, 1-propyne.

12. How can the following be distinguished by nmr spectroscopy: cyclohexene, 1-hexene, and 1-hexyne?

13. Deduce the structure of the compound C_5H_{10} that has the following nmr spectrum:

NMR spectrum of unknown, Problem 13.

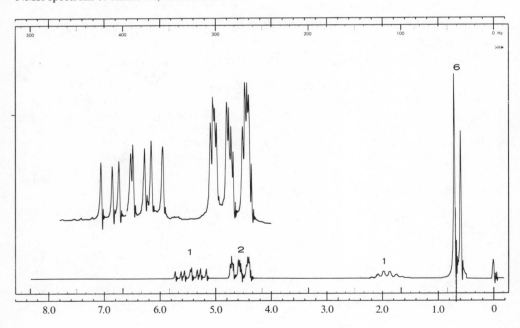

14. If the circulating electrons in acetylene cause the protons to be shielded, why are the protons found downfield from those of ethane?

15. Determine the number of sites of unsaturation possessed by each of the following molecular formulas.
    (a) $C_6H_{14}O$
    (b) C_6H_9Cl
    (c) $C_{10}H_8$
    (d) C_4H_9N
    (e) $C_3H_7NO_2$

16. A colorless liquid has the formula C_6H_{12}, and an nmr spectrum as shown. What is the structure of the compound?

NMR spectrum of unknown, Problem 16.

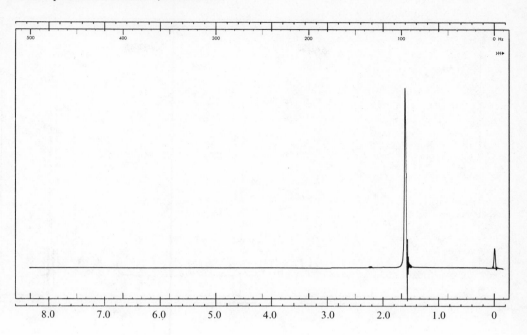

17.   An isomer of the compound in problem 16, also a colorless liquid, gave the nmr spectrum
      shown. What is its structure?

NMR spectrum of unknown, Problem 17.

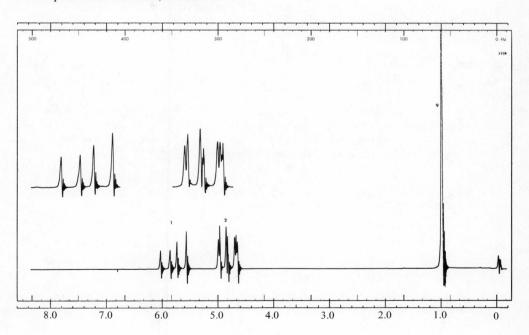

18.   The nmr spectrum of a compound $C_6H_{12}O$ is shown. What is the structure of the
      compound?

NMR spectrum of unknown, Problem 18.

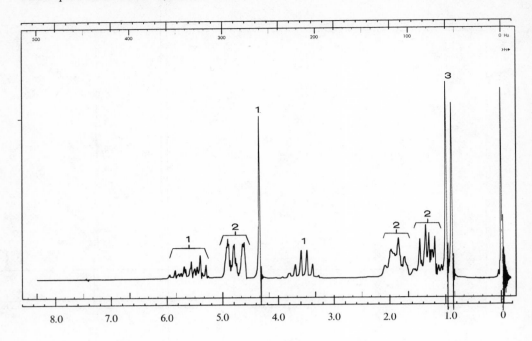

19. In which of the following properties will *cis*-3-methyl-2-pentene differ from the trans-
isomer?
    (a) Refractive index   (b) Dipole moment
    (c) Melting point   (d) Boiling point
    (e) Product of hydrogenation   (f) Rate of hydrogenation
    (g) Heat of hydrogenation   (h) Density
    (i) Heat of combustion   (j) Molecular weight

20. Limonene is found in orange peels, pine needles, and turpentine, and has the gross
    structure

$$H_3C-\underset{CH_3}{\overset{CH_2}{\underset{|}{C}}}$$

How many stereoisomeric forms of limonene are there? Circle each asymmetric carbon.
Complete hydrogenation of limonene produces $C_{10}H_{20}$; write the structural formula of
this product, and identify each asymmetric carbon. How many stereoisomers of the
tetrahydro compound are there? How many are optically active?

Optional Problem. Name the following alkenes by the IUPAC System, utilizing the
E, Z terminology to specify the configurations:

(a)
$$\underset{H}{\overset{CH_3}{>}}C=C\underset{CH_2CH_2CH(CH_3)_2}{\overset{H}{<}}$$

(b)
$$\underset{H}{\overset{F}{>}}C=C\underset{H}{\overset{Br}{<}}$$

(c)
$$\underset{H}{\overset{CH_3}{>}}C=C\underset{CH_2Cl}{\overset{Cl}{<}}$$

(d)
$$\underset{H}{\overset{CH_3}{>}}C=C\underset{\underset{H}{|}}{\overset{H}{<}}C=C\underset{CH_2CH_3}{\overset{H}{<}}$$

CHAPTER 8

FUNCTIONAL GROUPS CONTAINING OXYGEN MULTIPLY BONDED TO CARBON: THE CARBONYL GROUP

8.1   The Carbonyl Group

The $>C=O$ entity is referred to as the *carbonyl group*, and compounds containing this group are called *carbonyl compounds*. Figure 8.1 shows the structures of the common

Figure 8.1
Functional classes containing the carbonyl group.

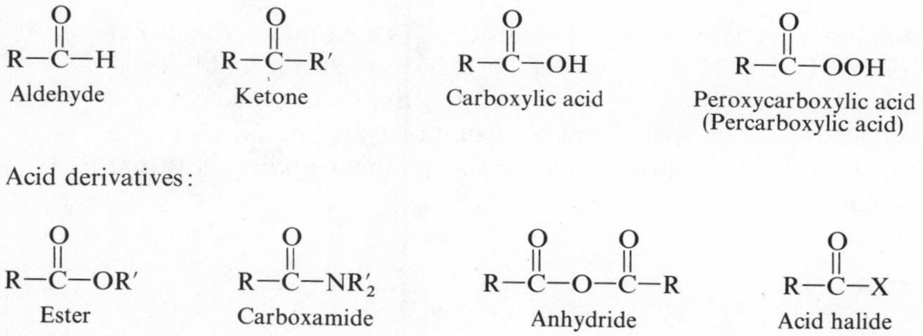

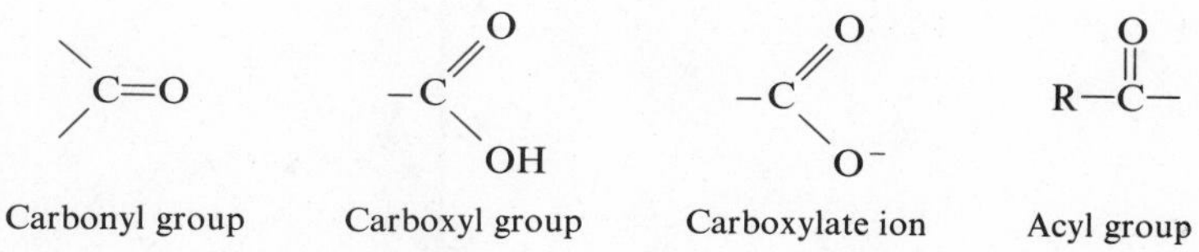

$$\underset{\text{Aldehyde}}{R-\overset{\overset{\textstyle O}{\|}}{C}-H} \qquad \underset{\text{Ketone}}{R-\overset{\overset{\textstyle O}{\|}}{C}-R'} \qquad \underset{\text{Carboxylic acid}}{R-\overset{\overset{\textstyle O}{\|}}{C}-OH} \qquad \underset{\substack{\text{Peroxycarboxylic acid}\\ \text{(Percarboxylic acid)}}}{R-\overset{\overset{\textstyle O}{\|}}{C}-OOH}$$

Acid derivatives:

$$\underset{\text{Ester}}{R-\overset{\overset{\textstyle O}{\|}}{C}-OR'} \qquad \underset{\text{Carboxamide}}{R-\overset{\overset{\textstyle O}{\|}}{C}-NR'_2} \qquad \underset{\text{Anhydride}}{R-\overset{\overset{\textstyle O}{\|}}{C}-O-\overset{\overset{\textstyle O}{\|}}{C}-R} \qquad \underset{\text{Acid halide}}{R-\overset{\overset{\textstyle O}{\|}}{C}-X}$$

functional classes of compounds which contain the carbonyl group. The functional groups themselves are referred to as follows:

$$\underset{\text{Carbonyl group}}{\overset{\diagdown}{\underset{\diagup}{}}C=O} \qquad \underset{\text{Carboxyl group}}{-\overset{\overset{\textstyle O}{\|}}{C}\diagdown_{OH}} \qquad \underset{\text{Carboxylate ion}}{-\overset{\overset{\textstyle O}{\|}}{C}\diagdown_{O^-}} \qquad \underset{\text{Acyl group}}{R-\overset{\overset{\textstyle O}{\|}}{C}-}$$

The simplest carbonyl-containing compound is formaldehyde, H_2CO, a gas which is very soluble in water. Most other carbonyl compounds are liquids, unless the molecular weight is high. Esters have fruity odors, and large cyclic ketones have very nice odors and are components of expensive perfumes. The carboxylic acids, the anhydrides and the acid halides have generally unpleasant odors.

The $C=O$ bond in compounds of the classes listed in Figure 8.1, like the $C=C$ bond of an olefin, is composed of one σ bond and one π bond. The carbonyl group may be pictured as being formed by the overlap of an sp^2 carbon orbital with a $2p_x$ oxygen orbital to form the σ bond, combined with sidewise overlap of $2p_z$ orbitals on carbon and oxygen to form the π bond (Figure 8.2). There is an unshared pair of electrons in the $2s$ orbital of oxygen, and another unshared pair in the $2p_y$ orbital.

Figure 8.2
The planar carbonyl group with unhybridized (p^3) oxygen. The lone pair in the $2s$ orbital on oxygen is not shown.

EXERCISE 8.1

Suggest an alternate formulation for the hybridization and bonding of a carbonyl group. What advantage might your alternate picture have over that shown in Figure 8.2?

Although the C=O bond is a very strong bond—176-179 kcal/mole, somewhat stronger than two C—O bonds (2 × 85.5 kcal/mole)—it is nevertheless a highly reactive double bond. The high reactivity is due to the electronegativity difference between carbon and oxygen, which leads to a very significant contribution by a dipolar resonance form in which oxygen is negative and carbon positive. Dipole moment studies show that the contribution of the polar form may be as high as 50%.

$$\underset{/}{\overset{\backslash}{}}C{=}\underset{\cdot\cdot}{\overset{\cdot\cdot}{O}}{:} \quad \leftrightarrow \quad \underset{/}{\overset{\backslash}{}}\overset{+}{C}{-}\underset{\cdot\cdot}{\overset{\cdot\cdot}{\bar{\bar{O}}}}{:}$$

In compounds in which the atom attached to the carbonyl group has occupied p orbitals, the actual bonding situation is complicated by the possibility of additional electron delocalization (resonance).

$$-\overset{\overset{\displaystyle \cdot\cdot O \cdot\cdot}{\|}}{C}\underset{\overset{\displaystyle}{:Y:}}{} \quad \leftrightarrow \quad -\overset{\overset{\displaystyle \cdot\cdot O \cdot\cdot \,-}{|}}{C}\underset{\overset{\displaystyle}{\cdot\cdot \overset{+}{Y}\cdot}}{}$$

The importance of the dipolar form increases as Y decreases in electronegativity from halogen to oxygen to nitrogen; note that as the contribution of the dipolar form increases, the double-bond character of the carbonyl group decreases.

A four-center π system is possible when Y is a vinyl group.

$$-\overset{\overset{\displaystyle O}{\|}}{C}{-}CH{=}CH{-} \quad \leftrightarrow \quad -\overset{\overset{\displaystyle O^{-}}{|}}{C}{=}CH{-}\overset{+}{C}H{-}$$

The double bonds in such a structure are conjugated like those in butadiene, and the student may wish to review that discussion (Sections 7.13–7.14).

EXERCISE 8.2

Two contributing resonance forms of methyl vinyl ketone are shown below. Which form is likely to make the more important contribution to the structure and why?

$$CH_3-\overset{\overset{\displaystyle O^-}{|}}{C}=CH-\overset{+}{C}H_2 \qquad\qquad CH_3-\overset{\overset{\displaystyle O^+}{|}}{C}=CH-\overset{-}{C}H_2$$
$$\text{(a)} \qquad\qquad\qquad\qquad \text{(b)}$$

EXERCISE 8.3

Draw a picture showing the atomic p_z orbitals of methyl vinyl ketone. What does your picture imply about the stereochemistry of the molecule?

8.2   Carbonyl Compounds as Acids and Bases

The Carbonyl Group as a Lewis Acid

There are many organic compounds in which a multiply bonded atom can accept a share in an electron pair, usually with a synchronous shift in electrons of the multiple bond. (In Section 7.17 the case where a multiple bond *donates* a shared electron pair was discussed.) We may add to our previous list (Section 4.3) of Lewis acids, *multiply bonded groups with a site of low electron density.* The most notable of such Lewis acids

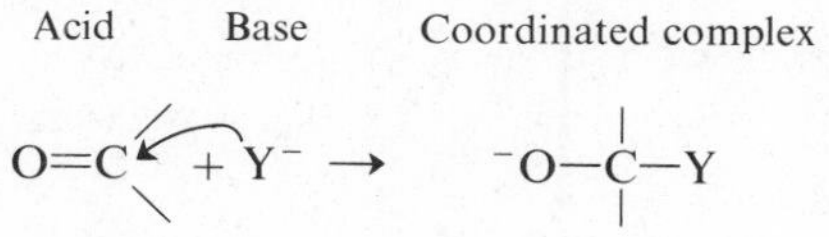

$$\text{Acid} \qquad \text{Base} \qquad \text{Coordinated complex}$$

$$O{=}C\overset{\displaystyle\frown}{\underset{\displaystyle\diagdown}{}} + Y^- \rightarrow \quad {}^-O-\overset{|}{\underset{|}{C}}-Y$$

is the carbonyl group. Note that the carbon atom involved does not have an unfilled orbital, but that an orbital is made available by an electron shift. This type of reaction, which involves addition across the $C{=}O$ bond, is one of the most important in all of organic chemistry.

An important classification for ionic reactions of organic molecules depends on a description of the "attacking" reagent. By the Lewis definition, an acid is any species capable of accepting an electron pair and a base is an electron-pair donor. Reagents which are electron-seeking (hence, Lewis acids) may be termed *electrophiles* (electron-loving); reagents which are electron-donating (hence Lewis bases) may be termed *nucleophiles* (nucleus-loving). Ionic reactions are then classified as *electrophilic* or *nucleophilic* according to the type of reagent involved. For instance, the equation shown above depicts a *nucleophilic addition* to a carbonyl group.

Do these fancy words describe anything new? The answer is yes. *Basicity* is assessed in terms of the position of the *equilibrium* between an electron donor and an acid (usually the proton). *Nucleophilicity*, on the other hand, is measured in terms of the *rate* of the reaction of the nucleophile with a substrate. (The word *substrate* is a general term for the molecule which is undergoing the reaction in question.) Consider the examples of methoxide, CH_3O^-, and methyl mercaptide, CH_3S^-. Methoxide is the stronger base but the mercaptide is the more powerful nucleophile. More will be said about basicity and nucleophilicity in later chapters.

$$\text{Bases}\begin{cases} CH_3O^- + H_2O \;\;\rightleftharpoons\; CH_3OH + HO^- \\ CH_3S^- + H_2O \;\;\rightleftharpoons\; CH_3SH + HO^- \end{cases}$$

$$\text{Nucleophiles}\begin{cases} CH_3O^- + \;\;{}^{\backslash}_{/}C{=}O \;\xrightarrow{\text{slow}}\; CH_3O{-}\overset{|}{\underset{|}{C}}{-}O^- \\ CH_3S^- + \;\;{}^{\backslash}_{/}C{=}O \;\xrightarrow{\text{fast}}\; CH_3S{-}\overset{|}{\underset{|}{C}}{-}O^- \end{cases}$$

It is easy to see that both proton acids and Lewis acids would be efficient catalysts for nucleophilic additions to the carbonyl group.

$$\;{}^{\backslash}_{/}C{=}O \;\xrightarrow{H^+}\; \left[\;{}^{\backslash}_{/}C{=}\overset{+}{O}{\underset{H}{\diagdown}} \;\;\leftrightarrow\;\; {}^{\backslash}_{/}\overset{+}{C}{-}O{\underset{H}{\diagdown}} \right]$$

Lewis acid   Stronger Lewis acid

$$Y^- + \;{}^{\backslash}_{/}C{=}\overset{+}{O}{\underset{H}{\diagdown}} \;\longrightarrow\; Y{-}\overset{|}{\underset{|}{C}}{-}OH$$

The protonated form of the carbonyl has more positive charge on carbon than does the original carbonyl, as shown. Attack by a nucleophile is thus facilitated.

The Carbonyl Group as a Lewis Base

The oxygen of the carbonyl group bears two lone pairs and, in addition, a high proportion of the electron density of the σ- and π-bonding electrons. As a consequence, the oxygen acts as a Lewis base, although it is 10^{12} to 10^{18} times less basic than the nitrogen of an amine.

$$\;{}^{\backslash}_{/}C{=}O \;\leftrightarrow\; {}^{\backslash}_{/}\overset{+}{C}{-}\overset{..}{O}{\underset{}{\diagdown}} \;\;\leftarrow\; \text{Lewis base}$$
$$\underset{\text{Lewis acid}}{}$$

Thus we find that while most carbonyl compounds except the very low molecular weight ones are insoluble in water, they dissolve in concentrated H_2SO_4 with formation of $R_2C{=}OH.^+$

Carbonyl Compounds as Proton Acids

We have seen that a carbonyl group may act both as a Lewis acid and as a Lewis base. Carbonyl compounds which contain a hydrogen bonded to an atom adjacent to the carbonyl group also may function as proton acids.

$$-\overset{O}{\underset{Y-H}{C\!\!\diagup\!\!\diagdown}} \;\;\underset{+H^+}{\overset{-H^+}{\rightleftharpoons}}\; \left[-\overset{O}{\underset{Y^-}{C\!\!\diagup\!\!\diagdown}} \;\leftrightarrow\; -\overset{O^-}{\underset{Y}{C\!\!\diagup\!\!\diagdown}} \right]$$

Increasing acidity $\left\downarrow\begin{array}{l} Y = CH_2 \;\; \text{Aldehydes and ketones, } pK_a \sim 19 \\ Y = NH \;\;\; \text{Amides, } pK_a \sim 15 \\ Y = O \;\;\;\;\; \text{Carboxylic acids, } pK_a \sim 5 \end{array}\right.$

The carboxylic acids are among the stronger organic acids; acetic acid (CH_3COOH) is 10^{11} times more acidic than ethanol. Although the uncharged resonance form is of major importance for most organic compounds, charged forms sometimes make significant contributions to the structure, and this is the case with the carboxylic acids.

$$R-C\begin{matrix}O\\\\OH\end{matrix} \leftrightarrow R-C\begin{matrix}O^-\\\\\overset{+}{O}H\end{matrix}$$

The form on the left is considerably more important than that on the right.

When the carboxylic acid ionizes, the resulting anion has two resonance forms which are equivalent.

$$R-C\begin{matrix}O\\\\O^-\end{matrix} \leftrightarrow R-C\begin{matrix}O^-\\\\O\end{matrix}$$

As discussed under Rules for the Use of the Resonance Method, page 152, resonance is more effective the more similar the energies of two resonance forms. Resonance therefore stabilizes the carboxylic acid, but it stabilizes the anion very much more.

This extra stabilization of the product on the right-hand side of the equation

$$R-C\begin{matrix}O\\\\OH\end{matrix} \rightleftharpoons R-C\begin{matrix}O\\\\O^-\end{matrix} + H^+$$

causes the equilibrium to be further to the right than if such resonance did not occur. The high acidity of carboxylic acids as compared to alcohols

$$R-OH \rightleftharpoons R-O^- + H^+$$

can be mainly attributed to this resonance effect.

EXERCISE 8.4

Why is resonance more important in the carboxylate ion than in the carboxyl group itself?

Among compounds of the type

$$R-\overset{\displaystyle O}{\underset{\displaystyle \|}{C}}-Y-H$$

the carboxylic acids are the most acidic. The amides, $RCONH_2$, are weakly acidic, essentially neutral compounds, as might be expected from the relative electronegativities of nitrogen and oxygen. At the opposite extreme, with Y a carbon atom in a compound such as a ketone, there is no three-atom delocalized system in the starting compound. There is, however, the possibility of electron delocalization in the anion, although the two resonance forms are not of equal energy.

$$R-C\begin{matrix}O\\\\CH_3\end{matrix} \underset{+H^+}{\overset{-H^+}{\rightleftharpoons}} \left[R-C\begin{matrix}O\\\\CH_2^-\end{matrix} \leftrightarrow R-C\begin{matrix}O^-\\\\CH_2\end{matrix} \right]$$

Keto form   Enolate ion

EXERCISE 8.5

Which of the two resonance forms of the enolate ion do you expect to make the major contribution to the structure?

A hydrogen on the carbon adjacent to the carbonyl group of a ketone is thus much more acidic ($pK_a \sim 19$) than the hydrogen of an alkane ($pK_a \sim 40$), but much less acidic than the proton of a carboxylic acid ($pK_a \sim 5$). Since a ketone is less acidic than water (pK_a 16), we usually would regard it as neutral, but this weak acidity is important in the chemical properties of such compounds (Sections 19.13–19.16).

When a hydrogen is attached to a carbon flanked by two carbonyl groups, the compound is considerably more acidic ($pK_a \sim 10$) than is an ordinary carbonyl compound, because of the added resonance stabilization imparted to the anion by the additional carbonyl group.

8.3   Keto–Enol Tautomerism

Protonation of either oxygen in a carboxylate anion produces the same structure—the carboxylic acid. With the enolate ion reprotonation may occur on carbon to produce the ketone, or it may occur on oxygen to produce an *enol* (*en-*, C=C; *-ol*, OH), which is equivalent to a vinyl alcohol. A ketone is in equilibrium with its enol under most conditions.

Keto–enol interconversion is subject to catalysis by acid or base, or, more accurately, a combination thereof. The process may occur stepwise or concertedly. Thus the base may remove the proton from carbon to give the enolate ion, which may protonate on oxygen to give the enol; or protonation may occur on oxygen to give the conjugate acid of the ketone, followed by abstraction of the proton on carbon by base. Alternatively, both of these proton transfers may occur simultaneously, and this is the way the process is usually written.

Except in the complete absence of acid or base, the keto and enol forms are rapidly interconvertible, and they exist in a mobile equilibrium the position of which depends upon the structural details of the compound and on the conditions (solvent, temperature, concentration, etc.).

Note that the keto and enol forms of a compound are distinct molecules. They are not to be confused with resonance forms, which have no real independent existence. A special name has been coined to describe the relationship between keto and enol forms. They are called *tautomers* of one another and their interconversion is referred to as *tautomerism*. Tautomers are easily and rapidly interconvertible under ordinary conditions. The keto and enol forms of cyclohexanone,

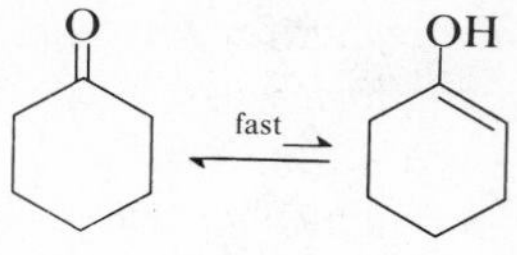

which differ from one another only in the relative position of a hydrogen atom, are known as tautomers, whereas methylenecyclohexane and 1-methylcyclohexene,

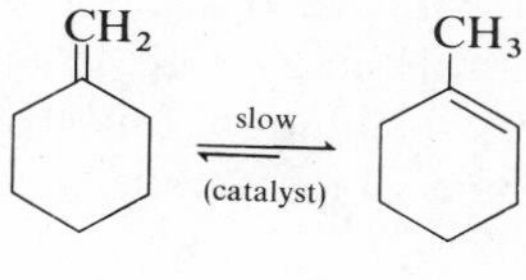

which exist independently under ordinary conditions, are simply structural isomers, not tautomers. The difference between structural isomers and tautomers is one of degree, not of kind.

For simple aldehydes and ketones equilibrium is far on the keto side, whereas 1,3-dicarbonyl compounds contain much more enol form.

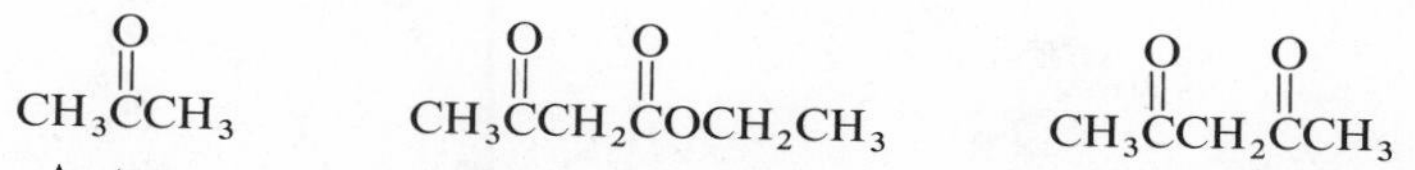

$\overset{O}{\overset{\|}{CH_3CCH_3}}$	$\overset{O\quad O}{\overset{\|\quad\|}{CH_3CCH_2COCH_2CH_3}}$	$\overset{O\quad O}{\overset{\|\quad\|}{CH_3CCH_2CCH_3}}$
Acetone	Ethyl acetoacetate	Acetylacetone
Less than 0.1 % enol	7.5 % enol	80 % enol

The existence of an appreciable amount of enol form in a 1,3-dicarbonyl compound is the result of stabilization by conjugation of the carbon–carbon double bond of the enol with the second carbonyl group and, where possible, by internal hydrogen bonding. The enol forms of most 1,3-dicarbonyl compounds exist in intramolecularly hydrogen-bonded ring structures described as *chelate rings* (from the Greek *chela* meaning "claw"). Exceptionally stable, usually crystalline, chelate salts are formed between β-dicarbonyl compounds and various metallic ions. It is necessary that the metal ion have low-lying unoccupied orbitals available for coordination.

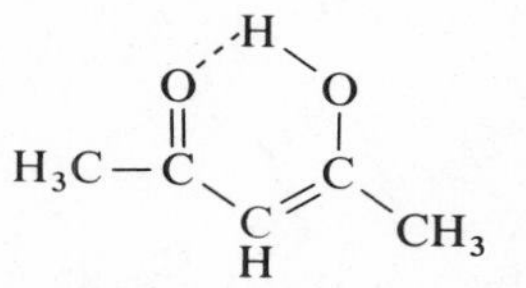

Enol of acetylacetone

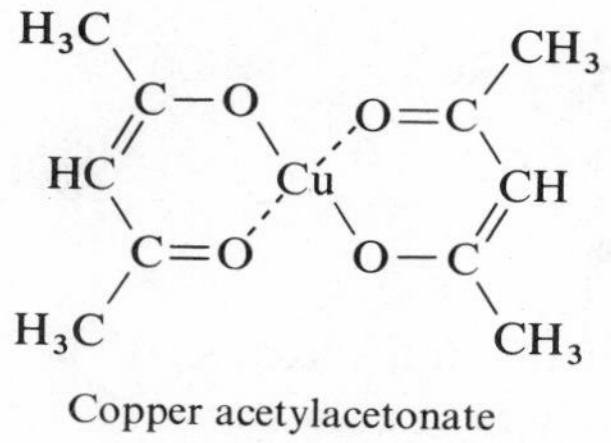

Copper acetylacetonate

SEPARATION OF TAUTOMERS. *Since long before the nature of tautomerization was understood, chemists have been fascinated with the challenge of isolating the simplest of the enols, vinyl alcohol; to date this feat has not been accomplished. The equilibrium heavily favors the aldehyde.*

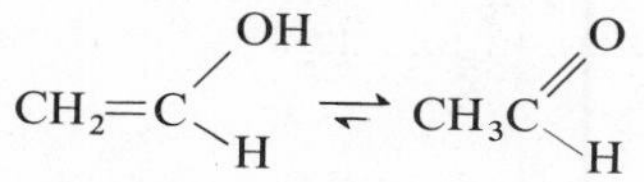

Vinyl alcohol   Acetaldehyde

Ethyl acetoacetate has always been considered as the classic case of keto–enol tautomerism. As early as 1911, the German chemist Ludwig Knorr† succeeded in separating and isolating both the keto and the enol forms of ethyl acetoacetate. The keto form crystallized from solutions at −78°C. When dry hydrogen chloride was passed into a solution of the sodium salt of ethyl acetoacetate at −78°C, the enol form was obtained as a glassy solid. When either isomer was permitted to reach room temperature, the equilibrium mixture was obtained.

EXERCISE 8.6

Ordinary glass contains acidic and basic sites which can catalyze keto–enol interconversion. By using specially treated quartz apparatus, in 1920 K. H. Meyer separated the two forms of ethyl acetoacetate by distillation. Since alcohols boil higher than ketones, it is surprising that the enol form boils lower than the keto form. Offer an explanation.

8.4   The Structures of Aldehydes and Ketones

If a carbonyl carbon is bonded to one or two hydrogens and to not more than one alkyl group, the resulting compound is an *aldehyde*. In a *ketone*, two alkyl groups flank the carbonyl.

Aldehydes, in principle and in practice are obtained by the oxidation of primary alcohols, whereas ketones are obtained by oxidation of secondary alcohols. Aldehydes are subject to further oxidation to yield carboxylic acids. In organic chemistry *oxidation* usually involves the removal of hydrogen, often coupled with the addition of oxygen or some other electronegative element. *Reduction* most frequently involves the addition of hydrogen and/or the removal of an electronegative element such as oxygen.

The nmr spectra of aldehydes and ketones give us useful structural information about these compounds, even though the carbonyl group itself gives no peak in the nmr spectrum. Hydrogen nuclei in the vicinity of the carbonyl group experience significant deshielding as a result of the electron-attracting character of the positively charged carbonyl carbon. Methyl hydrogens adjacent to the carbonyl group of aldehydes and ketones appear near $\delta 2$; methylenes ($-CH_2-CO-$) appear at slightly lower field, near $\delta 2.5$ (Figure 8.3 and Figure 8.4). A dramatic deshielding is observed in the case of aldehydic hydrogens, which are attached directly to the carbonyl carbon; such hydrogens appear near $\delta 10$ (Figure 8.3). Since almost no other types of hydrogen nuclei appear at such a low field, nmr spectroscopy provides an excellent method for the identification of aldehydes.

† Ludwig Knorr. 1859–1921. Born Munich. Universities of Wuerzburg and Jena.

Figure 8.3

NMR spectrum of acetaldehyde in $CDCl_3$ solution (offset 2.0 ppm). Note the characteristic low field resonance of the aldehydic quartet at δ 9.80.

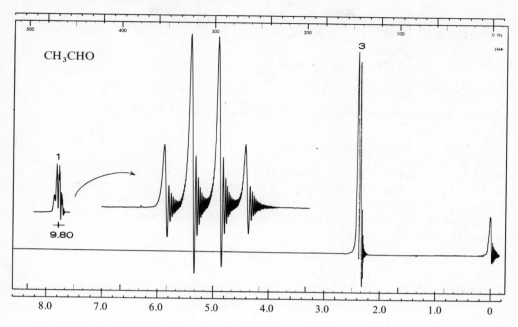

TECHNICAL NOTE ON NMR SPECTRA. *The commonly used charts for nmr spectra cover a range of 500 Hz (δ 0 to 8.33). An "offset" is required to bring any peaks onto the chart which fall outside this standard range. The offset does not apply to the lower curve in Figure 8.3, which runs the full length of the chart, but only to the upper partial trace beginning at the extreme left-hand edge. To determine the chemical shift of protons shown in an offset tracing, the offset in ppm is simply added to the values shown at the bottom of the chart. For example, in Figure 8.3 the aldehyde proton is seen on the offset trace centered at 7.80. The offset is given at 2.0 ppm. The chemical shift of the aldehyde proton is then 7.80 + 2.0 or δ 9.80. The large quartet is a "blow-up" of the δ 9.80 multiplet.*

Figure 8.4

NMR spectrum of methyl ethyl ketone.

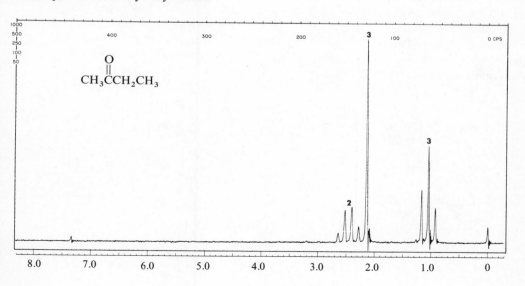

EXERCISE 8.7

Highly acidic protons such as in H_2SO_4 or acetic acid, are found near δ 10 to 15, and this is clearly due to the fact that they have a very low electron density around them. The proton attached to the carbonyl carbon of an aldehyde is not acidic. Why then, does it occur at such low field? Why is such a proton not acidic?

EXERCISE 8.8

Suggest complete interpretations of the spectra in Figures 8.3 and 8.4.

8.5   Nomenclature of Aldehydes and Ketones

The IUPAC names of aldehydes are formed by replacing the final -e of the hydrocarbon name by the ending -al. The aldehydic carbon is always number 1. Common names are derived from the common names of the corresponding carboxylic acids (Section 8.8) by replacing the ending -ic or -oic with -aldehyde. Common names are almost always used for aldehydes of five carbons or less.

$$CH_3CH_2COOH \qquad CH_3CH_2CHO \qquad CH_3CHCH_2CHO$$
$$\overset{\displaystyle CH_3}{\underset{}{\big|}}$$

Propionic acid   Propionaldehyde   Isovaleraldehyde
(Propanoic acid)   (Propanal)   (3-Methylbutanal)

In the IUPAC names, the positions of substituents on a parent structure are designated by numbers. A frequently used practice with common names is to indicate substituent positions by means of Greek letters, starting with α at the carbon *adjacent* to the principal functional group; ω is sometimes used to designate the last carbon in the chain regardless of the number.

$$\overset{\omega}{C}\cdots\overset{\varepsilon}{C}-\overset{\delta}{C}-\overset{\gamma}{C}-\overset{\beta}{C}-\overset{\alpha}{C}-X \qquad\qquad CH_3CH_2CHCHO$$
$$\qquad\qquad\qquad\qquad\qquad\qquad\qquad Br$$

α alpha δ delta
β beta ε epsilon
γ gamma ω omega α-Bromo-*n*-butyraldehyde

The IUPAC names of ketones are derived from the hydrocarbon name by adding the suffix -*one* to the name of the longest hydrocarbon chain which contains the carbonyl group, the location of which is specified by the lowest possible number placed just before the hydrocarbon name, or just before the suffix when used in conjunction with other suffixes. When a ketone is present along with other important functional groups, it is sometimes indicated by the prefix *oxo-* or *keto-* along with an appropriate number. The common names of ketones are formed by naming the hydrocarbon groups attached to the carbonyl group and adding the word *ketone*. Occasionally ketones are known by trivial names which reflect their origin.

$$\overset{\displaystyle O}{\underset{\displaystyle \|}{CH_3CH_2CCH_3}} \qquad \overset{\displaystyle O}{\underset{\displaystyle \|}{CH_2{=}CH{-}C{-}CH_3}} \qquad \overset{CH_3}{\underset{CH_3}{\diagup}}C{=}CHCCH_3$$

Methyl ethyl ketone   Methyl vinyl ketone   Mesityl oxide
(2-Butanone)   (3-Buten-2-one)   (4-Methyl-3-penten-2-one)

$$\overset{\displaystyle O}{\underset{\displaystyle \|}{Cl{-}CH_2{-}C{-}CH_3}} \qquad \overset{\displaystyle O\;\;Cl}{\underset{\displaystyle \|\;\;\;|}{CH_3CH_2C{-}CHCH_3}} \qquad \overset{\displaystyle O}{\underset{\displaystyle \|}{CH_3CCH_2CH_2COOH}}$$

Chloroacetone   2-Chloro-3-pentanone   4-Oxopentanoic acid
                    (α-Chlorodiethyl ketone)   (γ-Ketovaleric acid)
                                        (Levulinic acid)

EXERCISE 8.9

Name the following compounds (by any system of nomenclature):

(a) $CH_3CH_2CH_2CH_2CH_2CHO$

(b) $CH_3CHCH_2CH_2\overset{\overset{\displaystyle O}{\|}}{C}CH_3$
    $\quad\ \ |$
    $\quad\ CH_3$

(c) $CH_3\underset{\underset{\displaystyle H}{|}}{C}=\underset{\underset{\displaystyle H}{|}}{C}CH_2CH_2-\overset{\overset{\displaystyle O}{\|}}{C}-CH_2CH_2CH_2CH_2CH_3$

8.6   Properties of Aldehydes and Ketones

The physical properties of a number of representative and important aldehydes and ketones are given in Table 8.1. Most simple aldehydes and ketones have dipole moments near 2.7 D. Significant dipole association accounts for the boiling points of these compounds; the boiling points are intermediate between those of hydrocarbons and alcohols of similar molecular weights. The low molecular weight aldehydes have very pungent odors, while ketones, which are widely distributed in nature, often have very pleasant odors. A number of natural and synthetic ketones are used in perfumes and flavorings; others are important medicinal and biological materials.

Table 8.1   Physical Properties of Aldehydes and Ketones

Name	Structure	Mp, °C	Bp, °C
	Aldehydes		
Formaldehyde	CH_2O	-117	-19
Acetaldehyde	CH_3CHO	-123	21
Propionaldehyde	CH_3CH_2CHO	-81	48
n-Butyraldehyde	$CH_3(CH_2)_2CHO$	-97	75
n-Valeraldehyde	$CH_3(CH_2)_3CHO$	-51	93
n-Caproaldehyde	$CH_3(CH_2)_4CHO$	-56	129
Acrolein	$CH_2{=}CHCHO$	-87	53
	Ketones		
Acetone	CH_3COCH_3	-95	56
Methyl ethyl ketone	$CH_3COCH_2CH_3$	-86	80
Diethyl ketone	$CH_3CH_2COCH_2CH_3$	-39	102
3-Hexanone	$CH_3CH_2COCH_2CH_2CH_3$		124
t-Butyl methyl ketone	$(CH_3)_3CCOCH_3$	-53	106
Cyclopentanone	⬠=O	-58	130
Cyclohexanone	⬡=O	-31	156
Methyl vinyl ketone	$CH_3COCH{=}CH_2$		80
Mesityl oxide	$CH_3COCH{=}C(CH_3)_2$	-53	130
Biacetyl	$CH_3COCOCH_3$	-2	88
Acetylacetone	$CH_3COCH_2COCH_3$	-23	138

USES OF CARBONYL COMPOUNDS. *Biacetyl is a principal ingredient in the flavoring of margarine. Muscone, extracted from the scent glands of the male musk deer, is an expensive perfume ingredient. Camphor, obtained from the wood of the camphor tree native to Vietnam, Japan, and China, has been known and valued for medicinal purposes for many centuries; it is still frequently used, although it appears to have no therapeutic*

value other than its characteristic medicinal odor. Testosterone, the sex hormone respon-
sible for the development of male characteristics in man and other mammals, is obtained
commercially by extraction from bulls' testicles.

$$\begin{array}{c} O \quad O \\ \parallel \parallel \\ CH_3CCCH_3 \end{array}$$

Butane-2,3-dione
(Biacetyl)

Camphor
(1,7,7-Trimethylbicyclo-
[2.2.1]heptan-2-one)

Muscone
(3-Methylcyclopentadecanone)

Testosterone

Formalin, a 37% aqueous solution of formaldehyde, is familiar as a preservative of
biological specimens. Over 2.5 billion pounds of formalin is manufactured each year in
the United States, mainly for use in the resin and plastics industry. Acetaldehyde is
also an important industrial chemical, used in the synthesis of organic compounds.

   Acetone is by far the most important of the ketones. Over a billion pounds are used
annually in the United States. It is an excellent solvent for organic materials. Methyl
ethyl ketone is also used in large quantities as an industrial solvent.

8.7   The Structures of Carboxylic Acids

The carboxyl group, —COOH, formally a combination of a carbonyl and a hydroxyl
group, represents the oxidation state of a primary carbon just above that of an aldehyde.
The most apparent result of the combination of the two groups is a tremendous increase
in the acidity of the hydroxyl. Although ionization is far from complete, the carboxyl
group ionizes sufficiently in water to turn litmus red. The reasons for the acidity of the
carboxyl have already been discussed in Section 8.2.

   Acids form even stronger hydrogen bonds than do alcohols, because their O—H
bonds are more strongly polarized and the hydrogen bridge may be bonded to the more
negatively charged carbonyl oxygen rather than to an oxygen of another hydroxyl.
Carboxylic acids in the solid, liquid, and even to some extent in the vapor state exist as
cyclic dimers.

$$R-C \begin{array}{c} O \cdots H-O \\ \diagup \qquad \diagdown \\ \diagdown \qquad \diagup \\ O-H \cdots O \end{array} C-R$$

The electron density at the carboxyl hydrogen is very low and, as would be anticipated,
such protons appear in nmr spectra at unusually low field, near δ 11 to 13. In the nmr
spectrum of acetic acid in deuteriochloroform solution, a methyl singlet is observed at
δ 2.10 and the acidic proton singlet at δ 11.37. The nmr spectrum of a simple, common
carboxylic acid is shown in Figure 8.5.

EXERCISE 8.10

Give a detailed interpretation of the nmr spectrum shown in Figure 8.5.

Figure 8.5
NMR spectrum of a simple carboxylic acid.

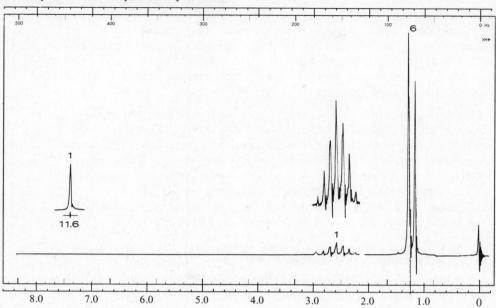

8.8   Nomenclature of Carboxylic Acids

The common names for a number of important carboxylic acids are shown in Table 8.2. Since these and names derived from them will be in constant use, the student should

Table 8.2   Carboxylic Acids

Acid	Structure	Mp, °C	Bp, °C	$pK_a^{25°}$
	Monocarboxylic Acids			
Formic	HCOOH	8	100.5	3.77
Acetic	CH_3COOH	17	118	4.76
Propionic	CH_3CH_2COOH	−22	141	4.88
n-Butyric	$CH_3CH_2CH_2COOH$	−5	163	4.82
n-Valeric	$CH_3CH_2CH_2CH_2COOH$	−35	187	4.81
Hexanoic (Caproic)	$CH_3(CH_2)_4COOH$	−2	205	4.85
Octanoic (Caprylic)	$CH_3(CH_2)_6COOH$	16	237	4.85
Decanoic (Capric)	$CH_3(CH_2)_8COOH$	31	269	—
Lauric (Dodecanoic)	$CH_3(CH_2)_{10}COOH$	43	—	—
Myristic (Tetradecanoic)	$CH_3(CH_2)_{12}COOH$	58	—	—
Palmitic (Hexadecanoic)	$CH_3(CH_2)_{14}COOH$	64	—	—
Stearic (Octadecanoic)	$CH_3(CH_2)_{16}COOH$	70	—	—
Glycolic	$HOCH_2COOH$	79	—	3.83
Lactic	$CH_3CHOHCOOH$	18	—	3.87
Acrylic	$CH_2{=}CHCOOH$	13	141	4.26
	Dicarboxylic Acids			
Oxalic	HOOC—COOH	190	—	1.46
Malonic	$HOOC—CH_2—COOH$	135d	—	2.80
Succinic	$HOOC—(CH_2)_2—COOH$	187	235	4.17
Glutaric	$HOOC—(CH_2)_3—COOH$	98	303	—
Adipic (Hexanedioic)	$HOOC—(CH_2)_4—COOH$	152	340	—
Pimelic (Heptanedioic)	$HOOC—(CH_2)_5—COOH$	105	—	—
Maleic	HOOC—CH=CH—COOH (*cis*)	131	—	—
Fumaric	HOOC—CH=CH—COOH (*trans*)	287	—	—

commit them to memory. Above six carbons, only those acids with an even number of carbon atoms are important, since they are the only ones that occur to any significant extent in natural sources. As we shall see later (Chapter 30), nature builds these longer chain acids by the combination of two-carbon acetic acid residues.

It is also important to know the common names of the simple dicarboxylic acids shown in Table 8.2. The names of the saturated dicarboxylic acids from C_2 through C_7 (oxalic, malonic, succinic, glutaric, adipic, pimelic) can be remembered by the first letters of the mnemonic: *Oh my, such good apple pie.*

A HISTORICAL NOTE. *Many of the common carboxylic acids were first isolated from natural sources, especially from fats, hence they are often referred to as "fatty acids." The common names, used before their chemical structures were known, refer to natural origin rather than to their structures. The irritation resulting from the bite of an ant is due to formic acid (*Latin *formica, ant), the principal ingredient of vinegar is acetic acid (*L. *acetum, vinegar), butyric acid (*L. *butyrum, butter) gives rancid butter its characteristic odor, valeric acid was isolated from valerian root (*L. *valere, to be strong), and caproic, caprylic, and capric acids (*L. *caper, goat) are responsible for the unsociable odor of goats.*

Acids having an isopropyl group at the end of a normal hydrocarbon chain may be named by adding the prefix *iso-* to the common name of the acid with the same total number of carbons.

$$CH_3CH_2CH_2CH_2COOH$$
Valeric acid

$$
\begin{array}{c}
CH_3 \\
| \\
CH_3CHCH_2COOH
\end{array}
$$
Isovaleric acid

Acids are often named as derivatives of a parent acid.

$$
\begin{array}{c}
CH_3 \\
| \\
CH_3CCOOH \\
| \\
CH_3
\end{array}
$$
Trimethylacetic acid
(Pivalic acid)

$$
\begin{array}{c}
CH_3 \\
| \\
CH_3CH_2CCH_2COOH \\
| \\
CH_3
\end{array}
$$
β,β-Dimethylvaleric acid

$$
\begin{array}{c}
CH_3CHCOOH \\
| \\
NH_2
\end{array}
$$
Alanine
(α-Aminopropionic acid)

In the IUPAC system, the final *-e* is dropped from the name of the longest-chain hydrocarbon which contains the carboxyl group and the suffix *-oic acid* is added. The carboxyl carbon is always numbered atom 1. Note that in the common names which use Greek letters, it is the carbon *adjacent* to the carboxyl which is called α, not the carboxyl carbon itself. The systematic name is seldom used for an acid with less than five carbons.

$$
\begin{array}{c}
CH_3 \qquad CH_3 \\
| \qquad\quad | \\
CH_3CHCH_2CH_2CHCOOH
\end{array}
$$
2,5-Dimethylhexanoic acid

$$CH_2{=}CH{-}(CH_2)_8{-}COOH$$
10-Undecenoic acid

When a carboxyl group appears as a substituent on a parent structure, it may be referred to by the prefix *carboxy-*. Alternatively, the parent hydrocarbon name may be used, followed by *carboxylic acid.*

2-Carboxycyclohexanone   Cyclobutanecarboxylic acid

The names for the carboxylate anions ($RCOO^-$) are formed from those of the acids by dropping the *-ic acid* and adding the suffix *-ate*. Salts of carboxylic acids are then named by first naming the cation, followed by the name of the carboxylate anion.

$$CH_3COO^-NH_4^+ \qquad \langle\ \rangle\!-\!COO^-Na^+ \qquad HOOCCH_2CH_2COO^-Na^+$$

Ammonium · · · · · · · · Sodium · · · · · · · · · · Sodium
acetate · · · · · cyclohexanecarboxylate · · · · hydrogen succinate

8.9   Properties of Carboxylic Acids

The melting and boiling point data given for representative carboxylic acids in Table 8.2 indicate that these substances have much higher boiling and melting points than do other classes of compounds of similar molecular weight. This is attributed to the strong intermolecular association through hydrogen bonds (Sections 4.20 and 8.7). The water solubility of acids more or less parallels that of alcohols, amines, and other compounds which water can solvate through hydrogen-bond formation. Formic, acetic, propionic, and butyric acid are completely miscible with water, isobutyric and valeric acid have borderline solubilities, and the higher acids are practically insoluble in water.

Carboxylic acids form the soluble sodium carboxylates on reaction with aqueous sodium hydroxide or sodium bicarbonate.

$$RCOOH + NaHCO_3 \rightarrow RCOO^-Na^+ + CO_2 + H_2O$$

The sodium salts of acids containing 12 or more carbons are only sparingly soluble in water and are useful as soaps (Section 8.11). Salts of carboxylic acids have the expected properties of high melting points and low solubilities in organic solvents.

USES OF CARBOXYLIC ACIDS. *Formic and acetic acids have a sharp acrid odor and a typical sour acid taste. The acids with four to eight carbons have exceptionally disagreeable odors. Obnoxious as they may be, in small concentrations they add delight to many flavors; blue cheese would never make it without valeric acid.*

All of the acids listed in Table 8.2 are available for commercial use as synthetic intermediates. By far the most important of these is acetic acid, which is used as a reactant and solvent in both laboratory and industrial processes. Acetic acid is marketed as glacial acetic acid (~99.5%), so-called because on cold days it freezes to an icelike solid. Over a million pounds is used annually in the United States.

Many acids and derivatives thereof are found in nature; they play important roles in animal and plant metabolism. Acetic acid, the end product of fermentation, is the fundamental building block used by organisms for the biosynthesis of a wide variety of natural products from fatty acids to natural rubber (Chapter 30).

8.10   Esters and Lactones

In a *condensation reaction*, two molecules unite, usually with the loss of water or other simple molecule. An *ester* is the product of a condensation reaction between a carboxylic acid and an alcohol.

$$\underset{\displaystyle R-\overset{\textstyle O}{\overset{\|}{C}}\!-\!\lceil OH + H\rceil\!-\!OR'}{} \rightarrow R-\overset{\textstyle O}{\overset{\|}{C}}\!-\!OR' + HOH$$

At one time it was thought that esterification was analogous to neutralization, and esters are still named as if they were "alkyl salts" of carboxylic acids.

CH_3COOH · · · · · CH_3COONa · · · · · $CH_3COOCH_2CH_3$
Acetic acid · · · · Sodium acetate · · · · · Ethyl acetate

$$CH_3CH_2COOCH_2CH{=}CH_2 \qquad CH_2{=}CHCOO\overset{\overset{\displaystyle CH_3}{|}}{\underset{\underset{\displaystyle CH_3}{|}}{C}}CH_3 \qquad ClCH_2COOCH{=}CH_2$$

Allyl propionate   *t*-Butyl acrylate   Vinyl chloroacetate

Sometimes the ester group may be considered a substituent on a parent compound.

2-Carbomethoxycyclohexanone   2-Acetoxycyclohexanone

Esters are somewhat less enolic than ketones, but a β-ketoester, such as 2-carbo-methoxycyclohexanone, contains at least a small percentage of enol at equilibrium.

EXERCISE 8.11

Write the structures of the two possible enol forms of 2-carbomethoxy-cyclohexanone. Actually, only one of these enol forms occurs in detectable amounts at equilibrium. Which one?

A cyclic ester is known as a *lactone*; the ring size is designated by the Greek letter corresponding to the position of the hydroxyl group with which the acid moiety is condensed.

β-Hydroxypropionic acid   β-Propiolactone

The most frequently encountered lactones are the strain-free five- and six- membered ring γ- and δ-lactones. γ- and δ-Hydroxy acids rarely exist as such. When prepared, such compounds spontaneously lose water and form lactones. γ- and δ-lactones are widely distributed in nature, especially in plant materials. The three-membered ring α-lactones are highly strained and exist only as transient reaction intermediates.

β-Valerolactone   γ-Valerolactone   δ-Valerolactone

Esters are generally insoluble in water and have boiling points slightly higher than hydrocarbons of similar molecular weight (Table 8.3). The volatile esters have

Table 8.3 Esters

Name	Bp, °C	Name	Bp, °C
Methyl formate	32	*n*-Butyl acetate	127
Methyl acetate	57	Ethyl propionate	99
Ethyl acetate	77	*n*-Butyl butyrate	166
n-Propyl acetate	102	Isoamyl isovalerate	194

characteristic fruity odors. Esters, along with ketones, are responsible for the flavor and fragrance of many fruits, flowers, and artificial flavorings.

The delicacy of natural flavors and fragrances is due to complex mixtures; for instance, perhaps more than 100 substances contribute to the flavor of ripe strawberries ("God could have made a better berry, but He didn't.") Cheap artificial flavorings such as used in lollipops are often single compounds or at the most simple mixtures. The odor and flavor of isoamyl acetate resembles that of bananas, isoamyl valerate that of apples, isobutyl propionate that of rum, and so on.

    Ethyl and butyl acetate are used as industrial solvents, especially in the formulation of lacquers. Higher boiling esters are used as softening agents (plasticizers) for resins and plastics, a number of which are themselves polyesters.

The nmr spectrum of methyl acetate contains two sharp singlets at δ 2.03 and 3.77. The assignment of these peaks can be made by considering methyl ether and acetone as model compounds.

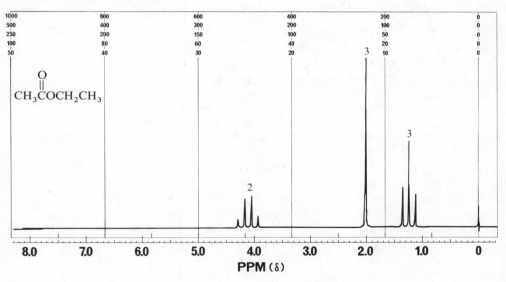

The nmr spectrum of ethyl acetate is shown in Figure 8.6.

Figure 8.6
NMR spectrum of ethyl acetate.

EXERCISE 8.12

Suggest how nmr spectroscopy could be used to differentiate between ethyl acetate (Figure 8.6) and methyl propionate.

8.11   Fats, Soaps, and Detergents

The naturally occurring fats, oils, and waxes, which are principally high molecular weight esters, are known collectively as *lipids*. Waxes are complex mixtures of alcohols, acids, and some long-chain alkanes, but the principal components are esters formed from long-chain fatty acids and long-chain alcohols. The most abundant ingredient in beeswax, the purified wax of the honeycomb of the bee, is myricyl palmitate.

$$\underset{\text{O}}{\overset{\text{O}}{\text{CH}_3(\text{CH}_2)_{14}\overset{\|}{\text{C}}-\text{O}(\text{CH}_2)_{29}\text{CH}_3}}$$

Fats (solids) and *oils* (liquids) are esters formed from the higher fatty acids (C_{12} to C_{22}) and glycerol; these esters are frequently called *glycerides*.

$$\begin{array}{c}
\text{CH}_2\text{O}-\overset{\overset{\displaystyle\text{O}}{\|}}{\text{C}}-\text{R} \\
| \\
\text{CHO}-\overset{\overset{\displaystyle\text{O}}{\|}}{\text{C}}-\text{R}' \\
| \\
\text{CH}_2\text{O}-\overset{\overset{\displaystyle\text{O}}{\|}}{\text{C}}-\text{R}''
\end{array}$$

Fats and oils are not *simple* glycerides, but contain a number of different fatty acids distributed more or less at random over the various glyceride molecules. (Thus one molecule may contain three stearate residues, another a palmitate and two stearates, another two palmitates and a myristate, etc.) The most important of the saturated fatty acids obtained by hydrolysis of fats and oils are lauric [$CH_3(CH_2)_{10}COOH$], palmitic [$CH_3(CH_2)_{14}COOH$], and stearic [$CH_3(CH_2)_{16}COOH$] acid. The most important of the unsaturated acids are the C_{18} acids: oleic, linoleic, and linolenic. The olefinic linkages in these compounds have the cis configuration.

$$\underset{18}{\text{CH}_3(\text{CH}_2)_7}\underset{10}{\overset{\text{H}}{\text{C}}}=\underset{9}{\overset{\text{H}}{\text{C}}}(\text{CH}_2)_7\underset{1}{\overset{\text{O}}{\overset{\|}{\text{C}}}}-\text{OH}$$

Oleic acid

$$\underset{18}{\text{CH}_3(\text{CH}_2)_4}\underset{13}{\overset{\text{H}}{\text{C}}}=\underset{1211}{\overset{\text{H}}{\text{C}}}\text{CH}_2\underset{10}{\overset{\text{H}}{\text{C}}}=\underset{9}{\overset{\text{H}}{\text{C}}}(\text{CH}_2)_7\underset{1}{\overset{\text{O}}{\overset{\|}{\text{C}}}}-\text{OH}$$

Linoleic acid

$$\underset{18}{\text{CH}_3}\underset{17}{\text{CH}_2}\underset{16}{\overset{\text{H}}{\text{C}}}=\underset{1514}{\overset{\text{H}}{\text{C}}}\text{CH}_2\underset{13}{\overset{\text{H}}{\text{C}}}=\underset{1211}{\overset{\text{H}}{\text{C}}}\text{CH}_2\underset{10}{\overset{\text{H}}{\text{C}}}=\underset{9}{\overset{\text{H}}{\text{C}}}(\text{CH}_2)_7\underset{1}{\overset{\text{O}}{\overset{\|}{\text{C}}}}-\text{OH}$$

Linolenic acid

Oils contain a higher percentage of glycerides of unsaturated fatty acids than do the fats.

POLYUNSATURATES AND HEALTH. *By a process called* catalytic hydrogenation, *it is possible to add hydrogen across the double bonds in unsaturated glycerides of oils, thereby converting them to semisolid or solid fats, depending on how far the process is taken. Many cooking fats are produced by hydrogenation of corn oil and cottonseed oil Margarines are made by hydrogenating oils to the consistency of butter, churning the product with skim milk, fortifying with vitamin A, and adding artificial color.*

In recent years dietary saturated fat has been implicated as a causative factor in atherosclerotic diseases, the most serious of which are coronary thrombosis and paralytic strokes. However, it might be noted that Eskimos, whose diet contains large quantities of highly saturated fat, seldom die of heart attacks. Because of possible health implications, oils such as corn oil and safflower oil which contain high percentages of linoleic acid ("polyunsaturates") are being used in increasingly larger quantities as foodstuffs. Semisolid cooking fats and margarines can be made from these "polyunsaturated fats" through the use of emulsifying agents rather than by hydrogenation as was the practice in the past.

DRYING OILS. *Certain oils are largely composed of highly unsaturated glycerides. Most notable of these are linseed oil (from flax seed) and tung oil (from the tung nut). Such oils polymerize to a tough, glossy polymer when exposed to the oxygen of the atmosphere. These oils are known as "drying oils," and they are of considerable use in the formulation of paints, especially for outside surfaces.*

Soaps and detergents are composed of molecules containing large hydrocarbon groups [the *hydrophobic* (water-fearing) group] and one or more polar groups [*hydrophilic* (water-loving) groups]. The nonpolar parts of such molecules dissolve in grease or oils and the polar portions are soluble in water. The cleansing properties of soaps and detergents depend upon their ability to form emulsions with fat-soluble materials in which the soap or detergent molecules surround the "dirt" in such a way as to enclose it within a water-solubilizing envelope (Figure 8.7). Solid particles of dirt become dispersed in the emulsion.

Figure 8.7
The emulsification of oil in water by soap. Nonpolar hydrocarbon chains dissolve in oil, polar ionic groups in water. The negatively charged droplets repel one another.

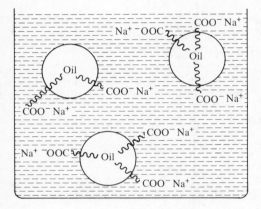

Soaps are made by the saponification of fats and oils. (Any reaction of an ester with a base to produce an alcohol and the salt of an acid is called a saponification *reaction.) The by-product in the manufacture of soaps is glycerin, from which the high explosive* nitroglycerin *is made. During World Wars I and II, housewives saved excess cooking fats and oils and turned them in for reclamation of the glycerin.*

$$\begin{array}{l} \quad\quad\quad\; \overset{\displaystyle O}{\overset{\displaystyle \|}{}} \\[-2pt] CH_2OCR \\[4pt] \quad\quad\quad\; \overset{\displaystyle O}{\overset{\displaystyle \|}{}} \\[-2pt] CHOCR' + 3NaOH \rightarrow \\[4pt] \quad\quad\quad\; \overset{\displaystyle O}{\overset{\displaystyle \|}{}} \\[-2pt] CH_2OCR'' \end{array}$$

$$\begin{array}{l} CH_2OH \quad\; RCOONa \\[4pt] CHOH \;+\; R'COONa \\[4pt] CH_2OH \quad\; R''COONa \\[4pt] \text{Glycerin} \quad\;\; \text{Soaps} \end{array}$$

Soaps, which are mixtures of the sodium salts of C_{12} and higher fatty acids, are ineffective cleansing agents in hard water (water containing salts of the heavier metals, especially iron and calcium). The soaps are precipitated from hard water as the insoluble iron or calcium salts (bathtub ring). On the other hand, the calcium and iron salts of alkyl hydrogen sulfates are soluble in water, and the sodium salts of these materials, known as *detergents*, are effective cleansing agents even in hard water. Such detergents

$$CH_3(CH_2)_{10}CH_2OSO_3^- Na^+$$

Sodium lauryl sulfate

contain straight alkyl chains in analogy to the natural fats; they are metabolized by bacteria in sewage treatment plants and hence are known as *biodegradable* detergents.

DETERGENTS AND THE POLLUTION PROBLEM. *By law, all detergents presently on the U.S. market are biodegradable. In the early 1960s enormous quantities of detergents which contained branched alkyl chains were being used. These detergents were not degraded by bacteria and appeared in the sewage outflow into rivers and streams, causing rivers as large as the Mississippi to become huge basins of suds.*

It is interesting to note that many very effective detergents do not foam in water. Although experiments have shown that the degree of sudsing has very little to do with the efficiency of a detergent, the housewife has come to associate sudsing with efficiency and manufacturers often add sudsing agents to their products.

8.12   Amides and Related Compounds

An *amide* is a derivative of a carboxylic acid formed by reaction with ammonia or an amine, with the elimination of a molecule of water.

$$RC\!\!\overset{O}{\underset{OH}{\big\langle}} + NH_3 \rightarrow RC\!\!\overset{O}{\underset{O^-}{\big\langle}}\ NH_4^+ \overset{\Delta}{\rightarrow} RC\!\!\overset{O}{\underset{NH_2}{\big\langle}} + H_2O$$

Ammonium salt   Amide

Amides are divided into subclasses depending on the number of substituents on nitrogen.

$RCONH_2$ $RCONHR'$ $RCONR'_2$

Primary amide   Secondary amide   Tertiary amide

Amides are named by dropping the *-ic acid* or *-oic acid* from the name of the parent acid and replacing it with the suffix *-amide*. Substituents on nitrogen are denoted by placing a capital *N* before the name of the substituent.

$$CH_3\overset{O}{\overset{\|}{C}}NH_2 \qquad CH_3CH_2CH_2CH_2\overset{O}{\overset{\|}{C}}NHCH_3 \qquad CH_3\underset{Cl}{\overset{O}{\overset{\|}{C}}HC}N(CH_3)_2$$

Acetamide   *N*-Methylpentanamide   *N,N*-Dimethyl-2-
                   (*N*-Methylvaleramide)   chloropropionamide

Cyclic amides are called *lactams*; their nomenclature follows directly from that of lactones.

γ-Butyrolactam   ε-Caprolactam

Imides contain two acyl groups attached to the same nitrogen. The cyclic imides are the most important.

Succinimide

The π-system of succinimide

EXERCISE 8.13

Based on structural considerations, what can you predict about the acid/base properties of succinimide?

Primary amides are solids with the exception of formamide, which melts at 2.5°C (Table 8.4). Primary and secondary amides are strongly associated through intermolecular hydrogen bonding. Dimethylformamide is highly polar and is a powerful solvent for both organic and inorganic materials even though it is aprotic.

Table 8.4   Amides

Name	Bp, °C (mp)[a]	Name	Bp, °C (mp)[a]
Formamide	210	*N*-Cyclohexylacetamide	(104)
Dimethylformamide	153	Urea	(132)
Acetamide	(82)	Ethyl carbamate	(49)
Propionamide	(79)	Succinimide	(125)

[a] Numbers in parentheses are melting points, the others are boiling points.

Ureas and urethanes are groups of compounds named for the simplest member of each group, urea and urethane (sometimes written urethan). They are very stable derivatives of carbonic acid, which itself is unstable and tends to decompose to water and carbon dioxide. Carbamic acid is similarly unstable and decomposes to ammonia and carbon dioxide.

$$\underset{\text{Carbonic acid}}{\overset{\displaystyle O}{\overset{\|}{HOCOH}}} \qquad \underset{\text{Carbamic acid}}{\overset{\displaystyle O}{\overset{\|}{NH_2COH}}} \qquad \underset{\text{Urea}}{\overset{\displaystyle O}{\overset{\|}{NH_2CNH_2}}} \qquad \underset{\substack{\text{Urethane}\\ \text{(Ethyl carbamate)}}}{\overset{\displaystyle O}{\overset{\|}{NH_2COC_2H_5}}}$$

$$\underset{\text{A disubstituted urea}}{\overset{\displaystyle O}{\overset{\|}{RNHCNHR'}}} \qquad \underset{\text{A urethane}}{\overset{\displaystyle O}{\overset{\|}{RNHCOR'}}}$$

8.13   The Structures of Amides

Recall that ammonia and the amines are pyramidal rather than planar, although the energy difference between the two forms is not very large (Section 4.14). In the case of

$$RC\overset{\displaystyle \ddot{O}}{\underset{\ddot{N}H_2}{\diagup}} \quad \leftrightarrow \quad RC\overset{\displaystyle \ddot{O}:^-}{\underset{\overset{+}{N}H_2}{\diagup}}$$

amides, the extra conjugation energy gained by allowing the lone pair on nitrogen (in a *p* orbital) to overlap with the 2*p* orbital on the carbonyl carbon is sufficient to make the planar (*sp²*) form of the nitrogen the more stable.

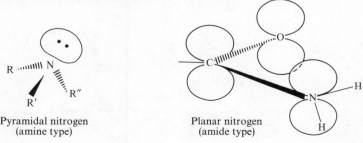

Pyramidal nitrogen (amine type)

Planar nitrogen (amide type)

As a consequence of the lone pairs on nitrogen being involved in delocalization with the carbonyl group, amides are much less basic than amines; protonation usually occurs on oxygen rather than on nitrogen. (Why?)

Simple amides are weakly basic or neutral compounds. If two carbonyl groups are attached to the same nitrogen, the electron withdrawal from nitrogen is even greater: The hydrogen on the nitrogen of an imide is acidic.

Rotation about a single bond at room temperature is usually so rapid that rotational isomers or conformers cannot be isolated, nor can they be detected by nmr spectroscopy. When the barrier hindering rotation is a formal covalent double bond, the isomers (e.g., cis and trans isomers of alkenes) are isolable, and they have different nmr spectra. If there is considerable double-bond character in the C—N bond of a simple amide, rotation about this bond should be restricted. Consider the example of N,N-dimethyl-formamide:

Restricts rotation

If rotation about the C—N bond were unhindered, the two N-methyl groups would appear identical in the nmr spectra. In actual fact, near room temperature the spectrum of N,N-dimethylformamide (Figure 8.8) shows two different kinds of methyl groups.

Figure 8.8
NMR spectrum of N,N-dimethylformamide at room temperature showing effect of hindered rotation about amide C—N bond.

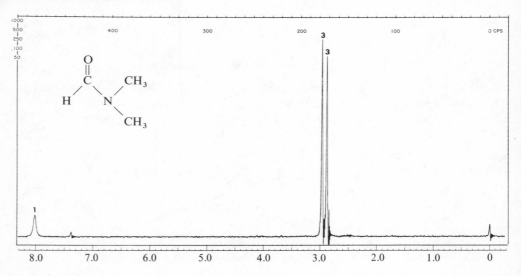

The methyl group which is cis to the oxygen absorbs at δ 2.97, while the methyl cis to the formyl hydrogen appears at δ 2.88.

It is interesting to note the effect of temperature on the nmr spectrum of *N,N*-dimethyl-formamide. As the temperature is raised the two methyl peaks begin to broaden. When a temperature of 111°C is reached, the two peaks coalesce into a single broad signal. At still higher temperatures, a single sharp signal is observed for the methyl groups. At the elevated temperatures, the methyl groups become "magnetically equivalent" because of rapid rotation about the C—N bond.

DETECTION OF SHORT-LIVED ISOMERS. *With the aid of nmr, it is possible to "see" isomers which are too short-lived to isolate. A familiar analogy is a whirling airplane propeller. Our eyes see the average position of the propeller (as a blurred circle) while a high-speed camera freezes the motion of the propeller, and shows it at a given instant. Similarly, since in nmr we are ordinarily concerned with differences of the order of a few cycles per second, isomers which are interconverting may be seen as an "average" or as a mixture of separate compounds, depending on how fast they interconvert. If the half-life for interconversion is of the order of several seconds or more, the nmr will see the separate isomers. When the half-life gets down to a fraction of a second, only an average nmr spectrum for the mixture of isomers will be seen. If we want to actually isolate in the laboratory samples of two interconverting isomers, they must have a half-life of the order of an hour to permit the physical manipulations to be carried out. We can therefore "see" in the nmr mixtures which interconvert too rapidly to be isolated in the laboratory. The interconversions become faster as the temperature is raised, and the half-life becomes shorter. Low-temperature nmr has been very useful in studying substances which interconvert too rapidly to actually isolate in the laboratory. (See also Section 6.8.)*

8.14   Acid Halides

Replacement of the hydroxyl group of a carboxylic acid by a halogen produces an *acid halide*. Although the acid fluorides, bromides, and iodides are known, only the acid chlorides are commonly encountered. Formyl chloride, HCOCl, is unstable and decomposes to carbon monoxide and hydrogen chloride at ordinary temperatures.

Carboxylic acid   Acid halide
(Acyl halide)

Acid halides are named by combining the names of the acyl group (RCO—) and that of the halide. Acyl groups are named by dropping the *-ic acid* from the name of the carboxylic acid and adding *-yl*. Acid halides derived from acids which have the suffix *-carboxylic acid* are named as carbonyl halides.

Acetic acid   Acetyl   Acetyl bromide

$CH_2{=}CHCH_2CH_2CH_2CH_2COCl$

6-Heptenoyl chloride

Cyclohexanecarbonyl chloride

Acid halides are insoluble in water but are readily hydrolyzed; the lower ones, such as acetyl chloride, react violently with water.

$$RCOCl + H_2O \rightarrow RCOOH + HCl$$

Owing to dipole association, the boiling points of acid halides are somewhat higher than those of hydrocarbons of similar molecular weights (Table 8.5). The acid halides have very irritating odors and are strong lachrymators (tear gases).

Table 8.5 Acid Halides

Name	Bp, °C	Name	Bp, °C (Mp)*
Acetyl fluoride	21	n-Butyryl chloride	102
Acetyl chloride	52	Stearyl chloride	(22)
Acetyl bromide	108	Phosgene (carbonyl chloride)	8
Propionyl chloride	80	Oxalyl chloride	62

* Number in parenthesis is melting point, the others are boiling points.

PHOSGENE. *The diacid chloride of carbonic acid—phosgene, $COCl_2$—was responsible for a high percentage of the war gas casualties of World War I. Its toxic action apparently is due to hydrolysis in the lungs with the liberation of hydrogen chloride. Carbon tetrachloride is one of the few organic liquids that can be used to extinguish flames. Even so, in hot fires it produces some phosgene, and carbon tetrachloride extinguishers should therefore be used only where there is good ventilation.*

In spite of its toxicity, phosgene is used in very large quantities as an industrial chemical, principally for the manufacture of intermediates in the foam-rubber industry. It is produced by the reaction of a mixture of chlorine and carbon monoxide.

$$CO + Cl_2 \xrightarrow[\text{carbon catalyst}]{\text{activated}} COCl_2$$

8.15   Acid Anhydrides and Ketenes

Acid anhydrides (Table 8.6) are formally derived by removal of one molecule of water

Table 8.6 Anhydrides

Name	Bp, °C	Name	Mp, °C
Acetic anhydride	140	Succinic anhydride	120
Propionic anhydride	168	Glutaric anhydride	56

from two molecules of acid.

$$\underset{\displaystyle RC}{\overset{\displaystyle O}{\|}}\!\!-\!\!OH + H\!\!-\!\!\underset{\displaystyle OCR}{\overset{\displaystyle O}{\|}} \xrightarrow{-H_2O} \underset{\displaystyle RCOCR}{\overset{\displaystyle O\quad O}{\|\quad\|}}$$

Both symmetric and mixed anhydrides are known: the former are by far the more important. These compounds are named by replacing the word *acid* with *anhydride*; for mixed anhydrides, both parent acids are named.

Acetic anhydride   Acetic butyric anhydride

Cyclic anhydrides are very easily formed from dibasic acids which can cyclize to five- or six-membered rings.

Succinic anhydride   Maleic anhydride   Glutaric anhydride

Substances formally derived from acids by splitting out a molecule of water as shown are known as *ketenes*. The parent compound, ketene, is derived from acetic acid.

Ketenes are rarely isolated and characterized because of their high reactivity; they are usually allowed to react *in situ* as generated.

8.16   NMR Spectra of Carbonyl Compounds. Summary

Nmr data have been discussed throughout this chapter as they pertained to specific types of compounds. (For aldehydes and ketones, see Section 8.4; for acids, Section 8.7; for esters, Section 8.10; and for amides, Section 8.13.) In this section we will summarize the applications of nmr to carbonyl-containing compounds.

The carbonyl group is electron-withdrawing, and it causes downfield shifts of 1–2 δ units for protons α to it. This is equally true whether the C=O group is part of an aldehyde, ketone, ester, acid, anhydride or acid halide.

Aldehydes and acids can be differentiated from the other carbonyl compounds by virtue of the proton: in –C(=O)H at about δ 10, or in –C(=O)OH at about δ 12. The aldehyde proton is likely to be coupled to α protons, and hence split, while the carboxyl proton will be unsplit.

In esters and amides, the alkyl protons on the carbons attached, respectively, to O and N are shifted downfield by about 3 and 2 δ units. The results of restricted rotation about the C—N bond in amides are usually evident in splitting of the peaks.

The molecular formula is used in conjunction with the nmr spectrum to deduce the structure of an unknown compound. Thus the formula $C_6H_{12}O$ and the fact that the nmr spectrum shows a line at δ 10.5 means the compound must be an aldehyde, since a carboxylic acid would require (at least) two oxygens.

EXERCISE 8.14

Interpret the nmr spectrum of ethyl *t*-butylacetate shown.

NMR spectrum of ethyl *t*-butylacetate.

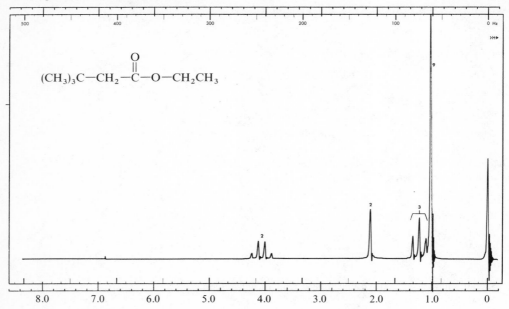

PROBLEMS

1. Consider the following two equilibria, each of which involves nucleophilic addition to a double bond.

   (a) $CH_3O^- + CH_2{=}O \rightleftharpoons CH_3OCH_2O^-$

   (b) $CH_3O^- + CH_2{=}CH_2 \rightleftharpoons CH_3OCH_2CH_2^-$

   In which of the two reactions would adduct formation be more favorable and why?

2. Why is acetic acid a stronger acid than acetone?

3. How many possible enol forms are there of methyl ethyl ketone? Which form is more stable? (*Hint*: See Section 7.10).

4. Predict the most stable conformation of butane-2,3-dione and justify your choice.

5. Which of the following structural isomers of $C_5H_{10}O$ could give rise to each of the nmr spectra described below?

3-Methylbutanal	2-Pentanone
3-Methyl-2-butanone	3-Pentanone
2,2-Dimethylpropanal	Pentanal

   (a) A triplet at δ 1.05 and a quartet at δ 2.47.
   (b) A doublet at δ 1.02, a singlet at δ 2.13 and a heptet at δ 2.22.
   (c) A doublet at δ 0.93 and a triplet at δ 9.74 (partial spectrum).
   (d) Two singlets.

6. Compare and contrast: *resonance forms*, *tautomers*, and *isomers*.

7. Draw structures for the following compounds:
   (a) *cis*-3-Penten-2-one   (b) 1,4-Cyclohexanedione
   (c) 3-Hydroxypentanal   (d) Nonanoic acid
   (e) γ-Aminobutyric acid   (f) Isovaleraldehyde
   (g) Sodium propionate   (h) β-Butyrolactone
   (i) *N*, *N*-Diethylformamide   (j) *t*-Butyl propionate
   (k) Stearyl chloride   (l) α,α'-Dimethylglutaric anhydride

8. In the nmr spectrum of ethanol in carbon tetrachloride, the hydroxyl proton appears over a wide range (δ 0.5 to 4), depending on concentration. In the same solvent, the position of the hydroxyl proton of acetic acid appears near δ 11 and is little affected by concentration. Explain.

9. The nmr spectrum of a compound $C_6H_{12}O_2$ consists only of two singlets. The ratio of the intensity of the singlet at δ 1.45 to that at δ 1.97 is 3:1. Suggest a structure for the compound.

10. Write systematic names for the following compounds:

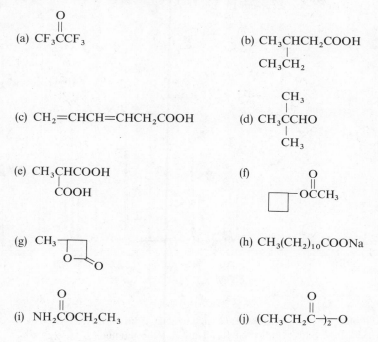

(a) $CF_3\overset{\overset{\displaystyle O}{\|}}{C}CF_3$

(b) CH_3CHCH_2COOH
    $\ \ \ \ \ \ \ |$
    $\ \ \ \ \ CH_3CH_2$

(c) $CH_2{=}CHCH{=}CHCH_2COOH$

(d) $CH_3\overset{\overset{\displaystyle CH_3}{|}}{\underset{\underset{\displaystyle CH_3}{|}}{C}}CHO$

(e) $CH_3CHCOOH$
    $\ \ \ \ \ \ |$
    $\ \ \ \ COOH$

(f)

(g) CH_3

(h) $CH_3(CH_2)_{10}COONa$

(i) $NH_2\overset{\overset{\displaystyle O}{\|}}{C}OCH_2CH_3$

(j) $(CH_3CH_2\overset{\overset{\displaystyle O}{\|}}{C}{\frac{}{}}_2O$

11. Suggest a structure for the compound $C_7H_{12}O_4$ on the basis of its nmr spectrum.

NMR spectrum of unknown, Problem 11.

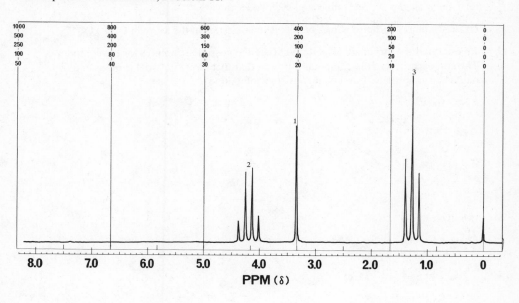

12. The hydrogens α to the carbonyl of an ester are less acidic than those of a ketone. Can you explain why, in terms of the difference in charge distribution brought about by induction and resonance in the two cases? Do you think the α hydrogens of an *N,N*-dialkylamide would be more or less acidic than those of esters and ketones? Explain.

13.   The nmr spectrum of acetoacetic ester (CH$_3$COCH$_2$COOEt) is shown. Can you interpret it fully, including the little peaks a and b?

NMR spectrum of ethyl acetoacetate, Problem 13.

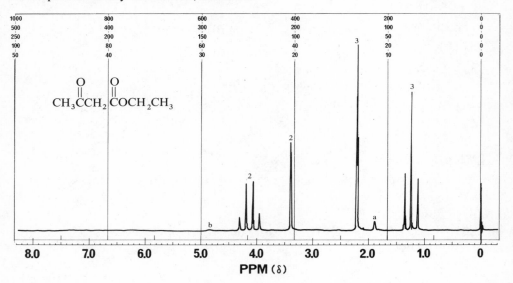

14.   Show in a diagram all of the orbitals of the valence shell of each atom for (a) acetyl chloride; (b) acrylic acid. In each case indicate hybridization and bond angles.

15.   Describe simple chemical methods that would allow you to separate the following mixtures and isolate each component in pure form.
       (a) n-Heptane and di-n-propylamine
       (b) Valeric acid and di-n-butylamine
       (c) Octanoic acid, n-decylamine, and cyclododecane

16.   Draw structures and give names of nine isomeric esters of the formula C$_5$H$_{10}$O$_2$.

17.   An ester had the formula C$_4$H$_6$O$_2$. What are the possible structures for the compound? The nmr spectrum of the compound showed that there were no vinyl protons and no methyl group present. Can you identify the compound?

CHAPTER 9

INFRARED SPECTROSCOPY

9.1 The Electromagnetic Spectrum

In previous chapters the structures and properties of many (in fact, most) of the known kinds of organic compounds have been discussed. In Chapter 5, the usefulness of nmr spectra in studying such structures was outlined. Another group of powerful methods for the study of structures makes use of electromagnetic spectra, and one of these methods, the one currently found to be the most useful, will be discussed in detail in this chapter.

If a molecule absorbs energy of electromagnetic radiation, it can undergo various types of *excitation*. This excitation might be electronic excitation, rotational excitation, excitation leading to a change in nuclear spin, excitation resulting in bond deformation, and so on; if the energy available approaches the ionization potential of the molecule, an electron can be ejected and ionization will occur. Since each mode of excitation requires a specific quantity of energy, the absorptions appear in different regions of the electromagnetic spectrum (Table 9.1).

Table 9.1 The Electromagnetic Spectrum

Region	Wavelength[a]	Excitation energy	Type of excitation
Gamma radiation, X rays, cosmic rays	< 100 nm	> 286 kcal	
Ultraviolet			
Vacuum	100–200 nm	286–143 kcal	Electronic
Quartz	200–350 nm	143–82 kcal	Electronic
Visible	350–800 nm	82–36 kcal	Electronic
Infrared[b]			
Near-infrared	0.8–2.0 μm	36–14.3 kcal	Overtones of bond deformations
Infrared	2–16 μm	14.3–1.8 kcal	Bond deformations
Far-infrared	16–300 μm	1.8–0.1 kcal	Bond deformations
Microwave	1 cm	10^{-4} kcal	Rotational
Radiofrequency	meters	10^{-6} kcal	Electron and nuclear spin transitions

[a] See Table 9.2 for explanation of units.

[b] Raman spectra can be determined by exposing a substance to intense high-energy (usually ultraviolet) radiation, and measuring light which is scattered by the substance and which is of different frequency than the incident radiation. From such spectra one can determine the same general kinds of things that are determined from infrared spectra.

When a molecule absorbs electromagnetic radiation in being excited from a state of lower energy to a state of higher energy, the frequency at which absorption occurs is given by the relationship

$$E = hv$$

where E is energy absorbed, v is the frequency of the elctromagnetic radiation, h is Planck's constant: 6.624×10^{-27} erg sec. Since the frequency, v, and the wavelength, λ, of the absorbed radiation are related, the energy can also be expressed in terms of wavelength:

$$v = c/\lambda$$
$$E = hv = hc/\lambda$$

where λ is wavelength and c is the velocity of light: 2.998×10^{10} cm/sec. The wave number, n, is defined as the reciprocal of the wavelength in centimeters, and is commonly used in place of wavelength to locate positions in spectra because the numerical values are of a convenient magnitude.

$$n = 1/\lambda$$

where n is in cm^{-1}.

The ultraviolet and infrared regions of the electromagnetic spectrum are further broken down into subregions, as shown in Table 9.1. The relationship $E = hc/\lambda$ shows that the energy of excitation is inversely proportional to the wavelength. Thus, as the wavelengths increase down Table 9.1, the energies decrease. At energies greater (wavelengths shorter) than those found in the ultraviolet region, the energy might be large enough to ionize the molecule, or even to cause nuclear transformations.

EXERCISE 9.1

The stretching of a C—H bond in an alkane leads to absorption at about 2900 cm^{-1} in the infrared. What wavelength does this correspond to? What is the energy change involved?

The terms *spectrometry* and *spectroscopy* are usually used interchangeably. A *spectrophotometer* is an instrument used to measure ultraviolet, visible, and infrared spectra. An instrument used to measure nuclear magnetic resonance or mass spectra is commonly referred to as a *spectrometer*. Other commonly used symbols and terms are defined in Table 9.2.

Table 9.2 Symbols and Definitions

Symbol	Definition
uv	Ultraviolet
ir	Infrared
Å	The unit Ångstrom, equal to 10^{-8} cm
μm[a]	The unit micrometer, equal to 10^{-6} meter
nm[a]	The unit nanometer, equal to 10^{-9} meter
cm^{-1}	The unit reciprocal centimeter (wave number), equal to 1/cm

[a] The units micron (μ) and millimicron (mμ) were used in the older literature, and are now gradually being displaced. They are equal to micrometer and nanometer, respectively.

An important point to remember is that a *discrete amount of energy* is required for each type of excitation. These are all quantized phenomena. Therefore radiation of a particular and characteristic frequency is absorbed for a given transition. Interpretation of an absorption spectrum is based on assigning absorptions of energy to the presence of certain structural features in the molecule. Data from absorption spectra, although valuable, are not always sufficient to lead to the complete, and correct, structure of the molecule being studied. Such data are most often used effectively in conjunction with chemical data.

9.2 Infrared Spectra

The breakdown of the infrared region of the electromagnetic spectrum into the three subregions near-infrared, infrared, and far-infrared is based arbitrarily on instrument design and cost. We shall discuss the wavelength region from 2.5 to 16 μm (in terms of wave numbers 4000 to 625 cm^{-1}), because it is the region generally used by the organic chemist for structural work.

Figure 9.1
Schematic diagram of a simple spectrophotometer.

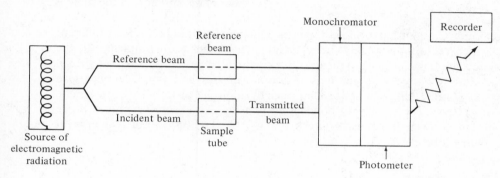

Figure 9.1 presents a schematic diagram of a spectrophotometer. From the reference beam, which has the same intensity as the incident beam, it is possible to obtain the intensity of the radiation which enters the sample tube. The difference between the intensity of the reference beam and that of the transmitted beam is a measure of the amount of radiation absorbed. The frequency of the radiation being examined is automatically varied by the *monochromator*. In the *photometer* the relative intensities of the reference and transmitted beams are compared. The percentage of the reference beam which is found in the transmitted beam is plotted as a function of wave number.

Figure 9.2 shows the infrared spectrum of *n*-hexane. Note that it is customary for infrared spectra to be plotted as light transmitted, not light absorbed, from 0 to 100%. Ordinary infrared spectra therefore show *maximum* absorption by a *minimum* on the chart, in contrast to nmr spectra where absorption is being plotted. In many parts of the spectrum the transmittance is close to 100%, meaning that the molecule is transparent to radiation of that frequency. Note the strong absorption bands at 2900 and 1450 cm^{-1}, which are the result of C—H stretching and bending motions, respectively. The absorption bands are not sharp lines because vibrational energy levels have a number of rotational levels associated with them, transitions between which cause the lines to broaden.

Infrared spectra can be obtained from materials as *neat* liquids (homogeneous liquids containing no solvents), as gases, as solids, or in solution. In the case of a liquid solution, a tube holding *only* the *solvent* can be placed in the reference beam (Figure 9.1). Absorption of the incident beam by the solvent in the sample tube is then automatically compensated for. This leaves the spectrum of the solute to be recorded.

The energy which is absorbed in exciting a molecule to a higher energy state is released when the molecule returns to a lower energy state. In the infrared region, this energy

Figure 9.2
Infrared spectrum of *n*-hexane as a neat liquid film.

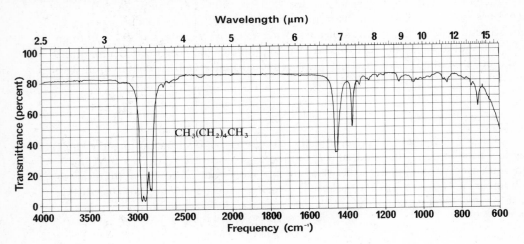

is released primarily as heat, which causes the temperature of the contents of the sample tube to rise.

Different kinds of atoms have different masses. Different kinds of bonds have different strengths, which are approximately independent of the other atoms attached to the atoms forming the bond in question (except for conjugated systems and other special cases). Therefore, different combinations of atomic masses and bond energies give systems which vibrate at different frequencies when the molecule absorbs electromagnetic energy. For example, the O—C—O bond in carbon dioxide absorbs energy of wave number 667 cm^{-1} when it bends, whereas the H—O—H bond absorbs energy at 1595 cm^{-1} when it bends.

O—C—O bend   H—O—H bend
$n = 667 \text{ cm}^{-1}$ $n = 1595 \text{ cm}^{-1}$

Different vibrational motions of the atom in the same molecule can also lead to absorption at different wave numbers. For example, consider the water molecule. The two hydrogens do not stretch independently, but rather their motions are coupled together, like those of two pendulums swinging on the same bar. This coupling leads to a symmetric motion in which both hydrogens stretch together, and an antisymmetric motion in which one hydrogen moves towards oxygen while the other moves away. An O—H bond isolated from the effects of coupling would have a stretching vibration which leads to absorption at 3700 cm^{-1} (midway between the symmetric and antisymmetric vibrations). A change in either of these motions requires absorption of different amounts of energy, and each of these changes leads to absorption at a different and characteristic frequency in the infrared spectrum. Therefore, the H_2O molecule has a total of three characteristic absorptions at different frequencies:

Symmetric   Antisymmetric   Bend
stretch   stretch
$n = 3655 \text{ cm}^{-1}$ $n = 3756 \text{ cm}^{-1}$ $n = 1595 \text{ cm}^{-1}$

IR Spectra of Hydrocarbons

The coupling of vibrational frequencies occurs most effectively when the frequencies are similar to one another. In organic molecules there are usually many C—C and many C—H bonds, and the frequencies from the vibrations of these atoms usually couple together to give very complicated spectra. However, certain characteristic features are discernible in hydrocarbon spectra. In the infrared spectrum of *n*-hexane (Figure 9.2) the strongest absorption bands are found at 2900 and 1450 cm^{-1}, resulting from the C—H stretching and bending, respectively. All molecules which contain alkyl groups show these absorption bands, so these are found in almost all infrared spectra of organic compounds. In addition, the symmetrical bending deformation of a methyl group leads to absorption at approximately 1380 cm^{-1}. The methyl at the end of any alkyl group shows this absorption, so a band at 1380 cm^{-1} is also found for most organic compounds.

EXERCISE 9.2

A compound has the formula C_5H_{10}, and it shows *no* absorption at 1380 cm^{-1} in the infrared. What is its structure?

The C≡C bond is stronger than the C=C bond, and the former is harder to stretch; C≡C stretching therefore leads to absorption at higher wave numbers than C=C stretching. The latter is, in turn, responsible for absorptions at higher wave numbers than is C—C. Because of the coupling together of many of the carbon–carbon stretching and the carbon–hydrogen bending modes, the 800–1400 cm^{-1} region of the spectrum of a typical molecule is usually very complicated, and the individual bands cannot be assigned to individual bonds. Rather, the whole region is a characteristic of the specific molecule. This part of the spectrum is called the *fingerprint region*, for obvious reasons.

The Relationships between Vibrational Frequencies and Bond Properties. To a crude approximation, all single bonds have similar bond strengths or stretching *force constants*, and the energy required to stretch a bond is given by

$$E = \tfrac{1}{2}k(\delta l)^2$$

The constant k is called the force constant, and it measures the stiffness of the bond. The quantity δl is the increment by which the bond is stretched (or compressed); this type of relationship is the classical one exhibited by weights stretching springs (Hooke's law).

For double bonds, X=Y, the force constants are about twice as big as for single bonds, and for triple bonds, X≡Y, the force constants are about three times as big as for single bonds. The vibrational frequency of X—Y in cm^{-1}, where the mass of Y is very large compared to that of X, is given by

$$v = \frac{1}{2\pi c}\sqrt{\frac{k}{m_X}}$$

where k is the force constant for bond stretching, m_X is the mass of atom X, and c is the velocity of light. For a constant X, the frequencies of vibration of X—Y, X=Y, and X≡Y are approximately $1, \sqrt{2}$, and $\sqrt{3}$. Also note that as m_X increases, the frequency decreases, since in this case v is proportional to $1/\sqrt{m_X}$.

Because the mass of hydrogen is so small, the H—Y frequencies are exceptionally high.

EXERCISE 9.3

The C—H stretching frequencies of alkanes are near 2900 cm^{-1}. Predict the values of the corresponding C—D frequencies, that is, where hydrogen is replaced by deuterium.

We can now construct a diagram summarizing the general regions of infrared absorption of carbon–carbon and carbon–hydrogen bonds (Figure 9.3).

The C—H stretching absorption occurs near 2900 (alkyl), 3100 (vinyl), and 3300 (acetylenic) cm^{-1}. Triple bonds absorb at 2100–2300 cm^{-1} and double bonds near

Figure 9.3
General regions of infrared absorptions of carbon–carbon and carbon–hydrogen bonds.

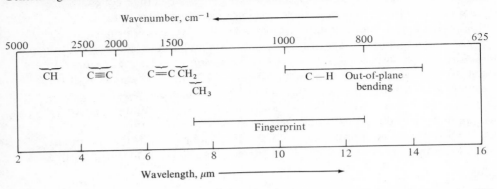

$1650\ cm^{-1}$. Vinyl hydrogens show strong "out-of-plane-bending" bands in the 700–$1000\ cm^{-1}$ region. The student will notice that many of these features are prominent in the spectrum methylenecyclohexane (Figure 9.4).

Figure 9.4
Infrared spectrum of methylenecyclohexane as a neat liquid film.

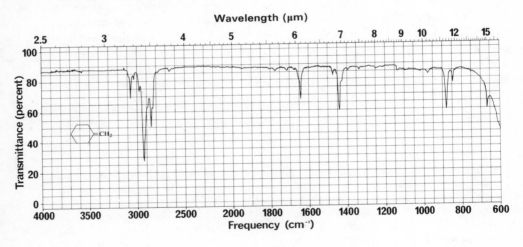

Figure 9.5
Infrared spectrum of 1-hexanol as a neat liquid film.

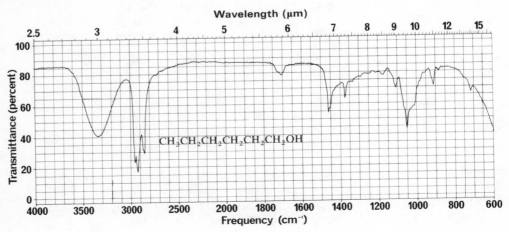

IR Spectra of Functional Groups

Infrared spectra are regularly used by organic chemists to help identify functional groups. By comparisons of the spectra in Figures 9.4–9.7 we will illustrate how the presence and absence of specific absorptions can be used to recognize the presence or absence of certain functional groups in a molecule.

The infrared spectrum of 1-hexanol, Figure 9.5, illustrates the characteristic O—H stretching absorption of a hydrogen-bonded alcohol—the strong, broad band at 3330 cm^{-1}—and also shows C—O absorption at 1060 cm^{-1}. In contrast, the spectrum of diethyl ether, Figure 9.6, does not have the O—H absorption at 3330 cm^{-1}, but does have strong absorption at 1125 cm^{-1} which is characteristic of a C—O stretching vibration.

Figure 9.6
Infrared spectrum of diethyl ether as a neat liquid film.

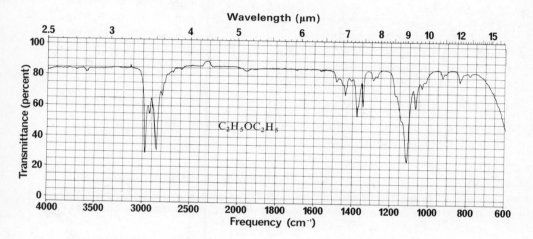

The infrared spectrum of ethyl butyrate, Figure 9.7, shows strong absorption in the 1730 cm^{-1} region due to the C=O stretching vibration. Figure 9.7 does not show the band characteristic of the O—H stretch of a hydrogen-bonded alcohol at 3330 cm^{-1} (Figure 9.5), but it has a C—O stretch at 1180 cm^{-1} (Figure 9.6). Figures 9.4–9.6 do

Figure 9.7
Infrared spectrum of ethyl butyrate as a neat liquid film.

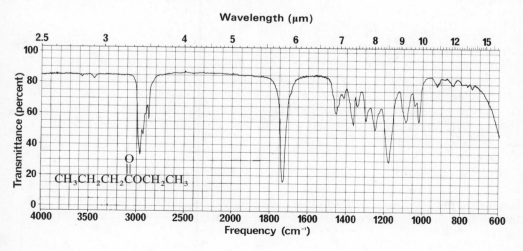

not show the strong absorptions at 1730 cm^{-1} characteristic of $C{=}O$ (Figure 9.7). We can conclude that the compound of Figure 9.7 contains a carbonyl group, but that those of Figures 9.4–9.6 do not; that Figure 9.4 represents a compound with none of the functional groups represented in Figures 9.5–9.7; that the compounds of Figures 9.5–9.7 all contain $C{-}O$ bonds. In this manner chemists can compare the spectra of known compounds with the spectrum of an unknown compound and often identify the functional groups present in the unknown.

With nmr spectra, the intensity of a peak is proportional to the number of protons contributing to that peak. With infrared spectra, there is no such simple relationship, but rather the intensity of a given peak is proportional to the *change in the dipole moment of the molecule which results from the absorption*. This change is, in general, not predictable in any simple way; however, there are some generalizations which can be made which are useful guides.

First, vibration of a polar bond ($C{-}O$, $C{=}O$, $C{-}Br$) is likely to lead to a larger change in the dipole moment of the molecule than is vibration of a less polar bond ($C{-}C$, $C{-}N$, $C{=}N$), and hence more-polar groups usually lead to stronger absorption bands than do less-polar ones. Second, vibration across a center of symmetry will lead to no change in dipole moment, and such vibrations lead to very weak absorptions (or none at all) in the infrared. Thus the $C{=}C$ stretching absorption near 1650 cm^{-1} is very weak in ethylene and in tetramethylethylene, but much stronger in propene and in isobutylene.

EXERCISE 9.4

The $-C{\equiv}C-$ stretching leads to moderate absorption in 1-butyne, but very weak absorption in 2-butyne. Why?

In practice, the infrared absorption of the carbonyl group proves to be of great value. The absorption is strong (Why?) and occurs in a region where few other bands are usually present. It is thus easy to locate and identify. The exact frequency of the $C{=}O$ absorption depends on a number of environmental variables and is well understood. If the frequency can be determined, much can be deduced concerning the environment. An ester absorbs at higher frequency than a ketone, while the absorption for an amide is at lower frequency. If a ketone is present in a ring, the absorption frequency is a function of ring size. (This is a purely mechanical effect; the frequency varies inversely with the $C{-}C{-}C$ angle at the carbonyl group.)

Carbonyl frequencies (cm^{-1})

| 1775 | 1740 | 1710 | 1700 | $n > 6$ |

Open-chain ketones have a $C{=}O$ frequency similar to that of cyclohexanone.

In general, conjugated systems absorb at lower frequencies than nonconjugated systems. For example, an aliphatic ketone absorbs at about 1710 cm^{-1}, whereas 2-cyclohexen-1-one (Figure 9.8), absorbs at 1680 cm^{-1}. Also, alkenes absorb at $1670–1640 \text{ cm}^{-1}$, whereas alkenes conjugated with a carbonyl group or another double bond absorb near 1600 cm^{-1}. The reason for these shifts can be seen in terms of resonance forms, using butadiene as an example:

$$CH_2{=}CH{-}CH{=}CH_2 \leftrightarrow {}^-CH_2{-}CH{=}CH{-}CH_2^+$$

Contributions from the ionic forms tend to make the double bonds weaker and the single bonds stronger. These forms do not contribute very much, so the shifts are not very large.

EXERCISE 9.5

An aliphatic aldehyde containing an unconjugated double bond shows C=O and C=C stretching at 1720–1740 and near 1650 cm^{-1}, respectively. Explain why crotonaldehyde (CH$_3$CH=CHCHO) shows the corresponding absorptions at 1700 cm^{-1} and 1630 cm^{-1}.

Figure 9.8

Infrared spectrum of 2-cyclohexen-1-one as a neat liquid film.

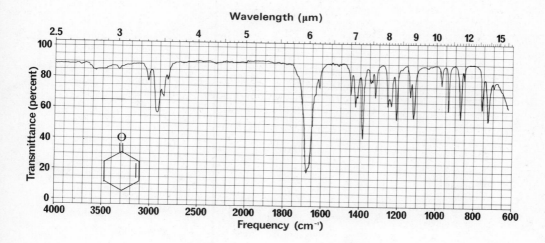

Thus we see that the carbonyl frequency in the infrared spectrum of a compound of unknown structure can provide us with various kinds of useful information. We can sometimes learn what kind of functional group the carbonyl is a part of. If the carbonyl group is part of a ring, or if it is conjugated, these facts may be evident.

Even though many absorption bands cannot be assigned to a specific vibration, thorough studies of the approximately 125,000 spectra reported for compounds of known structure have resulted in many empirical correlations. These correlations can be used to recognize structural features from the infrared spectra of compounds of unknown structure. In Table 9.3 are given some characteristic infrared absorption frequencies of functional groups. (A more complete table is given in the Appendix.)

9.3   Examples of the Use of Infrared Spectroscopy

To illustrate how infrared spectroscopy can be used to solve problems encountered in the laboratory, we will now examine two typical situations.

Example 1

A bottle containing 100 g of butanal was purchased from a chemical supplier. The supplier stated that the material was 99.9% pure. Since this level of purity was unsatisfactory for the purposes of the purchaser, he purified the butanal further and isolated 0.1 g of impurity. Since an infrared spectro-photometer was present in the laboratory, infrared spectra of the pure butanal and of the impurity were obtained.

The infrared spectrum of pure butanal is given in Figure 9.9. The carbonyl absorption is found at 1730 cm^{-1}, as expected for a saturated aliphatic aldehyde. Two bands due to the C—H stretching vibration of the aldehyde group are found at 2700 and 2800 cm^{-1}.

Table 9.3 Characteristic Infrared Absorption Frequencies of Functional Groups

Group	Class of compound	Range, cm^{-1}	Intensity
C—H	Alkane	2965–2850 (stretch)	strong
	—CH$_3$	1450 (bend)	medium
		1380 (bend)	medium
	—CH$_2$—	1465	medium
	Alkene	3095–3010 (stretch)	medium
		700–1000 (bend)	strong
	Alkyne	3300 (approx.)	strong
	Aldehyde	2900–2820	weak
		2775–2700	weak
C—C	Alkane	700–1200 (generally not useful)	weak
	Alkene[a]	1680–1620	variable
	Alkyne[a]	2260–2100	variable
C=O[a]	Ketone	1725–1705	strong
	Aldehyde	1740–1720	strong
	Carboxylic acid	1725–1700	strong
	Ester	1750–1730	strong
	Amide	1700–1630	strong
	Anhydride	1850–1800	strong
C—O	Alcohol, ester, carboxylic acid, ether	1300–1000	strong
—O—H	Alcohol		
	Monomer	3650–3590	variable and sharp
	H-bonded	3400–3200	strong and broad
	Carboxylic acid		
	H-bonded	3300–2500	variable and broad
—N—H	Primary amine and amide	3500 (approx.), Stretch[b]	medium
	Secondary amine and amide	3500, Stretch[b]	medium
C≡N	Nitrile[a]	2260–2240	medium
C—X	Fluoride	1400–1000	strong
	Chloride	800–600	strong
	Bromide	600–500	strong
	Iodide	500 (approx.)	strong

[a] Not conjugated. Conjugation of a multiple bond lowers the stretching frequency about 30 cm^{-1}.
[b] Lower if hydrogen bonded.

Figure 9.9
Infrared spectrum of butanal as a neat liquid film.

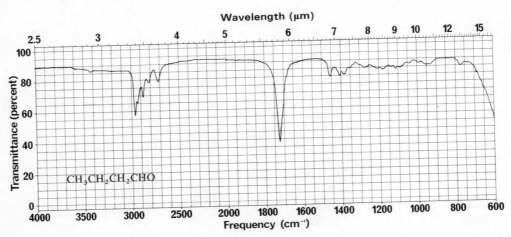

The infrared spectrum of the impurity is given in Figure 9.10. Strong carbonyl absorption can be seen at 1710 cm^{-1}. This absorption (and the fact that absorptions expected of other functional groups such as —CHO, COOH, etc., are absent) suggests that the impurity is a saturated aliphatic ketone.

Figure 9.10
Infrared spectrum (neat liquid film) of impurity isolated from commercial butanal and identified as butanone.

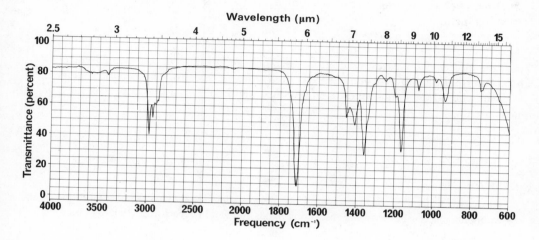

The impurity was submitted for nmr analysis and an nmr spectrum identical to the one in Figure 8.4 was obtained. Thus, the impurity was butanone, an isomer of butanal.

Example 2

Students in an organic chemistry laboratory were given rancid butter and asked to isolate and identify the ingredient which gives it the characteristic

Figure 9.11
Infrared spectrum (neat liquid film) of unknown identified as butyric acid.

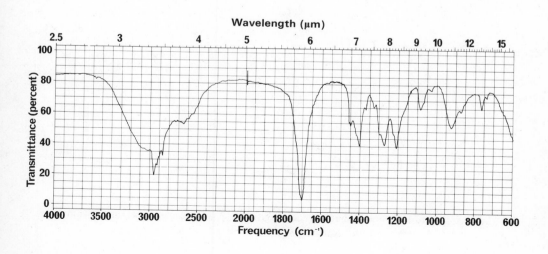

rancid odor. They found that extraction of the rancid butter with base removed the odor, and acidification of the basic extract regenerated it. After considerable work, an acidic compound responsible for the odor was isolated. Its infrared spectrum is given in Figure 9.11. The carbonyl absorption at 1700 cm^{-1} is characteristic of an aliphatic carboxylic acid. The OH stretching vibration region extends from 3600 to 2500 cm^{-1}, because of hydrogen bonding. This broad type of absorption band is characteristic of a carboxylic acid. The students found that their infrared spectrum was superimposable on the infrared spectrum of butyric acid. Other chemical and spectroscopic data agreed with that structural assignment.

There are additional classes of compounds, not yet discussed, for which useful structural information can be obtained from their infrared spectra. The pertinent facts will be given when these compounds are taken up. See the table in the Appendix for a summary.

PROBLEMS

1. How would infrared spectroscopy be useful in distinguishing between the following compounds? Cite characteristic absorption bands you would expect from each.

   (a) 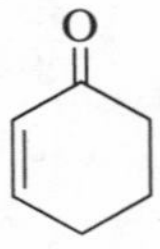   and

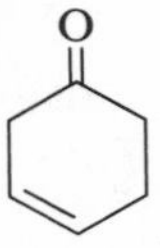

   (b)   CH$_3$CCH$_3$ and   CH$_3$CH$_2$CH=O

   (c)   CH$_3$—◯—COH   and   ◯—C—O—CH$_3$

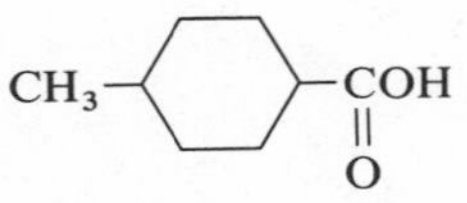

   (d)   CH$_3$C≡N   and   CH$_3$C≡C—H

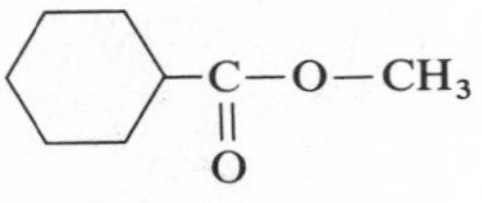

   (e) 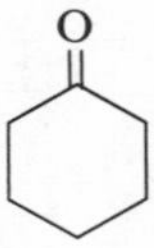   and   CH$_3$

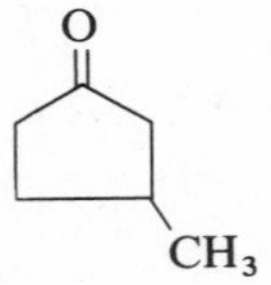

   (f) 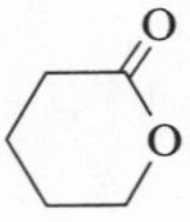   and

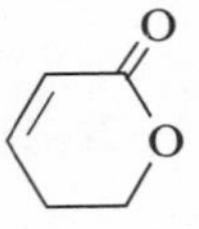

2. The infrared spectrum of 3-methylbutanoic acid is given. (a) Assign as many of the absorption bands as you can. (b) What would you expect the nmr spectrum to look like?

Infrared spectrum of 3-methylbutanoic acid as a neat liquid film, Problem 2.

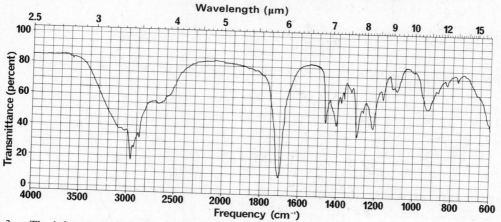

3. The infrared spectrum of an unknown compound is shown and its nmr spectrum is also given. The combustion analysis gave 88.2% C and 11.8% H. Suggest a structure for the unknown. Fully interpret the nmr spectrum and assign as many of the absorption bands in the infrared spectrum as you can.

Infrared spectrum of unknown, Problem 3, as a neat liquid film.

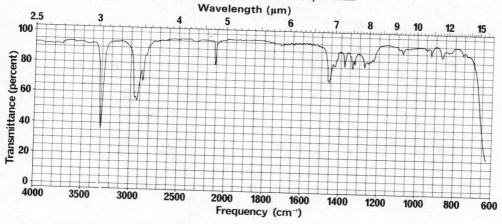

NMR spectrum of unknown, Problem 3.

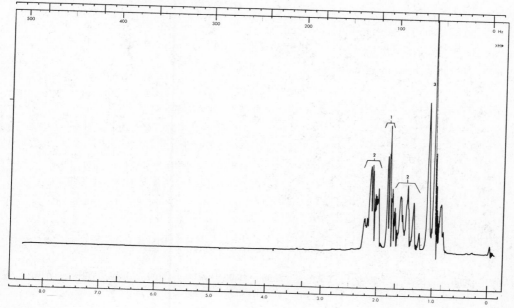

4. The infrared and nmr spectra of a compound of formula C_3H_7NO are given. Interpret the spectra and suggest a structure which is consistent with these data.

Infrared spectrum of unknown, Problem 4, as a neat liquid film.

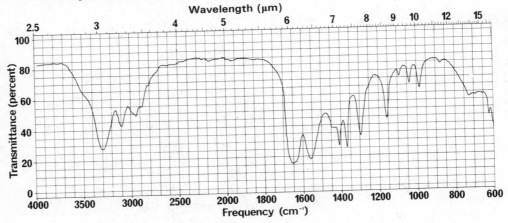

NMR spectrum of unknown, Problem 4, in methylene chloride solution.

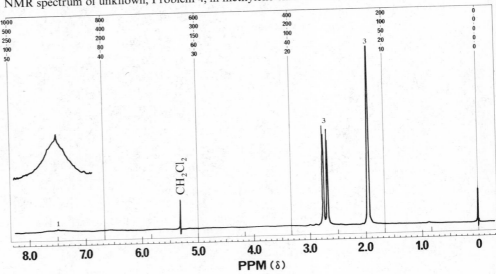

5. The infrared spectrum of butenone is given. Compare it with the spectra in Figures 9.4 and 9.10. List and interpret the differences.

Infrared spectrum of butenone as a neat liquid film.

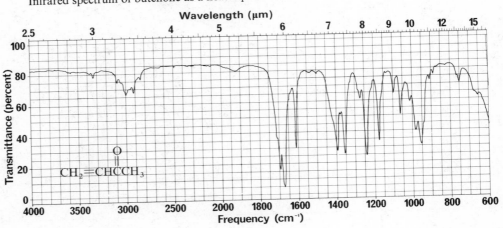

6. An unknown compound was analyzed and gave the formula C_4H_8O upon elemental analysis and molecular weight determination. Its infrared spectrum shows strong absorption at 1070 cm^{-1}, but no absorption in the $1600-1800 \text{ cm}^{-1}$ region. Its nmr spectrum consists of a multiplet centered at δ 1.8 and a multiplet centered at δ 3.7, of relative areas $1:1$. What is the unknown compound?

7. The progress of the oxidation of 2-propanol to acetone can be followed by infrared spectroscopy. Suggest how this might be done.

Optional Problem. Butanal shows strong carbonyl absorption at 1730 cm^{-1}. When the ^{16}O of butanal is replaced by ^{18}O, at what frequency will the carbonyl band be observed?

CHAPTER 10

OTHER FUNCTIONAL GROUPS CONTAINING MULTIPLY BONDED HETEROATOMS

10.1   Groups with Carbon–Nitrogen Multiple Bonds

Imines are nitrogen analogs of aldehydes and ketones.

$$
\begin{array}{cc}
\overset{\displaystyle H}{\underset{}{R-C=O}} & \overset{\displaystyle R'}{\underset{}{R-C=O}} \\
\text{Aldehyde} & \text{Ketone}
\end{array}
$$

$$
\begin{array}{cc}
\overset{\displaystyle H}{\underset{}{R-C=NH}} & \overset{\displaystyle R'}{\underset{}{R-C=NH}} \\
\text{Aldimine} & \text{Ketimine} \\
& \text{Imines}
\end{array}
$$

Most imines are readily hydrolyzed to carbonyl compounds and ammonia or amines.

$$
{>}C{=}N{\diagup}^{H} \ \xrightarrow{\text{H}_2\text{O}} \ {>}C{=}O + NH_3
$$

$$
{>}C{=}N{\diagup}^{R} \ \xrightarrow{\text{H}_2\text{O}} \ {>}C{=}O + H_2NR
$$

Hydrazones and *oximes* ($R_2C{=}NNH_2$ and $R_2C{=}NOH$, where R may be alkyl or H) are imines derived from hydrazine (NH_2NH_2) and hydroxylamine (NH_2OH), respectively; they are usually stable crystalline materials. The nitrogen of an imine is sp^2-hybridized, and isomerism can occur about the carbon–nitrogen double bond. The imine type of nitrogen does not invert as easily as does the ammonia type.

Acetone hydrazone   Isomeric oximes from acetaldehyde

EXERCISE   10.1

Consider the following two structures for acetone oxime:

(a) $\underset{CH_3}{\overset{CH_3}{\diagdown}}C=N\overset{OH}{\diagup}$ (b) $\underset{CH_3}{\overset{CH_3}{\diagdown}}C=N-OH$

Can structure (b) be ruled out simply on the basis of the hybridization available to the nitrogen atom? Explain how a spectroscopic method could be used to demonstrate that structure (a) is correct.

Nitriles contain the cyano group, $-C{\equiv}N$, and may be considered as organic derivatives of hydrogen cyanide.

$H-C{\equiv}N:$ $R-C{\equiv}N:$
Hydrogen cyanide   Nitrile

The electronic structure of nitriles is similar to that of acetylene—both the carbon and nitrogen are *sp*-hybridized; the lone pair on nitrogen is in an *sp* orbital (Figure 10.1).

Figure 10.1
The electronic structure of a nitrile.

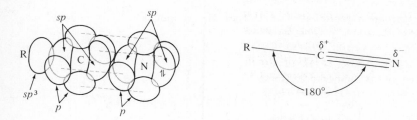

The cyano group, like the carbonyl group, is capable of stabilizing an adjacent *carbanion* (see page 170). (A carbon atom which contains a lone pair and carries a negative charge is called a *carbanion*.)

$$-\overset{\overset{\displaystyle H}{|}}{\underset{|}{C}}-C{\equiv}N \;\rightleftharpoons\; \left[-\overset{|}{\underset{|}{\bar{C}}}-C{\equiv}N \;\leftrightarrow\; {>}C{=}C{=}\bar{N}\right] + H^+$$

EXERCISE   10.2

In theory could propionitrile, CH_3CH_2CN, exist in more than one tautomeric form? If so, how many forms could there be? Draw them.

The names of nitriles are derived from those of the acids to which they may be hydrolyzed.

$$R-C{\equiv}N + H_2O \xrightarrow[\text{base catalyst}]{\text{acid or}} R-COOH + NH_3$$

The ending *-ic acid* is dropped and replaced by the suffix *-onitrile*. In polyfunctional compounds, the *cyano* group may be named as a substituent.

$$ClCH_2CH_2CH_2C{\equiv}N \qquad NCCH_2COOH \qquad CH_3CN$$

4-Chlorobutyronitrile   Cyanoacetic acid   Acetonitrile
                                                    (methyl cyanide)

Nitriles have significant dipole moments and are highly associated in the liquid state. Their boiling points are somewhat higher than those of alcohols of comparable molecular weights. Most nitriles have an odor reminiscent of that of hydrogen cyanide, and they are moderately toxic. *Acetonitrile* is an excellent polar solvent for both ionic and covalent materials.

Less-Common Types of Compounds Containing Carbon–Nitrogen Multiple Bonds. Other classes of compounds which contain carbon–nitrogen multiple bonds include the *isocyanides, isocyanates,* and *carbodiimides.*

$$CH_3{-}N{=}C: \qquad CH_3{-}N{=}C{=}O \qquad CH_3{-}N{=}C{=}N{-}CH_3$$

Methyl isocyanide   Methyl isocyanate   Dimethylcarbodiimide

Isocyanides (also known as isonitriles) are best noted for their unusual structures and unbelievably disagreeable odors. They, along with carbon monoxide, are among the very few stable compounds which contain divalent carbon. This stability is due in part to contributions by polar resonance forms.

$$:C{=}\ddot{O}: \leftrightarrow :\overset{+}{C}{-}\overset{-}{\underset{..}{O}}: \leftrightarrow :\overset{-}{C}{\equiv}\overset{+}{O}:$$

$$R{-}\ddot{N}{=}C: \leftrightarrow R{-}\overset{-}{\underset{..}{N}}{-}\overset{+}{C}: \leftrightarrow R{-}\overset{+}{N}{\equiv}\overset{-}{C}:$$

Isocyanates and carbodiimides are nitrogen analogs of ketenes. They are important laboratory reagents and are used in the plastics and polymer industries.

10.2   Groups with Nitrogen–Oxygen Double Bonds

The nitro group ($-NO_2$) is electronically similar to the carboxylate anion ($-CO_2^-$) and can be written as two equivalent resonance forms.

Note that the nitrogen bears a full positive charge and the oxygens each bear one-half of a negative charge. The nitro group is highly electronegative and nitro compounds are polar substances of high boiling points but of surprisingly low water solubility.

The nitro group is named as a substituent on a parent compound.

$$CH_3NO_2 \qquad \underset{\underset{NO_2}{|}}{CH_3CHCH_3} \qquad \underset{\underset{NO_2}{|}}{CH_3CHCH_2COOH}$$

Nitromethane   2-Nitropropane   3-Nitrobutyric acid

The nitro group is capable of stabilizing a negative charge on an adjacent atom to a pronounced degree; thus nitromethane is sufficiently acidic to dissolve in aqueous sodium hydroxide. (The prefix *aci-* indicates the acid (enol) form of a compound.)

Nitromethane   *aci*-Nitromethane

Reprotonation of the salt may occur on either carbon or oxygen. Initial protonation is usually on oxygen to give the strongly acidic *aci* tautomer, which is analogous to the enol of a ketone and which slowly reverts to the more stable nitro form.

EXPLOSIVES. *A number of the simple nitro compounds are useful as reagents and solvents.* Nitro compounds, nitrates (*esters of nitric acid*), and nitramines (N-*nitroamines*) are among the most important classes of shock-sensitive high explosives.

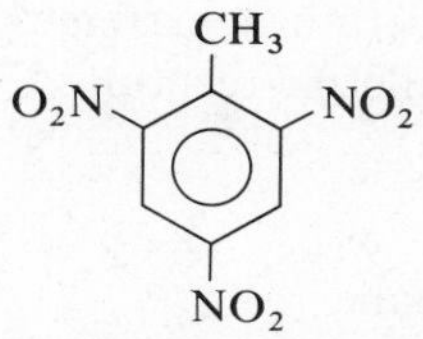

2,4,6-Trinitrotoluene
(TNT)

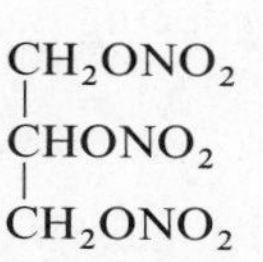

Glyceryl trinitrate
(Nitroglycerin)

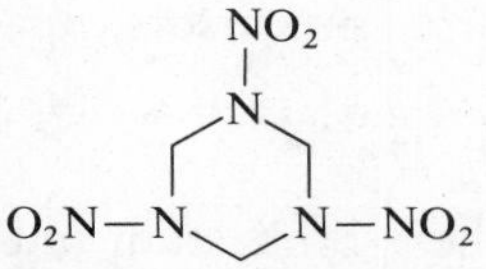

1,3,5-Trinitro-1,3,5-triazane
(Cyclonite or RDX)

Nitroso Compounds. Compounds containing the *nitroso* group ($-N=O$) are rather rare. Primary and secondary *C*-nitroso compounds are unstable and dimerize or rearrange to the tautomeric oximes.

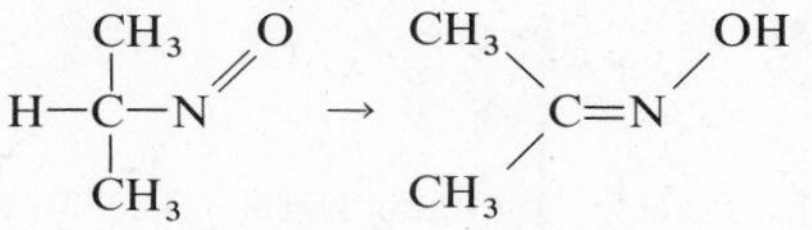

2-Nitrosopropane   Acetone oxime

The tertiary derivatives exist as blue monomers in the gas phase or in dilute solution but are usually isolated as colorless to orange dimeric solids or liquids.

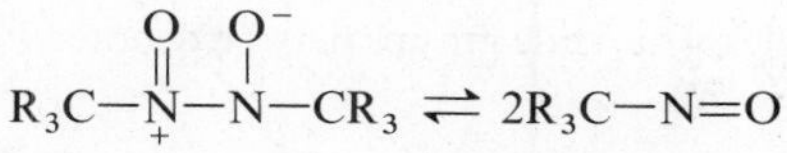

Dimer   Monomer
                          (Blue color)

Compounds of the structure $R-O-N=O$ are called *nitrites* and are esters of nitrous acid. The *N*-nitroso derivatives of secondary amines are stable.

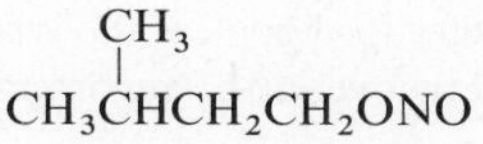

Isoamyl nitrite 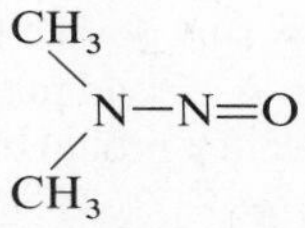   *N*-Nitrosodimethylamine
                          (Dimethylnitrosamine)

10.3   Groups with Nitrogen–Nitrogen Multiple Bonds

The nitrogen–nitrogen triple bond in N_2 is the strongest covalent bond known (226 kcal/mole). It is not surprising that most compounds containing nitrogen–nitrogen double bonds tend to decompose or react in such a way as to yield molecular nitrogen.

Azo compounds contain the grouping $-N=N-$. Compounds of the type $R-N=N-H$ are very unstable and rapidly decompose to RH and N_2. The stability of the disubstituted compounds, $R-N=N-R$, is dependent on the nature of the R group. Azomethane ($CH_3-N=N-CH_3$) is a yellow liquid which is stable to about 400°C.

EXERCISE 10.3

Should geometrical isomerism be possible about the $-N=N-$ bond?

The most important of the *diazo compounds* is the parent substance, diazomethane.

$$CH_2=\overset{+}{N}=\overset{-}{\ddot{N}}: \leftrightarrow \overset{-}{\ddot{C}}H_2-\overset{+}{N}\equiv N: \leftrightarrow \overset{-}{\ddot{C}}H_2-\overset{..}{N}=\overset{+}{\ddot{N}}:$$

Diazomethane,
Bp −23°C, yellow gas

Diazomethane is one of the most interesting and useful reagents in organic chemistry despite the fact that it is highly explosive, unstable at room temperature, extremely toxic, and made from precursors capable of producing dangerous allergic reactions.

EXERCISE 10.4

Predict the hybridization and the bond angles of diazomethane.

Other Compounds Containing Nitrogen–Nitrogen Multiple Bonds. The stability of *diazonium ions* $(R-\overset{+}{N}\equiv N:)$ is dependent on the structure of the R group. Alkanediazonium salts have never been isolated; reactions that might have been expected to produce them instead produce nitrogen and an alkyl derivative, such as a halide. Only aromatic diazonium salts have been isolated (see Section 22.7).

$$[CH_3-\overset{+}{N}\equiv N \; Cl^-] \rightarrow N_2 + CH_3Cl$$

Azides are organic derivatives of the unstable and highly toxic hydrazoic acid (HN_3). The lower molecular weight azides are often explosive.

$$R-N=\overset{+}{N}=\overset{-}{\ddot{N}}: \leftrightarrow R-\overset{-}{\ddot{N}}-\overset{+}{N}\equiv N: \leftrightarrow R-\overset{..}{\ddot{N}}-\overset{..}{N}=\overset{+}{\ddot{N}}:$$

The nomenclature of azides is patterned after that of halides. The azide groups may be denoted by the prefix *azido.*

$$CH_3N_3 \qquad CH_3CH_2CH_2\overset{\overset{\displaystyle O}{\displaystyle \|}}{C}-N_3 \qquad N_3CH_2CH_2COOH$$

Methyl azide   Butyryl azide   3-Azidopropionic acid

Multiple Bonds to Boron. Although there are no known compounds of the types $RB=O$, $RB=NR$, $RB=CR_2$, or $RB=BR$, there is evidence for partial double-bond character for bonds of the type $B-Y$, where the atom Y possesses a lone pair. A π bond may be formed by overlap of a p orbital on atom Y containing a lone pair, with the vacant p orbital on boron.

$$\overset{\diagdown}{\underset{\diagup}{}}B-\ddot{Y} \leftrightarrow \overset{\diagdown}{\underset{\diagup}{}}\overset{-}{B}=\overset{+}{Y}$$

The fact that trialkoxyboranes, $B(OR)_3$, and triaminoboranes, $B(NR_2)_3$, are very weak Lewis acids has been ascribed to such bonding, which would reduce the effective electron deficiency at boron. Apparently, significant nitrogen–boron π bonding occurs in borazines (Section 4.18) and related compounds (Section 12.2).

10.4   Properties of the Orbitals of the Third Principal Shell.

Multiple Bonding and Second-Row Elements

In this section the general characteristics of multiple bonding by second-row elements are discussed. In subsequent sections functional groups containing the second-row elements sulfur, phosphorus, and silicon will be presented.

Second-row elements have their bonding electrons in the third principal shell, which differs from the second in three major respects:

1. The number of electrons which can be accommodated, and hence *the total number and type of orbitals within the shell*. A filled second shell has the configuration $2s^2 2p^6$, whereas a filled third shell is $3s^2 3p^6 3d^{10}$.

2. *The number of nodes for each orbital*. The second-shell orbitals have one node, while the third-shell orbitals each have two.

3. *The relative size of the orbitals*. The electron density is concentrated further out as the value of the principal quantum number increases. The probability of finding an electron is highest beyond the last (farthest out) node in any given lobe of an orbital.

The s and p orbitals of the second and third shells are compared in Figure 10.2. The $3s$ and $3p$ orbitals form hybrids and σ bonds which are similar to those from $2s$ and $2p$ orbitals, except that the angles tend to be somewhat different (Sections 4.12 and 4.14). A more important difference is that the $3p$–$3p$ π bonds between second-row elements are weak, and in fact rarely form.

Figure 10.2
The s and p orbitals of the second and third principal shell.

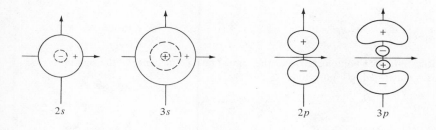

Why Do Second-Row Elements Form Poor p–p π Bonds? The reasons for this reluctance of $3p$ orbitals to form π bonds are not well understood. With the large nuclei of the second row the bonds are quite long, so that $3p$ overlap is not very effective. In the case of the $2p$–$3p$ π bond it may be further suggested that the radial node of the $3p$ orbital occurs in such a way as to decrease the net effective overlap of the two orbitals.

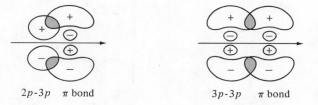

Second-row elements can engage in more complicated bonding schemes through the use of their d orbitals. The five $3d$ orbitals, which in contrast to the p orbitals do not all have the same shapes when shown in the usual way (Figure 10.3), can form σ bonds with s, p, or d orbitals or hybrids thereof, or π bonds with p and d orbitals.

The π bonds that have a major influence on the chemistry of the second-row elements are p–d π bonds. The d_{xz}, d_{yz}, and d_{xy} orbitals have the advantage that their lobes are directed somewhat toward the p orbitals of the second atom and their signs are correct for bonding (see Figure 10.4).

Figure 10.3
The shapes of the 3d orbitals.

Most often involved in σ bonds:

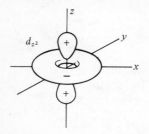

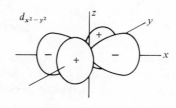

Most often involved in π bonds:

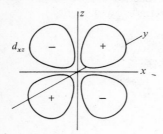

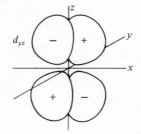

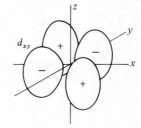

Overlap and Bonding. Recall that for bonding to occur there must be a coincidence of the sign of the wave function. This is illustrated in Figure 10.4.

Figure 10.4
Effect on bonding of the sign of the wave function.

Net overlap = 0. No bonding interaction

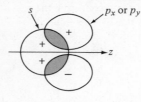

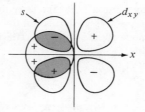

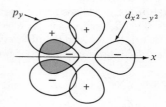

Net overlap leading to bonding

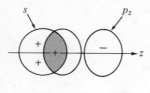

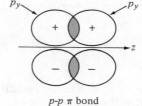

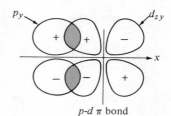

   s-p σ bond   *p-p* π bond   *p-d* π bond

Hybrids of d Orbitals. The nature of the d orbitals is such that hybridization with s and p orbitals may lead to a number of alternative geometries (Figure 10.5). Certain of these hybridizations will prove useful in discussing bonding in molecules containing atoms with low-lying empty d orbitals.

Figure 10.5

Some hybridization schemes involving *d* orbitals. Heavy arrows show the directions in which the lobes point. Bond angles are given.

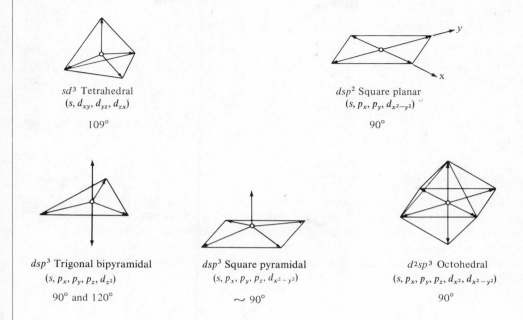

sd^3 Tetrahedral
$(s, d_{xy}, d_{yz}, d_{zx})$

109°

dsp^2 Square planar
$(s, p_x, p_y, d_{x^2-y^2})$

90°

dsp^3 Trigonal bipyramidal
$(s, p_x, p_y, p_z, d_{z^2})$

90° and 120°

dsp^3 Square pyramidal
$(s, p_x, p_y, p_z, d_{x^2-y^2})$

$\sim$ 90°

d^2sp^3 Octahedral
$(s, p_x, p_y, p_z, d_{x^2}, d_{x^2-y^2})$

90°

EXERCISE 10.5

As was mentioned in Chapter 5, it is possible to use nuclear magnetic resonance techniques to examine nuclei other than hydrogen. In the fluorine magnetic resonance spectrum of SF_4 two distinct triplets of equal intensity are observed. Fluorine has a spin of $\frac{1}{2}$. Using this data, can you suggest a structure for SF_4?

More on Lewis Acids

Why is silicon tetrafluoride so very reactive in contrast to carbon tetrafluoride, which is a very inert substance? The answer is that the silicon atom in silicon tetrafluoride with its low-lying empty *d* orbitals can act as a Lewis acid by expansion of its octet.

$$\textit{Acid} \qquad \textit{Base} \qquad \textit{Coordinated complex}$$

(*sp³* tetrahedral)   (*d²sp³* octahedral)

Other examples of this type of acid–base reaction include:

$$\textit{Acid} \qquad \textit{Base} \qquad \textit{Coordinated complex}$$

$$PCl_3 + ROH \rightarrow [\overset{+}{RO}-\overset{-}{P}Cl_3] \rightarrow PCl_2OH + RCl$$
$$\underset{H}{|}$$

$$SF_4 + F_2 \rightarrow SF_6$$

Interestingly, SF_6, with no more orbitals available as reaction sites, is one of the most stable molecules known; it is inert to oxygen in an electric discharge and can be recovered unchanged from molten potassium hydroxide.

Our completed list of types of Lewis acids important to organic chemistry includes

1. Simple cations, for example, H^+, Li^+, Ag^+, Cl^+, CH_3^+.

2. Compounds whose central atom has an incomplete octet, for example, BF_3, $AlCl_3$, $FeBr_3$, $MgBr_2$.

3. Multiply bonded groups with a site of low electron density, for example,

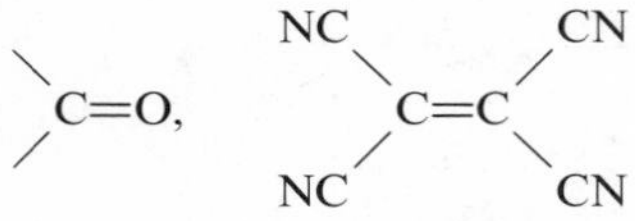

4. Compounds in which the octet of the central atom can be expanded, for example, SiF_4, $SbCl_5$, PCl_3, SO_2, SO_3, Br_2, I_2.

10.5   Sulfur Compounds

Sulfur, like other second-row elements, forms very weak p–p π bonds. Thus thiocarbonyl compounds, in which the π bond of the C=S grouping is formed from overlap of the carbon $2p$ and sulfur $3p$ orbitals, are much less stable than the corresponding carbonyl compounds and consequently fairly uncommon. For example, thioaldehydes and many thioketones readily dimerize, trimerize, or polymerize to yield compounds containing only sigma bonds.

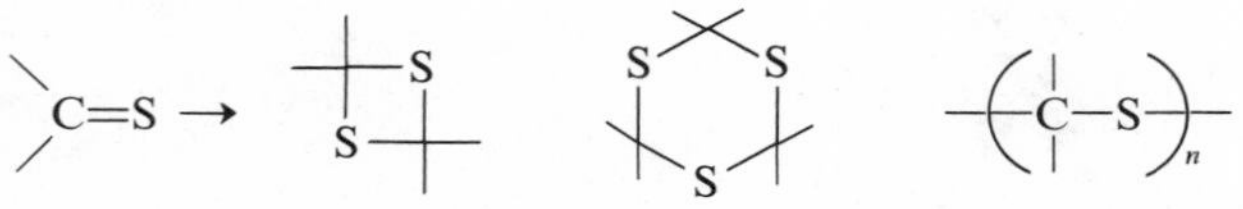

Dimer   Trimer   Polymer

The more stable thiocarbonyl compounds are those containing substituents which decrease the double-bond character of the thiocarbonyl grouping.

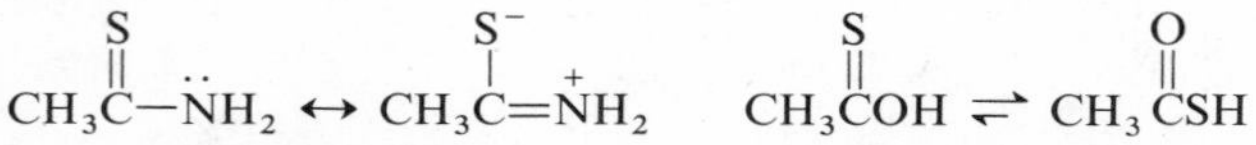

Thioacetamide   Thioacetic acid

The most common organic chemical containing the C=S grouping is carbon disulfide (CS_2), which is a useful solvent.

Perhaps the most striking example of the reluctance of sulfur to form $3p$–$3p$ π bonds is provided by elemental sulfur, which, unlike O_2, is most stable in the cyclic S_8 form.

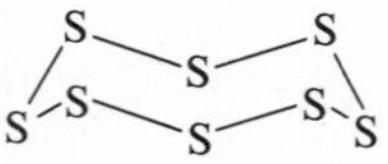

Sulfur,
stable S_8 form

The p–d π bonding so important in the chemistry of second-row elements is illustrated here by consideration of the structure of dimethyl sulfoxide. Acetone is shown for comparison.

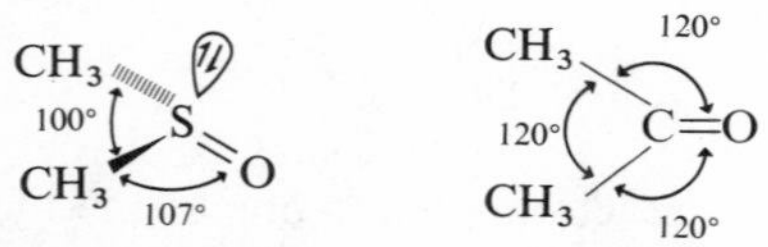

Dimethyl sulfoxide   Acetone
(DMSO)

The S—O sigma bond is formed by overlap of a sulfur sp^3 orbital with the oxygen $2p_x$ orbital (Figure 10.6a). There remain on oxygen the filled $2p_y$ and $2p_z$ orbitals. Two of the vacant sulfur d orbitals are situated so as to be properly oriented for π overlap with these p orbitals (Figure 10.6b). Bonding of the type illustrated by oxygen donating electron density back to empty sulfur orbitals is sometimes described as "back-bonding".

Figure 10.6
Bonding in dimethyl sulfoxide: (a) σ bonds; (b) π bonds (there are two situated at right angles to one another, xz and xy).

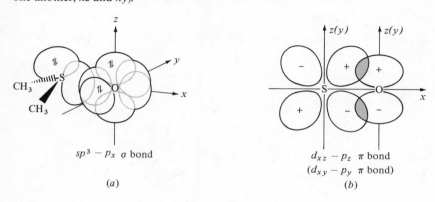

$sp^3 - p_x$ σ bond

(a)

$d_{xz} - p_z$ π bond
($d_{xy} - p_y$ π bond)

(b)

Dimethyl sulfoxide can, then, be regarded as a resonance hybrid of the following electronic structures:

These p–d π bonds are not very strong and the electron pairs belong mostly to oxygen, as evidenced by the fact the sulfoxides have high dipole moments (~ 3.9 D) and act as Lewis bases primarily at the oxygen atom.

For sulfur in higher oxidation states, π bonding from oxygen to sulfur again appears to be important, for example,

Dimethyl sulfone   Methanesulfonic acid

In such cases the participating vacant orbitals on sulfur may well be of a hybrid nature, involving some $4s$ and/or $4p$ character.

BONDING IN SULFUR COMPOUNDS. *The nature of sulfur bonding has been and remains a subject of some controversy. In the current scientific literature, sulfoxides are represented by the following formulations:*

We shall use the symbolism $>$S$=$O, *not to represent a double bond in the classical sense, but to remind us that significant back-bonding does occur. The bond order of such a bond, based on bond distances and energies, appears to be just less than 2.*

There is no doubt that sulfur is capable of expanding its octet. We have already mentioned SF_4 and SF_6. A few analogous organic compounds are known, for example

$$C_6H_5SF_3 \qquad\qquad CF_3SF_5$$

Phenylsulfur trifluoride†   Trifluoromethylsulfur pentafluoride

Apparently the combination of high electronegativity and small size of the fluorine make such structures possible. To date there are no known compounds that have more than three carbons σ-bonded to a single sulfur atom.

Both the sulfoxide and sulfone groups are capable of stabilizing an adjacent negative charge.

$$\underset{\overset{\|}{\text{CH}_3\text{SCH}_3}}{\overset{O}{}} + NaH^{\dagger\dagger} \longrightarrow \underset{\overset{\|}{\text{CH}_3\text{SCH}_2^-}}{\overset{O}{}} Na^+ + H_2$$

$$\underset{\underset{\|}{\overset{\|}{\text{CH}_3\text{SCH}_3}}}{\overset{O}{}}_{O} + NaH \longrightarrow \underset{\underset{\|}{\overset{\|}{\text{CH}_3\text{SCH}_2^-}}}{\overset{O}{}}_{O} Na^+ + H_2$$

EXERCISE   10.6

Write the resonance forms which contribute to the structure of the anion of dimethyl sulfone.

An *ylide* is an internal salt formed by removal of a proton from a carbon adjacent to a heteroatom bearing a positive charge. Some of the sulfur ylides are important reagents in synthesis.

$$\underset{\underset{\text{CH}_3}{\overset{|}{}}}{\overset{+}{\text{CH}_3\text{SCH}_3}} \; Cl^- \quad \xrightarrow[\text{DMSO}]{\text{NaH}^{\dagger\dagger}} \quad \underset{\underset{\text{CH}_3}{\overset{|}{}}}{\overset{+\quad-}{\text{CH}_3\text{S}-\text{CH}_2}} \leftrightarrow \underset{\underset{\text{CH}_3}{\overset{|}{}}}{\text{CH}_3\text{S}=\text{CH}_2}$$

Trimethylsulfonium chloride   Dimethylsulfonium methylide

Undoubtedly *d*-orbital participation contributes to the stability of the ylides and anions described above.

Sulfur. A Summary. A number of typical sulfur compounds, most of which contain multiply bonded sulfur, are listed here along with their common and/or systematic names.

Sulfoxides and related compounds

$$\underset{\text{CH}_3\text{CH}_2\text{SCH}_3}{\overset{\overset{O}{\|}}{}} \qquad \underset{\text{CH}_3\text{SCH}_2\text{COOH}}{\overset{\overset{O}{\|}}{}} \qquad \underset{\text{CH}_3\text{SCH}_3}{\overset{\overset{NH}{\|}}{}}$$

Ethyl methyl sulfoxide   Methanesulfinylacetic acid   Dimethylsulfilimine

Sulfones and related compounds

$$\underset{\underset{O}{\overset{\|}{}}}{\underset{\text{CH}_3\text{CH}_2\text{SCH}_3}{\overset{\overset{O}{\|}}{}}} \qquad \underset{\underset{O}{\overset{\|}{}}}{\underset{\text{CH}_3\text{SCH}_2\text{COOH}}{\overset{\overset{O}{\|}}{}}} \qquad \underset{\underset{O}{\overset{\|}{}}}{\underset{\text{CH}_3\text{SCH}_3}{\overset{\overset{NH}{\|}}{}}}$$

Ethyl methyl sulfone   Methanesulfonylacetic acid   Dimethylsulfoximine

---

† The phenyl group (C_6H_5—) has rather special structural properties. It will be discussed in detail in Chapter 11.

†† NaH is a strong base which reacts with even weakly acidic compounds to give the sodium salt of the compound and H_2; for example, NaH + ROH $\longrightarrow$ RONa + H_2.

Sulfenic acids and derivatives

CH_3SOH
Methanesulfenic acid
(unstable)

CH_3SCl
Methanesulfenyl chloride

CH_3SNH_2
Methanesulfenamide

Sulfinic acid and derivatives

$$\overset{O}{\underset{}{\overset{\|}{CH_3\overset{}{S}OH}}}$$
Methanesulfinic acid

$$\overset{O}{\overset{\|}{CH_3\overset{}{S}Cl}}$$
Methanesulfinyl chloride

$$\overset{O}{\overset{\|}{CH_3\overset{}{S}OCH_3}}$$
Methyl methanesulfinate

Sulfonic acids and derivatives

$$\overset{O}{\underset{O}{\overset{\|}{CH_3\overset{}{\underset{\|}{S}}OH}}}$$
Methanesulfonic acid

$$\overset{O}{\underset{O}{\overset{\|}{CH_3\overset{}{\underset{\|}{S}}NH_2}}}$$
Methanesulfonamide

δ-Butanesultone

Miscellaneous compounds

$$\overset{O}{\overset{\|}{CH_3OSOCH_3}}$$
Dimethyl sulfite

$$\overset{O}{\underset{O}{\overset{\|}{CH_3O\overset{}{\underset{\|}{S}}OCH_3}}}$$
Dimethyl sulfate

$$\overset{S}{\overset{\|}{CH_3CH_2OCSCH_3}}$$
O-Ethyl *S*-methyl xanthate

EXERCISE 10.7

What types of isomers should be possible for each of the following compounds?

(a) Dimethyl sulfone   (b) Methyl ethyl sulfoxide   (c) CH_3—⬡—$S{=}O$

10.6 Phosphorus and Silicon Compounds

Bonding in phosphorus compounds is characteristic of bonding in second-row elements as discussed and given more detailed analysis for some representative sulfur compounds. Once again we see a strong trend away from p–p π bonding and an increased reliance on p–d π bonding. Silicon does not participate in formal p–p π double bonds, but can use $3d$ orbitals to expand its octet.

Phosphorus. A Summary. Names and structures of representative phosphorus compounds are given below.

$$\overset{CH_3}{\underset{CH_3}{\overset{|}{CH_3\overset{}{P}{=}O}}}$$
Trimethylphosphine
oxide

$(C_6H_5)_3{-}P{=}CH_2 \leftrightarrow (C_6H_5)_3{-}\overset{+}{P}{-}\overset{-}{C}H_2$
Methylenetriphenylphosphorane
(Triphenylphosphonium methylide)

$(C_6H_5)_5{-}P$
Pentaphenylphosphorane

$$\overset{OCH_3}{\underset{OCH_3}{\overset{|}{CH_3O{-}\overset{}{P}{=}O}}}$$
Trimethyl phosphate

$$\overset{OH}{\underset{OH}{\overset{|}{CH_3\overset{}{P}{=}O}}}$$

$$\begin{array}{c} \text{OH} \\ | \\ CF_3P{=}O \\ | \\ CF_3 \end{array}$$

Bis(trifluoromethyl)phosphinic acid

Phosphorus and sulfur differ in that phosphorus can better accommodate higher coordination states. Although SF_4 and SF_6 are stable compounds, and SCl_4 is a known but unstable material, compounds of the type R_4S and $(RO)_4S$ are unknown. Phosphorus compounds of the general type PCl_5 (which exists in the solid state as $PCl_4^+ PCl_6^-$), R_5P, $(RO)_5P$, R_6P^-, and $(RO)_6P^-$ are known. The penta-coordinate phosphorus compounds have trigonal bipyramidal structures and the hexa-coordinate compounds apparently have octahedral structures.

Silicon. A Summary. Since silicon is normally tetracovalent and apparently is unable to participate in *p–p* π bonding, no compounds of the types

$$>Si{=}C<, \quad >Si{=}O, \quad >Si{=}N-, \quad \text{or} \quad >Si{=}Si<$$

are known. The formation of the previously mentioned anion, SiF_6^{2-}, indicates that silicon, like other second-row elements, can expand its octet by utilizing the $3d$ orbitals. Apparently *p–d* π back-bonding results in partial double-bond character for a number of bonds of the type

$$\begin{array}{c} \diagdown \\ -Si-\ddot{Y} \\ \diagup \end{array} \leftrightarrow \begin{array}{c} \diagdown \\ -\overset{-}{Si}{=}\overset{+}{Y} \\ \diagup \end{array}$$

where Y = halogen, nitrogen, oxygen, or an unsaturated carbon group. Such *d*-orbital participation results in a lower dipole moment, higher bond energy, and a shorter bond length than might have been expected on the basis of ordinary single bonds.

10.7   Spectroscopic Analysis

Infrared

Table 10.1 lists the characteristic vibrational frequencies of the more important functional groups discussed in this chapter. It is important to note that carbon–nitrogen vibrational bands are usually much less intense than the corresponding carbon–oxygen bands.

Table 10.1   Typical Infrared Absorption Characteristics

Functional group	Frequency range, cm^{-1}	Intensity
$>C{=}N$	1640–1670	medium
$-C{\equiv}N$	2210–2260	weak
$-NO_2$	1515–1570	strong
	1320–1390	strong
$>S{=}O$	1040–1060	strong
$>SO_2$	1300–1340	strong
	1135–1160	strong
$\geqq Si-C\leqq$	690–890	strong
$\geqq Si-O-$	1000–1100	strong

For the nitro and sulfone groups, two characteristic bands are always present. These correspond to symmetric and antisymmetric stretching.

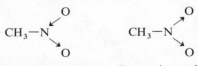

Antisymmetric stretching   Symmetric stretching
vibration : 1570 cm^{-1} vibration : 1380 cm^{-1}

NMR

The chemical shifts of methyl derivatives of selected functional groups discussed in this chapter are shown.

$$CH_3CN \quad CH_3NO_2 \quad CH_3SCH_3 \quad CH_3\overset{\overset{\displaystyle O}{\|}}{S}CH_3 \quad CH_3\overset{\overset{\displaystyle O}{\|}}{\underset{\underset{\displaystyle O}{\|}}{S}}CH_3 \quad (CH_3)_2Si(OCH_3)_2$$

$$\delta\,2.0 \qquad \delta\,4.3 \qquad \delta\,2.1 \qquad \delta\,2.5 \qquad \delta\,2.6 \qquad \delta\,0.1 \quad \delta\,3.6$$

The chemical shift observed for a compound CH_3X is dependent on the electron density surrounding the hydrogen nuclei. The electron density in turn is a function of the electronegativity of the group X. If more than one group is present, as in $Y-CH_2-X$, an additive effect of the two groups X and Y on the chemical shifts of the hydrogen nuclei might be anticipated. To a first approximation this has been found to be true. Table 10.2

Table 10.2   NMR Shielding Constants

X *or* Y	Shielding constant	X *or* Y	Shielding constant
$-CH_3$	0.8	$-I$	1.8
$>C=C<$	1.3	$-C_6H_5{}^a$	1.8
$-C\equiv C-$	1.4	$-Br$	2.3
$-COOR$	1.6	$-OR$	2.4
$-NR_2$	1.6	$-Cl$	2.5
$-SR$	1.6	$-OH$	2.6
$-C\equiv N$	1.7	$-OCOR$	3.1
$-COR$	1.7	$-OC_6H_5{}^a$	3.2

[a] The formula C_6H_5 represents the phenyl group, to be discussed in Chapter 11.

lists the *shielding constants* for selected X and Y groups. To calculate the approximate chemical shift for a disubstituted methylene group, the sum of the appropriate shielding constants for X and Y is added to 0.2 (the δ value for methane).

$$\delta = 0.2 + \sum \text{shielding constants}$$

Thus the value for the methylene protons of CH_3O-CH_2-CN is found as follows:

$$\delta = 0.2 + 2.4(OR) + 1.7(CN) = 4.3$$

The observed value is δ 4.2. The chemical shifts of compounds **HXYZ** can be calculated in like manner, but the values obtained are much less accurate.

PROBLEMS

1. Draw an orbital model of $CH_2{=}NCH_3$ showing all of the valence atomic orbitals.

2. Give acceptable names for the following compounds:
    (a) $CH_3\underset{\underset{\displaystyle NO_2}{|}}{C}HCH_3$
    (b) $CH_3\underset{\underset{\displaystyle ONO}{|}}{C}HCH_3$
    (c) $CH_3\underset{\underset{\displaystyle ONO_2}{|}}{C}HCH_3$

3. Predict the hybridization of the carbons and nitrogen atoms in the following compounds:
    (a) $CH_3-N{=}C{=}O$
    (b) $CH_3-N{=}C{=}N-CH_3$
    (c) $Li^+ \ {}^-CH_2NO_2$
    (d) CH_3OCN

4. Give examples of four different types of Lewis acids and a characteristic acid–base reaction of each.

5. Draw structures for the following compounds:
   (a) 3-Methylcyclohexanone oxime
   (b) 1-Acetoxy-1-cyanocyclopentane
   (c) Isovaleronitrile
   (d) 2,5-Dinitrohexane
   (e) Azoethane
   (f) Cyclobutyl azide
   (g) Ethyl methyl sulfone
   (h) Propane-2-sulfonic acid
   (i) N,N-Dimethylethanesulfonamide
   (j) Diethyl sulfate

6. Estimate the chemical shift of the boldface protons in each of the following compounds:
   (a) $\textbf{CH}_2Cl_2$
   (b) $HC{\equiv}C\textbf{CH}_2OH$
   (c) $C_6H_5\textbf{CH}_2OCOCH_3$
   (d) $\textbf{CH}_2(COOCH_2CH_3)_2$
   (e) $CH_3\textbf{CH}_2I$
   (f) $\textbf{CH}Br_3$

7. The infrared spectrum of compound A (C_4H_7N) exhibited a moderate band at 2250 cm^{-1}. Its nmr spectrum contained a doublet at δ 1.33 (6H), and a heptet at δ 2.72 (1H). What is the structure of A?

8. The strongest bands in the infrared spectrum of compound B ($C_4H_{10}O_2S$) were 1150 and 1330 cm^{-1}. The nmr spectrum of B reveals a triplet at δ 1.32 (3H), and a quartet at δ 3.03 (2H). What is the structure of B?

9. The following data were obtained on compound C:
   Elemental analysis: C, 29.2%; H, 4.9%; N, 11.3%; Cl, 28.7%
   Nmr spectrum: triplet, δ 1.10 (3H)
   multiplet, δ 2.32 (2H)
   triplet, δ 5.80 (1H)
   IR spectrum: strong bands at 1383 and 1553 cm^{-1}
   What is the structure of C?

10. Why is the stretching frequency characteristic of a nitrile so much higher than that of an imine?

11. Unknown compound $C_6H_{14}OS$, an oily substance with an odor suggestive of garlic, gives the nmr and the ir spectra shown. Suggest a structure for the compound.

NMR spectrum of unknown compound, Problem 11.

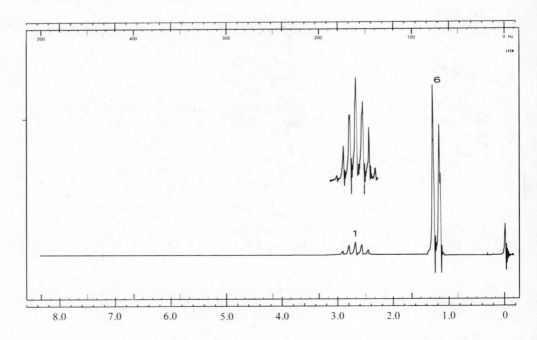

Infrared spectrum (neat liquid film) of unknown compound, Problem 11.

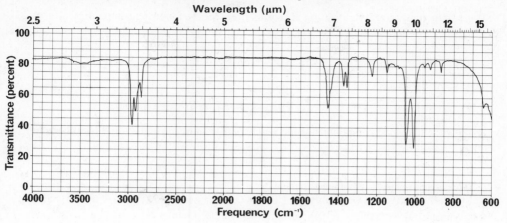

12.   A compound $C_5H_{10}O_2S$, gave the nmr and the ir spectra shown. On the basis of these data, suggest a structure.

NMR spectrum of unknown compound, Problem 12.

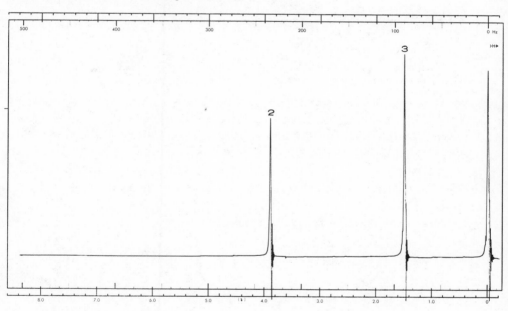

Infrared spectrum (chloroform solution) of unknown compound, Problem 12.

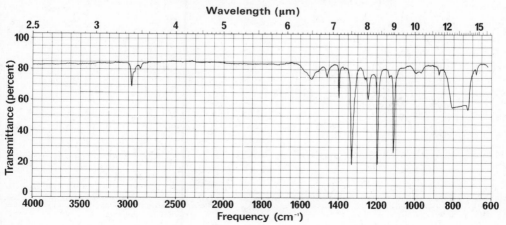

Optional Problems

1. Suggest structures (give hybridization of central atom) for the following compounds:

    (a) PF_6^- (b) $(CH_3)_2PF_3$ (c) $(CH_3)_4Si$

2. Are the following compounds likely to exist? Justify your answer in each case.

$$
\underset{\text{(a) }CH_3-P=P-CH_3}{} \qquad
\overset{\displaystyle O}{\underset{\text{(b) }CH_3-\overset{\|}{Si}-CH_3}{}} \qquad
\text{(c) }NF_5
$$

3. Which of the following compounds would you expect to have the higher dipole moment and why?

    $(CH_3)_3PO$ $(CH_3)_3NO$
    Trimethylphosphine   Trimethylamine
    oxide   oxide

4. Both oximes and sulfoxides are configurationally stable: Oximes have cis and trans forms, and sulfoxides of the type RR′SO can be resolved into enantiomers. Amines $R_1R_2R_3N$, on the other hand, are not configurationally stable and cannot be resolved. Can you suggest a reason for this difference?

CHAPTER 11

BENZENE AND AROMATICITY

11.1   Benzene

A large group of compounds isolated during the nineteenth century was given the general term "aromatic," because so many of them had pleasant odors. The parent compound of this series was found to be a hydrocarbon, C_6H_6, which was given the name *benzene*. The most conspicuous property of benzene was revealed by the earliest experiments: Although the molecular formula indicated a high degree of unsaturation, the compound did not show the typical reactivity associated with unsaturated hydrocarbons. Benzene underwent rather few reactions and these proceeded slowly and often required heat and catalysts. This is in contrast to ordinary alkenes, which react with many reagents rapidly, often almost instantaneously. The connection between the structure of an organic molecule and its odor remains obscure, but in time the original meaning of the expression was abandoned, and the term *aromatic compounds* came to mean unsaturated compounds which show a low degree of reactivity. Today, a compound is said to be aromatic if it is "benzene-like" in its properties.

The structure of benzene concerned chemists from the time the compound was first discovered in 1825 until the structure was finally determined in 1931. There were a great many possibilities proposed, including one which was substantially correct. The attack on this problem made by early chemists was extremely ingenious and will be discussed in Section 16.1. For now, we will only say that what was close to the correct structure was proposed by Kekulé in 1865. Kekulé wrote the structure as I. There were

I   II   III

two points which this structure did not adequately explain. First, there was no obvious reason why this compound would not show the reactivity of other alkenes. Second, it was found that a 1,2-disubstituted benzene, such as 1,2-dimethylbenzene, was a single isomer, rather than the two (II and III) that would seem to be required by formula I. Kekulé therefore suggested that the double bonds were not rigidly fixed, but continuously moved around the ring; this would explain why the 1,2-disubstituted compound was a single isomer. The early chemists were forced to conclude that, for some reason which they could not understand at that time, such a motion of the double bonds about the ring led to a lack of chemical reactivity.

With the development of the quantum theory, the structure of benzene finally became understandable. Today we write the two Kekulé forms with the aid of a double-headed arrow to indicate that neither structure adequately represents the molecule, but both structures together do. This is referred to as *resonance*. When the atomic orbitals which make up the π system in benzene are considered (IV), as will be done in more detail in the next few pages, it becomes apparent that the relationship between each adjacent

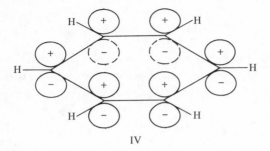

IV

pair of atoms is the same, just as the sum of the two Kekulé forms would imply. Another way to look at it is to imagine that instead of the bond being double between one pair of carbons and single between another pair, there is one and one-half bonds between each pair. With this idea in mind, benzene rings are often written with dotted lines or circles as indicated.

The student should not gain the impression that the resonance hybrid of benzene sometimes has one Kekulé form, and sometimes the other. The rhinoceros provides a useful analogy. The rhinoceros may be considered to be a hybrid of a unicorn and a dragon. That does not mean that sometimes a rhinoceros is a unicorn, and sometimes a dragon, but rather that he is always a rhinoceros. Most important, the rhinoceros is real, while the unicorn and the dragon are imaginary. Similarly, benzene is always a single structure, related to the Kekulé forms but different from them. Finally, benzene is real, while the Kekulé forms are imaginary.

As the parent compound of a series, benzene has been of considerable theoretical interest. Since the molecule contains 12 nuclei and 42 electrons, however, even a rather crude solution to the Schroedinger equation describing the system is quite formidable. The σ system of the benzene molecule is relatively unexceptional; it is the π system which leads to the interesting structural aspects of the molecule. Since the π system is orthogonal to (i.e., does not overlap) the σ system, it can be studied mathematically independently of the σ system. When this is done, one needs only to consider six electrons moving in the potential field of the σ system, and this reduces the problem to the point where a useful approximate solution to the Schroedinger equation is possible.

Figure 11.1
The orbital energies of the π systems (E_π) of ethylene and benzene.

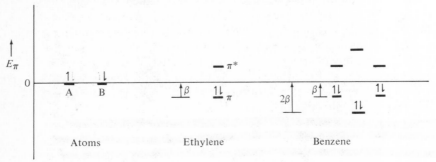

As shown in Figure 11.1, we can consider what happens when the p orbitals of two carbon atoms are joined together to yield the π system of ethylene (Section 7.2), and then consider what happens when the π systems of three ethylenes are joined together to yield the π system of benzene. Each atom contributes one orbital and one electron. When the two carbons are joined together to form ethylene, they form a π-bonding and a π^*-antibonding orbital. In the ground state the bonding orbital contains two electrons, and these electrons have an energy of 2β (1β for each electron). The quantity β is called the *resonance integral*, and it is a negative number, so that larger values for β correspond to lower energies and more stable systems. The bonding and antibonding π orbitals of ethylene can be written in terms of the atomic wave functions:

$$\psi_\pi^* = \psi_A - \psi_B \quad \text{(antibonding)}$$

$$\psi_\pi = \psi_A + \psi_B \quad \text{(bonding)}$$

If we now allow three ethylene π systems to come together to form the π system of benzene, we find that the orbital energies which are obtained by solution of the Schroedinger equation are as indicated in Figure 11.1. The total π energy of the benzene molecule is calculated to be 8β, or 2β greater than the three separate ethylenes. This difference of 2β is called the *conjugation energy* (Section 7.14) of benzene, meaning the stabilization energy which benzene has that is above and beyond that which the three separate ethylenes would have. Sometimes this *extra* resonance energy of 2β is called the "resonance energy" of benzene (meaning beyond that of a single Kekulé form). Since even ethylene already has considerable resonance energy (both π and σ), it seems less ambiguous to use "conjugation energy" when that is what is really meant.

The π Orbitals of Benzene. The π orbital in benzene which is of lowest energy is perfectly symmetrical; it can be written as $\psi_{\pi_1} = \psi_A + \psi_B + \psi_C + \psi_D + \psi_E + \psi_F$. It is roughly similar to two donuts above and below the planes of the carbon atoms (Figure 11.2). The next two π orbitals

Figure 11.2
The benzene π orbitals.

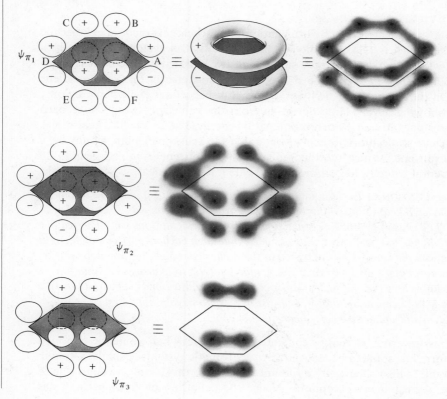

(ψ_{π_2} and ψ_{π_3}) are degenerate (have the same energies) and hence exhibit certain mathematical peculiarities. The two orbitals taken together give a symmetrical distribution for the four electrons, which looks the same as the distribution present in ψ_1. Separately, these two orbitals look as pictured in Figure 11.2. Each of these three π orbitals contains two electrons in the ground state.

As might be suspected, the carbon–carbon bond lengths in benzene are all equal, and they have a length (1.40 Å) which is in between that found for ordinary double bonds (1.33 Å) and that of ordinary single bonds (1.53 Å).

The effect of the conjugation energy of benzene can perhaps best be seen with the aid of an energy diagram (Figure 11.3). The hydrogenation of cyclohexene is exothermic

Figure 11.3
Heats of hydrogenation and stability: benzene, cyclohexadiene, and cyclohexene.

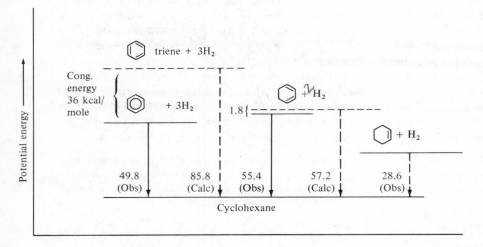

by 28.6 kcal/mole, as indicated. The hydrogenation of 1,3-cyclohexadiene is exothermic by 55.4 kcal/mole, which is 1.8 kcal/mole less than twice that of cyclohexene. The lack of additivity shows that the diene is more stable than two isolated double bonds (cyclohexenes) would be. This 1.8 kcal/mole is the conjugation energy of cyclohexadiene (Section 7.15). On the other hand, the hydrogenation of benzene is exothermic by only 49.8 kcal/mole, showing a very large deviation from the value that would have been expected for a "cyclohexatriene" with no conjugation energy ($3 \times 28.6 = 85.8$ kcal/mole). Clearly the benzene molecule is much more stable (36 kcal/mole) than would be a simple "cyclohexatriene." Since the theoretical conjugation energy of benzene is 2β and the experimental value is 36 kcal/mole, the value for β in this case is 18 kcal/mole.

EXPERIMENTAL EVALUATION OF β. *It should be noted that the value of β obtained in this way from benzene is 18 kcal/mole, while that obtained from butadiene was 7 kcal/mole (Section 7.14). The reason for the discrepancy is that when calculations were carried out for ethylene, butadiene, and benzene, it was assumed that each carbon–carbon bond length in each molecule was the same. The difference in the numerical values obtained for β is a measure of the accuracy of this approximation. Unfortunately, to improve the situation requires that we know how the energies of the σ components of the bonds vary as a function of distance. This is not accurately known, and just how to go beyond this first approximation is a problem still under study by theoretical chemists.*

This very great lowering in energy content compared to what would be expected from a Kekulé form has come to be associated with aromatic systems. Usually, a system which is very stable is also chemically quite unreactive, but this is only a rough rule to which there are a great many exceptions. Hence the definition of "aromaticity" has become a little bit muddled, because some people have used it to refer to unsaturated systems of unusual thermodynamic stability, while others have used it to refer to un-reactive systems. There are some compounds which are aromatic by one definition, but not by another, which leads to some confusion.

In Section 7.15, the conjugation energy of polyenes was discussed. Conjugation energy can be of major importance only when two or more of the resonance forms contributing to the structures are similar in energy. With butadiene there are four principal resonance forms:

$$CH_2=CH-CH=CH_2 \leftrightarrow \overset{-}{C}H_2-CH=CH-\overset{+}{C}H_2 \leftrightarrow \overset{+}{C}H_2-CH=CH-\overset{-}{C}H_2$$

$$\leftrightarrow \overset{\uparrow}{C}H_2-CH=CH-\overset{\downarrow}{C}H_2$$

but the first form is much more important than the other three. Conjugation energy from the other three forms lowers the total energy, but not by very much (3.5 kcal/mole). Benzene, on the other hand, shows two Kekulé forms of equal energy

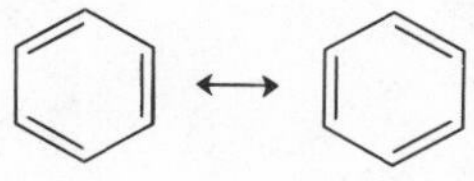

and here the conjugation greatly lowers the total energy (by 36 kcal/mole).

11.2   Benzene Derivatives

Alkylbenzenes are structurally unexceptional, and they are usually named in a simple way. Methylbenzene has the trivial name *toluene*.

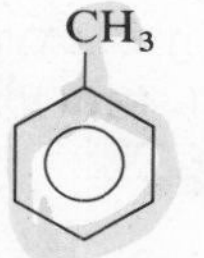

Toluene 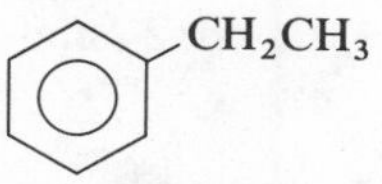   Ethylbenzene 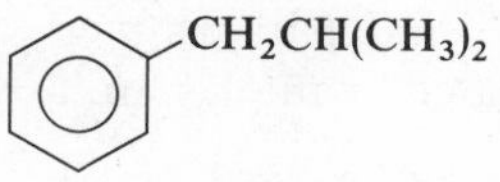   Isobutylbenzene

The substituent 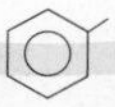 (often abbreviated as ϕ, Ph, or C_6H_5-) is called the *phenyl* group.

Sometimes the symbol *Ar* is used to represent any aromatic (aryl) group just as R is used to represent an alkyl group.

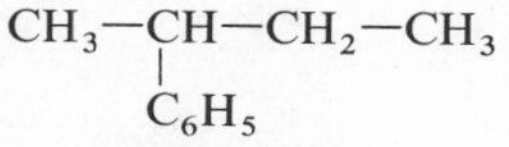

$$CH_3-CH-CH_2-CH_3 \qquad CH_3-CH-CH-CH-CH_2-CH_3 \qquad C_6H_5C{\equiv}CH$$

$$\underset{C_6H_5}{|} \qquad\qquad \underset{C_6H_5}{|}\ \underset{CH_3}{|}$$

2-Phenylbutane 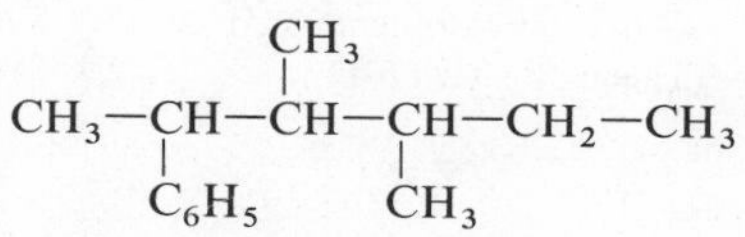   3,4-Dimethyl-2-phenylhexane   Phenylacetylene

For many other substituents, the nomenclature is straightforward; some compounds have trivial (common) names which are widely used. If there are two substituents on a benzene ring, the words *ortho* (*o*), *meta* (*m*), and *para* (*p*) are used to describe their relationship, as illustrated here for the dimethylbenzenes, which are called *xylenes*.

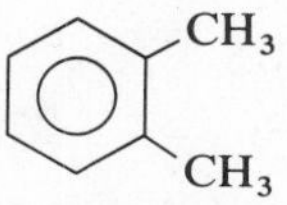

o-Xylene 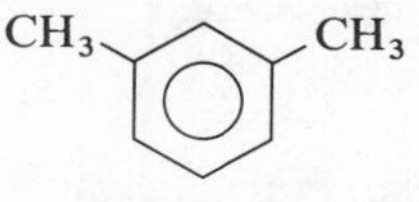   *m*-Xylene 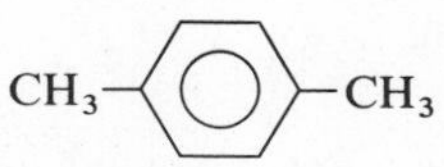   *p*-Xylene

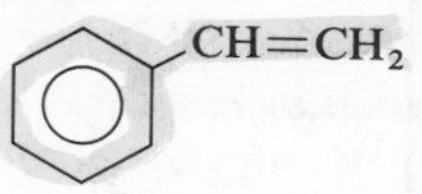

Styrene 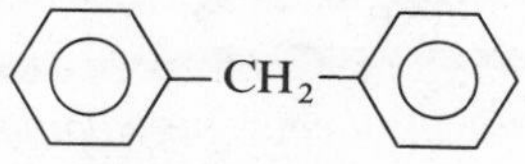   Diphenylmethane

Vinylbenzene has the common name *styrene*; it is a compound widely used in the plastics industry.

The group $PhCH_2-$ is quite common and has the name *benzyl*; thus $PhCH_2Cl$ is called *benzyl chloride*.

Phenol is the popular name for hydroxybenzene, and the monomethyl phenols are known as *cresols*. Phenol containing a small amount of water is a liquid at room temperature; in this form it is often referred to in pharmacy as *carbolic acid*. *Lysol* and similar products are powerful antiseptics and have the characteristic odor of phenol and the cresols. Phenol was the first compound to be used extensively as an antiseptic in medicine (Lister, 1867). Phenol is used today mainly as a starting material in the plastics industry.

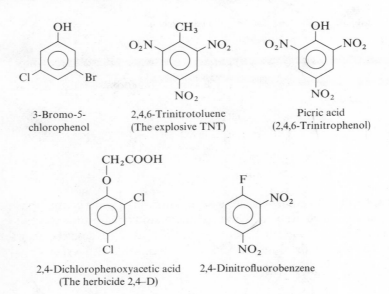

Phenol	*o*-Bromophenol

o-Cresol	*m*-Cresol	*p*-Cresol

For more highly substituted rings, a numbering system is used, the root function being understood to be at position 1, and the numbering proceeding around the ring in the direction which gives the lowest numbers to other substituents. Thus, *meta*-bromophenol could be called 3-bromophenol (not 5-bromophenol), it being understood the hydroxyl is at position 1. The ortho and para isomers could be called 2- and 4-substituted, respectively. More complicated examples are as follows:

3-Bromo-5-chlorophenol	2,4,6-Trinitrotoluene (The explosive TNT)	Picric acid (2,4,6-Trinitrophenol)

2,4-Dichlorophenoxyacetic acid (The herbicide 2,4-D)	2,4-Dinitrofluorobenzene

PHENOLS IN NATURE. *A great many phenols and phenol ethers occur in nature. Only a very few of these with special interest can be mentioned here.* o-*Hydroxybenzoic acid, known as* salicylic acid, *can be obtained from the willow tree (genus Salix). Its methyl ester is the flavoring constituent of oil of wintergreen and a common ingredient of liniments. Although it is not a naturally occurring compound, acetylsalicylic acid is of enormous importance as the common analgesic* aspirin.

Thymol *is the flavoring constituent of thyme ; because of its pleasant flavor, it is a favorite antiseptic ingredient in mouthwashes.* Eugenol *is responsible for the flavor of cloves. Clove oil is often used as an antiseptic by dentists because it contains this phenol. Closely related to eugenol is the cyclic acetal* safrole. *Safrole is a principal constituent of sassafras oil and has a strong odor characteristic of root beer.*

Certain phenols have powerful physiological effects. For example, the irritating constituents of poison ivy and poison oak contain the 1,2-dihydroxybenzene system (catechol) substituted in the 3 position by a long alkyl chain of a variable degree of unsaturation. A complex phenol known as (−)-tetrahydrocannabinol has been shown to be the major active principle of marijuana.

Safrole   Eugenol   Thymol   Aspirin

Methyl salicylate   Poison ivy irritants   (−)-Tetrahydrocannabinol

Benzaldehyde, *benzoic acid,* acetophenone, *and* benzophenone are the simplest and most fundamental of the aromatic carbonyl compounds.

Benzaldehyde   Benzoic acid   Acetophenone   Benzophenone

Benzaldehyde, sometimes known in pharmacy as oil of bitter almonds, is the active ingredient of almond flavor. β-Phenylacrolein is commonly known as *cinnamaldehyde* and is responsible for the flavor of cinnamon. Natural vanilla flavoring is mainly due to the phenolic aldehyde, *vanillin.* Since vanillin is available as a cheap by-product of the paper industry, it is much used not only as a flavoring agent but also for such purposes as masking the unpleasant odor of paint. *Salicylaldehyde* has an odor like bitter almonds, and is used in perfumery.

Cinnamaldehyde   Vanillin   Salicylaldehyde

The amino derivative of benzene is known as *aniline* and the corresponding amino toluenes are known as *toluidines.* Aniline and the toluidines are important starting materials in the synthetic dye industry. Both *p*-aminobenzoic acid and the ortho isomer, known as *anthranilic acid*, are biochemical intermediates of some importance. In addition, methyl anthranilate is a constituent of natural grape aroma and finds use as a synthetic grape flavor.

Aniline   *p*-Toluidine   *p*-Aminobenzoic acid   Methyl anthranilate

SOME AMINES OF PHYSIOLOGICAL IMPORTANCE. *Many derivatives of β-phenylethylamine are of considerable medicinal interest, probably because the basic unit of this amine forms part of the structure of the natural hormone,* adrenalin *(epinephrine). Adrenalin is involved in the function of the nervous system and causes such effects as an increase in blood pressure and an acceleration of the heart beat. α-Methyl-β-phenylethylamine is the synthetic drug known as* benzedrine *or* amphetamine; *it is a powerful stimulant for the nervous system. 3,4,5-Trimethoxy-β-phenylethylamine, known as* mescaline, *is the active ingredient of the peyote cactus, which has been used for centuries by Indians of the southwestern United States as a ceremonial hallucinogen.*

$C_6H_5CH_2CH_2NH_2$

β-Phenylethylamine

Adrenalin

Mescaline

$C_6H_5CH_2CHCH_3$
NH_2

Benzedrine

If more than one benzene ring is present in a compound, they are distinguished for purposes of nomenclature by primes which are added to the numbers of the second ring.

4,4′-Dibromobenzophenone   2,4-Dinitro-4′-methylbiphenyl

11.3   Resonance in Benzene Derivatives

The structures and physical properties of many benzene derivatives (such as the halobenzenes and the alkylbenzenes) are rather unexceptional. On the other hand, phenol, aniline, and related compounds exhibit some properties which require special comment.

In a molecule such as phenol, there exists the possibility of resonance between a lone pair of electrons on the oxygen and the aromatic ring. Thus a number of resonance forms may be written for phenol. When the phenol molecule ionizes to yield the phenoxide ion, the latter also has a number of resonance forms, as shown in Figure 11.4. Note that both phenol and its anion have two Kekulé forms. In addition they each have three other charged forms with the negative charge in an ortho or para position. In phenol

Figure 11.4
The resonance forms of phenol and phenoxide ion.

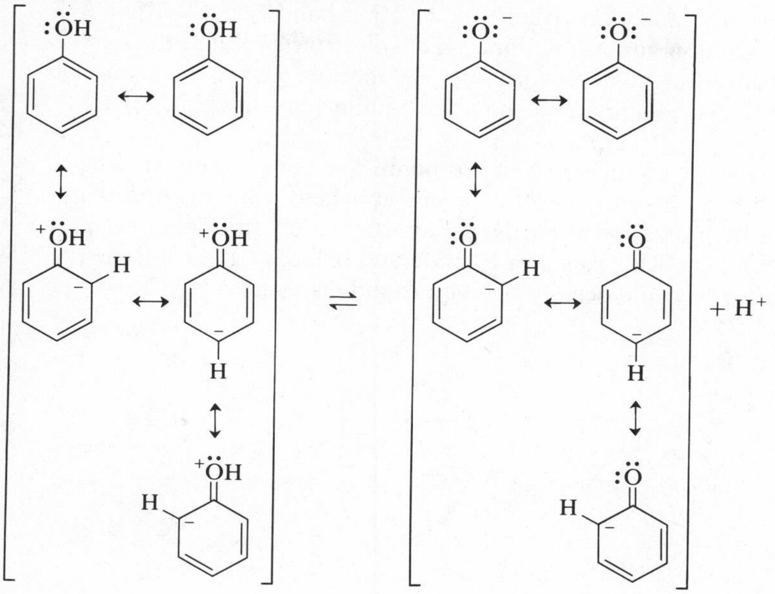

itself these charged forms contribute much less to the hybrid than do the Kekulé forms, because charge separation costs energy, and high-energy forms cannot stabilize the hybrid much. The resonance forms of the phenoxide ion in which the charge is in the ring, on the other hand, require no charge separation; the charge is simply delocalized. Hence these forms stabilize the anion very much. If we compare the acidity of cyclohexanol and phenol, we might predict that the resonance in the aromatic case, which is completely absent in cyclohexanol and its anion, will stabilize the phenoxide ion more than it stabilizes phenol. Hence, phenol should be more acidic than cyclohexanol; it is, by about $6\,\text{p}K$ units (one million times). Thus while alcohols are "neutral" in the sense that their acidity is no more than that of water, phenols are in fact acids—they are comparable with hydrogen cyanide or hydrogen sulfide in acidity, and they react with sodium hydroxide, essentially to completion, to yield phenoxide ions.

Aniline also shows resonance interaction between the lone pair (from nitrogen in this case) and the ring (Figure 11.5). Aniline and other amines are bases, and they react with acids to form salts of the ammonium type. While phenol is a stronger acid than cyclohexanol, aniline is a weaker base than cyclohexylamine (by about $5\,\text{p}K$ units).

Figure 11.5
The resonance forms of aniline and anilinium ion.

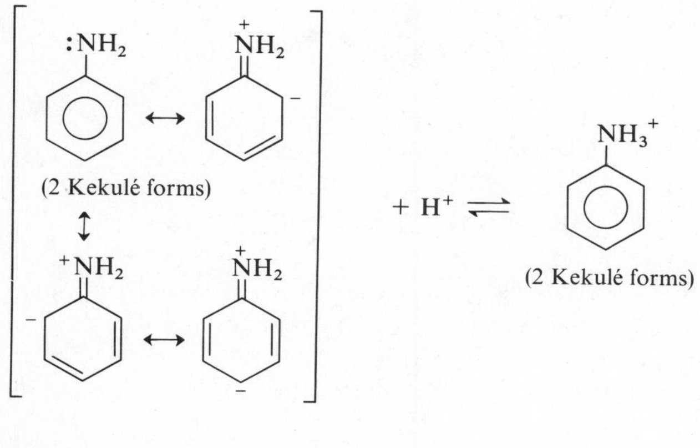

The lower basicity of aniline and the higher acidity of phenol stem from the same cause. Aniline has two Kekulé forms and three charged forms in which the negative charge is at an ortho or para position. The anilinium ion, on the other hand, has two Kekulé forms, and that is all. The anilinium ion has no lone pair of electrons, because the lone pair of aniline is engaged in covalent bond formation in the ion. Hence, resonance stabilizes the free base, but not the cation, and shifts the equilibrium shown in Figure 11.5 to the left.

The geometry of aniline deserves comment on at this point. The benzene ring and the attached nitrogen lie in a plane, while the two hydrogens attached to the nitrogen lie out of this plane, so that the hybridization at nitrogen is approximately sp^3. The overlap of this sp^3 orbital with the π system of the ring is only moderately effective. If the nitrogen were hybridized sp^2, the lone pair could occupy a p orbital, and resonance with the ring

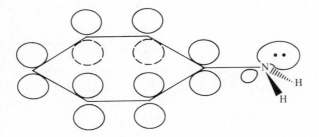

would be improved. Such hybridization would, however, require bond angle deformation as discussed for simple amines in Section 4.14, and the energy lowering due to resonance, if the nitrogen were to become planar, would not be sufficient to overcome the increase in energy due to angular deformation. The nitrogen therefore remains pyramidal.

To a first approximation, an amino group attached to a benzene ring will always have similar properties, regardless of other group(s) attached to the ring. The same is true of phenols or carboxylic acids; hence, it is convenient to study these compounds by classes.

To a second approximation, however, we find a good deal of variation within a class. As an example, we may consider the phenols, and observe how their acidities change as substituents are placed on the ring.

If we examine Figure 11.4, we note that the distribution of negative charge into the ring is more important in the anion than in the phenol itself. Thus, we find that if a substituent which tends to stabilize the presence of negative charge is placed on the ring, then the anion will be stabilized relative to the phenol, and the phenol will become more acidic. Conversely, if a substituent is placed on the ring which tends to stabilize positive charge and destabilize negative charge, then the phenol will become a weaker acid. In Table 11.1 are shown the pK_a's of a few substituted phenols.

Table 11.1   The Acidities of Substituted Phenols

Phenol	pK_a
2,4,6-Trinitro–	0.38
2,4-Dinitro–	4.00
p-NO$_2$–	7.14
m-NO$_2$–	8.35
p-COOEt–	8.50
m-Br–	9.11
H–	9.94
p-CH$_3$–	10.19

The presence of an electron-donating group (p-CH_3–) decreases the acidity of phenol by about 0.25 pK units or a factor of 2. The electron-attracting groups increase the acidity. The p-nitro group increases the acidity of phenol by approximately 600 times. A nitro group is a powerful electron-withdrawing group, both by induction and by resonance. Thus, resonance forms of the types shown contribute to the great acidity of p-nitrophenol.

The presence of additional nitro groups increases the acidity still further, so that finally 2,4,6-trinitrophenol (picric acid) has an acidity similar to that of the mineral acids. It is more than 3 billion times as acidic as phenol itself. Note that resonance forms such as those shown are effective only if the nitro group is in a position ortho or para to the hydroxyl. A m-nitro group has a qualitatively similar effect but only from induction, so that it will increase the acidity of a phenol but not by very much (40 times, vs 600 times for the para).

Similarly, the effect of a nitro group in aniline tends to decrease its base strength and increase the acidity of the anilinium salt. Thus, for the salts of aniline and p-nitro-aniline, the pK_a's are approximately 5 and 2, respectively.†

EXERCISE 11.1

Show by means of resonance forms why a p-nitro group decreases the base strength of aniline.

If resonance is important in a molecule, then it will not be possible to adequately represent the molecule with a single Kekulé structure. The inadequacy of such a single Kekulé structure may be detected experimentally in a great many ways; from heats of hydrogenation, from pK measurements, from nmr, and so on, and these methods are all useful. The most general way to determine the importance of resonance, although of limited accuracy, is from heat of combustion measurements, since almost all organic compounds burn. The other methods are limited, since few compounds can be hydro-genated, few are acids, the nmr is not always interpretable, and so on. Typical organic compounds have heats of combustion on the order of 1000 kcal/mole. This means that very precise work (to 0.1% accuracy) still gives errors of the order of 1 kcal/mole. To calculate the conjugation energy of a molecule, one can sum up known values for the heats of combustion of all the C—C bonds, the C=C bonds, the C—H bonds, and so on, in the molecule for the principal Kekulé form. (The numbers will be given and the method discussed in detail in Chapter 13.) The calculated value for the heat of combustion is then compared with the experimental value. Strain energy, if present, can also be allowed for (Section 3.5). If the actual heat of combustion is lower than calculated, the actual compound is more stable than the Kekulé form implies, and the difference between the calculated and observed values is the conjugation energy.

In Table 11.2 are given the conjugation energies for many of the compounds discussed in this chapter, as derived from heats of combustion. Additional examples of more complicated systems are given in Table 11.3 (Section 11.9).

---

† The base strength of an amine is often indicated with the aid of a pK_b, which is related to the pK_a of the ammonium salt in the following way: pK_a + pK_b = 14 (in water), see page 60.

Table 11.2   Conjugation Energies Derived from Heats of Combustion (kcal./mole)

Compound	Structure	$-\Delta H_{\mathrm{calcd}}{}^{a}$	$-\Delta H_{\mathrm{obs}}$	Conjugation energy
1,3-Butadiene	$CH_2{=}CH{-}CH{=}CH_2$	611.5	608	3.5
trans-1,3-Pentadiene	$CH_3CH{=}CH{-}CH{=}CH_2$	766.1	762	4.1
2-Methyl-1,3-butadiene (Isoprene)	$CH_2{=}\underset{\underset{CH_3}{\vert}}{C}{-}CH{=}CH_2$	765.2	762	3.2
Benzene		825.1	789	36.1
Toluene	CH_3	979.0	944	35.0
Aniline	NH_2	861.7	824	37.7
Phenol	OH	785.2	749	36.2

a The calculated heats of combustion are obtained as described in Chapter 13.

11.4   Nuclear Magnetic Resonance and Infrared Spectra of Benzene Derivatives

NMR

The nmr spectrum of benzene itself shows only a sharp singlet at δ 7.37 from the six equivalent hydrogens. This is a considerably larger δ value than those found for alkenes, and the reason for this large value is an important one. Because the π system of benzene is quite polarizable, a magnetic field induces a flow of these electrons around the ring in the same way that such a field would introduce a flow of electrons in a loop of wire. This ring current in turn generates an induced magnetic field which tends to reinforce the applied field felt by the protons, as illustrated in Figure 11.6.

Figure 11.6
The π electron flow and induced field resulting when benzene is placed in a magnetic field (H_0).

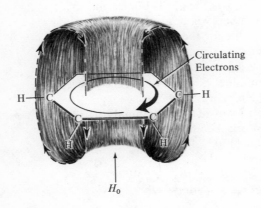

Circulating Electrons

H_0

Ring-Current-Induced Chemical Shifts. The effect of the ring current here should be contrasted with that observed for acetylene (Section 7.21). Note from Figure 11.6 that if protons are placed over the face of the benzene ring, rather than in the plane of the ring, a shift to higher field is predicted. This is exactly what is observed in compounds such as the paracyclophanes.

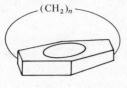

n-Paracyclophane

For $n = 8$, the side-chain protons located in the π cloud of the ring are found at $\delta -0.3$.

Toluene shows an nmr spectrum consisting of two sharp singlets: δ 7.17 (area = 5) and δ 2.34 (area = 3). The aromatic protons are nonequivalent in principle, but in practice they are equivalent in the nmr (same chemical shift) and hence they do not couple. (This is frequently found to be the case with aromatic protons.) *p*-Xylene also has an nmr spectrum consisting of two sharp singlets: δ 7.05 (area 2) and δ 2.28 (area 3).

EXERCISE 11.2

Offer an explanation for the fact that the aromatic protons of the series benzene, toluene, and *p*-xylene show a small but definite upfield shift.

The nmr spectrum of benzaldehyde is shown in Figure 11.7. Note the complex aromatic pattern. The aromatic protons are all similar, but not equivalent, and the resulting pattern cannot be interpreted in any simple way.

Figure 11.7
NMR spectrum of benzaldehyde.

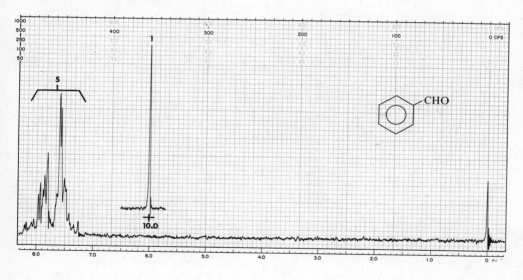

IR

The C—H stretching frequency is a function of the hybridization of the carbon and is found in the range of 3000–3100 cm^{-1} for both aromatic rings and alkenes. The C=C stretching frequency is lower in an aromatic ring (1500–1600 cm^{-1}) or conjugated olefin (about 1600 cm^{-1}) than for an unconjugated olefin (about 1650 cm^{-1}), which reflects the relative bond strengths of the different bonds. These absorption bands are not usually very strong.

In Section 9.2, the effect on the carbonyl stretching frequency by conjugation of the carbonyl group with a double bond was discussed. The same kind of shift to lower frequency (about 30 cm^{-1}) is observed for a carbonyl group when it is conjugated with an aromatic ring. (Why?)

Determination of the Substitution Pattern in a Benzene Derivative. In simple olefins, the very strong C—H out-of-plane-bending bands in the 800–1000 cm^{-1} range often permit a positive assignment of stereochemistry around the double bond. Analogous absorption bands are obtained from aromatic rings, and the exact frequencies often permit the assignment of the substitution pattern present. For many compounds, the following strong bands are observed:

Monosubstituted:	690–710 cm^{-1}	*o*-Disubstituted: 735–770 cm^{-1}
	730–770 cm^{-1}	*p*-Disubstituted: 800–860 cm^{-1}
m-Disubstituted:	750–810 cm^{-1}	

With complicated molecules it sometimes is found that there are so many bands in the 700–1000 cm^{-1} region that no conclusions are possible.

EXERCISE 11.3

The infrared spectra of *o*-, *m*-, and *p*-bromotoluene are shown in Figure 11.8, and labeled A, B, and C. Which is which?

Figure 11.8
Infrared spectra of *o*, *m*, and *p* isomers of bromotoluene (Exercise 11.3).

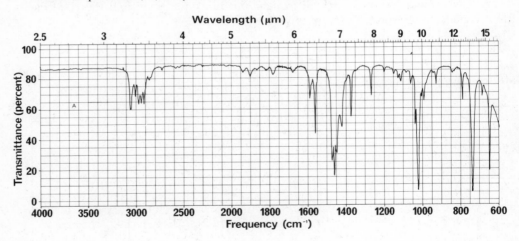

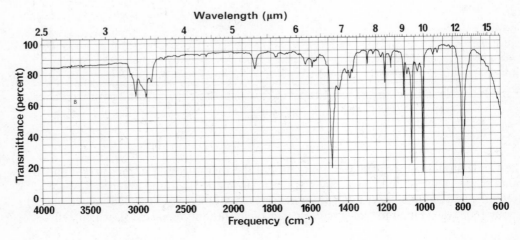

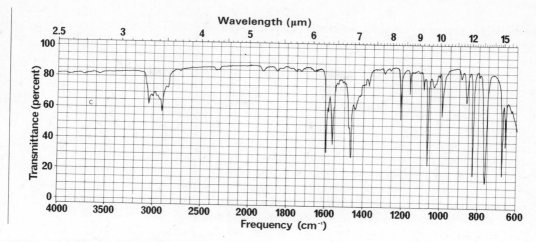

11.5   Biphenyl and Its Derivatives

The structure of biphenyl has been studied with some care, and it has been found that the molecule has the two rings coplanar in the crystal, but in the gas phase one ring is

Crystalline
(coplanar)

Gaseous
(rotated)

rotated some 42° with respect to the other. Clearly the resonance between the rings tends to keep the system coplanar. When the molecule has such a geometry, however,

$\longleftrightarrow$ $\longleftrightarrow$ $\longleftrightarrow$ etc.

the ortho and ortho' hydrogens are closer together than the sum of their van der Waals radii. Hence in the gas phase, the molecule twists until a minimum of energy is reached. Staying planar involves too much van der Waals repulsion, while twisting 90° causes too much loss of resonance energy, and a compromise is reached. When the molecules are packed into a crystal, the *intermolecular* van der Waals attractions are greater if the rings are coplanar, as this allows for a more compact crystal. Hence, although an isolated molecule prefers to be nonplanar, the greater intermolecular attractions for the planar form cause this to be the stable form in the crystal. Usually a molecule in a crystalline phase exists in a single conformation. In the gas phase or in solution, most substances exist as conformational mixtures. The predominant conformation in solution is usually, but not necessarily, the conformation found in the crystal. For example, *n*-butane is mostly in the anti conformation in solution, and exclusively in this conformation in the crystal.

If a biphenyl has some or all of its ortho hydrogens replaced by larger groups, these will interfere even more seriously with the other ortho groups when the molecule is planar. 2,2′-Dicarboxy-6,6′-dinitrobiphenyl, for example, has such bulky groups interfering with one another that the molecule cannot become planar at all.

2,2′-Dicarboxy-6,6′-dinitrobiphenyl
(6,6′-Dinitrodiphenic acid)

The molecule therefore exists in *two* isomeric forms:

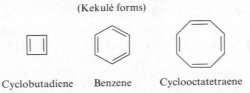

Careful inspection of these structures will show that they are enantiomers. (Use models if this is not clear.) To interconvert them, it is necessary to go through an intermediate in which the rings are coplanar. The bulky ortho groups prevent that, so these enantiomers are quite stable.

Thus we have two extremes. In a simple disubstituted biphenyl, such as 4,4'- or 3,3'-dibromobiphenyl, in which the bromines are too far apart to interfere with one another, two enantiomers exist and there is a small barrier to their interconversion.

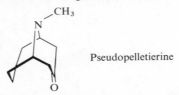

fast

3,3'-Dibromobiphenyl

This barrier is so small, however, that the enantiomers are in equilibrium. At the other extreme, the 2,2'-dicarboxy-6,6'-dinitrobiphenyls are separated by such a large barrier that they cannot be interconverted. In between these extremes are molecules which cover the whole range. 2,2'-Dibromobiphenyl, for example, can be resolved and is optically stable at very low temperatures, but it racemizes slowly at room temperature. The corresponding diiodo compound, with larger interfering groups, is racemized more slowly. It is stable at room temperature, but racemizes upon heating. (See also Section 6.2 and page 140.)

11.6   Hückel's Rule

Since benzene was such a stable compound, early chemists sought to prepare the lower and higher vinylogs, cyclobutadiene and cyclooctatetraene, respectively.

(Kekulé forms)

Cyclobutadiene   Benzene   Cyclooctatetraene

Cyclobutadiene has not really been isolated to date (page 244). The higher vinylog of benzene is of some historical interest.

The first preparation of "cyclooctatetraene" was announced by Willstätter[†] and co-workers in two papers published in 1911 and 1913. The approach used was a chemical degradation of the pomegranate alkaloid *pseudopelletierine*, which contains a cyclooctane carbon skeleton, bridged through the 1 and 5 positions by an *N*-methylamino group. Chemists long wondered whether Willstätter's hydrocarbon really was cyclo-

Pseudopelletierine

[†] Richard Willstätter. 1872–1942. Universities of Zurich, Berlin, and Munich. Nobel Prize, 1930.

octatetraene, and during the years 1939–1943 there appeared several papers challenging his structure. The evidence put forward against formulation of the Willstätter product as 1,3,5,7-cyclooctatetraene was based on the similarity of the product to styrene ($C_6H_5CH{=}CH_2$), on the fact that catalytic dehydrogenation of cyclooctene gave styrene and not cyclooctatetraene, and on the anomalous results obtained with open-chain compounds that were investigated as models for the last steps in the Willstätter synthesis. In 1946, a remarkably simple route to cyclooctatetraene by catalytic tetra-merization of acetylene appeared in the literature. This synthesis was an outgrowth of an extensive study of the chemistry of acetylene during 1928–1944 conducted by W. Reppe[†] and his collaborators in Germany, which was not published until after the end of World War II. There was no question that this compound was cyclooctatetraene. In 1947, A. C. Cope[††] and C. G. Overberger[††] were able to show by a direct compari-son of the physical and chemical properties, that the products obtained by the Willstätter and Reppe methods were identical.

From the point of view of quantum mechanics, an aromatic system is one that con-tains a closed shell of π electrons; hence it is a molecular π system which corresponds to a rare gas configuration in atomic systems. The organic chemist, however, often uses the term *aromatic* to mean benzene-like, that is, unreactive, so that the word must always be used in context if the meaning is to be unambiguous.

As was noted by E. Hückel[†††] (1931), when the Schroedinger equation is solved for the π system of a regular, planar, monocyclic polyene, the orbital energies which are calculated have a very simple characteristic pattern. There is always one orbital of lowest energy, followed by pairs of orbitals of increasing energy, and finally a single orbital of highest energy. Thus, if we look at the orbital energies for cyclobutadiene, benzene, cyclooctatetraene, and cyclodecapentaene, assuming they are regular and planar, we see that the orbital energies have the pattern shown in Figure 11.9. There is a single

Figure 11.9
The orbital energies for the π systems of some cyclic polyenes if they are assumed regular and planar.

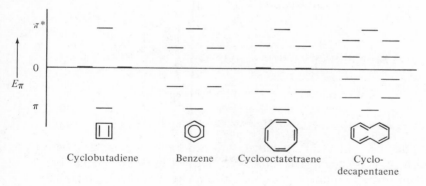

orbital of lowest energy and one of highest energy. In between, there are pairs of orbitals of equal energies. A system like one of these will have aromatic, or closed-shell, stability when the π system contains two electrons (which fills the lowest shell), or six electrons (which fills the lowest two shells), or ten electrons (which fills the lowest three shells), and so on, until all of the bonding orbitals are filled.

  [†] Walter Reppe. Born 1892, Foeringen, Germany. Badische Anilin und Soda-Fabrik, Ludwigshafen, Germany.

  [††] Arthur C. Cope. 1909–1966. Born Dunreith, Indiana. Bryn Mawr College, Columbia University, Massachusetts Institute of Technology.

    Charles G. Overberger. Born 1920. Polytechnic Institute of Brooklyn, University of Michigan.

[†††] Erich Hückel. Born 1896, Charlottenburg, Germany. Universities of Stuttgart and Marburg.

Hückel devised a simple rule for predicting whether or not such systems would be aromatic. The rule is that if the number of π electrons is equal to 2 + 4n, where n equals 0, 1, 2, 3, . . . , the system will be aromatic; otherwise it will not. The rule results because it takes two electrons to fill the lowest orbital and four to fill each succeeding shell, so that 4n in addition to the two for the lowest shell will always yield a closed-shell configuration, as shown for benzene and cyclodecapentaene in Figure 11.10.

Figure 11.10
Closed-shell configurations of the π systems of benzene and cyclodecapentaene.

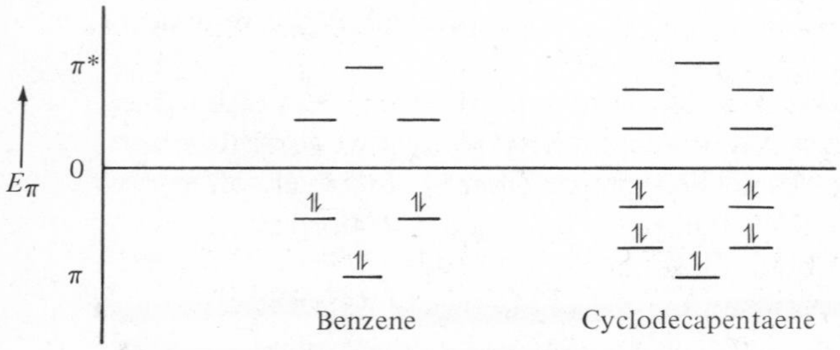

While Hückel's rule predicts that a 10-carbon cyclic polyene should have a closed-shell π system, the compound is not as stable as is benzene. The problem is the σ system. If the compound were to have all cis double bonds, the σ angle strain would be very large; such a compound probably would not exist but would polymerize by reaction with itself. If two of the double bonds each had trans stereochemistry, as shown, cyclodecapentaene might exist in the conformation shown.

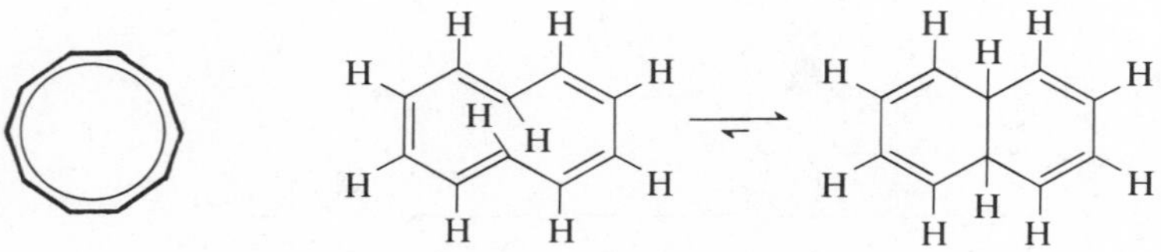

All cis double
bonds

Two trans double
bonds

Dihydronaphthalene

The only trouble with this structure is that there are two hydrogens inside where there really is not much room for them. The molecule could not in fact be planar, but would have to buckle in order to allow a place for these hydrogens. This compound has actually been detected, but it is in equilibrium with the bicyclic structure, dihydronaphthalene, and exists almost exclusively in the latter form. The conjugation of the system is interrupted by noncoplanarity, and hence Hückel's rule is not strictly applicable.

The fact that benzene has a high degree of stability is understandable from Hückel's rule, and the low degree of stability of cyclodecapentaene is a case of sigma strain; the lack of stability of what appear to be otherwise reasonable compounds is also explainable. Cyclobutadiene, for example, looks to be simply a smaller vinylog of benzene. One might think that it should have a similar conjugation energy and a corresponding degree of stability, except perhaps for the strain of the σ system. In fact, as mentioned previously, cyclobutadiene has never been isolated (in the ordinary way). It is possible to prepare the compound, and it will exist for a few seconds, so that it might be studied if one moved fast, but the compound is certainly not stable in the usual sense. If we examine the orbital energy diagram (Figure 11.11a) for the molecule, we can see why.

Figure 11.11
The π orbitals of cyclobutadiene.

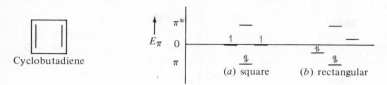

Cyclobutadiene

(a) square   (b) rectangular

The π system contains four electrons, and hence does not satisfy Hückel's rule. Two go into the lowest orbital, and two are left to be distributed between the next two orbitals.

More about Cyclobutadiene. Hund's rule applies to molecular systems as it does to atoms. It states that the most stable arrangement for the two electrons of cyclobutadiene above the lowest orbital is in different orbitals, with their spins parallel. This means that the ground state of a square-planar cyclobutadiene molecule should be that of a diradical, rather than of a covalent substance. On this basis, it is not surprising that the compound lacks the stability of an aromatic system. Since there are 4π electrons, Hückel's rule is, of course, not satisfied, as it requires 2, 6, or 10 π electrons for a stable aromatic system.

Actually, cyclobutadiene has an alternative structure open to it. If the molecule were to have alternating long and short bonds, and a rectangular shape, then Hückel's rule does not apply. Solution of the Schroedinger equation for the rectangular molecule gives the orbital energy diagram shown (Figure 11.11b), and the ground state contains a closed shell of electrons. It is simply a conjugated diene (the rectangular shape means that it has only one Kekulé form), highly strained because of the four-membered ring. Theory indicates the rectangular form to be of lower energy than the square form, but definite experimental evidence is lacking at present.

Cyclooctatetraene is another molecule which Hückel's rule predicts should not be aromatic. As discussed on page 242 the actual molecule is stable enough to be isolated, but the heat of hydrogenation shows that it possesses a very small conjugation energy. In this case, the molecule is not in fact a diradical as the orbital energy diagram indicates (Figure 11.12), but avoids the difficulty by being nonplanar. The nonplanar system has

Figure 11.12
The π orbitals of cyclooctatetraene.

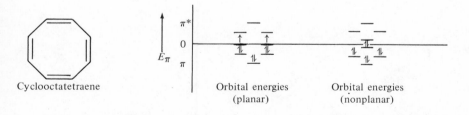

Cyclooctatetraene

Orbital energies
(planar)

Orbital energies
(nonplanar)

orbital energies as shown, so that a closed shell (but little conjugation energy, Table 11.3) is possible with eight electrons. The σ system plays an important part in determining the geometry of this molecule. For sp^2-hybridized carbon atoms, bond angles of about 120° are optimal, whereas the interior angle of a regular planar octagon is 135°. By puckering of the ring to give a tub conformation, the σ system can be very much stabilized.

Planar
conformation

Tub
conformation

Since the π system was not especially stabilized by the planar conformation, the σ system dominates the situation. The molecule is in fact a typical polyene, rather than an aromatic system. The experimental value for the conjugation energy of cyclooctatetraene is only 3.8 kcal/mole. The nmr spectrum shows a single sharp resonance line at δ 5.78, characteristic of a polyene rather than of an aromatic system.

Hückel's rule is seen from the above examples to be a simple tool for predicting whether compounds of this general type may or may not be aromatic. There are many other related types of systems which have been prepared, and new ones are prepared from time to time. Some of these will be discussed in later parts of this and subsequent chapters. The generalization regarding stability seems to hold quite well.

11.7   Condensed Ring Systems

Naphthalene is the simplest member of the class of compounds said to possess *condensed ring systems*.

Naphthalene

The relationship between naphthalene and benzene is clearly evident. Naphthalene has three Kekulé forms, as illustrated, and it has more resonance stabilization than does benzene. It is interesting to note that in two of the three Kekulé forms, the bonds of the type between atoms 1 and 2 are double, while the bonds of the types between atoms 2 and 3, between atoms 1 and 9, and between atoms 9 and 10 are single. In line with the implications of the Kekulé forms, it is found that the bond length between atoms 1 and 2 is relatively short, 1.37 Å, while the other bonds mentioned above are relatively long, averaging 1.42 Å. (These numbers should be compared with the benzene bond length, 1.40 Å.) Thus, the Kekulé forms yield a good rough measure of the bond orders. More exact bond orders can be obtained from direct solution of the Schroedinger equation.

The IUPAC nomenclature for naphthalene derivatives can be illustrated by 1-bromonaphthalene and 1-methyl-3-isopropylnaphthalene, which have the structures

The nomenclature often used for simple naphthalene compounds is based on the fact that there are only two different kinds of positions in naphthalene itself. Carbon 1 is called α, carbon 2 is β. All other positions are either α or β by symmetry. Thus, 2-hydroxynaphthalene is sometimes named 2-naphthol but more often β-naphthol.

β-Naphthol α-Naphthylamine

It is possible to fuse additional rings together in a line, and *anthracene, naphthacene, pentacene, hexacene,* and so on, are known aromatic substances.

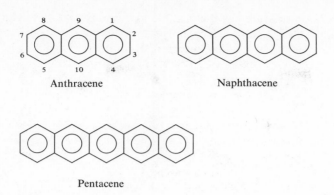

Anthracene   Naphthacene

Pentacene

The rings need not be fused together in a straight line. For example, we have *phenanthrene, pyrene, benzpyrene, triphenylene, coronene,* and *hexahelicene.*

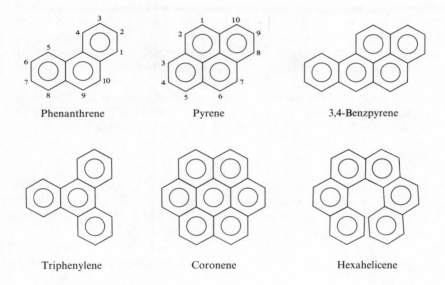

Phenanthrene   Pyrene   3,4-Benzpyrene

Triphenylene   Coronene   Hexahelicene

EXERCISE 11.4

By considering the five Kekulé forms of phenanthrene, decide which bond will be the shortest.

These multi-ring compounds are all stable, and numbers of Kekulé forms may be written for them. For naming derivatives of these compounds, the numbering systems indicated are employed in a straightforward manner. Each of these compounds (except hexahelicene) is planar, and generally the bond lengths are similar but not identical, as the Kekulé forms would indicate. Perhaps the most exceptional characteristic of any of this group of compounds is the very high degree of carcinogenic (cancer-producing) character shown by benzpyrene. A number of molecules which contain fused aromatic rings are known to be powerful carcinogens. Such compounds often result when organic materials are heated to high temperatures, and they are believed to be responsible for the rather high incidence of skin cancer among people who work with coal tar, and of lung cancer among cigarette smokers.

HEXAHELICENE. *Hexahelicene is especially interesting because it exists in two enantiomeric forms. It is not planar, but is rather like a* helix *(or screw) having but one turn. A helix is dissymmetric or chiral.*

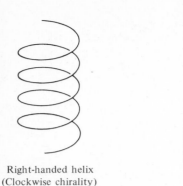

Right-handed helix
(Clockwise chirality)

Left-handed helix
(Counterclockwise chirality)

Hexahelicene exists in two enantiomeric forms. Such helical compounds possess enormous optical rotations. Thus, while a specific rotation (α) for a typical organic compound might be 20° at the sodium D line, for hexahelicene the value is 3700°.

When the number of fused rings becomes infinite in two directions, graphite results. Graphite sheets are individually very strong. Only van der Waals forces hold the individual sheets together, however. The sheets can slip parallel to one another quite easily since they are not pulled apart in this process, and even van der Waals forces do not have to be overcome. Graphite thus has the unusual property of being a *solid lubricant.*

It might be noted that all of the molecules discussed in this section have the right number of electrons to be aromatic systems according to Hückel's rule, and they all have large resonance energies (Table 11.3). It should be pointed out that Hückel's rule

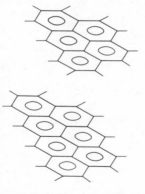

properly applies only to monocyclic compounds, although obviously it gives satisfactory predictions for multi-ring compounds also.

11.8   Aromatic Heterocyclic Compounds

The simple common heterocycles can be divided into two fundamentally different types, the six-membered rings and the five-membered rings. It is not simply a matter of the number of atoms in the ring—the electronic structures for the two different ring sizes are also quite different. As an example of the six-membered heterocyclic rings, we might consider *pyridine,* in which one of the carbon atoms in benzene has been replaced by a nitrogen atom. The Kekulé forms for pyridine are analogous to those of benzene.

Pyridine

In addition, because of the higher electronegativity of nitrogen as compared to carbon, resonance forms of the charge type which places negative charge on nitrogen and positive charge on carbon contribute much more to the structure in pyridine than they would in benzene. Thus we have additional important resonance forms for pyridine as follows:

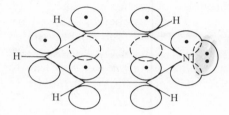

If we examine the six atomic orbitals which make up the π system of pyridine, we find that they are quite analogous to those in benzene. An additional feature of pyridine is the lone pair of electrons on nitrogen, which is to be found in an orbital of approximately sp^2 hybridization which lies in the plane of the ring. Note that there is no hydrogen

Pyridine

attached to the nitrogen. The six molecular π orbitals of pyridine divide into three antibonding (empty) and three bonding (full) orbitals. They are quite similar to those of benzene, though they are distorted somewhat due to the electronegativity of the nitrogen. The compound thus obeys Hückel's rule and is aromatic.

The electron pair in the sp^2 orbital belongs not to the π system, but rather to the σ system. When pyridine is protonated to form the pyridinium ion, the added proton is attached to this pair.

Pyridinium ion

The ion is also an aromatic system. Since the lone pair on the nitrogen of pyridine occupies an sp^2 orbital, it is less available for bonding than that of an aliphatic amine (sp^3). (Why?) The pK_a of pyridinium ion is 5, compared to about 10 for an aliphatic ammonium ion. Pyridine is thus comparable to aniline in base strength and is a 100,000 times weaker base than aliphatic amines.

The five-membered heterocyclic rings are a somewhat more extensive group than are the six-membered ring heterocycles. We might consider *pyrrole* as a typical example. Pyrrole has a single Kekulé form and a number of charged forms. Although the charged forms do not contribute as much to the compound as another Kekulé form would, they are able to confer considerable stability to the system. While the six-membered aromatic rings have conjugation energies of the order of 20–35 kcal/mole, the corresponding quantities for the five-membered rings are generally 15–30 kcal/mole.

Pyrrole, in contrast to pyridine, has a hydrogen attached to the nitrogen. The lone pair of the nitrogen is in the p orbital which goes to make up a part of the π system.

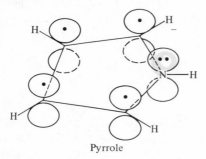

Pyrrole

This allows for six electrons in the π system, one from each carbon atom and two from the nitrogen. Thus, the energies of the molecular orbitals look as shown in Figure 11.13. There are five orbitals containing six electrons; Hückel's rule is obeyed, and we have an aromatic system. Note that the six electrons specified by Hückel's rule can be provided by six atoms, each contributing one electron (pyridine), or have five atoms, one of which contributes two electrons (pyrrole). Other numbers of *atoms* can also lead to aromatic systems if the number of electrons is correct (Chapter 12); it is the number of π electrons that Hückel's rule is concerned with.

Figure 11.13
The π molecular orbital energies for pyrrole.

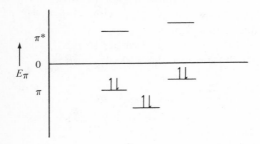

There are other heterocyclic rings analogous to pyrrole in which the place of nitrogen is taken by another atom. It is only necessary that this atom be capable of forming sigma bonds to the carbons and have an unshared pair of electrons in a properly oriented p orbital for formation of the aromatic π system. Oxygen and sulfur satisfy these requirements nicely, and they form corresponding heterocycles which are named *furan* and *thiophene*, respectively.

Furan   Thiophene

Aromaticity in these systems can be understood in terms of the importance of the ionic resonance forms. These ionic forms are relatively more important with sulfur, and less important with oxygen. The order of electronegativities is C, S, N, O, with oxygen being so electronegative that the electron pair is to a large extent localized on the oxygen. The conjugation energy of furan (16 kcal/mole) is therefore much less than that of pyrrole (21 kcal/mole), which is in turn less than that of thiophene (29 kcal/mole) (see Table 11.3).

Compounds such as *imidazole* contain both a pyridine-type nitrogen and a pyrrole-type nitrogen in the five-membered ring.

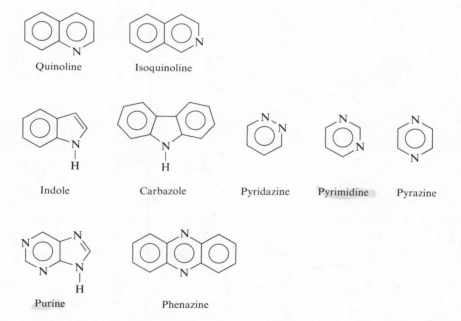

Imidazole

Note that in this case there is a hydrogen attached to one nitrogen and not to the other; therefore the resonance forms are as indicated and the nitrogens are not equivalent to one another. One nitrogen is of the pyridine type, the other is of the pyrrole type. By acid–base proton transfers, the two types of nitrogens can interchange. This system is biologically of great importance (Section 28.8).

More Complicated Heterocycles. Additional compounds are known which contain a pyridine-type nitrogen and a sulfur or oxygen atom also. These are, respectively, the thiazoles and oxazoles.

Thiazole   Isothiazole   Oxazole   Isoxazole

Finally, many of the previously discussed structural features can be combined into the same molecule, so that we have such compounds as *quinoline* and *isoquinoline*.

Quinoline   Isoquinoline

Indole   Carbazole   Pyridazine   Pyrimidine   Pyrazine

Purine   Phenazine

These compounds contain the same structural features over and over again, but in different combinations. The chemistry of some of the more important ones will be taken up in Chapter 28.

11.9   Other Aromatic Systems

Many higher vinylogs of benzene have been synthesized in the last few years, mostly by F. Sondheimer† and his students. In order to facilitate discussion of these compounds, a

---

† Franz Sondheimer. Born 1926, Stuttgart. Syntex, Mexico; Weizmann Institute, Israel; and University College, London.

Table 11.3 Conjugation Energies Derived from Heats of Combustion[a] (kcal./mole)

Compound	Structure	$-\Delta H_{calcd}{}^a$	$-\Delta H_{obs}$	Conjugation energy
Benzene		825.1	789	36.1
Biphenyl		1584.7	1514	70.7
Naphthalene		1311.4	1250	61.4
Azulene		1312.3	1279	33.3
Anthracene		1796.3	1712	84.3
Phenanthrene		1797.7	1705	92.7
Pyridine		697.7	675	22.7
Pyrrole		599.2	578	21.2
Furan		522.7	507	15.7
Thiophene		640.7	612	28.7
Cyclooctatetraene		1098.8	1095	3.8
18-Annulene		2466.3	2346.8	119.5

[a] The calculated heats of combustion are obtained as described in Chapter 13.

nomenclature has been invented which refers to completely conjugated cyclic polyenes as *annulenes*. Cyclodecapentaene is more conveniently called 10-annulene. Reasonable structures can be written for cyclic polyenes containing 18 or 24 carbon atoms, for example,

18-Annulene   24-Annulene

The first of these should be aromatic according to Hückel's rule, while the second should not. Both of these compounds have been prepared and their nmr spectra have been recorded. At room temperature, 18-annulene shows two broad peaks at $\delta\,8.9$ and $\delta\,-1.8$, with an intensity ratio of $2:1$. The large peak is in the typical aromatic region and must result from the protons outside the ring, while the absorption at the negative δ value must be from the protons inside the ring (see Figure 11.6). At higher temperatures (above 110°C) these two peaks merge, indicating that the ring is turning inside out, making the protons all equivalent. The conjugation energy for 18-annulene calculated from the heat of combustion is 120 kcal/mole, and it seems proper to consider this compound as aromatic. In contrast to what was observed for 18-annulene, it was found that the nmr spectrum of 24-annulene shows a sharp singlet at $\delta\,6.84$, which is in the range for a normal (not aromatic) polyene.

The conjugation energies of the compounds discussed in this chapter are important quantities and numerical energy values for some simple compounds were given in Table 11.2. Additional values for heterocyclic compounds, fused systems, and annulenes are given in Table 11.3.

ELECTRONIC SYSTEMS RELATED TO 10-ANNULENE. *As mentioned earlier (Section 11.6), at least part of the instability of 10-annulene arises because the two hydrogens in the middle of the molecule interfere with one another. It might be possible to prepare an analogous compound in which the two center carbons are replaced by pyridine-type nitrogens. With this compound there would be no problem of central hydrogens interfering with one another, because there are none. It has not yet proved possible to synthesize the compound, however. Another alternative would be to replace the two hydrogens by another group, for example, a CH_2 group. Such a compound has been prepared, as have heterocyclic analogs.*

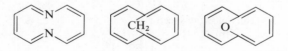

These compounds are generally considered to be aromatic, although the geometries are not exactly the planar ones that are preferred for aromatic systems.

PROBLEMS

1. Benzene has two important resonance forms, and 18 forms of lesser importance. Draw them. What are the first two called?

2. The hydrogenation of styrene is exothermic by 76.9 kcal/mole.
   (a) From the data in the text, calculate the conjugation energy between the aromatic ring and the olefinic double bond.
   (b) What carbon–carbon bond lengths do you anticipate in this molecule?

3.   Name the following:

(a)

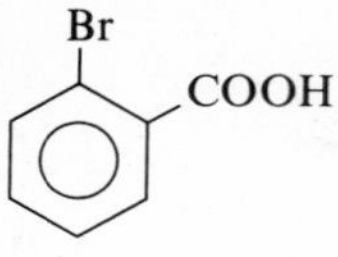

(b)

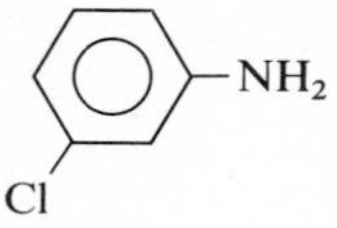

(c)

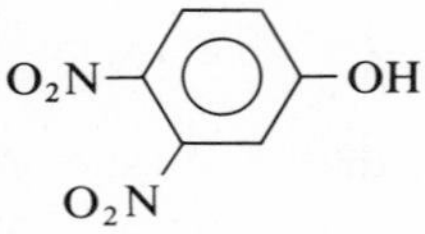

(d)

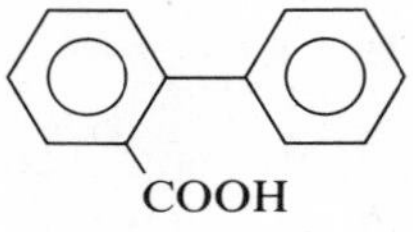

(e)

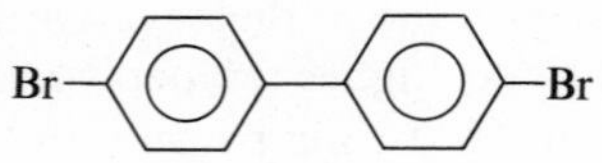

(f)

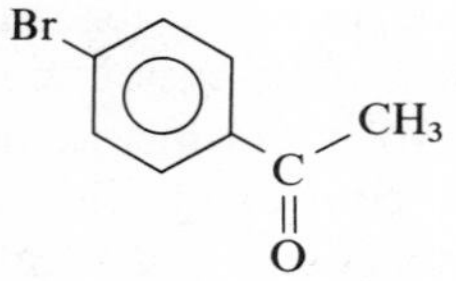

4.   Draw structures for the following:
(a) *p*-Isopropylbenzoic acid
(b) *p*-Toluenesulfonic acid
(c) *o*-Nitroaniline
(d) *m*-(*sec*-Butyl)phenylacetylene
(e) Benzamide
(f) Ethyl 2,4-dichlorobenzoate

5.   List the phenols below in order of increasing acid strength. (*Hint*. Draw resonance forms.)

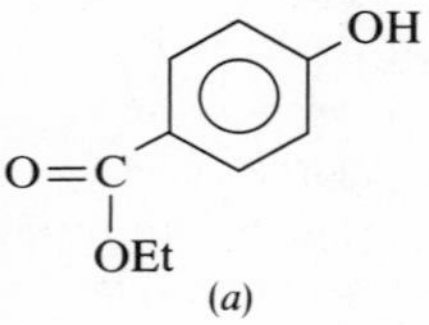

(a) 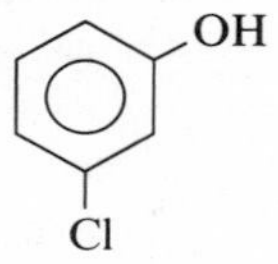   (b) 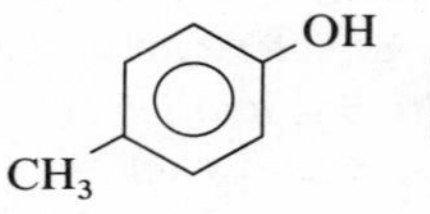   (c) 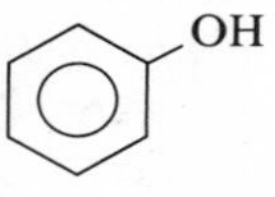   (d)

6.   A compound having the molecular formula C_7H_8O shows a broad, intense band at 3300 in the infrared and an nmr spectrum which consists of three sharp singlets: δ 3.68 (area = 1), δ 4.43 (area = 2) and δ 7.21 (area = 5). What is the structure?

7.   Give a structure consistent with each of the following spectra:
(a) C_4H_9Br
    (i) doublet, δ 1.04 6H
    (ii) multiplet, δ 1.95 1H
    (iii) doublet, δ 3.33 2H

(b) $C_{10}H_{14}$
    (i) singlet, δ 1.30 9H
    (ii) singlet, δ 7.28 5H

(c) $C_9H_{11}Br$
    (i) quintet, δ 2.15 2H
    (ii) triplet, δ 2.75 2H
    (iii) triplet, δ 3.38 2H
    (iv) singlet, δ 7.22 5H

8.   Hydrocarbon A, C_6H_6, gave an nmr spectrum with two signals, δ 6.55 and δ 3.84, with an area ratio of 2:1. When warmed for 3 hours in pyridine solution, A was quantitatively converted to benzene. Gentle hydrogenation of A gave B, C_6H_{10}, which showed no absorption in the 1650 cm^{-1} region of the infrared, and showed only one broad peak in the nmr (δ 2.34). What are the structures of A and B?

9.   The nmr spectrum of a compound $C_8H_8O_2$ is shown. Interpret the spectrum as fully as you can. What is the structure of the compound?

NMR spectrum (deuterochloroform solution) of unknown, Problem 9.

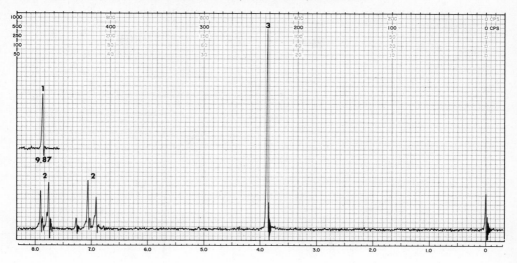

10.   Draw a diagram showing all of the valence shell atomic orbitals for imidazole, indicating the hybridization of each.

11.   The resonance hybrid for furan has a single Kekulé form, and four important charged structures. Draw them.

12.   The following molecules have dipole moments as indicated:

A	B	C
1.58 D	3.95 D	6.87 D

(a) Which way do these moments point?
(b) Explain the value of the moment of C compared to A and B.
(*Hint:* Draw the most important ionic resonance form of C.)

D	E

(c) What is the magnitude of the moment of D? Considering the moments of C and D, what moment would you predict for E?

(d) Actually, the latter has a moment of only 4.11 D. Why do you suppose that is?

13.   Phenanthrene and anthracene are isomers. Draw all the Kekulé forms of each. From these forms, can you explain the observed difference in the conjugation energies of the two compounds (Table 11.3)?

NMR spectrum of unknown, Problem 14.

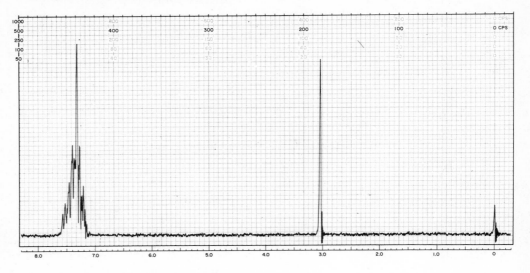

Infrared spectrum of unknown, Problem 14.

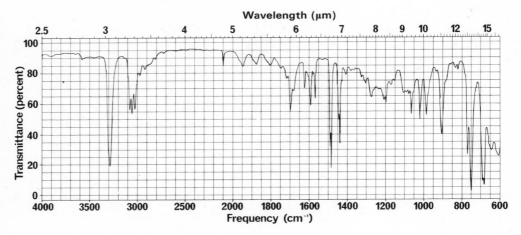

14.   The nmr and infrared spectra of a compound C_8H_6 are shown. Interpret the spectra as fully as you can. What is the structure of the compound?

15.   It is experimentally observed that compared to benzene, which is fairly inert, pyrrole is very reactive toward electrophiles. Pyridine will react with a powerful base like amide ion, while benzene will not. Explain.

16.   Using resonance forms and your knowledge of inductive and resonance effects, explain for each compound in Table 11.1 (page 236) why it is a weaker acid than the compound above it in the table, and why it is a stronger acid than the compound below it.

Optional Problems

1.   On page 154 is given a diagram of the π energy levels of butadiene (Fig. 7.15), and the conjugation energy of the molecule is calculated. A similar diagram (Fig. 11.1) is given for benzene on page 228. Assume that cyclodecapentaene (p. 243) is planar. (a) Is it aromatic? Why? (b) Sketch a similar diagram for the molecule. (c) The π molecular orbitals come in pairs, except for the highest and lowest, and solution of the Schroedinger equation gives the following energies (units of β): $+2.00$, $+1.62$, $+1.62$, $+0.59$, $+0.59$, -0.59, -0.59, -1.62, -1.62, -2.00. Calculate the conjugation energy. (d) The molecule is actually not planar. What will the lack of coplanarity do to the actual conjugation energy? Why?

2. The nmr spectrum of is shown. What conclusions can you draw from this spectrum?

NMR spectrum of 1,6-methanocyclodecapentaene, Optional Problem 2.

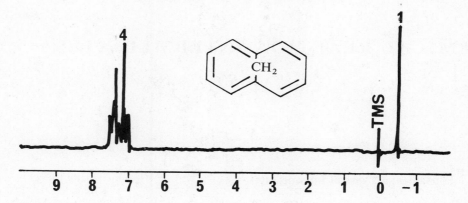

CHAPTER 12

CHEMICAL REACTION INTERMEDIATES

12.1   Fundamental Types of Intermediates

There are a variety of organic molecules which most often occur not as stable compounds, but only as transient intermediates in chemical reactions. Some intermediates have conventional bonding at carbon which may be represented by typical valence-bond structures. In others, carbon has fewer than four covalent bonds. Such structural types ordinarily are very unstable, and thus have only a transitory existence; but under certain circumstances they are of sufficient stability to be isolated and studied. The four most common kinds of intermediates with fewer than four covalent bonds at carbon are typified by the following specific examples related to methane:

$$CH_3^+ \qquad :CH_3^- \qquad CH_3\cdot \qquad :CH_2$$

| Carbonium ion, or methyl cation | Carbanion, or methyl anion | Methyl radical | Carbene, or methylene |

The methyl radical is simply the carbon radical that results when cleavage of methane occurs to give a hydrogen atom. This type of reaction is called *homolytic cleavage*, the breaking of an electron-pair bond in which one electron goes to each fragment.

$$H_3C:H \rightarrow H_3C\cdot \ \cdot H \qquad \text{Homolytic cleavage}$$

In *heterolytic cleavage* both electrons of an electron-pair bond go to the same fragment. The methyl cation, a *carbonium ion*, results when the hydrogen carries away the pair of electrons to give a hydride ion. The methyl anion, a *carbanion*, results from heterolytic cleavage to give a proton.

$$\left.\begin{array}{l} H_3C:H \rightarrow H_3C^+:H^- \\ H_3C:H \rightarrow H_3C:^-H^+ \end{array}\right\} \text{Heterolytic cleavages}$$

The final type of intermediate is a *carbene*, or methylene, which in a formal sense may be derived by having methyl anion lose hydride, or by having methyl cation lose a proton, or by having methyl radical lose a hydrogen atom.

The four types of intermediates discussed differ in the number of electrons surrounding the carbon atom. This in turn leads to structural differences. The structures of carbonium ions and carbanions can readily be predicted by analogy with trimethylboron and ammonia, respectively. Ammonia is isoelectronic with the methyl anion, which means that the two molecules have identical electronic structures and hence the same fundamental type of geometry (pyramidal sp^3 hybridization). Trimethylcarbonium ion is similarly isoelectronic with trimethylboron; the central carbon is trigonally (sp^2) hybridized and in the same plane as the three atoms attached to it.

Carbanion	Ammonia	Trimethylcarbonium ion	Trimethylboron

Methyl cation itself should be analogous to borane (BH_3), but the latter does not exist (Section 4.18). The geometry of the methyl radical is more difficult to predict, and it is also less well established experimentally. It appears that carbon radicals are either planar or else easily inverted pyramids, and it seems likely that either structure may exist, depending on what substituents are attached to the carbon atom. The geometry and other properties of these intermediates are further discussed in the following sections. Aromatic ions and radicals are specifically considered in Section 12.6.

IMPORTANCE OF MOLECULAR GEOMETRY. *The geometries of intermediates are chemically important for a number of reasons. If a planar intermediate such as a carbonium ion is formed during the course of a chemical reaction and exists for a reasonable length of time, then any product which is formed from that carbonium ion will have the carbon atom at which the carbonium ion was formed racemized during the course of the reaction. A planar carbonium ion $R_1 R_2 R_3 C^+$ possesses a plane of symmetry and lacks optical activity (as long as the R groups themselves are not dissymmetric). On the other hand, a tetrahedral species such as $R_1 R_2 R_3 C^-$ does not have a symmetry plane if $R_1 \neq R_2 \neq R_3$, and is therefore dissymmetric at any given instant. Thus an optically active starting material would give an optically inactive carbonium ion, which would necessarily give optically inactive products. On the other hand, a pyramidal intermediate such as a carbanion or an alkyl radical could react to give an optically active product. However, if the pyramid were to exist for a relatively long time, it might invert and hence the resulting product might be partially or completely racemized. These ideas will be amplified in later chapters.*

12.2   Carbonium Ions

Carbonium ion intermediates occur in a great many chemical reactions, and they are pretty well understood. The cycloheptatrienyl cation (see Section 12.6 for its electronic structure) is an exceptionally stable carbonium ion, which can be isolated and studied. It is a carbonium ion which is stabilized by resonance to a very high degree. At the other extreme is the methyl cation, which is so unstable that it has never even been detected as an intermediate in any ordinary chemical reaction. In between these two extremes there exists a whole spectrum of carbonium ions; some can be isolated, some are detectable but not isolable, and others can be generated only under extreme conditions, such as by bombardment of a suitable molecule with a high-energy electron beam.

Some representative carbonium ions are listed below in the order of their decreasing relative stability (in solution). The relative stabilities of the first four ions are easily understood on the basis of conjugation. The cycloheptatrienyl (tropylium) ion (which is discussed further on page 273) has seven equivalent Kekulé forms. Detailed calculations on this ion predict a very large conjugation energy, and the high degree of stability found experimentally (Section 12.6) is exactly what is expected for this molecule.

If triphenylmethyl bromide is placed in a solvent which supports charge, such as aqueous alcohol, it is rapidly ionized. The resulting triphenylcarbonium ion reacts with the solvent, however, and does not accumulate in large concentration. If triphenylmethyl bromide is placed in a solvent which solvates charged species, but with which

Cycloheptatrienyl   Triphenylcarbonium   Benzyl   Allyl cation   t-Butyl cation
cation   ion   cation
(Tropylium)   (Trityl)

Isopropyl   Ethyl   Methyl   Vinyl   Phenyl
cation   cation   cation   cation   cation

the ion cannot react (e.g., liquid sulfur dioxide), it is found that the compound dissociates into ions which are stable under these conditions and can be quantitatively determined by measuring the electrical conductivity of the solution.

$$Ph_3C\!-\!Br \xrightleftharpoons{liq. SO_2} Ph_3C^+ + Br^-$$

Eight Kekulé forms in which the positive charge is on the central carbon atom can be written for the trityl ion. These same eight Kekulé forms can be written for the neutral triphenylmethyl compound. Since both Ph_3CBr and Ph_3C^+ are stabilized equally by Kekulé resonance, this type of resonance does not influence the dissociation equilibrium. The ion, however, is additionally stabilized by nine resonance forms in which the charge is dispersed into the rings.

It is this delocalization of the charge over the whole molecule that results in the high degree of stabilization of the ion which was not present in the neutral molecule and which is responsible for the relatively great stability of this ion.

Dyes Derived from Triphenylmethane. A number of substituted triphenylcarbonium ions are quite stable. Many in fact are used as dyes because their extended conjugated systems show absorption in the visible part of the spectrum, and the compounds are therefore colored.

Malachite green   etc.

Fuchsine or *magenta* is a dye composed mainly of *pararosaniline*. The hexamethyl derivative of pararosaniline (where each hydrogen on nitrogen is replaced by a methyl) is a bluish violet dye called *crystal violet*.

Pararosaniline

The next member of our series is the benzyl cation (phenylcarbonium ion). Obviously the same type of resonance forms which stabilize the triphenylcarbonium also exist here, but there are fewer of them and their effect is not so pronounced. A solution of benzyl chloride in liquid sulfur dioxide does not conduct electricity to any appreciable extent: The equilibrium in liquid sulfur dioxide lies far to the left.

However, if a strong Lewis acid is added to halide, it is possible to detect the ion.

The rate of reaction of an organic halide with silver ion (silver nitrate in aqueous alcohol) is a useful measure of the stability of the carbonium ion which is formed by ionization. Triphenylmethyl bromide and benzyl bromide each give an almost instantaneous precipitate of silver bromide when dissolved in alcoholic silver nitrate. From the fast reaction we may infer that the ion is quite stable (Chapter 14). In fact, the times required for the corresponding bromides to react with silver ion to give the carbonium ions listed on page 260 are increasingly longer as we proceed along the series of decreasing stability.

The allyl cation has but two resonance forms,

$$CH_2=CH-CH_2^+ \leftrightarrow {}^+CH_2-CH=CH_2$$

but they are equivalent; this ion has a stability similar to that of the benzyl cation. [Sometimes the allyl cation is represented by the symbol $(CH_2 \cdots CH \cdots CH_2)^+$. This kind of symbol is somewhat misleading and will be avoided in this text.]

For the remaining carbonium ions on our list, stabilization is not so simply explained. Chemists debated for many years about the reasons for the observed order of stability of alkylcarbonium ions: tertiary > secondary > primary. The *t*-butyl cation, very stable for an alkylcarbonium ion, has a stability similar to that of the allyl cation, while the secondary and primary methyl-substituted carbonium ions are successively less stable. The stability of alkylcarbonium ions is now explained in terms of two effects, hyperconjugation and induction, both mentioned in Chapter 7 as contributing to the properties of alkyl-substituted olefins.

An *inductive effect* results when atoms of different electronegatives are bonded together. If a methyl group is bound to an olefinic carbon, as in propene for example, there will be a shift of electrons from the methyl toward the attached doubly bonded carbon, because the latter is more electronegative (Section 7.9). Now consider the effect of replacing a hydrogen of carbonium ion by a methyl group.

Carbonium ion   Methylcarbonium ion

Clearly we have an sp^3 orbital from the methyl overlapping an sp^2 orbital from the ionic carbon. This is similar to the situation in propene (Section 7.9). In addition, the ionic carbon carries a positive charge which causes it to be even more electronegative. The result is that we expect, and find, that the presence of a methyl group has a substantial stabilizing effect on the carbonium ion.

The second important effect leading to stabilization of a carbonium ion by an attached alkyl group is referred to as *hyperconjugation*. Propene, for example, is stabilized by resonance of the kind illustrated:

$$
\underset{\underset{\text{H}}{|}}{\overset{\overset{\text{H}}{|}}{\text{H}-\text{C}}}-\text{CH}=\text{CH}_2 \leftrightarrow \underset{\underset{\text{H}}{|}}{\overset{\overset{\text{H}^+}{|}}{\text{H}-\text{C}}}=\text{CH}-\text{CH}_2^- \leftrightarrow \underset{\underset{\text{H}^+}{}}{\overset{\overset{\text{H}}{|}}{\text{H}-\text{C}}}=\text{CH}-\text{CH}_2^- \leftrightarrow
$$

$$
\text{H}^+ \; \underset{\underset{\text{H}}{|}}{\overset{\overset{\text{H}}{|}}{\text{C}}}=\text{CH}-\text{CH}_2^-
$$

Such resonance is not very effective, because the ionic forms have one less covalent bond than does the ordinary Kekulé form. These ionic forms would be analogous to a form such as $\text{CH}_3^- \text{H}^+$ for methane, and clearly such forms are much less important than those with covalent bonds. Since ionic forms of this type can be written only by "sacrificing" a covalent bond, the type of resonance referred to above for propene is sometimes called *sacrificial hyperconjugation*.

For an alkyl-substituted carbonium ion, however, one can write hyperconjugative resonance forms which have the *same number* of covalent bonds as the principal structure:

$$
\underset{\underset{\text{H}}{|}}{\overset{\overset{\text{H}}{|}}{\text{H}-\text{C}}}-\text{CH}_2^+ \leftrightarrow \underset{\underset{\text{H}}{|}}{\overset{\overset{\text{H}^+}{|}}{\text{H}-\text{C}}}=\text{CH}_2 \leftrightarrow \text{H}^+ \; \underset{\underset{\text{H}}{|}}{\overset{\overset{\text{H}}{|}}{\text{C}}}=\text{CH}_2 \leftrightarrow \underset{\underset{\text{H}^+}{}}{\overset{\overset{\text{H}}{|}}{\text{H}-\text{C}}}=\text{CH}_2
$$

This type of resonance is referred to as *isovalent hyperconjugation*, and it is a good deal more important than is sacrificial hyperconjugation.

For a long time there was considerable ambiguity in the interpretation of the experimental facts. There was no doubt that methyl substitution stabilized a carbonium ion. The question was, Did the stability result from induction, or did it result from hyperconjugation? The answer is that both are important, and since the two effects work in the same direction, it is not easy to disentangle them. Theory says they should be comparable in importance.

EXERCISE 12.1

Draw all of the hyperconjugative resonance forms of isopropyl cation.

The stability afforded to a carbonium ion by the combined action of the inductive and resonance effects of a methyl group is very significant. The stabilization energies resulting from the substituents attached to the positively charged carbons in Table 12.1 have been measured by electron bombardment in a mass spectrometer (gas phase). Theoretical calculations reproduce these numbers very well.

Direct experimental studies of carbonium ions became possible in the 1960s when Olah† showed that it was possible to prepare many simple ones under conditions where they were stable, and to study them by means of their nmr spectra. Alkyl fluorides, for

† George Olah. Born 1927, Budapest, Hungary. Technical University of Budapest, Dow Chemical of Canada, Case Western Reserve University.

Table 12.1   Stabilization Energies of
Substituted Carbonium Ions

Ion	Energy kcal/mole
CH_3^+	0
$CH_3CH_2^+$	36
$(CH_3)_2CH^+$	66
$(CH_3)_3C^+$	84
$CH_2{=}CHCH_2^+$	58

example, react with the powerful Lewis acid antimony pentafluoride to yield carbonium ions.

$$R{-}F + SbF_5 \xrightarrow{\text{liq. } SO_2} R^+SbF_6^-$$

The nine methyl protons of *t*-butyl fluoride in sulfur dioxide are observed in the nmr at δ 1.3. When antimony pentafluoride is added to the solution, the protons are seen as a sharp singlet at δ 4.35. The large downfield shift of the methyl protons is expected since the positively charged carbon exerts large inductive and hyperconjugative effects on these protons.

Similarly, isopropyl fluoride shows the methyl protons at δ 1.23, while in $SbF_5{-}SO_2$, these are shifted to δ 5.06. The secondary proton in isopropyl fluoride is seen at δ 4.64, and in the carbonium ion it is shifted to δ 13.50!

12.3   Carbanions

As with carbonium ions, carbanions exhibit a whole spectrum of stabilities. Nitromethane, for example, is sufficiently acidic to react with aqueous alkali (Section 10.2) because the anion formed has a high degree of stability.

The stability of this ion is largely a result of the electronegativity of the oxygen atoms of the nitro group. There is a sizable inductive effect as well as a powerful resonance effect, both of which withdraw negative charge from carbon into the nitro group. The acidity of nitromethane bears a closer resemblance to that of nitric acid than it does to that of methane, and the order of acidities may be written:

pK_a -1.4 10   40

Electronegative atoms or groups, depending on their ability to withdraw electrons, will lead to more or less stable carbanions. The more common groups are listed in order of decreasing electron withdrawing ability.

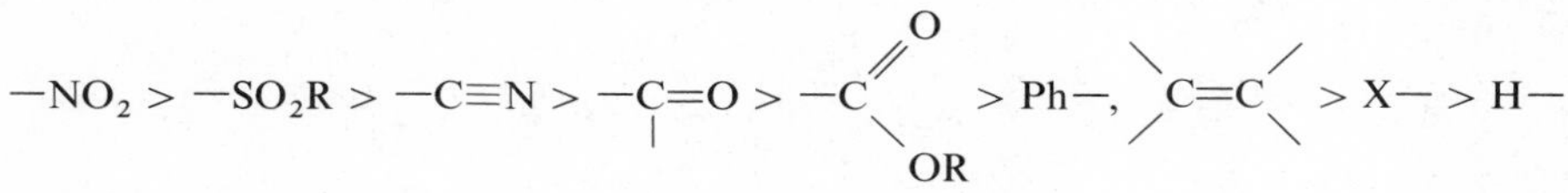

$$-NO_2 > -SO_2R > -C{\equiv}N > -\overset{|}{C}{=}O > -C\overset{O}{\underset{OR}{\diagdown}} > Ph-, \diagup\!C{=}C\!\diagdown > X- > H-$$

A single nitro group attached to carbon causes nitromethane to be sufficiently acidic to react with alkali. A group in the range from $-SO_2R$ to $-CO_2R$ is not electronegative enough to yield a compound with measurable acidity relative to water, but two such groups attached to the same carbon will remarkably enhance the acidity of a C—H bond. Whereas ethyl acetate does not react with sodium ethoxide to any appreciable extent, malonic ester does:

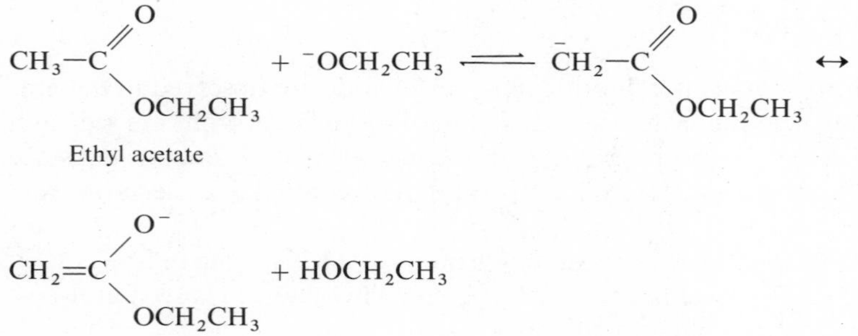

$$CH_3-C\overset{O}{\underset{OCH_2CH_3}{\diagdown}} + {}^-OCH_2CH_3 \rightleftharpoons {}^-CH_2-C\overset{O}{\underset{OCH_2CH_3}{\diagdown}} \leftrightarrow$$

Ethyl acetate

$$CH_2{=}C\overset{O^-}{\underset{OCH_2CH_3}{\diagdown}} + HOCH_2CH_3$$

but

$$CH_3CH_2O\overset{O}{\overset{||}{C}}CH_2\overset{O}{\overset{||}{C}}OCH_3CH_3 + {}^-OCH_2CH_3 \rightleftharpoons HOCH_2CH_3 +$$

Malonic ester

$$CH_3CH_2O\overset{O}{\overset{||}{C}}-\overset{-}{C}H-\overset{O}{\overset{||}{C}}OCH_2CH_3 \leftrightarrow$$

$$CH_3CH_2O\overset{O^-}{\overset{|}{C}}{=}CH-\overset{O}{\overset{||}{C}}OCH_2CH_3 \leftrightarrow CH_3CH_2O\overset{O}{\overset{||}{C}}-CH{=}\overset{O^-}{\overset{|}{C}}OCH_2CH_3$$

On the other hand, if a strong enough base is used, reaction will occur even with ethyl acetate.

$$CH_3\overset{O}{\overset{||}{C}}OCH_2CH_3 + NH_2^- \rightleftharpoons {}^-CH_2\overset{O}{\overset{||}{C}}OCH_2CH_3 + NH_3$$

The carbanions which are greatly stabilized by resonance are planar insofar as the delocalized electronic system is concerned. Thus the nitromethane anion has all of its atoms in a plane, with trigonal hybridization at both carbon and nitrogen.

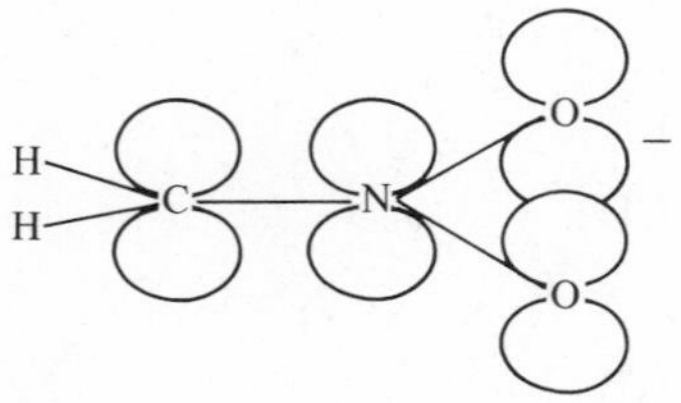

Malonic ester anion is similar; only the hydrogens on the ethyl groups lie out of the molecular plane:

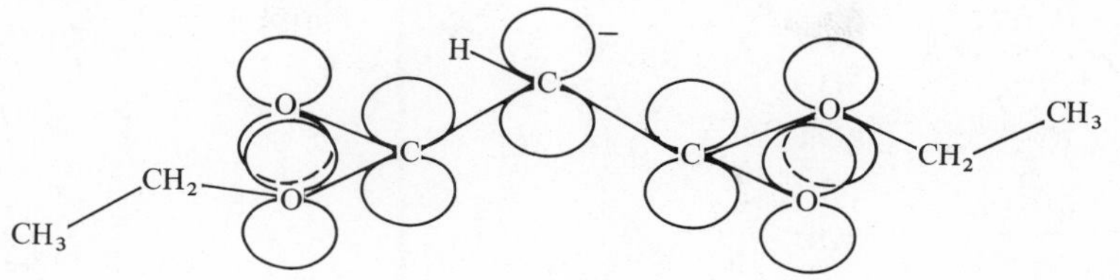

Because of the relatively low electronegativity of the carbons of the ring, the phenyl group resonance forms of the type shown do not give nearly as much stabilization to a carbanion as is provided by groups such as nitro or cyano.

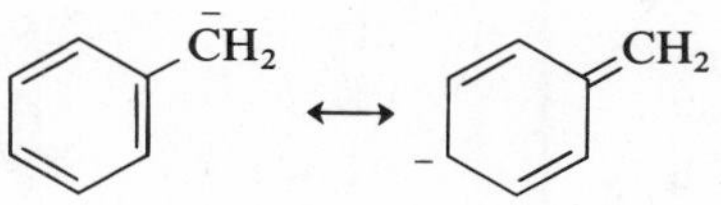

The geometry of the benzyl anion has not yet been directly studied. However, the ion is isoelectronic with aniline, and is likely to be geometrically similar to it also. Aniline, recall, is not a planar molecule—the nitrogen has a roughly tetrahedral geometry (Section 11.3). While resonance in aniline would be more effective with a planar nitrogen, other factors (analogous to ammonia, Section 4.14) keep the nitrogen pyramidal. Similarly it may be supposed that the methylene carbon of the benzyl anion is likely to be pyramidal.

Relative Acidities of Some Common Compounds. Table 12.2 gives a list of common compounds which have acidities or basicities of interest. A study of this table will help the student to summarize the material on acidity that has been covered in this and previous Chapters. It should be emphasized that the *relative acidities* are important, not the numerical values of the pK_a's. In fact, for pK_a's outside the range 0–16, the numerical values are very approximate.

Table 12.2 pK_a Values for Many Types of Acids

Acid	Base	Approximate pK_a
FSO_3H	FSO_3^-	-12
RNO_2H^+	RNO_2	-12
$ArNO_2H^+$	$ArNO_2$	-11
$HClO_4$	ClO_4^-	-10
HI	I^-	-10
$RCNH^+$	RCN	-10
H_2SO_4	HSO_4^-	-9
$RCH{=}\overset{+}{O}H$	$RCH{=}O$	-8
$ArSO_3H$	$ArSO_3^-$	-7
HCl	Cl^-	-7
$ArOH_2^+$	$ArOH$	-7
RSH_2^+	RSH	-7
$RCR{=}\overset{+}{O}H$	$RCR{=}O$	-7
$RCOR{=}\overset{+}{O}H$	$RCOR{=}O$	-6.5
$RCOH{=}\overset{+}{O}H$	$RCOH{=}O$	-6

Table 12.2   pK_a Values for Many Types of Acids—*continued*

Acid	Base	Approximate pK_a
$\overset{\displaystyle HCH}{\underset{\displaystyle \overset{\|}{OH^+}}{}}$	$\overset{\displaystyle HCH}{\underset{\displaystyle \overset{\|}{O}}{}}$	−4
$\overset{\displaystyle R_2O^+}{\underset{\displaystyle \overset{\|}{H}}{}}$	ROR	−3.5
ROH_2^+	ROH	−2
H_3O^+	H_2O	−1.74
HNO_3	NO_3^-	−1.4
$\overset{\displaystyle RCNH_2}{\underset{\displaystyle \overset{\|}{OH^+}}{}}$	$\overset{\displaystyle RCNH_2}{\underset{\displaystyle \overset{\|}{O}}{}}$	−1
HSO_4^-	SO_4^{2-}	1.99
HF	F^-	3.17
HONO	NO_2^-	3.29
$ArNH_3^+$	$ArNH_2$	3–5
RCOOH	$RCOO^-$	4–5
H_2CO_3	HCO_3^-	6.35[a]
H_2S	HS^-	7.00
ArSH	ArS^-	8
$CH_3COCH_2COCH_3$	$CH_3CO\overset{-}{C}HCOCH_3$	9
NH_4^+	NH_3	9.24
ArOH	ArO^-	9–11
RCH_2NO_2	$R\overset{-}{C}HNO_2$	10
R_3NH^+	R_3N	10–11
RNH_3^+	RNH_2	10–11
HCO_3^-	CO_3^{2-}	10.33
$R_2NH_2^+$	R_2NH	11
CH_3COCH_2COOEt	$CH_3CO\overset{-}{C}HCOOEt$	11
RSH	RS^-	12
$NCCH_2CN$	$NC\overset{-}{C}HCN$	12
$EtOOCCH_2COOEt$	$EtOOC\overset{-}{C}HCOOEt$	13
$MeSO_2CH_2SO_2Me$	$MeSO_2\overset{-}{C}HSO_2Me$	14
		14–15
H_2O	OH^-	16
CH_3OH	CH_3O^-	16
RCH_2OH	RCH_2O^-	18
R_2CHOH	R_2CHO^-	18
$PhC{\equiv}CH$	$PhC{\equiv}C^-$	18.5
R_3COH	R_3CO^-	19
$RCOCH_2R$	$RCO\overset{-}{C}HR$	19–20
		20
		23
$ROOCCH_2R$	$ROOC\overset{-}{C}HR$	24.5
RCH_2CN	$R\overset{-}{C}HCN$	25
$RCONH_2$	$RCONH^-$	25

Table 12.2   pK_a *Values for Many Types of Acids—continued*

Acid	Base	Approximate pK_a
HC≡CH	HC≡C$^-$	25
ArNH$_2$	ArNH$^-$	25
Ar$_3$CH	Ar$_3$C$^-$	31.5
A$_2$CH$_2$	Ar$_2$CH$^-$	33
MeSOCH$_2$R	MeSOCHR	33.5
NH$_3$	NH$_2^-$	34
ArCH$_3$	ArCH$_2^-$	35
CH$_2$=CH$_2$	CH$_2$=CH$^-$	36.5
PhH	Ph$^-$	37
cyclo-C$_3$H$_6$	cyclo-C$_3$H$_5^-$	39
CH$_4$	CH$_3^-$	40
C$_2$H$_6$	C$_2$H$_5^-$	42
(CH$_3$)$_2$CH	(CH$_3$)$_2$C$^-$	44
cyclo-C$_6$H$_{12}$	cyclo-C$_6$H$_{11}^-$	45

^{a} The pK_a for H_2CO_3 is actually about 4. The value 6.35 includes the equilibrium CO_2 + $H_2O \rightleftharpoons H_2CO_3$.

EXERCISE 12.2

Compare the acidities of NH_3 with $PhNH_2$ and $RCONH_2$ (Table 12.2). Can you explain the differences? How might you estimate the acidity of *p*-nitroaniline?

12.4   Carbon Radicals

Most simple carbon radicals, such as the methyl and *t*-butyl radicals, are highly reactive species. Even if they are kept out of contact with various other substances they cannot be obtained in any appreciable concentration because they react with one another by dimerization and disproportionation:

$$CH_3CH_2 \cdot + CH_3CH_2 \cdot \rightarrow CH_3CH_2CH_2CH_3 \qquad \text{Dimerization}$$

$$CH_3CH_2 \cdot + CH_3CH_2 \cdot \rightarrow CH_3CH_3 + CH_2=CH_2 \quad \text{Disproportionation}$$

Under normal circumstances the reactions are nearly instantaneous, are irreversible, and go to completion. For a free radical to exist as such in solution for an indefinite time, it would seem necessary that the stability of the radical be at least comparable with that of the covalent compound it would form upon dimerization.

The alkyl radicals are increasingly stable in the order

$$CH_3 \cdot < CH_3CH_2 \cdot < (CH_3)_2CH \cdot < (CH_3)_3C \cdot$$

a fact which can be attributed to hyperconjugation (as with the corresponding carbonium ions).

Benzyl and allyl radicals are more stable than the simple alkyl radicals.

$$\langle\bigcirc\rangle\text{—}\dot{C}H_2 \longleftrightarrow \langle\bigcirc\rangle\text{=}CH_2 \longleftrightarrow \text{etc}$$

$$CH_2\text{=}CH\text{—}CH_2 \longleftrightarrow \dot{C}H_2\text{—}CH\text{=}CH_2$$

Nonetheless, they dimerize almost instantaneously. The triphenylmethyl radical, on the other hand, is found to survive if it is kept in dilute solution. At higher concentration it is mostly dimeric, but the dimerization is reversible.

$$2\ (C_6H_5)_3C\cdot \rightleftharpoons \text{dimer}$$

THE DISCOVERY OF A STABLE FREE RADICAL. *In the year 1900 a very remarkable paper appeared in the* Journal of the American Chemical Society *and also in the* Berichte der Deutschen Chemischen Gesellschaft, *by a chemist names Moses Gomberg.† Gomberg was interested in completely phenylated alkanes and had previously prepared tetraphenylmethane, a synthesis which had frustrated a number of eminent chemists. He then set himself the task of synthesizing hexaphenylethane. He began with triphenylchloromethane and attempted to join two molecules together by means of a Wurtz reaction.*

$$2R\text{—}Cl + 2Na \rightarrow R\text{—}R + 2NaCl$$

This was a method sometimes used to prepare hydrocarbons. Gomberg isolated from the reaction a white crystalline solid, which melted at 185°C, and which he thought was hexaphenylethane.

As a chemist always does when trying to establish the structure of a new compound, Gomberg analyzed his product for carbon and hydrogen. He was surprised to find that the analysis showed 88% carbon and 6% hydrogen, a total of only 94%. Repeated analyses gave the same result. He concluded that the compound he had obtained was not hexaphenylethane, a hydrocarbon, but rather a compound containing 6% of some other element, probably oxygen.

He first thought that the oxygen might have come from impure starting materials, but when all of these were carefully purified and free of oxygen, the same results were obtained.

The oxygen could have come from the air, although it seemed unlikely that molecular oxygen would react at room temperature with a hydrocarbon. However, he carried out the reaction under an atmosphere of carbon dioxide. In this case, the compound he obtained had a melting point of 147°C, not 185°C. This substance was eventually purified, and on analysis gave the correct composition for hexaphenylethane: 93.8% carbon and 6.2% hydrogen. When this material was dissolved in benzene, it gave a yellow solution. When a small amount of air was admitted to the container, the yellow color disappeared. After a few minutes, the yellow color reappeared again. When more oxygen was admitted, the same thing happened: The color disappeared and slowly reappeared. This change could be repeated many times, but finally the color disappeared for good, and evaporation of the solvent yielded the compound of melting point 185°C.

Gomberg finally concluded that the compound having a melting point of 185°C was the peroxide

$$(C_6H_5)_3C\text{—}O\text{—}O\text{—}C(C_6H_5)_3$$

which he confirmed by preparing an authentic specimen in a different way. The hydrocarbon

† Moses Gomberg. 1866–1947. Born Elisabetgrad, Russia. University of Michigan.

which had a melting point of 147°C would then presumably be hexaphenylethane, but it was behaving in a very curious manner. The spontaneous cleavage of a carbon–carbon bond by oxygen was a previously unknown reaction. Gomberg therefore proposed that he had prepared a stable free radical "The experimental evidence presented above forces me to the conclusion that we have to deal here with a free-radical, triphenylmethyl, $(C_6H_5)_3C\cdot$." Gomberg's proposal was finally accepted, and it now seems clear that this is what happens. The metal abstracts a chlorine atom from triphenylchloromethane, and forms the free radical, triphenylmethyl. Two of these radicals then combine to form a dimer. Prior to 1967, it was assumed that this dimer was indeed hexaphenylethane. The carbon–carbon bond would be a very weak one in hexaphenylethane, because of the steric repulsions between the phenyl groups, and because the radical which could be generated by dissociating the molecule would be a fairly stable one. Thus an equilibrium might exist between the free radicals and the hydrocarbon. The equilibrium actually tends to favor a dimeric hydrocarbon; the material which exists as free radicals amounts to about 2% in a 1 molar solution, 10% in a 0.01 molar solution, and nearly 100% in a very dilute solution.

Triphenylmethyl radical is yellow, while both the dimeric hydrocarbon and the peroxide are colorless. The solution of the dimeric hydrocarbon is yellow because of the radical present in the equilibrium mixture. When oxygen is admitted to the solution, the triphenyl-methyl radical reacts rapidly to form the peroxide (remember that molecular oxygen is a diradical!), and the yellow color disappears. The equilibrium is then re-established by the dissociation of more dimer, and the yellow color reappears. Only after all of the dimeric hydrocarbon has been converted to peroxide does the yellow color fail to reappear.

Many other dimeric hydrocarbons, presumed to be substituted hexaarylethanes, were prepared, and the existence of the corresponding triarylmethyl radicals was substantiated in a number of ways. The most convincing evidence for the free radical nature of these materials lies in properties which arise from the odd electron. If two electrons occupy the same orbital, their spins and the corresponding magnetic moments exactly cancel one another. A free radical, however, has a net magnetic moment from the odd electron, and such a material is paramagnetic. The paramagnetism of the compound can be detected in a magnetic field, and in addition, it is possible to observe a paramagnetic resonance absorption spectrum, which comes about in a similar manner to that of an nmr spectrum. Instead of aligning a nuclear moment with or against the field, the electron's magnetic moment is being aligned for such a radical.

Since hexaphenylethane would be such a sterically crowded compound, one might ask why the radicals would tend to add in this orientation anyway. Why wouldn't they instead prefer to add as shown.

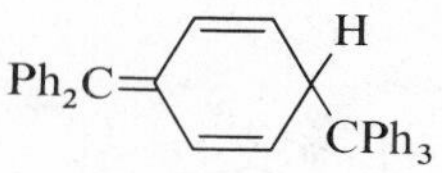

In 1968 a paper appeared in Tetrahedron Letters which described the nmr spectra of some supposed hexaphenylethanes. It was found that, in fact, the dimers were not hexa-phenylethanes, but were rather of the type shown above. Such a dimer is not particularly stable, because the resonance energy of one benzene ring has been lost. It seems that hexaphenylethane is to date still an unknown compound.

Why is triphenylmethyl radical so stable? There are two important reasons. The first is resonance.

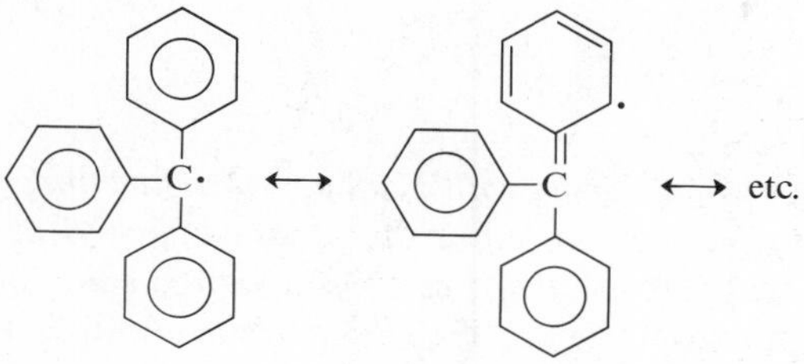

Many forms may be written with the odd electron displaced from the central carbon atom into the phenyl groups. This high degree of delocalization makes the radical quite stable. The second reason for stability is that the *dimer* is relatively unstable. The phenyl groups are very bulky, and any way of forming the dimer leads to a rather unstable structure. It has been found that hexacyclohexylethane does not dissociate into radicals, so the resonance in the triphenyl radical is an *essential* feature for its stability. The steric compression in the dimer doubtlessly contributes to its easy dissociation, but just how much is uncertain.

Just as carbonium ions range from highly unstable to quite stable, so do free radicals. The stable extreme is represented by N,N-diphenylpicrylhydrazyl, which is a commercially available material. Thus in many laboratories one can find on the shelf a bottle full of free radicals.

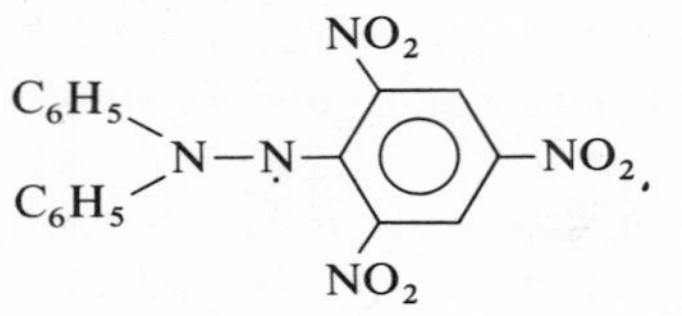

$$
\begin{array}{c}
C_6H_5 \\
\diagdown \\
\quad N-\overset{\cdot}{N}-\!\!\!\bigcirc\!\!\!-NO_2, \\
\diagup \\
C_6H_5
\end{array}
$$

with NO_2 groups at top (ortho), NO_2 (ortho bottom), and NO_2 (para)

N,N-Diphenylpicrylhydrazyl

12.5   Carbenes

There are two different types of electronic structures that might be visualized for carbene. The two valence-shell electrons which are not used for bonding could be in the same orbital (in which case another orbital would be empty and the molecule might be formally looked upon as being at the same time a carbanion and a carbonium ion).

Alternatively, the two electrons could be in different orbitals and the molecule might be looked upon as a diradical. In this case the electrons might have their spins either paired (singlet) or unpaired (triplet); the latter would be expected to be the more stable. The singlet species with two singly occupied orbitals will normally be an excited state of the singlet in which both electrons are in the same orbital (unless the orbitals are degenerate). Such an excited state will have but a fleeting existence, as it will quickly decay to its ground state. These possible states can best be understood with reference to the energy diagram in Figure 12.1.

Figure 12.1
The relationships between the various possible electronic structures of a typical carbene.

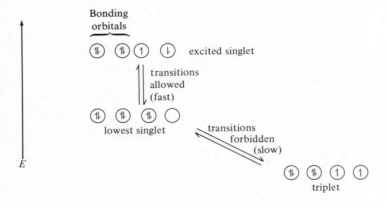

THE MULTIPLICITY OF A MOLECULE. *A* singlet *is a molecule with a unique wave function and no unpaired electrons. A* doublet *and* triplet *have wave functions that can be written in two and three ways as a consequence of the presence of one and two unpaired electrons, respectively. In general, the number of unpaired electrons is one less than the* multiplicity.

The triplet carbene and the singlet carbene with two paired electrons in the same orbital are expected to be of roughly comparable energies; it appears that one or the other of these structures may exist, depending on the circumstances. Usually the triplet is the ground state and the singlet is an excited state, but a few cases are known (e.g., the dihalocarbenes CX_2) where the singlet is the ground state. Transitions between singlets and triplets are forbidden and occur slowly. Hence one can sometimes prepare a singlet carbene and have it react chemically before it has a chance to become a triplet. Alternatively the singlet can be allowed to go over to the triplet before a reaction is carried out. The chemical behavior of the singlet and triplet will ordinarily be somewhat different.

Hybridization in a Carbene. The carbene which has both electrons in the same orbital would have a singlet ground state, and, in line with the discussion given in Section 4.2, the empty orbital would be a p orbital. There would be a high concentration of s character in the orbital which contained the electron pair, and the bonding orbitals to the hydrogens would probably be something close to sp^2 in character. Thus the R—C—R bond angle would be around 120°.

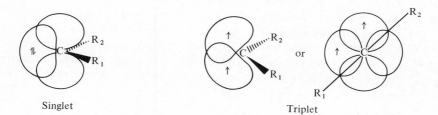

Singlet   Triplet

For the carbene in which the two valence-shell electrons not used in bonding occupy separate orbitals, the s orbital might be used fully for bonding; in this case we would have a linear molecule with sp hybrid orbitals used for bond formation. The extra electrons would be in pure p orbitals. The latter two orbitals are degenerate, and, applying Hund's rule, the two electrons should have their spins parallel. One can also imagine some s character being placed into the nonbonding orbitals, which would yield an angular rather than a linear molecule. There is evidence for the existence of such angular triplets in certain complex molecules. While both the singlet and the triplet carbene intermediates have been detected in chemical reactions and studied to some extent, little is known experimentally regarding their physical properties.

A carbene can react in different ways, depending upon whether it is in a singlet or triplet state. In the singlet state, a carbene is essentially a carbonium ion and a carbanion; it generally will react as though it were a carbonium ion first and a carbanion second. If the molecule is in a triplet state, it behaves more like a free radical. Obviously, the outcome of the reaction would be expected to be, and is, different in the two cases.

12.6   Aromatic Ions and Radicals

As discussed in the previous chapter, Hückel's $4n + 2$ rule has been a valuable aid for predicting when aromatic character in a π system might be anticipated. The rule has only to do with the presence or absence of filled electronic shells, not with the number of atoms present nor the charge on the molecule. It therefore applies to ions, as well as to the molecules previously discussed.

Let us now consider the cyclopentadienyl system. The cyclopentadienyl radical consists of five carbons which are arranged in a regular planar pentagon. The molecule is neutral, and it is a free radical rather than a normal covalent substance. It is written with resonance forms as indicated:

The atomic orbitals which make up the π system can be pictured as shown, and it is seen that the system is quite analogous in this sense to benzene.

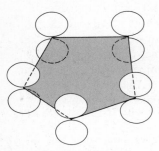

π Atomic orbitals
of cyclopentadienyl

The radical is quite reactive, however, and is not a stable chemical compound. It contains five π electrons, and if we put the electrons into the orbitals in accord with the energy diagram (Figure 12.2), we see that the outer (bonding) shell is not full. We are missing one electron. In fact, if one electron is added to the system, a much more stable species results. It is experimentally awkward to add an electron to the radical. But a cyclopentadienyl anion, with six π electrons can be conveniently generated in a different way. If cyclopentadiene is treated with a strong base, a proton is removed to give the anion (the cyclopentadienide ion).

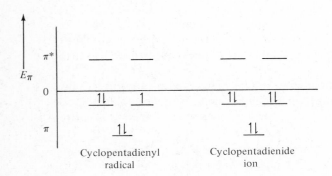

Cyclopentadiene   Cyclopentadienide
                                      ion

Hydrocarbons in general are very nonacidic, and it is most unusual to be able to form a carbanion from a hydrocarbon with a base such as sodium methoxide or sodamide. The ion forms in this case because of the unusual stability of the filled-shell configuration. The π-energy diagram of cylopentadienyl anion is as shown (Figure 12.2) for the ion with six electrons.

Figure 12.2
The cyclopentadienyl system.

EXERCISE 12.3

Write the Kekulé forms (5) of the cyclopentadienide ion.

There is a great similarity between pyrrole (Section 11.8) and cyclopentadienide ion.

The nitrogen atom in pyrrole supplies two electrons to the π system, and in the cyclopentadienide case, one carbon atom supplies two electrons by being an anion. The latter has a higher degree of symmetry than the former, and hence pairs of π orbitals which are of similar energy in pyrrole (Figure 11.13) are degenerate in the anion (Figure 12.2), but the overall analogy should be clear.

Next, consider the cycloheptatrienyl radical.

Cycloheptatrienyl
radical

Cycloheptatriene

It has the electronic configuration shown in Figure 12.3 and is not a closed-shell compound. Naturally it is not a stable species, and it cannot be isolated and stored in a bottle. On the other hand, if the system loses one electron, it forms a stable cation, with the

Figure 12.3
The cycloheptatrienyl system.

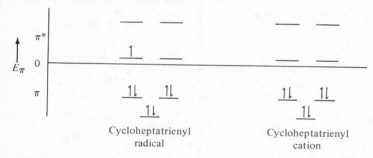

Cycloheptatrienyl
radical

Cycloheptatrienyl
cation

electronic configuration shown in Figure 12.3. Cycloheptatrienyl bromide, for example, exists as a salt rather than as a covalently bound compound. It dissolves in water, and behaves as an ionized salt in solution.

Cycloheptatrienyl cation
(Tropylium ion)

The cycloheptatrienyl cation is sometimes referred to by the trivial name *tropylium ion*. This name is derived from *tropolone*, a ring system which is found in a few naturally occurring compounds. In 1945, Dewar† noted that two Kekulé forms could be written for

† Michael J. S. Dewar. Born 1918, Ahmednagar, India. Queen Mary's College, Universities of London, Chicago, and Texas.

the then unknown compound (if the hydroxyl proton is allowed some average position

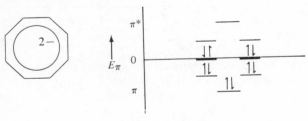

Tropolone

or disregarded). He correctly suggested that such ring systems were present in several natural products which had been isolated earlier, but the structures of which were unknown. All of the carbon–carbon bonds in tropolone have lengths of 1.40 Å, and heat of combustion measurements show that it has a conjugation energy of about 20 kcal/mole.

EXERCISE 12.4

Interpret the conjugation energy of tropolone in terms of Hückel's rule.

Compounds containing the cyclopropenyl cation system are also well known, and are reasonably stable, considering the strain present in the system. The synthesis of the first of these compounds was reported by Breslow[†] in 1958. Note that the cyclopropenyl cation follows Hückel's rule.

Recall that cyclooctatetraene is an eight-π-electron system, and that it is nonplanar and not aromatic. On the other hand, adding two electrons to the π system of cyclooctatetraene does produce an aromatic system (Figure 12.4), which is found to be planar and regular (D_{8h} symmetry). Cyclooctatetraenide dianion is not, however, a particularly stable system, because of the unfavorable electrostatic situation developed by the double negative charge. However, it does have a closed-shell structure, and it is stable when kept away from air and water.

Figure 12.4
The cyclooctatetraene dianion.

Azulene is an isomer of naphthalene which contains a five-membered ring fused to a seven-membered ring. It is aromatic and has two Kekulé forms. The most spectacular property of this compound is its intense blue color, which is very unusual for such a simple molecule. The conjugation energy of azulene is considerable (33 kcal/mole), but less than that of the isomeric naphthalene (61 kcal/mole). Part of the difference doubtless stems from the fact that the σ system in naphthalene is unstrained, while that in azulene is moderately strained. It is also found that azulene possesses a dipole moment of 1.0 D. Since most hydrocarbons are nonpolar, this, too, is quite unusual. If we recall, however, that cyclopentadienide is a particularly stable anion, and that cycloheptatrienyl cation is aromatic, we might guess that azulene would have an imbalance in the charge distribution of the π system. The seven-membered ring could take on a partial positive charge,

† Ronald Breslow. Born 1931, Rahway, New Jersey. Columbia University.

and the five-membered ring a negative one. This is what is found.

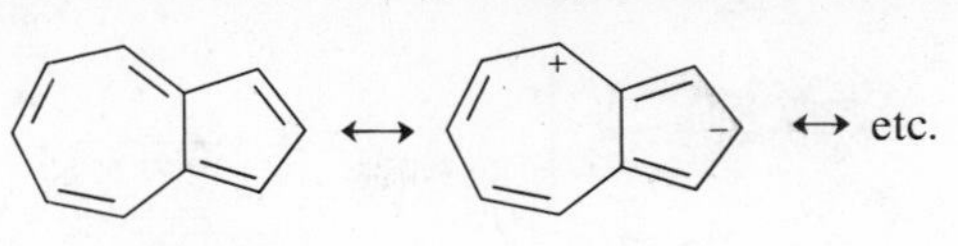

Azulene

EXERCISE 12.5

Would you expect that heptafulvalene 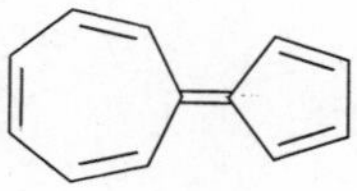 might be aromatic? Explain.

Bond Lengths in Azulene. The two Kekulé forms suggest that the peripheral bonds should all be similar to benzene in bond order and bond length, and further, that the central bond has a low bond order and is longer. The experimental values (X-ray diffraction) are 1.39 ± 0.05 for the peripheral bonds and 1.48 ± 0.01 for the central bond.

Some Additional Kinds of Aromatic Systems. Among the less common aromatics are heterocycles which contain electron-deficient atoms. Boron, for example, when bound to three other atoms has an empty *p* orbital left over. It is quite analogous to a carbonium ion structurally and chemically. Just as the cycloheptatrienyl ion is a stable cation, following Hückel's rule, so there are analogous boron compounds, one example of which is illustrated:

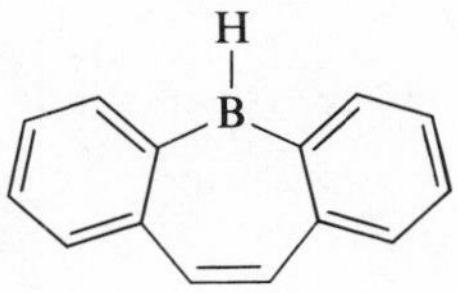

The parent compound of the series (boracycloheptatriene, without the additional fused benzene rings) has not yet been prepared.

An electron-deficient atom adjacent to an atom with a lone pair yields a π system similar to that found between two doubly bonded carbon atoms. The following are illustrative examples of such aromatic compounds containing this kind of hetero system.

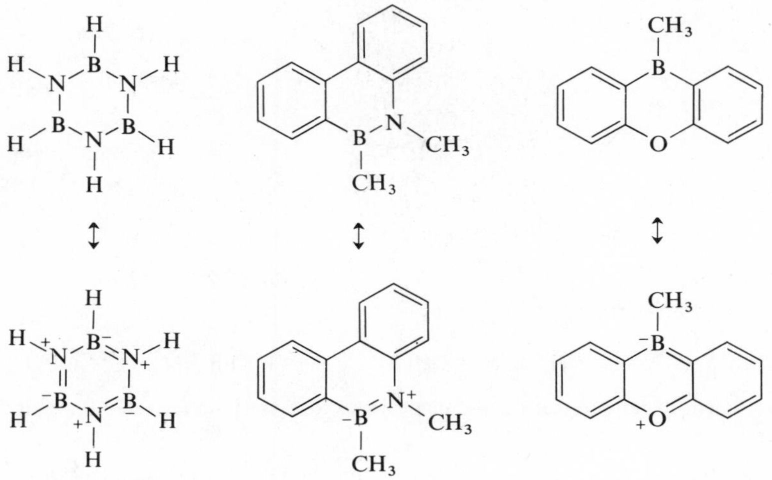

Borazine

Finally, there is a class of compounds referred to as *metallocenes*, which contain rings that have managed to attain aromaticity through interaction with a metal. Perhaps the best known and most studied of this class is *ferrocene*, which is formally considered as being two cyclopentadienyl radicals held together by an iron atom. By donating two of its electrons, one to each of the cyclopentadienyl rings, the iron atom (formally) reaches a comfortable $+2$ oxidation state, while the relatively unstable radical is converted to the relatively stable cyclopentadienide-type anion. The whole thing is held together as a neutral electronically stable molecule. Such a compound is sometimes referred to as a π *complex*, and there are quite a number of different types of π complexes now known. Cyclopentadienylmanganese tricarbonyl, and benzenechromium tricarbonyl are other typical examples.

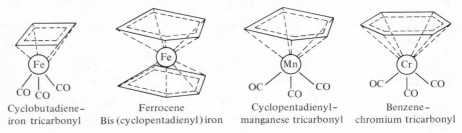

| Cyclobutadiene– iron tricarbonyl | Ferrocene Bis (cyclopentadienyl) iron | Cyclopentadienyl– manganese tricarbonyl | Benzene– chromium tricarbonyl |

It is interesting to note that while cyclobutadiene itself, as discussed earlier, is not a stable substance, it forms a complex with iron and three carbon monoxide molecules which is perfectly stable.

PROBLEMS

1. Sketch the atomic orbitals of the following species, indicating how many electrons are in each. Also indicate hybridization and bond angles.
   (a) CH_3^+ (b) CH_3^- (c) $CH_3\cdot$

2. Define: homolytic, isoelectronic, carbene, sacrificial hyperconjugation.

3. Do you anticipate that pentalene (⬡⬡) will be a stable aromatic system? Why?

   Answer the same questions for pentalene dianion.

4. Discuss the aromaticity or lack of it for the following:

   (a)   (b)   (c)   (d)   (e)

   (f)   (g)   (h)

5. List in order of increasing stability:

   Ph_2CH^+, $(CH_3)_2CH^+$, $CH_2{=}CH^+$, $CH_2{=}CHCH_2^+$, $CH_3CH_2^+$, $PhCH_2^+$, $p\text{-}CH_3OPhCH_2^+$

6. How many isovalent hyperconjugative resonance forms for the trimethylcarbonium ion are there? Draw them.

7. Tropolone has a measured heat of combustion that is 20 kcal lower than that calculated.

   Tropolone

   Its dipole moment is 3.71 D; that of 5-bromotropolone is 2.07 D. Tropolone is both acidic ($K_a \sim 10^{-7}$) and weakly basic, forming a hydrochloride in ether.

(a) What class of compounds does tropolone resemble? Is it adequately represented by the formula given above?

(b) Using both valence-bond and orbital structures, account for the properties of tropolone.

(c) In what direction is the dipole moment of tropolone? Is this consistent with the structure you have proposed?

(d) The infrared spectrum of tropolone shows a broad band at about 3150 cm^{-1} which changes only slightly upon dilution. What does this tell you about the structure of tropolone?

8. When $C_6H_5-\underset{\underset{\text{OH}}{|}}{\overset{\overset{\text{C}_6\text{H}_5}{|}}{C}}-CH_2CH_3$ is dissolved in $FSO_3H-SbF_5-SO_2$, the nmr spectrum of the solution is as shown.

NMR spectrum of unknown compound, Problem 8.

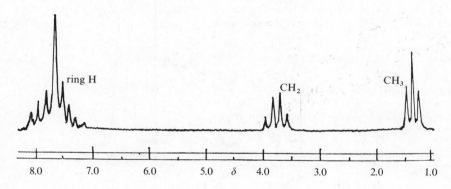

What is the structure of the species under observation?

9. Draw a picture of the benzyl cation showing the bond angles and hybridization of the valence orbitals associated with the benzyl carbon. Repeat for the *p*-nitro derivative, this time showing also the π system of the ring and the orbitals of the nitro group.

10. Acetoacetic ester ($CH_3\overset{\overset{\text{O}}{||}}{C}CH_2\overset{\overset{\text{O}}{||}}{C}OC_2H_5$) reacts with EtO^- to form a stable anion. Draw the principal resonance forms (3) of this ion. Sketch the atomic orbitals which make up the delocalized system in this anion.

11. List in order of acidity, the strongest acid first:

NH_3, CH_4, CH_3COOH, H_2O, C_6H_5OH, $CH_2=CH_2$, $C_6H_5NH_2$,

p-$NO_2C_6H_4NH_2$, *p*-ClC_6H_4OH, $HCOOH$, $CH_2(COOEt)_2$, C_2H_5OH, *t*-$BuOH$

12. Repeat Problem 9 for the benzyl anion.

13. Explain why hyperconjugation is rather unimportant in toluene, but more important in the *p*-methylbenzyl cation.

14. Draw the resonance forms for *N,N*-diphenylpicrylhydrazyl (page 270) and show why it is so stable.

15. If ⬡CH₂–CH(H)(Cl) were to be dissolved in SbF_5-SO_2, what compound would you expect to form? How might you show whether or not it did form?

16. Would you expect that triphenylcarbonium ion would have all of the carbon atoms in the same plane? Explain.

Optional Problem. When C₆H₅—C——C—CH₃ is dissolved in FSO₃H–SbF₅–SO₂,

the nmr spectrum of the solution is as shown.

NMR spectrum of unknown compound, Optional Problem 1.

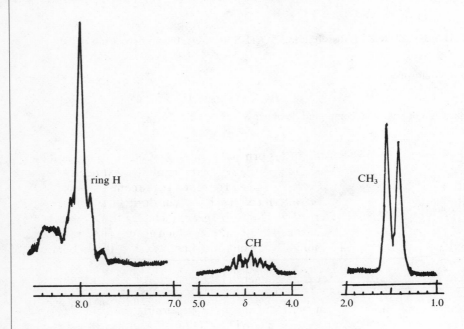

Interpret the above facts.

CHAPTER 13

APPLICATIONS OF THERMODYNAMICS

13.1   Basic Concepts

A major part of organic chemistry is the transformation of compounds to other compounds by means of *chemical reactions*. The first eleven chapters of this text dealt with the compounds which are the starting materials and end products of the common organic reactions. Chapter 12 discussed transient intermediates that occur during the course of such reactions. This chapter is concerned with the *energetics* (actually the *thermodynamics*) of these reactions. Here will be outlined the principles which govern the positions of equilibrium and the basic ideas upon which one must base considerations of the feasibility of different reactions.

Thermodynamics is the study of the flow of *energy* in a system. It is a basic subject which is equally applicable to engineering problems, living systems, and the behavior of organic molecules. The importance of thermodynamics in governing the behavior of chemical systems was first fully appreciated by Willard Gibbs,† who developed the methods and applications to a high degree. Heat can be looked upon as the most elementary form of energy, for any kind of energy, be it electrical, mechanical, or what have you, can be quantitatively converted into heat, while not all other kinds of energy can be quantitatively interconverted. For example, electrical energy can be quantitatively transformed into heat, but not into mechanical energy, because of friction. Therefore the energetics of a system can always be discussed in an exact way in terms of the *heat content* of the system, while other kinds of energy equivalents, such as mechanical work, are much more complicated.

Early scientists recognized what has been called the "conservation of energy," which is sometimes more elegantly called the *first law of thermodynamics*: Energy (including its equivalent in mass) cannot be created or destroyed, but the amount within an *isolated* system always remains constant.

The first law can be expressed as follows:

$$\Delta E = q - W$$

where ΔE is the change in the internal energy of the system, q is the heat added to the system, and W is the work done by the system.

The first law is an experimental fact. It cannot be derived or deduced from anything more fundamental. It just is. It is valuable because it has been tested by thousands of separate experiments, and it has been found to be true without exception.

Consider the process of heating a liter of oxygen from 25 to 30°C in a sealed vessel. Since the process is carried out at constant volume, the system does no work against its surroundings, so $W = 0$, and $\Delta E = q$; that is, the change in the energy of the system is

† Willard J. Gibbs. 1839–1903. Born New Haven, Connecticut. Yale University.

just equal to the heat added. If we know the heat added to the oxygen, we can specify exactly the change in the internal energy of the oxygen that takes place upon heating it from the initial to the final state.

For processes as they are ordinarily carried out on the planet Earth (which are the ones in which the organic chemist is usually most interested), if the system is open to the air, the process will not occur at constant volume, but rather at constant pressure. Consider repeating the above experiment with the oxygen in a container of variable volume (such as a cylinder containing a piston) so that the pressure on the system is exactly 1 atm throughout the experiment. In this case, the oxygen will expand upon heating, and it will occupy a larger volume in the final than in the initial state. In expanding, the oxygen has done work against the atmosphere—it has expanded against the resisting pressure of the atmosphere. In this case, the increase in the energy of the oxygen is the heat put in, less the amount of work done by the system in expanding, $p\Delta v$, where p is the pressure within the system and v is the volume of the system.

In this case, $q = \Delta E + p\Delta v$. It now proves convenient to define a quantity *enthalpy*, which is given the symbol H, such that for this last experiment $\Delta H = q$. The enthalpy is sometimes called the *heat content*, and for systems *at constant pressure*, H proves to be more useful than E, since it measures the amount of heat we must really put into a system to achieve a given result. Enthalpy and energy are related by the equation $\Delta H = \Delta E + \Delta(pv)$, or, since p is a constant in this case, $\Delta H = \Delta E + p\Delta v$. When we put numbers into this equation, we find that for gases the $p\Delta v$ term contributes an appreciable amount to ΔH, but for liquids, solids, and solutions, $p\Delta v$ is insignificantly small compared to ΔE. This is because gases expand quite a lot upon heating, but liquids and solids do not. Hence for solids, liquids, and solutions (which covers most cases in which organic chemists are interested) $E = H$, to a good approximation. Henceforth this approximation will be used without comment, but it must be recalled that it is an approximation, and it is *not* a good one for gases.

The early scientists found, after much discussion and experimenting, that there is more to thermodynamics than the first law. This "more" has to do with the fact mentioned before, that while one can quantitatively convert various forms of energy into heat, one cannot convert heat quantitatively into mechanical work. From this fact the second and third laws of thermodynamics were eventually developed. We will deal only briefly with the second and third laws because they are less important than the first law for present purposes.

Our objective is to be able to predict the relative enthalpies of different states for the purpose of predicting whether or not it might be possible for any given chemical reaction to proceed. Any chemical reaction can be written as an equilibrium. (Reactions which do not go at all, or which go to completion, are simply reactions for which the equilibrium constant has a value near zero or approaching infinity, respectively.)

Sometimes a reaction has a favorable equilibrium but still fails to proceed. Such a reaction is permitted to occur by thermodynamics, but not by kinetics; *this kind of situation will be taken up in the next chapter.*

It has been found that the equilibrium constant of a reaction depends on the enthalpy change (ΔH) and also on another quantity called the *entropy* change (ΔS). These quantities, together with the absolute temperature, give the *free energy* change (ΔG) according to the relationship $\Delta G = \Delta H - T\Delta S$, where T is the absolute temperature. It is the free energy which is related to the equilibrium constant.

The student should recall that if ΔG equals zero for a change, the system is at equilibrium, while if ΔG is negative, the process tends to proceed. A positive value for ΔG means that the reaction tends to go backward, from the final state toward the initial state.

Since energies are always relative terms, there has to be a standard relative to which energies are measured. It is convenient to define a *standard state of substance* as the state (solid, liquid, or gas) of the substance as it occurs *at 25°C and 1 atmosphere of pressure.*

For a substance in its standard state, it is said to have an enthalpy, entropy and free energy relative to its elements in their standard states, and a superscript zero is used to denote standard states. Thus the equation $C(s) + O_2(g) = CO_2(g)$, $\Delta H° = -94.05$ kcal/mole, means that when 1 mole of solid carbon reacts with 1 mole of oxygen gas to yield 1 mole of carbon dioxide gas (at 25°C and 1 atm), the heat content of the system decreases by 94.05 kcal/mole. Thus 94.05 kcal/mole of heat is evolved. (A negative sign of $\Delta H°$ means that the enthalpy change is a driving force tending to make the reaction go in the forward direction, while a positive sign means the reverse.) The *heat of formation* of CO_2 is said to be -94.05 kcal/mole. There exist many compilations of heats of formation of chemical compounds, and they are a useful aid in predicting the feasibility of untried chemical reactions.

For substances in their standard states, then

$$\Delta G° = \Delta H° - T\Delta S°$$

and the relationship between $\Delta G°$ and the equilibrium constant K is

$$\Delta G° = -RT \ln K$$

where $\ln K$ means the natural logarithm of K, R is the gas constant required to give the right-hand side of the equation the same dimensions as desired for the left (the numerical value is 0.00199 kcal/mole °K if ΔG is to be in kcal per mole), and T is the absolute temperature (°K). Thus, from the data in heat of formation tables we could calculate equilibrium constants, except for the quantity $\Delta S°$, the entropy change. Now very often this entropy change is small and we can forget about it. This is not always true, however, so that some discussion of entropy is now in order.

Entropy is a measure of probability; the more probable a state is, the more positive its entropy. As an example, consider the ionization of a monobasic acid RCOOH, and compare it with that of a dibasic acid $R(COOH)_2$.

The K_a of an acid is given by

$$K_a = \frac{[H^+][R-COO^-]}{[R-COOH]}$$

For a monobasic acid, RCOOH, there is a K_a as defined above which has a numerical value which can be measured. For the dibasic acid there are twice as many carboxyl groups per mole as with the monobasic acid; if everything else is equal, there is twice as great a probability that a carboxyl will ionize. At equilibrium the H^+ concentration will be twice as high as with the monobasic acid, and K_a will be twice as large. Clearly this is an entropy factor, since the enthalpy change upon ionization is assumed to be the same for the mono and dibasic acids.

The entropy of a system is given by

$$S = R \ln P$$

where P is the total possible number of states available to it. Thus a perfectly ordered system, as approximated by most crystals at 0°K has $P = 1$, and hence $S = 0$. If the system becomes more disordered, there are more possible arrangements it may assume, and P (and of course S) increases. In general, disorder and entropy tend to increase, and we can only overcome disorder through the expenditure of energy. This is why both entropy and enthalpy together must be considered in calculating an equilibrium constant.

The *third law of thermodynamics* states that a perfect crystal at 0°K has an entropy of zero. A perfect crystal is ordered in three dimensions, and at 0°K the molecules are all in their quantum states of lowest energy, therefore $P = 1$, and from the above equation, $S = 0$.

The *second law of thermodynamics* states that any process that occurs in a bounded system will lead to $\Delta S \geqslant 0$ for the system as a whole. If entropy is considered as disorder, this means that the universe as a whole tends to disorder. One can order part of the universe, but only at the expense of even greater disorder somewhere else.

The second and third laws of thermodynamics are important to our basic understanding of the universe in which we live, but they are pretty abstract as they have been stated, and it is not obvious how they apply to the subject at hand. We want now to look at some everyday examples of the usefulness of entropy to the chemist.

It is usually found that for organic reactions of the type

$$A + B \rightleftharpoons C + D \tag{1}$$

where A, B, C, and D are relatively nonpolar and are in relatively nonpolar solvents, the entropy change is small, and useful predictions can be made on the basis of enthalpies alone. There are exceptions, however, so that such predictions should be regarded as only first approximations.

For a reaction of the types

$$A \rightleftharpoons B + C \tag{2}$$

or

$$A + B \rightleftharpoons C \tag{3}$$

where there is a different number of molecules on the left side of the equation from that on the right side, the entropy change is usually large, and it favors the side of the equation which has the greater number of particles; thus, $\Delta S°$ is near zero for Equation (1), positive for (2), and negative for (3). The reason for the signs of these entropy changes can be seen in terms of disorder. Suppose A, B, C, and D correspond to marbles colored red, black, white, and green, respectively. Equation (1) describes a mole (say a bucketful) of each red and black marbles (all mixed together) being converted to a bucket full of white and green ones similarly mixed. Evidently there has not been any ordering or disordering in the process. Equation (2), on the other hand, corresponds to an ordered system (all red) going to a disordered system of black and white. Similarly, Equation (3) describes a disordered system becoming ordered; thus (2) corresponds to a positive ΔS, while for (3), ΔS is negative. A negative entropy (increasing order) for a reaction *tends* to prevent it from proceeding, but it does not by itself prevent it from proceeding.

A negative value for ΔS tends to prevent a reaction from proceeding, but if ΔH is negative and large enough to yield a negative ΔG, the reaction will proceed. The universe as a whole will still be more disordered as demanded by the second law, because the heat evolved will raise the molecules of the surroundings into higher quantum states and give more disorder overall.

If we apply these ideas to chemical systems, reactions that cause the total number of molecules to increase have favorable entropies, while if the number of molecules decreases, the entropy is unfavorable. The entropy of B + C in typical cases may exceed that of A by about 20 cal/deg mole or so, a very respectable amount, as $T\Delta S$ may then amount to several kilocalories per mole. An entropy unit (eu) has the units of calories per degree per mole (cal/deg mole). Note that these are calories, not kilocalories.

Ordinarily $\Delta H°$ for a chemical reaction is temperature independent. On the other hand, since $\Delta G°$ also contains a term $T\Delta S°$, it is often quite dependent on temperature. The variation with temperature of the $T\Delta S°$ contribution will have a very predictable effect on $\Delta G°$, if $\Delta S°$ or at least its sign can be estimated. If we consider the following specific reaction (the hydrogenation of benzene to cyclohexane) it clearly has a large negative entropy.

$$\Delta G° = \Delta H° - T\Delta S°$$

So if the entropy is negative, the term $(-T\Delta S°)$ is making a positive contribution to $\Delta G°$. In spite of this, the reaction proceeds to completion at room temperature, because the value of $\Delta H°$ is negative and overwhelmingly large. Suppose, however, that we heat the reaction mixture to a high temperature. Since T is larger, the $(-T\Delta S°)$ term becomes more important and it tends to push the reaction to the left. What we find is that above 300° C we can push the reaction essentially to completion to the left.

Here, then, we have a reaction which can be made to go in either direction by changing the temperature, and the trend is one which is clearly predictable from thermodynamics. In fact, it is generally true that if a reaction has a large number of molecules going to a smaller number, the equilibrium constant will be larger at lower temperatures than at higher temperatures, while if we consider the reverse reaction, which has a small number of molecules going to a larger number, the equilibrium constant will increase with increasing temperature. This analysis is most applicable, of course, to nonpolar systems. With reactions of ionic materials, or in water solvent, solvation phenomena may completely upset these simple predictions.

13.2   Bond Energies

It is often desirable to know what the heat of formation of a substance is when the quantity has never been experimentally determined. For example, one might want to predict whether some reaction will go, when one of the products is a compound which has never been prepared. In such cases it would be useful to be able to estimate what the heat of formation of a compound will be. To this end, tables of so-called "bond energies" have been prepared. These tables are based on the simple idea that the energy of a molecule can be expressed as the sum of the energies of the individual bonds in the molecule. This is a first approximation. A second approximation will allow corrections, to change the energy of a bond slightly, depending on the environment in which the bond is located. The student should be aware that such tables and techniques exist, although we will not have occasion to make much use of them in this text.

In the previous section the point was made that entropies associated with equilibria of the type with which organic chemists are generally concerned will often be small or negligible, and in most cases can be roughly estimated. Hence a study of equilibria becomes, to a first approximation, a study of enthalpies of reactions, which we will consider equivalent to energies of reactions.

It has been known since the time of Kekulé that most molecules can be considered as having the atoms joined together in a pairwise manner. Thus the molecule

$$\begin{array}{c} a \\ | \\ b-C-Cl \\ | \\ c \end{array}$$

has a carbon–chlorine bond, the behavior of which is approximately independent of the nature of a, b, and c. This approximation of pairwise bonding is clearly not true for conjugated systems, the B_2H_6 molecule, or other special cases, but it is a good approximation for most organic molecules.

If we consider the bonding orbitals in a typical molecule (abcC—Cl), we might reason as follows: We have five atoms (or however many are required by the nature of a, b, and c), four of which each contribute one atomic orbital, while the carbon contributes four orbitals. We will obtain eight molecular orbitals of the following form:

$$\psi_{\sigma_1} = a\psi_{Cl} + b\psi_{C_1} + c\psi_{C_2} + d\psi_{C_3} + e\psi_{C_4} + f\psi_a + g\psi_b + h\psi_c$$

$$\psi_{\sigma_2} = a'\psi_{Cl} + b'\psi_{C_1} + c'\psi_{C_2} + d'\psi_{C_3} + e'\psi_{C_4} + f'\psi_a + g'\psi_b + h'\psi_c$$

$$\psi_{\sigma_3} = a''\psi_{Cl} + b''\psi_{C_1} + c''\psi_{C_2} + \cdots$$

Table 13.1 Bond Contributions and Corrections Used in the Klages–Wheland Method for Calculating Heats of Combustion[a]

Bond	Contribution kcal	Types of compound in which used
C—H	54.0	All types
C—C	49.3	All types
C=C	121.2	Ethylene
	119.1	Monosubstituted ethylenes
	117.4	*cis*-1,2-Disubstituted ethylenes, including 6-membered rings
	115.7	*cis*-1,2-Disubstituted ethylenes in 5-membered rings
	116.4	*trans*-1,2-Disubstituted ethylenes
	115.5	1,1-Disubstituted ethylenes
	114.0	Trisubstituted ethylenes
	112.0	Tetrasubstituted ethylenes
C≡C	202.6	Acetylene
	197.7	Monosubstituted acetylenes
	193.6	Disubstituted acetylenes
N—H	30.5	All types
C—N	33.0	All types
C=N	60.3	All types
C≡N	97.6	All types
O—H	7.5	Alcohols[b]
C—O	10.0	All types
C=O	26.5	Formaldehyde
	19.8	Other aldehydes
	13.5	Ketones
S—H	67.0	All types
C—S	69.0	All types
C—Cl	2.9	All types
C—Br	26.6	All types
C—I	38.7	All types

Correction for:

Tertiary carbon atom[c]	−1.7
Quaternary carbon atom	−4.2
Secondary alcohol	−3.6
Tertiary alcohol	−8.8
Acetal	−3.0
Methoxyl group	+3.0
5-Membered ring	+6.0
6-Membered ring	+1.0

[a] These figures are taken from F. Klages, *Chem. Ber.*, **82**, 358, (1949), as modified by G. W. Wheland, "Resonance in Organic Chemistry," John Wiley and Sons, New York, 1955. These articles may be consulted for further details.

[b] For water, the value is 5.25 kcal, or half of the heat of vaporization.

[c] This value applies to saturated compounds, not to olefins.

where ψ_{Cl} is the chlorine orbital being used for bonding, ψ_{C_1}, ψ_{C_2}, ψ_{C_3}, and ψ_{C_4} are the four orbitals from carbon used for bonding, and ψ_a, ψ_b, ψ_c are the orbitals contributed by a, b, and c. The coefficient a measures the contribution of ψ_{Cl} to the molecular orbital ψ_{σ_1}, while a' measures the contribution of ψ_{Cl} to ψ_{σ_2}, and so on.

Now, since we know it is a good approximation to consider the atoms bound together pairwise, the orbitals for the description of such a system must have many of these coefficients equal to (or nearly) zero. If ψ_{σ_1} is the carbon–chlorine bond, for example, that means that the coefficients a and b are large, while the rest (c–h) are nearly zero. If ψ_{σ_2} is the C—a bond, then c' and f' are large, while a', b', d', e', g', and h' are all near zero.

We conclude then, both from classical structural formulas and from the molecular orbital viewpoint, that a molecule (excluding the special types mentioned) can, to a first approximation, be represented as the sum of a number of pairwise interactions, or bonds. We ought, then, to be able to assign bond energies to each kind of bond, C—H, C—Cl, C—C, C=C, and so on, and by adding the bond energies for a molecule, find its total energy. This kind of approach is not exact, remember; it would be if all the small coefficients in the molecular orbitals were zero, but they aren't, they are just small. There have been a number of methods proposed for obtaining the bond energies we want, different approximations which differ in detail. We will use here the method of Klages, which is a good one, but not the only one. This method enables us to calculate the heat of combustion rather than the more abstract bonding energy.

In Table 13.1 are listed various kinds of bonds and the contribution each will make to the heat of combustion. Methane, for example, is calculated to have a heat of combustion of $(4 \times 54.0) = 216.0$ kcal/mole, while that for ethane is $(49.3 + 6 \times 54.0) = 373.3$ kcal/mole. It is found that in general more highly branched compounds have smaller heats of combustion than do straight chains, so corrections are introduced to allow for this. Thus, neopentane is more stable than *normal* pentane by 4.2 kcal/mole, while isopentane is more stable than the *normal* isomer by 1.7 kcal/mole. These differences appear to come from interactions between atoms which are not bound to one another, but are neighbors one or two atoms further removed. While the first approximation, then, would include only bound atom interactions, the next, much better approximation of Klages allows for these close neighbor interactions. Thus, the increased stability of olefins when they are methylated, which was discussed in Chapter 7, is well accounted for.

Note that the Klages–Wheland method is an empirical one. That is, it was devised by measuring the heats of combustion of a large number of compounds, and then picking the numbers in Table 13.1 so as to give the best duplication of the experimental facts. In principle, one could arrive at these numbers from theory—by solution of the Schroedinger equation. This has been done too, but the numbers from theory are not (yet) as good as those from experiment.

Using the values in Table 13.1, we can quantitatively predict heats of combustion for a great variety of simple compounds. From the heats of combustion, which are *relative* heat contents, we can calculate the enthalpy changes for reactions. For example, consider the reaction of vinyl alcohol to yield acetaldehyde (tautomerization).

$$\underset{298.6\ \text{kcal/mole}}{CH_2=C\!\!\begin{array}{c} OH \\ H \end{array}} \rightleftharpoons \underset{285.1\ \text{kcal/mole}}{CH_3-C\!\!\begin{array}{c} O \\ H \end{array}} \qquad \Delta H^\circ = -13.5\ \text{kcal/mole}$$

We can determine the relative heat contents of these compounds as follows: For each compound we have the following bonds, together with the numbers from Table 13.1:

Vinyl alcohol			Acetaldehyde		
C—H	$54.0 \times 3 =$	162.0	C—H	$54.0 \times 4 =$	216.0
C—O	10.0	10.0	C—C		49.3
O—H	7.5	7.5	C=O (aldehyde)		19.8
C=C (monosubst.)		119.1			285.1
		298.6			

The vinyl alcohol has the greater heat content, thus we have to add heat to the right-hand side of the equation to balance it. Hence, the reaction is exothermic by 13.5 kcal/mole and proceeds to the right. If we assume $\Delta S^\circ = 0$ for the reaction, we can calculate the equilibrium constant: $\Delta G^\circ = \Delta H^\circ = -RT \ln K$. Thus, $-13,500 = -(1.99)(298) \ln K$, and solving, $K = 10^{9.9}$, which is consistent with the observation that the amount of vinyl alcohol in acetaldehyde is undetectably small.

Conjugation energies are obtained for compounds by comparing their experimental heats of combustion with the values calculated for the Kekulé forms; thus, for benzene we calculate from Table 13.1 a heat of combustion of $(3 \times 117.4) + (3 \times 49.3) + (6 \times 54.0) + 1.0 = 825.1$ kcal/mole. The actual molecule has a heat of combustion of 789 kcal/mole; this extra stability of the actual molecule $(825.1 - 789.0 = 36.1$ kcal/mole$)$ is the conjugation energy. The conjugation energies in Tables 11.2 and 11.3 were determined in this way.

Strain energies in molecules can also be obtained as the difference between the value calculated from the table (which assumes no strain) and the experimental value, as was discussed in Section 3.5.

Conjugation energies tend to stabilize a molecule and lead to experimental heats of combustion which are lower than calculated. Strain energies, on the other hand, destabilize a molecule and yield experimental heats of combustion which are larger than calculated.

Often one may have not a value for a heat of combustion, but instead a heat of hydrogenation, or a pK_a value. These values can sometimes be used in place of heats of combustion to calculate the same sorts of information. There are often advantages to using such numbers. The heat of hydrogenation of a typical olefin may, for example, be about 50 kcal/mole, while its heat of combustion may be 1000 kcal/mole. This means that a 1% error in the heat of hydrogenation will give the final energy to an accuracy of 0.5 kcal/mole, while this kind of accuracy from a heat of combustion would require a measurement of the total heat evolved to an accuracy of 0.05%. The determination of equilibria from heat of combustion data suffers from the fact that we are usually looking at the small difference between large numbers, and experimental errors are very serious. The same is true for conjugation energies. It should be especially noted that when one wants to compare a series of values, say for conjugation energies of a group of compounds, the exact numbers obtained by the Klages–Wheland method will be somewhat different from those obtained by other methods, but the relative values will be similar by any method. One must be careful to refrain from comparing the quantitative values for such quantities unless they are all calculated by the same method.

PROBLEMS

1. Define and give a symbol (if any) for: thermodynamics, first law, energy, enthalpy, free energy, entropy, heat of formation.

2. For each of the following reactions, predict which way the equilibrium will be shifted by an increase in temperature.

(a) $CH_2=CH_2 + CH_3\overset{\displaystyle O}{\underset{\displaystyle \|}{C}}-OH \rightleftharpoons CH_3CH_2O-\overset{\displaystyle O}{\underset{\displaystyle \|}{C}}-CH_3$

(b)

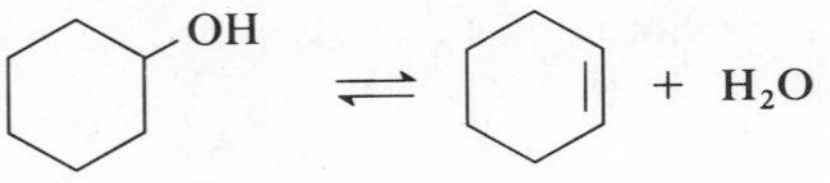

(c)

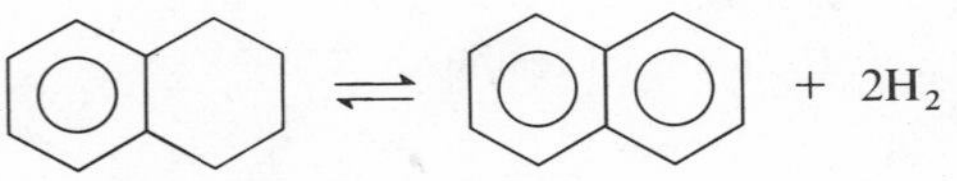

(d)

(e) $HOCH_2CH_2OH + CH_3C=O \underset{CH_3}{\rightleftharpoons} \quad + H_2O$

3. For a reaction $A + B \rightleftharpoons C + D$, $\Delta H° = -2.40$ kcal/mole, $\Delta S° = -1.0$ eu.
   (a) Calculate $\Delta G°$ for the reaction at 25°C.
   (b) Calculate the equilibrium constant (K) for the reaction.
   (c) Calculate K for the reaction at 100°C.
   (d) In order to get the reaction to go as far to the right as possible, is a high temperature more or less favorable than a low temperature? Why?

4. Triphenylmethyl radicals are stable in dilute solution, but dimerize to a considerable extent in concentrated solution.
   (a) From the data on page 269, calculate K for the following reaction at 25°C.

   $2(C_6H_5)_3C \cdot \rightleftharpoons dimer$

   (b) Calculate $\Delta G°$ for the above reaction.
   (c) The absolute value of the $\Delta S°$ for the above reaction is about 20 eu. Is this number positive or negative?
   (d) Calculate $\Delta H°$ for the reaction.
   (e) Which way will the equilibrium shift if the temperature is raised? Why?

5. On page 35 it was stated that the conformation of cyclohexane is the chair form to the extent of more than 99% at room temperature. If the chair form has a lower free energy than the twist-boat by 5 kcal/mole, what is the value of the equilibrium constant, boat $\xrightarrow{K}$ chair?

6. Consider the equilibrium between the anti and gauche conformations of *n*-butane (Section 3.3).

For the reaction as written, $\Delta H° = 0.8$ kcal/mole. There is only one form or state for the anti conformation, but there are two forms (*d* and *l*) for the gauche as shown. (The student may wish to review the details of this particular example, which was discussed in Section 6.2, especially Figure 6.1.) The entropy is thus 0 for the anti form, and $R \ln 2 = 1.4$ eu for the gauche form. Thus, for the above reaction, $\Delta S° = +1.4$ eu.

(a) Calculate the percent of the *n*-butane which is gauche at 25°C.

(b) Repeat the calculation for a temperature of 500°C.

(c) From the above sets of calculations, can you reach any conclusions about the effect of entropy on equilibrium?

(d) What would the composition of the equilibrium mixture be at 0°K? Can you make a general statement concerning equilibria at very low temperatures?

Optional Problems

1. Using the table on page 284, which pertains to reactions at 25°C, calculate the enthalpy change for each of the reactions in Problem 2. Assuming that equilibrium can be reached, predict which reactions will occur at 25°C, and suggest how the others might be forced to occur. [For (c), take the heat of combustion of hydrogen gas as 58.4 kcal/mole, and assume that the conjugation energy of naphthalene is 24 kcal/mole greater than that of benzene.]

2. For the reaction

it is believed that the equilibrium constant K is about 100 at room temperature, which means the product is more stable than the reactant by 2.8 kcal/mole. The conjugation energy of the product tetraene is about 4 kcal/mole. From the numbers in Table 13.1, calculate the difference in energy between the two molecules. Using the experimental data above, decide whether 10-annulene has more or less conjugation energy than steric repulsion energy, and by how much.

3. From the data in Table 13.1, which way does the following reaction proceed, to the right, or to the left? What is the equilibrium constant?

$$CH_3-C\equiv N \rightleftharpoons CH_2=C=NH$$

4. The experimental value for the heat of combustion of biphenylene is 1481 kcal/mole. What can you deduce from that value?

CHAPTER 14

CHEMICAL KINETICS

14.1   Reaction Mechanisms

A study of thermodynamics (Chapter 13) allows us to predict whether or not a reaction can proceed. Thermodynamics is concerned with the relative enthalpies and entropies of the reactants and products in a chemical equilibrium; from these quantities and the absolute temperature we are able to calculate the free energy of reaction, ΔG. A negative value for ΔG indicates that the thermodynamics is favorable for the reaction to proceed in the forward direction. However, this does not necessarily ensure that the reaction will occur. Thermodynamics can only tell us where the equilibrium position lies between the reactants and products; it cannot tell us how to get from one to the other. The rate at which a reaction will proceed to equilibrium may be tremendously large or nearly zero, and from a practical point of view, a reaction proceeding at a near-zero rate does not go, no matter what thermodynamics tells us about equilibrium. If thermodynamics tells us a reaction will not proceed under a certain set of conditions, there is no use trying it in the laboratory—it simply won't work. However, if thermodynamics tells us that a reaction should occur, there is still the question of whether or not it will have a rate fast enough to be useful. To understand the rate of a reaction, we have to understand the sequence of steps which occur from the starting materials to the final products, and we have to know what kinds of intermediates are formed during the reaction. The *mechanism* of a chemical reaction describes the detailed, stepwise pathway by which reaction occurs. A knowledge of the mechanism of a reaction will help us choose the proper conditions to employ to cause a thermodynamically favorable reaction to proceed to the desired products in good yield.

Ideally, knowledge of a reaction mechanism implies that we know the exact positions of all of the atoms in the molecules, including solvent molecules, at all times during the reaction. Additionally, we should know the nature of the interactions and/or bonds between these atoms, the energy of the system at all stages, and the rate at which all changes occur. This, of course, presents us with a very complicated problem, and, except for the simplest of gas-phase reactions, we cannot expect at present to be able to determine all of these things. Therefore, we are content to say that we have a basic understanding of the mechanism of a chemical reaction if we know the structures of all of the intermediate compounds that are formed, and if we can describe in general terms how each individual step of the reaction takes place. We want to know which bonds are being broken and which are being formed, which atoms are attacking other atoms and how readily this is occurring.

Mechanisms are not necessarily proven. Rather, the preferred mechanism for any given reaction is that which remains after all reasonable alternatives are excluded, and which stands up to scientific test. The mechanism must account not only for the products of the reaction, but also for the stereochemistry observed. For example, when bromine is added to cyclopentene the product is *trans*-1,2-dibromocyclopentane; and the mechanism for this reaction must account for the exclusive trans addition.

If *intermediates* are postulated in a mechanism, all attempts should be made to detect them by either chemical or physical methods. In many cases this is not possible, but we can often reject possible intermediates by preparing them separately, introducing them into the reaction, and showing that the same products are not formed. For example, when *t*-butyl chloride is allowed to react in dilute aqueous sodium hydroxide solution, a mixture of *t*-butyl alcohol and isobutylene is produced. If *t*-butyl alcohol is placed in this same reaction medium, it does not give isobutylene. We may then conclude that *t*-butyl alcohol is not an intermediate in the conversion of *t*-butyl chloride to isobutylene under these conditions.

t-Butyl chloride   *t*-Butyl alcohol   Isobutylene

The mechanism proposed for a reaction must also account for the changes in products and/or reaction rates caused by changes in the medium or the temperature or by added catalysts. Finally, the mechanism must account for the *kinetics* of the reaction.

14.2   Reaction Kinetics

Kinetics is concerned with motion. In chemistry, kinetics deals with the rate of a chemical reaction, with all factors that influence this rate, and with the explanation of the rate in terms of the reaction mechanism. Contrast kinetics with thermodynamics: Whereas *time* is the fundamental variable of kinetics, it is not one of the thermodynamic variables. A study of the kinetics of a reaction is one of the most important methods of obtaining information about the reaction mechanism. Moreover, a typical organic molecule may react in several different ways, and the path that the reaction follows is controlled by the *relative rates* of the various competing processes. It is by understanding the effects which the reaction variables (concentration, temperature, solvent, etc.) have on the various rates that the chemist can choose the proper conditions to make the desired reaction predominate.

Consider first the hypothetical reaction between A and B to give C:

$$A + B \rightarrow C$$

Let us suppose that we find that the rate of this reaction is dependent upon the concentrations of both A and B. In other words, if either concentration is doubled, the rate is doubled; or, if both concentrations are doubled, the rate is quadrupled. The rate of the reaction may be measured by observing the appearance of product C with time, or the disappearance of reactants A or B with time. A simple *rate equation* can express this:

$$\text{Rate} = \frac{d[\text{C}]}{dt} = \frac{-d[\text{A}]}{dt} = k[\text{A}][\text{B}]$$

The differential expression $d[\text{C}]/dt$ refers to the incremental amount of product C produced during an incremental amount of time (t). Thus the rate equals the appearance of product ($d[\text{C}]$) vs time (dt), *or* the disappearance of starting material ($-d[\text{A}]$) vs time (dt). Note also that $-d[\text{B}]/dt$ equals the rate of reaction. The proportionality constant k is called a *rate constant*. The rate expression is an experimentally determined quantity, and it describes the kinetic order of a reaction. The reaction given above is a *second-order* reaction, because the right-hand side of the rate equation is the product of two concentrations. A reaction of this type may also be bimolecular, implying that a simple collisional process between two molecules A and B causes reaction to occur. *Molecularity* refers to the number of molecules or particles involved in a collisional process, whereas the *order of a reaction* is the sum of the exponents of the concentration terms in the rate expression. Molecularity is a theoretical concept, and reaction order is something which has to be determined experimentally.

For any rate expression such as

$$Rate = k[A]^a[B]^b[C]^c$$

the order of reaction, n, is equal to $a + b + c$, and each individual exponent is the order with respect to that component. The reaction $A + B \rightarrow C$ discussed above is second-order overall, first order in A and first order in B. For this reaction, the observed second-order kinetics support a simple bimolecular mechanism for the reaction. However, other mechanisms may be involved. Consider the same reaction, but now let us assume that it occurs in two steps as shown, where I is some intermediate:

$$A + B \xrightarrow{slow} I \xrightarrow{fast} C$$
$$Rate = k[A][B]$$

Because the second step is fast, the first step is the key one and is called the *rate-determining step*. This first step is bimolecular and shows second-order kinetics. *The kinetics of the overall reaction are identical with the kinetics of the rate-determining step* because the rate of the reaction is equal to the rate of the slowest step.

The observation of second-order kinetics for the reaction in question does not allow a distinction between the two mechanisms: a bimolecular collision between A and B to give C directly, or a *slow* bimolecular collision between A and B to give an intermediate I which subsequently decomposes to C in a fast step. More information is needed to decide between the two alternatives. However, all mechanisms that do not involve a bimolecular reaction as the only step, or as the slow one of many steps, or as a fast step prior to the rate-determining step, are excluded by the observation of second-order kinetics.

The following reaction might be a first-order reaction:

$$D \rightarrow E$$
$$Rate = \frac{d[E]}{dt} = \frac{-d[D]}{dt} = k[D]$$

The rate of this reaction is proportional only to the concentration (to the first power) of D. This reaction could show a mechanism which simply involves unimolecular decomposition of D to E.

Let us also consider another mechanism for the conversion of D to E:

$$D \xrightarrow{slow} I \xrightarrow{fast} E$$

The rate expression for this mechanism, which is two-step, also has the form

$$Rate = k[D]$$

because the unimolecular reaction of D—the first step—is the slow step of the overall process. There is a way by which we can distinguish between the one-step and the two-step, first-order mechanisms for the conversion of D to E. This would be to detect the occurrence of the intermediate I.

14.3 Collision Theory

Up to this point, we have written rate expressions for various reactions in terms of a rate constant, k. Every reaction has a characteristic rate constant; and, if the reaction has several steps, each step is associated with a rate constant. Obviously one important feature that causes one reaction to occur in preference to another reaction, or that causes one step in a multistep sequence to be slower than the other steps, is the magnitude of the individual rate constants. Two important theories are concerned with an understanding of the factors that make one rate constant larger than another. The first of these is derived from the kinetic theory of gases, and is called *collision theory*. (The second, transition-state theory, will be discussed in the next section of this chapter.)

The rate at which a chemical reaction between two molecules (say A and B) occurs *cannot* be faster than the rate at which they collide. Thus a knowledge of the number of collisions taking place per unit time should give us information about the rate of a reaction. Certainly, increasing the concentrations of A and B will increase the frequency of collisions, because there are more molecules to collide (doubling the concentration of A should double the frequency of collisions, etc.). An increase in temperature should also increase the rate of collisions, because the molecules will move faster and collide more often. However, under a given set of concentration and temperature conditions, we find that only a small fraction of the total collisions that occur (usually about one in every 10^{15} collisions) leads to successful reaction. This can be partly accounted for by stating that in order for a collision to be effective in leading to a reaction, a certain minimum amount of energy is required. This minimum amount of energy that must be provided by a collision for reaction to take place is called the *activation energy*, E_a.

When collisions occur with less than this amount of energy, they are elastic; the atoms bounce apart and no reaction takes place. Even when a reaction in the forward direction is favored by the thermodynamics (in other words energy would be given off if the reaction were completed), activation energy is required to get the reaction to go. The reason is that, although the bonds in the products are more stable than those in the reactants, bonds must be broken (requiring energy) before new bonds are completely formed as the reaction proceeds. In other words, the atoms are required to adopt a certain geometrical arrangement which is of higher energy than that of either the starting materials or the products. This region of highest energy on the reaction pathway is called an *activated complex*. Figure 14.1 shows an energy diagram for a simple, one-step conversion of reactants (R) to give products (P). The point X corresponds to the atomic arrangement and energy of the activated complex. This does not define an intermediate compound; rather it is the highest-energy state through which reactants must pass in order to get to product. The difference between the average energy of the starting molecules and the energy of the complex X is the activation energy, E_a, of the forward reaction

Figure 14.1
Collision theory energy diagram.

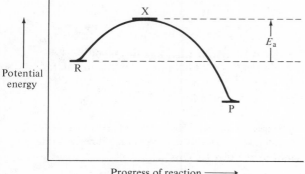

(R → P). Only those starting materials which possess at least this amount of energy *more* than the average energy will be able to react on collision. Most of the particles do not have so much energy; these simply undergo elastic collisions, and no reaction occurs.

The Arrhenius Equation. It can be shown that the rate of reaction may be expressed as

$$\text{Rate} = Ze^{-E_a/RT}$$

where e is the base of natural logarithms (2.72) and Z is the number of collisions per unit time. The $e^{-E_a/RT}$ term simply expresses the fraction of successful collisions; those for which the molecules (atoms) possess the necessary energy (E_a or greater).

A few reactions, such as those between gaseous atoms, follow this rate expression quite well; however, most other reactions, especially those between molecules, do not. Apparently, in the reactions between molecules some collisions have the required excess energy to result in a reaction, but the particles collide with the wrong orientation. The term P refers to that fraction of energetically suitable collisions in which the molecules have the correct orientation for a reaction to occur, and it is called the *probability factor*. The final form of the rate expression is therefore

$$\text{Rate} = PZe^{-E_a/RT}$$

Both E_a and P are intimately associated with the reaction mechanism, and they can be evaluated by studying the temperature dependence of the rate.

14.4   Transition-State Theory

A more modern approach to reaction rates, and one which is applicable to reactions in solution, is the *transition-state theory* (sometimes called the *absolute rate theory*). The objective of this theory is to bring to bear on the problem of reaction mechanisms the very powerful principles of thermodynamics. This is the theory that is most generally applied in organic chemistry today. It is somewhat similar to collision theory in that both are concerned with a configuration of highest energy (an energy barrier) through which starting materials must pass to arrive at products. Instead of dealing with collisions and collision probabilities, transition-state theory says that the rate of reaction is determined by the rate of passage of a system through a transition state.

Actually, the region of configuration space at the top of the energy barrier is called the transition state, *and a species (or system) in the transition state is known as an* activated complex. *The transition state is the state in which the change over from reactants to products occurs. We will use the two terms synonymously. Transition state is often abbreviated as* ‡ *(double dagger).*

This *rate of passage* is proportional to the concentration of the transition-state species, and the concentration of the species in the transition state is determined by an equilibrium constant, because the transition-state species is in equilibrium with the starting materials.

According to the transition-state theory, the rate constant (k) for a reaction is given by the equation

$$k = \frac{k_B T}{h} \exp\frac{-\Delta G^{\ddagger}}{RT}$$

which is usually referred to as the *Eyring†* equation. The symbols have the following meanings: k_B is Boltzmann's constant, h is Planck's constant, T is the absolute temperature, R is the gas constant, and $\Delta G^{\ddagger}$ is the free energy of activation, which is related to the enthalpy and entropy of activation in the usual way ($\Delta G^{\ddagger} = \Delta H^{\ddagger} - T\Delta S^{\ddagger}$). [The symbolism exp(X) is often used instead of e^X to mean e to the exponent X.]

Origin of the Eyring Equation. The source of Eyring's equation can be outlined here. If we allow an equilibrium to occur between the starting materials and the transition state, there exists an

† Henry Eyring. Born 1901, Colonia Juarez, Chihuahua, Mexico. University of Utah.

equilibrium constant denoted as $K^{\ddagger}$; it is defined like other equilibrium constants as

$$K^{\ddagger} = \frac{[\text{transition state}]}{[\text{starting materials}]}$$

Statistical mechanics has been used to show that *all* transition states go on to their respective products at the same rate; this universal rate constant is $k_B T/h$. At 25°C, $k_B T/h = 6 \times 10^{12} \text{ sec}^{-1}$. Thus the rates of all chemical reactions can be expressed as

$$\text{Rate} = \frac{k_B T}{h} [\text{transition state}]$$

and from the expression defining $K^{\ddagger}$, we can write

$$\text{Rate} = \frac{k_B T}{h} K^{\ddagger} [\text{starting material}]$$

The rate constant, k, of any reaction would be equal to $K^{\ddagger} k_B T/h$. The rate constant at any given temperature is thus proportional to the equilibrium constant $K^{\ddagger}$. Applying the principles of thermodynamics (Chapter 13), we see that

$$\Delta G^{\ddagger} = \Delta H^{\ddagger} - T\Delta S^{\ddagger} = -2.303 RT \log K^{\ddagger}$$

and hence

$$k = \frac{k_B T}{h} \exp\frac{-\Delta G^{\ddagger}}{RT}$$

The student should always remember that $\Delta G^{\ddagger}$ will be a positive number (or sometimes zero), because energy must usually be supplied to get a reaction to occur. $\Delta G^{\ddagger}$ for a given reaction can be obtained by measuring the rate constant at a given temperature, and both $\Delta H^{\ddagger}$ and $\Delta S^{\ddagger}$ can be obtained by determining the variation of rate with T.

Energy diagrams for organic reactions can also be drawn in transition-state theory terminology. Figure 14.2 depicts the same reaction ($R \rightarrow P$) that was shown in terms of collision theory in Figure 14.1. The reaction coordinate is a quantity which expresses the degree of reaction from 0 to 100% (along the path from reactants to products).

Figure 14.2
Transition-state theory free energy diagram.

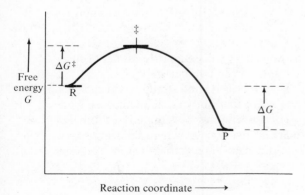

The difference between the average standard free energies of the reactants and the energy of the transition state is $\Delta G^{\ddagger}$, the free energy of activation for the forward reaction. The difference in standard free energy of the reactants and the products, ΔG, is also indicated on the diagram. Note that ΔG is a thermodynamic quantity; it tells us only what kind of energy flow to expect if the reaction can be made to occur, and it has nothing to do with the rate of the reaction. The rate of the reaction is determined by $\Delta G^{\ddagger}$.

The diagram of Figure 14.2 is that for a one-step reaction. There is only one transition state, and no intermediate compounds are involved. A transition-state free energy diagram is shown in Figure 14.3 which corresponds to the two-step reaction

$$R + R' \xrightarrow{\text{slow}} I \xrightarrow{\text{fast}} P$$

in which the first step is the rate-determining step. Since the first step is rate-determining, the first transition state is of higher energy. The intermediate I is a true compound; it occurs at an energy minimum on the path. A two-step reaction will have two transition states and one intermediate between reactants and products. The student should also note the important fact that $\Delta G^{\ddagger}$ for the forward reaction is the energy difference between the reactants and the highest-energy transition state, and $\Delta G^{\ddagger}$ for the reverse reaction would be the free energy difference between P and this same highest-energy transition state. If $\ddagger_1$ is the transition state of higher energy for the forward reaction, it is the transition state of higher energy for the reverse reaction.

Figure 14.3
Energy diagram for a two-step reaction.

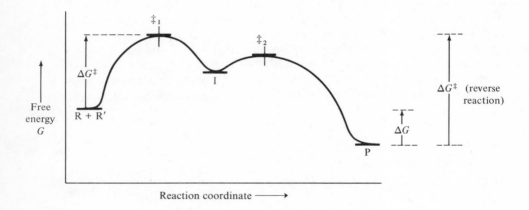

In a multistep reaction, the number of transition states will equal the number of steps, and the number of intermediates will be one less than the number of steps.

We might point out here the general relationship between bond strength and chemical reactivity: namely, there is none. Bond strengths are thermodynamic quantities, while chemical reactivity is a kinetic phenomenon. The student may be tempted to think that strong bonds mean low reactivity, but there are so many cases where this is not true, it is best at this point to consider bond strengths and chemical reactivities as independent quantities.

14.5   Catalysis

A *catalyst* is a substance which accelerates a chemical reaction, but which is not itself altered during the overall process. Because the rate of a reaction is determined by the activation energy, the catalyst functions by providing a new reaction pathway which has a lower activation energy. The common example used to illustrate the action of a catalyst is the reaction between an alkene and hydrogen. In Section 7.10, we learned that when an alkene is hydrogenated to give an alkane, heat is evolved (i.e., the reaction is exothermic). However, despite the favorable thermodynamics, no reaction occurs when the alkene and hydrogen are simply mixed together. This is because the activation energy for this reaction is too high. When a dispersed metal such as palladium or platinum is added, the uptake of hydrogen is smooth and quantitative. The metal catalyst serves to lower the activation energy for the overall reaction. This effect is shown graphically in Figure 14.4 with the aid of an energy diagram. Note that the ΔG of reaction is not altered by addition of the catalyst; the rate is merely increased. The catalyst is not consumed in the overall reaction.

Figure 14.4
Free energy diagram for the hydrogenation of an alkene with and without a catalyst.

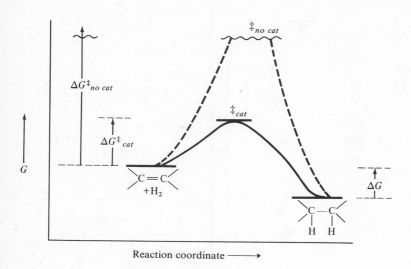

Dispersed metals such as palladium or platinum are typical of *heterogeneous catalysts*; they are insoluble and provide a surface, on which reaction can occur. An active area of present-day research involves a study of metallic compounds which are soluble in organic solvents and can function as *homogeneous catalysts*. To be sure, we do not know exactly how catalysts act to lower the activation energies of reactions in all cases, but we can usually write specific mechanisms to account for the actions of most homogeneous catalysts.

The most important and frequent cases of catalytic action in solution involve acids and bases. An example of a reaction that is catalyzed specifically by hydroxide ion (*specific base catalysis*) is the hydrolysis of an epoxide.

An epoxide   A *vic*-glycol

The accepted mechanism for this reaction is that hydroxide ion attacks the epoxide in a slow step to give an intermediate hydroxy alkoxide, which then reacts very rapidly with water to produce glycol and regenerate hydroxide ion.

Hydroxy alkoxide

Thus hydroxide is not consumed in the reaction; it is a true catalyst. The kinetics of the reaction, Rate = k[epoxide][$^-$OH], are in accord with this mechanism.

Note that the rate expression tells us the molecular formula and the charge of the transition state, apart from solvent. Thus in the base-catalyzed epoxide opening reaction in the previous paragraph, the transition state contains the elements of epoxide and OH$^-$; the molecular formula is (epoxide · OH)$^-$, but the kinetics does not tell us which atoms are attached to which, or where the charge is located. Thus

all correspond to the observed kinetics.

This same reaction is also catalyzed by acids; the mechanism for the acid-catalyzed hydrolysis of an epoxide is:

It is found experimentally that the rate is given by the following expression:

Rate = k_{obs}[epoxide][H$^+$]

and the term [H$^+$] means that we have acid catalysis.

EXERCISE 14.1

(a) Sometimes a reaction A + B $\longrightarrow$ C will be found where the rate (d[C]/dt) does not change when the concentration of B is increased. What can you say about the rate expression? What does this mean regarding A with respect to the transition state?

(b) Sometimes a reaction $A + B \longrightarrow C$ will be found where the rate ($d[C]/dt$) *increases* with time. Explain.

The Kinetics of Epoxide Opening. The rate of the epoxide opening reaction is given by

$$\text{Rate} = k_2[\text{epoxide} \cdot \text{H}^+][\text{H}_2\text{O}]$$

However, since water is the solvent as well as the reactant, it will not be seen in the experimental rate law. (The solvent does not appear in any experimental rate law, because it is always present in huge excess, and its concentration does not vary. Thus the effect of the water is experimentally lumped into k_2, and we observe an apparent k_1, call it $k_{\text{app}} = k_2[\text{H}_2\text{O}]$.) Hence

$$\text{Rate} = k_{\text{app}}[\text{epoxide} \cdot \text{H}^+]$$

We do not know the concentration of epoxide $\cdot$ H^+, however; we only know the concentration of epoxide and of H^+ which are added. These things are restated by the equilibrium constant, K_1, as follows:

$$\frac{[\text{epoxide} \cdot \text{H}^+]}{[\text{epoxide}][\text{H}^+]} = K_1$$

or

$$[\text{epoxide} \cdot \text{H}^+] = K_1[\text{epoxide}][\text{H}^+]$$

Our rate expression then becomes

$$\text{Rate} = k_{\text{app}}K_1[\text{epoxide}][\text{H}^+]$$

When we determine the rate experimentally, we find

$$\text{Rate}_{\text{obs}} = k_{\text{obs}}[\text{epoxide}][\text{H}^+]$$

If the mechanism is correct as written, obviously $k_{\text{obs}} = k_{\text{app}}K_1$.

In some cases, *all acids* and *all bases* (in the Lewis sense, not just H^+ and ^-OH) which are present in solution can catalyze a reaction. For example, when acetic acid is dissolved in water, the acids H_3O^+, HOAc, and H_2O are present, as are the bases ^-OAc, ^-OH, and H_2O. If each of the acids can catalyze the reaction, we see *general acid catalysis*. If all bases act as catalysts, we have *general base catalysis*. It is usually easy to distinguish between specific acid catalysis and general acid catalysis by examining the effect that buffer solutions with the same pH have on the rate. The pH of a solution is a measure of H_3O^+ concentration, and the reaction rate would be the same in various buffer solutions of the same pH if specific acid catalysis is present. On the other hand, if we use acetate buffer solutions in which the concentrations of acetic acid and acetate ion are increased (but constant pH is maintained), the rate would increase if general acid catalysis is involved.

14.6   Competitive Reactions. Relative Rates

It was mentioned earlier (Section 14.2) that the reaction path followed by an organic molecule is controlled by the relative rates of the various competing processes. In other words, most organic reactions are *kinetically controlled*. We can illustrate this common situation by use of Figure 14.5, which is an energy diagram showing the conversion of A to B. However, compound A can also react to give a by-product C under these conditions. The relative amounts of products B and C are determined by their relative rates of formation, which in turn depend on the relative values of $\Delta G^{\ddagger}$ for each process. The student will recognize that we have said nothing at all about whether B is more stable than C, or vice versa. As long as the reactions are kinetically controlled, we will obtain more of B than C, because $\text{B}^{\ddagger}$ is of lower energy than $\text{C}^{\ddagger}$ ($\Delta G_{\text{B}}^{\ddagger} < \Delta G_{\text{C}}^{\ddagger}$). Contrast this situation with a reaction which is reversible and (when it comes to equilibrium) *thermodynamically controlled*. If the reaction shown in Figure 14.5 did come to equili-

Figure 14.5
Free energy diagram for competitive reactions of A.

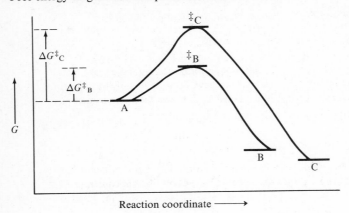

brium, we would get more C than B, since C has the lower free energy. Many examples of each situation are known, and in certain reactions, the ratios of competing products can be varied between thermodynamic and kinetic control at will by choice of experimental conditions.

EXERCISE 14.2

Listed below are several hypothetical situations that might apply to the competitive reaction of A to give either B or C (such as shown in Figure 14.5). Given each of these conditions, how may we alter the reaction variables (temperature, solvent, concentrations, etc.) so as to improve the product ratio B/C; that is, obtain more B and repress the formation of C?

(a) The reaction $A \rightarrow C$ has a less negative $\Delta S^{\ddagger}$ than the reaction $A \rightarrow B$.

(b) The reaction to give B proceeds as follows, $A \xrightarrow{\text{slow}} \text{ions} \xrightarrow{\text{fast}} B$; whereas the reaction $A \rightarrow C$ is a unimolecular decomposition of A not involving ions.

(c) Each of these reactions requires another reagent Z. However, the reaction $A + Z \rightarrow B$ is second order (rate $= k[A][Z]$), but the reaction to give C is unimolecular ($A \xrightarrow{\text{slow}} I \xrightarrow[Z]{\text{fast}} C$; rate $= k[A]$ because Z is not involved before or during the rate-determining transition state).

(d) The reaction $A \rightarrow B$ is acid-catalyzed, and the reaction $A \rightarrow C$ is not susceptible to acid catalysis.

There is another aspect of our concern with relative rates that we should examine now. Consider a series of similar compounds, A, A', and A", that are undergoing a reaction to give similar products, B, B', and B". Each of the starting materials has the same functional group and each reacts by the same mechanism. The only difference is that the structures have been altered slightly. Through an understanding of the mechanism of the reaction and the effects of structure on reactivity, we should be able to predict the relative rates of reaction of A, A', and A". A case in point would be the relative rates of the first-order hydrolysis of methyl bromide (MeBr), isopropyl bromide (*i*-PrBr), and *t*-butyl bromide (*t*-BuBr). The mechanism for the reaction may be given in general terms as

$$R-Br \xrightarrow{\text{slow}} R^+ + Br^-$$
(a carbonium ion)

$$R^+ + H_2O \xrightarrow{\text{fast}} R\overset{+}{O}H_2$$

$$R\overset{+}{O}H_2 \xrightarrow{\text{fast}} ROH + H^+$$

We need be concerned here only with the first step, since it is rate-determining. Further-more, we shall assume that the standard free energies of all three bromide starting materials and all three alcohol products (methanol, isopropyl, and *t*-butyl alcohols) are nearly the same. In order to predict the relative rates we must be able to estimate the relative free energy differences between the starting materials and their respective tran-sition states. Since the starting materials are of approximately the same free energy, it is the transition-state energies that we must estimate. We don't know the detailed structures of the transition states; *but*, because the ionization reaction to give carbonium ion is quite *endothermic*, we can predict that the relative stabilities of the carbonium ions should reflect themselves in the relative energies of the transition states leading to them. It was stated in Section 12.2 that the order of stabilities of carbonium ions is tertiary > secondary > primary. Therefore, the tertiary bromide should ionize to give carbonium ion much more easily than the other bromides. The idea that the transition-state energy and hence the rate of reaction is reflected in the carbonium ion energy is an example of the *Evans-Polanyi principle*, which is useful in predicting relative rates of very similar reactions. Figure 14.6 clearly shows that the relative rates of hydrolysis of these bromides is *t*-BuBr > *i*-PrBr > MeBr.

Figure 14.6
Energy diagram for the rate-determining steps in the hydrolysis of methyl, isopropyl, and *t*-butyl bromides.

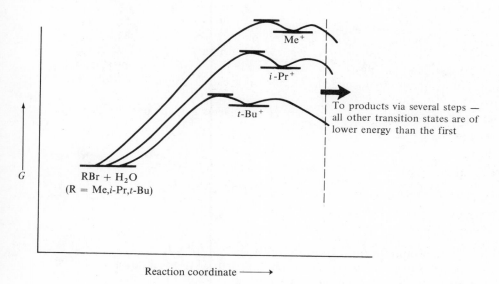

14.7   Isotope Effects on Reaction Rates

When an isotope is substituted for an atom in a molecule, the chemical properties of the material are not qualitatively altered. Often, however, the rate at which chemical reactions take place differs from one isotopic species to the next. The differences in rate caused only by isotopic substitution are called *kinetic isotope effects*, and they are usually small.

There are three basic kinds of kinetic isotope effects, termed primary, secondary, and solvent isotope effects. *Primary kinetic isotope effects* arise because a bond to the particular atom replaced by its isotope is being broken during the rate-determining step of a reaction. In the case of *secondary isotope effects*, a bond to the isotope is not being broken, but the isotopic substitution is sufficiently close to the reaction center so that changes in the vibrational frequencies in the nonreacting bonds can influence the rate. The *solvent isotope effect* can often be observed because a change in solvent from one containing a light isotope to one having a heavy isotope (for example, H_2O vs D_2O) alters the physical properties of the solvent, and solvent properties can influence the rates of reactions in solution. We will not consider the latter two isotope effects to any further extent in this text, although they have been shown to be quite valuable in certain mechanistic studies.

Primary kinetic isotope effects can be of relatively large magnitude, and they are always expressed in terms of the rate ratio $k_{\text{light isotope}}/k_{\text{heavy isotope}}$. The value for this ratio is always greater than 1; that is, the compound containing the light isotope reacts somewhat faster than that with the heavy isotope, and ratios of 2–5 are typical. The *smaller* the ratio of the atomic weights of the two isotopic atoms, the larger the primary isotope effect. This, of course, means that isotope effects involving the substitution of deuterium for hydrogen (k_H/k_D, ratio of masses $1:2$) and tritium for hydrogen (k_H/k_T, ratio of masses $1:3$) will be the largest observable. The great majority of isotope effect studies have been made by using the relatively cheap and available deuterium in place of hydrogen.

EXERCISE 14.3

Heavy water (D_2O) is frequently used for studies of solvent isotope effects. $H_2^{18}O$ is just as heavy, and is not very expensive, but is almost never used for such studies. Can you suggest a reason for the preference for D_2O?

The primary kinetic isotope effect can be a tremendous tool in the elucidation of reaction mechanisms. Not only does the detection of a primary isotope effect such as k_H/k_D tell us that the bond to hydrogen is being broken in the rate-determining step, but the magnitude and temperature dependence of this value can give us information as to the structure of the transition state.

An example of the use of primary deuterium isotope effects is given in the following reactions:

$$(CH_3)_2CHBr + NaOC_2H_5 \rightarrow CH_3CH{=}CH_2 + NaBr + C_2H_5OH$$

$$(CD_3)_2CHBr + NaOC_2H_5 \rightarrow CD_3CH{=}CD_2 + NaBr + C_2H_5OD$$

$$k_H/k_D = 6.9 \text{ at } 25°C$$

The detection of a substantial primary kinetic isotope effect definitely indicates that a C—H bond is being broken in the rate-determining step. This observation excludes many mechanistic possibilities for this elimination reaction. Thus the mechanism

$$(CH_3)_2CHBr \xrightarrow{\text{slow}} (CH_3)_2\overset{+}{C}H \xrightarrow[\text{fast}]{\text{NaOEt}} CH_2{=}CHCH_3 + EtOH + Na^+ + Br^-$$

would *not* show such an isotope effect, since the C—H bond is not broken in the rate-determining step. The observation of such a large kinetic isotope effect therefore excludes this as a possible mechanism for the reaction. (The correct mechanism for this reaction will be discussed in Section 17.6.)

Origin of the Primary Kinetic Isotope Effect. This effect is a result of the zero-point vibrational energy (E^0) of the molecule. A $0°K$, where nearly all molecular motion is frozen out, there still resides some vibrational energy in a bond. In other words, the atoms are still free to vibrate about an average bond length (Heisenberg uncertainty principle). The zero-point energy for a bond to a heavy atom is lower than for the light isotope; for example, the zero-point energy for a C—H bond is 8.3 kcal/mole, and for a C—D bond it is about 6 kcal/mole, making a difference of

~ 2.3 kcal/mole. Now consider a reaction involving the breaking of a carbon–hydrogen bond in the rate-determining step. The process should be more facile than breaking the same bond to deuterium, because of the 2.3-kcal difference in zero-point energy. In fact, if the transition state for this reaction involved the extreme situation of having the C—H (and C—D) bond completely broken, the difference in activation energies would be 2.3 kcal/mole, which corresponds to a $k_H/k_D = 48$ at 25°C. However, in ordinary cases this never occurs, because bond making also occurs in the transition state. Therefore, the transition states will show a zero-point energy difference which cancels a part of the zero-point energy difference of the ground state. Thus, the transition-state difference is always smaller than the ground-state difference. At 25°C, typical values for k_H/k_D range from 3 to 8. Figure 14.7 depicts the origin of the primary kinetic isotope effect.

Figure 14.7
Origin of kinetic isotope effect, k_H/k_D.

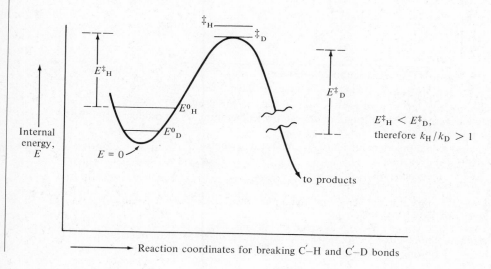

Reaction coordinates for breaking C′–H and C′–D bonds

PROBLEMS

1. Define and give a symbol (if any) for:
   (a) Free energy of activation
   (b) Rate constant
   (c) Mechanism
   (d) Intermediate
   (e) Catalyst
   (f) Kinetically-controlled reaction
   (g) Thermodynamically-controlled reaction
   (h) Primary kinetic isotope effect
   (i) Order of reaction

2. Derive the rate equations for the following reactions. (Rate expressions are ordinarily given in terms of the materials put into the reaction, and not in terms of intermediates that occur during the reaction, and this policy should be followed here.)

   (a) $A \xrightarrow{\text{slow}} [B + C] \xrightarrow{\text{fast}}$ products

   (b) $A + B \xrightarrow{\text{slow}} C \xrightarrow[+D]{\text{fast}} E \xrightarrow{\text{fast}}$ products

   (c) $C_6H_5CH_2CH_2Br + OH^- \xrightarrow{\text{slow}} C_6H_5CH=CH_2 + Br^- + H_2O$

3. A reaction has the following stoichiometry:

   $A + 2B + C \rightarrow D$

When A, B, and C were all present in concentrations of $0.1M$, the initial rate $(d[D]/dt)$ of the reaction was found to be 0.002 moles liter^{-1} sec^{-1}. When the concentration of A was doubled, the rate was 0.004, when the concentration of B was doubled, the rate was 0.002, and when the concentration of C was doubled, the rate was 0.008 moles liter^{-1} sec^{-1}. Assuming that the rate expression is of the form: rate $= k[A]^a[B]^b[C]^c$, deduce the rate expression, and calculate the rate constant k.

4. Consider the following competitive reaction: $C \rightleftharpoons A \rightleftharpoons B$. A free energy vs reaction coordinate diagram is given:

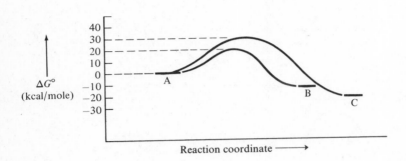

(a) If the reaction were run a short length of time at low temperature, which product would predominate? Why?
(b) Which product would predominate under thermodynamic control?
(c) What is $\Delta G^{\ddagger}$ for the reaction $A \rightarrow C$?
(d) What is $\Delta G^{\ddagger}$ for the reaction $B \rightarrow A$?
(e) What is ΔG^0 for the reaction $A \rightarrow B$?
(f) Calculate the amounts of B and C present after a reaction of A has gone to completion at 25°C under equilibrium control.

5. Draw an approximation of a free energy vs reaction coordinate diagram for the reaction represented by the following mechanism:

$$CH_2=CH_2 + Br_2 \xrightarrow{\text{slow}} H_2\overset{+}{C}-CH_2 + Br^- \xrightarrow{\text{fast}} BrCH_2CH_2Br$$

6. Repeat Problem 5 for the reaction

$$CH_3CH_2CH_2CH_2OH + HBr \underset{\text{fast}}{\rightleftharpoons} CH_3CH_2CH_2CH_2\overset{+}{O}H_2 + Br^- \xrightarrow{\text{slow}}$$

$$CH_3CH_2CH_2CH_2Br + H_2O$$

7. The rate of reaction of 3-bromopentane with sodium thiocyanate (NaSCN) is second order. If the rate is 3×10^{-6} moles per liter per second in a solution containing $0.1M$ RBr and $0.1M$ NaSCN, what would the rate be in a solution which is $0.2M$ RBr and $0.2M$ NaSCN?

Optional Problems

1. Derive the rate equations for the following reactions:

    (a) $A + B \underset{K_{eq}}{\overset{\text{fast}}{\rightleftharpoons}} C \xrightarrow[\text{slow, +D}]{} $ products

    (b) $CHCl_3 + OH^- \underset{K_{eq}}{\overset{\text{fast}}{\rightleftharpoons}} {}^-CCl_3 + H_2O \xrightarrow{\text{slow}} :CCl_2 + Cl^-$

2. The dimerization of benzaldehyde in the presence of cyanide ion as the catalyst (the *benzoin condensation*) has the following rate law: Rate $= [C_6H_5CHO]^2[CN^-]$.

The proposed mechanism is

$$C_6H_5\overset{\underset{|}{H}}{C}{=}O + CN^- \rightleftharpoons C_6H_5\overset{\underset{|}{H}}{\underset{CN}{C}}{-}O^- \rightleftharpoons C_6H_5\overset{H}{\underset{CN}{\bar{C}}}{-}OH$$

$$\| \quad C_6H_5\overset{H}{C}{=}O$$

$$C_6H_5\overset{\underset{|}{O}}{\underset{H}{C}}{-}\overset{OH}{C}C_6H_5 + CN^- \rightleftharpoons C_6H_5\overset{O^-}{\underset{CN}{C}}{-}\overset{OH}{\underset{H}{C}}C_6H_5 \rightleftharpoons C_6H_5\overset{HO}{\underset{CN}{C}}{-}\overset{O^-}{\underset{H}{C}}C_6H_5$$

Which step is rate-determining?

CHAPTER 15

REACTIONS OF ALKENES AND ALKYNES

Most organic chemists today spend most of their time carrying out organic reactions. In the chemical industry reactions are ordinarily carried out to furnish compounds which are useful for some practical purpose, and which can be prepared from materials which nature has chosen to furnish us in abundance. Many compounds are prepared in large tonnage amounts for use in the preparation of plastics, synthetic fibers, paints, and other commercial products. Other compounds are prepared in small amounts because they are suspected of having properties which may make them useful as pharmaceuticals, or because they are desired for study of their spectroscopic properties, or other properties which are scientifically interesting, or may prove to be of practical value.

The first 12 chapters of this text have discussed, from the point of view of their structures and physical properties, the organic molecules and molecular fragments with which the organic chemist commonly deals. Chapters 13 and 14 gave brief discussions of the thermodynamic and kinetic principles which govern the interconversion of these molecules and fragments. The next 9 chapters of this volume will be concerned with specific reactions which organic molecules undergo. A few simple chemical reactions occur in which just one bond is broken and remade, but typical organic reactions involve sequential events in which several bonds are broken and formed. These reactions are all subject to the laws of thermodynamics and to the principles of kinetics. Any reaction which proceeds does so because the system as a whole is able to achieve a lower energy by virtue of the reaction occurring. As has been explained earlier, however, the fact that thermodynamics would permit a reaction to occur does not necessarily mean that we are going to succeed in carrying out the reaction in the laboratory.

With the brief theoretical introduction of the previous chapters, we can now profitably study chemical reactions and try to fit into the framework of our previous understanding the wide variety of facts which are to be uncovered in the following chapters. It should be remembered, however, that historically, organic chemistry began as a purely experimental science. The early organic chemists knew nothing of thermodynamics or kinetics, and they did not have spectroscopic tools available to help them in their studies. They developed their science exclusively on the basis of the chemical reactions which compounds underwent. Even today, far more discoveries are made by the experimental chemist in the laboratory than are made by the theoretician.

The reactions of organic molecules are for the most part the reactions of functional groups. The double bond in ethylene undergoes pretty much the same reactions as does the double bond in 1-butene, or in styrene, or in vinyl bromide, or in most other alkenes. The substituents attached to the olefin may modify these reactions, but for the most part they do not really change them. Therefore, it proves expedient to divide our study of reactions according to the functional groups involved in the reactions. A study of the Table of Contents for Chapters 15–23 will show how this division has been made. We will commence this study with the carbon–carbon multiple bonds.

15.1 Additions to the Carbon–Carbon Double Bond

The chemistry of alkenes is very largely the chemistry of the carbon–carbon double bond. In Section 7.2 we learned that a carbon–carbon double bond consists of a strong σ bond and a weaker π bond. The π bond is represented by two rather diffuse lobes of electron density, one above and one below the plane defined by the six atoms (see Figure 7.4). The kinds of reactions that we would expect to occur with alkenes on the basis of thermodynamics are those in which the weak π bond is broken and is replaced by two new, stronger σ bonds. The geometry of an alkene is such that the π electrons are sterically quite accessible (Section 7.2), and such reactions are therefore often kinetically favorable also. A reaction of this type is called an *addition reaction*; it may be represented in its most general form as

$$\ce{C=C} + \text{X-Y} \rightarrow \underset{\underset{\text{X} \quad \text{Y}}{|\quad|}}{\ce{C-C}}$$

In the addition reaction, an unsaturated molecule and another reagent combine to give a single saturated compound. The product molecule contains two new σ bonds, whereas the reactant molecules possessed one π bond (the alkene) and one σ bond (the reagent X—Y).

We may now ask the question, What kind of reagents are best for participating in these addition reactions to carbon–carbon double bonds? The electron-donor (Lewis base) properties of the π bond in alkenes were discussed in Section 7.17. Quite obviously, reagents that tend to seek electrons (electrophilic reagents or Lewis acids) in chemical reactions would be expected to add most easily to the double bond of an alkene. *Electrophilic addition* is the characteristic reaction of alkenes, and a substantial portion of our discussion in this chapter will be devoted to the wide variety of such additions and their mechanisms.

In contrast, electron-donating nucleophilic reagents are quite unreactive toward carbon–carbon double bonds, unless there are substituents present on the olefin having a high degree of electron-attracting power. Addition reactions of this type will be examined in detail in Section 19.17.

Free-radical reagents—atoms or molecules containing an unpaired electron—are also mildly electrophilic and can undergo *free-radical additions* to alkenes. These reactions are quite general and will also be discussed in this chapter.

15.2 Hydrogenation of Alkenes

In several places previously (Section 7.10, Section 14.5) we have mentioned the catalytic hydrogenation of alkenes. Not only do quantitative data on heats of hydrogenation provide a useful measure of the relative stabilities of alkenes, but the hydrogenation reaction itself is a valuable preparative method for alkanes. This process is the most general way to convert a carbon–carbon double bond into a carbon–carbon single bond. Many other kinds of functional groups do not react under the normal conditions of hydrogenation, and we are able to carry out transformations such as that of an unsaturated alcohol into a saturated alcohol, an unsaturated ester into a saturated ester, or an unsaturated ether into a saturated ether.

Some typical examples of heterogeneous, catalytic hydrogenation are shown.

$$\underset{\underset{\text{CH}_3}{|}}{\overset{\overset{\text{CH}_3}{|}}{\ce{CH_3-C-CH_2-}}}\overset{\overset{\text{CH}_3}{|}}{\ce{C=CH_2}} + \ce{H_2} \xrightarrow{\text{Pd}} \underset{\underset{\text{CH}_3}{|}}{\overset{\overset{\text{CH}_3}{|}}{\ce{CH_3-C-CH_2-}}}\underset{\underset{\text{H}}{|}}{\overset{\overset{\text{CH}_3}{|}}{\ce{C-CH_3}}}$$

[Note how much more resistant the double bonds in an aromatic compound are to hydrogenation than are simple double bonds.]

The catalysts normally employed for the hydrogenation of alkenes to alkanes at low pressure (1–4 atm) and moderate temperature (0–100°C) contain noble metals such as platinum, palladium, or rhodium. Raney nickel, an active form of nickel (obtained by reaction of a nickel–aluminium alloy with aqueous sodium hydroxide, which dissolves out the aluminum and leaves a nickel powder with a large surface area), is mainly used for medium to high pressure work. Reductions over platinum employ the finely divided metal obtained by the reduction of platinum oxide. Palladium and rhodium catalysts are usually deposits of the metal on the surface of inert supports such as carbon, alumina, or barium sulfate. All of these catalysts apparently function by allowing the alkene and the hydrogen to be chemically adsorbed (weak bonding) on the surface. This brings the two molecules into close contact. Reaction occurs by simultaneous addition of a hydrogen atom to each carbon of the double bond; the alkane product is then rapidly desorbed from the surface.

The fact that catalytic hydrogenation is a reaction that takes place on a bulky metal surface has two other implications, each of which is well supported by experiment. The first is that the *fewer the number and size of the substituents* that are attached to the double bond, the more easily the compound will fit onto the catalytic surface, and the *faster* will be the rate of hydrogenation. Relative rates of hydrogenation of alkenes fall off in the order ethylene > monosubstituted > disubstituted > trisubstituted > tetrasubstituted double bonds. Thus selective hydrogenation of one double bond in the presence of another is often possible.

The second implication is that both hydrogens become attached to the same side of the double bond to give a product resulting from cis addition. Two examples of preferential cis hydrogenation are shown. The product of cis hydrogenation of *cis*-2,3-diphenyl-2-butene exists predominantly in the more stable conformation in which the phenyl groups are anti to one another.

Another reagent that also leads to cis addition of hydrogen to an alkene is *diimide* (HN=NH, an unstable substance which is generated *in situ*, Section 22.5). Diimide is sometimes used to advantage in situations where catalytic hydrogenation is impractical.

$$
\begin{array}{c}
\text{H} \diagdown \diagup \text{CH}_2\text{OH} \\
\text{C} \\
\| \\
\text{C} \\
\text{HOCH}_2 \diagup \diagdown \text{H}
\end{array}
+ [\text{HN}=\text{NH}] \rightarrow \text{N}_2 + \text{HOCH}_2\text{CH}_2\text{CH}_2\text{CH}_2\text{OH}
$$

Of course many other unsaturated functional groups can be catalytically hydrogenated, and such cases will be examined in later chapters.

15.3   Electrophilic Additions to Alkenes. Additions of Acids (H—Z)

Proton acids, H—Z, are typical of the electrophilic reagents that add to alkenes. In the appropriate medium sufficiently strong proton acids, such as sulfuric acid (H—OSO$_3$H), the hydrogen halides (H—Cl, H—Br, and H—I), and trifluoroacetic acid (CF$_3$COO—H) react readily with alkenes. Weaker acids such as water (H—OH) and acetic acid (CH$_3$COO—H) do not add by themselves, but such additions are catalyzed by the presence of a trace of a strong acid. (No stereochemistry is implied in the following.)

$\xrightarrow{\text{H}_2\text{SO}_4}$

$$
\begin{array}{c}
\mid\mid \\
-\text{C}-\text{C}- \\
\mid\mid \\
\text{H}\text{OSO}_3\text{H}
\end{array}
$$

Alkyl hydrogen sulfate

$\xrightarrow{\text{HBr}}$

$$
\begin{array}{c}
\mid\mid \\
-\text{C}-\text{C}- \\
\mid\mid \\
\text{H}\text{Br}
\end{array}
$$

Alkyl bromide

$\xrightarrow{\text{HCl}}$

$$
\begin{array}{c}
\mid\mid \\
-\text{C}-\text{C}- \\
\mid\mid \\
\text{H}\text{Cl}
\end{array}
$$

Alkyl chloride

$\xrightarrow{\text{CF}_3\text{COOH}}$

$$
\begin{array}{c}
\mid\mid \\
-\text{C}-\text{C}- \\
\mid\mid \\
\text{H}\text{O}-\text{C}-\text{CF}_3 \\
\| \\
\text{O}
\end{array}
$$

Alkyl trifluoroacetate

$\xrightarrow{\text{H}_2\text{O, H}^+}$

$$
\begin{array}{c}
\mid\mid \\
-\text{C}-\text{C}- \\
\mid\mid \\
\text{H}\text{OH}
\end{array}
$$

Alcohol

$\xrightarrow{\text{CH}_3\text{COOH, H}^+}$

$$
\begin{array}{c}
\mid\mid \\
-\text{C}-\text{C}- \\
\mid\mid \\
\text{H}\text{O}-\text{C}-\text{CH}_3 \\
\| \\
\text{O}
\end{array}
$$

Alkyl acetate

From a synthetic standpoint, the most important of these reactions is the acid-catalyzed hydration of alkenes to produce alcohols. With reactive alkenes, the hydration may be accomplished by stirring or shaking the alkene with a relatively dilute sulfuric or phosphoric acid solution. For less-reactive alkenes the hydration is done in two stages: The alkene is mixed with concentrated sulfuric acid to give the alkyl hydrogen sulfate (addition of sulfuric acid), which is then hydrolyzed by diluting the solution with water and heating. The alcohols ethanol, isopropyl alcohol, and t-butyl alcohol are made on an industrial scale by hydration of the appropriate alkene. Observe the following:

$$CH_2{=}CH_2 \xrightarrow{98\% \; H_2SO_4} CH_3CH_2OSO_3H \xrightarrow[\text{heat}]{H_2O} CH_3CH_2OH + H_2SO_4$$

$$CH_3CH{=}CH_2 \xrightarrow{80\% \; H_2SO_4} \underset{\underset{\displaystyle OSO_3H}{|}}{CH_3CHCH_3} \xrightarrow[\text{heat}]{H_2O} \underset{\underset{\displaystyle OH}{|}}{CH_3CHCH_3} + H_2SO_4$$

$$\underset{CH_3}{\overset{CH_3}{\diagup}}C{=}CH_2 \xrightarrow[25°C]{10\% \; H_2SO_4} CH_3{-}\underset{\underset{\displaystyle OH}{|}}{\overset{\overset{\displaystyle CH_3}{|}}{C}}{-}CH_3$$

The hydration of propylene *gives only isopropyl alcohol—not* n-*propyl alcohol*; the hydration of isobutylene *gives only* t-*butyl alcohol—not isobutyl alcohol*. These facts will be quite understandable when we discuss the mechanisms of electrophilic additions.

The typical aqueous solution is unsuitable for the addition of a hydrogen halide to an alkene because hydration of the alkene competes. What is usually done is to pass the dry hydrogen halide gas directly into the alkene or into a solution of the alkene in an in-different solvent such as ether or benzene. Another method is to generate the hydrogen halide *in situ* by adding the alkene to a concentrated phosphoric acid solution of an alkali halide.

$$\text{(cyclohexene)} + KI \xrightarrow{95\% \; H_3PO_4} \text{(iodocyclohexane)}$$

The addition under electrophilic conditions of a hydrogen halide to an alkene is seldom used as a preparative method for *simple* alkyl halides, because these compounds can usually be prepared more easily by other procedures.

The mechanism for all of the electrophilic additions listed at the beginning of this section may be presented in the most general sense as a two-step, polar process.

rate-determining electrophilic attack $\quad \underset{\diagup}{\overset{\diagdown}{}}C{=}C\underset{\diagdown}{\overset{\diagup}{}} + H^+Z^- \xrightarrow{\text{slow}} -\underset{\underset{\displaystyle H}{|}}{\overset{|}{C}}-\overset{|}{\underset{+}{C}}- + Z^-$

fast nucleophilic attack on a carbonium ion $\quad -\overset{|}{\underset{\underset{\displaystyle H}{|}}{C}}-\overset{|}{\underset{+}{C}}- + Z^- \xrightarrow{\text{fast}} -\overset{|}{\underset{\underset{\displaystyle H}{|}}{C}}-\overset{|}{\underset{\underset{\displaystyle Z}{|}}{C}}-$

The first step is rate-determining; it involves attack by a proton (the proton is the initiating electrophile in these additions) at the electron-rich π bond of the alkene to generate an intermediate carbonium ion. In the subsequent step, the carbonium ion reacts very rapidly with an available nucleophile.

EXERCISE 15.1

For each of the additions listed on page 307, what is the corresponding nucleophile?

It is not at all difficult to explain why the first step is the slow step in the sequence. Carbonium ions, especially simple alkyl cations, are reactive species (Sections 12.1, 12.2). A reaction involving the generation of such energetic intermediates will be quite endothermic with an accompanying high activation energy (slow). The reaction of a carbonium ion with a nucleophile (Lewis base) to give a covalent product is exothermic and is expected to have a low activation energy (rapid).

This mechanism is completely consistent with the fact that a strong acid is needed to cause the proton transfer. It is also consistent with the fact that if other nucleophiles are present in the reaction medium, these can compete for the carbonium ion. For example, if HCl is added to an alkene in acetic acid solvent, a *mixture* of an alkyl chloride and an alkyl acetate is formed, because the intermediate carbonium ion may be captured by either chloride ion or by acetic acid.

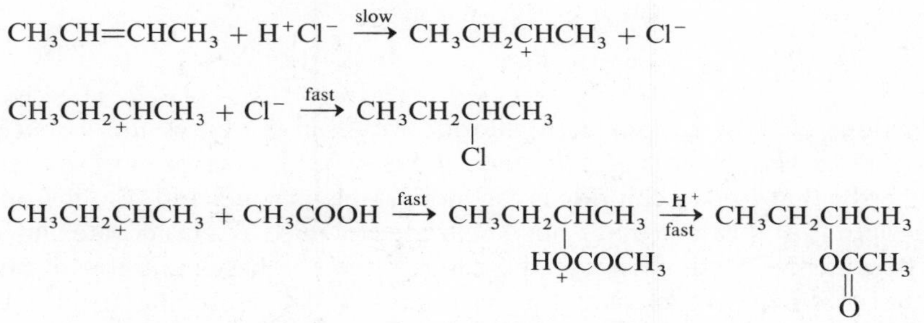

$$CH_3CH{=}CHCH_3 + H^+Cl^- \xrightarrow{\text{slow}} CH_3CH_2\overset{+}{C}HCH_3 + Cl^-$$

$$CH_3CH_2\overset{+}{C}HCH_3 + Cl^- \xrightarrow{\text{fast}} \underset{\underset{Cl}{|}}{CH_3CH_2CHCH_3}$$

$$CH_3CH_2\overset{+}{C}HCH_3 + CH_3COOH \xrightarrow{\text{fast}} \underset{\underset{\overset{+}{H}OCOCH_3}{|}}{CH_3CH_2CHCH_3} \xrightarrow[\text{fast}]{-H^+} \underset{\underset{\underset{O}{\parallel}}{\underset{OCCH_3}{|}}}{CH_3CH_2CHCH_3}$$

The stepwise polar mechanism can also account for the *orientation of addition*, the *relative reactivities of alkenes*, and the *rearrangements* which sometimes occur during the course of electrophilic additions. Since the key step in this mechanism is the transfer of a proton to the alkene to generate a carbonium ion, a knowledge of the properties of carbonium ions should be translatable into an understanding of stepwise electrophilic additions.

Addition of an unsymmetrical reagent, H—Z, to an unsymmetrical alkene can presumably give two products.

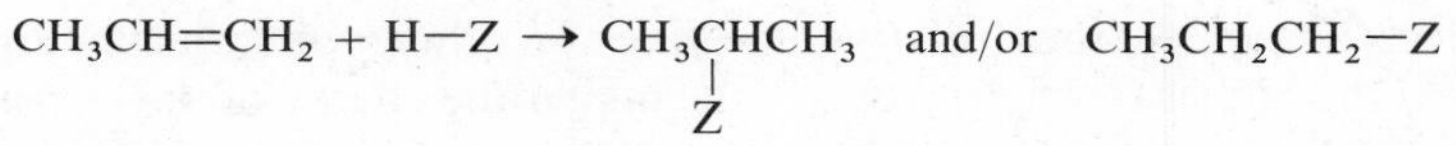

$$CH_3CH{=}CH_2 + H{-}Z \rightarrow \underset{\underset{Z}{|}}{CH_3CHCH_3} \quad \text{and/or} \quad CH_3CH_2CH_2{-}Z$$

In fact, however, such additions give predominant and often exclusive formation of only one of the two. We have already noted that the hydration of propylene gives only iso-propyl alcohol, and that the hydration of isobutylene gives only *t*-butyl alcohol. These are cases of specific orientation; following are two other examples ·

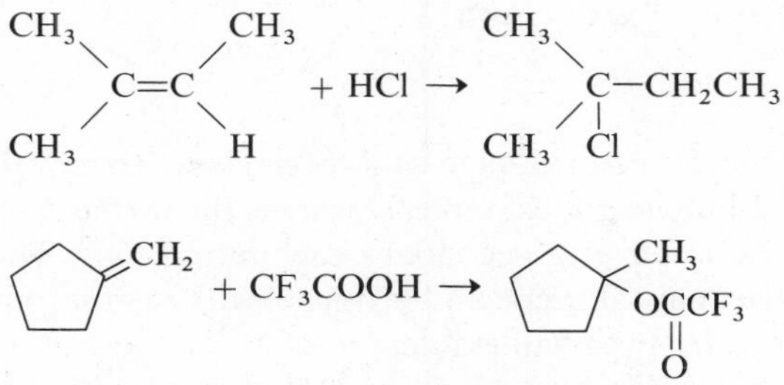

$$\underset{CH_3}{\overset{CH_3}{{>}}}C{=}C\underset{H}{\overset{CH_3}{{<}}} + HCl \rightarrow \underset{CH_3}{\overset{CH_3}{{>}}}\underset{Cl}{\overset{|}{C}}{-}CH_2CH_3$$

On the basis of this mechanism for stepwise, polar additions to alkenes and by using carbonium ion theory we can understand the orientations observed in the above reactions. Moreover, these theoretical principles should allow us to predict orientation in the stepwise addition of any unsymmetrical electrophilic reagent to an unsymmetrical alkene.

Consider the addition of hydrogen chloride to isobutylene. Two different intermediate carbonium ions could be formed by addition of the proton to one or the other of the double-bond carbons.

$$\underset{CH_3}{\overset{CH_3}{\diagdown}}C=CH_2 + H^+ \xrightarrow{slow} \underset{CH_3}{\overset{CH_3\diagdown\ \ \diagup CH_3}{\overset{+}{C}}} \xrightarrow{Cl^-} (CH_3)_3C-Cl$$

t-Butyl cation   t-Butyl chloride

and/or

$$CH_2=C\underset{CH_3}{\overset{CH_3}{\diagup}} + H^+ \xrightarrow{slower} \underset{CH_3}{\overset{CH_3\diagdown}{CH\overset{+}{C}H_2}} \xrightarrow{Cl^-} (CH_3)_2CHCH_2-Cl$$

Isobutyl cation   Isobutyl chloride

Subsequent reactions of these cations with chloride would give t-butyl and isobutyl chlorides; *but only t-butyl chloride is actually formed.* Why? Two explanations are open to us. It can either be that t-butyl chloride is the more stable product and results from *thermodynamic control*; or it can be that t-butyl chloride is formed at a faster rate under *kinetic control.* Because the reaction is not readily reversible under these conditions, it can be concluded that thermodynamic control is not operative. Therefore, the reaction is kinetically controlled, and the alkyl chloride which is obtained corresponds to the carbonium ion which is most easily formed (because the carbonium ion is generated in the rate-determining step).

We recall from our discussion in Chapter 12 that the order of relative stabilities of carbonium ions is tertiary > secondary > primary. When a proton is added to iso-butylene, we predict that the t-butyl cation will be generated more rapidly than the less stable isobutyl cation (a primary carbonium ion). We are not simply saying that the tertiary carbonium ion is formed faster than the primary carbonium ion because the former is more stable. Rather we are implying that the transition state leading to tertiary cation is of lower energy than that leading to primary cation, because the transition states resemble the cations and reflect their relative stabilities. In other words the lines in Figure 14.6 do not cross; the higher the energy of R^+, the higher the energy of the transition state leading to it (the *Evans–Polanyi principle*, page 299).

The *relative reactivities* of different alkenes in electrophilic addition reactions are determined in the same way. The order of reactivity of alkenes toward electrophiles is usually

$$\underset{R}{\overset{R}{\diagdown}}C=CH_2 > RCH=CHR \geqslant RCH=CH_2 > CH_2=CH_2$$

The 1,1-disubstituted alkenes (isobutylene is an example) will react faster than will 1,2-disubstituted alkenes (*cis*- and *trans*-2-butene are examples) because the former can give tertiary carbonium ions, whereas the latter give secondary carbonium ions. The 1,2-disubstituted alkenes and 1-alkenes (such as 1-butene and propene) will form secondary carbonium ions and thus will react faster than will ethylene.

EXERCISE 15.2

Why do you suppose propene and *trans*-2-butene react at approximately the same rate in such electrophilic additions?

An interesting situation arises with substituted alkenes of the type $Y-CH=CH_2$, where Y is a group that is *more electronegative* (electron-attracting) than hydrogen. The two possibilities for H—Z additions are

$$Y-CH=CH_2 \begin{array}{c} \xrightarrow{H^+} Y-CH_2-\overset{+}{C}H_2 \xrightarrow{Z^-} YCH_2CH_2Z \\ \\ \xrightarrow{H^+} Y-\overset{+}{C}HCH_3 \xrightarrow{Z^-} \underset{Z}{YCH-CH_3} \end{array}$$

One might expect that the reaction to give YCH_2CH_2Z would predominate, because the carbonium ion that has the positive charge located as far as possible from the electron-attracting group Y should be the more stable. However, if the atom of group Y which is attached to the doubly bonded carbons carries an unshared pair of electrons, the carbonium ion that has the positive charge on the same carbon is stabilized by electron delocalization. Note that the resonance form on the right gives each atom a full octet.

$$\overset{..}{Y}-\overset{+}{C}H-CH_3 \leftrightarrow \overset{+}{Y}=CH-CH_3$$

Groups or atoms such as CH_3O-, $Br-$, $Cl-$, $F-$ meet these requirements, and experimentally it is found that products of the type $ZYCHCH_3$ are formed. Apparently the conjugative stabilization of the cation more than compensates for the electron-attracting power of the substituents.

$$CH_2=CHBr + HCl \rightarrow \underset{Cl}{CH_3CH-Br}$$

unstable

These two offsetting phenomena also influence the reactivities of alkenes of this type. For $YCH=CH_2$, electrophilic additions are slower than those of ethylene if Y = halogen; but they are faster if Y = $-OR$, $-OOCR$.

EXERCISE 15.3

Predict the major product of the reaction $F_3C-CH=CH_2 \xrightarrow{HCl}$?

The addition of an acid to certain alkenes leads to a mixture of products, even though only one addition product should have been obtained on the basis of considerations regarding simple carbonium ion stabilities. This is because the initially formed carbonium ion will, if it is feasible to do so, *rearrange* to a more stable cation by the 1,2 shift of a hydrogen with its bonding electrons.

$$\underset{\overset{|}{C}-\overset{|}{C}-}{\overset{\overset{\displaystyle H}{|}}{\quad}\overset{+}{\quad}} \xrightarrow{\text{hydride shift}} \underset{-\overset{|}{C}-\overset{|}{C}-}{\overset{+}{\quad}\overset{\overset{\displaystyle H}{|}}{\quad}}$$

Such 1,2 rearrangements are quite prominent in carbonium ion chemistry when a primary or secondary cation can rearrange to the much more stable tertiary carbonium ion. For example, addition of HCl to 3-methyl-1-butene gives not only 2-chloro-3-methylbutane, but also 2-chloro-2-methylbutane.

$$CH_3-\underset{\underset{CH_3}{|}}{\overset{\overset{H}{|}}{C}}-CH=CH_2 \xrightarrow{H^+} CH_3-\underset{\underset{CH_3}{|}}{\overset{\overset{H}{|}}{C}}-\overset{+}{C}HCH_3 \xrightarrow{Cl^-} CH_3-\underset{\underset{H_3C}{|}}{\overset{\overset{H}{|}}{C}}-\underset{\underset{Cl}{|}}{C}HCH_3$$

3-Methyl-1-butene

2-Chloro-3-methyl-
butane

$$\downarrow \begin{array}{l} \text{rearrangement} \\ \text{via 1,2 H shift} \end{array}$$

$$CH_3-\underset{\underset{CH_3}{|}}{\overset{+}{C}}-CH_2CH_3 \xrightarrow{Cl^-} CH_3-\underset{\underset{CH_3}{|}}{\overset{\overset{Cl}{|}}{C}}-CH_2CH_3$$

2-Chloro-2-methyl-
butane

The proton addition step initially gives a secondary carbonium ion (methylisopropyl-carbonium ion). Rearrangement to a tertiary carbonium ion by a 1,2-hydride shift competes with reaction of the secondary carbonium ion with chloride ion. A mixture of two alkyl chlorides is obtained, one of which has an unexpected structure. Rearrangements of this type are in general limited to migration of a group from the carbon adjacent to the carbonium ion. Alkyl groups can migrate also, especially when there is no hydrogen properly positioned to do so, as will be discussed in Section 17.3.

15.4   Additions of Halogens. Stereochemistry

The halogens bromine and chlorine react smoothly with alkenes to give 1,2-dihalides (*vic*-dihalides) as addition products. The reaction is usually carried out by mixing the two reactants in an inert solvent like carbon tetrachloride or ether. As long as high

$$\underset{CH_3}{\overset{CH_3}{\diagdown}}C=CH_2 + Br_2 \rightarrow CH_3\underset{\underset{Br}{|}}{\overset{\overset{CH_3}{|}}{C}}-CH_2Br$$

$$CH_3(CH_2)_3CH=CH_2 + Br_2 \rightarrow CH_3(CH_2)_3\underset{\underset{Br}{|}}{C}HCH_2Br$$

$$ClCH=CHCl + Cl_2 \rightarrow Cl_2CHCHCl_2$$

temperatures and excessive exposure to light are avoided, a polar electrophilic addition process occurs. Free-radical additions of bromine (and of hydrogen bromide) to alkenes can also be made to occur; the mechanism for the homolytic addition of hydrogen bromide to alkenes will be discussed in Section 15.7. Iodine does not ordinarily undergo electrophilic additions to alkenes, but free-radical additions of iodine have been accomplished.

The polar mechanism for the addition of halogens to alkenes may be considered, as a first approximation, to be a simple two-stage process. The first step is an electrophilic attack of bromine at the double bond, resulting in heterolytic cleavage of the π bond of

$$\diagup\hspace{-0.3em}C=C\hspace{-0.3em}\diagdown + \ddot{\underset{\cdot\cdot}{Br}}-\ddot{\underset{\cdot\cdot}{Br}} \rightarrow -\overset{|}{\underset{|}{\underset{:\ddot{Br}:}{C}}}-\overset{+}{\underset{|}{C}}\diagdown + :\ddot{\underset{\cdot\cdot}{Br}}:^-$$

or (Cl—Cl)

$$-\overset{|}{\underset{:\ddot{Br}:}{C}}-\overset{+}{\underset{|}{C}}\diagup + :\ddot{\underset{\cdot\cdot}{Br}}:^- \rightarrow -\overset{|}{\underset{\underset{Br}{|}}{C}}-\overset{|}{\underset{\underset{Br}{|}}{C}}-$$

the alkene *and* of the bromine–bromine bond. A carbonium ion and a bromide ion are first generated, and then react in the second step (nucleophilic attack at a carbonium ion) to give the product. This mechanism resembles very closely that involved in the electrophilic addition of a proton acid to an alkene (page 308).

There is much evidence in support of the basic features of this process. First of all, halogens are very definitely electrophilic reagents; their most important reactions are with nucleophiles (in the additions to alkenes, the nucleophile is the electron-rich π bond of the alkene). As anticipated on the basis of electrophilic attack by halogen, the more highly alkyl-substituted alkenes add halogens faster than does ethylene. Secondly, if a cationic intermediate is involved in these reactions, other nucleophiles that might be present in solution should be able to react with this species in competition with the originally generated halide ion. For example, when the bromination of ethylene is carried out in an aqueous medium, not only is 1,2-dibromoethane produced, but also 2-bromoethanol. If sodium chloride is present, a mixture of 1,2-dibromoethane, 2-bromo-1-chloroethane, and 2-bromoethanol results. The bromination of ethylene in methanol gives both the dibromide and 2-bromo-1-methoxyethane.

$$CH_2{=}CH_2 \xrightarrow{Br_2} \underset{\underset{Br}{|}}{CH_2{-}\overset{+}{C}H_2} + Br^-$$

in H_2O → $BrCH_2CH_2Br + BrCH_2CH_2OH$

in $H_2O + Cl^-$ → $BrCH_2CH_2Br +$
$BrCH_2CH_2Cl + BrCH_2CH_2OH$

in CH_3OH → $BrCH_2CH_2Br +$
$BrCH_2CH_2OCH_3$

The student should recognize that attack at the carbonium ion by the electrically neutral, nucleophilic reagents water and methanol proceeds as follows:

$$BrCH_2\overset{+}{C}H_2 + R{-}\overset{..}{\underset{..}{O}}{-}H \rightarrow BrCH_2CH_2 {-}\overset{\overset{R}{|}}{\underset{..}{O}}{-}H \xrightarrow{-H^+} BrCH_2CH_2OR$$

$$(\text{or any } {-}\overset{|}{\underset{|}{C}}{^+})$$

The actual mechanism of the addition of Br_2 to an alkene must, however, be a little more complicated than that suggested above, which does not account for the stereochemistry of the addition of halogens to alkenes. Halogens add to alkenes to give *trans*-1,2-dihalides (Figure 15.1). Naturally, the fact that the addition of bromine to ethylene or to 1-hexene (page 312) is trans cannot be detected, because there are no diastereomers of 1,2-dibromoethane and 1,2-dibromohexane. In order to determine the stereochemistry of such addition reactions, we must utilize alkenes that show cis, trans isomerism (for example, cyclohexene and *trans*-2-butene in Figure 15.1), so that we may determine which diastereomeric product is formed.

It does not seem reasonable that a simple carbonium ion intermediate can account for trans addition of halogens to alkenes. This can be appreciated by examining the situation that would occur if the simple two-stage mechanism operated in the addition of bromine to *cis*-2-butene (Figure 15.2). The carbonium ion intermediate would be the 3-bromo-2-butyl cation, which has sp^2 hybridization. Bromide should be able to attack equally well from the top or bottom of this planar carbon cation, leading to a mixture of the *meso-* and *dl*-2,3-dibromobutanes (paths a and b in Figure 15.2). Moreover, there seems to be no real reason why rotation about the central bond could not occur to give a conformational isomer of the cation, which could also be attacked from either side

Figure 15.1
Trans addition of halogens to alkenes.

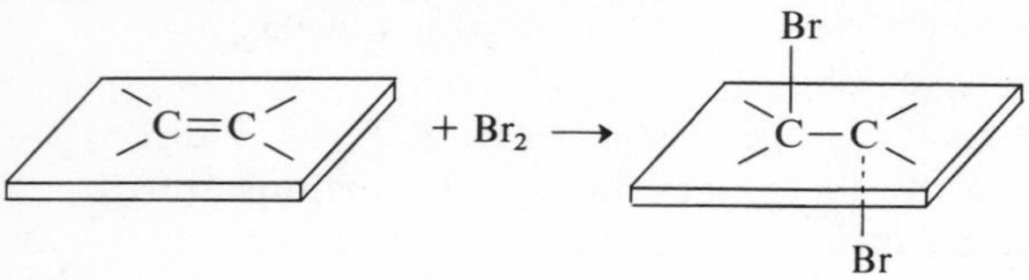

Examples:

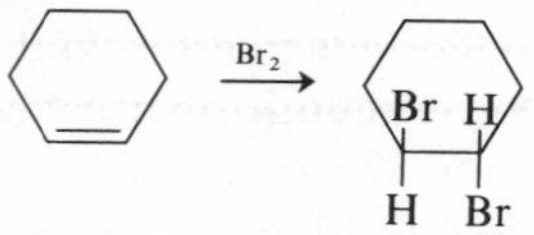

trans-1,2-Dibromocyclohexane

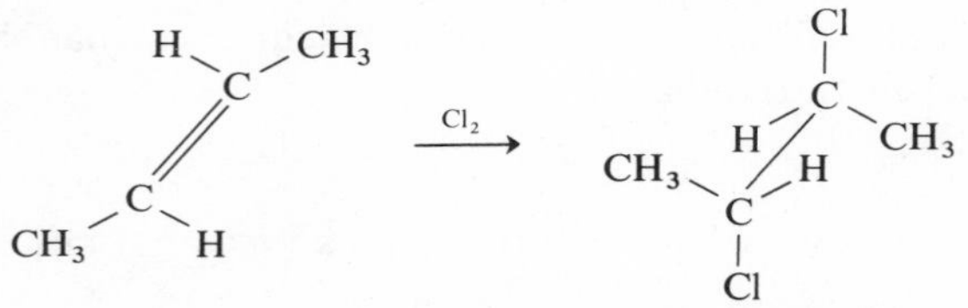

meso-2,3-Dichlorobutane

(paths c and d in Figure 15.2). However, only *dl*-2,3-dibromobutane (from exclusive trans addition) is formed in the reaction.

Figure 15.2
Possible products from addition of bromine to *cis*-2-butene if a simple planar carbonium ion is an intermediate.

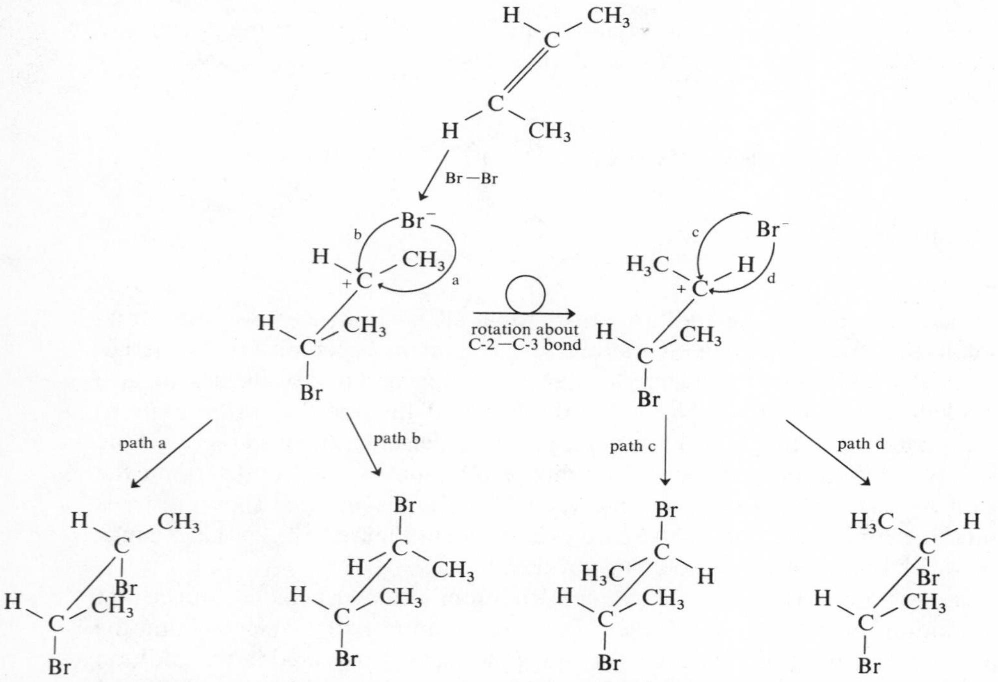

rotation about
C-2—C-3 bond

path a   path b   path c   path d

meso-2,3-Dibromobutane   *dl*-2,3-Dibromobutane   *meso*-2,3-Dibromobutane   *dl*-2,3-Dibromobutane
(not observed   (one enantiomer)   (not observed   (one enantiomer)
experimentally)   experimentally)

The trans stereospecificity in halogen additions to alkenes is now commonly explained in terms of a *bridged intermediate* in which bromine (or chlorine) is simultaneously bonded to both carbon atoms of the double bond. Attack of halide ion, or any other nucleophile, is forced to occur on the side opposite the bridging group, and this results in the formation of trans addition product.

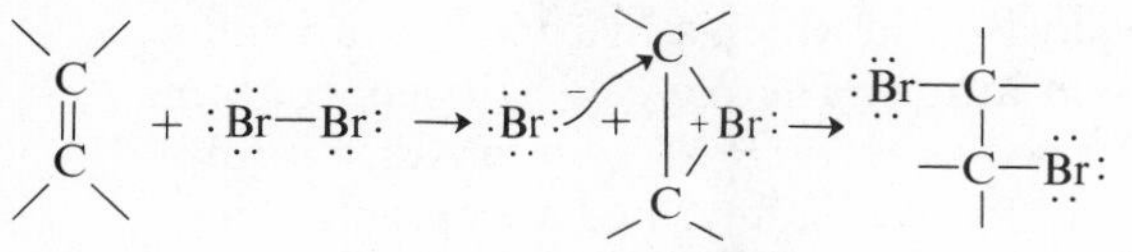

A bromonium ion

Any positively charged halogen ion is called a *halonium ion* (*chloronium, bromonium,* etc.). The bridged intermediate in this mechanism may be called a bromonium ion because the halogen formally carries the positive charge.

Halonium ions are not purely imaginary. Iodonium salts such as those shown are well known and quite stable crystalline compounds.

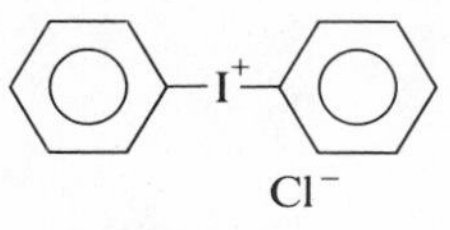

Diphenyliodonium
chloride

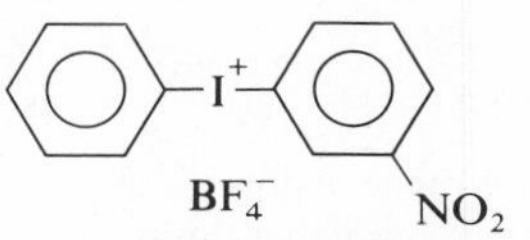

3-Nitrodiphenyliodonium
fluoborate

The corresponding bromonium and chloronium salts have been isolated, but little is known of their chemistry.

With the intervention of halonium ion intermediates, the exclusive production of *trans*-1,2-dibromocyclohexane from the bromination of cyclohexene, *meso*-2,3-dichloro-butane from the chlorination of *trans*-2-butene, and *dl*-2,3-dibromobutane from the bromination of *cis*-2-butene can be nicely accounted for.

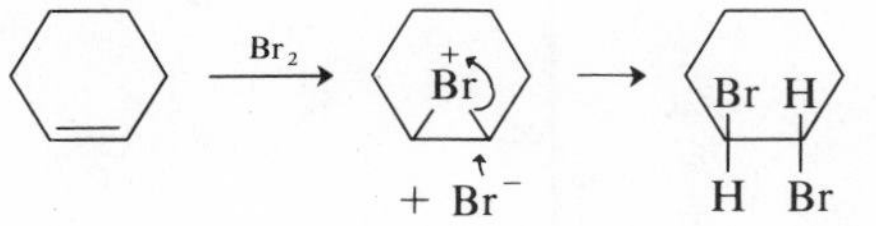

trans only

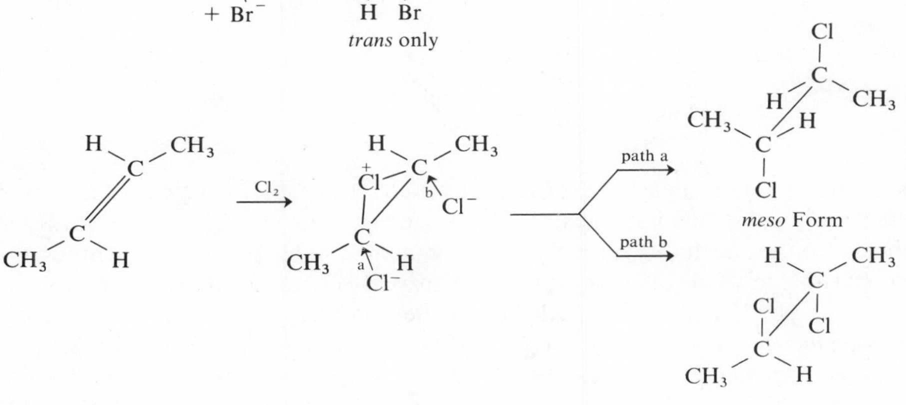

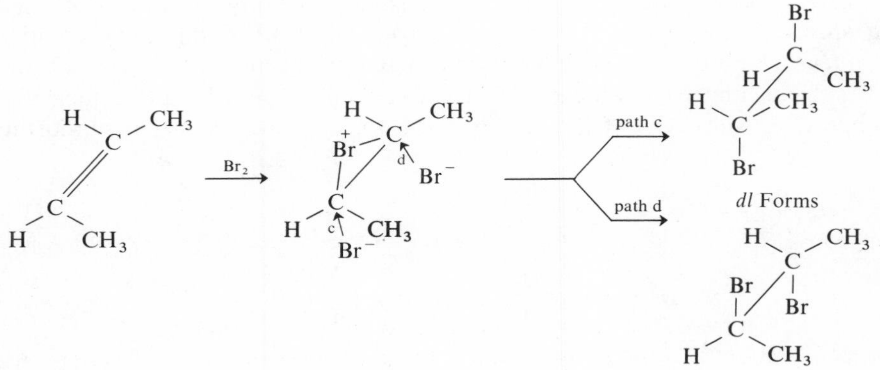

meso Form

dl Forms

15.5   Halohydrin Formation

Hypochlorous acid (HO—Cl) and hypobromous acid (HO—Br) are weak acids, and do not react in the way that strong proton acids do. Instead, they add to the double bond of an alkene to give products called *halohydrins* in which a hydroxyl group and a halogen atom are attached to adjacent carbon atoms. The oxygen–halogen bond in hypochlorous and hypobromous acids is polarized as $HO^{\delta-}$—$X^{\delta+}$. Halohydrin formation occurs by electrophilic attack at the π bond to give an intermediate halonium ion. Opening of this bridged ion from the opposite side by hydroxide or water produces the product.

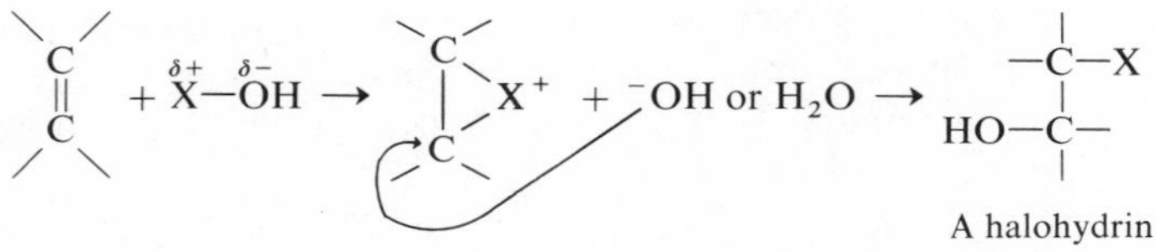

A halohydrin

$$CH_2{=}CH_2 + HOBr \rightarrow BrCH_2CH_2OH$$

2-Bromoethanol
(Ethylene bromohydrin)

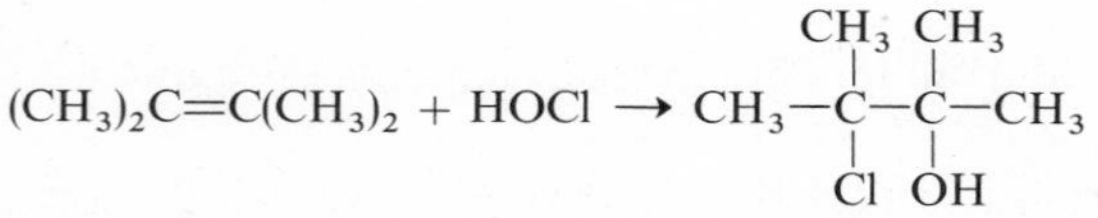

(3-Chloro-2,3-dimethyl-2-butanol)

Because a bridged halonium ion is the intermediate, additions of hypohalous acids to alkenes occur with trans stereospecificity.

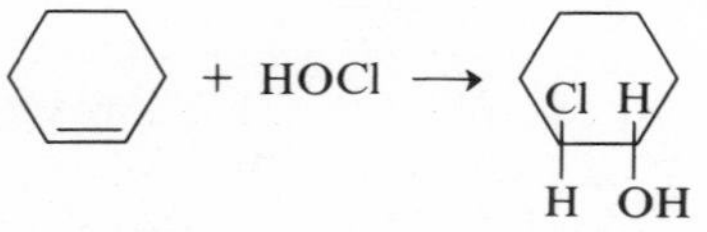

trans-2-Chlorocyclohexanol

Hypohalous acids are unsymmetrical electrophilic reagents. In their reactions with unsymmetrically substituted alkenes, two isomeric products are theoretically possible. Nevertheless, only one halohydrin is usually obtained. The preferred orientation is readily explicable in terms of carbonium ion theory. It is possible to extend the conclusions from the H—Z additions to alkenes in the following way: *In the electrophilic addition of an unsymmetrical and highly polarized reagent $Y^{\delta+}$—$Z^{\delta-}$ to an unsymmetrical alkene, the predominant product will be that predicted by the initial addition of Y^+ to give the more stable carbonium ion.* This generalization will hold regardless of whether the true intermediate is a simple, open carbonium ion (as in H—Z additions) or a bridged ion (as in HO—X additions). The reasoning is that a bridged ion generated by addition of Y^+ to an unsymmetrical alkene is "unsymmetrically bridged," and attack by the nucleophile $Z{:}^-$ will occur at the carbon atom that can best assist in supporting a positive charge.

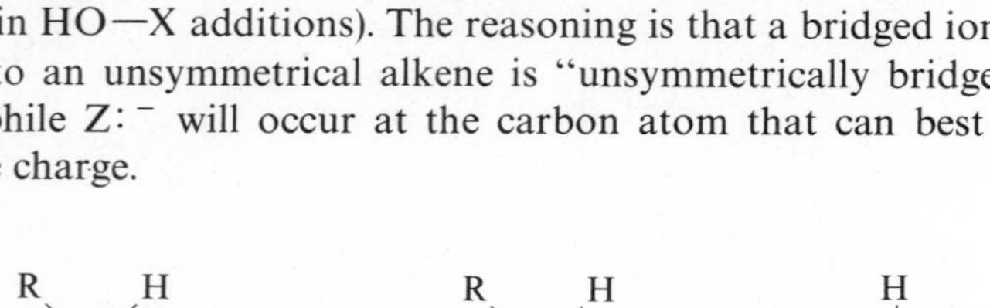

or

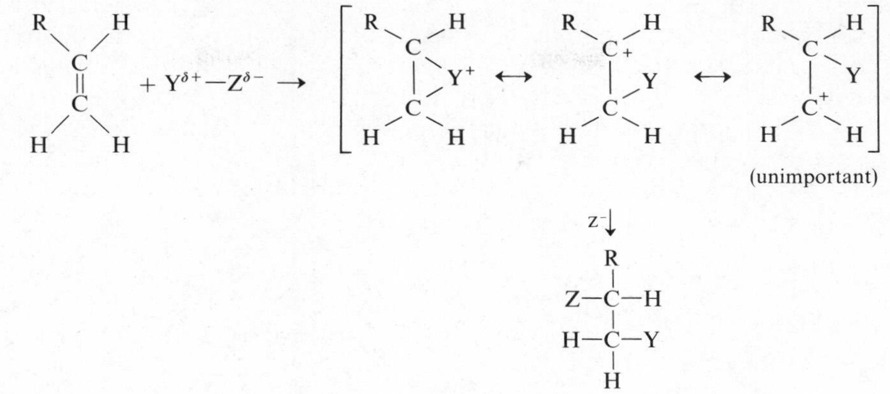

(unimportant)

Thus

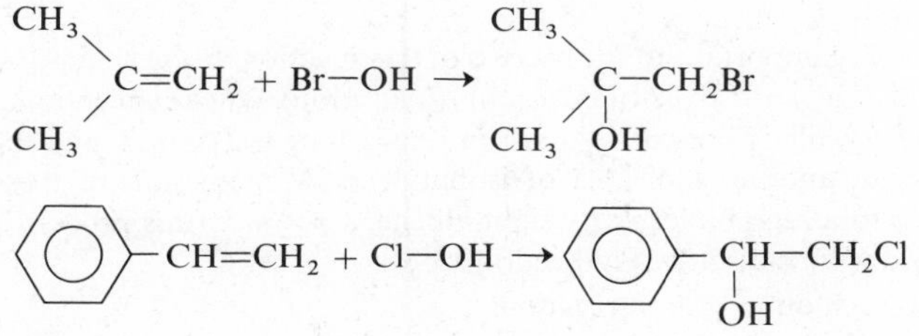

Other reagents which fall into this category are $I^{\delta+}-Cl^{\delta-}$, $NO^{\delta+}-Cl^{\delta-}$, and $ClHg^{\delta+}-Cl^{\delta-}$.

15.6   Dimerization

A carbonium ion is also an electrophilic species and as such is capable of initiating addition to the double bond of an alkene. The simplest case of a reaction that proceeds by this pathway is the *dimerization* of isobutylene. In the presence of 60 % sulfuric acid, isobutylene is transformed into a mixture of isomeric alkenes containing eight carbon atoms.

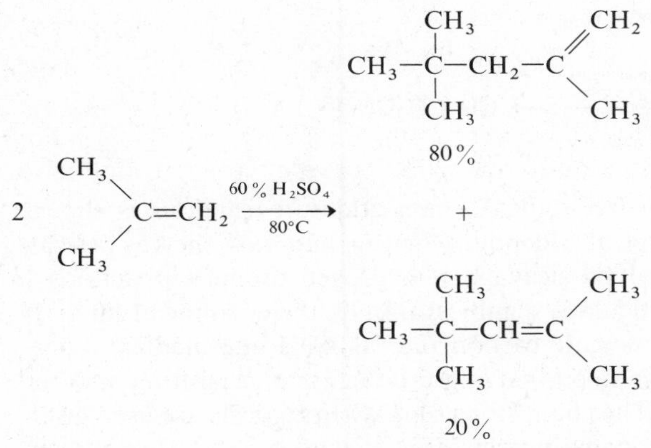

The less highly substituted olefin is more stable in this case, because the more highly substituted one has a serious repulsion as a result of the bulky *t*-butyl group being cis to a methyl.

The mechanism for this reaction involves three steps: (1) reversible addition of a proton to isobutylene to give the *t*-butyl cation; (2) addition of the *t*-butyl cation to another molecule of isobutylene to generate a new eight-carbon tertiary carbonium ion; and (3) loss of a proton to give the dimeric alkene. Loss of a proton from an adjacent carbon is a very common mode of reaction of carbon cations when reasonably good nucleophiles are not present. The tertiary carbonium ion produced in the dimerization reaction can lose a proton in either of two different directions, which results in the formation of a mixture of two, isomeric eight-carbon alkenes.

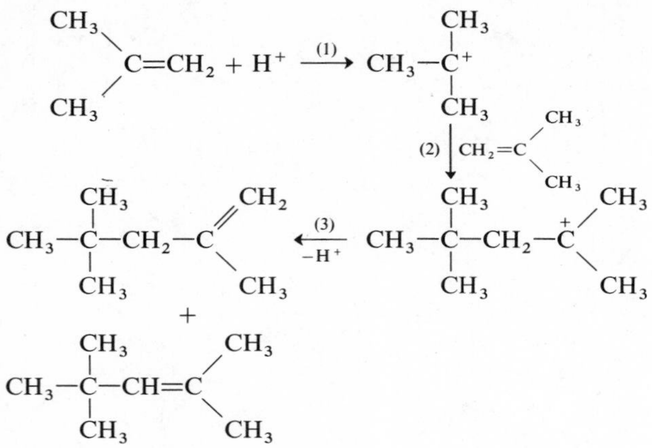

The strength of the sulfuric acid is very important to the success of this reaction. If the acid is too dilute, water will react with the *t*-butyl cation to give *t*-butyl alcohol (hydration). When concentrated sulfuric acid is used, no good nucleophile is present to assist in removal of the proton, and the eight-carbon cation may react with another molecule of isobutylene. A succession of these addition steps will eventually lead to a high molecular weight alkene, a *polymer* (this process is called cationic polymerization, and will be discussed in Section 15.14).

Other alkenes can also undergo such dimerization reactions.

15.7   Free-Radical Additions. Hydrogen Bromide

In the absence of peroxides and in polar media, hydrogen bromide undergoes a slow addition to propylene to form only isopropyl bromide, in complete accord with a carbonium ion mechanism (Section 15.3). When peroxides, light, or other free-radical initiators are present, rapid addition occurs to give *n*-propyl bromide—*the direction of addition is exactly opposite to that found in electrophilic additions.*

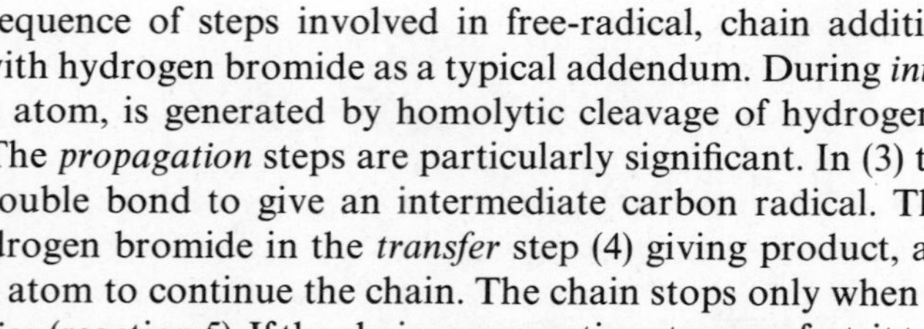

The sequence of steps involved in free-radical, chain addition reactions is shown below, with hydrogen bromide as a typical addendum. During *initiation*, the key radical, bromine atom, is generated by homolytic cleavage of hydrogen bromide (reactions 1 and 2). The *propagation* steps are particularly significant. In (3) the bromine atom adds to the double bond to give an intermediate carbon radical. This intermediate reacts with hydrogen bromide in the *transfer* step (4) giving product, and generating another bromine atom to continue the chain. The chain stops only when radicals are used up in *termination* (reaction 5). If the chain-propagating steps are fast, it takes only a few bromine atoms to generate many molecules of product (long reaction chains). This is the case with hydrogen bromide additions to alkenes, and only traces of peroxides are required.

Initiation steps

$$R-O-O-R \xrightarrow{\text{heat}} 2\,RO\cdot \qquad (1)$$

A peroxide   A radical

$$RO\cdot + H-Br \longrightarrow ROH + Br\cdot \qquad (2)$$

$$(\text{or } H-Br \xrightarrow{\text{light}} H\cdot + Br\cdot)$$

Propagation steps

$$\sideset{}{}{\mathop{C}}=C + Br\cdot \rightarrow -\overset{|}{\underset{|}{C}}-\overset{|}{\underset{|}{\underset{Br}{C}}}- \quad \text{(addition)} \tag{3}$$

$$-\overset{|}{\underset{|}{\underset{Br}{C}}}-\overset{|}{\underset{\cdot}{C}}- + H-Br \rightarrow -\overset{|}{\underset{|}{\underset{Br}{C}}}-\overset{|}{\underset{|}{\underset{H}{C}}}- + Br\cdot \quad \text{(transfer)} \tag{4}$$

Termination step

$$R'\cdot + R\cdot \rightarrow R'-R \tag{5}$$

(where R· and R'· are any atom or radical combination)

EXERCISE 15.4

Suggest three termination products (R'—R) that can be formed and will interrupt the above propagation sequence.

The direction of hydrogen bromide addition to an unsymmetrical alkene by the radical-chain mechanism is determined by which carbon of the double bond the bromine atom becomes attached to in the addition step (3). The two possibilities with propylene are

$$CH_3CH=CH_2 + Br\cdot \rightarrow CH_3\dot{C}HCH_2Br \xrightarrow{HBr} CH_3CH_2CH_2Br + Br\cdot$$

A secondary radical   *n*-Propyl bromide

or

$$CH_3CH=CH_2 + Br\cdot \nrightarrow CH_3CH-\dot{C}H_2 \xrightarrow{HBr} CH_3CHCH_3 + Br\cdot$$
$$\underset{Br}{|}\phantom{CH_2 \xrightarrow{HBr} CH_3CH}\underset{Br}{|}$$

A primary radical   Isopropyl bromide

The preferred pathway is determined by the relative stabilities of the intermediate radicals. Clearly, the 1-bromo-2-propyl radical, a secondary radical, is more stable than the primary 2-bromo-1-propyl radical, since the stabilities of alkyl radicals are in the order tertiary > secondary > primary (Section 12.5). The product is, therefore, *n*-propyl bromide.

MARKOVNIKOV'S RULE. *Long before the mechanisms for hydrogen halide additions to alkenes were understood, Markovnikov† published a paper, in 1868, entitled* Materials on the Question of the Mutual Effects of Atoms in Chemical Compounds. *In this work he formulated an empirical rule for predicting orientation in the "ionic" additions of hydrogen halides to unsymmetrical alkenes. This now famous rule accommodated all facts known then and even now. The* Markovnikov rule *states that* the hydrogen of a hydrogen halide will add to the carbon atom of the double bond having the greatest number of attached hydrogen atoms and the halogen will add to the least hydrogenated carbon of the double bond. *The principles discussed in Section 15.3 provide theoretical foundation for his statement, and allow us to expand the scope of the rule to account for orientation in all* electrophilic additions *to unsymmetrical alkenes. Statement of a generalized Markovnikov rule is given in Section 15.5. Additions to alkenes producing products in accord with this rule are commonly referred to as* Markovnikov additions *giving* Markovnikov products.

† V. V. Markovnikov. 1838–1904. Born in Russia. Kazan, Odessa, and Moscow Universities.

The fact that hydrogen bromide could add to unsymmetrical alkenes under certain conditions to give abnormal products—that is, products with structures opposite to those predicted by the Markovnikov rule—was reported in 1933. Credit for recognizing that the abnormal addition, sometimes called the "peroxide effect," occurs by way of a free-radical, chain process goes to Kharasch[†] *and Mayo.*[††] *Orientation in free-radical additions to unsymmetrical alkenes is predicted on the basis that the chain-carrying radical will add to the alkene to give the more stable radical intermediate These types of additions are sometimes called* anti-Markovnikov additions *and they lead to* anti-Markovnikov products.

The most efficient radical additions to alkenes are those for which long reaction chains exist, since each initiation can then lead to many molecules of the product. For the chain to be long, the two chain-propagating steps (reactions 3 and 4) must be rapid so that termination is improbable. Can we predict when we will have a favorable situation? A consideration of bond dissociation energies allows us to calculate the energetics of these two steps. For hydrogen bromide additions, the addition step (3) has $\Delta H = -11$ kcal/mole, and the transfer step (4) shows $\Delta H = -5$ kcal/mole. *Both* reactions are exothermic, and the overall sequence is exothermic by 16 kcal/mole. The activation energies for these kinds of exothermic processes are small; therefore, the reactions proceed rapidly.

Hydrogen iodide does not react with alkenes by a radical-chain mechanism. Consideration of the energetics gives us a clue as to why. Although the transfer step is exothermic ($\Delta H = -27$ kcal/mole), the addition step is endothermic ($\Delta H = +7$ kcal/mole). An iodine atom is too stable to add to alkenes efficiently. Free-radical additions of hydrogen chloride to alkenes can only be made to occur under special conditions. The energetics are opposite to those shown by hydrogen iodide additions, but the overall result is the same. With hydrogen chloride, the addition step is very exothermic (-26 kcal/mole); however the transfer step is endothermic ($+5$ kcal/mole), because the H—Cl bond strength is much greater than that of H—Br. Only hydrogen bromide has favorable energetics for both steps. These numbers are summarized in Figure 15.3.

Figure 15.3
Reaction coordinate diagram for propagation steps of the radical addition of HX to ethylene.

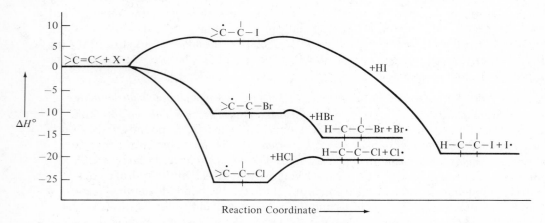

An atom with a lone pair of electrons will stabilize a radical on the attached carbon by resonance. Thus we find the following:

$$CH_2{=}CHCl + HBr \xrightarrow{h\nu} BrCH_2CH_2Cl$$

[†] Morris S. Kharasch. 1895–1957. Born Kremenetz, Ukraine. University of Chicago.
[††] Frank R. Mayo. Born 1908, Chicago, Illinois. U.S. Rubber Company, G.E. Research Laboratory, Stanford Research Institute.

And of course

$$CH_2{=}CHCH_2Br + HBr \xrightarrow{\text{peroxides}} BrCH_2CH_2CH_2Br$$

EXERCISE 15.5

Explain in detail the orientation obtained in the last two examples.

15.8 Other Radical Additions

There are numerous other compounds which can be made to undergo radical-chain addition to alkenes. The mechanisms of these reactions are similar to those of hydrogen bromide, and to predict orientation we only need to know the nature of the chain-carrying radical. Reagents such as hydrogen sulfide (H—SH), carbon tetrachloride (Cl—CCl$_3$), and bromotrichloromethane (Br—CCl$_3$) are especially useful for synthetic reactions.

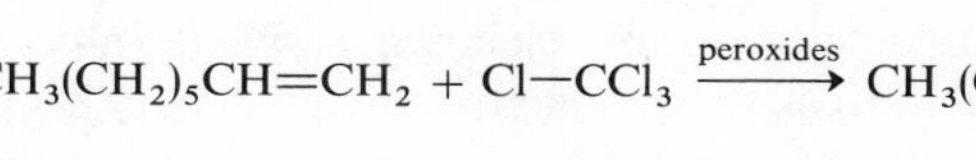

$$CH_3(CH_2)_5CH{=}CH_2 + Cl{-}CCl_3 \xrightarrow{\text{peroxides}} CH_3(CH_2)_5\underset{\underset{Cl}{|}}{C}HCH_2CCl_3$$

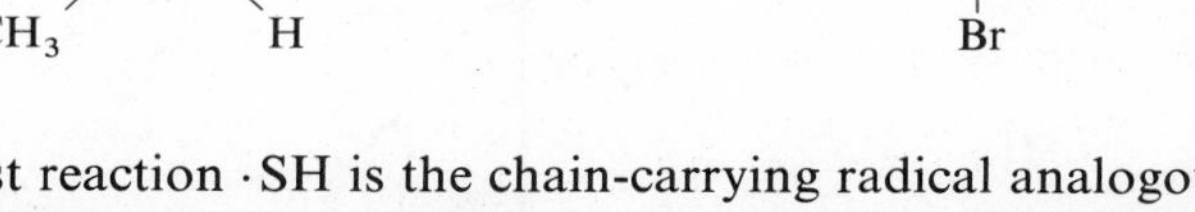

In the first reaction ·SH is the chain-carrying radical analogous to X· in the hydrogen halide additions. In each of the last two examples, ·CCl$_3$ is the chain-carrying radical.

From a consideration of the energetics, it can be predicted, and experimentally verified, that radical-chain additions of water (H—OH) and ammonia (H—NH$_2$) to alkenes will not occur. Thus the anti-Markovnikov hydration or amination of an alkene by a radical process is not synthetically feasible.

15.9 Hydroboration of Alkenes

Several Group III hydrides will add smoothly to alkenes to give trialkyl metal compounds. Diborane (B$_2$H$_6$) additions have been studied most extensively. In such reactions, diborane functions as if it were the hypothetical monomer, borane (BH$_3$). The addition proceeds in a stepwise fashion via successive additions of each boron–hydrogen bond to the alkene. In the case of highly hindered alkenes, the reaction may stop after one or two additions.

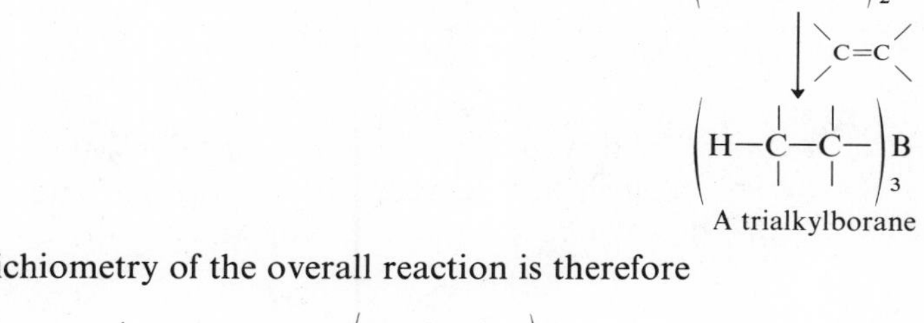

A trialkylborane

The stoichiometry of the overall reaction is therefore

This reaction, discovered and developed by H. C. Brown,† is called *hydroboration*; it is of tremendous synthetic utility because the trialkylboron compounds undergo many useful transformations. Most often the addition products are not isolated, but are treated in the same reaction vessel with the necessary reagents to carry out further conversions.

> The solvents used for hydroboration are ethers, particularly tetrahydrofuran and diethylene glycol methyl ether ["diglyme," $CH_3O(CH_2)_2O(CH_2)_2OCH_3$]. Diborane can be generated by the reaction between sodium borohydride ($NaBH_4$) and boron trifluoride (BF_3), either *in situ* (in the presence of the alkene) or in a separate vessel.

There are two significant aspects of hydroboration that greatly enhance the usefulness of the reaction. With an unsymmetrically substituted alkene such as 1-butene, hydroboration proceeds so that the boron becomes preferentially attached to the less-substituted carbon atom of the double bond.

$$6\ CH_3CH_2CH{=}CH_2 + B_2H_6 \longrightarrow 2\ (CH_3CH_2CH_2CH_2)_3B$$

Tri-n-butylborane

This is consistent with electrophilic character in the addition, because a boron–hydrogen bond is polarized as $H^{\delta-}{-}B^{\delta+}$ (e.g., the hydrogen is more electronegative than boron).

Hydroboration is a stereospecific reaction; the hydrogen and the boron become attached to the *same side of the double bond*. This overall cis-addition is best explained in terms of a *one-step, four-center* process (Figure 15.4).

Figure 15.4
The cis addition mechanism for hydroboration.

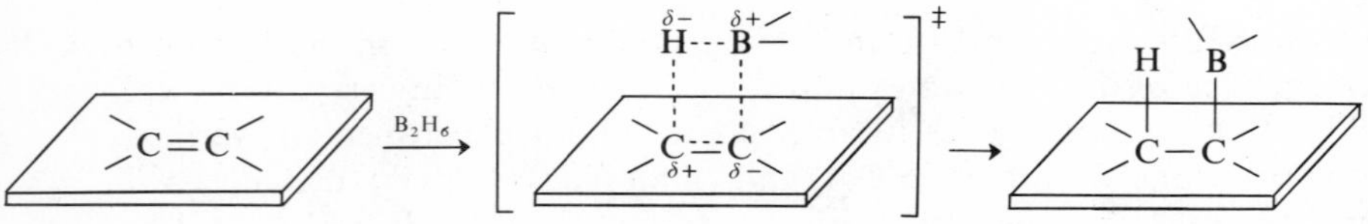

Example:

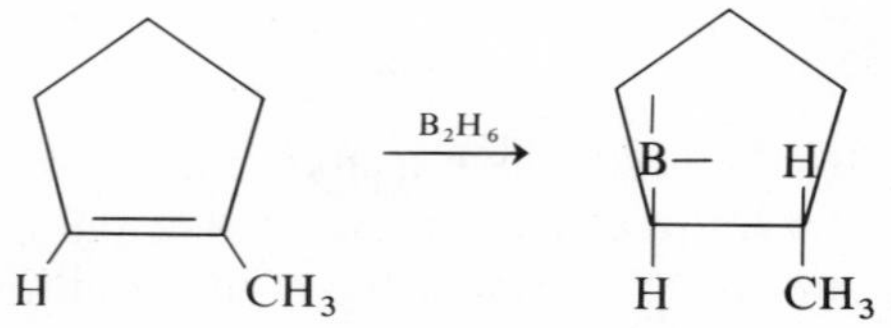

Carbonium ions are not intermediates in hydroboration; therefore, rearrangements do not occur.

One of the most important of the general reactions of alkylboron compounds is oxidation with alkaline hydrogen peroxide to the corresponding alcohol.

$$R_3B + 3\,H_2O_2 \xrightarrow[25°]{^-OH} 3\,R{-}OH + B(OH)_3$$

If the hydroboration reaction is coupled with a subsequent oxidation, "anti-Markovnikov" hydration (addition of water) of an alkene is achieved. Furthermore, the oxidation reaction is stereospecific; and anti-Markovnikov, cis addition of water is the overall

---

† Herbert C. Brown. Born 1922, London, England. Wayne State and Purdue Universities.

result with diastereomeric alkenes. Examples of the *hydroboration–oxidation* sequence are

$$CH_3CH_2CH_2CH{=}CH_2 \xrightarrow{B_2H_6} \xrightarrow{H_2O_2, \ ^-OH} CH_3CH_2CH_2CH_2CH_2OH$$

$$\underset{\underset{CH_3}{|}}{CH_3CH_2C}{=}CH_2 \xrightarrow{B_2H_6} \xrightarrow{H_2O_2, \ ^-OH} \underset{\underset{CH_3}{|}}{CH_3CH_2CHCH_2OH}$$

Mechanism. The generally accepted mechanism for the alkaline hydrogen peroxide oxidation of an organoborane involves nucleophilic attack by the hydroperoxide anion, leading to an intermediate hydroperoxyboron species which then rearranges to a borate ester. Subsequent alkaline hydrolysis of the borate gives the alcohol.

$$R_2B{-}OR \xrightarrow[\substack{repeat \\ twice}]{^-OOH} \underset{A \ borate}{(RO)_3B} \xrightarrow{3H_2O} 3\,ROH + B(OH)_3$$

The alkylboranes are stable to water, to aqueous mineral acids, and to aqueous alkalis. However, they are readily cleaved to alkanes by the action of carboxylic acids (acetic and propionic acids are most often used). Therefore hydroboration–acid hydrolysis is a means of effecting cis hydrogenation of alkenes (and also alkynes, Section 15.15). That the hydrogenation is indeed cis is shown in the reaction with deuterated diborane.

Mechanism. Cleavage of the carbon–boron bond by protonation may be considered an example of electrophilic substitution of boron by hydrogen. A six-center mechanism can be proposed which is consistent with the observations that the reaction proceeds with retention of configuration at carbon and that carboxylic acids are more effective than mineral acids.

Synthetic Reactions of Organoboranes. There are numerous other reactions which make organo-boranes highly versatile synthetic intermediates:

Amination

$$\diagdown B{-}R + H_2NOSO_3H \longrightarrow R{-}NH_2$$

Hydroxylamine-*O*-
sulfonic acid

Alkylation of α-haloesters and α-haloketones

$$\diagdown B{-}R + BrCH_2\overset{\overset{O}{\|}}{C}{-}OR' \xrightarrow{\text{KO-}t\text{-Bu}} RCH_2\overset{\overset{O}{\|}}{C}{-}OR'$$

$$\diagdown B{-}R + BrCH_2\overset{\overset{O}{\|}}{C}R' \xrightarrow{\text{KO-}t\text{-Bu}} RCH_2\overset{\overset{O}{\|}}{C}R'$$

Carbonylation
  to ketones

$$-B\diagup^{R}_{\diagdown R} \xrightarrow[\text{H}_2\text{O, 100°C}]{\text{CO}} \xrightarrow[\text{H}_2\text{O}_2]{^-\text{OH}} R{-}\overset{\overset{O}{\|}}{C}{-}R$$

  to aldehydes

$$\diagdown B{-}R \xrightarrow[\text{LiHAl(O-}t\text{-Bu)}_3]{\text{CO}} \xrightarrow[\text{buffer}]{\text{H}_2\text{O}_2} R{-}\overset{\overset{O}{\diagup\!\!\!\diagdown}}{C}\diagdown_H$$

  to trialkylcarbinols

$$R{-}\overset{\overset{R}{|}}{\underset{|}{B}}_{R} \xrightarrow[\text{100°C}]{\text{CO}} \xrightarrow[\text{H}_2\text{O}_2]{^-\text{OH}} R_3C{-}OH$$

Each of these electrophilic substitution reactions proceeds with retention of configuration at carbon.

Aluminum–hydrogen bonds also react with alkenes, to give trialkylaluminum compounds. The chemistry is similar to that in hydroboration. Since aluminum is cheaper than boron, organo-aluminum chemistry is of greatest interest to the chemical industry. Another valuable reaction is represented by the addition of carbon–aluminum bonds to ethylene. The product, a mixture of medium molecular weight tri-*n*-alkylaluminums, can be oxidized to primary alcohols of a size useful in the manufacture of detergents.

$$Al(C_2H_5)_3 + n\,CH_2{=}CH_2 \xrightarrow{\text{pressure}} \left[CH_3CH_2{-}(CH_2CH_2)_{\overline{n}}\right]_3 Al$$

$$\text{air}\downarrow$$

$$CH_3CH_2(CH_2CH_2)_nOH$$

(where $n = 3$ to 6)

15.10   Epoxidation, Hydroxylation, and Ozonolysis

Oxidations of alkenes can provide a useful route to compounds having oxygen attached to the originally doubly bonded carbons. Several different types of oxidizing agents are employed, depending upon the nature of the product desired.

When an alkene is allowed to react with an organic peracid (Sections 8.1, 20.16), the π bond is broken and a three-membered cyclic ether, called an *epoxide* or *oxirane*, results. Typical of the peracids that are used are perbenzoic ($C_6H_5CO_3H$), mono-perphthalic (*o*-HOOC-$C_6H_4CO_3H$), and peracetic (CH_3CO_3H) acids.

A peracid   An epoxide
(oxirane)

Cyclohexene
oxide

Organic peracids are known to be electrophilic species; therefore, the rate of their reactions with alkenes increases with substitution of electron-releasing groups (e.g., alkyl groups) at the double bond. Alkenes with three or four alkyl substituents are readily epoxidized with peracids, whereas terminal alkenes ($RCH{=}CH_2$) react more slowly. The epoxidation of alkenes with peracids is thought to proceed by the pathway shown.

In accord with this mechanism are the observations that peracids having strongly electron-withdrawing groups (such as trifluoroperacetic acid, CF_3CO_3H) cause epoxidation with enhanced rates, and that the epoxidation reaction is not catalyzed by strong acids.

The most striking demonstration of the electrophilic nature of a peracid is the fact that alkenes which are conjugated with the strongly electron-withdrawing carbonyl group

do not react to give epoxides, because resonance makes the alkene double bond highly electron-deficient.

The epoxidation of alkenes with peracids is a stereospecific reaction, proceeding via cis addition to the double bond.

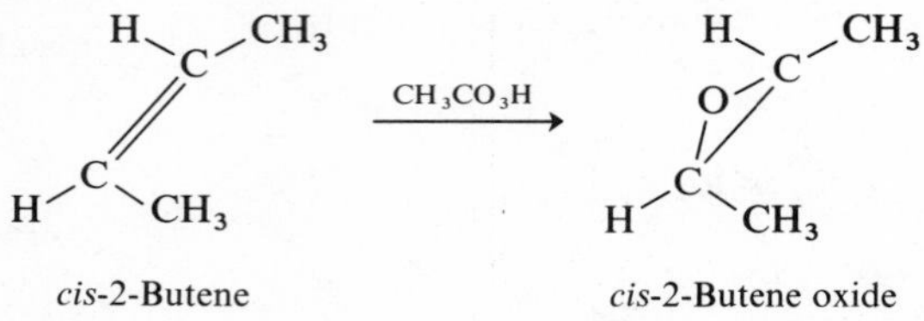

cis-2-Butene   *cis*-2-Butene oxide

Depending upon the peracid employed and upon the reaction conditions, the epoxide first formed may not survive as such, but may undergo ring-opening to give a 1,2-hydroxy ester. Hydrolysis of this product leads to a 1,2-diol (a *vicinal glycol*).

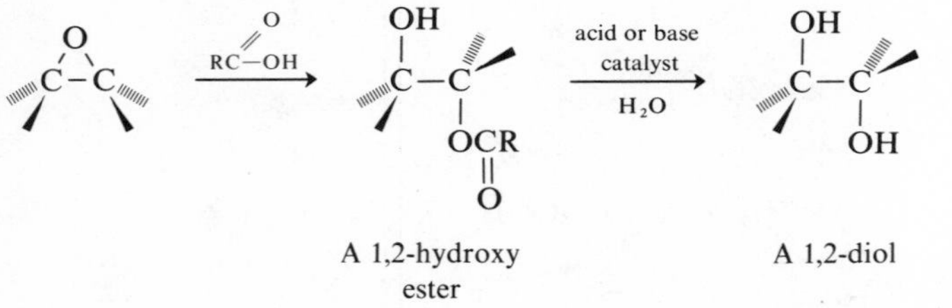

A 1,2-hydroxy   A 1,2-diol
ester

For example, when the epoxidation of an alkene is carried out with performic acid, the epoxide cannot be isolated because it rapidly reacts to give a hydroxyformate, as a result of the high acidity of formic acid. The overall sequence of reaction of an alkene with 30–90% hydrogen peroxide and formic acid (via HCOOOH), followed by alkaline hydrolysis to the 1,2-diol, results in the net addition of two –OH groups to the double bond. This process is called *hydroxylation* of the alkene. Most importantly, the stereo-chemistry of the two key stages—the epoxidation, which is cis, and the opening of the epoxide, which involves inversion at one of the carbon atoms—provides a clean method for trans hydroxylation.

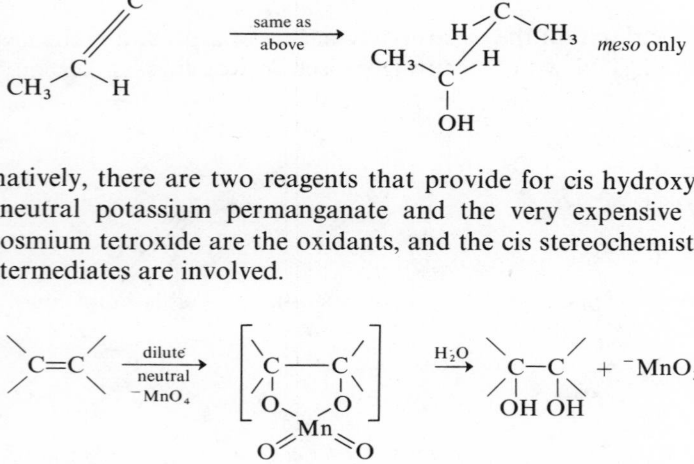

trans only

meso only

Alternatively, there are two reagents that provide for cis hydroxylation of alkenes. Dilute, neutral potassium permanganate and the very expensive and highly toxic reagent osmium tetroxide are the oxidants, and the cis stereochemistry results because cyclic intermediates are involved.

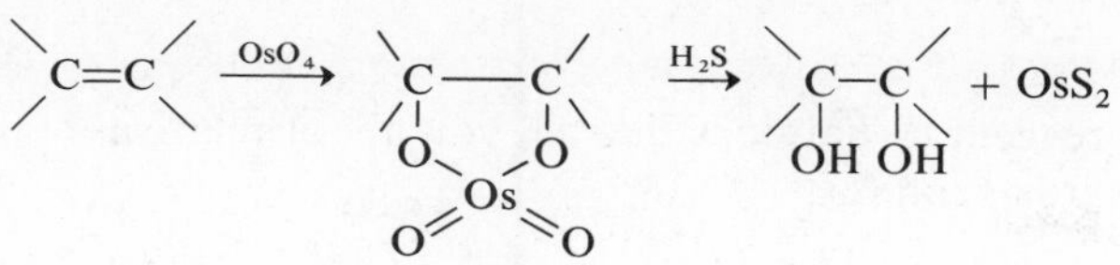

Thus

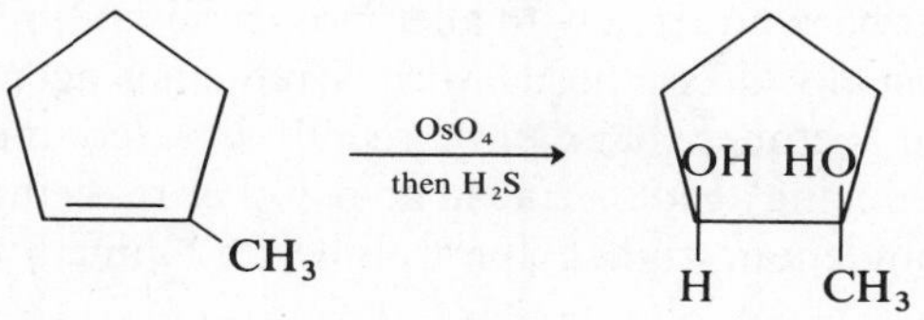

The hydroxylation with OsO_4 is quite clean. On the other hand, $KMnO_4$ reacts with vicinal diols to give ketones or carboxylic acids, and it is difficult to stop the reaction at the diol stage.

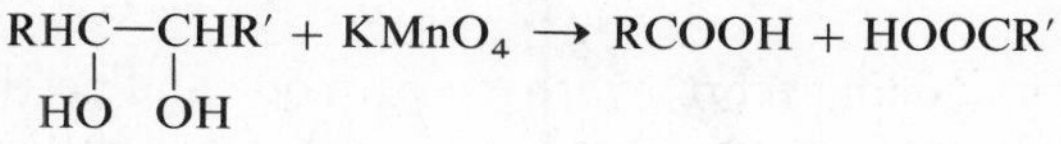

$$RHC—CHR' + KMnO_4 \rightarrow RCOOH + HOOCR'$$
$$\underset{HO\ \ \ OH}{|\ \ \ \ \ |}$$

EXERCISE 15.6

Show with perspective drawings that the hydroxylation of *trans*-2-butene with OsO_4 gives *dl*-2,3-butanediol.

The reaction between alkenes and ozone occurs readily at low temperatures to cleave the double bond. The product obtained is called an ozonide (*normal ozonide*).

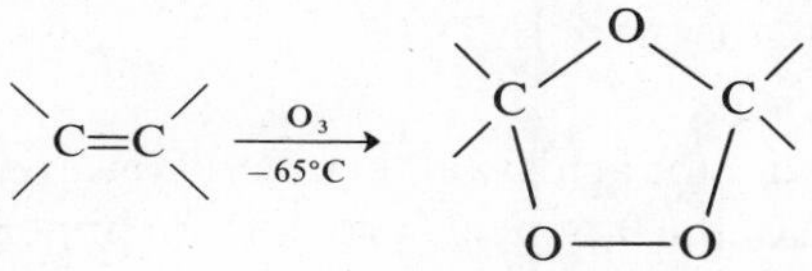

An ozonide

Ozonization apparently proceeds in several stages. First, electrophilic addition of ozone produces the unstable cyclic *molozonide* in which the π bond of the alkene has been replaced by two carbon–oxygen bonds. The molozonide decomposes into two fragments, which then may recombine in an alternative way to give the ozonide. This is illustrated below for 1-butene.

Ozone: $\overset{+}{O}=\overset{+}{O}-\overset{-}{O} \leftrightarrow \overset{+}{O}-O-\overset{-}{O} \leftrightarrow \overset{-}{O}-O-\overset{+}{O}$

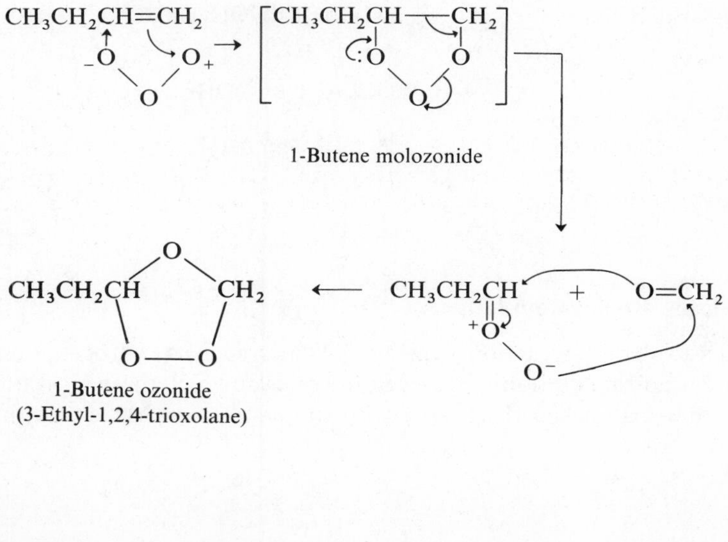

1-Butene molozonide

1-Butene ozonide
(3-Ethyl-1,2,4-trioxolane)

EXERCISE 15.7

Ozone is an electrophilic reagent. What does this tell you about relative reactivities of alkenes towards ozone?

Ozonides, like most compounds containing oxygen–oxygen bonds (*peroxidic* bonds), are hazardous. Obviously, ozonizations must be conducted with all appropriate caution. Ozonides are seldom isolated. They are usually decomposed with a reducing agent (*reductive work-up*) to yield aldehydes and/or ketones that can be readily isolated and identified. The most commonly employed reducing agent is zinc in acid. Other reducing agents used include hydrogen-palladium, iodide ion, triphenylphosphine, and dimethyl sulfide.

Sometimes the ozonide is decomposed by adding more hydrogen peroxide and acetic acid (*oxidative work-up*), and any aldehyde product is oxidized to an acid, which is then isolated.

The method can be used preparatively for aldehydes (or acids) and ketones. However, the great utility of ozonization is that identification of the fragments provides an important method of locating the position of a double bond in an alkene of unknown structure.

$$(CH_3)_2CHCH_2CH_2CH_2CH=CH_2 \xrightarrow[\text{2. H}_2\text{O, Zn}]{\text{1. O}_3} (CH_3)_2CHCH_2CH_2CH_2CHO + CH_2O$$

$$CH_3(CH_2)_7CH=CH(CH_2)_7C\!\!\begin{array}{c}O\\\diagup\\\diagdown\\OH\end{array} \xrightarrow[\text{2. H}_2\text{O}_2/\ \text{acetic acid}]{\text{1. O}_3} CH_3(CH_2)_7COOH$$
$$+$$
$$HOOC(CH_2)_7COOH$$

15.11   Additions to Dienes. Conjugate Additions

Conjugated dienes undergo all of the reactions typical of alkenes, such as hydrogenation, and electrophilic and free-radical additions. However, the rates at which these reactions occur with 1,3-dienes are usually faster than those with simple alkenes. Moreover, the products resulting from two-step addition reactions are usually mixtures, resulting from competing *1,2 addition* (on adjacent carbon atoms) and *1,4* (or *conjugate*) *addition* pathways.

Consider as a typical example the addition of hydrogen chloride to butadiene. Electrophilic attack of a proton should lead initially to the most stable cationic intermediate. With 1,3-dienes, addition of the proton to a terminal carbon atom of the conjugated system will generate an allylic cation—clearly the most stable of the possible carbonium ions. The allylic cation is resonance-stabilized; the positive charge resides mainly on two carbon atoms. Attack at one of these positions by chloride ion will give 3-chloro-1-butene (the 1,2-addition product), and attack at the other will give 1-chloro-2-butene (the 1,4 adduct).

$$CH_2=CH-CH=CH_2 \xrightarrow{\text{H}^+\text{Cl}^-} [CH_3\overset{+}{C}H-CH=CH_2 \leftrightarrow CH_3CH=CH-\overset{+}{C}H_2]$$

$$\begin{array}{ccc} \underset{\text{addition}}{1,2} \Big\downarrow Cl^- & & Cl^- \Big\downarrow \underset{\text{addition}}{1,4} \\[1em] CH_3\underset{|}{C}HCH=CH_2 & & CH_3CH=CHCH_2Cl \\ Cl & & \\ \text{3-Chloro-1-butene} & & \text{1-Chloro-2-butene} \end{array}$$

The proportions of the two products vary markedly, depending upon the solvent, the temperature, and the time of reaction. At low temperatures ($-60°C$), 1,2 addition predominates over 1,4 addition to give 3-chloro-1-butene and 1-chloro-2-butene in a ratio of about 4:1. If the reaction is allowed to proceed at higher temperatures ($25°C$), or if the reaction mixture generated at $-60°C$ is allowed to stand at $25°C$ for a period of time, or if either pure isomer is heated for a prolonged period, the ratio of 3-chloro-1-butene to 1-chloro-2-butene is found to be about 1:4. Thus, at higher temperatures *equilibrium* is rapidly established between the two adducts; and the position of equilibrium tells us that 1-chloro-2-butene is more stable than 3-chloro-1-butene. However, the product ratio produced at low temperatures indicates that 3-chloro-1-butene is formed more rapidly than its isomer. We have a situation where *kinetic control* of product formation dominates at low temperatures, and *thermodynamic control* occurs at higher temperatures, under conditions where equilibrium can be established. Considering only the second steps in the overall addition of hydrogen chloride to 1,3-butadiene, we can conclude from the above data that the ΔG for reaction between the allylic cation and chloride ion to give 1,4 adduct ($\Delta G_{1,4}$) is more negative than $\Delta G_{1,2}$; but $\Delta G^{\ddagger}_{1,4}$ is more positive than $\Delta G^{\ddagger}_{1,2}$.

EXERCISE 15.8

Construct a free energy vs reaction coordinate diagram to illustrate the data given in the previous paragraph.

Other examples of conjugate additions to 1,3-dienes are shown below:

$$CH_2=CH-CH=CH_2 + Br_2 \rightarrow BrCH_2\underset{\underset{Br}{|}}{C}HCH=CH_2 + BrCH_2CH=CHCH_2Br$$

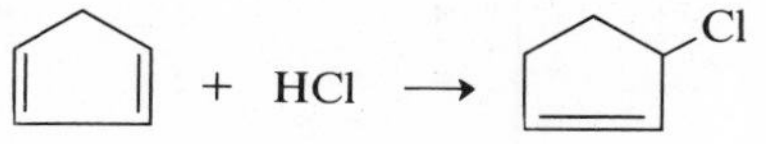

+ HCl ⟶ Cl   [Here, the 1,2 adduct and the 1,4 adduct are identical]

$$CH_2=\underset{\underset{CH_3}{|}}{C}-CH=CH_2 + HCl \rightarrow CH_3-\underset{\underset{CH_3}{|}}{\overset{\overset{Cl}{|}}{C}}-CH=CH_2 + CH_3-\underset{\underset{CH_3}{|}}{C}=CHCH_2Cl$$

EXERCISE 15.9

Why are 3-chloro-2-methyl-1-butene and 1-chloro-2-methyl-2-butene *not formed* in this last reaction?

15.12   Cycloadditions. The Diels–Alder Reaction

One of the most valuable methods for the preparation of six-membered ring alkenes is the Diels–Alder reaction.† This reaction involves the 1,4 addition of an alkene to a conjugated diene. It is called a *cycloaddition* because a cyclic compound is produced by the combination of two molecules in a process that involves a conversion of two π bonds to two σ bonds. To be more explicit, this reaction is called a [4 + 2] *cycloaddition* because it requires combination of a four-π-electron system (the 1,3-diene) with a two-π-electron system (the alkene, called a *dienophile*).

A 1,3-diene   A dienophile   Adduct

Since the adduct is a six-membered ring alkene, it must have a cis double bond. This means that in order for the reaction to occur, the diene must be the *s-cis* conformation. [The terminology *s-cis* and *s-trans* refers to the geometric arrangement about a single bond (*s*), and, of course, these are conformations rather than stereoisomers.] Most acyclic dienes exist predominantly in the *s-trans* form, but the energy barrier for conversion to *s-cis* is quite low (about 5 kcal/mole) since this is merely a conformational isomerization.

s-cis-1,3-Butadiene   *s-trans*-1,3-Butadiene
(undergoes Diels–Alder reaction)

Cyclic dienes such as 1,3-cyclopentadiene and 1,3-cyclohexadiene are fixed in the *s-cis* conformation, and they react readily as the diene in the Diels–Alder reactions.

The reaction proceeds most rapidly when the dienophile is substituted by electron-attracting groups, such as —COR (a conjugated aldehyde or ketone), —COOR (a conjugated acid or ester), or —C≡N (a conjugated nitrile). On the other hand, the reaction is faster when electron-donating groups (alkyl groups) are present on the diene.

20%

† Otto Diels. 1876–1954. Born Hamburg. University of Kiel. Nobel Prize 1950.
  Kurt Alder. 1902–1958. Born Könegshütte. A student of Diels. University of Cologne. Nobel Prize 1950.

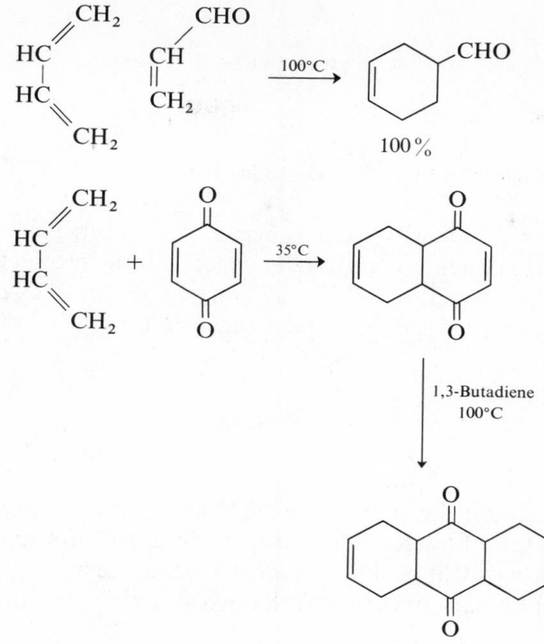

100 %

1,3-Butadiene
100°C

The configurations of the diene and the dienophile are retained in the products. This means that both new σ bonds are being formed in the transition state (although one may be formed to a greater extent than the other). A reaction that involves the simultaneous making and breaking of several bonds in the transition state, with no intermediates being generated, is called a *concerted reaction*.

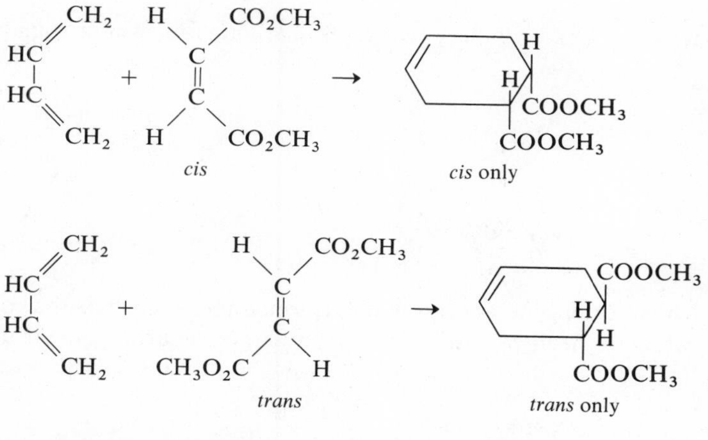

cis   *cis* only

trans   *trans* only

Finally, when cyclic dienes are used, two isomeric products are possible. In general, the adduct with the endo configuration (having the double bond of the adduct and the unsaturated substituent of the dienophile portion closest together in space) is usually much preferred over the exo adduct.

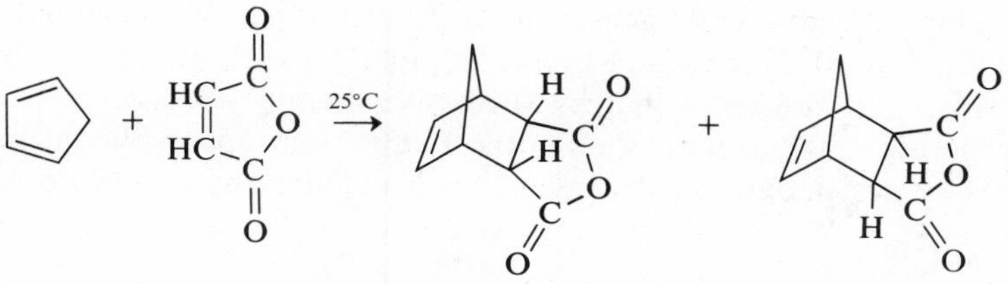

endo adduct (favored)   exo adduct (minor)

endo adduct (favored)   exo adduct (minor)

When a 1,5-hexadiene, which contains a diallylic system, is heated, a very intriguing rearrangement occurs whereby atoms and bonds become interchanged, but the product of the rearrangement has the same gross structure as did the starting material. For example, if 1,5-hexadiene itself is heated at about 300°C, it rearranges to itself.

This is a *degenerate* rearrangement, because the product is the same as the starting material. The rearrangement can be detected by, for example, deuterium substitution, because the location of the deuterium atoms will be different after rearrangement.

Another way is to provide a substitution pattern such that the two structures are not equivalent.

This general rearrangement of a diallylic system to a new diallylic system is called the *Cope rearrangement.*

These reactions are concerted, bond-switching processes involving four-center transition states.

A similar reaction, which is not degenerate but which is much more facile, is that of *cis*-divinylcyclopropane, which is itself not isolated, but undergoes rearrangement as formed.

Notice that it is the same type of rearrangement, diallyl ⇌ diallyl. A tremendous increase in rate for the divinylcyclopropane case is provided by the favorable geometry and release of ring strain in opening the cyclopropane ring.

The most remarkable molecule that undergoes facile, degenerate divinylcyclopropane rearrangements is tricyclo[3.3.2.0^{4,6}]deca-2,7,9-triene, popularly called *bullvalene*. In 1962, William von E. Doering† predicted that by successive divinylcyclopropane rearrangements, each of the 1,209,600 arrangements of the 10 C—H groups in bullvalene can be converted into the others, making all 10 carbon atoms and all 10 hydrogen atoms appear equivalent.

_____

† William von E. Doering. Born 1917, Forth Worth, Texas. Columbia, Yale, and Harvard Universities.

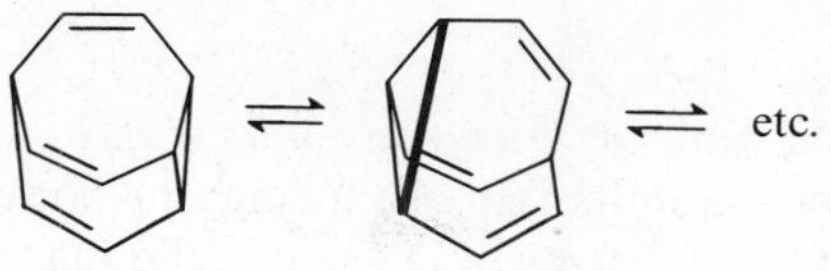

Bullvalene

Since that time, bullvalene has been prepared by several groups. At low temperatures, the nmr spectrum shows four chemically distinct types of hydrogens, indicating that the rearrangement has been stopped. Above 80°C only a single, sharp peak is observed at δ 4.22, showing that the degenerate rearrangement is occurring rapidly.

15.13   Additions Yielding Cyclopropanes

Attachment of a divalent carbon atom to both carbon atoms of an alkene is an extremely simple and useful way of producing cyclopropanes. Several important research break-throughs in recent years have provided practical methods for effecting this conversion.

The most convenient and selective way to convert an alkene to a cyclopropane is to allow iodomethylzinc iodide (ICH_2ZnI, a reagent which is unstable and is usually generated *in situ* from diiodomethane and zinc which has been alloyed with copper) to react with the alkene. Zinc iodide is eliminated and the $>CH_2$ group becomes bonded to both carbon atoms of the double bond. This is a methylene-transfer reaction: and, although the simplest carbene, methylene ($:CH_2$) is *not* actually an intermediate, iodomethylzinc iodide may be called a *carbenoid species* (meaning a reagent which reacts so as to transfer a carbene).

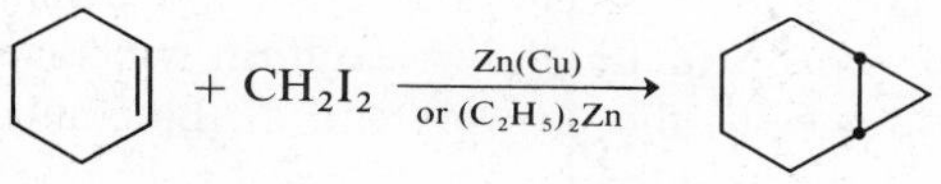

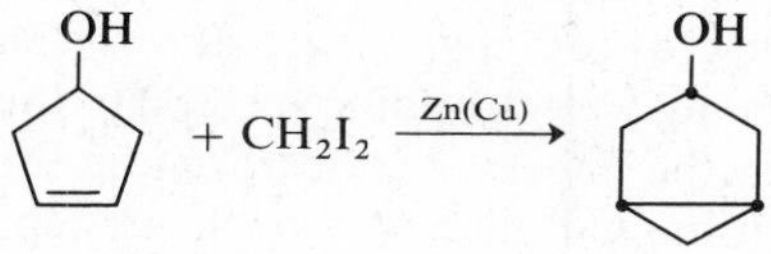

True carbenes are electrophilic, highly reactive intermediates that will add to the double bond of an alkene. Such reactions are stereospecific cis additions to the double bond (under proper conditions). The more stable carbenes, since they give fewer side reactions, are the ones that are most practical (work best). Dihalocarbenes have been especially useful.

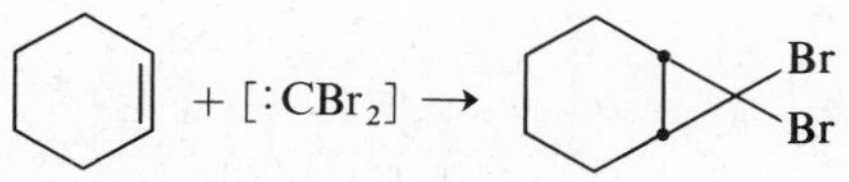

Dibromocarbene

($:CBr_2$ is generated by the reaction of dry KO-*t*-Bu and $CHBr_3$; or by decomposition of $C_6H_5HgCBr_3$.)

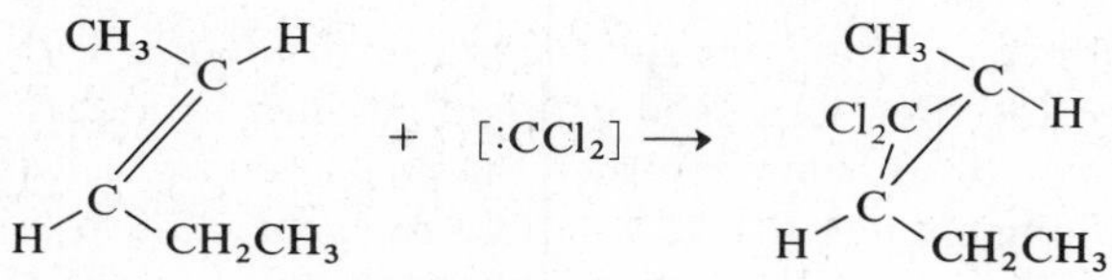

($:CCl_2$ is generated by the reaction of dry KO-*t*-Bu and $CHCl_3$; or by the thermal decomposition of $Cl_3CCOONa$.)

15.14   Polymerization

Among the chief products of the organic chemical industry today are *polymers*, high molecular weight compounds with recurring structural units that are formed by combinations of simpler *monomers*. The extensive variety of classes of polymers, the many kinds of polymerization processes, and the uses of polymers will be discussed in detail in Chapter 25. An introduction to the subject is given here, as this chapter is concerned with the chemistry of alkenes, which are very important monomers. Three of the technically important methods of polymerization of alkenes may be understood by extension of the basic mechanisms for simple additions that have been examined in earlier sections of this chapter. It is our purpose in this section to briefly evaluate the mechanisms for cationic, anionic, and free-radical polymerizations of alkenes.

Polymerization of an alkene, called *vinyl polymerization*, can be generalized as follows:

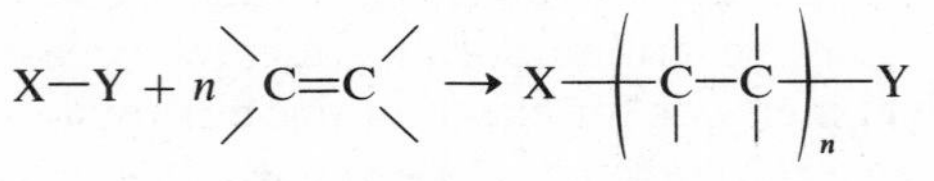

$$X{-}Y + n \underset{/}{\overset{\backslash}{C}}{=}\underset{\backslash}{\overset{/}{C}} \rightarrow X{-}\!\!\left(\!\!\begin{array}{cc} | & | \\ C{-}C \\ | & | \end{array}\!\!\right)_{\!n}\!\!{-}Y$$

A monomer   *A polymer*

The reagent X—Y initiates the combination of many monomer units. It may function as a true catalyst and be regenerated at the end of the polymerization sequence; or it may actually end up as part of the polymer (as shown above). If the latter is true, then X– and Y– become the *end groups* of the polymer chain; however, only two end groups occur for many, many alkene structural units.

Alkene polymerizations are, in effect, chain processes. An initiating species adds to the alkene to generate a reactive intermediate. This triggers the rapid, successive additions of many molecules of alkene (*propagation*). Finally, polymerization will stop (*termination*) when either a reactive species attaches to the growing end of the chain, or the end of the growing chain ejects a small species. Obviously, the mechanisms of vinyl polymerization will depend on the type of initiator that is used.

Cationic polymerization means that the end of the growing chain is a cation. The polymerization is initiated by addition of an acid (a strongly electrophilic species) to the alkene. If good nucleophilic reagents are not present, the intermediate carbonium ion will add to another alkene to give a longer chain cation. Continuation of these steps will lead to a polymer cation. Termination can finally occur by loss of a proton from the growing end of the chain.

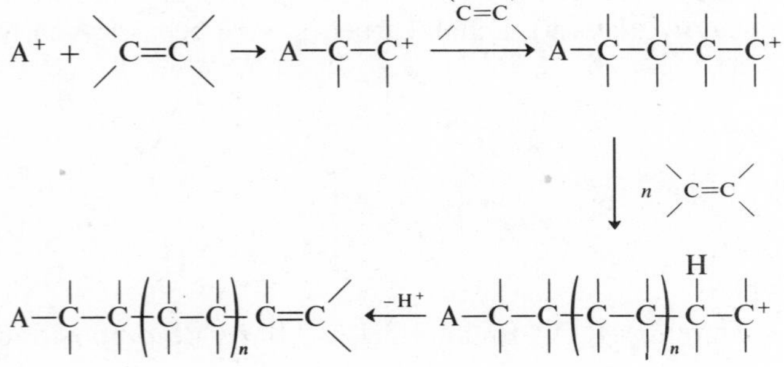

The acids used to initiate cationic polymerization are sulfuric and hydrofluoric acids, aluminum chloride, or boron trifluoride. For successful cationic polymerization, the alkene should have electron-donating substituents in order that the growing cation will be sufficiently stable to survive long enough to add to another alkene, and so on. Thus, ethylene does not undergo cationic polymerization, but isobutylene does so readily, to give polyisobutylene. The first two steps of the proton-catalyzed polymerization of isobutylene are identical to those in dimerization (Section 15.6).

$$n \; CH_2{=}C\overset{\displaystyle CH_3}{\underset{\displaystyle CH_3}{\big<}} \quad \xrightarrow[\substack{CH_3Cl \\ -100°C}]{AlCl_3} \quad {\Big(}CH_2{-}\underset{\displaystyle CH_3}{\overset{\displaystyle CH_3}{\underset{|}{\overset{|}{C}}}}{\Big)}_n$$

Polyisobutylene

Pure polyisobutylene is a tacky, rubbery material used in pressure-sensitive adhesives. In order for polyisobutylene to serve as a synthetic rubber, it must be *cross-linked*. This cross-linking is done by causing chemical bonds to be formed between the polymer chains, thus converting the long chains to a three-dimensional network, which increases the molecular weight and restricts the movement of the chains with respect to one another. Polyisobutylene, being completely saturated, has no convenient sites for cross-linking. About 2% of isoprene is therefore *copolymerized* with the isobutylene to provide these sites. The resulting polymer is known as *butyl rubber*, and this is the material from which most inner tubes are made.

$$\Big({-}CH_2{-}\underset{CH_3}{\overset{CH_3}{\underset{|}{\overset{|}{C}}}}\Big)_n {-}CH_2{-}CH{=}\overset{CH_3}{\overset{|}{C}}{-}CH_2{-}\Big(CH_2{-}\underset{CH_3}{\overset{CH_3}{\underset{|}{\overset{|}{C}}}}{-}\Big)_n$$

Polyisobutylene–isoprene copolymer

Butyl rubber

For *anionic polymerization*, the initiator is a powerful nucleophilic reagent (for example, $:NH_2^-$). Addition to the alkene gives a carbanion, and successive additions to other molecules of the alkene give a high molecular weight anion.

$$B:^- + \overset{\diagdown}{\diagup}C{=}C\overset{\diagup}{\diagdown} \;\rightarrow\; B{-}\overset{|}{\underset{|}{C}}{-}\overset{|}{\underset{|}{C}}:^- \xrightarrow{\; n \; \diagdown C{=}C \diagup \;} B{-}\overset{|}{\underset{|}{C}}{-}\overset{|}{\underset{|}{C}}\Big({-}\overset{|}{\underset{|}{C}}{-}\overset{|}{\underset{|}{C}}{-}\Big)_{n-1}\overset{|}{\underset{|}{C}}{-}\overset{|}{\underset{|}{C}}:^-$$

$$\Big\downarrow H^+$$

$$B{-}\overset{|}{\underset{|}{C}}{-}\overset{|}{\underset{|}{C}}\Big({-}\overset{|}{\underset{|}{C}}{-}\overset{|}{\underset{|}{C}}{-}\Big)_{n-1}\overset{|}{\underset{|}{C}}{-}\overset{|}{\underset{|}{C}}{-}H$$

Any reaction that destroys the carbanion on the end of the chain will stop the polymerization.

Perhaps the most important example of anionic polymerization is that of isoprene. Natural rubber is all-*cis*-1,4-polyisoprene; when isoprene is polymerized by means of a specially prepared lithium dispersion, the product is a nearly all *cis*-1,4-polyisoprene called *coral rubber*.

$$n \; CH_2{=}\underset{\underset{CH_3}{|}}{C}{-}CH{=}CH_2 \xrightarrow[\text{dispersion}]{Li} \left(\underset{\underset{CH_2}{|}}{\overset{CH_3}{|}}C{=}C\overset{H}{\underset{CH_2}{|}} \right)_n$$

Isoprene   Coral rubber

Simple alkenes will not polymerize under anionic conditions because nucleophilic additions do not occur readily to alkene double bonds. Anionic polymerization is useful only when the alkene is substituted with groups that stabilize carbanions.

Obviously *free-radical polymerizations* follow a course very similar to that shown for radical-chain additions in Section 15.7. Decomposition of a peroxide generates an alkoxy free radical which adds to the alkene to give a carbon radical. Stepwise addition to other alkene molecules (chain propagation) gives a polymer radical. Chain termination would involve any reaction resulting in the destruction of free radicals.

$$RO{\cdot} + \underset{/}{\overset{\backslash}{C}}{=}\underset{\backslash}{\overset{/}{C}} \longrightarrow RO{-}\overset{|}{\underset{|}{C}}{-}\overset{|}{\underset{|}{C}}{\cdot}$$

$$n \;\; \underset{/}{\overset{\backslash}{C}}{=}\underset{\backslash}{\overset{/}{C}}$$

$$RO{-}\overset{|}{\underset{|}{C}}{-}\overset{|}{\underset{|}{C}}\left(\overset{|}{\underset{|}{C}}{-}\overset{|}{\underset{|}{C}}\right)_{n-1}\overset{H}{\underset{|}{C}}{-}\overset{|}{\underset{|}{C}}{\cdot}$$

disproportionation

$$RO{-}\overset{|}{\underset{|}{C}}{-}\overset{|}{\underset{|}{C}}\left(\overset{|}{\underset{|}{C}}{-}\overset{|}{\underset{|}{C}}\right)_{n-1}\underset{\backslash}{\overset{/}{C}}{=}\underset{\backslash}{\overset{/}{C}} + RO{-}\overset{|}{\underset{|}{C}}{-}\overset{|}{\underset{|}{C}}\left(\overset{|}{\underset{|}{C}}{-}\overset{|}{\underset{|}{C}}\right)_{n-1}\overset{H}{\underset{|}{C}}{-}\overset{|}{\underset{|}{C}}{-}H$$

Ethylene may be polymerized in this way to give a polyethylene of low crystallinity having from 100 to 1000 monomer units. Butadiene is also polymerized under free-radical conditions, as is styrene ($C_6H_5CH{=}CH_2$). In fact, most industrial vinyl polymerizations are carried out under free-radical conditions (Section 25.3).

15.15 Additions to Alkynes. Reductions of Alkynes

Alkynes are unsaturated compounds, and like alkenes they undergo addition reactions. The carbon–carbon triple bond (two π bonds and one σ bond) determines the chemistry of alkynes. In most reactions the triple bond reacts in the same way as does a double bond, except (of course) that for additions to the triple bond *2 moles* of a reagent can be consumed.

$$-C{\equiv}C- + X{-}Y \longrightarrow \underset{/}{\overset{X}{\overset{\backslash}{C}}}{=}\underset{\backslash}{\overset{Y}{\overset{/}{C}}} \xrightarrow{X-Y} -\overset{X}{\underset{X}{C}}{-}\overset{Y}{\underset{Y}{C}}-$$

The catalytic hydrogenation of an alkyne will proceed in two stages—the uptake of 1 mole of hydrogen to give an alkene, which reacts further to give the alkane.

$$CH_3CH_2C{\equiv}CH \xrightarrow[Ni]{+2H_2} CH_3CH_2CH_2CH_3$$

The reduction of an alkyne to the double-bond (alkene) stage is of both theoretical and practical importance. If the triple bond is not at the end of a chain (not a 1-alkyne), the addition of 1 mole of hydrogen can give a *cis*-alkene (by cis addition of hydrogen) or a *trans*-alkene (by trans addition of hydrogen). The isomer preferentially formed is determined by the type of reducing agent used. With few exceptions, the *trans*-alkene is the major product obtained by reduction of an alkyne with sodium (or lithium) in liquid ammonia.

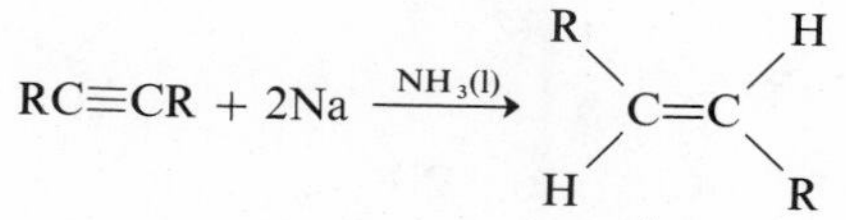

$$RC\equiv CR + 2Na \xrightarrow{NH_3(l)}$$

trans

$$CH_3(CH_2)_2C\equiv C(CH_2)_2CH_3 \xrightarrow{Na, NH_3}$$

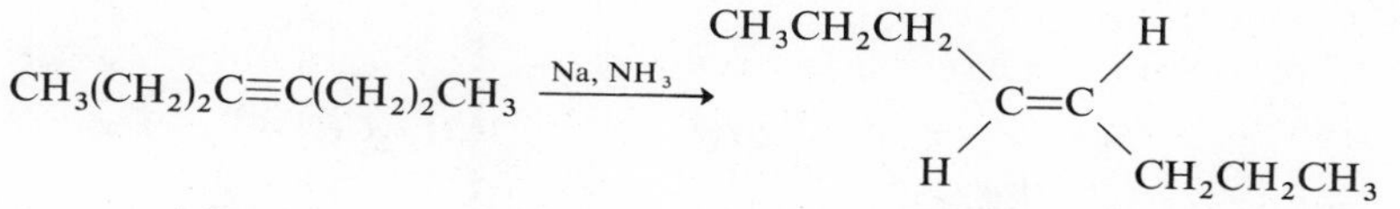

4-Octyne   *trans*-4-Octene

Two general methods can be employed for the reduction of an alkyne to a *cis*-alkene. Predominantly *cis*-alkenes can be prepared by hydrogenation of alkynes in the presence of "deactivated" catalysts. Typical of these catalysts is palladium on barium sulfate deactivated by quinoline

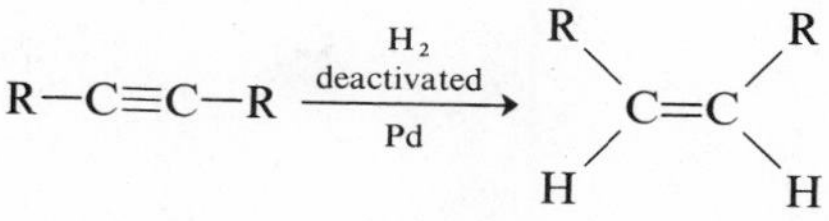

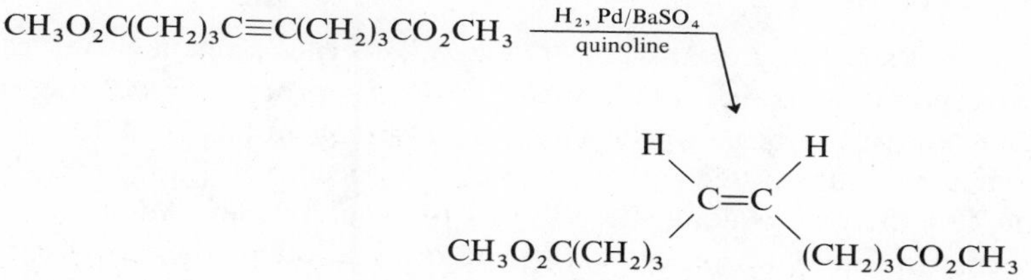

$$R-C\equiv C-R \xrightarrow[\text{Pd}]{\substack{H_2 \\ \text{deactivated}}}$$

$$CH_3O_2C(CH_2)_3C\equiv C(CH_2)_3CO_2CH_3 \xrightarrow[\text{quinoline}]{H_2, Pd/BaSO_4}$$

A newer method involves the addition of B—H across the triple bond of an alkyne, similar to the hydroboration of an alkene. The addition is a stereospecific cis process; and with an unsymmetrical alkyne the direction of addition is anti-Markovnikov. Hydrolysis of the vinylborane with acetic or propionic acid occurs cleanly and stereospecifically.

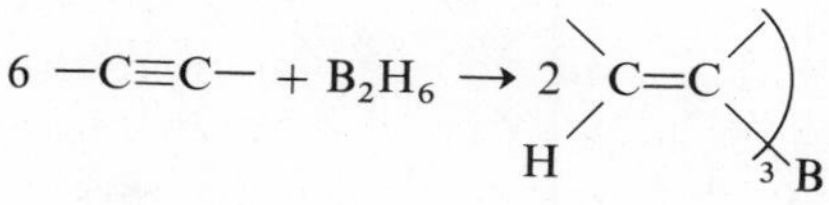

$$6 \, -C\equiv C- \, + B_2H_6 \rightarrow 2$$

A vinylborane

$$\xrightarrow{CH_3COOH}$$

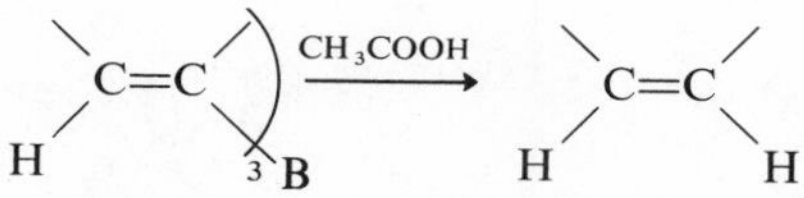

A *cis*-alkene

Thus the overall process represents cis hydrogenation of an alkyne.

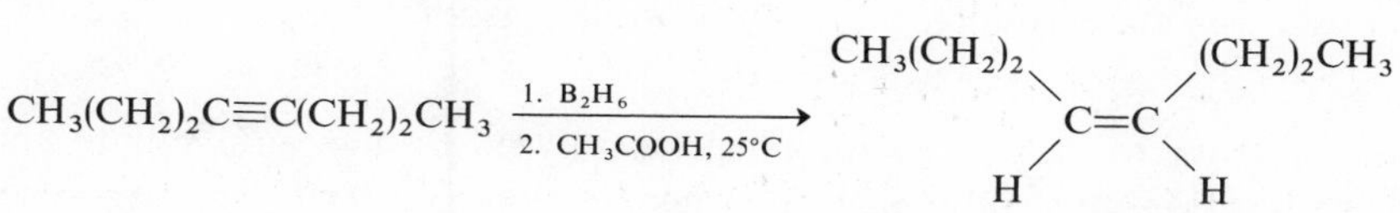

$$CH_3(CH_2)_2C\equiv C(CH_2)_2CH_3 \xrightarrow[\text{2. } CH_3COOH, 25°C]{\text{1. } B_2H_6}$$

cis-4-Octene

The vinylboranes can also be oxidized with alkaline hydrogen peroxide to give aldehydes (if the double bond is on the end of the chain), or ketones (if the double bond is internal).

$$CH_3(CH_2)_3C\equiv CH \xrightarrow{R_2B-H} CH_3(CH_2)_3CH=CHBR_2 \xrightarrow[^-OH]{H_2O_2}$$

$$CH_3(CH_2)_4\overset{O}{\underset{H}{C}} \xleftarrow{\text{tautomerize}} [CH_3(CH_2)_3CH=CHOH]$$

Hexanal

$$CH_3(CH_2)_2C\equiv C(CH_2)_2CH_3 \xrightarrow{R_2B-H} \underset{H}{\overset{CH_3(CH_2)_2}{\diagdown}}C=C\underset{BR_2}{\overset{(CH_2)_2CH_3}{\diagup}}$$

$$\downarrow H_2O_2, \ ^-OH$$

$$CH_3(CH_2)_3\underset{\underset{O}{\|}}{C}(CH_2)_2CH_3 \xleftarrow{\text{tautomerize}} [CH_3(CH_2)_2CH=\underset{\underset{OH}{|}}{C}-(CH_2)_2CH_3]$$

4-Octanone

15.16   Other Additions to Alkynes

Electrophilic reagents add smoothly to alkynes. In general, alkynes are somewhat less reactive than the corresponding alkenes. Electrophilic additions proceed in two stages; however, the reaction can usually be stopped after 1 mole of reagent has been added if the alkene produced has been substituted with electronegative (deactivating) groups. The substituted ethylene can then be isolated or allowed to react further. Additions of unsymmetrical reagents to 1-alkynes proceed with the orientation predicted by consideration of the possible cationic intermediates.

$$HC\equiv CH + Br_2 \rightarrow \underset{H}{\overset{Br}{\diagdown}}C=C\underset{Br}{\overset{H}{\diagup}} \xrightarrow{Br_2} Br_2CH-CHBr_2$$

$$CH_3C\equiv CH + HCl \rightarrow CH_3\underset{\underset{Cl}{|}}{C}=CH_2 \xrightarrow{HCl} CH_3\underset{\underset{Cl}{|}}{\overset{\overset{Cl}{|}}{C}}CH_3$$

EXERCISE 15.10

How would you prepare $CH_3-\underset{\underset{Br}{|}}{\overset{\overset{Cl}{|}}{C}}-CH_3$ from $CH_3C\equiv CH$? Show from the

mechanism why this product, rather than another isomer, would be obtained.

The addition of water to alkynes is specifically catalyzed by mercuric sulfate and sulfuric acid. The reaction must proceed by oxymercuration; α-mercury ketones react readily with acid to give the free ketones. Markovnikov's rule is obeyed.

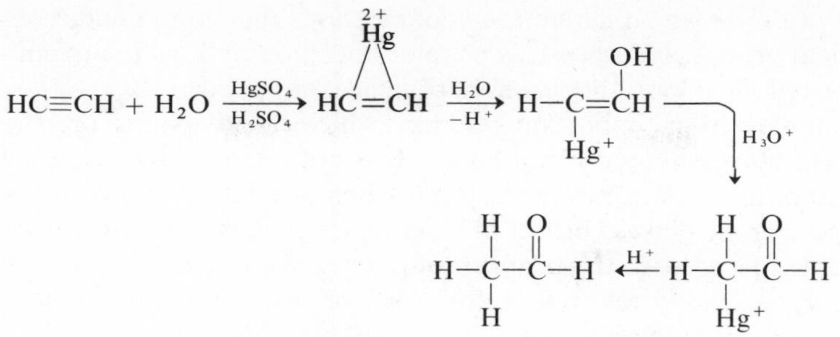

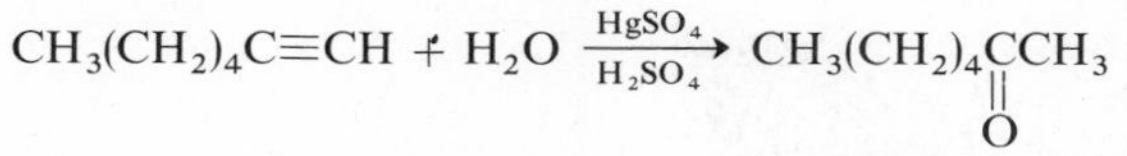

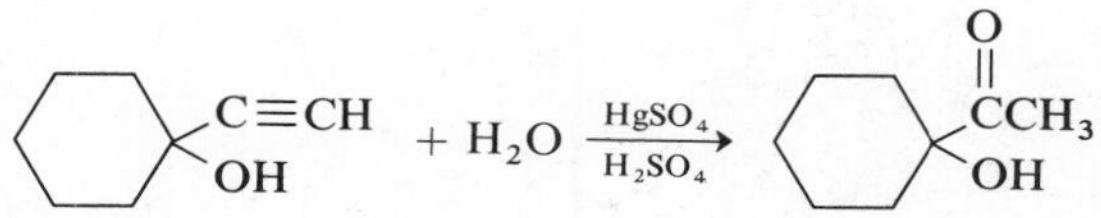

$$HC\equiv CH + H_2O \xrightarrow[\text{H}_2\text{SO}_4]{\text{HgSO}_4} HC = CH \xrightarrow[-\text{H}^+]{\text{H}_2\text{O}} H - C = CH \xrightarrow{\text{H}_3\text{O}^+}$$

$$H - C - C - H \xleftarrow{\text{H}^+} H - C - C - H$$

$$CH_3(CH_2)_4C\equiv CH + H_2O \xrightarrow[\text{H}_2\text{SO}_4]{\text{HgSO}_4} CH_3(CH_2)_4CCH_3$$

The additions of compounds containing —OH groups (alcohols, acids, water) to acetylenes are often specifically catalyzed by mercuric, cuprous, and nickelous salts. An example of commercial significance is the preparation of vinyl acetate.

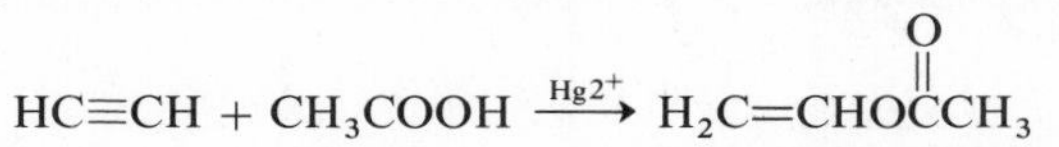

$$HC\equiv CH + CH_3COOH \xrightarrow{\text{Hg}^{2+}} H_2C = CHOCCH_3$$

Vinyl acetate

EXERCISE 15.11

What is the product from the hydration of propyne in the presence of $HgSO_4/H_2SO_4$? Write out the detailed mechanism of the reaction.

Alkynes can serve as dienophiles in Diels–Alder reactions with 1,3-dienes.

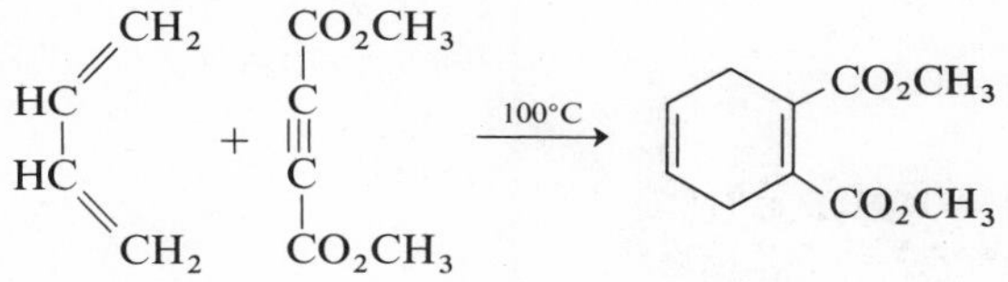

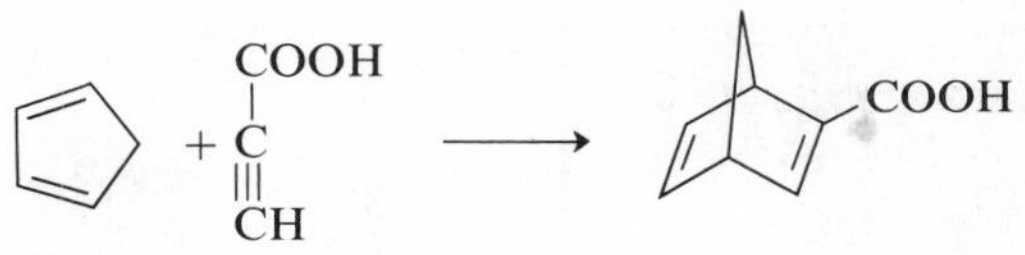

EXERCISE 15.12

Would you expect vinylacetylene (CH_2=CH—$C\equiv CH$) to function as a diene in the Diels–Alder reaction? Explain.

15.17 Summary of Synthetic Methods for Alkenes and Alkynes

One of the most important areas within the discipline of organic chemistry is *synthesis*—the preparation of required compounds from others that are available. Suppose we have a bottle of compound A, and we need another compound B; but suppose (as is usually the case) that there is no known reaction which will convert A to B, that is, A $\nrightarrow$ B. It may be possible to convert A to another compound C, which can, in turn, be converted to B, that is, A $\rightarrow$ C $\rightarrow$ B. Typical syntheses usually involve several steps (via intermediate compounds such as C in this example) to the final product, and the choice of good synthetic schemes is something of an art. Obviously, in order to plan syntheses it is necessary to know the different kinds of reactions that compounds containing specific functional groups undergo. This chapter and those following are concerned with the reactions of the important classes of organic compounds.

In this section are summarized the important reactions which can be used to prepare alkenes and alkynes from *other classes* of compounds. It is not intended nor expected that the student learn all of these reactions at this point. Each of these reactions will be taken up later in the appropriate place. This list of reactions is given for later reference, so that when the student is faced with the problem of how to synthesize an alkene or alkyne, this section may be readily referred to for a list of the important synthetic methods, as well as for cross references to where each method is discussed.

1. Alkenes
  a. Dehydrohalogenation of alkyl halides (Sections 17.5, 17.6)

$$-\underset{\underset{H}{|}}{\overset{|}{C}}-\underset{\underset{X}{|}}{\overset{|}{C}}- + KOH \xrightarrow[\text{solvent}]{\text{alcohol}} \overset{\diagdown}{\underset{\diagup}{C}}=\overset{\diagup}{\underset{\diagdown}{C}} + KX + H_2O$$
$$\qquad\qquad\qquad\text{(or other bases)}$$

$$(CH_3)_2CHCH_2CH_2Br + KOH \xrightarrow{\text{alcohol}} (CH_3)_2CHCH=CH_2$$

$$BrCH_2\underset{\underset{Br}{|}}{CHCH_2Br} + NaOH \rightarrow BrCH_2\underset{\underset{Br}{|}}{C}=CH_2$$

  b. Dehydration of alcohols (Section 18.6)

$$-\underset{\underset{H}{|}}{\overset{|}{C}}-\underset{\underset{OH}{|}}{\overset{|}{C}}- \xrightarrow[\text{heat}]{\text{acid}} \overset{\diagdown}{\underset{\diagup}{C}}=\overset{\diagup}{\underset{\diagdown}{C}} + H_2O$$

$$(C_6H_5)_2\underset{\underset{OH}{|}}{C}-CH_3 \xrightarrow{H_2SO_4} (C_6H_5)_2C=CH_2$$

$$\underset{CH_3}{\overset{CH_3\diagdown}{\diagup}}\underset{\underset{OH}{|}}{C}-CH=CH_2 \xrightarrow{\text{catalyst}} CH_2=\underset{\underset{CH_3}{|}}{C}-CH=CH_2$$

  c. Dehalogenation of vicinal dihalides (Sections 17.6, 17.11)

$$-\underset{\underset{X}{|}}{\overset{|}{C}}-\underset{\underset{X}{|}}{\overset{|}{C}}- + Zn\ (or\ NaI) \rightarrow \overset{\diagdown}{\underset{\diagup}{C}}=\overset{\diagup}{\underset{\diagdown}{C}} + ZnX_2\ (or\ 2NaX + I_2)$$

$$(CH_3)_3CCH_2\underset{\underset{Br}{|}}{CHCH_2Br} \xrightarrow{Zn} (CH_3)_3CCH_2CH=CH_2$$

  d. Pyrolysis of quaternary ammonium hydroxides (Section 21.2).

$$-\underset{\underset{H}{|}}{\overset{|}{C}}-\underset{\underset{\overset{+}{N}(CH_3)_3}{|}}{\overset{|}{C}}- \xrightarrow[\text{-OH}]{\text{heat}} \overset{\diagdown}{\underset{\diagup}{C}}=\overset{\diagup}{\underset{\diagdown}{C}} + (CH_3)_3N + H_2O$$

$$\overset{\displaystyle H}{\underset{\displaystyle CH_2\overset{+}{N}(CH_3)_3}{\bigcirc}} \xrightarrow[-OH]{100°C} \bigcirc{=}CH_2$$

e. Pyrolysis of esters and xanthates (Section 20.16)

$$-\overset{|}{\underset{H}{C}}-\overset{|}{\underset{OCR}{C}}- \xrightarrow{heat} \overset{\diagdown}{\diagup}C{=}C\overset{\diagup}{\diagdown} + RCOOH$$

$$(CH_3)_3CCHCH_3 \xrightarrow{350°C} (CH_3)_3CCH{=}CH_2$$
$$\underset{\underset{O}{\parallel}}{OCCH_3}$$

f. Pyrolysis of amine oxides (Section 22.3)

$$-\overset{|}{\underset{H}{C}}-\overset{|}{\underset{\overset{\downarrow}{N}(CH_3)_2}{C}}- \xrightarrow{heat} \overset{\diagdown}{\diagup}C{=}C\overset{\diagup}{\diagdown} + (CH_3)_2NOH$$

$$CH_2{=}CHCH_2CH_2CH_2\overset{\downarrow}{N}(CH_3)_2 \xrightarrow{130°C} CH_2{=}CHCH_2CH{=}CH_2$$

g. The Wittig reaction (Section 19.10)

$$\overset{\diagdown}{\diagup}C{=}O + \overset{\diagdown}{\diagup}C{=}P(C_6H_5)_3 \rightarrow \overset{\diagdown}{\diagup}C{=}C\overset{\diagup}{\diagdown} + (C_6H_5)_3P{=}O$$

$$\bigcirc{=}O + C_6H_5CH{=}P(C_6H_5)_3 \rightarrow \bigcirc{=}CHC_6H_5$$

h. Reductions of alkynes (Section 15.15)

$$RC{\equiv}CR \xrightarrow{[H]} RCH{=}CHR$$

2. Alkynes
   a. Dehydrohalogenation of 1,2-dihaloalkanes (Section 17.6)

$$-\overset{H}{\underset{X}{\overset{|}{C}}}-\overset{H}{\underset{X}{\overset{|}{C}}}- \xrightarrow[base]{strong} \overset{H}{\underset{X}{\overset{\diagdown}{\diagup}}}C{=}C\overset{\diagup}{\diagdown} \xrightarrow[base \; (NaNH_2)]{stronger} -C{\equiv}C-$$

$$C_6H_5\underset{Br}{\overset{|}{CH}}-CH_2Br \xrightarrow{2NaNH_2} C_6H_5C{\equiv}CH$$

b. Reaction of metal acetylides with alkyl halides (Section 17.1)

$$RC{\equiv}\overset{-}{C}\overset{+}{N}a + R'Cl \rightarrow R-C{\equiv}C-R' + NaCl$$

$$HC{\equiv}CNa + CH_3(CH_2)_3Cl \rightarrow HC{\equiv}C-(CH_2)_3CH_3$$

PROBLEMS

1. A compound of molecular formula C_6H_{10} absorbs only *1 mole* of hydrogen on catalytic hydrogenation. The nmr spectrum is rather simple in that it corresponds to a compound with high symmetry; it shows a two-proton vinyl resonance at $\delta\,4.82$, a four-proton resonance at $\delta \sim 2.22$, and a four-proton resonance at $\delta \sim 1.65$. What is the structure?

2. Draw structures for the products expected from reaction of 2-methyl-1-butene with the following reagents. (If no reaction occurs, write "no reaction.")
   (a) H_2, Ni   (b) Br_2 (c) Cl_2 (d) HBr
   (e) H_2SO_4 (f) H_2O, H^+ (g) Br_2, H_2O (h) NaCl, H_2O
   (i) HOCl   (j) ICl   (k) HOBr

3. A compound of molecular formula C_6H_{12} shows only one unsplit peak in the nmr spectrum at $\delta\,1.77$. What is its structure?

4. Draw structures for the products expected from reaction of cyclopentene with each of the reagents (a)–(k) of Problem 2 (*Pay particular attention to stereochemistry*).

5. A compound C_4H_6 was dissolved in liquid ammonia containing sodamide ($NaNH_2$), and then ethyl bromide was added. After an hour the solution was diluted with water, and an organic layer separated. Distillation of the organic material gave a compound C_6H_{10}, the nmr spectrum of which is shown.

NMR spectrum of unknown C_6H_{10}, Problem 5.

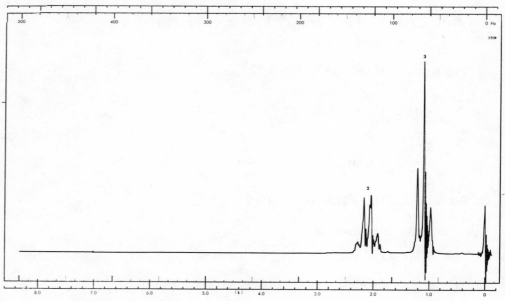

Interpret the spectrum and suggest a structure for the compound C_6H_{10}.

The compound C_6H_{10} was treated for several hours with excess sodamide in liquid ammonia. Ammonium chloride was added to the solution, then water, and an organic layer separated. Distillation gave a compound C_6H_{10}, which was an isomer of the previous compound. How did it form and what was it? Predict where in the infrared and nmr spectra characteristic absorption will be found which can be used to prove the structure of this compound.

6. Write a mechanism for the addition of HCl to 1-propene showing how the mechanism accounts for the exclusive production of 2-chloropropane.

7. Write a mechanism to account for the following isomerization:

$$\text{(cyclohexane ring)}\!=\!CH_2 \xrightarrow[\text{catalyst}]{H^+ \text{ (trace)}} \text{(cyclohexene ring)}\!-\!CH_3$$

8. The two compounds allyl bromide, $CH_2=CHCH_2Br$, and 2-bromopropene,

$$CH_2=C\overset{\displaystyle CH_3}{\underset{\displaystyle Br}{\big<}}$$

show the following nmr spectra. Which spectrum corresponds to 2-bromopropene? Explain.

NMR spectra of allyl bromide and 2-bromopropene, Problem 8.

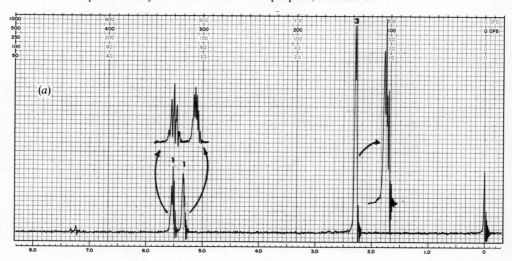

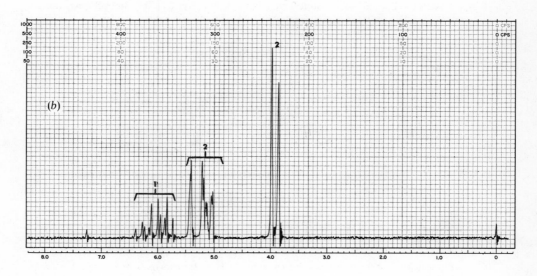

9. Write mechanisms to account for the fact that the additions of HBr to ethyl acrylate ($CH_2=CHCOOC_2H_5$) under both *ionic* and *radical-chain* conditions give only $BrCH_2CH_2COOC_2H_5$.

10. In the presence of peroxides or under the influence of light, 1-octene reacts with
    (a) $BrCCl_3$ to give 1,1,1-trichloro-3-bromononane
    (b) CCl_4 to give 1,1,1,3-tetrachlorononane
    (c) C_6H_5SH to give $n\text{-}C_8H_{17}SC_6H_5$
    Show all steps in the most probable mechanism for each of these reactions.

11. Draw structures for and name the diastereomers which would result from the reaction of *trans*-2-butene with
    (a) Br_2
    (b) Dil. neutral $KMnO_4$
    (c) C_6H_5COOOH
    (d) HCOOOH/HCOOH, then ⁻OH
    (e) HOCl
    (f) B_2H_6, then H_2O_2/⁻OH

12. What are the structures of the alkenes which give the following carbonyl compounds after ozonization?
    (a) CH_2O and cyclopentanone
    (b) Only acetone
    (c) CH_3CHO and CH_2O and $OHCCH_2CHO$
    (d) CH_3COCH_3 and $(CH_3)_2CHCH_2CH_2CH_2CHO$
    (e) $CH_3COCH_2CH_2CH_2CH_2CHO$

13. Draw the structures of the diene and the dienophile that would give the following products in a Diels–Alder reaction.

    (a)
    (b)
    (c)
    (d)

14. Write the structure of the *alkene* that will react with the reagents listed to give the desired product.
    (a) With B_2H_6, then H_2O_2/⁻OH to give $(CH_3)_2CHCH_2CH_2OH$
    (b) With HBr and peroxides to give 1,2-dibromopropane
    (c) With Br_2 to give *dl*-3,4-dibromohexane
    (d) With $CHBr_3$ and KO-*t*-Bu to give *trans*-2,3-dimethyl-1,1-dibromocyclopropane
    (e) With CF_3COOH to give 1-methylcyclohexyl trifluoroacetate

    (f) With CH_2I_2/Zn—Cu to give [structure]—OH

    (g) With OsO_4, then H_2S to give *meso*-2,3-butanediol

    (h) With H_2O/H^+ to give [structure with CH_3 and OH]

15. Draw structures for the products (more than one may be possible) from reaction of butadiene and the following reagents:
    (a) HCl
    (b) Br_2
    (c) HOCl
    (d) CH_2=$CHCOOCH_3$
    (e) *cis*-HOOCCH=CHCOOH
    (f) Butadiene (a Diels–Alder reaction)
    (g) O_3, then Zn/H_2O

16. An unknown hydrocarbon has the formula $C_{10}H_{16}$. It absorbs 2 moles of hydrogen on catalytic hydrogenation. Upon reaction with 1 mole of HCl, two different monochlorides $(C_{10}H_{17}Cl)$ are obtained. The hydrocarbon does not react with maleic anhydride in a Diels–Alder reaction. Treatment with excess ozone followed by Zn, H_2O gives acetone and

    OHC—C—CH_2CH_2CHCHO
         ‖ |
         O CH_3

    What is the structure of the hydrocarbon and why does it not undergo a Diels–Alder reaction?

17. Suggest a mechanism for the reaction:

PhCOOOH + → O + PhCOOH

18. Draw structures for the products expected from the reactions of *trans*-3-methyl-2-pentene with the following reagents. (If no reaction occurs write "no reaction.")
    (a) HBr
    (b) HBr, peroxides
    (c) B_2H_6, then H_2O_2/OH^-
    (d) PhCOOOH
    (e) H_2O, peroxides
    (f) HCOOOH/HCOOH, then OH^-
    (g) Cold, dilute, neutral $KMnO_4$
    (h) H_2S, peroxides
    (i) O_3 then, Zn, H_2O
    (j) $CHCl_3$ + KO-*t*-Bu
    (k) CH_2I_2 + Zn—Cu
    (l) H_2SO_4
    (m) NH_4OH, peroxides

19. Draw structures for the products expected from reaction of cyclohexene with each of the reagents (a)–(m) of Problem 18. *Pay particular attention to the stereochemistry.*

20. Draw structures for the products expected from reaction of 1-butyne with the following reagents:
    (a) 1 mole of H_2, Pd/$BaSO_4$
    (b) 2 moles of H_2, Ni
    (c) 1 mole of Cl_2
    (d) 2 moles of Cl_2
    (e) Ag^+
    (f) 1 mole of HCl
    (g) 2 moles of HCl
    (h) R_2B—H, then CH_3COOH
    (i) R_2B—H, then $H_2O_2/^-OH$
    (j) H_3O^+, $HgSO_4$
    (k) O_3, then H_2O
    (l) CF_2=CCl_2, heat
    (m) $NaNH_2$

21. Draw structures for the products expected from reaction of 2-butyne with the following reagents:
    (a) 1 mole of H_2, Pd/$BaSO_4$
    (b) B_2H_6, then CH_3CH_2COOH
    (c) Na, NH_3(liq)
    (d) 2 moles of Br_2
    (e) H_3O^+, $HgSO_4$
    (f) 2 moles of HCl
    (g) O_3, then H_2O
    (h) B_2H_6, then $H_2O_2/\overline{O}H$

CHAPTER 16

AROMATIC SUBSTITUTION

16.1 The Structure of Benzene

Benzene has been known since 1825, and it is perhaps by now the most thoroughly studied and best known of all organic compounds. The structure of the molecule presented an extremely difficult problem to the early organic chemists, not because it was particularly complicated, but rather because it was the first example of delocalized bonding which they met, and it did not seem to fit in with what was then known about molecular structure.

The results of a great many careful experimental investigations (outlined below) led the early chemists to the conclusion that benzene was best represented by a pair of Kekulé forms (Section 11.1). Until the concepts of delocalized electrons and resonance were forthcoming in the late 1920s, however, it was not really possible for them to understand just why benzene required two Kekulé forms to describe its structure. Nor was it clear why benzene was so stable. The experimental facts were simply accepted that a molecule such as benzene, for which one could write two Kekulé forms, generally appeared to be best described as the sum of the two forms and that such compounds showed a much higher degree of stability, or resistance to chemical reactions, than analogous compounds for which one could write but a single Kekulé structure. (The student may wish to review the rules for the use of the resonance method, page 152.)

A HISTORICAL NOTE ON THE STRUCTURE OF BENZENE. *The formula C_6H_6 could correspond to a great many different physical structures, if Kekulé's rules of valence are used as the only guide. Structures I–VI all fit the molecular formula and satisfy Kekulé's rules of valence.*

$$CH_2=CH-C\equiv C-CH=CH_2$$

$$CH_3-C\equiv C-C\equiv C-CH_3$$

I II III IV V VI

The early chemists were able more or less to eliminate most of the structures from consideration, however, because of the chemical behavior of the benzene molecule. Benzene is rather inert as organic substances go. For example, it does not react with aqueous potassium permanganate, or with bromine in carbon tetrachloride, or with concentrated sulfuric or nitric acid (at room temperature). As was discussed in Chapter 15, olefins and acetylenes typically undergo reactions with these reagents with the greatest of ease. Conjugated olefins are even more reactive, and the open-chain compound,

1,3,5-hexatriene (VII), for example, reacts vigorously with all of these reagents at room temperature.

$$CH_2=CH-CH=CH-CH=CH_2$$

VII

Chemical reactivity may be misleading, however, if one is not using a proper analogy. Benzene is a system in which the electrons are highly delocalized, and even though we might draw a structure for it which resembles a triene, the molecule itself is actually quite different from hexatriene. The early chemists recognized this fact also, and hence did not discount structures I–VI as possible ones for benzene on the basis of reactivity alone. Their attack on the problem made important use of the number of isomers into which benzene derivatives could be converted.

One of the observations made during the last century was that benzene, while less reactive than alkenes, could be induced to undergo chemical reactions by simply using more vigorous reaction conditions. Thus, while benzene does not react with bromine in carbon tetrachloride, it will do so when heated to its boiling point, if a suitable Lewis acid (such as ferric bromide) is added as a catalyst. When benzene reacts with bromine under these conditions, however, it does not simply add bromine as does an olefin. Rather, it replaces a hydrogen by bromine. The reaction can be written as follows:

What the early chemists observed was that it was possible to replace just one hydrogen of the benzene molecule by bromine under proper conditions. Now the interesting fact was noted that only a single product of the formula C_6H_5Br was obtained from this reaction. This suggested that all six of the hydrogens in the benzene molecule had to be located on equivalent positions; otherwise isomeric compounds would have been obtained. On this basis the Dewar formula (II) can be tentatively eliminated. There are two different types of hydrogens in this molecule, and only if one group of hydrogens is tremendously less reactive than the other group could II correspond to benzene. Similarly, compounds IV and V have different types of hydrogens, and can tentatively be eliminated from consideration. Only structures I, III, and VI have all of their hydrogens equivalent.

Next consider what happens when bromobenzene (C_6H_5Br) is allowed to react with another mole of bromine in the presence of a Lewis acid catalyst. The reaction is relatively slow but will proceed, and three isomeric products are obtained. They have the formula $C_6H_4Br_2$ and are called dibromobenzenes. *If VI is the structure of benzene, then bromobenzene would have structure VIII, and there would be only two isomeric dibromides which could be formed from it (IX and X). Since three isomeric dibromobenzenes are actually obtained, structure VI can be eliminated as a possibility for benzene.*

The above considerations are typical of those employed to attack the problem of the structure of benzene. Such experimental evidence very quickly leads to consideration of only structures I and III for benzene. Structure III would be capable of yielding a single monobromide and three dibromides, as observed. For structure I, there would be a single monobromide possible, but unless the double bonds were free to move about, there would be four possible dibromides (XI–XIV). If we put a bromine at any position and number that position 1, then the second bromine may be on the adjacent carbon in either of two directions, either the direction pointed out by the double bond (XI), or the position pointed out by the single bond (XII). Thus if the double bonds remain fixed, 1,2-dibromobenzene (which is XI), and 1,6-dibromobenzene (which is XII) are different substances. The student may convince himself, by examining models if necessary, that 1,3-dibromobenzene (XIII) and 1,5-dibromobenzene correspond to the identical structure. Thus, if benzene had the structure of a single Kekulé form, it would yield four dibromides rather than three. Since only three dibromides are found, it can be concluded that benzene could not have structure I.

If benzene is a resonance hybrid of two Kekulé structures, then it can be written as structure XV, in which case dibromide XI and dibromide XII become the same dibromide, XVI.

XI   XII   XIII   XIV

XV

XVI   XVII   XVIII   XIX

Hence the resonance hybrid structure of benzene satisfies the experimental data which are available, as does the Ladenburg formula for benzene (III).

It can be proved that benzene has structure XV rather than structure III in a somewhat more subtle manner. XVI, XVII, and XVIII each have a plane of symmetry; they are each superimposable upon their mirror images, and therefore none of these structures can exist in optically active forms. Structure III, on the other hand, yields three dibromides, one of which (XIX) is not superimposable upon its mirror image, and hence can exist in optically active forms. Since no optical activity has ever been detected in a simple disubstituted benzene derivative, one may infer that structures such as XIX do not correspond to such derivatives. Thus, it is possible to eliminate structure III as the formula for benzene.

As can be seen from the foregoing outline, it was quite difficult for the early chemists to establish the structures of unknown compounds. They were forced to carry out very laborious studies to determine what we now consider to be simple facts. Obviously, it is much easier for modern-day chemists with the techniques now available to reach conclusions of a similar complexity.

16.2   The Mechanism of Electrophilic Aromatic Substitution. Halogenation

We will now examine some of the chemical properties of the benzene ring, and, in the light of our knowledge about the resonance energy of the molecule (Chapter 11), try to understand why the reactions of benzene are so different from those of alkenes, which the benzene molecule formally appears to resemble. As a typical example, let us compare the reaction of molecular bromine with an alkene, on one hand, and with benzene, on the other.

The reaction of bromine with an alkene was discussed in Section 15.4. The bromine adds via a bridged bromonium ion intermediate that is attacked by bromide ion to give a vicinal dibromide. The Br_2 molecule is a poor electrophile and as such does not react directly with benzene at a rate fast enough for the reaction to be useful. However, the addition of a Lewis acid as catalyst causes the bromine–benzene reaction to proceed readily. The function of the Lewis acid is to convert the weak electrophile Br_2 into the much more powerful electrophile Br^+. What occurs is not the addition of two bromine atoms across the double bond, but *substitution* of one bromine for one hydrogen.

$$\bigcirc + Br_2 \xrightarrow[\text{heat}]{FeBr_3} \bigcirc\!\!-Br + HBr$$

75 % yield

The reaction of Br^+ with an alkene is analogous to the reaction between Br_2 and an alkene.

$$H_2C{=}CH_2 + Br^+ \rightarrow H_2\overset{Br^+}{\overset{\diagup\,\diagdown}{C{-}C}}H_2 \tag{1}$$

$$H_2\overset{Br^+}{\overset{\diagup\,\diagdown}{C{-}C}}H_2 \xrightarrow{Br^-} \overset{Br}{\overset{|}{C}}H_2{-}\overset{}{\underset{\underset{Br}{|}}{C}}H_2 \tag{2}$$

In Section 15.4 evidence was discussed for the formation of the bridged intermediate ion rather than an intermediate in which bromine adds directly to one carbon atom, leaving the other as a carbonium ion (see Figure 15.2). Formation of such a carbonium ion would be unfavorable, because a Lewis acid—the positively charged carbon which has an open *p* orbital—and a Lewis base—the bromine covalently bound to carbon, which has unshared electron pairs—would be situated very near to each other. They prefer instead to form the three-centered intermediate.

Both types of intermediate can also be written for the reaction between bromine and benzene.

$$\bigcirc + Br^+ \rightarrow \text{(bridged)} \quad or \quad \text{(open carbonium)} \tag{3}$$

The carbonium ion in the benzene case is not nearly so unfavorable. The charge is delocalized over five carbon atoms, instead of being concentrated at one. If the bromine adds also to the adjacent carbon to form the three-centered intermediate, the charge which was highly delocalized would become more localized upon bromine. This seems to be an unfavorable and unlikely event, and it is believed (although there is no proof on this point) that the intermediate in fact has the structure of the open carbonium ion. This type of structure as a definite reaction intermediate corresponding to an energy minimum on the reaction coordinate diagram (as opposed to a transition state which would correspond to an energy maximum) was discussed by Wheland† many years ago, and it has subsequently become known as a *Wheland intermediate*.

† George W. Wheland. Born 1907. University of Chicago.

The Wheland intermediate (or the bridged bromonium ion intermediate, for which the student may as an exercise reformulate the following equations) could undergo attack by bromide ion, to give the dibromide.

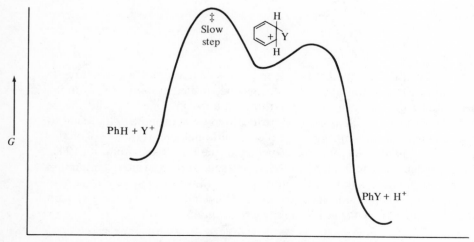

$$(4)$$

Alternatively, the attacking bromide ion may act as a base, and abstract a proton from the carbon to which the bromine is attached, as shown:

$$+ \quad HBr \qquad\qquad (5)$$

From the experimental fact that the product of the reaction is bromobenzene, it appears that the second of these alternatives, reaction (5) is the one that actually takes place.

The best evidence that the Wheland intermediate actually is an intermediate and not just a transition state comes from isotope effects (Section 14.7). In most electrophilic substitution reactions of benzene, the reaction proceeds at the same rate regardless of whether hydrogen, deuterium, or tritium is being replaced by the electrophile (Br^+, or as the case may be). The C—H bond must not, therefore, be broken in the slow step of the reaction. There must consequently be two steps to the reaction, the slow step (the attack on the ring by the electrophile), and a separate step in which the C—H bond is broken. Since the C—H bonds of benzene show no tendency to break spontaneously, this step must follow the other one. These facts require that the reaction coordinate diagram for the typical electrophilic substitution of benzene look as shown in Figure 16.1.

There must be two potential energy barriers corresponding to the two steps. The second one must be lower than the first, but it cannot be negligible. If it were larger than or comparable to the first barrier, or if it were negligible, there would be some C—H bond breaking in the rate-determining part of the reaction, and hence an isotope effect would be observed.

Figure 16.1
Energy diagram for electrophilic substitution of benzene.

Reaction coordinate ——————▶

Returning now to the fact that benzene undergoes substitution rather than addition, let us see if we can understand why in terms of a reaction coordinate diagram. We may formulate such a diagram for an olefin with the following points in mind. We begin with an olefin plus a bromine molecule, and we end with a dibromoalkane. The latter must have a lower energy than the former. As was described in Section 15.4, there are experiments that convince us that the bridged bromonium ion is an intermediate in this reaction. It seems likely that this intermediate has a higher energy than does the starting material. Since it is an intermediate, and it has a finite lifetime, it must have a barrier to reaction by either path (back to starting material, or forward to product). We can therefore draw the reaction coordinate diagram for the whole addition process as indicated in Figure 16.2 (top curve).

Figure 16.2
Energy diagrams for brominations. The circled numbers correspond to the reaction numbers in the text.

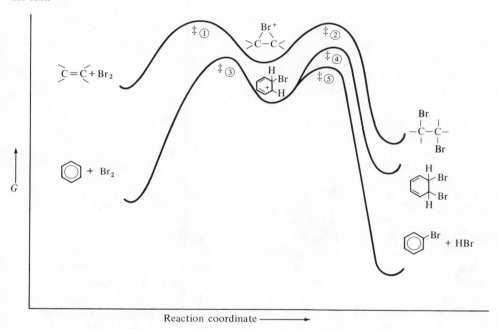

Next, consider the same process using benzene in place of ethylene in the reaction. Since benzene has a very sizable resonance energy, we might consider that we are starting from a point much lower down than we did in the case of ethylene (Figure 16.2, bottom curve).

While we might think of benzene as more stable than ethylene for present purposes, we should note that benzene contains many more atoms than does ethylene, and hence the heat of combustion of a mole of benzene is in fact larger than that of a mole of ethylene.

Since the resonance energy of benzene would have been lost in the dibromide which would result from direct addition, this dibromide product will have a higher energy than does the starting material. Because of the diene resonance, we still can write the energy of this dibromide below that of the dibromide from ethylene. Again, because of the evidence that the Wheland intermediate is a real intermediate rather than a transition state (see below), we need energy barriers separating it both from the starting material and from the product. Since bromobenzene is obtained as the kinetic (as well as the thermodynamic) product of the reaction, there is a lower barrier to reaction of the intermediate by the path which yields bromobenzene (reaction 5) than by the path which yields the dibromide (reaction 4). Hence we can draw this reaction sequence as indicated in Figure 16.2.

We may now summarize the similarities and differences between the reaction of bromine with ethylene, and the reaction of bromine with benzene. Benzene has a large stabilization energy from resonance which is lacking in ethylene. Hence while a powerful electrophile such as Br^+ will attack either one by adding to the pi electrons, which in this case are acting as a Lewis base, the subsequent portions of the reactions differ in the two cases. With ethylene, an addition reaction takes place, by Br^- adding to the other ethylenic carbon atom. With benzene, because of the resonance energy of the aromatic ring, the Wheland intermediate finds its more desirable to have the bromide ion abstract a proton from the carbon to which one bromine is already bound, so that benzene undergoes an *electrophilic substitution reaction*, rather than an electrophilic addition reaction.

The complete mechanism for the bromination of benzene may be written as follows:

$$Br_2 + FeBr_3 \rightleftharpoons Br^+ + FeBr_4^-$$

Benzene and other aromatic compounds similarly undergo a chlorination reaction in the presence of a suitable catalyst. A chloronium ion Cl^+ is generated from chlorine and a Lewis acid, and Cl^+ attacks the aromatic ring in the same way as does Br^+.

Iodobenzene can be obtained from benzene and I_2. Nitric acid is ordinarily used as the essential catalyst in this case. The exact function of the nitric acid is obscure, but presumably it converts I_2 into a more reactive species, probably I^+. In practice, aromatic iodo compounds are not ordinarily prepared by direct iodination, but rather via an amino compound (Section 22.7).

The direct fluorination of benzene is not practical under ordinary conditions, because fluorine is such a powerful oxidizing agent that it reacts explosively with most organic materials. It is possible to fluorinate benzene directly under special conditions, however. Ordinarily, fluorinated benzenes are prepared in a less direct manner (Section 22.7).

There are four types of electrophilic aromatic substitution reactions that are of primary importance in synthetic organic chemistry. There are also a number of additional minor cases which will not be discussed here. The four important reactions are the following:

1. *Halogenation*

$$X_2 + ArH \xrightarrow{\text{Lewis acid}} ArX + HX$$

2. *Nitration*

$$HNO_3 + ArH \xrightarrow{H_2SO_4} ArNO_2 + H_2O$$

3. *Sulfonation*

$$H_2SO_4 + ArH \longrightarrow ArSO_3H + H_2O$$

4. *Friedel–Crafts Reactions*

$$R-X + ArH \xrightarrow{\text{cat.}} Ar-R + HX$$

$$\overset{O}{\overset{\|}{R}C}-X + ArH \xrightarrow{\text{cat.}} Ar-\overset{O}{\overset{\|}{C}}-R + HX$$

Halogenation has been discussed in this section. The other reactions will be discussed in the following three sections.

16.3   Nitration

The nitration of benzene may be carried out by mixing together nitric acid and benzene in the presence of concentrated sulfuric acid and heating the mixture.

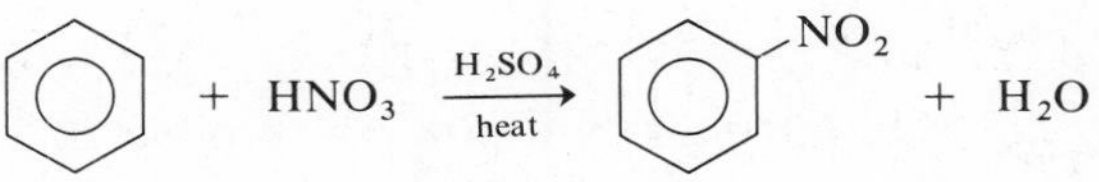

85% yield

This is an electrophilic substitution reaction, quite analogous to the halogenations previously discussed.

EXERCISE 16.1

Draw the Lewis structure and principal resonance forms for NO_2^+.

The electrophilic agent is NO_2^+ (nitronium ion); the nitric and sulfuric acids simply generate NO_2^+. The sulfuric acid, being an extremely strong acid, protonates the nitric acid to give $H_2NO_3^+$, which can lose water to form NO_2^+. Sulfuric acid facilitates this reaction by tying up the water formed. The NO_2^+ ion then attacks the benzene ring, and the usual sequence of events follows. We can write the full mechanism of the reaction as

$$H_2SO_4 + HNO_3 \rightleftharpoons HSO_4^- + H-\overset{+}{\underset{H}{O}}-NO_2$$

$$H_2ONO_2^+ \rightleftharpoons H_2O + NO_2^+$$

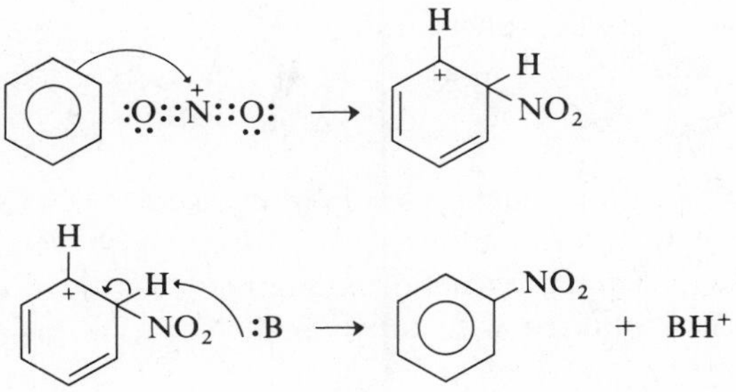

where B: may be H_2O, HSO_4^-, or NO_3^-. Benzene itself is a molecule of average reactivity as aromatic rings go. Highly reactive aromatic compounds (phenol, for example) will react with nitric acid alone, in the absence of sulfuric acid, to give nitro derivatives. In this case the small amount of nitronium ion liberated by self-ionization is sufficient to cause nitration. (The reaction mechanisms in these cases may be more complex, especially in organic solvents.) For relatively unreactive aromatic rings, one may use *fuming nitric and fuming sulfuric acids* and heat the mixture to a relatively high temperature.

Fuming nitric acid is HNO_3 containing NO_2, and fuming sulfuric acid is H_2SO_4 containing SO_3. They are more powerful nitrating and sulfonating agents than the concentrated acids themselves.

The reaction mechanism is the same in each case, but the reactions of different kinds of rings have different activation energies. The reaction conditions are simply chosen to yield a convenient rate of reaction.

When the mechanism for the nitration of benzene was originally proposed, the NO_2^+ ion was a hypothetical species. From studies of the infrared and Raman spectra of mixtures of nitric and sulfuric acids, it has more recently been possible to identify lines in the spectra which had been anticipated for the NO_2^+ ion. In addition, it has proven possible to isolate crystalline salts which contain the nitronium ion, for example, nitronium perchlorate ($NO_2^+ClO_4^-$).

16.4   Sulfonation

Benzene will slowly react with sulfuric acid at elevated temperatures. The product of the reaction is benzenesulfonic acid.

The mechanism of the reaction involves the initial generation of sulfur trioxide (SO_3) from the sulfuric acid. Sulfur trioxide is a relatively powerful electrophile because the sulfur atom is electron-deficient, and it attacks the benzene ring in the usual way. The generation of sulfur trioxide from sulfuric acid and the entire reaction sequence occur as follows:

$$2H_2SO_4 \rightleftharpoons SO_3 + H_3^+O + HSO_4^-$$

The reaction proceeds more easily if fuming sulfuric acid is used in place of concentrated sulfuric acid, as the SO_3 concentration is higher. If the sulfuric acid is diluted with water, the sulfuric acid is solvated and deactivated so that the reaction will not go. Neither does sulfonation occur when the sulfuric acid is diluted with nitric acid. Nitration takes place instead.

The sulfonation of benzene differs somewhat from the previously discussed reactions in that it is reversible at high temperature. If benzenesulfonic acid is treated with superheated steam, it is converted into benzene and sulfuric acid.

This reaction is also an aromatic substitution reaction, and the mechanism is exactly the same as was written for the sulfonation of benzene, except that the steps occur in the reverse order.

The nitration of benzene, and most halogenations of benzene, are irreversible. It is possible at high temperatures to reduce iodobenzene to benzene with hydriodic acid (the other compound formed is iodine). The other reactions mentioned are irreversible in a practical sense. Thus, it is not possible to convert nitrobenzene into benzene and nitric acid by any known direct method. The equilibria are simply too one-sided, or the activation energies are too high, to make this feasible. (Nitrobenzene can be converted into benzene, but more roundabout reaction schemes are required.)

Sulfonation also differs from the other electrophilic substitution reactions of benzene in that a small isotope effect is observed with deuterated benzenes. Since the effect is quite small, it seems that the energy barriers to attack by SO_3 and to proton removal are of similar size (Section 14.7).

EXERCISE 16.2

Figure 16.1 shows the reaction coordinate diagram for a typical aromatic substitution reaction such as nitration or bromination. Draw a similar diagram for sulfonation.

As a practical matter, aromatic sulfonic acids are not usually prepared and handled as such. They tend to be very corrosive, hygroscopic, nonvolatile, water-soluble, and generally unpleasant. Fortunately they are usually desired as intermediates rather than for themselves. If isolation is necessary, sulfonic acids are sometimes obtained as their salts, but more often as the corresponding acid chlorides (called *arenesulfonyl chlorides*). Benzene, for example, reacts with chlorosulfonic acid (2 moles) as follows:

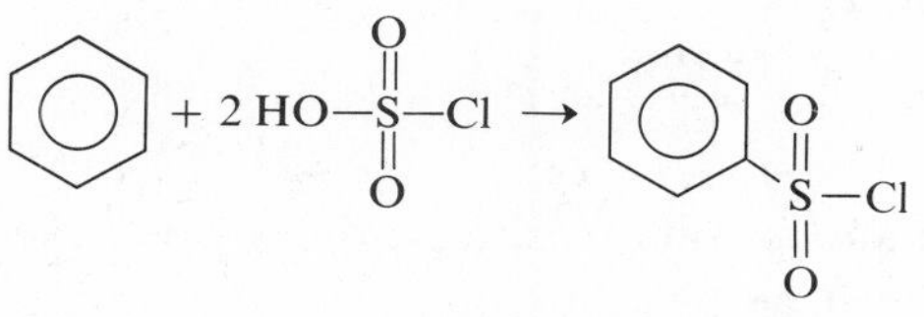

Chlorosulfonic   Benzenesulfonyl
acid   chloride

EXERCISE 16.3

Suggest a mechanism for the reaction of benzene with chlorosulfonic acid.

Most arenesulfonyl chlorides (except the parent benzenesulfonyl chloride), in contrast to the corresponding acids, are nice crystalline compounds which are relatively unreactive and easy to work with.

16.5   Friedel–Crafts Reactions

We can divide Friedel–Crafts reactions into two general types: *alkylations* and *acylations*. The alkylations appear to be the most straightforward at first glance. An example of a Friedel–Crafts alkylation is the following:

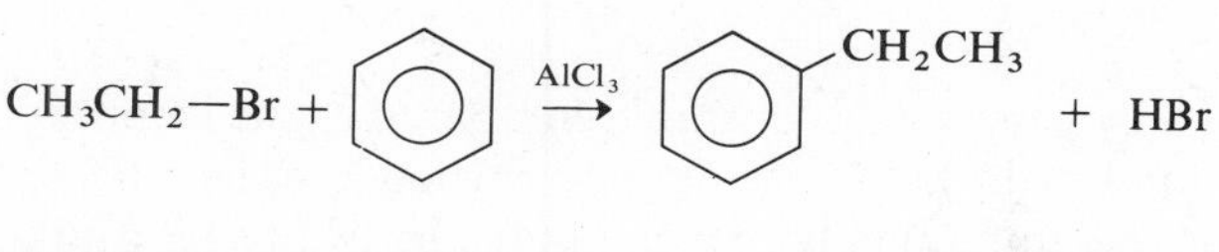

An alkyl halide such as ethyl bromide, by treatment with a suitable Lewis acid (aluminum chloride in this case), is converted to either a free carbonium ion ($CH_3CH_2^+$), or else to a polarized complex which behaves very much as we would expect the carbonium ion to behave. Then this carbonium ion or complex, being a powerful electrophile, attacks the benzene ring in the usual way. The mechanism for the process is

$$CH_3CH_2—Br + AlCl_3 \longrightarrow CH_3CH_2—\overset{+}{Br}—\bar{A}lCl_3 \rightleftharpoons CH_3\overset{+}{C}H_2 + \bar{A}lCl_3Br$$

We have previously discussed the structures of carbonium ions (Sections 12.1, 12.2) and mentioned that they are powerful Lewis acids. They are isoelectronic with organic boron compounds, because they contain a p orbital in which there are no electrons. It was also mentioned in Chapter 12 that carbonium ions have widely differing stabilities; the t-butyl cation is a good deal more stable than is the isopropyl cation, which in turn is more stable than the ethyl cation. In general, a tertiary carbonium ion is a good deal more stable than a secondary, which in turn is more stable than a primary. Benzyl cations are also quite stable. With halides that yield relatively stable carbonium ions, lesser amounts of catalyst are needed, or a weaker Lewis acid may be employed (such as $GaCl_3$, $FeCl_3$, or $ZnCl_2$).

Since Friedel–Crafts alkylations involve carbonium ions, rearrangements present a very serious limitation to the synthetic utility of the reaction. Whereas ethyl bromide will react with a Lewis acid and benzene to yield ethylbenzene, and isopropyl bromide will similarly react to yield isopropylbenzene,

n-propyl bromide will react under the same conditions to afford largely isopropylbenzene:

The mechanism for the reaction of a normal bromide to give an iso product is as follows:

$$CH_3CH_2CH_2—Br \xrightarrow{AlCl_3} CH_3CH_2\overset{+}{C}H_2$$

1,2 H shift

The n-propyl cation which is originally generated is unstable compared to the isopropyl cation, and it turns out to be easy for a hydride to migrate from carbon 2 to the adjacent carbon. Hence the unstable n-propyl cation quickly rearranges to the isopropyl cation. The latter then reacts in the ordinary way. The results of such rearrangements are that Friedel–Crafts alkylations usually give rearranged side chains attached to the benzene ring. Often carbon atoms will migrate, in place of or in addition to hydride ions.

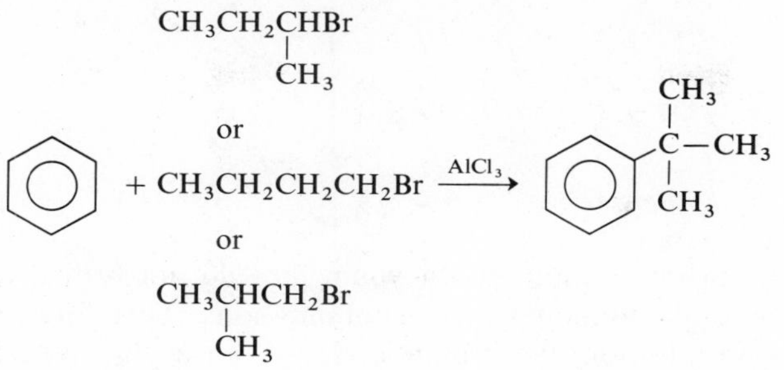

$$
\underset{\substack{\text{CH}_3\text{CH}_2\text{CHBr} \\ | \\ \text{CH}_3}}{}
$$

$$\text{or}$$

$$\bigcirc + \text{CH}_3\text{CH}_2\text{CH}_2\text{CH}_2\text{Br} \xrightarrow{\text{AlCl}_3}$$

$$\text{or}$$

$$\underset{\substack{| \\ \text{CH}_3}}{\text{CH}_3\text{CHCH}_2\text{Br}}$$

There are a variety of ways in which one may generate carbonium ions other than by the reaction of a halide with a strong Lewis acid. For example, one may allow ethylene or ethanol to react with sulfuric acid, and either of these processes will generate the ethyl cation. It is often possible to utilize an olefin or an alcohol in the presence of a suitable Lewis acid, in place of a halide in a Friedel–Crafts reaction. The following two examples are of considerable commercial importance:

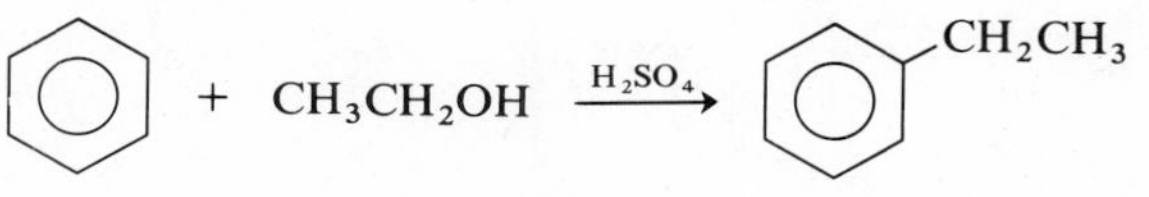

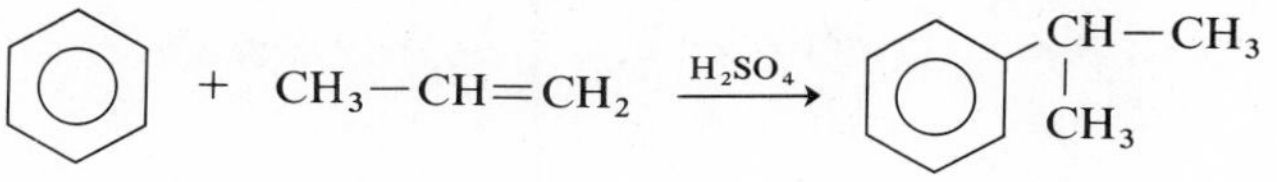

$$\bigcirc + \text{CH}_3\text{CH}_2\text{OH} \xrightarrow{\text{H}_2\text{SO}_4} \bigcirc\text{—CH}_2\text{CH}_3$$

$$\bigcirc + \text{CH}_3\text{—CH}\text{=CH}_2 \xrightarrow{\text{H}_2\text{SO}_4} \underset{\substack{| \\ \text{CH}_3}}{\bigcirc\text{—CH}\text{—CH}_3}$$

Ketones (or aldehydes) can also sometimes be used as alkylating agents. The insecticide DDT is prepared from chloral and chlorobenzene.

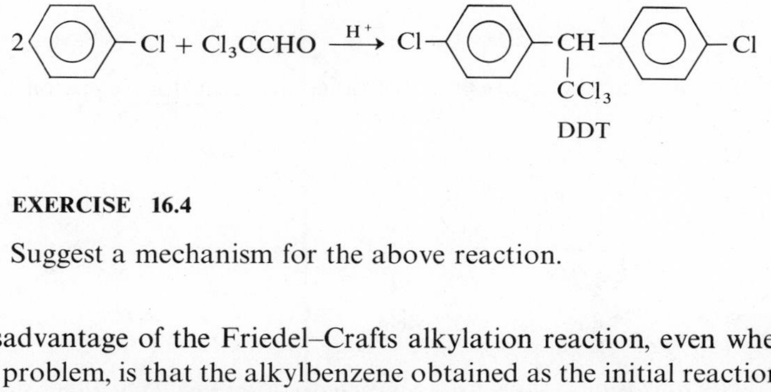

$$2\bigcirc\text{—Cl} + \text{Cl}_3\text{CCHO} \xrightarrow{\text{H}^+} \text{Cl}\text{—}\bigcirc\text{—}\underset{\substack{| \\ \text{CCl}_3}}{\text{CH}}\text{—}\bigcirc\text{—Cl}$$

DDT

EXERCISE   16.4

Suggest a mechanism for the above reaction.

A disadvantage of the Friedel–Crafts alkylation reaction, even when rearrangement is not a problem, is that the alkylbenzene obtained as the initial reaction product is more reactive than benzene itself, and dialkylation as a side reaction may be a serious problem.

Because of the rearrangement reactions which typically occur with carbonium ions, and the problem of polyalkylation, Friedel–Crafts alkylation reactions are a good deal less useful than one might have supposed at the outset. Fortunately, there is a modification of the Friedel–Crafts method which is suitable for the preparation of compounds such as *n*-propylbenzene which are not obtained cleanly by the direct alkylation procedure. The modification is referred to as the *Friedel–Crafts acylation reaction*. One begins with an acid chloride, rather than with an alkyl chloride. For example, instead of propyl chloride the reaction is carried out with propionyl chloride.

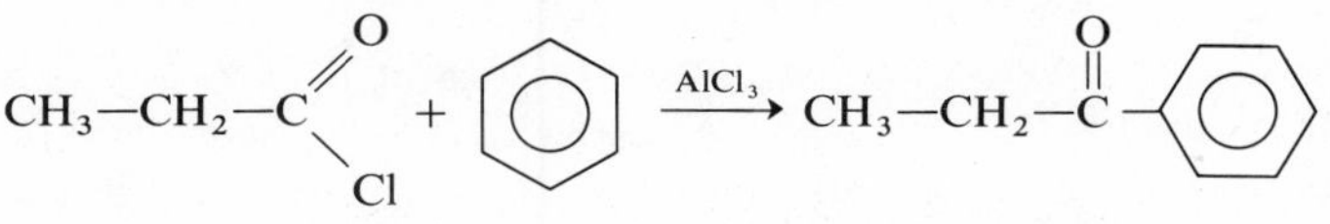

$$\underset{\substack{\\ \text{Cl}}}{\text{CH}_3\text{—CH}_2\text{—C}}\overset{\text{O}}{\diagup} + \bigcirc \xrightarrow{\text{AlCl}_3} \text{CH}_3\text{—CH}_2\overset{\overset{\text{O}}{\|}}{\text{—C}}\text{—}\bigcirc$$

90% yield

In this case the product of the reaction is a ketone, ethyl phenyl ketone. The reaction proceeds through an *acylium ion*,

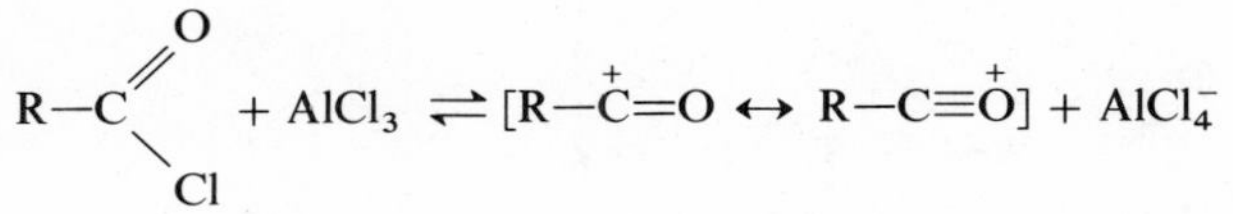

$$R-\overset{O}{\underset{Cl}{\overset{\|}{C}}} + AlCl_3 \rightleftharpoons [R-\overset{+}{C}=O \leftrightarrow R-C\equiv\overset{+}{O}] + AlCl_4^-$$

An acylium ion

rather than through an ordinary carbonium ion, and acylium ions do not ordinarily undergo the rearrangement reactions common with carbonium ions. Therefore, *an unrearranged ketone is obtained*. In addition, the aromatic ring of an acylbenzene is much less reactive toward electrophiles than benzene itself, and diacylation is not a significant side reaction.

To complete the preparation of an alkylbenzene, the ketone from the Friedel–Crafts acylation is converted to a hydrocarbon by removal of the carbonyl oxygen. This may be accomplished by a number of methods, which are discussed in Section 19.12. The Friedel–Crafts acylation reaction thus proves to be a much more useful synthetic procedure than does the more direct alkylation reaction.

Some additional examples of acylation are

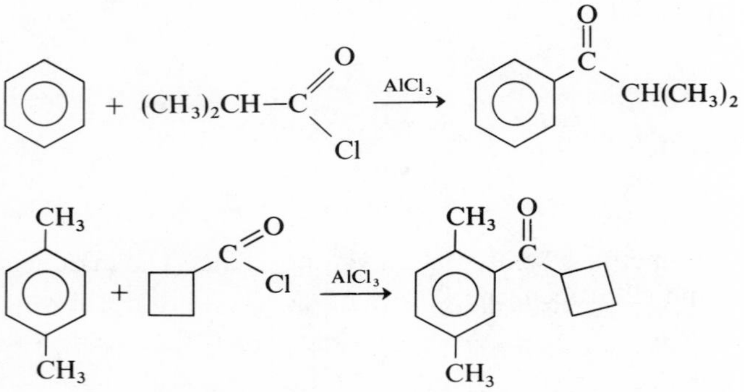

An especially useful application of acylation is an intramolecular reaction resulting in ring closure.

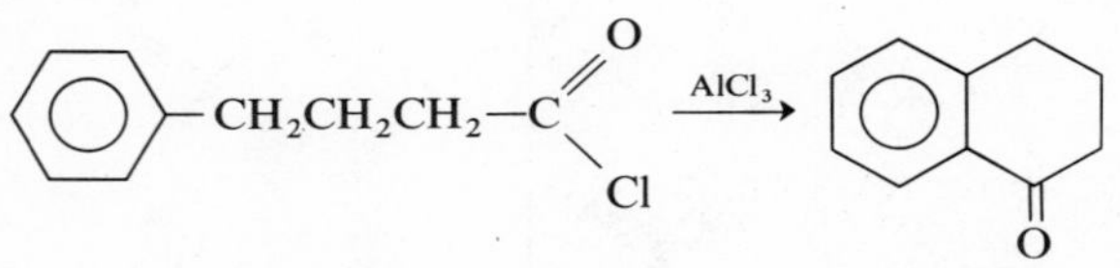

90% yield

In carrying out Friedel–Crafts acylations, one must employ more than one equivalent of catalyst (AlCl$_3$) because the ketone formed is basic enough to form a salt with the Lewis acid, and reduce the catalytic activity of the latter.

Friedel–Crafts acylations can also be carried out using an anhydride as the acylating agent.

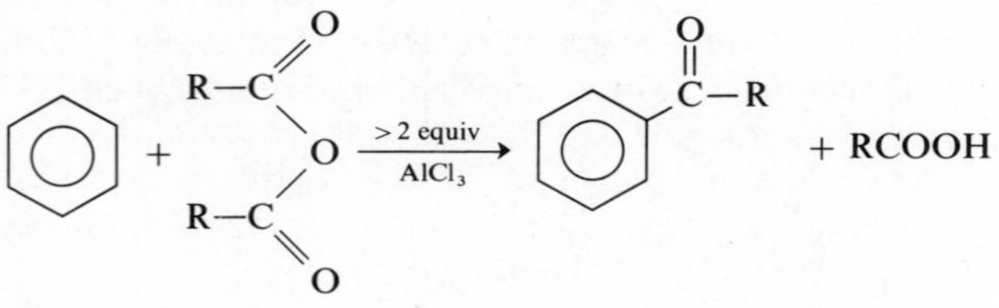

The generation of the acylium ion (the active electrophile) from the anhydride and aluminum chloride can be shown as

$$R-C\overset{\displaystyle O}{\Big\langle} \quad R-C\overset{\displaystyle O}{\Big\langle}$$

Greater than two equivalents of $AlCl_3$ must be used because one is tied up by the acid (from the anhydride) and the other is complexed to the product ketone. Cyclic anhydrides may be used very effectively for this reaction.

80% yield

EXERCISE 16.5

Write out the complete mechanism for the Friedel–Crafts acylation of toluene by acetyl chloride, using aluminum chloride as the catalyst.

16.6   Activation Effects of Substituents

As shown in Figure 16.2, for the bromination of benzene the rate-determining step of the reaction is the formation of the Wheland intermediate. This seems generally to be true for electrophilic aromatic substitutions. The benzene ring is supporting a considerable amount of positive charge in the transition state. If we recognize that the transition state looks very much like the Wheland intermediate and draw its resonance forms, we find that the positive charge is mostly localized on positions ortho and para to the attacking electrophile.

The meta positions contain an increased amount of positive charge also, from induction, but the bulk of the charge is located at the positions indicated.

Since all electrophilic substitutions of aromatic rings in general proceed through the same type of intermediate, and since this intermediate contains an excess of positive charge, it seems clear that any substituent on the benzene ring which offers to stabilize the positive charge will lower the energy of the intermediate. Conversely, any substituent on the ring which tends to destabilize this positive charge by withdrawing electrons from the ring, will tend to destabilize the intermediate. If the Wheland intermediate is stabilized, the transition state is also stabilized, and such a stabilization will lead to a faster reaction. (Evans–Polanyi principle, page 299.) On the other hand, if the Wheland intermediate is destabilized, the transition-state energy is increased relative to the ground-state energy, and the reaction will be slower.

It is an easy task to divide the possible substituents which might be attached to a benzene ring into two categories: firstly, those which are electron-donating, which will stabilize the positive charge in the ring, and which lead to a faster reaction; and, secondly, those which are electron-withdrawing, which will destabilize the transition state and will lead to a slower reaction. If the substitution of a group on the benzene ring makes the compound more reactive toward electrophilic substitution, the group is said to be an *activating group*, while if the substitution of a group on the ring slows the rate of reaction, the group is referred to as a *deactivating group*. The situation may be qualitatively summarized by saying that electron-donating groups are activating, while electron-attracting groups are deactivating.

The effect which a group can have on the rate of reaction may be very large indeed. The difference between the rate of reaction of phenol (which contains a powerful activating group) and nitrobenzene (which contains a powerful deactivating group) under the same conditions is often a factor of a million or more. This means that a reaction of phenol which may proceed at a convenient rate (requiring an hour, say) might, with nitrobenzene under the same conditions, require 1 million hours (about 100 years), and such a reaction would not be of much practical use.

Let us now look at the various common types of groups, and try to decide which will be electron-donating and which will be electron-withdrawing. Armed with this knowledge, we can make qualitative predictions as to which groups will be activating and which will be deactivating. More important, once we understand how the electron attracting or donating properties of a group may be determined from a consideration of the structure of the group, then we are prepared to extend the ideas to any other group in which we may be interested. It is possible to put activating effects on a quantitative basis, but here we are concerned only with a qualitative understanding of the subject.

As has been mentioned in earlier chapters, there are two mechanisms by which a group may withdraw or donate electrons from or to the attached moiety (the benzene ring in this case): the *inductive effect* and the *resonance effect*. Suppose we take five groups as a representative sampling and see what we are able to predict about the activating properties of these groups on the basis of what we already know. We will choose the methyl, amino, nitro, carboxyl, and chloro groups.

Can we put these compounds in order according to their reactivity with an electrophilic reagent?

Compared to benzene, toluene should be more reactive by virtue of the inductive effect of the methyl group and the hyperconjugation effect. Recall that when a carbon sp^3 orbital is attached to an sp^2 orbital of carbon, there is an electron donation in the direction of the sp^2 carbon. (The student may wish to review the discussion on pages 144 and 261.) While hyperconjugation is of some importance in the ground state of toluene, it is *sacrificial* hyperconjugation (Section 12.2). The effect is a good deal more important in the Wheland intermediate, where it becomes *isovalent* hyperconjugation.

Thus toluene, and alkylbenzenes in general, are more reactive than benzene itself. Alkyl groups are found to be relatively weak activating groups, however.

Next, consider the aniline molecule. The electronegativity of an sp^2 carbon orbital is between that of an sp^3 orbital of nitrogen (which is more electronegative) and a p orbital of nitrogen (which is less electronegative). Since the bonding orbitals from amino nitrogens are ordinarily between p and sp^3 in character, the nitrogen in a molecule of the aniline type is similar to the attached carbon in electronegativity, and the inductive effect of the amino group attached to the benzene ring is small. There is, however, a very large resonance effect. The lone pair of electrons on nitrogen is partly delocalized into the aromatic ring, as shown by the resonance forms below:

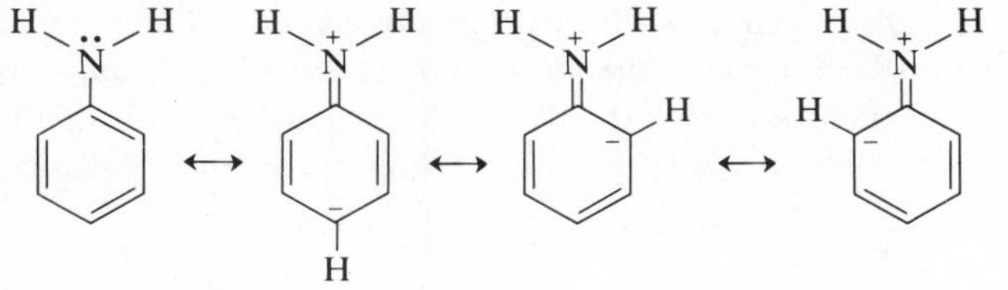

Compared to toluene, where electrons are supplied to the ring by resonance from the C—H σ bond, here the electrons being supplied are nonbonding ones, and they are not held nearly as tightly by the nitrogen as are the C—H bonding electrons in toluene. The aniline molecule has an excess of electrons available to the aromatic ring by resonance, and it is therefore highly reactive toward electrophilic reagents. (Recall that it is this resonance that makes aniline such a weak base, relative to aliphatic amines, Section 11.3.) We will postpone a discussion of the Wheland intermediate which results when an electrophile attacks aniline until the next section. At this point we only note that the aniline molecule is very much more reactive toward electrophiles than is toluene, which in turn is considerably more reactive than is benzene.

Now let us examine benzoic acid. Here an sp^2 carbon from the benzene ring is bound to an sp^2 carbon from the carboxyl group, and the inductive effect which results does not come directly from this bond, but only from atoms further away. In the carboxyl group, two oxygen atoms are attached to the carbonyl carbon. These exert a substantial electron-withdrawing effect upon the carboxyl carbon, because of the high electronegativity of the oxygens. This removal of electrons from the carboxyl carbon by oxygen increases the electronegativity of the carboxyl carbon, which in turn then withdraws electrons inductively from the benzene ring.

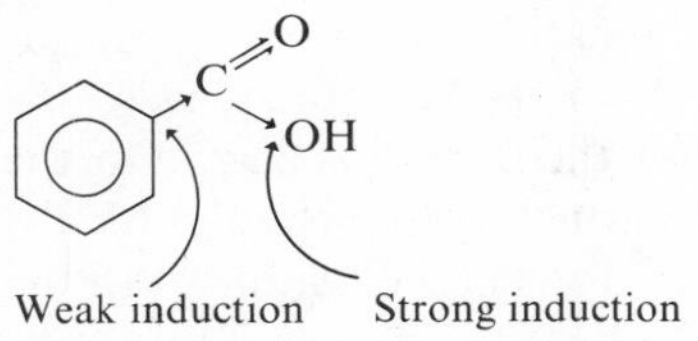

Weak induction   Strong induction

Therefore, the inductive effect of the carboxyl group deactivates the ring, but this effect is not very large.

In addition, there is a resonance effect involving the carboxyl group. Some of the important resonance forms of benzoic acid are as follows:

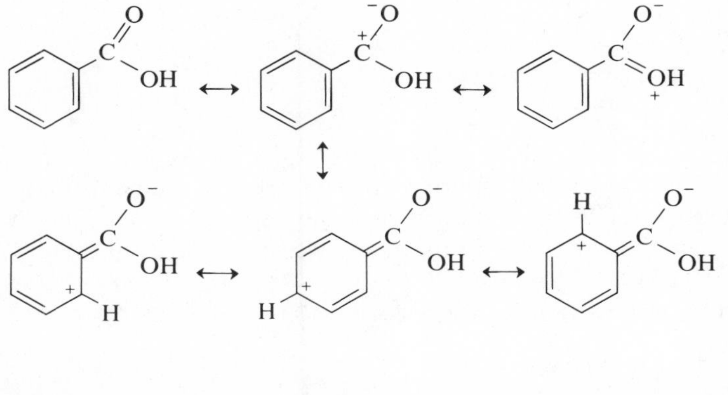

Notice that some of these forms place a positive charge in the benzene ring, while none of them place a negative charge in the benzene ring. Because the first two forms are relatively more important than the others, the resonance effect of the carboxyl group is only moderate, but both the resonance and the inductive effects of this group lead to deactivation. Relative to benzene then, benzoic acid is unreactive toward electrophiles. In our series of compounds, the reactivity order so far is aniline > toluene > benzene > benzoic acid.

Nitrobenzene is a deactivated molecule, and all of the inductive and resonance arguments which apply to the carboxyl group apply equally to the nitro group, but quantitatively the effects are larger. The nitro group withdraws electrons inductively more effectively than the carboxyl group because the nitrogen atom of the nitro group has sp^2 hybridization and is more electronegative than the sp^2-hybridized carbon of the carboxyl group. The nitro group is also an electron-withdrawing group by resonance, as the forms shown will illustrate:

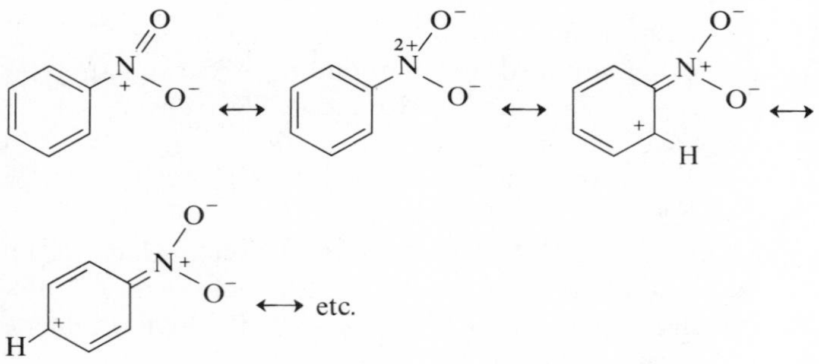

The nitro group is the most powerful electron-withdrawing group of those we have considered, in fact it is one of the most powerful of all.

Chlorobenzene is somewhat more complicated than the previously examined molecules. In toluene, the methyl group is an electron-donating group, both by resonance (hyperconjugation) and by induction. In aniline, there is a large resonance effect and a small inductive effect. With benzoic acid and nitrobenzene, both resonance and induction tend to withdraw electrons from the ring. Chlorobenzene differs from all of these, in that it shows large inductive and resonance effects, but they are in opposite directions and nearly cancel one another. Chlorine is highly electronegative and clearly the inductive effect of chlorine is to withdraw electrons from the aromatic ring. On the other hand, chlorine has one of its unshared pairs of electrons in a p orbital which is parallel to the p orbitals of the benzene ring, and these electrons can be donated to the ring, in analogy to the kind of donation discussed for aniline. While the nitrogen of aniline is a very good electron donor by resonance, the chlorine is not as good, both because of the high electronegativity of the chlorine atom, and because of the poor $2p(C)$–$3p(Cl)$ orbital overlap (Section 10.4).

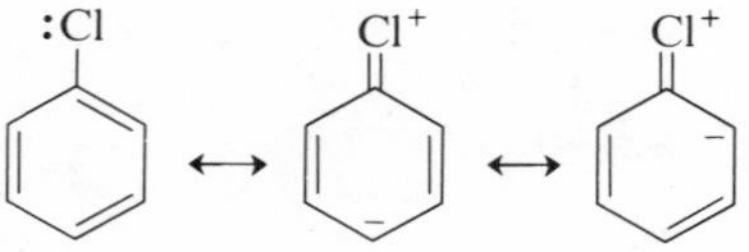

As one might guess, the inductive effect of chlorine wins out over the resonance effect, and the chlorine atom deactivates the benzene ring, but not by very much. The six compounds we have considered may now be arranged in order of reactivity as follows:

aniline > toluene > benzene > chlorobenzene > benzoic acid > nitrobenzene

Our rationalizations are consistent with the available experimental facts. For the nitration reaction (under similar but not identical conditions) the following relative rate constants were obtained:

PhOH	PhCH$_3$	PhH	PhCl	PhCOOH	PhNO$_2$
1000	25	1.0	0.30	0.004	0.0001

(Aniline is converted to the rather unreactive anilinium salt by nitric acid, so it cannot be directly compared in the above sequence. When such a complication does not arise, aniline is usually more reactive than phenol.)

The principles that have been discussed are very general ones, and they can be applied to any other functional group to determine whether it is activating or deactivating. It is convenient to have a simple symbolism which will summarize the type of discussion given above. If a group takes on a negative charge by *induction*, the group is said to possess a $-I$ effect. If the group takes on a positive charge by induction, it is said to possess a $+I$ effect. Similarly, if the group takes on a negative charge by *resonance*, it is said to possess a $-R$ effect, while if it takes on a positive charge by resonance, it is said to possess a $+R$ effect. A $+I$ or $+R$ effect tends to make the substituent positive and the ring negative, and these are activating effects. A $-I$ or $-R$ effect tends to put negative charge on the substituent and positive charge in the ring, and they are therefore deactivating. The amino group of aniline is a $+R$ group. The methyl group in toluene is a $+R$, $+I$ group. The nitro group of nitrobenzene is said to be $-R$, $-I$ since it withdraws electrons by both mechanisms. Finally, the chlorine atom in chlorobenzene is said to be $+R$, $-I$.

EXERCISE 16.6

Using the kinds of arguments given previously to decide which groups were activating and which were deactivating, decide whether or not the groups

$$-CF_3 \text{ and } -C\overset{\displaystyle N-Ph}{\underset{\displaystyle CH_3}{\diagup}}$$

will be activating, and their approximate positions in the series shown on page 360.

In Table 16.1 are listed the more common substituents found on aromatic rings. These have been divided into strong and weak activators and deactivators, and the R and I characteristics of each are indicated.

Table 16.1   Classification of Common Substituent Groups According to Their Activating Effects on Electrophilic Aromatic Substitutions

Activating groups	Deactivating groups
Powerful	
$-NH_2, -NHR, -NR_2,$	$-NO_2 \, (-R, -I)$
$-OH, -O^- \, (+R)$	$-NR_3^+ \, (-I)$
Intermediate	
$-OR, -NHCOR \, (+R, -I)$	$-C\equiv N, -CHO, -COR,$
	$-COOH \, (-R, -I)$
Weak	
$-Ph \, (+R)$	$-F, -Cl, -Br, -I \, (+R, -I)$
$-Alkyl \, (+R, +I)$	

EXERCISE 16.7

Why is $-NH_2$ a more powerful activating group than $-NHCOCH_3$?

16.7   Orientation Effects of Substituents

If there is already one substituent present on a benzene ring, an incoming electrophilic agent can attack at any of three positions, and a mixture of ortho-, meta-, and para-substituted products might be expected. It was found by the early chemists that the relative orientations of the substituents in the reaction products did not ordinarily depend in a qualitative way upon what the incoming electrophile was. Rather, the orientation of the product depended upon what kind of substituent was already present on the benzene ring when the reaction was carried out. Nitrobenzene, for example, always gave a reaction product which was a meta-substituted nitrobenzene, regardless of whether the reaction was nitration, sulfonation, bromination, or some other electrophilic substitution.

Next the observation was made that the reaction product was one of two general types and that the substituents on the ring could be classified according to which type of reaction product they produced. Of the compounds specifically discussed in the previous section, nitrobenzene and benzoic acid both gave very largely meta-substituted derivatives upon electrophilic substitution. The nitro and carboxyl groups were therefore called *meta directors*, since they directed the incoming electrophile into the meta position. The remaining substituents discussed above—the amino and methyl groups, and the chlorine atom—gave very little meta-substituted product, but instead gave a mixture of ortho and para isomers. These groups, therefore, were called *ortho, para directors*. All substituents fall into one or the other of these two classes. A substituent is either a meta director, or it is an ortho, para director.

Interpretation of these observations, developed more or less simultaneously and independently by two English chemists, Sir Robert Robinson and Sir Christopher Ingold,[†] was one of the triumphs of the early electronic theory of organic chemistry. To understand the ideas set forth by these two men, we might begin with nitrobenzene. If nitrobenzene is brominated, the reaction product is almost exclusively *meta*-bromonitrobenzene. Can we understand why in terms of the $-I$ and $-R$ effects of the nitro group? The $-I$ effect of the nitro group tends to withdraw electrons from the benzene ring; mostly it withdraws electrons from the atoms nearest to the nitro group. Thus the $-I$ effect by itself will tend to pull electrons away from the ortho positions to a large extent, from the meta positions to a lesser extent, and from the para position to an even smaller extent. Since these electrons are needed for bond formation to the attacking electrophile, the $-I$ effect would suggest that the electrophile would prefer to attack at the para position, where the electron density is the highest, the meta position being a second choice, and the ortho position being the poorest choice of all. These considerations do not lead to a correct prediction of the reaction product, so we need to look further. Suppose we look at the $-R$ effect of the nitro group. The following resonance forms appear to be important:

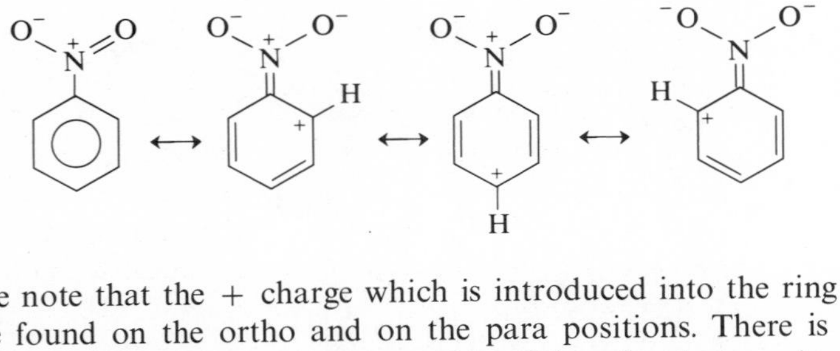

Now we note that the + charge which is introduced into the ring by the nitro group is to be found on the ortho and on the para positions. There is no resonance form which puts the + charge on a meta position. Thus the electron density is higher on the meta position than on the other positions, as far as the results of this resonance are concerned. Resonance considerations, therefore, suggest that the electrophile would

† Sir Robert Robinson. Born 1886, Rufford/Chesterfield, England. Liverpool, Manchester, and Oxford Universities. Nobel Prize 1947.

Sir Christopher K. Ingold. Born 1893, Ilford, England. University College, London.

attack at the meta position, which is what is observed. The resonance effect tends to reduce the electron density at the ortho and para positions, making reaction there very unfavorable. The inductive effect reduces the electron density at all of the ring atoms, making reaction anywhere relatively unfavorable. Hence the attack by an electrophile on the nitrobenzene molecule is difficult and the reaction proceeds slowly; but when it does go, it goes in such a way as to yield a meta-substituted product.

The above interpretation is based upon an examination of the ground state of the nitrobenzene molecule. Frequently, chemists make predictions as to where aromatic substitution will occur on the basis of such a consideration of the ground state. *This is not the strictly correct method of approach, however.* The rate of reaction at any given position is governed by the difference in free energy between the ground state and the transition state corresponding to substitution at that position. Thus, to decide whether the nitrobenzene would substitute in the ortho, meta, or para position, we really ought to examine the transition states which result from substitution at these different positions. Since these three transition states all are produced from the same ground state, the transition state which is formed preferentially will be the one which is of lower energy. Recalling that the Wheland intermediate is a good approximation to the transition state, we may consider the intermediates which will result from meta and from para substitution. Let us examine first the case where there is present on the ring a substituent such as methyl, which shows $+I$ and $+R$ effects. Subsequently, similar intermediates having a substituent such as nitro, which shows $-I$ and $-R$ effects, will be considered.

If the electrophile (Y^+) attacks toluene at the para position, the resulting intermediate has three important resonance forms:

Para attack

On the other hand, if the attack is at the meta position, the resonance forms of the resulting intermediate are as follows:

Meta attack

If we now compare the resonance forms which result from para attack with those which result from meta attack, there appears to be one resonance form which we can set apart from the others. The inductive effect of the methyl group, or the effect of any group attached to the ring, is most strongly felt at the carbon where the attachment is made, so induction favors para substitution over meta. In addition, for para substitution

Favored by induction   (three forms)
Hyperconjugative forms

there are three hyperconjugative forms. (There are none for meta substitution.) These inductive and resonance effects tend to stabilize the Wheland intermediate for para substitution to a larger degree than they tend to stabilize the Wheland intermediate for meta substitution. Therefore, the methyl group is found to be a para director rather than a meta director. One can likewise write very favorable resonance forms for the ortho-substituted Wheland intermediate:

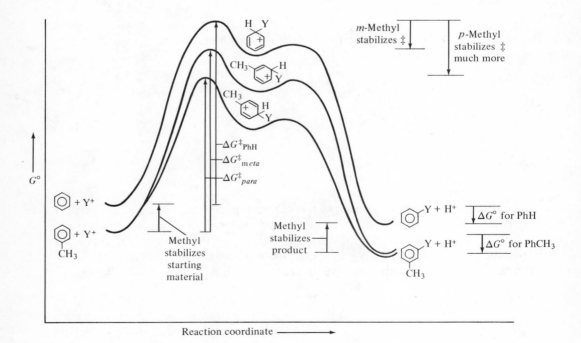

Favored by induction   (three forms)

Hence the methyl group leads to an especially favorable transition state from attack at either the ortho or para position. For the meta-substituted Wheland intermediate, corresponding resonance forms are not possible; the positive charge is at best one carbon removed from the point of attachment of the methyl group. The methyl group does stabilize the meta-substituted intermediate a little bit compared to the analogous intermediate in benzene, but it stabilizes the ortho or para-substituted intermediates considerably more. Consequently the ortho- and para-substituted Wheland intermediates resulting from toluene are lower in energy than the meta-substituted one. The energy of the corresponding transition state is similarly lower, and thus the methyl group is an ortho, para director and an activating group (see Figure 16.3).

Figure 16.3

A reaction coordinate diagram for the electrophilic substitution of benzene and toluene.

If we now turn our attention to nitrobenzene, the argument follows a path parallel to that used for toluene. The meta- and para-substituted intermediates which result from attack by an electrophile on nitrobenzene have the resonance forms shown:

Para attack

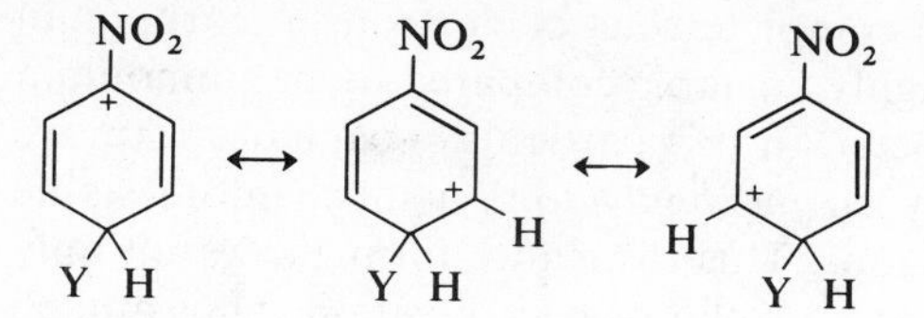

Meta attack

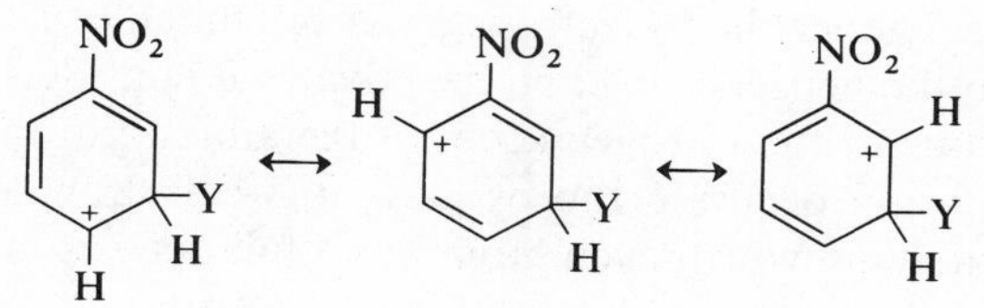

EXERCISE 16.8

Write out the resonance forms for substitution of nitrobenzene at the ortho position and compare these with the forms shown for substitution at the meta and para positions.

In this case, one form (the one at the upper left) is particularly *unfavorable*. The nitrogen of the nitro group carries a partial positive charge, and a resonance form which places a positive charge on the carbon to which the nitro group is attached contributes very little to the stability of the Wheland intermediate. The para-substituted Wheland intermediate therefore has only two resonance forms contributing effectively to its structure, whereas the meta-substituted one has three. The latter situation is, of course, more favorable. Thus the meta-substituted Wheland intermediate is more stable and the transition state leading to it is of lower energy. The nitro group is thus a meta director, as well as a deactivating group.

The amino group is a powerful ortho, para director. The Wheland intermediate which results when aniline is attacked by an electrophile at the para position has a number of resonance forms:

Para attack

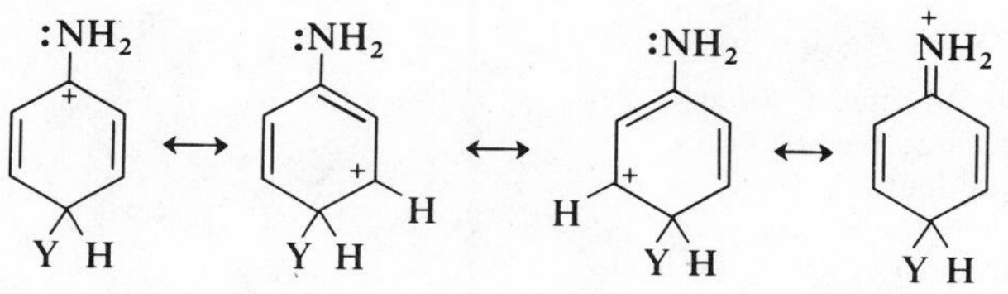

The corresponding intermediate for meta attack has the following resonance forms:

Meta attack

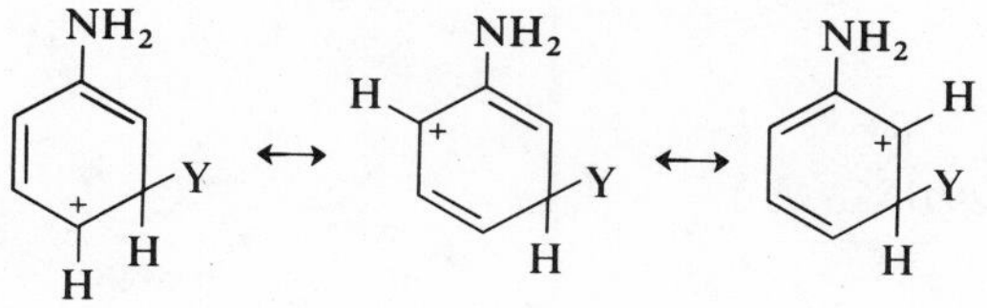

For these intermediates, the most important form is

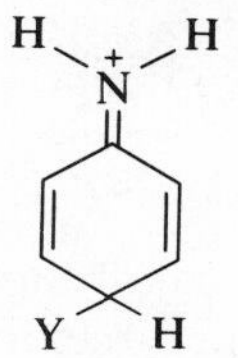

That this particular form is especially important can be seen by noting that in this form, and only in this form, each of the atoms has a complete octet of electrons. A carbonium ion, with its sextet of electrons, tends to be highly unstable compared to an ammonium ion, in which the nitrogen has a completed octet. In this particular resonance form we have essentially an ammonium ion (actually an *immonium* ion), a much more stable sort of thing than the alternative carbonium ions. This resonance form can result only if the substitution into the ring has occurred at an ortho or para position. Thus aniline is a powerful ortho, para director, as well as a powerful activating group.

Finally, we may consider chlorobenzene. The very high electronegativity of the chlorine atom effectively withdraws electrons from the benzene ring and deactivates it considerably. The chlorine atom is partly analogous to the nitrogen atom of the amino group in aniline, however, in that if the substitution occurs ortho or para, one can draw a resonance form for the Wheland intermediate in which each atom has a full octet.

The result of these two opposing effects is that the chlorine in chlorobenzene is an ortho, para director, but the compound reacts quite slowly, and the chlorine is in fact a deactivating group.

EXERCISE 16.9

Explain (using resonance forms) why chlorobenzene substitutes ortho as well as para.

Now we may summarize the experimental evidence available concerning the directive influence of various groups, and note that the behavior of each group can be understood on the basis of the foregoing discussion (see Table 16.2).

Table 16.2   Classification of the Common Substituent Groups According to Their Oriental Directing Effects on Electrophilic Aromatic Substitutions

Ortho, para directors	Meta directors
Powerful	
$-NH_2, -NHR, -NR_2,$ $-OH, -O^-$	$-NO_2, -NH_3^+, -NR_3^+$
Intermediate	
$-OR, -NHCOCH_3$	$-C{\equiv}N, -SO_3H$
Weak	
$-R, -Ph, -F,$ $-Cl, -Br, -I$	$-CHO, -COR,$ $-COOR, -COOH$

EXERCISE 16.10

Explain and show by means of resonance forms why $-Ph$ is an ortho, para director. Why do you suppose $-NH_3^+$ is a meta director?

It is important that the student remembers which of the common functional groups are activators and deactivators (Table 16.1), and which groups are ortho, para directors and meta directors (Table 16.2). In general, groups which have a *lone pair of electrons* on the atom attached to the ring are activators and ortho, para-directors ($-\text{NH}_2$, $-\text{OCH}_3$, etc.), the halogens being a special case. If the atom attached to the ring bears a positive charge, partly or completely (check all resonance forms), it will be a meta

director ($-\text{NH}_3^+$; $-\text{CF}_3$; $-\text{C}\underset{Z}{\overset{O}{\langle}} \leftrightarrow -\overset{+}{\text{C}}\underset{Z}{\overset{O\_}{\langle}}$; etc.).

The foregoing arguments may be extended to include an electrophilic aromatic substitution taking place on a benzene ring which carries two substituents, such as *p*-nitrotoluene. Where will the incoming group go? The methyl group tries to direct the incoming group ortho (the para position is blocked). The nitro group is trying to direct it meta. In this case the two substituents cooperate and both direct the incoming group to the same carbon. The reaction product is therefore easy to predict.

Suppose, however, that the same two groups are present in a meta relationship. What orientation will the substitution product of *meta*-nitrotoluene have?

Ordinarily an incoming group will not go in between any two groups already present for steric reasons. Of the remaining positions, the methyl tries to direct the incoming group into the positions indicated by the large arrows, whereas the nitro group tries to direct it to the position indicated by the small arrow. Experimentally, it is found that activating groups win out over deactivating groups, so the product will be a mixture of the isomers shown.

Finally, consider electrophilic substitution of *p*-bromoanisole.

As one would expect, the powerful activator wins out over a weaker activator (which wins out over a deactivator), and the product is

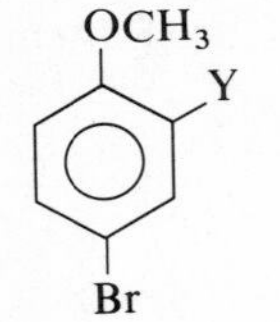

EXERCISE 16.11

What will be the principal product(s) from an electrophilic aromatic substitution reaction with each of the following molecules?

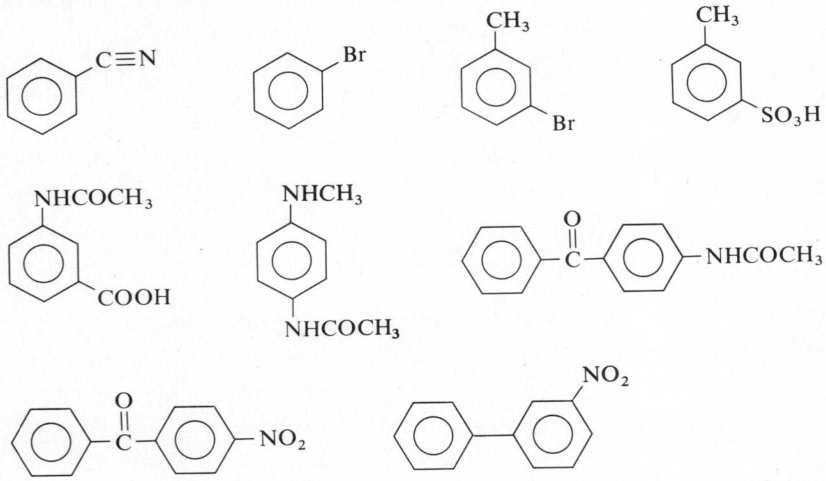

16.8   Substitution in Fused Ring Systems

The reaction of an aromatic compound with an electrophile to yield a substitution product is quite a general one. Benzene and substituted benzenes undergo this kind of reaction, and so do almost all other aromatic compounds. Naphthalene, for example, reacts with various electrophiles to substitute at one of the two types of available positions. (The student may wish to review the earlier discussion of naphthalene, Section 11.7.) Most reactions take place at the 1 position (the α position). The bromination of naphthalene, for example, proceeds as follows:

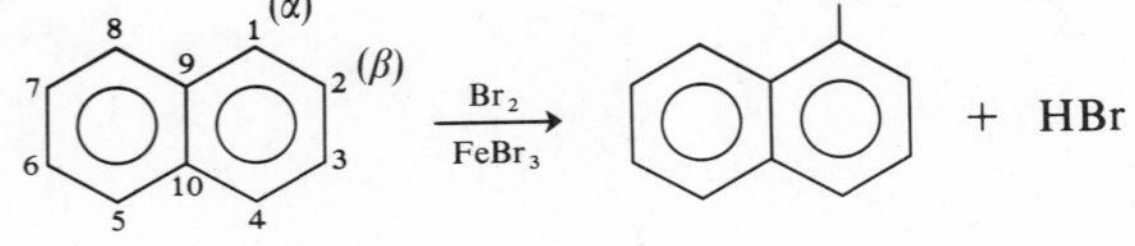

Similarly, the nitration of naphthalene yields α-nitronaphthalene, and sulfonation at low temperature yields α-naphthalenesulfonic acid.

The tendency for naphthalene to substitute α rather than β can be understood in terms of the Wheland intermediates. Direct solution of the Schroedinger equation for the two cases indicates that the α-substituted intermediate is of lower energy. In terms of resonance forms, this is perhaps best seen by noting that the α-substituted intermediate has two resonance forms (apart from the forms which involve the other ring), while the β-substituent intermediate has but one.

α *Substitution*   β *Substitution*

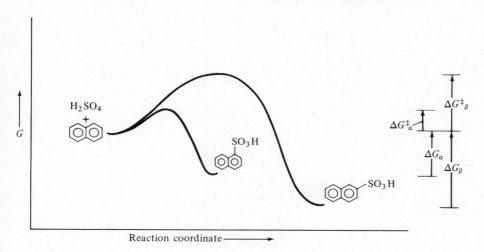

At high temperatures, napthalene can be sulfonated in the 2, or β position. The reason for the temperature dependence of the reaction product in this case stems from the fact that the sulfonation reaction is reversible. The α position is more reactive, and hence if the reaction is kinetically controlled, α substitution results. β-Naphthalenesulfonic acid is the more stable isomer, however, so that if thermodynamic control takes over, then the β isomer predominates. At a sufficiently high temperature, the α-naphthalene sulfonic acid is formed reversibly, and the more stable β isomer is formed slowly, but rather irreversibly. The reaction coordinate diagram for the sulfonation of naphthalene is illustrated in Figure 16.4 and should be carefully studied by the student. ΔG_β is more

Figure 16.4

The sulfonation of naphthalene. (For clarity, the Wheland intermediate is not shown.)

negative than ΔG_α, so that if equilibrium is established, the β isomer predominates. $\Delta G_\beta^\ddagger$ is larger than $\Delta G_\alpha^\ddagger$, however, so that the α product is more rapidly formed. The α isomer is the product of kinetic control of the reaction, while the β isomer is the product of thermodynamic control. We can summarize the sulfonation of naphthalene as follows:

From the experimental point of view, it is possible to prepare either the 1- or the 2-naphthalenesulfonic acid by choosing the proper temperature at which to carry out the reaction.

EXERCISE 16.12

Which of the naphthalenesulfonic acids will be obtained at 50°? at 170°C?
Why do you suppose the β isomer is thermodynamically more stable?

Aromatic sulfonic acids are especially useful because they are converted to phenols upon fusion with alkali. The α- and β-naphthols are thus easily available compounds; they are useful intermediates in the preparation of a number of important dyes.

α-Naphthol

β-Naphthol

Friedel–Crafts acylations proceed easily with naphthalene, and if the reaction is carried out in an indifferent solvent such as carbon disulfide, substitution occurs at the α position. If nitrobenzene is used as the solvent, it is complexed with the aluminum chloride and the acid chloride, and the attacking electrophile becomes quite bulky. In this case, reaction occurs predominantly at the β position.

As the above examples indicate, naphthalene usually undergoes electrophilic substitution at the α position. It is possible to obtain β-substituted products in only a few special instances.

Now, if a monosubstituted naphthalene undergoes electrophilic substitution, what position will the incoming electrophile attack? The answer to this question is a little more complex than in the benzene case. It depends, as in benzene, on the nature of the substituent already present on the naphthalene nucleus, and in addition, it depends on the location of that substituent.

Suppose we examine α-substituted naphthalenes first, and consider where attack will take place if there is an activating group present, or if there is a deactivating group present. In general, an activating group will activate the ring in which it is located, and the second substituent will then enter this same ring. If there is a deactivating group present, it deactivates the ring in which it is located. The incoming substituent therefore goes into the other ring.

As usual, electron-donating groups are ortho, para directors, while electron-withdrawing groups are meta directors. For example, if there is a hydroxyl group present in the 1 position of naphthalene, the incoming group will preferentially enter position 4, and to a lesser extent 2.

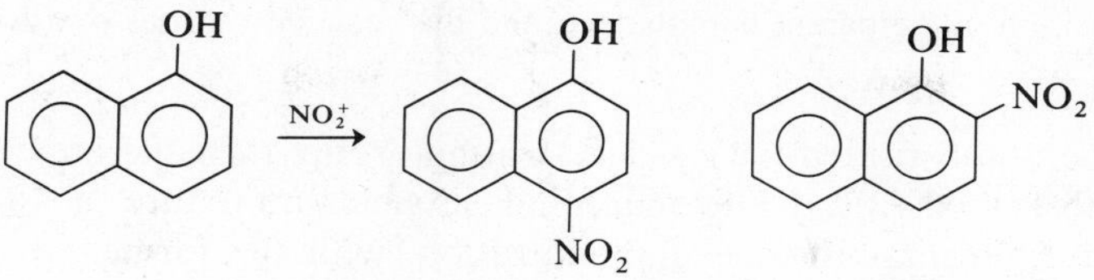

Mostly   Some

EXERCISE 16.13

Explain, using resonance forms, the orientation observed in the nitration of
α-naphthol.

Dinitration of α-naphthol gives the 2,4-dinitro derivative, which is the dye *Martius
Yellow*.

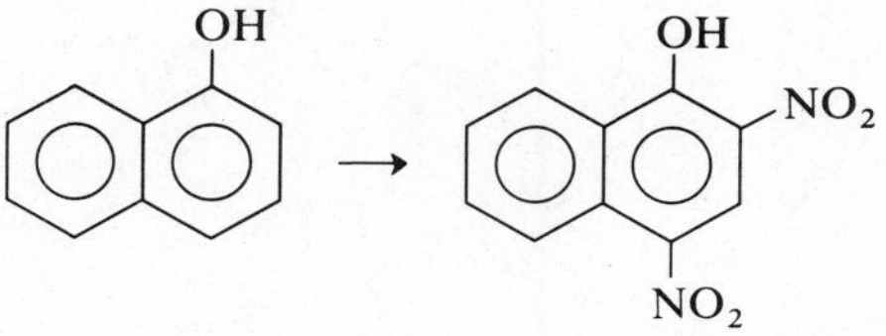

If the hydroxyl is located at position 2, then the incoming group will attack position 1
(an α position), rather than position 3 (a β position).

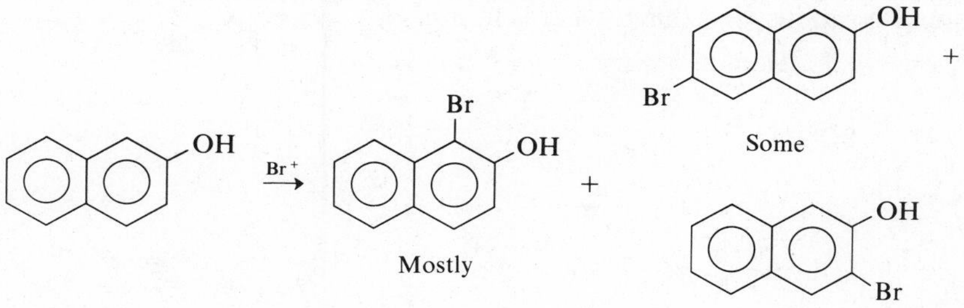

Mostly

Some

Trace

6-Position Activation. Why does the 2-hydroxyl activate the 6 position more than it does the
3 position? There does not appear to be any simple explanation for this fact, but an analogy
is found with the stabilities of the benzoquinones, the para-isomers of which are considerably
more stable than the ortho-isomers (Section 16.9). The Wheland intermediates for substitution
at positions 6 or 1 in β-naphthol have resonance forms analogous to the quinones. The preferential

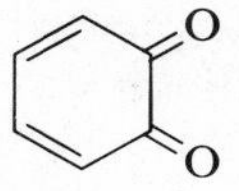

o-Benzoquinone 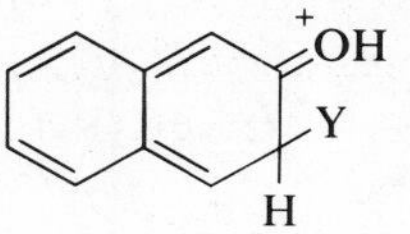   *o*-Quinone
type

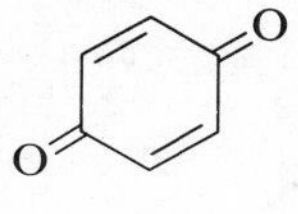

p-Benzoquinone

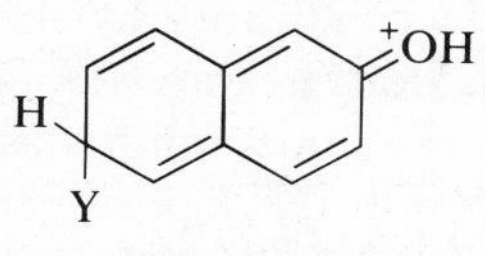

p-Quinone
type

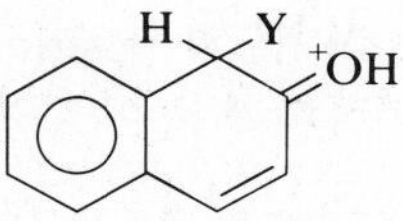

Best
(2 Kekulé
forms)

attack at position 4 over position 2 in the case of a 1-substituted naphthalene, or at position 1 rather than 3 in a 2-substituted naphthalene, is merely a reflection of the fact that an α position is more reactive than a β position in the parent naphthalene, and this reactivity carries over to these derivatives.

If one ring in naphthalene is substituted with a deactivating group, then the attack will take place on the unsubstituted ring. 1-Nitronaphthalene yields a mixture of 1,8-dinitronaphthalene and 1,5-dinitronaphthalene upon nitration, with the former predominating. The incoming reagent attacks the ring which does not contain the nitro group, and which is therefore the more reactive ring. Substitution occurs at an α position, and the 1,8 isomer is formed preferentially because it has a 1,3 (metalike) relationship to the nitro group already present, whereas position 5 has a 1,4 relationship. Thus, if the resonance forms are written out, there is one with a +charge at C-5, but no analogous one for C-8.

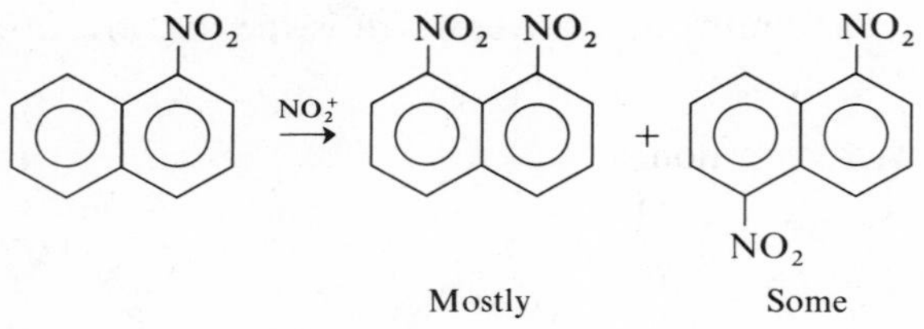

Mostly   Some

EXERCISE 16.14

Draw the resonance forms discussed in the preceding paragraph.

One would predict, then, that β-naphthalenesulfonic acid would substitute preferentially at the 5 and 8 positions, and this is what is found.

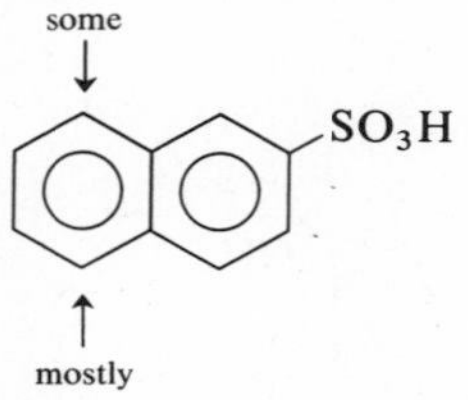

Substitution reactions take place very readily on both anthracene and phenanthrene, and each yields a 9-substituted derivative predominantly. (The numbering system is given in Section 11.7.)

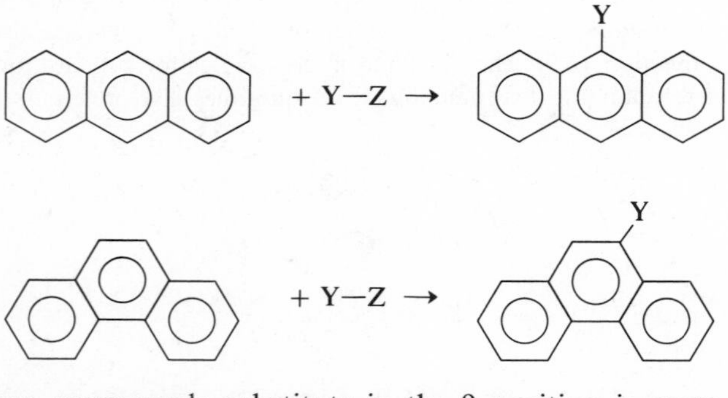

That these compounds substitute in the 9 position is more or less indicated by the Kekulé forms. Even if groups are attached to both the 9 and 10 positions in anthracene, the resulting 9,10-dihydro compound still has four Kekulé forms, the same number as anthracene itself. Thus anthracene undergoes aromatic substitution at the 9 position, or other kinds of additions at the 9,10 positions, fairly easily. The reactivity of anthracene towards substitution is in between that of benzene and that of a simple olefin.

EXERCISE 16.15

Draw the structures of 1,5-dinitroanthracene; 2-bromo-9-anthracenesulfonic acid; 1,9-dimethylphenanthrene.

Anthracene undergoes a Diels–Alder reaction with maleic anhydride at the 9,10 positions.

Phenanthrene is nearly as reactive as anthracene. If we add hydrogens to the 9,10 double bond, we see that the resulting compound, which is a substituted biphenyl, has four Kekulé forms. Phenanthrene itself has five. The loss is rather smaller than in the case of a compound like benzene, where addition across any double bond leads us from a compound with two Kekulé forms to something with only one Kekulé form. Phenanthrene therefore adds reagents rather easily to the 9,10 double bond; or more often, it substitutes at the 9 position.

In Section 7.16, it was mentioned that the product of the coefficients of the atomic wave functions at two centers yields a quantity referred to as the *bond order*. If we solve the Schroedinger equation for the π systems of naphthalene, anthracene, and phenanthrene, we find that the bond orders for the different bonds are very close to those obtained by a consideration of the Kekulé forms. In naphthalene, for example, the 1,2 bond is double in two of the three Kekulé forms, whereas the 2,3 bond is double in only one of the three Kekulé forms. This implies that the 1,2 double bond is of higher bond order than is the 2,3 double bond. Theory therefore requires the 1,2 double bond to be shorter, and X-ray diffraction measurements show that this is the case.

For phenanthrene, four of the five Kekulé forms contain a double bond between the 9 and 10 positions. This double bond is therefore practically olefinic in character. Thus it is found that phenanthrene will actually add bromine at the 9,10 position.

Note that phenanthrene has five Kekulé forms, while the 9,10 adduct still has four, a relatively small percentage change. Anthracene similarly *adds* bromine 9,10 for the same reason as in the case of phenanthrene.

EXERCISE 16.16

From the numbers in Tables 11.2 and 11.3, how much conjugation energy is lost in each of the following additions?

(c) Phenanthrene $\longrightarrow$ 9,10-dihydrophenanthrene
(d) Anthracene $\longrightarrow$ 9,10-dihydroanthracene
Compare your calculated numbers with available experimental facts.

for 2nd quiz

16.9   Oxidation Reactions of Aromatic Compounds. Quinones

The benzene ring is quite resistant to oxidation, so it is possible to oxidize toluene, for example, to benzoic acid;

or, in general

The balancing of oxidation–reduction equations involving organic molecules is often more difficult than it looks, and this topic will be discussed in Section 23.2.

Oxidation of toluene proceeds by way of the benzyl radical. Ethylbenzene oxidizes to give a methylbenzyl radical, which is also converted in several steps to benzoic acid, carbon dioxide, and water. Similarly, isopropylbenzene is oxidized to benzoic acid. On the other hand, *t*-butylbenzene has no hydrogen on the benzyl carbon, and it cannot lose a hydrogen atom to yield a stable benzyl radical. It does not oxidize under these conditions but is recovered unchanged. Just as alkylbenzenes are oxidized to benzoic acid, so dialkylbenzenes are oxidized to the corresponding dicarboxylic acids. The latter have the trivial names *phthalic*, *isophthalic*, and *terephthalic* acids, depending on the relationship of the carboxyl groups.

Phthalic acid   Phthalic anhydride   Isophthalic acid Terephthalic acid
  mp 231°C   mp 131°C   mp 348°C   mp 300°C

Oxidation is used commercially to prepare aromatic carboxylic acids from alkylbenzenes. It is also a technique useful in establishing the structures of complex molecules by converting them to smaller, known molecules. For example, permanganate oxidation of the methyl ether of *estrone*, a human estrogenic hormone, yields 4-methoxyphthalic acid:

Estrone   4-Methoxyphthalic acid

Ordinary oxidation reactions frequently involve attack by an electrophile (something formally equivalent to O^+). Therefore, while benzene itself is quite resistant to oxidation, substituted benzenes which are reactive toward electrophiles are also reactive toward oxidizing agents. 2,4-Diaminotoluene, for example, does not react with an oxidizing agent to give the diaminobenzoic acid, but instead the ring is attacked. The various processes which occur are not well understood, but most of the molecule is converted to carbon dioxide and water, and in this case the methyl group of the molecule survives as the methyl group in acetic acid.

Groups which deactivate the ring toward aromatic substitution also deactivate it toward oxidation, and hence compounds like *p*-nitrotoluene or 2-bromo-1,4-dimethyl-benzene are oxidized to the corresponding carboxylic acids in good yield.

Phthalic acid is a cheap industrial chemical available from the controlled oxidation of naphthalene.

Substituted naphthalenes are oxidized at the more activated ring.

Quinones are a class of compounds which, although not aromatic, are conveniently considered at this point because they <u>are oxidation products of aromatic compounds</u>.

Mild oxidation of 1,2- or 1,4-dihydroxybenzene (known as *catechol* and *hydroquinone*, respectively) converts them to the corresponding quinones.

Catechol   *o*-Benzoquinone

Hydroquinone   p-Benzoquinone   Resorcinol

Note that the quinones have but one Kekulé form and are not aromatic. Also note that no such thing as a *meta*-quinone exists, and no reasonable structure can be written for such a molecule. Oxidation of 1,3-dihydroxybenzene (resorcinol) yields only carbon dioxide and water.

Quinones are themselves mild oxidizing agents, those substituted by electronegative groups being somewhat more powerful. Chloranil and dicyanodichloroquinone are especially useful ones.

Chloranil

2,3-Dichloro-5,6-dicyano-
1,4-benzoquinone

PHOTOGRAPHY. *A practical use of the hydroquinone–quinone oxidation–reduction system is in photography. When the tiny grains of silver bromide in a photographic emulsion are exposed to light, a stable activated form of silver bromide is produced; the activation apparently involves the generation of some sort of a crystal defect. Subsequently, when the emulsion is developed, the function of the developer is to react with the activated silver bromide crystals and reduce them to silver metal more rapidly than the ordinary silver bromide crystals are reduced. The developer may be an aqueous alkaline solution of hydroquinone and sodium sulfite. The reaction which takes place is as follows:*

AgBr* = activated silver bromide

The unreduced silver bromide is then removed with sodium thiosulfate ("fixing"), and the finely divided silver metal which remains in the emulsion constitutes the familiar photographic negative. The sodium sulfite in the developer serves a number of functions, one being that of an antioxidant, or preservative. Many commercial compounds similar

*to, but slightly different from hydroquinone (e.g., substituted hydroquinones and
p-aminophenols), are utilized in various kinds of developers.*

QUINONES IN NATURE. *Many complex quinones are found to occur in nature. Vitamin* K_1
is a 1,4-naphthoquinone.

Vitamin K_1

The yellow pigment lawsone *is obtained from the leaves of a tropical shrub* henna
(Lawsonia inermis), *which is cultivated in Egypt. Lawsone is a quinone which dyes
wool and silk an orange shade. A paste made from powdered henna leaves has been
used to tint the hair red. Mohammed is said to have dyed his beard with henna.*

Lawsone

Coenzyme Q_{10}

*Coenzyme Q is a term applied to a group of related quinones which are essential
in the biologically important oxidative phosphorylation reaction. From 1 ton of pig
heart it was possible to isolate 37 g of pure* Q_{10}, *and the structure was established to
be that shown.*

Many insects, as well as other arthropods, have developed the use of p-benzoquinones
for defensive purposes. The carabid beetle Eleodes longicollis *produces and stores a
defensive secretion whose chief active components are* p-benzoquinone, methyl-p-
benzoquinone, *and* ethyl-p-benzoquinone. *These are sprayed directly at an attacking
predator from glands located in the tip of the abdomen. Similar quinonoid secretions
are found in a variety of spiders and millipedes. The* bombardier beetle *has the most
dramatic delivery system for his defensive quinones. They are ejected by mixing a
25% solution of hydrogen peroxide (containing hydroquinones) with a mixture of
enzymes which catalyze the decomposition of the peroxide into oxygen and water,
as well as the oxidation of the hydroquinones to quinones. The decomposition attains
explosive violence, and temperatures up to 100°C have been measured in the resultant
quinone jet propelled by the heated reactants.*

More about Quinones. Substituted quinones can be obtained from oxidation of the corresponding
substituted dihydroxybenzenes or aminophenols, or even from the phenols (in poorer yield). In
fact, the hydroxyl group activates the aromatic ring enough to make phenol itself easily susceptible
to oxidation.

Phenol

p-Benzoquinone

p-Benzoquinone is obtained in quite low yield because it is susceptible to further oxidation and
products of higher molecular weight are formed. The initial oxidation leads to the formation of a

phenoxyl radical which may be oxidized further to the quinone or can undergo other radical reactions:

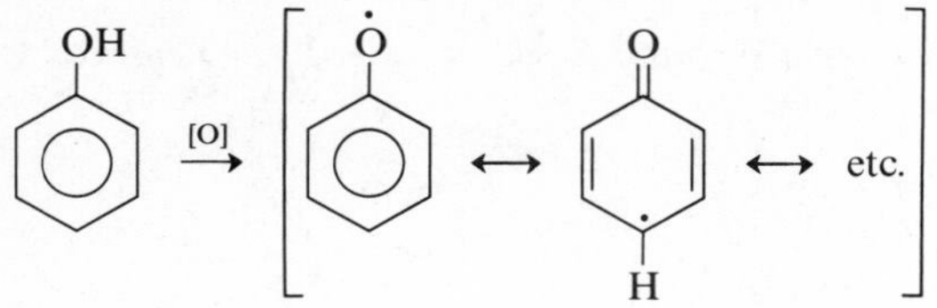

The analogous radical from 2,4,6-tri-*t*-butylphenol is relatively stable, since the bulky *t*-butyl groups effectively fend off would-be attacking reagents. The radical is dark blue and can be trapped by butadiene.

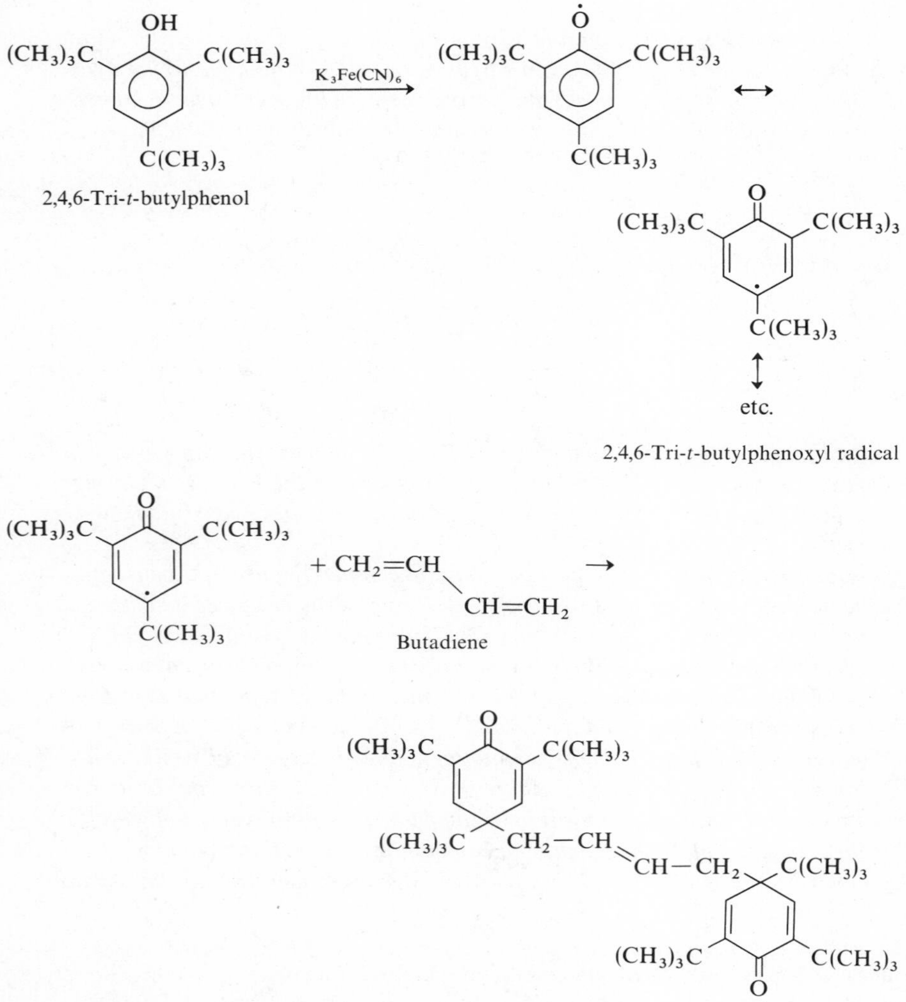

2,4,6-Tri-*t*-butylphenol

2,4,6-Tri-*t*-butylphenoxyl radical

Butadiene

A number of quinones from fused ring systems are known; these are available by oxidation of the corresponding dihydroxy compounds.

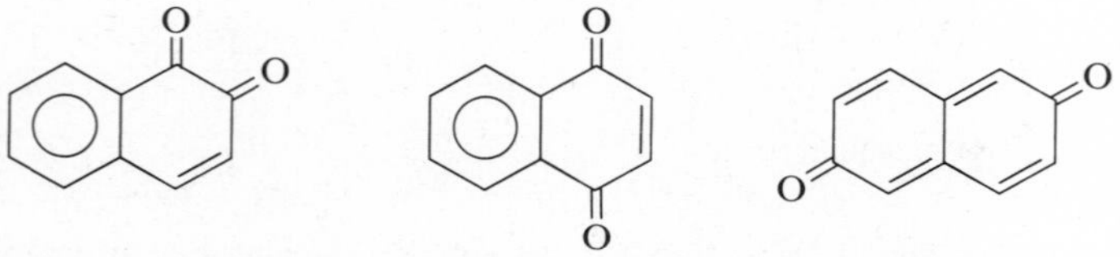

1,2-Naphthoquinone   1,4-Naphthoquinone   2,6-Naphthoquinone

Anthracene and phenanthrene, which are especially reactive at the 9,10 positions, can be oxidized directly to the corresponding quinones.

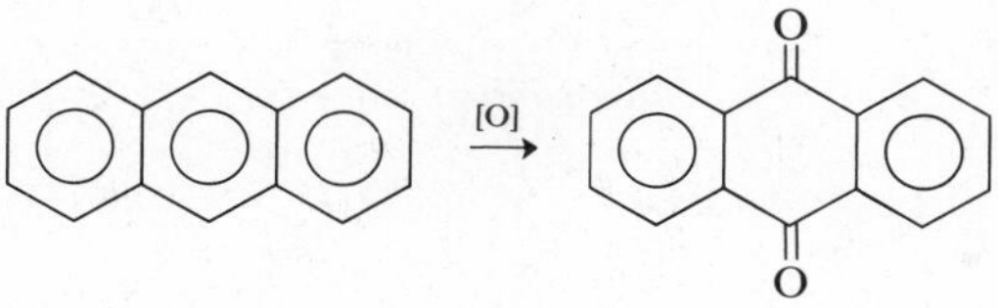

Anthraquinone

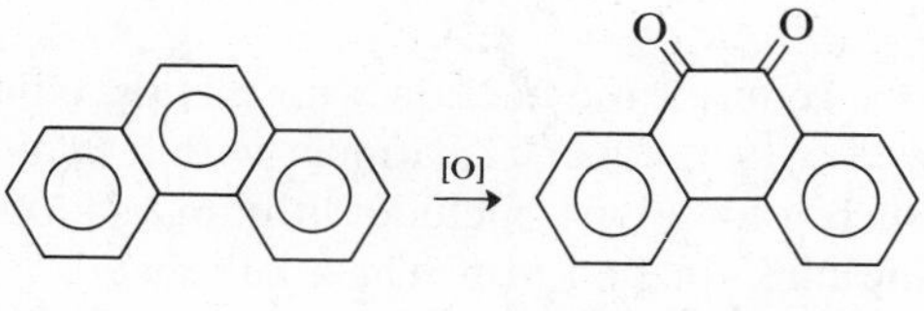

Phenanthraquinone

Most simple organic molecules do not absorb light in the visible region of the spectrum, and consequently they are colorless or white. Quinones, even the simplest ones, are highly colored. *p*-Benzoquinone is bright yellow, and the ortho isomer is deep red. Simple quinones, being really just unsaturated ketones, are reactive toward oxygen; they are not very stable in air. Anthraquinone and many substituted quinones are quite stable. Because of their colors, some of them are used as dyes. *Alizarin* was the first natural dye to be prepared synthetically (1868).

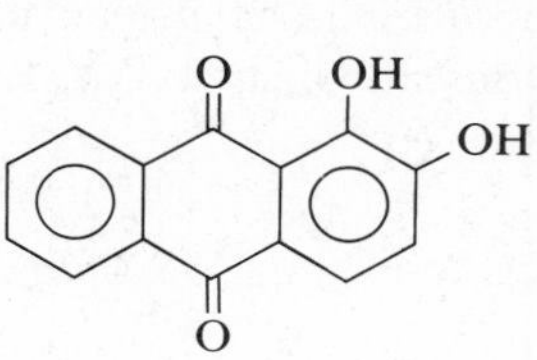

Alizarin

EXERCISE 16.17

Is alizarin more or less stable than the isomer shown? Explain. How could you tell these isomers apart?

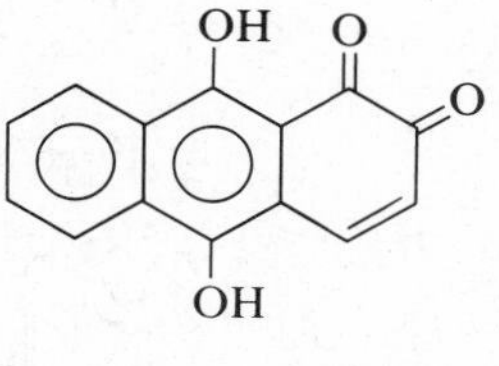

When *p*-benzoquinone is mixed with hydroquinone in alcohol, dark green crystals separate. This substance is called *quinhydrone*, and it is a molecular complex composed of equimolar amounts of quinone and hydroquinone. It dissociates slightly in solution.

16.10 Reduction Reactions of Aromatic Compounds

The reduction of an aromatic ring by hydrogen and a catalyst (hydrogenation) tends to be much slower and more difficult than is the corresponding reaction of an alkene. The reason is, of course, that reduction of the aromatic ring has to overcome the resonance energy of the ring (Chapter 11). It is possible to reduce benzene by using a very active catalyst (such as platinum) and favorable reaction conditions (such as acetic acid as the solvent). Under these circumstances the reduction can be brought about at room temperature. At much higher temperatures, even a less active nickel catalyst is adequate for reducing the benzene ring as long as the system is maintained under a high pressure of hydrogen to prevent the equilibrium from shifting back toward the starting products. (For a discussion of the position of equilibrium, see Section 13.1.)

A large variety of organic molecules can be reduced by reaction with metals, either in the presence of a proton donor or followed by subsequent treatment with a proton donor. Metals commonly employed in such reductions include lithium, sodium, potassium, and calcium as well as zinc, magnesium, tin, and iron. The alkali metals and calcium can be used as solutions in liquid ammonia (bp $-33°C$); all may be used as suspensions in inert solvents, protic solvents, or mixtures thereof. It might seem logical that such reductions are effected by the hydrogen liberated by the reaction of the metal with the hydroxylic solvent.

$$Na + NH_3 \rightarrow NaNH_2 + \tfrac{1}{2}H_2$$

In actual fact, the formation of hydrogen during these reductions is normally an undesirable side reaction. Dissolving-metal reductions are reactions in which an electron is transferred from the metal to the molecule being reduced.

$$M° + A \rightarrow M^+ + A^{\cdot -}$$

Metal   Electron   Metal   Radical anion
         acceptor   cation   (an anion with an unpaired electron)

It is possible to reduce the aromatic ring with potent metallic reducing agents, such as one of the alkali metals. Thus, lithium in ammonia (metallic lithium dissolved in liquid ammonia, *not* lithium which has been allowed to react with ammonia to form lithium amide) containing alcohol will reduce the benzene ring (1,4 addition) via the steps shown.

Lithium is usually a more potent reducing agent than is sodium. It has often been found advantageous to use various amines as solvents, rather than ammonia, because alkali metals are usually more reactive in the amine solvents. In addition, these solvents dissolve more organic compounds, and are liquids with more convenient boiling points. The reduction of an aromatic ring by an alkali metal in an amine (or ammonia) solvent is usually referred to as the *Birch reduction*.[†] It is quite a useful reaction, although relatively few substituents in the benzene ring are capable of withstanding it. Toluene and anisole,

† Arthur J. Birch. Born 1915, Sydney, Australia. Universities of Sydney, Manchester (England), and Australian National University, Canberra.

for example, undergo the reaction as shown.

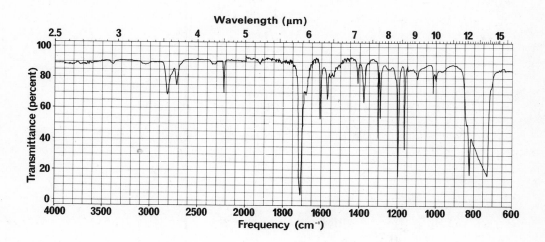

EXERCISE 16.18

Write the detailed mechanism for the conversion of anisole to 3-cyclohexenone.

The halobenzenes and phenol do not undergo this reaction. The former are simply reduced to benzene, whereas the latter forms the phenoxide ion, which is resistant to reduction. More complicated molecules can be reduced to varying degrees, depending upon the reaction conditions chosen.

PROBLEMS

1. The infrared spectrum of a compound C_8H_5NO is shown. Can you deduce the structure of the compound?

Infrared spectrum of unknown compound, Problem 1.

Wavelength (μm)

(infrared spectrum graph: Transmittance (percent) vs Frequency (cm⁻¹), ranging from 4000 to 600)

Frequency (cm⁻¹)

2. Write the mechanisms for the reaction: ethylene + Cl_2 → 1,2-dichloroethane; and for the reaction: benzene + Cl_2 → chlorobenzene + HCl.

3. (a) Write a balanced equation for the aromatic substitution reaction of bromine with *p*-xylene and sketch the reaction coordinate diagram. If one adds an iron catalyst to the reaction mixture, the substitution is greatly accelerated. (b) What change occurs in the reaction coordinate diagram? (c) Draw all of the resonance forms of the Wheland intermediate.

4. Write the mechanism for the reaction shown:

$$CH_3-\langle\bigcirc\rangle-SO_3H + H_2O \xrightarrow[\text{steam}]{\text{superheated}} CH_3-\langle\bigcirc\rangle + H_2SO_4$$

5. A volatile, colorless liquid compound was isolated from petroleum. The infrared spectrum of the compound is shown. The nmr spectrum has two singlets at $\delta\,2.32$ and $\delta\,7.17$, which integrate to give a ratio of $1:1.65$, respectively. The combustion analysis gave 91.4% carbon and 8.7% hydrogen. What is the structure of the compound?

Infrared spectrum of unknown compound, Problem 5.

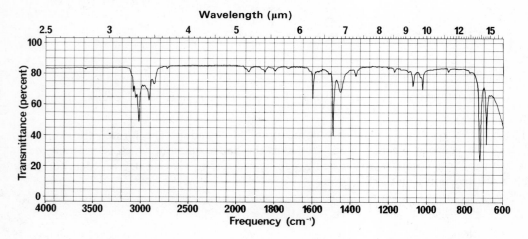

6. List the following molecules in order of increasing acid strength. (1 = least acidic.) Explain, using resonance forms where appropriate.

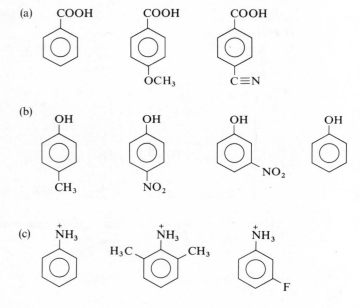

7. Show by means of resonance forms why a methyl group is an ortho, para director, both by hyperconjugation and by induction.

8. Starting from benzene, how would you synthesize m-bromonitrobenzene? How would you synthesize the para isomer?

9. Complete the following:

(a) $HNO_3 + H_2SO_4 +$ ⬡—CH_3 ⟶

(b) CH_3CHCH_2Cl +
   |
   CH_3

   [structure: 1,4-dichlorobenzene] $\xrightarrow[\Delta]{AlCl_3}$

(c) [benzene ring with NO_2] + HNO_3 $\xrightarrow[H_2SO_4]{\Delta}$

(d) [benzene ring with CH_3] + $CH_3CH_2CH{-}\overset{\overset{\displaystyle O}{\|}}{C}{-}Cl$ $\xrightarrow{AlCl_3}$
   |
   CH_3

(e) [benzene ring with Cl and CH_3] + Br_2 $\xrightarrow{Fe}$

(f) [benzene ring with NO_2 and Cl] $\xrightarrow[\substack{H_2SO_4 \\ \Delta}]{HNO_3}$

(g) [benzene ring with CH_3] + HCl $\xrightarrow{\Delta}$

(h) $CH_3O{-}$[benzene ring]${-}$[benzene ring]${-}NO_2$ $\xrightarrow{HNO_3}$

(i) [benzene ring]${-}COOH$ + Cl_2 $\xrightarrow{Fe}$

(j) $NO_2{-}$[benzene ring] + $CH_3\overset{\overset{\displaystyle O}{\|}}{C}{-}Cl$ $\xrightarrow{AlCl_3}$

10. Anisole was treated with iodine and nitric acid, and a compound C_7H_7IO was isolated from the reaction mixture. The nmr spectrum of the compound is shown. What is the structure of the compound?

NMR spectrum of unknown compound, Problem 10.

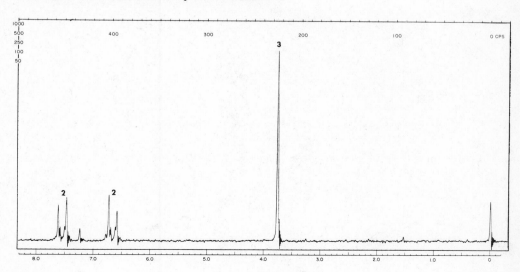

11. Show by means of resonance forms why the carboethoxyl group (—COOEt) is a meta director. Repeat for the cyano group (—C≡N).

12. Outline a synthesis of *p*-bromoacetophenone starting from benzene, acetyl chloride, and inorganic reagents.

13. At which ring carbons would electrophilic aromatic substitution occur in the following compounds?

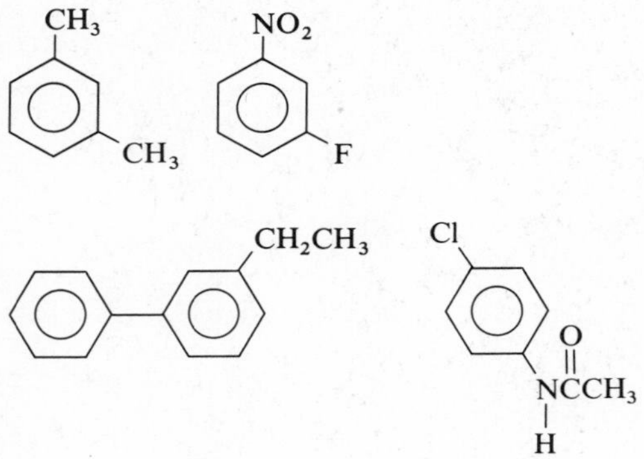

14. Complete the following:

(a) 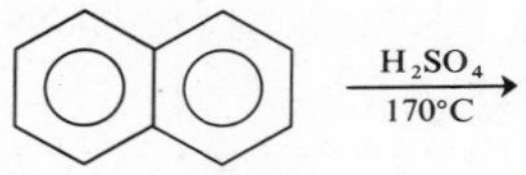 $\xrightarrow[170°C]{H_2SO_4}$

(b) $\xrightarrow[AlCl_3]{PhNO_2}$

(c) $\xrightarrow{Br_2}$

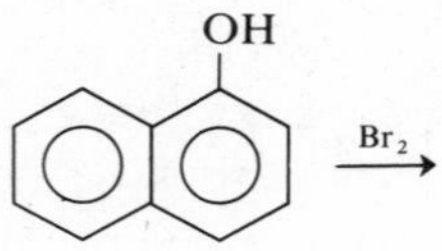

(d) 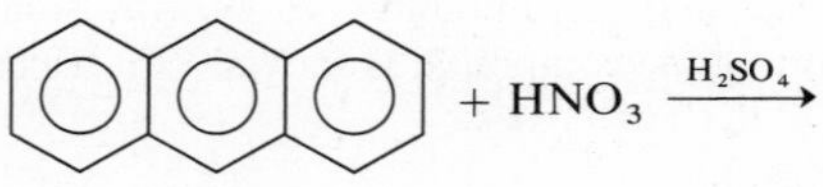 + HNO_3 $\xrightarrow{H_2SO_4}$

(e) 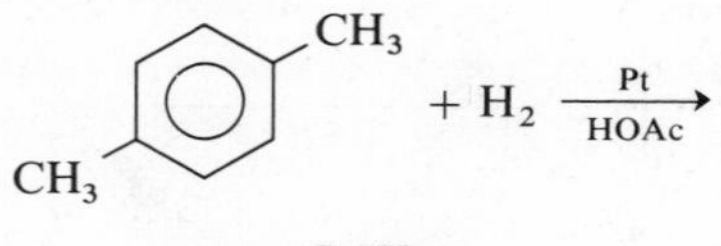 + H_2 $\xrightarrow[HOAc]{Pt}$

(f) 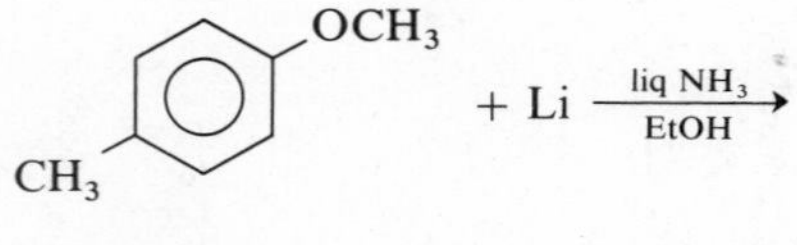 + Li $\xrightarrow[EtOH]{liq\ NH_3}$

(g) Product of reaction (f) + H_3O^+ $\xrightarrow{\Delta}$

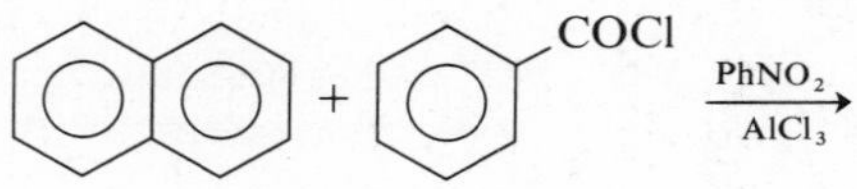

(h) 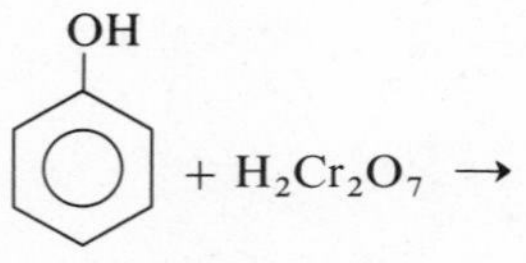 + $H_2Cr_2O_7$ →

(i) 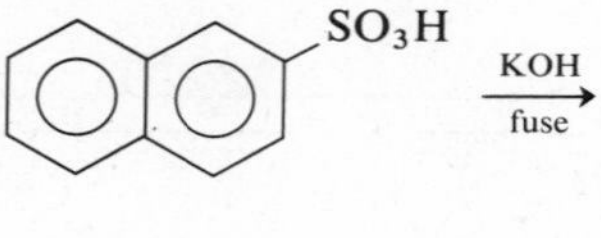 $\xrightarrow[fuse]{KOH}$

(j)

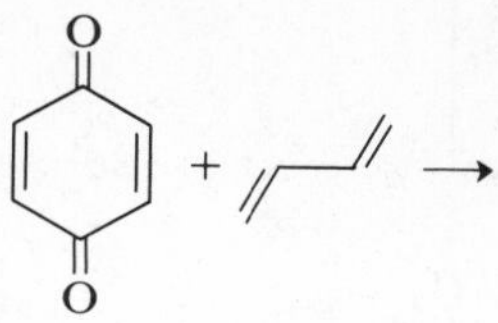

(k)

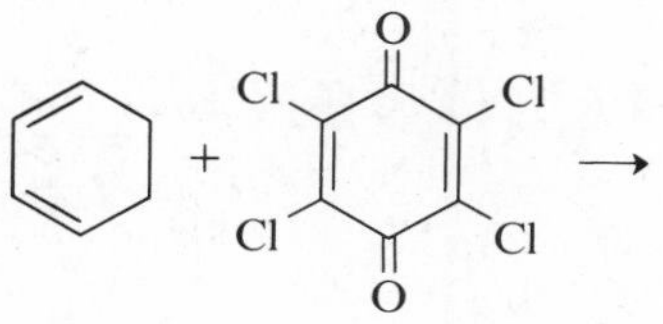

15. Outline a synthesis of 1,4-naphthoquinone from naphthalene.

16. A compound (A) of unknown structure has the formula C_9H_{10}. How many sites of unsaturation does it have? Its nmr spectrum shows a singlet (area 3) at $\delta\,2.3$, a multiplet (area 3) at $\delta\,5$, and a multiplet (area 4) at $\delta\,7$. When A was treated with ozone, and the reaction mixture was treated with hydrogen peroxide, a compound (B) was isolated, $C_8H_8O_2$. B showed an nmr spectrum as follows: singlet (area 3) $\delta\,2.3$, multiplet (area 4) $\delta\,7.2$, singlet (area 1) $\delta\,12$. When B was oxidized with hot aqueous potassium permanganate, another compound (C) was isolated, $C_8H_6O_4$, which showed an nmr spectrum as follows: multiplet (area 4) $\delta\,7.4$, singlet (area 2) $\delta\,12$. Upon heating with P_2O_5, C was converted to phthalic anhydride. What are the structures of A, B, and C?

17. Fluorobenzene is more reactive toward electrophilic substitution reactions than is chlorobenzene, even though fluorine is more electronegative than chlorine. Explain.

18. A certain benzene derivative, C_8H_{10}, can be converted into two and only two isomeric monobromo derivatives in which the bromine can be established as being attached to the ring. No trace of a third isomer can be found by the most sensitive means. What structure does this evidence indicate?

19. Which of the following benzene derivatives is most easily sulfonated? Which would be the best solvent in which to carry out a Friedel–Crafts alkylation of benzene? Which would give the smallest number of isomers on monobromination? Which would be the best starting material from which to synthesize 2-chloro-4-nitroethyl-benzene?
    (a) Benzene
    (b) Ethylbenzene
    (c) Chlorobenzene
    (d) Nitrobenzene
    (e) *m*-Xylene
    (f) Benzotrichloride ($C_6H_5CCl_3$)

CHAPTER 17

REACTIONS OF ORGANIC HALOGEN COMPOUNDS

17.1 Reactions with Nucleophiles and Bases

Since the terms *acid*, *base*, *electrophile*, and *nucleophile* are used frequently in this chapter, they will be defined again here. Lewis acids (electrophiles) bond *to* an electron pair, whereas Lewis bases *provide* an electron pair for bonding. These are thermodynamic phenomena, and relative basicity and relative acidity are determined from equilibrium values. A *nucleophile* is a reagent which has an available pair of electrons, usually non-bonded electrons, with which it attacks another atom to form a new covalent bond. Relative nucleophilicities are obtained from relative rates of reactions, and nucleophilicity is, therefore, a kinetic phenomenon.

Several factors play a role in affecting the relative nucleophilicities of reagents: the basicity (since nucleophiles are also Lewis bases); the polarizability of the attacking electron pair; and the solvation shell surrounding the attacking nucleophile. Consequently basicity and nucleophilicity are not synonymous, but they *are* related. For example, thiophenoxide, $C_6H_5S^-$, is a much better nucleophile than phenoxide, $C_6H_5O^-$, although this order is the reverse of their relative basicities (see Section 8.2). This can be explained by the less tightly held and more polarizable electron cloud on sulfur. The electrons on sulfur are more available for attack on a positive center. As another example, the highly polarizable *iodide ion* is a very weak base but a powerful nucleophile. On the other hand, fluoride ion is much more basic than iodide ion, but fluoride is an extremely poor nucleophile.

In this chapter the nucleophilic substitution and base-catalyzed elimination reactions of alkyl halides will be examined, and the mechanisms of these reactions will be discussed. These are two competing reactions of an alkyl halide with a nucleophile, and they can be summarized as:

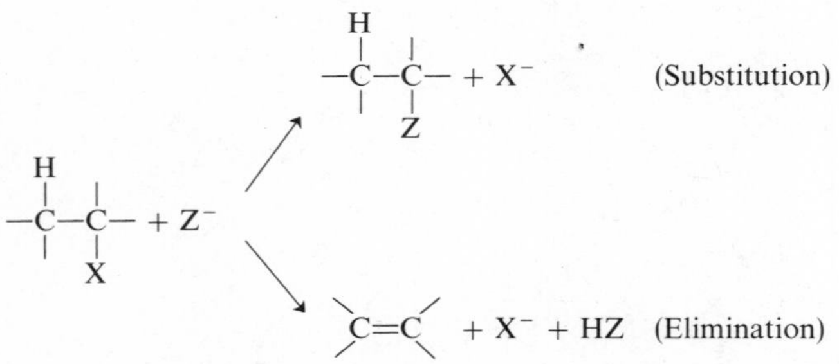

In the following few sections we will discuss these reactions, as well as the variations in the halide structure, in the nature of the nucleophile or base, and in the reaction conditions, which are found to influence this competition.

Nucleophilic Substitution Reactions

Whereas most aryl halides (for example, chlorobenzene) exhibit little tendency to react with nucleophiles, alkyl halides react with a wide variety of nucleophiles. Nucleophilic substitution reactions of alkyl halides are widely used for the synthesis of many classes of organic compounds, such as alcohols, alkynes, amines, esters, ethers, and nitriles. Elimination of hydrogen halide with formation of an alkene competes with simple displacement of the halide ion; if elimination is the predominant path, it provides a tool for the synthesis of alkenes.

The general equation for nucleophilic substitution involves a nucleophile reacting with an alkyl halide, which results in replacement of halide ion (called a *leaving group*) by the nucleophile:

$$R\text{---}X \quad + \quad Z^- \rightarrow R\text{---}Z + X^-$$

Alkyl   Nucleophile   Leaving
halide   Group

or

$$R\text{---}X \quad + \quad :Z \rightarrow R\text{---}Z^+ + X^-$$

Alkyl   Nucleophile   Leaving
halide   group

The student should note that the nucleophile supplies the electron pair for bonding to the atom being attacked, and the leaving group departs *with* a pair of electrons. If the attacking nucleophile is the solvent, the reaction is called a *solvolysis reaction*. As can be seen from Table 17.1, the nucleophile can either be an anion, such as RO^-, $HC\equiv C^-$, or ^-CN, or it can be a neutral species with a pair of unshared electrons, such as $:NH_3$ or $:P(C_6H_5)_3$. Nucleophilic substitution reactions are not limited to halides, but occur readily with other compounds which can furnish good leaving groups; a commonly encountered example is the reaction of an alkyl sulfonate with a nucleophile in which a sulfonate ion is displaced.

$$R\text{---}O\text{---}\overset{\overset{\displaystyle O}{\|}}{\underset{\underset{\displaystyle O}{\|}}{S}}\text{---}R' \quad + \quad Z^- \rightarrow R\text{---}Z + {}^-O_3SR'$$

An alkyl sulfonate   Nucleophile   Leaving group

Among the sulfonate esters, the *p*-toluenesulfonates (tosylates) and methanesulfonates (mesylates) are most commonly employed. The reactivities of these compounds toward nucleophiles, in both substitution and elimination reactions, are similar to the reactivities of the corresponding bromides. Other good leaving groups are H_2O, N_2, CO_2, and similar stable molecules (Evans–Polanyi principle, page 299).

$$CH_3CH_2\text{---}O\text{---}\overset{\overset{\displaystyle O}{\|}}{\underset{\underset{\displaystyle O}{\|}}{S}}\text{---}\langle\!\!\bigcirc\!\!\rangle\text{---}CH_3 + CN^- \rightarrow CH_3CH_2C\equiv N + {}^-O_3S\text{---}\langle\!\!\bigcirc\!\!\rangle\text{---}CH_3$$

Ethyl tosylate

$$\langle\!\!\bigcirc\!\!\rangle\text{---}CH_2\text{---}O\text{---}\overset{\overset{\displaystyle O}{\|}}{\underset{\underset{\displaystyle O}{\|}}{S}}\text{---}CH_3 + EtO^- \xrightarrow{\text{EtOH}} \langle\!\!\bigcirc\!\!\rangle\text{---}CH_2OEt + CH_3SO_3^-$$

Benzyl mesylate

Table 17.1   Synthetically Important Reactions of Alkyl Halides with Nucleophiles and Bases

Substitution by a nucleophile			*Product*
$R-X + HO^-$	$\rightarrow R-OH$	$+ X^-$	Alcohol
$R-X + R'-O^-$	$\rightarrow R-O-R'$	$+ X^-$	Ether
$R-X + R'-CO_2^-$	$\rightarrow R-O_2CR'$	$+ X^-$	Ester
$R-X + :NH_3$ (excess)	$\rightarrow R-NH_2$	$+ HX$	Primary amine
$R-X + R_3N$	$\rightarrow R_4N^+X^-$		Quaternary ammonium salt
$R-X + N_3^-$	$\rightarrow R-N_3$	$+ X^-$	Azide
$R-X + H-C\equiv C^-$	$\rightarrow R-C\equiv C-H$	$+ X^-$	Alkyne
$R-X + {}^-CN$	$\rightarrow R-CN$	$+ X^-$	Nitrile
$R-X + \geqslant C^-$	$\rightarrow \geqslant C-R$	$+ X^-$	A new C—C bond
$R-X + H\bar{C}(CO_2R')_2$	$\rightarrow R-CH(CO_2R')_2$	$+ X^-$	Substituted malonate
$R-X + R'-\underset{\underset{O}{\|}}{C}-\bar{C}H-CO_2R''$	$\rightarrow R'-\underset{\underset{O}{\|}}{C}-\underset{\underset{R}{\|}}{C}H-CO_2R$	$+ X^-$	Substituted β-ketoester
$R-X + HS^-$	$\rightarrow R-SH$	$+ X^-$	Mercaptan
$R-X + R'S^-$	$\rightarrow R-S'-R'$	$+ X^-$	Sulfide
$2R-X + S^{2-}$	$\rightarrow R-S-R$	$+ 2X^-$	Sulfide
$R-X + :P(C_6H_5)_3$	$\rightarrow [R-P(C_6H_5)_3]^+X^-$		Phosphonium salt
$R-X + I^-$	$\rightarrow R-I$	$+ X^-$	Iodide

Elimination by a Base

$$-\underset{\underset{X}{\|}}{\overset{\overset{H}{\|}}{C}}-\overset{\|}{C}- + B^- \rightarrow -C=\overset{\|}{C}- + 2HB + X^- \qquad \text{Alkene}$$

$$-\underset{\underset{H}{\|}}{\overset{\overset{H}{\|}}{C}}-\underset{\underset{X}{\|}}{\overset{\overset{X}{\|}}{C}}- \xrightarrow{B^-} -HC=CX- + BH + X^- \qquad \text{Vinyl halide}$$

$$-\underset{\underset{X}{\|}}{\overset{\overset{H}{\|}}{C}}-\underset{\underset{X}{\|}}{\overset{\overset{H}{\|}}{C}}- \xrightarrow{B^-} -HC=CX- + BH + X^- \qquad \text{Vinyl halide}$$

$$-HC=CX- \xrightarrow{B^-} -C\equiv C- + BH + X^- \qquad \text{Alkyne}$$

Elimination Reactions

The general equation for elimination reactions shows the net loss of H—X from the halide to form an alkene:

$$-\underset{\underset{X}{\|}}{\overset{\overset{H}{\|}}{C}}-\overset{\|}{C}- + B^- \rightarrow \hspace{0.3em} {\Large\diagup}C=C{\Large\diagdown} \hspace{0.3em} + X^- + HB$$

Alkyl   Base   Alkene   Halide Acid
halide   ion

or

$$-\underset{\underset{X}{\|}}{\overset{\overset{H}{\|}}{C}}-\overset{\|}{C}- + :B \rightarrow \hspace{0.3em} {\Large\diagup}C=C{\Large\diagdown} \hspace{0.3em} + X^- + HB^+$$

Alkyl   Base   Alkene   Halide Acid
halide   ion

Since the proton that is lost is on the carbon atom *beta* to the halogen, this reaction is called *β elimination.* From these equations, it can be seen that β elimination is the reverse process of addition to an alkene, which was discussed in Chapter 15. When X is a halogen atom, the process is called *dehydrohalogenation*. Actually, elimination can also occur readily when —X is any good leaving group, such as $^-OSO_2R'$.

Synthetic Use of Nucleophilic Substitution and Elimination Reactions

A number of useful general reactions of alkyl halides with nucleophiles are presented in Table 17.1 in order to emphasize the utility of these synthetically important reactions.

If it is intended to carry out an elimination reaction rather than a substitution, one of the following bases is ordinarily used: alcoholic KOH, *t*-BuOK in *t*-BuOH, certain tertiary amines (particularly quinoline), $NaNH_2$. There is always a competition between substitution and elimination, but these reagents are, generally speaking, better bases than nucleophiles, while alternatives such as aqueous KOH or sodium acetate tend to be better nucleophiles than bases.

We can briefly examine here the use of the reactions shown in Table 17.1 in synthesis. Alcohols, ethers, and esters can all be synthesized by reaction of halides with OH^-, OR^-, or $RCOO^-$, respectively. Some examples are shown.

$$n\text{-}C_6H_{13}\text{—CH—Br} + HO^-Na^+ \xrightarrow{H_2O} n\text{-}C_6H_{13}\text{—CH—OH} + Na^+Br^-$$
$$\underset{\text{2-Bromooctane}}{\overset{|}{CH_3}} \qquad\qquad \underset{\text{2-Octanol}}{\overset{|}{CH_3}}$$

$$CH_3\text{—CH—O}^-Na^+ + CH_3I \rightarrow CH_3\text{—CH—O—CH}_3 + Na^+I^-$$
$$\underset{\text{Sodium isopropoxide}}{\overset{|}{CH_3}} \quad \underset{\substack{\text{Methyl}\\\text{iodide}}}{} \quad \underset{\text{Isopropyl methyl ether}}{\overset{|}{CH_3}}$$

$$\overset{\displaystyle O}{\overset{\|}{} }$$
$$C_4H_9\text{—CH—Cl} + CH_3\overset{\|}{C}\text{—O}^-Na^+ \rightarrow C_4H_9CH\text{—O—}\overset{\|}{C}CH_3 + NaCl$$
$$\underset{\text{2-Chlorohexane}}{\overset{|}{CH_3}} \quad \underset{\text{Sodium acetate}}{} \quad \underset{\text{2-Hexyl acetate}}{\overset{|}{CH_3}}$$

EXERCISE 17.1

Outline syntheses of the following compounds from suitable nucleophiles and halides:

(a) $CH_3CH_2CH_2O\text{—CH}_3$

(b) $CH_3CHCH_2CH_2O\text{—}\overset{\overset{\displaystyle O}{\|}}{C}CH_2CHCH_3$
$\overset{|}{CH_3}\overset{|}{CH_3}$

(c) $CH_3CH\text{—O—}\overset{\overset{\displaystyle O}{\|}}{C}CH_2CH_2\overset{\overset{\displaystyle O}{\|}}{C}\text{—O—CHCH}_3$
$\overset{|}{CH_3}\overset{|}{CH_3}$

Nucleophilic nitrogen compounds react with halides in a manner similar to alkoxides. For example, the azide anion will displace halide.

$$CH_3CH_2CH\text{—Br} + NaN_3 \rightarrow CH_3CH_2CH\text{—N}_3 + NaBr$$
$$\underset{\text{2-Bromobutane}}{\overset{|}{CH_3}} \quad \underset{\substack{\text{Sodium}\\\text{azide}}}{} \quad \underset{\text{2-Butyl azide}}{\overset{|}{CH_3}}$$

The organic azides are themselves of limited interest, but upon reduction they yield amines, which are very useful compounds (discussed in detail in Chapter 21).

$$\text{CH}_3\text{CH}_2\underset{\underset{\text{CH}_3}{|}}{\text{CH}}-\text{N}_3 \xrightarrow[\text{cat.}]{\text{H}_2} \text{CH}_3\text{CH}_2\underset{\underset{\text{CH}_3}{|}}{\text{CH}}-\text{NH}_2 + 2\,\text{NH}_3$$

2-Butyl azide   2-Aminobutane

Amines (and ammonia) also react with halides, and this reaction is sometimes useful for synthesis (Section 21.1).

$$\text{CH}_3-\!\!\bigcirc\!\!-\text{CH}_2\text{CH}_2\underset{\underset{\text{CH}_3}{|}}{\overset{\overset{\text{CH}_3}{|}}{\text{N}}}\!\!: \;+\; \text{CH}_3-\text{I} \;\rightarrow\; \text{CH}_3-\!\!\bigcirc\!\!-\text{CH}_2\text{CH}_2\underset{\underset{\text{CH}_3}{|}}{\overset{\overset{\text{CH}_3}{|}}{\overset{+}{\text{N}}}}\text{CH}_3 \; \text{I}^-$$

$$\text{ClCH}_2\text{CO}_2\text{H} + 2\,\text{NH}_3 \rightarrow \text{H}_2\text{NCH}_2\text{CO}_2\text{H} + \text{NH}_4^+\text{Cl}^-$$

Chloroacetic acid   Glycine

An extremely useful kind of reaction is that between a halide and a carbon anion. Simple alkyl carbanions are not very satisfactory for such reactions, but many kinds of relatively stable carbanions can be used. Cyanide is a suitable example.

$$\text{CH}_3\text{CH}_2\text{CH}_2\text{CH}_2\text{Cl} + \text{Na}^+\text{CN}^- \rightarrow \text{CH}_3\text{CH}_2\text{CH}_2\text{CH}_2\text{CN} + \text{Na}^+\text{Cl}^-$$

1-Chlorobutane   Valeronitrile

This reaction represents an easy way to lengthen a chain by one carbon atom, and is a widely used synthetic procedure. It works well for almost all primary and many secondary halides, but *never for tertiary halides*.

As mentioned in Sections 4.19 and 17.10, a Grignard reagent has carbanion character; and while such organomagnesium halides will not react with most ordinary halides, smooth reaction occurs with "active" halides such as allylic and benzylic halides.

$$\bigcirc\!\!-\text{CH}_2\text{Cl} + \text{CH}_3\text{CH}_2\text{MgCl} \rightarrow \bigcirc\!\!-\text{CH}_2\text{CH}_2\text{CH}_3 + \text{MgCl}_2$$

Benzyl chloride   Ethylmagnesium   *n*-Propylbenzene
chloride

$$\text{CH}_2\!\!=\!\!\underset{\underset{\text{Br}}{|}}{\text{C}}\text{CH}_2\text{Br} + \text{C}_6\text{H}_5\text{MgBr} \rightarrow \text{CH}_2\!\!=\!\!\underset{\underset{\text{Br}}{|}}{\text{C}}\text{CH}_2\text{C}_6\text{H}_5 + \text{MgBr}_2$$

2,3-Dibromopropene   Phenylmagnesium
bromide

In Section 7.20 it was pointed out that 1-alkynes, $\text{R}-\text{C}\equiv\text{C}-\text{H}$, show enhanced acidity relative to other hydrocarbons. The acid–base reaction between a 1-alkyne and a strong base will lead to a salt.

$$\text{R}-\text{C}\equiv\text{C}-\text{H} + \text{NaNH}_2 \rightarrow \text{R}-\text{C}\equiv\text{C}^-\text{Na}^+ + \text{NH}_3$$

Sodium   A sodium
amide   alkynide

$$\text{R}-\text{C}\equiv\text{C}-\text{H} + \text{CH}_3\text{CH}_2\text{CH}_2\text{CH}_2\text{Li} \xrightarrow[\text{solvent}]{\text{inert}} \text{RC}\equiv\text{C}^-\,\text{Li}^+ + \text{CH}_3\text{CH}_2\text{CH}_2\text{CH}_3$$

n-Butyllithium   A lithium
alkynide

Several of these alkynides are commercially available, for example, propynylsodium ($CH_3C{\equiv}CNa$) and propynyllithium ($CH_3C{\equiv}CLi$). The alkynides are nucleophilic reagents, and they enter into nucleophilic substitution reactions by attacking the carbon atom of an alkylating agent with displacement of a leaving group. The net result of this reaction is alkylation of the alkynide to produce a new alkyne.

$$RC{\equiv}C^-M^+ + R'CH_2 - X \longrightarrow RC{\equiv}CCH_2R' + M^+ + X^-$$
$$X = -Br \text{ or}$$
$$-OSO_2R''$$

In general, this reaction is limited to situations where the alkylating agent (the alkyl bromide or alkyl sulfonate) is primary and unbranched on the β-carbon atom. Despite this limitation, this represents a useful method for the production of many alkynes, as the examples shown below illustrate.

$$HC{\equiv}CNa + CH_3CH_2CH_2CH_2Br \xrightarrow{\text{liq. NH}_3} CH_3CH_2CH_2CH_2C{\equiv}CH + NaBr$$
1-Hexyne

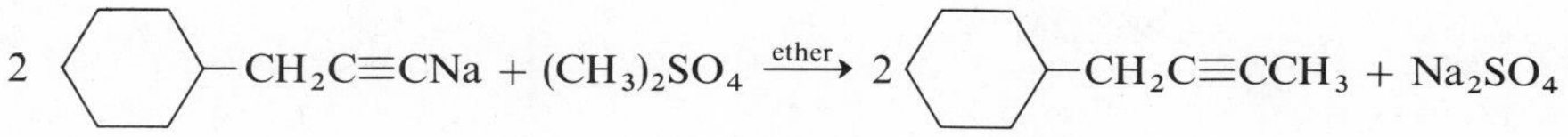

$$2\ \langle{\bigcirc}\rangle{-}CH_2C{\equiv}CNa + (CH_3)_2SO_4 \xrightarrow{\text{ether}} 2\ \langle{\bigcirc}\rangle{-}CH_2C{\equiv}CCH_3 + Na_2SO_4$$
1-Cyclohexyl-
2-butyne

$$CH_3CH_2CH_2C{\equiv}CNa + CH_3CH_2CH_2Br \xrightarrow{\text{liq. NH}_3}$$
$$CH_3CH_2CH_2C{\equiv}CCH_2CH_2CH_3 + NaBr$$
4-Octyne

The anions from diethyl malonate and acetoacetic ester react with halides to form new carbon–carbon bonds. These reactions are very useful from a synthetic point of view, but only when taken in conjunction with other reactions. Further discussion of these points will be postponed until Section 20.16.

$$\underset{\text{Ethyl sodioacetoacetate}}{CH_3\overset{O}{\overset{\|}{C}}{-}\overset{-}{C}H{-}\overset{O}{\overset{\|}{C}}{-}OC_2H_5} + \underset{n\text{-Butyl bromide}}{n\text{-}C_4H_9{-}Br} \rightarrow \underset{\text{Ethyl }n\text{-butylacetoacetate}}{CH_3\overset{O}{\overset{\|}{C}}{-}\underset{CH_2CH_2CH_2CH_3}{\overset{|}{C}H}{-}\overset{O}{\overset{\|}{C}}{-}OC_2H_5} + Na^+Br^-$$

Sulfur and phosphorus atoms not bound to electronegative atoms are excellent nucleophiles. The reactions are similar to those of the corresponding oxygen and nitrogen compounds.

$$\underset{CH_3}{CH_3CH_2\overset{|}{C}HBr} + Na^+HS^- \rightarrow \underset{CH_3}{CH_3CH_2\overset{|}{C}HSH} + Na^+Br^-$$

$$\underset{CH_3}{CH_3CH_2\overset{|}{C}HSH} + \overset{+}{K}\overset{-}{O}H \rightarrow \underset{CH_3}{CH_3CH_2\overset{|}{C}HS^-K^+} \xrightarrow{CH_3I} \underset{CH_3}{CH_3CH_2\overset{|}{C}HSCH_3} + K^+I^-$$
$$+ H_2O$$

EXERCISE 17.2

Why is RS^- a better nucleophile than $SO_4^=$?

EXERCISE 17.3

Complete the following:

$CH_3CH_2CH_2CH_2I + Na_2S \rightarrow$ $CH_3CH_2CH_2CH_2 S^- Na^+$ $+ Na$

$Ph\,CH_2Br + Ph_3P \rightarrow$ $PhCH_2PPh_3$

$CH_3CH_2Br + CH_3COO^- \rightarrow$ $CH_3CH_2OOCCH_3$

All of the nucleophilic substitution reactions discussed up to this point work well with primary halides and fairly well with secondary halides, although elimination tends to be a serious competing side reaction with secondary halides. On the other hand, tertiary halides give poor yields of substitution products, often no yield at all. Elimination usually predominates over substitution with tertiary halides.

$$CH_3-\underset{\underset{CH_3}{|}}{\overset{\overset{Br}{|}}{C}}-CH_2CH_3 \xrightarrow{\text{KOH}} \underset{CH_3}{\overset{CH_3}{}}C=C\underset{CH_3}{\overset{H}{}}$$

Major product under
most conditions

An example of a double elimination to yield an alkyne is the following:

$$\text{Ph}-\underset{\underset{Br}{|}}{\overset{}{C}}H-\underset{\underset{Br}{|}}{\overset{}{C}}H_2 + 2Na^+NH_2^- \rightarrow \text{Ph}-C\equiv C-H + 2NH_3 + 2Na^+Br^-$$

1,2-Dibromo-1-
phenylethane

Phenylacetylene

In Table 17.2 are listed some additional reactions of alkyl halides which are not of interest for synthetic purposes, but which are sometimes used in mechanistic studies. (They are generally slow reactions.)

Table 17.2   Other Reactions of Alkyl Halides with Nucleophiles[a]

$R-X + H_2O$	$\rightarrow ROH$ $+ HX$	Alcohol
$R-X + R'-OH$	$\rightarrow R-O-R'$ $+ HX$	Ether
$R-X + R'-CO_2H$	$\rightarrow R-O_2CR'$ $+ HX$	Ester
$R-X + R'-SH$	$\rightarrow R-S-R'$ $+ HX$	Sulfide

[a] If the nucleophile in these examples is also being used as the solvent, the reactions are called *solvolysis reactions*.

17.2   The S_N2 Mechanism

Nucleophilic substitution reactions have been extensively investigated both kinetically and stereochemically. Two mechanistic extremes are required to explain the experimental data. One mechanism will be discussed in this section and the other in the following section. Whether a particular halide reacts by one mechanism or the other depends on such factors as the structural features of the alkyl halide and the nucleophile, and the effects of the solvent and other reaction conditions. Again, it should always be kept in mind that alkyl derivatives with leaving groups other than halide also readily undergo nucleophilic substitution. One of the first investigators in this field of research was C. K. Ingold, and most of our knowledge of these mechanisms is due to work by his research group. Many nucleophilic substitution reactions are found experimentally to be first order in alkyl halide and first order in the nucleophile (Section 14.2):

$$Rate = k[R\,X][Z^-]$$

Reactions which show these overall second-order kinetics are given the notation S_N2, for substitution (S), nucleophilic (N), bimolecular (2). Examples are:

$$CH_3-Cl + Na^+I^- \xrightarrow[\text{(S}_N2)]{\text{acetone}} CH_3-I + NaCl \downarrow$$

$$Rate = k[CH_3Cl][I^-]$$

$$CH_3CH_2Br + OH^- \xrightarrow{H_2O} CH_3CH_2OH + Br^-$$

$$Rate = k[CH_3CH_2Br][OH^-]$$

The stereochemical outcome of this reaction is also a key to the mechanism. The S_N2 reaction is *always* accompanied by *inversion of configuration* at the carbon atom originally bonded to the halogen atom. This phenomenon can be observed experimentally if this carbon atom is asymmetric and the reaction is carried out on a single enantiomer.

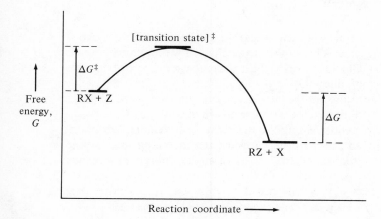

2(S)-Chlorobutane   2(R)-Butanol

A second way to demonstrate this inversion process is to examine the reaction of a compound containing two asymmetric centers and to note its conversion to a diastereomer.

cis-3-Methylcyclopentyl bromide   *trans*-3-Methylcyclopentyl cyanide

The energy diagram in Figure 17.1 represents the S_N2 reaction in terms of an energy maximum which must be overcome in the bimolecular collision between R—X and Z⁻

Figure 17.1
A free energy diagram for a typical S_N2 reaction.

in order for reaction to occur (Section 14.4). The commonly accepted pictorial representation of the transition state for the S_N2 reaction shows a new bond forming between carbon and Z^- (the nucleophile) as the bond between carbon and halogen (the leaving group) is simultaneously breaking:

Reactants

Transition state
(an energy maximum)

From a molecular orbital viewpoint, the carbon at which substitution is occurring has rehybridized from sp^3 in the starting halide to sp^2 at the transition state. In this state, the attacking and leaving groups simultaneously overlap with the p orbital which is perpendicular to the plane containing the other three orbitals on carbon.

Transition state

The more electronegative X and Z groups bear the bulk of the excess negative charge (if the nucleophile is an anion) through all stages of the reaction. In a shorthand form, nucleophilic substitution is depicted by using arrows to show the movements of the electron pairs during the attack:

$$Z^- + R\!-\!X \rightarrow Z\!-\!R + X^-$$

Such inversion of configuration is often referred to as Walden† inversion, after its discoverer.

EXERCISE 17.4

Write the molecular formulas of the transition states for the two reactions for which the rate expressions are given on page 395. From the discussion in the previous paragraph, draw the transition states for those two reactions on page 395. Do the transition states you have drawn have the molecular formulas demanded by the kinetics?

This proposed mechanism is also consistent with the observation that the rates of S_N2 reactions increase as the attacking species is changed to one which is more nucleophilic. For example, the nucleophile $CH_3CH_2O^-$ gives S_N2 displacement rates approximately 10^5 times faster than the less nucleophilic :NO_3^-.

Furthermore, this mechanism accounts for the fact that S_N2 reactivities of alkyl halides *decrease* as the rear side of the alkyl halide becomes more crowded, making attack by the nucleophile more difficult. Methyl halides should be the most reactive in S_N2 displacements, because only three hydrogen atoms project toward the incoming nucleophile. Primary alkyl halides present no great problem, because a single unbranched carbon

† Paul von Walden. 1863–1957. Born Latvia. Universities of Riga (Latvia), Rostock, and Tübingen.

chain attached to the carbon at which inversion is occurring can orient itself out of the way. The steric hindrance to nucleophilic attack is greater with secondary halides, but reaction will still occur at a reasonable rate. With tertiary halides and with halides that are highly branched at the β-carbon atom, this steric factor is quite severe. This is illustrated below with *t*-butyl and neopentyl halides.

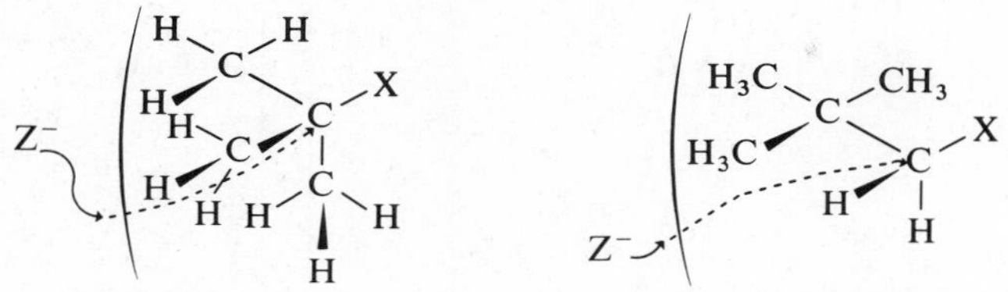

t-Butyl halide   Neopentyl halide

Backside attack
hindered

Even though neopentyl halides are primary halides, they react about 100,000 times more slowly than the corresponding methyl halides. It is reasonable to conclude that tertiary halides will react very slowly, if at all, by an S$_N$2 mechanism. The order of reactivity in S$_N$2 reactions is therefore

Methyl > Primary > Secondary ≫ Neopentyl, Tertiary

Primary allylic halides and primary benzylic halides are quite reactive in S$_N$2 substitutions. Actually, these compounds react faster than normal primary halides.

Steric factors in the attacking nucleophile have also been studied. Attack by quinuclidine on isopropyl iodide in nitrobenzene is 700 times faster than attack by triethylamine. In quinuclidine the substituents are tied back, whereas in triethylamine the freely rotating substituents screen approach to the nitrogen part of the time.

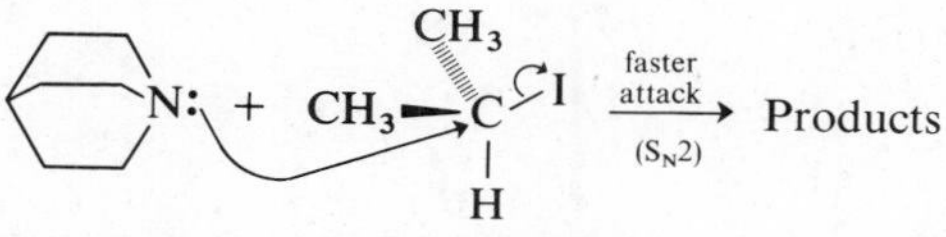

Quinuclidine   Isopropyl iodide

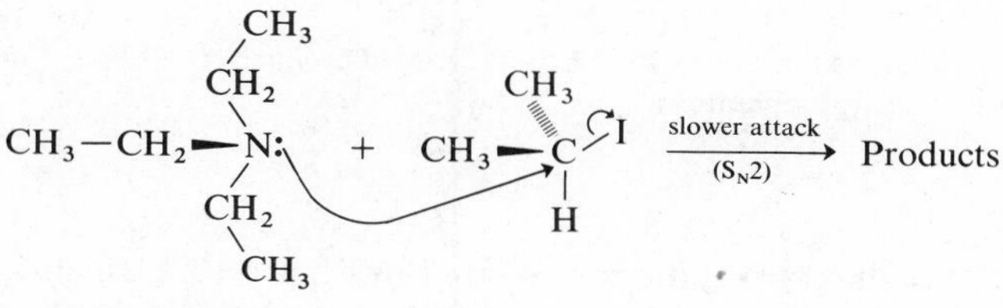

Triethylamine

EXERCISE 17.5

Draw the structures of the substitution products of the above two reactions.

Solvents of high polarity solvate ions better than solvents of low polarity, and these polarity differences affect the rates of S$_N$2 reactions. For example, an increase in solvent polarity *slows* the reaction between hydroxide ion and methyl bromide.

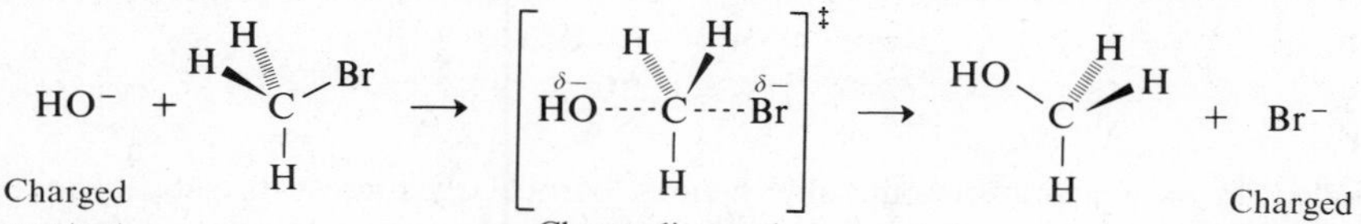

Charged   Charge dispersal   Charged
reactant   product

Figure 17.2
Effect of solvent polarity on an S_N2 reaction.

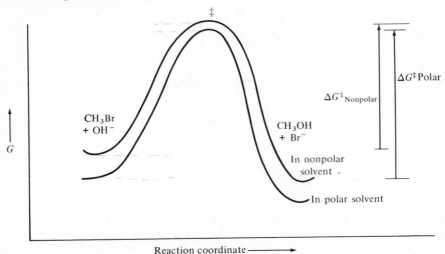

The charge is more dispersed in the transition state than it is in the reactants. If the polarity of the solvent is increased, the solvation lowers the energy of each charged species in solution. The smaller the ion, the more important the solvation. The more polar solvent therefore solvates the starting materials better than it does the transition state. Hence, as the solvent polarity increases, the rate of reaction slows down. Figure 17.2 will help to make this clear. A reaction such as the one shown in Figure 17.2 involves only a *dispersal of charge* in the transition state and is therefore not very sensitive to changes in the polarity of the solvent, because no large difference in charge develops between reactants and transition state. In contrast, the rate of reaction of ammonia with methyl bromide is greatly increased by an increase in solvent polarity, owing to the developing *charge separation* in the transition state.

$$H_3N: \ + \quad \ \longrightarrow \quad \left[H_3\overset{\delta+}{N}----C----\overset{\delta-}{Br} \right]^{\ddagger} \quad \longrightarrow \quad H_3\overset{+}{N} \quad + \quad Br^-$$

Uncharged reactants   Transition state—   Charged products
                           charge separation

EXERCISE 17.6

Draw a reaction coordinate diagram analogous to that in Figure 17.2 which shows why the rate of reaction of methyl bromide with ammonia is accelerated by an increase in solvent polarity.

EXERCISE 17.7

Predict the effect of increasing solvent polarity on the following nucleophilic substitution reaction:

$$R\overset{+}{N}(CH_3)_3 + OH^- \longrightarrow ROH + N(CH_3)_3$$

Explain.

The S_N2' Reaction. In the reaction of some allyl halides, particularly those with substituents on the carbon bearing the halogen, a product is formed from attack on the γ carbon. For example, triethylamine and α-methylallyl chloride form 85% of rearranged product, in addition to the $S_N 2$ product.

$$C_2H_5-\overset{\overset{\displaystyle C_2H_5}{|}}{\underset{\underset{\displaystyle C_2H_5}{|}}{N}}: \; +CH_2\!=\!\!CH\!-\!\overset{\overset{\displaystyle CH_3}{|}}{CH}\!-\!Cl \xrightarrow[\text{(S}_N2')]{\text{benzene}} (C_2H_5)_3\overset{+}{N}\!-\!CH_2\!-\!CH\!=\!C\!\!\!\begin{array}{l}CH_3\\ \\ H\end{array} + Cl^-$$

Triethylamine   α-Methylallyl   85%
             chloride

$$\left(+ CH_2\!=\!CH\!-\!\overset{\overset{\displaystyle CH_3}{|}}{CH}\!-\!\overset{+}{N}(C_2H_5)_3 \right)$$

from $S_N 2$ reaction

The formation of the rearranged product is first order in amine and first order in α-methylallyl chloride; and the mechanism, a variation of the ordinary $S_N 2$, is referred to as $S_N 2'$.

To summarize, then, the characteristics of the $S_N 2$ mechanism are these: (1) the reaction is bimolecular and typically shows second-order kinetics; (2) inversion of configuration occurs at the carbon substituted; (3) the reaction is quite sensitive to steric hindrance; and (4) the reaction is rather insensitive to the polarity of the solvent (unless charges are formed or destroyed in approaching the transition state).

17.3   The $S_N 1$ Mechanism

In the previous section it was mentioned that alkyl halides undergo nucleophilic substitution reactions by two mechanisms. The first mechanism is $S_N 2$ and the second is a nucleophilic (N), substitution (S), and unimolecular (1), referred to as $S_N 1$. An example of the mechanism is the reaction of benzhydryl chloride with fluoride ion in liquid sulfur dioxide solution.

$$(C_6H_5)_2CHCl + F^- \xrightarrow[\text{(S}_N1)]{\text{SO}_2} (C_6H_5)_2CHF + Cl^-$$

Benzhydryl chloride   Benzhydryl fluoride

It is experimentally found that increasing the fluoride ion concentration does not speed up the reaction; the experimental rate equation, therefore, is

$$\text{Rate} = k[(C_6H_5)_2CHCl]$$

Not only is the initial rate of the reaction independent of fluoride ion concentration, but it is the same as the rate of reaction of benzhydryl chloride with other nucleophiles, such as triethylamine and pyridine.

If an optically active alkyl halide is allowed to react under conditions favoring the $S_N 1$ mechanism, nearly complete racemization occurs; for example,

$$CH_3\underset{\underset{\displaystyle H}{|}}{\overset{\overset{\displaystyle C_6H_5}{|}}{C}}\!-\!Cl \xrightarrow[-HCl]{80\% \text{ aqueous acetone}} CH_3\underset{\underset{\displaystyle H}{|}}{\overset{\overset{\displaystyle C_6H_5}{|}}{C}}\!-\!OH \; + \; HO\!-\!\underset{\underset{\displaystyle H}{|}}{\overset{\overset{\displaystyle C_6H_5}{|}}{C}}\!CH_3$$

1(S)-Phenylethyl   1(S)-Phenylethanol   1(R)-Phenylethanol
    chloride
(optically active)   (98% racemization; 2% inversion)

$$\text{Rate} = k[C_6H_5\!-\!\underset{\underset{\displaystyle CH_3}{|}}{CH}\!-\!Cl]$$

These data are most easily explained by an initial rate-determining ionization of the alkyl halide to a carbonium ion and a halide ion, followed by attack of a nucleophile on the carbonium ion.

Rate-determining step—doesn't involve nucleophile

$$R—X \xrightarrow{\text{slow}} R^+ + X^-$$

Subsequent fast step

$$R^+ + Z^- \longrightarrow R—Z$$

or

$$R^+ + Z: \longrightarrow R—Z^+$$

The fact that the proposed rate-determining step does not involve the nucleophile explains the first-order kinetics and also explains the observation that the initial rate is the same, no matter which nucleophile is attacking. The formation of a planar, sp^2-hybridized carbonium ion (Section 12.1) which can be attacked with equal probability from either side accounts for the racemization observed.

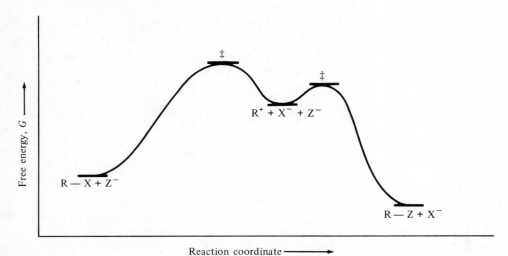

An energy diagram for a reaction proceeding by an S_N1 mechanism is shown in Figure 17.3; the carbonium ion intermediate, R^+, represents an energy minimum.

Figure 17.3
A free energy diagram for a typical S_N1 reaction.

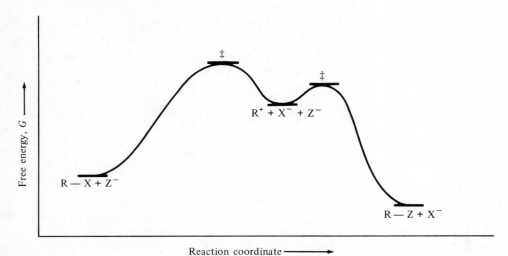

EXERCISE 17.8

The rate expression for the reaction of methyl bromide with hydroxide ion is

$$-\frac{d(CH_3Br)}{dt} = k[CH_3Br][OH^-]$$

while that for the corresponding reaction of *t*-butyl bromide is

$$-\frac{d(t\text{-}BuBr)}{dt} = k[t\text{-}BuBr]$$

Write balanced equations for these reactions. Deduce the molecular formula of the transition state in each case. Suggest structures to correspond to the formulas of the transition states.

An example of the S_N1 mechanism was given on page 399 for the formation of racemic 1-phenylethanol from optically active 1(S)-phenylethyl chloride. The key intermediate is the carbonium ion formed in the slow step of the reaction.

Of course, the carbonium ion is not free, but has solvent attracted to it and is, therefore, *solvated*. When the anion is still associated with the cation after ionization, an *ion pair* is formed. Dissociation of the ion pair may lead to a *symmetrically solvated cation*.

If cations are symmetrically solvated, they give a completely racemized product when they react with nucleophiles. However, most cations are not sufficiently stable to exist in solution long enough to become symmetrically solvated.

Experimentally, one type of ion pair is not sufficient to explain all the data. An ion pair in which the anion influences the cation, even though solvent is between them, is experimentally distinguishable from the "tight" ion pair shown above.

In the phenylethyl chloride example, reaction before formation of a symmetrically solvated cation accounts for the 2% excess net inversion which accompanies racemization; the nucleophile reacts preferentially at the side away from the departing anion. The benzylic carbonium ion from 1-phenylethyl chloride is relatively stable and does exist long enough for the chloride ion to move away, resulting in the high degree of racemization. Higher percentages of net inversion are observed for halides forming less stable carbonium ions, which are more rapidly attacked by the nucleophile before symmetrical solvation can occur.

In the transition state of the rate-determining step for the S_N1 reaction, the C—X bond is lengthening and charge separation occurs:

$$R-X \rightarrow [\overset{\delta+}{R}\cdots\overset{\delta-}{X}]^{\ddagger} \rightarrow R^+ + X^-$$

Transition state—
charge separation

Therefore an increase in solvent polarity causes a large increase in rate by stabilizing the developing charges.

Lewis acids, such as Ag^+ and Hg^+, enhance the reactivity of alkyl halides in S_N1 reactions. The effect is catalytic, reducing the activation energy required to reach the transition state; the metal cation complexes with the halogen atom, drawing electrons toward itself and weakening the R—X bond.

$$R-\overset{\cdot\cdot}{\underset{\cdot\cdot}{X}}\colon Ag^+ \rightarrow R^+ + AgX\downarrow$$

Catalysis by silver ion

The order of reactivity of halides in the S_N1 reaction is $RI > RBr > RCl > RF$, as would be predicted from C—X bond strengths (page 62).

Let us now examine the effects of the structure of the R group on the relative rates of S_N1 reactions. Since a carbonium ion is being generated in the formation of the transition state, alkyl halides which lead to the most stable carbonium ions should react fastest (see Section 12.2). With simple aliphatic halides, the order is therefore

Tertiary ≫ Secondary > Primary

Allylic and benzylic halides react about as rapidly as do simple tertiary halides. This is because a resonance-stabilized cation is generated in the rate-determining step.

$$CH_2{=}CH{-}CH_2{-}Cl \xrightarrow[\substack{\text{dioxane} \\ (S_N1)}]{\text{aqueous}} [CH_2{=}CH{-}\overset{+}{C}H_2 \leftrightarrow \overset{+}{C}H_2{-}CH{=}CH_2] \xrightarrow[\text{H}_2\text{O}]{\text{fast}}$$

$$CH_2{=}CHCH_2OH$$

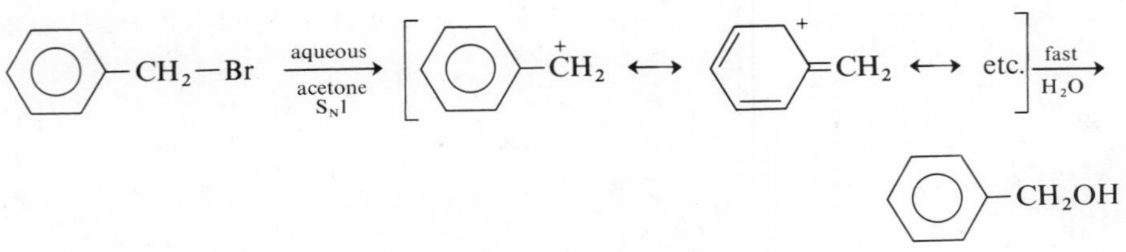

$$\langle\bigcirc\rangle{-}CH_2OH$$

benzylic halide with an electron-donating ($+$R or $+$I) substituent in the ortho or para position of the ring should react faster than the unsubstituted compound. An example is *p*-methoxybenzyl bromide.

Here the *p*-methoxy group greatly assists in resonance stabilization of the benzylic cation.

Halides of the type YCH$_2$X should undergo S$_N$1 reactions quite readily if Y is a group such as RÖ$-$, R$_2$N$-$, or RṠ$-$. These Y groups have at least one unshared pair of electrons on an atom directly attached to the carbon which is becoming positively charged. Thus the carbonium ion will be greatly stabilized.

$$CH_3O-CH_2-Cl \xrightarrow[(S_N1)]{methanol} [CH_3O-\overset{+}{C}H_2 \leftrightarrow CH_3\overset{+}{O}=CH_2] \xrightarrow{fast} CH_3O-CH_2-OCH_3$$

Vinyl and aryl halides *do not* react easily under S$_N$1 conditions. This is because vinyl cations ($\overset{}{\underset{}{C}}=\overset{}{\underset{}{C}}_+$) and aryl cations (⬡$+$) are relatively unstable and therefore difficult to form under ionization conditions.

EXERCISE 17.9

Why is vinyl cation less stable than ethyl cation?

A test for the reactivity of halides under S$_N$1 conditions is to place the halide in solution in aqueous alcoholic silver nitrate. Silver halide precipitates instantly with ionic halides and with reactive covalent halides. The longer it takes for a precipitate to form, the less reactive is the halide by the S$_N$1 mechanism.

Carbonium ions prefer to have planar, trigonal hybridization (*sp*^{2}) (Section 12.1). A halide (even a tertiary halide) which must ionize to give a carbonium ion that cannot attain planarity should react slowly, if at all, in the S$_N$1 substitution. An example is 1-chloronorbornane.

Very little reaction

1-Chloronorbornane

The rigidity of this system prevents a bridgehead carbonium ion from becoming planar (and it also prevents rearside solvation of the carbonium ion), so no reaction occurs.

Further evidence that the S$_N$1 reaction proceeds via a carbonium ion mechanism is the observation that rearrangement may occur. For example, neopentyl iodide in water, with silver nitrate present, rearranges to a 2-methyl-2-butyl derivative (an example of the Wagner–Meerwein rearrangement).

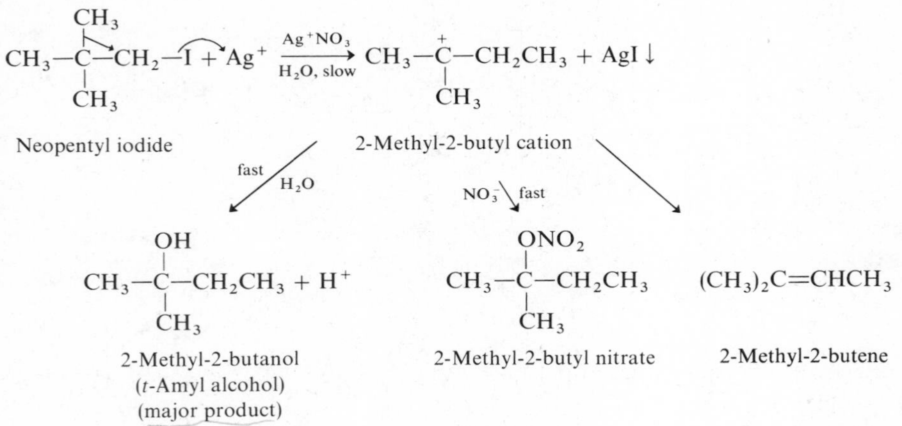

Neopentyl iodide

2-Methyl-2-butyl cation

2-Methyl-2-butanol
(*t*-Amyl alcohol)
(major product)

2-Methyl-2-butyl nitrate

2-Methyl-2-butene

One way to account for the products is to say that a primary carbonium ion is formed first from the neopentyl iodide; this would certainly rearrange rapidly to the more stable, tertiary, 2-methyl-2-butyl cation by a 1,2-methyl shift.

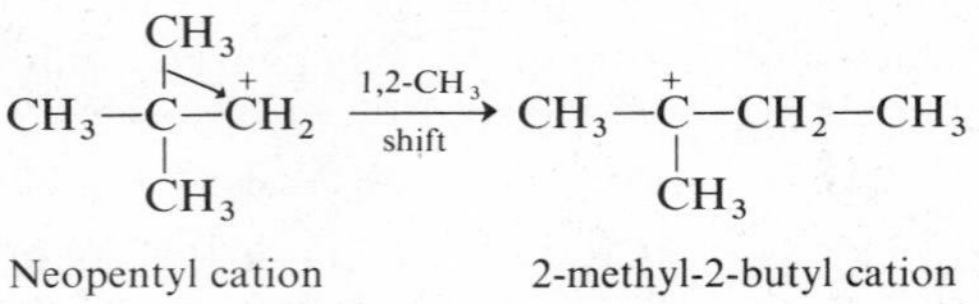

Neopentyl cation

2-methyl-2-butyl cation

However, the migration of the methyl appears to be concerted with ionization, and the neopentyl cation never really forms. Instead, the methyl group migrates to the developing positive charge on the carbon bearing the iodide as ionization occurs. This adjacent methyl group migrates with its pairs of electrons, and at the transition state it is partially bonded to both carbon atoms. Products from the neopentyl cation are not observed. The rate of S_N1 hydrolysis of neopentyl bromide in wet formic acid is about the same as that of *n*-propyl bromide. (Compare with the rate difference between neopentyl halide and a simple primary halide in an S_N2 reaction, page 397.) Typically, S_N1 reactions are not slowed by steric hindrance. Note that the methyl group does not appear to accelerate the reaction to a detectable extent, either.

An example in which the migrating alkyl group is part of a ring system is

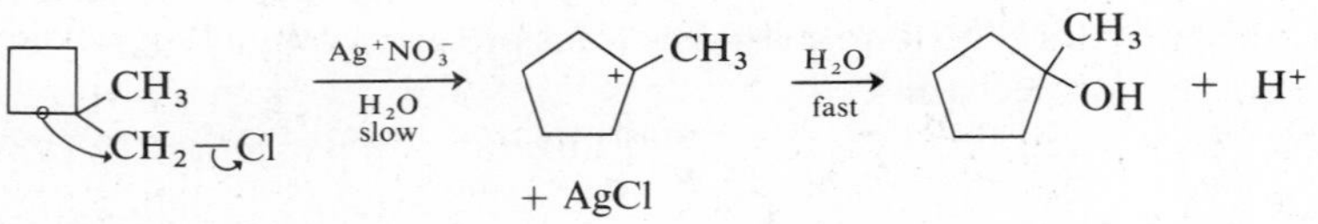

+ AgCl

EXERCISE 17.10

Predict the order of reactivity of the following compounds with ethanol in an an S_N1 reaction:

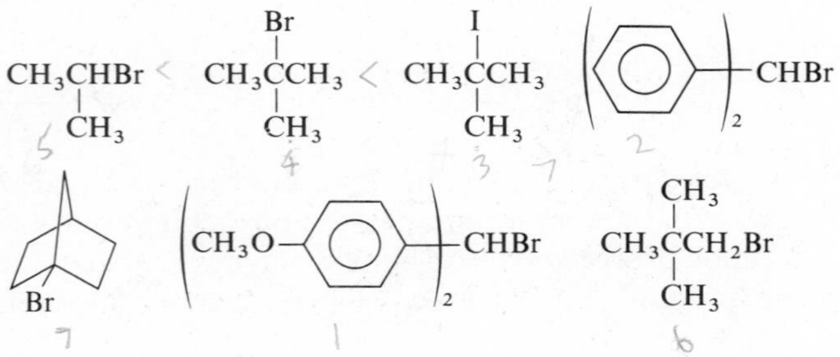

Another example of a type of rearrangement that occurs during S_N1 reactions is the *allylic rearrangement*. For example:

$$
\underset{CH_3}{\overset{CH_3}{\diagdown}}C{=}CHCH_2Cl \xrightarrow[\substack{acetone\\(S_N1)}]{aqueous}
\left[
\begin{array}{c}
\underset{CH_3}{\overset{CH_3}{\diagdown}}C{=}CH\overset{+}{C}H_2 \\[2em]
\updownarrow \\[2em]
\underset{CH_3}{\overset{CH_3}{\diagdown}}\underset{+}{C}{-}CH{=}CH_2
\end{array}
\right]
\xrightarrow[fast]{H_2O}
\begin{array}{c}
\underset{CH_3}{\overset{CH_3}{\diagdown}}C{=}CHCH_2OH \\[2em]
+ \\[2em]
\underset{CH_3\;\;OH}{\overset{CH_3}{\diagdown}}C{-}CH{=}CH_2
\end{array}
$$

The resonance-stabilized allylic cation can be attacked by a nucleophile at two positions, leading to a mixture of products.

The Cyclopropylcarbinyl Cation. Three products, two from rearrangement, are formed from cyclopropylcarbinyl chloride in water.

$$
\overset{CH_2Cl}{\triangle} \xrightarrow[S_N1]{H_2O} \overset{CH_2OH}{\triangle} \quad + \quad \overset{OH}{\square} \quad + \quad CH_2{=}CHCH_2CH_2{-}OH
$$

Cyclopropylcarbinyl   48%   47%   5%
chloride   Cyclopropylcarbinol   Cyclobutanol   3-Buten-1-ol

The rearrangement products can be explained by migration of σ bonds of the cyclopropyl ring.

$$
\underset{CH_2}{\overset{CH_2}{\diagdown}}\overset{a}{\underset{b}{\diagup}}\underset{CH}{\overset{CH_2^+}{}} \xrightarrow{a} \overset{CH_2-CH_2}{\underset{CH_2-\overset{+}{C}}{|\qquad|}}\underset{H}{} \xrightarrow{H_2O} \underset{OH}{\square} \quad + H^+
$$

$$
\xrightarrow{H_2O}
$$

$$
\xrightarrow[b]{} \underset{\overset{+}{C}H_2}{\overset{CH_2}{|}}CH_2 \xrightarrow{H_2O} HOCH_2CH_2CH{=}CH_2 + H^+
$$

$$
\triangleright{-}CH_2OH \; + \; H^+
$$

Nearly the same product distribution is obtained if cyclobutyl chloride and 1-chloro-3-butene are solvolyzed in water. Apparently the three chlorides ionize to form common carbonium ion intermediates.

A cationic center adjacent to a cyclopropane ring appears to have unusual stability. This requires a structure for the carbonium ion which implies charge delocalization over more than one carbon atom. This special type of σ-electron delocalization is different from the classical π-electron delocalization seen in the allylic and benzylic systems. Therefore, the cyclopropylcarbinyl cation has been described as a *nonclassical carbonium ion* (Figure 17.4), to distinguish it from the classically stabilized ions.

$$
^+CH_2{-}CH{=}CH_2
$$
$$
\updownarrow
$$
$$
CH_2{=}CH{-}\overset{+}{C}H_2
$$

"Classical" allyl
cation

$$
\overset{\delta^+}{\underset{\delta^+H_2C\text{-----}CH_2\delta^+}{\overset{CH_2}{\diagup|\diagdown}}}CH
$$

Proposed "nonclassical"
Cyclopropylcarbinyl
cation

The dashed lines are used to indicate partial bonds, that is, bonds present in some but not all of the resonance forms. Note that three of the carbons become equivalent by resonance—one is different from the others.

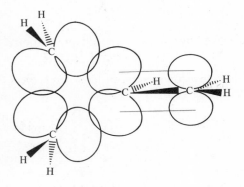

Nonclassical σ-electron delocalization has been proposed for other systems also.

Figure 17.4
Orbital representation of "nonclassical" cyclopropylcarbinyl cation.

EXERCISE 17.11

Why does 4(R)-chloro-*trans*-2-pentene racemize upon heating in benzene?

4(R)-Chloro-*trans*-2-pentene

We may ask ourselves now, What predictions can we make as to whether a given alkyl halide (or alkyl sulfonate) undergoes substitution by the S_N1 or by the S_N2 mechanism? and, Can we choose conditions to favor S_N1 over S_N2 or vice versa? A low concentration of nucleophile will favor the S_N1 reaction; the higher the concentration of nucleophile, the more probable is an S_N2 attack of nucleophile on the alkyl halide. (Why?) The S_N1 reaction is also favored over S_N2 when a poor nucleophile is used. For example, neopentyl bromide forms ethyl neopentyl ether via an S_N2 reaction with the aggressive ethoxide ion, whereas it produces ethyl 2-methyl-2-butyl ether via an S_N1 reaction with the less nucleophilic ethanol.

Thus, it is possible to exercise some control over the course of nucleophilic substitution reactions of alkyl halides by carefully choosing proper nucleophiles, concentrations, solvents, and halides.

In summary, the characteristics of a substitution reaction proceeding by an S_N1 mechanism are: (1) the reaction is unimolecular and typically is first order; (2) racemization is typical, but other stereochemical phenomena are sometimes observed (partial inversion of configuration has been discussed; retention of configuration is also possible and will be discussed in the next section); (3) the reaction is insensitive to steric hinderance, except in very special cases; (4) the reaction is greatly accelerated by polar solvents; and (5) rearrangements are frequent.

By way of a practical guide, the following halides always react by an S_N1 mechanism:

Tertiary halides
Secondary benzyl or allyl halides such as

$$PhCHCH_3$$
$$|$$
$$Br$$

Other halides which give carbonium ions at least as stable as the ions obtained from tertiary halides

Primary halides, on the other hand, undergo S_N2 reactions except with groups like neopentyl, for which the S_N2 process is very slow. Neopentyl types can often be made to undergo S_N2 reactions by use of conditions such as nonpolar solvents, or strong nucleophiles; and if they do, they give simple (unrearranged) substitution products. Rearrangement is inconsistent with an S_N2 mechanism and strong evidence for an S_N1 reaction. (It is not absolute proof of an S_N1, because some radical and carbene intermediates also undergo rearrangement.)

Secondary halides typically give results which indicate simultaneous S_N1 and S_N2 reactions. Thus for the reaction of isopropyl bromide with base, the rate equation is; Rate $= k_1 (i\text{-PrBr}) + k_2 (i\text{-PrBr})(OH^-)$, where k_1 and k_2 are similar in magnitude.

$$(CH_3)_2CHBr + OH^- \rightarrow (CH_3)_2CHOH + Br^-$$

It is possible to accelerate one component of the reaction at the expense of the other by the various methods previously discussed.

EXERCISE 17.12

Compare and contrast the S_N1 and S_N2 reactions by reference to the paragraphs on pages 407 and 399. Explain all of the similarities and differences.

17.4   Neighboring Group Participation

If a nucleophilic group is contained in the same molecule as a good leaving group, it is possible for an *intramolecular* nucleophilic substitution to occur. This is called *neighboring group participation*. For example, 4-chlorobutanol in water undergoes an intramolecular S_N2 reaction with ring closure to give tetrahydrofuran.

4-Chlorobutanol   Tetrahydrofuran

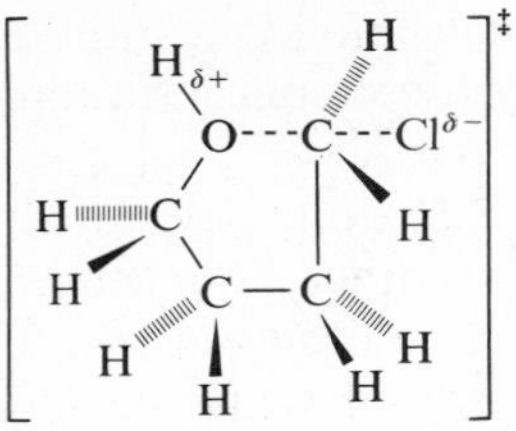

Transition state

$$\text{Rate} = k[\text{HOCH}_2\text{CH}_2\text{CH}_2\text{CH}_2\text{Cl}]$$

The rate is first order in 4-chlorobutanol, although the reaction is more like a simple S_N2 reaction than like an S_N1 reaction; that is, it is a displacement, not an ionization followed by an addition. The chain length is critical; the probability of the hydroxyl group being in the vicinity of the carbon bearing the chlorine atom drops off as the chain length increases. The reaction of 4-chlorobutanol is even faster in the presence of a base. This is because the base converts the alcohol group (the internal nucleophile) into an alkoxide, which is a much better nucleophile for intramolecular displacement of chloride.

When neighboring group participation occurs during the rate-determining step, the reaction may occur faster than predicted. In such a case, the neighboring group is said to have *anchimerically assisted* the displacement, resulting in a rate increase. For example, 2-phenyl-1-propyl chloride undergoes S_N1 solvolysis with rearrangement much more rapidly than the analogous isobutyl chloride discussed in the previous section. The difference in rate between the two chlorides has been explained by proposing that the phenyl group and its pair of electrons migrate concurrently with the ionization, anchimerically assisting the ionization, without requiring the formation of the high-energy primary carbonium ion as an intermediate.

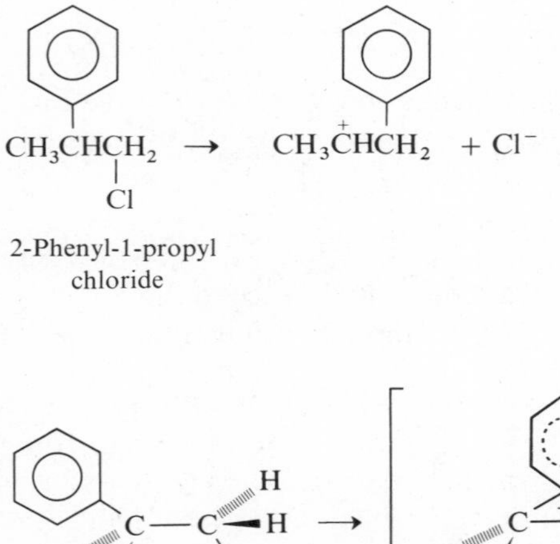

2-Phenyl-1-propyl
chloride

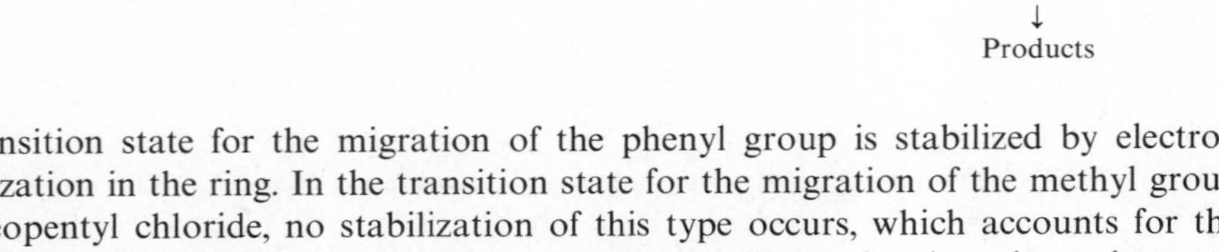

Transition state

A phenonium
ion
↓
Products

The transition state for the migration of the phenyl group is stabilized by electron delocalization in the ring. In the transition state for the migration of the methyl group from neopentyl chloride, no stabilization of this type occurs, which accounts for the rate difference. *Phenonium ions* can be discrete intermediates; they have been shown to exist by means of stereochemical studies.

EXERCISE 17.13

Draw a reaction coordinate diagram for the solvolysis of β,β,β-triphenylethyl chloride in acetic acid, paying special attention to the phenonium ion intermediate. What would be the difference in this diagram if the phenonium ion were a transition state instead of an intermediate?

Structurally, phenonium ions are quite analogous to the Wheland intermediates involved in electrophilic aromatic substitution, of which this is really a special case. Resonance structures for the phenonium ion from the solvolysis of 2-phenylethyl bromide are shown.

Displacement of bromide from 2-(p-hydroxyphenyl)ethyl bromide in the presence of ethoxide is 10^6 times faster than from 2-(p-methoxyphenyl)ethyl bromide. This can be explained by stabilization of an intermediate by the electrons on oxygen and is another example of neighboring group participation.

(The intermediate I has been independently prepared and undergoes the reaction shown.)

Two factors have been cited so far in this section as evidence for neighboring group participation: (1) the rate of the reaction is faster than expected; and (2) the displacement is intramolecular with no external nucleophile taking part in the rate-determining step. A third factor involves the configuration about an asymmetric center; this will be taken up in Section 18.4.

17.5 The E1 Mechanism

As we have seen, nucleophilic substitution reactions which are unimolecular, kinetically first order, and which are characterized by rearrangement and racemization (via a carbonium ion mechanism) are designated S_N1. Halides which form stable carbonium ions by ionization are the most reactive in this mechanism. Actually, S_N1 reactions are usually accompanied by a considerable amount of β elimination. For example, t-butyl bromide in ethanol reacts to give 81 % t-butyl ethyl ether (substitution product) and 19 %

2-methylpropene (the elimination product).

$$CH_3-\overset{\overset{\displaystyle CH_3}{|}}{\underset{\underset{\displaystyle CH_3}{|}}{C}}-\overset{+}{\underset{\underset{\displaystyle H}{|}}{O}}CH_2CH_3 + Br^- \rightarrow$$

$$CH_3CH_2\overset{..}{O}H + CH_3-\overset{\overset{\displaystyle CH_3}{|}}{\underset{\underset{\displaystyle CH_3}{|}}{C}}-Br$$

t-Butyl bromide

$$\overset{S_N1}{\nearrow}$$

$$\overset{E1}{\searrow}$$

$$CH_3-\overset{\overset{\displaystyle CH_3}{|}}{\underset{\underset{\displaystyle CH_3}{|}}{C}}-OCH_2CH_3 + HBr$$

t-Butyl ethyl ether

$$CH_2=C\overset{\displaystyle CH_3}{\underset{\displaystyle CH_3}{\Big\langle}} + Br^- + CH_3CH_2\overset{+}{\underset{\underset{\displaystyle H}{}}{O}}\overset{\displaystyle H}{\Big\langle}$$

2-Methylpropene

This kind of β elimination is also first order, and it proceeds through a carbonium ion mechanism. It is called an *E1 reaction;* for elimination (E) unimolecular (1). The rate-determining step is the ionization of the *t*-butyl bromide to form the carbonium ion. Ethanol (the nucleophile and base) has two alternatives in the subsequent fast step: (1) to remove a β-hydrogen atom of the carbonium ion to form the alkene, or (2) to attack the carbon bearing the positive charge.

$$CH_3-\overset{\overset{\displaystyle CH_3}{|}}{\underset{\underset{\displaystyle CH_3}{|}}{C}}-Br \xrightarrow{\text{slow}} CH_3-\overset{\overset{\displaystyle CH_3}{|}}{\underset{\underset{\displaystyle CH_3}{|}}{\overset{+}{C}}} + Br^-$$

$$CH_3CH_2\overset{..}{O}H + H-CH_2-\overset{+}{\underset{\underset{\displaystyle CH_3}{}}{C}}\overset{\displaystyle CH_3}{} \xrightarrow[\text{fast}]{\text{E1}} CH_3CH_2\overset{+}{\underset{\underset{\displaystyle H}{}}{O}}\overset{\displaystyle H}{} + CH_2=C\overset{\displaystyle CH_3}{\underset{\displaystyle CH_3}{}}$$

or

$$CH_3CH_2\overset{..}{O}H + CH_3-\overset{+}{C}\overset{\displaystyle CH_3}{\underset{\displaystyle CH_3}{}} \xrightarrow[\text{fast}]{S_N1} CH_3CH_2\overset{+}{\underset{\underset{\displaystyle H}{|}}{O}}-\overset{\overset{\displaystyle CH_3}{|}}{\underset{\underset{\displaystyle CH_3}{|}}{C}}-CH_3 \xrightarrow{-H^+} CH_3CH_2O\overset{\overset{\displaystyle CH_3}{|}}{\underset{\underset{\displaystyle CH_3}{|}}{C}}CH_3$$

Since the S_N1 and E1 reactions occur from the *same* intermediate carbonium ion, E1 reactions show the same effect of structure on reactivity as do S_N1 reactions. The leaving group usually cannot influence the relative amounts of E1 and S_N1 reactions, since they occur after the leaving group has departed. The main reaction condition which determines the relative amounts of elimination and substitution products is the temperature. In general, elimination is favored by a temperature rise. E1 elimination generally is more prevalent from a tertiary alkyl halide than from a secondary, because a more stable, highly substituted alkene can usually be formed from the intermediate carbonium ion. However, S_N1 reactions generally are faster than E1 under these conditions (polar nucleophilic solvent, absence of strong bases), and the main reaction products are usually those of substitution, not elimination.

If the base can attack two nonequivalent β-hydrogens, the hydrogen atom which gives the more substituted, that is, more stable, alkene is preferentially lost. Thus, 2-methyl-2-butyl bromide in 80% ethanol–20% water yields 60% S_N1 products, 32% 2-methyl-2-

butene, and only 8% of the less stable alkene, 2-methyl-1-butene.

$$
\begin{array}{ccc}
& \text{CH}_3 & \text{CH}_3 & \text{CH}_3 \\
& | & | & | \\
\text{CH}_3\text{CH}_2\text{—C—Br} & \longrightarrow \text{CH}_3\text{CH}_2\text{—C}^+ & \xrightarrow{-\text{H}^+} \text{CH}_3\text{CH}=\text{C} & + \\
& | & \backslash & \backslash \\
& \text{CH}_3 & \text{CH}_3 & \text{CH}_3
\end{array}
$$

2-Methyl-2-butyl
bromide

2-Methyl-2-butene
32%

$$
\begin{array}{c}
\text{CH}_2 \\
\parallel \\
\text{CH}_3\text{CH}_2\text{—C} \qquad + \underline{60\% \text{ substitution}} \\
\backslash \\
\text{CH}_3
\end{array}
$$

2-Methyl-1-butene   (ethers and alcohols)
8%

This tendency of a halide or an alcohol to eliminate so as to preferentially form the most substituted olefin is called the *Saytzev rule* (Section 21.2).

Neopentyl bromide in ethanol forms 2-methyl-2-butene as well as the S_N1 product, ethyl 2-methyl-2-butyl ether.

$$
\begin{array}{l}
\qquad\qquad\qquad\qquad\qquad\qquad\qquad\qquad\qquad\quad \text{CH}_3 \\
\qquad\qquad\qquad\qquad\qquad\qquad\qquad\qquad\qquad\quad \text{CH}_2 \\
\quad \text{CH}_3 \qquad\qquad\qquad\qquad \text{CH}_3 \qquad\qquad\qquad\quad \text{O} \\
\quad | \qquad\qquad\qquad\qquad\quad\quad | \qquad\qquad\qquad\qquad\quad | \\
\text{CH}_3\text{—C—CH}_2\text{—Br} \xrightarrow{\text{CH}_3\text{CH}_2\text{OH}} \text{CH}_3\text{—C}=\text{CH—CH}_3 + \text{CH}_3\text{—C—CH}_2\text{CH}_3 \\
\quad | \qquad\qquad\qquad\qquad\qquad\qquad\qquad\qquad\qquad\qquad\quad | \\
\quad \text{CH}_3 \qquad\qquad\qquad\qquad\qquad\qquad\qquad\qquad\qquad\quad \text{CH}_3
\end{array}
$$

Neopentyl bromide   2-Methyl-2-butene   Ethyl 2-methyl-2-
butyl ether

17.6   The E2 Mechanism

β-Elimination products are typically found to result to a greater or lesser extent when a substitution reaction is carried out under S_N2 conditions. For example, when isopropyl bromide is attacked by a nucleophile that is also a strong base, such as OH^- or $CH_3CH_2O^-$, propene is formed in addition to propanol or ethyl propyl ether. This elimination is bimolecular and second order (first order in alkyl halide and first order in ethoxide), and is therefore called an *E2 reaction.*

$$
\begin{array}{l}
\qquad\qquad\qquad\qquad\qquad\qquad \xrightarrow{\text{E2}} \text{CH}_3\text{CH}_2\text{OH} + \text{CH}_2=\text{CHCH}_3 + \text{Br}^- \\
\qquad\qquad\qquad\qquad\qquad\qquad\qquad\qquad\qquad\quad 80\% \\
\text{CH}_3\text{CH}_2\text{O}^- + \text{CH}_3\text{CHCH}_3 \\
\qquad\qquad\qquad\qquad | \\
\qquad\qquad\qquad\quad \text{Br} \qquad\qquad\qquad\qquad\qquad\qquad \text{CH}_3 \\
\qquad\qquad\qquad\qquad\qquad\qquad\qquad\qquad\qquad\qquad\quad | \\
\qquad\qquad\qquad\qquad \xrightarrow{\text{S}_N2} \text{CH}_3\text{CH}_2\text{O—CH} \qquad + \quad \text{Br}^- \\
\qquad\qquad\qquad\qquad\qquad\qquad\qquad\qquad\qquad\qquad\quad \backslash \\
\qquad\qquad\qquad\qquad\qquad\qquad\qquad\qquad\qquad\qquad\qquad \text{CH}_3 \\
\qquad\qquad\qquad\qquad\qquad\qquad\qquad 20\%
\end{array}
$$

The elimination of H and Br is concerted, that is, concurrent with the formation of the double bond. Thus an E2 reaction does not proceed through an intermediate carbonium ion and is not accompanied by rearrangements such as are found in E1 eliminations.

In the presence of strong base and a solvent which is not too polar (e.g., ethanol), S_N2 and E2 reactions usually occur in preference to S_N1 and E1 processes. The E2 usually wins out over the S_N2. Hence from a synthetic point of view, if we want to carry out a substitution reaction with a tertiary halide, we will choose a polar solvent, low temperature, and dilute weakly basic conditions (S_N1 conditions). If we want an elimination to occur, we will use strong base, less polar (e.g. alcoholic) solvent, and a high temperature (E2 conditions).

$$CH_3-\underset{\underset{CH_3}{|}}{\overset{\overset{CH_3}{|}}{C}}-Br \xrightarrow[25°C,\ HCO_3^-]{H_2O} CH_3-\underset{\underset{CH_3}{|}}{\overset{\overset{CH_3}{|}}{C}}-OH \qquad (S_N1)$$

$$CH_3-\underset{\underset{CH_3}{|}}{\overset{\overset{CH_3}{|}}{C}}-Br \xrightarrow[EtOH]{EtO^-,\ 100°C} CH_2=C\overset{CH_3}{\underset{CH_3}{\diagdown}} \qquad (E2)$$

Such E2 conditions also give good yields of alkenes with secondary and primary bromides and sulfonates.

Experimental observations on the stereochemistry of the products of E2 eliminations lead to the conclusion that the reaction is stereospecific, with trans elimination occurring. A trans elimination can be represented with the β-hydrogen atom, the halogen atom, and the two carbon atoms bearing them in a single plane, with the β-hydrogen and the halogen atom oriented as far apart as possible, in what is better called an *anti-coplanar* relationship.

Anti-coplanar relationship

This mechanism is analogous to the S_N2 reaction insofar as the electron pair of the C—H bond can be considered to displace the halide ion in a backside attack. The coplanar relationship is preferred so that the orbitals on carbon can overlap to form a π bond as the elimination proceeds.

The anti relationship allows Z^- to attack hydrogen at a position as distant as possible from the electronegative X, analogous to the stereochemical preference observed for the S_N2 reaction.

A trans and diaxial relationship of the H and leaving X is preferred in the cyclohexane system because only in this way can the system have anti-coplanar geometry.

(Equatorial Cl)   (Axial Cl)
     Chlorocyclohexane   Cyclohexene

The elimination occurs from the axial conformation, although the equatorial conformation is more stable and is present in greater amount.

If the β hydrogen and the departing halide cannot assume an anti-coplanar relationship owing to the rigidity demanded by a cyclic system, *or* if no hydrogen is available which is anti-coplanar, cis elimination can occur through a syn-coplanar relationship.

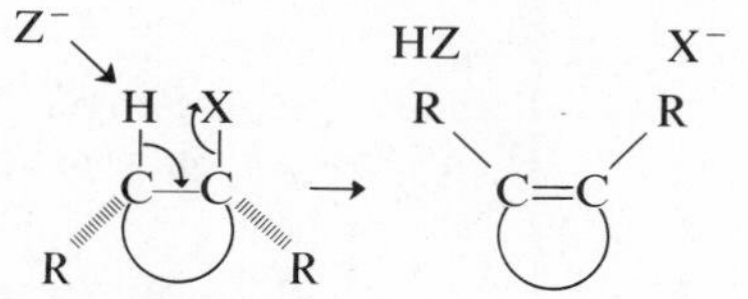

Syn-coplanar

In *exo*-norbornyl chloride the trans hydrogen (H_a) cannot easily achieve an anti-coplanar arrangement relative to the chlorine, and the molecule therefore preferentially undergoes a cis elimination.

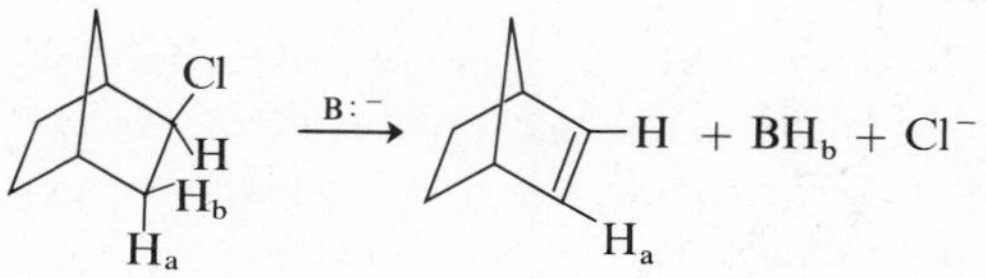

exo-Norbornyl
chloride

EXERCISE 17.14

How do you suppose one actually tells in the laboratory whether it was H_a or H_b that was lost in the above experiment?

Actually, a number of cases have been discovered recently in which syn-coplanar E2 elimination competes, at least to a small extent, with anti-coplanar E2 reactions, when both are possible.

If an anti-coplanar geometry is allowed, an E2 reaction of an alkyl halide or tosylate will also preferentially give the most highly substituted alkene (e.g., the most stable). Two examples are the following reactions:

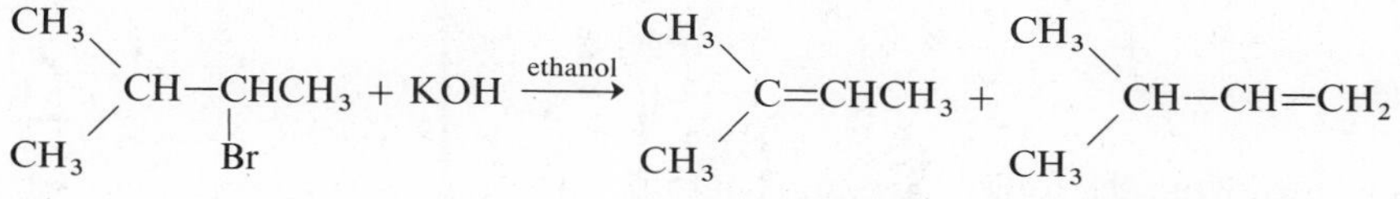

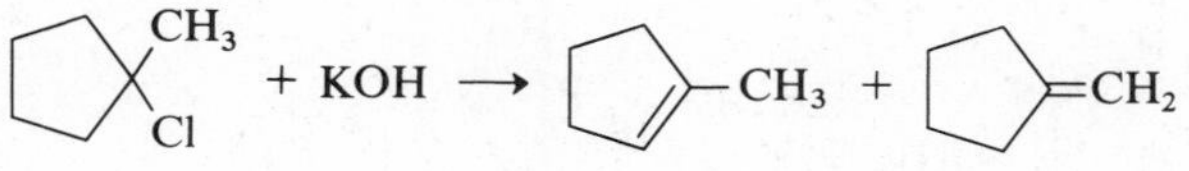

The situation that occurs with a typical secondary aliphatic halide of at least four carbon atoms is most interesting. For example, less steric interaction results in the butane conformation in which the methyl groups are anti to one another, than when they are gauche (Section 3.3). If we look at conformations of the alkyl halide $RCH_2CHR'X$ we see that the necessity for an anti-coplanar relationship and the lower energy that would result by having R and R' anti, rather than gauche, taken together, explain the predominant formation of *trans*- rather than *cis*-alkenes from E2 reactions.

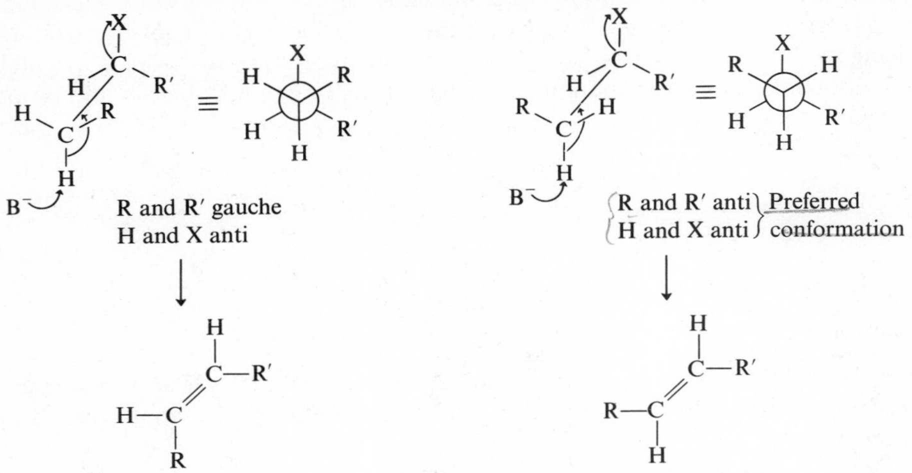

R and R' gauche
H and X anti

(R and R' anti) Preferred
(H and X anti) conformation

cis-Alkene

trans-Alkene

*The student may now be able to see why anti-coplanar and syn-coplanar are better
descriptive terms for the E2 mechanism than cis or trans. The anti-coplanar process can
give either a* trans- *or a* cis-alkene *(see above). Furthermore, with cyclic compounds,
although the terms cis and trans elimination are useful, they can be misleading.
The reason that small cyclic halides (C₄ to C₇) prefer trans elimination is that only
with the leaving groups (H and X) trans can the anti-coplanar geometry be attained.*

An example is the dehydrobromination of 2-bromobutane, in which R and R' are CH_3.
trans-2-Butene strongly predominates over *cis*-2-butene in the product. Since the more
highly substituted double bond is of lower energy, 2-butene strongly predominates over
1-butene also.

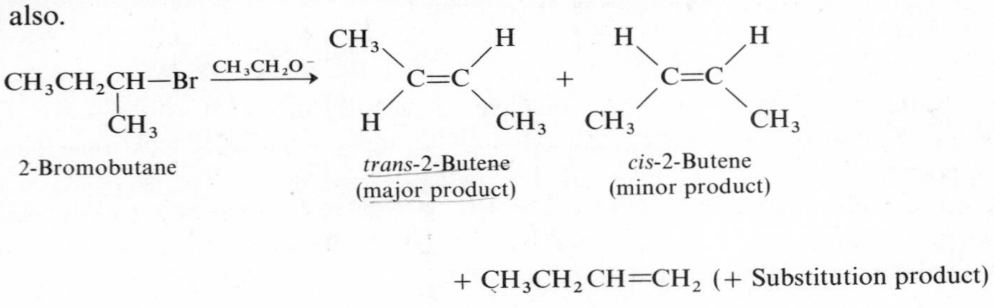

2-Bromobutane

trans-2-Butene
(major product)

cis-2-Butene
(minor product)

$+ CH_3CH_2CH=CH_2$ (+ Substitution product)

1-Butene
(minor product)

1-Butene is formed from the following conformation:

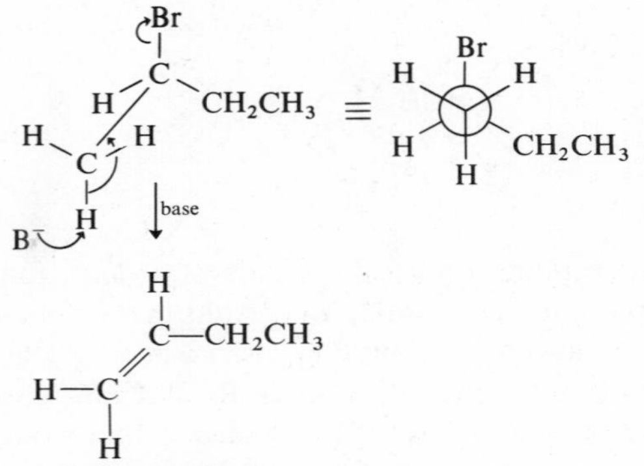

(minor product)

Both the direction of elimination (orientation) and the stereochemistry of the alkene (cis or trans) resulting from E2 reaction of halides and sulfonates are sensitive to reaction conditions. Such effects as caused by the steric size of the attacking base, the steric size of the substrate, the strength of the base, and the solvent can all alter the observed product ratios. We will not go into details here.

The anti-coplanar relationship present in the transition state of the ordinary E2 reaction demands that diastereomeric compounds give different alkenes. *meso*-2,3-Dibromobutane gives *cis*-2-bromo-2-butene, whereas the *dl*-dibromide eliminates to form the trans isomer.

meso-2,3-Dibromobutane   *cis*-2-Bromo-2-butene

dl-2,3-Dibromobutane   *trans*-2-Bromo-2-butene
(only one enantiomer is shown)

The relative amounts of products from competing S_N2 and E2 reactions depend on a number of factors. In general, tertiary halides give more elimination than do primary halides because a more stable, substituted alkene can be formed and because S_N2 attack is sterically hindered; secondary halides are intermediate in behavior. Increasing the temperature usually increases the percentage of elimination for a particular reaction.

The Carbanion Elimination Mechanism. The E2 mechanism involves a concerted cleavage of C—H and C—X bonds and formation of the carbon–carbon double bond. In the E1 mechanism, the C—X bond ionizes to a carbonium ion from which a proton is subsequently eliminated. In certain other reactions, the proton is removed in a step *prior* to the elimination of the halide ion:

A carbanion

This mechanism can only be important if a highly stabilized carbanion is formed.

Dehydrohalogenation of alkyl halides is an important reaction for the preparation of alkynes. Dihalides, such as 1,1-dichloropropane and 1,2-dichloropropane, and vinyl halides, such as 1-chloro-1-propene, are used.

Sodamide causes 1-alkynes to form where possible, because of the formation of the thermodynamically stable alkynide ion. Hydroxide or alkoxide, however, are not strong enough bases to form alkynides; when they are used, the thermodynamically more stable internal alkynes predominate.

$$CH_3-\underset{\underset{Cl}{|}}{\overset{\overset{Cl}{|}}{C}}-CH_2-CH_3 \xrightarrow{NH_2^-} H-C{\equiv}C-CH_2CH_3 \xrightarrow{NH_2^-} {}^-C{\equiv}C-CH_2CH_3$$

$$\xrightarrow{{}^-OCH_3} CH_3-C{\equiv}C-CH_3 \qquad \downarrow{}^{H^+}$$

$$HC{\equiv}C-CH_2CH_3$$

Vinyl halides are intermediates in the formation of alkynes from dichloroalkanes, and these suffer further dehydrohalogenation.

While H—X is often eliminated from a halide with base, the elimination of other fragments is also possible under certain conditions. A 1,2-dihalide will smoothly eliminate halogen upon treatment with iodide ion; for example,

$$\overset{\diagdown}{\underset{\diagup}{-C}}-\overset{C-X}{\underset{\diagdown}{C}}- \rightarrow \overset{\diagdown}{\underset{\diagup}{C}}{=}\overset{\diagup}{\underset{\diagdown}{C}} + IX + X^-$$

$$I^- \to X$$

Note that one halogen is removed without its bonding electrons (formally, as a halonium ion), while the other departs as halide. An anti-coplanar orientation of the two halogens is favored.

Reactive metals lead to a similar reaction.

$$-\overset{|}{\underset{|}{C}}-\overset{X}{\underset{X}{C}}- + Zn \rightarrow \overset{\diagdown}{\underset{\diagup}{C}}{=}\overset{\diagup}{\underset{\diagdown}{C}} + ZnX_2$$

Any good leaving group will function in place of the halide ion.

$$\overset{\diagdown}{\underset{\diagup}{-C}}-\overset{OCH_3}{\underset{X}{C}}- \overset{Zn}{\rightarrow} \overset{\diagdown}{\underset{\diagup}{C}}{=}\overset{\diagup}{\underset{\diagdown}{C}} + ZnX(OCH_3)$$

$$\overset{\diagdown}{\underset{\diagup}{-C}}-\overset{OSO_2C_6H_4CH_3}{\underset{X}{C}}- \overset{I^-}{\rightarrow} \overset{\diagdown}{\underset{\diagup}{C}}{=}\overset{\diagup}{\underset{\diagdown}{C}} + XI + CH_3C_6H_4SO_3^-$$

Specific examples are

$$CH_3CH_2\underset{Br}{\overset{|}{C}H}CH_2Br \overset{I^-}{\rightarrow} CH_3CH_2CH{=}CH_2$$

17.7   Alpha Elimination

A special type of elimination in which both groups are lost from the same carbon atom is called α *elimination*. For example, *t*-butoxide ion removes a proton from tribromo-methane in an acid–base equilibrium. In a subsequent step, the tribromocarbanion loses bromide ion from the same carbon to which the proton had been attached, yielding dibromocarbene, a very reactive intermediate which can be trapped by having an alkene, such as cyclohexene, present in the reaction mixture (Section 15.13).

$$(CH_3)_3C-O^- + H-CBr_3 \rightleftharpoons (CH_3)_3CO-H + {}^-CBr_3$$

    t-Butoxide   Tribromomethane   *t*-Butyl alcohol   Tribromocarbanion

From the discussion from Section 17.2 up to this section it can be seen that attack of nucleophiles on alkyl halides can be very complex, with S_N1 or S_N2 reactions occurring simultaneously along with E1 or E2; α elimination and carbanion mechanisms are also possible. In order to predict how a particular alkyl halide and nucleophile will react, it is essential to understand the above mechanisms and the factors that influence them. Thus one must have a firm grasp of kinetics and transition-state theory, stereochemistry, carbonium ion and carbanion stability, steric factors, and the effect of solvent polarity.

17.8   Nucleophilic Aromatic Substitution

Alkenes, because of their π electrons, show reactions which are predominantly those of Lewis bases; they are subject to attack by electrophilic reagents (Section 15.3). Aromatic compounds behave similarly, and for the same reason. The usual situation, in which an alkene or an aromatic compound acts as a Lewis base and is subject to attack by electro-philes, can be overturned under certain circumstances. If one or more powerful electron-withdrawing groups are attached to the unsaturated system, it is possible that the double bond will not act as a Lewis base (with an easily accessible pair of electrons), but rather will act as a Lewis acid or electron acceptor. In the latter case, the double bond will be subject to attack by nucleophilic species (Lewis bases). As might be anticipated from our earlier studies, electron-deficient alkenes tend to undergo nucleophilic *addition* reactions whereas electron-deficient aromatic compounds tend to undergo nucleo-philic *substitution* reactions.

A halogen attached to a saturated carbon atom is ordinarily displaced readily by a suitable nucleophile at temperatures below 100°C, as was discussed in the previous sections. On the other hand, bromobenzene and chlorobenzene are completely inert to reaction under these conditions. They react with aqueous sodium hydroxide, for example, only at temperatures of over 300°C. Thus a halogen atom attached to an aromatic ring (or to an olefinic double bond as, for example, in vinyl bromide) is, in general, fairly inert to substitution by nucleophiles (by either S_N2 or S_N1 mechanisms). If a powerful electron-withdrawing group is attached to the aromatic ring in a position ortho or para to the halogen atom, however, substitution can occur much more easily.

These are *bimolecular nucleophilic substitution reactions;* the mechanism involves formation of an intermediate analogous to that formed in electrophilic aromatic substitutions:

These anionic intermediates are sometimes called Meisenheimer complexes, *and several have been isolated. For example,*

As with the electrophilic substitution of an aromatic ring, the addition process is not completed, but instead the halogen is displaced. The electron-withdrawing groups, nitro groups in these examples (and in most important other cases), stabilize the intermediate both by induction and by delocalization of the negative charge.

If there are two or more electron-withdrawing groups present in the ortho and para positions on the aromatic ring, the intermediate is even more stable, and the substitution reaction proceeds even more easily.

Thus, any aromatic compound which contains a good leaving group such as halide, and a moderately strong "activating group" (or better, several of them) in the ortho or para position, will be subject to substitution by moderately good nucleophiles.

Note that an activating group for nucleophilic substitution is a group with $-I$ and $-R$ characteristics. This is opposite to what is required for an activating group in electrophilic aromatic substitution (Section 16.7).

The activating group must be in a position ortho or para to the leaving group; if it is in the meta position, it has very little activating effect. An examination of the resonance forms of the intermediate shows why.

The negative charge is not delocalized to the carbon atom bearing the nitro group in any of the resonance contributors. Therefore, the *m*-nitro is not in a position to stabilize the negative charge of the intermediate very well, either by induction or by resonance.

The mechanism of nucleophilic aromatic substitution can be described as an addition–elimination process.

Nucleophilic aromatic substitution has much in common with electrophilic aromatic substitutions.

Nucleophilic aromatic substitution

Electrophilic aromatic substitution

However, the effect of a substituent and the nature of both the leaving group and attacking reagent will be reversed in the two cases. In the first case Z^- must be a nucleophile, and X^- a good leaving group (one which is comfortable with the negative charge). In the electrophilic case, Z^+ and Y^+ must be electrophiles, and Y^+ should bear the charge the more comfortably if the thermodynamic driving force of the reaction is to be in the right direction. The activating and orienting effects of a substituent are also opposite in the two cases. Nucleophilic substitution involves the formation of an intermediate which carries a negative charge. A group with $-I$ and $-R$ effects (such as $-NO_2$), if located ortho or para to the attacked site, will stabilize the intermediate and the anion leading to it, and such a group will accelerate the reaction. In the electrophilic case, the presence of a group with $-I$ and $-R$ effects (such as $-NO_2$) destabilizes the intermediate and the corresponding transition state, and slows the reaction. This destabilization is most serious when the group is ortho or para to the attacked site. If the leaving group is a proton typically the electrophilic substitution process will occur at the meta position (see Section 16.7).

Figure 17.5
Free energy diagram for a typical nucleophilic aromatic substitution reaction.

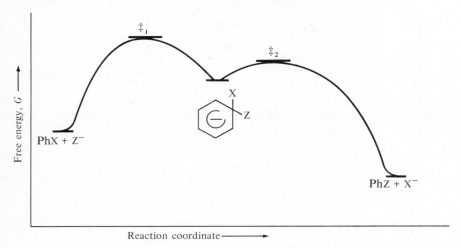

We also can compare and contrast bimolecular aromatic and aliphatic nucleophilic substitution reactions. The latter involve no intermediate (S_N2) but simply a transition state as shown in Figure 17.1. Nucleophilic aromatic substitution, on the other hand, involves an intermediate and two transition states (see Figure 17.5), of which the first one is ordinarily of higher energy.

EXERCISE 17.15

Predict the product of the reaction shown:

Draw a free-energy–reaction coordinate diagram for the reaction.

Relative Reactivities of Halogens in Nucleophilic Substitutions. The rate of reaction is usually determined by the height of the first barrier, rather than that of the second (Figure 17.5). In aliphatic nucleophilic substitution reactions, the alkyl halides react with nucleophiles in the order RI > RBr > RCl > RF. The C—I bond is the weakest, the C—F bond the strongest, and the order of reactivity is as would be expected on that basis. The total spread in reactivity is very large, with R—I being more reactive than R—F by something on the order of a million times. In nucleophilic aromatic substitution, it makes little difference which halide is the leaving group, since the C—X bond is not broken in the rate-determining step. Rate differences between ArI and ArF are therefore usually small, a factor of 10 or less. Interestingly, the fluoride ordinarily reacts *faster* than does the iodide in this case, because the powerfully electronegative fluorine helps to stabilize the negative charge being developed in the slow (first) step of the reaction more than does the less electronegative iodine. Thus the fluoride is thought to undergo the first (addition) step faster than the iodide, while the iodide is faster in the elimination step. The addition step is the slow step of the overall reaction, however, so it is observed that the fluoride reacts faster than the iodide. These ideas are summarized in the reaction coordinate diagram, Figure 17.6.

Figure 17.6
Free energy diagram of typical nucleophilic aromatic substitution reactions of ArI and ArF.

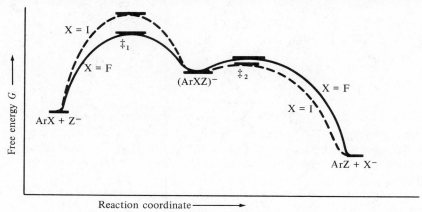

Nucleophilic Displacement via Conjugate Additions. An example of a nucleophilic substitution reaction of a halogen attached to an alkene bond is the displacement of chloride from ethyl 3-chloro-2-butenoate by thiomethoxide.

$$CH_3-\underset{\underset{Cl}{|}}{C}=CH-CO_2C_2H_5 + CH_3S^- \rightarrow CH_3-\underset{\underset{CH_3S}{|}}{C}=CH-CO_2C_2H_5 + Cl^-$$

This reaction, which is not typical of alkenes, proceeds because of the formation of a resonance-stabilized intermediate.

Reactants $\rightarrow$ $\left[CH_3-\underset{\underset{Cl}{|}}{\overset{\overset{SCH_3}{|}}{C}}-\overset{-}{C}H-\overset{\overset{O}{\diagup\diagup}}{C}-OC_2H_5 \leftrightarrow CH_3\overset{\overset{SCH_3}{|}}{C}-CH=\overset{\overset{O^-}{\diagup}}{C}\diagdown_{OC_2H_5} \right]$ $\rightarrow$ Products

Chloride is subsequently eliminated from the intermediate. The intermediate is similar to intermediates formed in *Michael addition reactions*, to be discussed in Section 19.17.

17.9   Reactions with Benzyne as an Intermediate

During the 1950s it was found by J. D. Roberts† and his group at Cal Tech, following an earlier suggestion by Georg Wittig†† and his collaborators at Heidelberg, that it is

---

† John D. Roberts. Born 1918, Los Angeles. Massachusetts Institute of Technology and California Institute of Technology.
†† Georg Wittig. Born 1897. Berlin, Universities of Freiburg, Tübingen, and Heidelberg.

possible to obtain what appears to be a nucleophilic substitution with even normally unreactive aromatic compounds (such as bromobenzene) when a sufficiently strong base is used as the nucleophile. Ammonia will not displace bromide from bromobenzene, even upon prolonged heating in a sealed tube. The amide ion, which may be obtained by allowing ammonia to *react* with sodium, does however, react readily with bromobenzene (even at very low temperatures). The product of the reaction is aniline, and it would at first appear to have been produced by an ordinary nucleophilic aromatic substitution.

Aniline

In fact, things are not so simple. If we treat *p*-bromotoluene with sodamide, we find that the reaction product is not just *p*-toluidine; but rather, it is a mixture of *m*- and *p*-toluidine.

p-Toluidine   *m*-Toluidine

The formation of the meta isomer appears to require some reaction mechanism *other* than a simple substitution process. It was deduced that the reaction of a simple aromatic halide with strong base actually goes in several steps. In the first step, bromobenzene, for example, undergoes an elimination reaction to give a highly strained alkyne, which then adds the elements of ammonia to give aniline. The addition process is believed to occur in two steps. First, amide ion attacks the triple bond to give a carbanion, which in turn abstracts a proton from ammonia, producing aniline and regenerating amide ion.

When this scheme is applied to the reaction of *p*-bromotoluene the triple bond is formed in the 3,4 position. The amide ion can add at either C-3, or at C-4, resulting in *m*- and *p*-toluidine, respectively.

This process is quite analogous to the formation of an alkyne from a vinyl halide (Section 17.6), and to the addition of a nucleophile to an alkyne. The reactive alkyne intermediate obtained in this case is called *benzyne*, and it must have a structure which is unusual indeed!

As discussed in Section 7.18, an alkyne will, if unstrained, have linear geometry with *sp* hybridization of the two carbon atoms. Benzyne *cannot* have such a geometry because the ring constrains the bond angles to something near 120°, rather than the preferred 180°. The acetylenic carbon atoms must have a hybridization which is near to sp^2. The benzyne molecule is, therefore, very strained and highly reactive. It is not surprising that such a molecule reacts very rapidly with any nucleophile which happens to be available and that no benzyne has been isolated.

Orientation in Reactions Proceeding via a Benzyne Intermediate. Because of the peculiar geometry of benzyne, the two orbitals lying in the plane of the ring have very poor overlap and the resulting bond is weak. The bond is a deformed π bond in which the atomic orbitals are not parallel (*p*), but point somewhat away from one another (sp^2). It is the most reactive bond in the molecule and the one which undergoes nucleophilic attack. If there are substituents on the ring, they can only interact with this component of the triple bond by induction. The resonance effect only comes into play insofar as the π-electron system of the benzyne ring is concerned. Thus if we take *p*-bromo-anisole and treat it with a sufficiently powerful base, it is converted into 4-methoxybenzyne.

4-Methoxybenzyne

The amide ion may now attack at either the para or at the meta position. Two different carbanions may be generated and subsequently protonated.

The inductive effect of the methoxyl group stabilizes the ion from para attack more than it does that from meta attack, and hence the product is *p*-methoxyaniline.

EXERCISE 17.16

Predict the product of the reaction of *p*-bromodimethylaniline with sodamide in liquid ammonia. Explain.

17.10   Preparation of Organometallic Compounds from Halides

In Section 4.19 organometallic reagents containing carbon-to-metal bonds were discussed. These compounds are very useful intermediates for the syntheses of organic compounds. In fact, Grignard reagents (organomagnesium compounds, prepared from organic halides and magnesium), are among the most useful reagents available to the organic chemist. In this section, we will discuss the preparation of organometallic compounds. The next section will discuss the reactions of organometallic compounds with organic halides.

A common method for the preparation of an organometallic compound is by reaction of an organic halide with a metal. The reactivity of halides with metals increases as the halogen atom varies from F down to I. The reactivity of the resulting organometallic compound increases with the percent of ionic character of the carbon-to-metal bond. From Table 4.9, page 78, it can be seen that the C—Na bond is approximately 47% ionic, whereas the C—Hg bond is much less ionic (9%); the C—Mg bond is intermediate, being 35% ionic. In each case the polarization of the carbon–metal bond is in the same direction; the metal has excess positive charge, and the organic fragment bears a partial negative charge. It is generally helpful to recall that this negative charge is present on carbon, and the chemical reactions which organometallic compounds undergo are typically those of carbanions and nucleophiles.

Sodium reacts easily with most halides, and the resulting organosodium compounds are so reactive that they frequently attack the starting halide or solvent as soon as they are formed. In contrast, mercury is amalgamated with sodium in order to increase its reactivity. The formation of a Grignard reagent represents an intermediate situation. An organic halide and magnesium react in ether to form what is referred to as RMgX.

$$R—X + Mg \xrightarrow{\text{ether}} RMgX$$
A Grignard reagent

As was mentioned in Section 4.19, the structure of the Grignard reagent is more complicated than indicated by the formula RMgX, because the ether coordinates with the magnesium. This interaction with the solvent inhibits the reagent from attacking unreacted halide. Fluorides do not react with magnesium in ether. Alkyl chlorides tend to react slowly, and aryl chlorides do not react. Bromides and iodides both react readily with magnesium, but bromides are more often used in practice because they are cheaper and more readily available.

$$Br—\overset{\bigcirc}{\underset{}{\bigcirc}}—Cl + Mg \xrightarrow{\text{ether}} BrMg—\overset{\bigcirc}{\underset{}{\bigcirc}}—Cl$$

Since the carbon-to-magnesium bond is polarized with partial negative charge on carbon and positive charge on magnesium, rearrangements of the carbonium ion type (Section 17.3) are not commonly associated with the formation of Grignard reagents. For example, the Grignard reagent can be prepared from neopentyl chloride without any rearrangement.

$$CH_3—\overset{\overset{\displaystyle CH_3}{|}}{\underset{\underset{\displaystyle CH_3}{|}}{C}}—CH_2—Cl + Mg \xrightarrow{\text{ether}} CH_3—\overset{\overset{\displaystyle CH_3}{|}}{\underset{\underset{\displaystyle CH_3}{|}}{C}}—\overset{\delta-}{C}H_2—\overset{\delta+}{M}gCl$$
Neopentylmagnesium chloride

Tetrahydrofuran is commonly used as a solvent in the preparation of Grignard reagents from the less reactive vinyl halides and aryl chlorides.

$$\text{C}_6\text{H}_5\text{—Cl} + \text{Mg} \xrightarrow{\text{tetrahydrofuran}} \text{C}_6\text{H}_5\text{—MgCl}$$

Chlorobenzene   Phenylmagnesium chloride

$$\text{CH}_2{=}\text{CH—Br} + \text{Mg} \xrightarrow{\text{tetrahydrofuran}} \text{CH}_2{=}\text{CH—MgBr}$$

Vinyl bromide   Vinylmagnesium bromide

Often an initiator such as a trace of iodine, methyl iodide, or especially 1,2-dibromo-ethane, is added. The initiators are believed to function by reacting rapidly with the metal, thereby cleaning the surface and promoting reaction between metal and halide. It is important that the reaction be kept dry, as traces of water inhibit the initiation.

Vicinal dihalides $-\overset{|}{\underset{X}{\text{C}}}-\overset{|}{\underset{X}{\text{C}}}-$ do not form Grignard reagents, but react with magnesium

to give alkenes $\diagdown\text{C}{=}\text{C}\diagup$; for example,

$$\underset{\underset{\text{Br}}{|}}{\text{CH}_2}-\underset{\underset{\text{Br}}{|}}{\text{CH}_2} + \text{Mg} \xrightarrow{\text{ether}} \text{CH}_2{=}\text{CH}_2 + \text{MgBr}_2$$

1,2-Dibromoethane   Ethylene

Compounds of the type $-\overset{|}{\underset{X}{\text{C}}}-\overset{|}{\underset{OR}{\text{C}}}-$ similarly undergo elimination, rather than Grignard formation.

$$\underset{\underset{\text{Br}}{|}}{\text{CH}_3\text{CH}}-\underset{\underset{\text{OCH}_3}{|}}{\text{CHCH}_3} \xrightarrow{\text{Mg}} \text{CH}_3\text{CH}{=}\text{CHCH}_3 + \text{MgBrOCH}_3$$

Other reactive metals such as zinc and sodium also give this type of reaction (Section 17.6). Likewise, 1,3-dihalides eliminate halogen to give cyclopropane.

$$\text{Br—CH}_2\text{—CH}_2\text{—CH}_2\text{—Br} + \text{Mg} \xrightarrow{\text{ether}} \underset{\text{CH}_2}{\text{CH}_2\diagup\diagdown\text{CH}_2} + \text{MgBr}_2$$

1,3-Dibromopropane   Cyclopropane

If the halogen atoms in dihaloalkanes are further apart, or if the two halogen atoms are on a benzene ring (not ortho), mono- or di-Grignard formation occurs rather than elimination.

$$\text{Br—(CH}_2)_n\text{—Br} + 2\text{Mg} \xrightarrow{\text{ether}} \text{BrMg—(CH}_2)_n\text{—MgBr}$$
$$n > 3 \qquad\qquad\qquad\qquad\quad n > 3$$

A di-Grignard reagent

$$\text{Br—C}_6\text{H}_4\text{—Br} + 2\text{Mg} \xrightarrow{\text{tetrahydrofuran}} \text{BrMg—C}_6\text{H}_4\text{—MgBr}$$

p-Dibromobenzene

Zinc and an alkyl halide will react to form an organozinc compound similar to the Grignard reagent.

$$\text{R—X} + \text{Zn} \rightarrow \text{R—ZnX}$$

The organozinc reagent that has most often been employed in syntheses of organic compounds is formed from an α-halo ester and zinc. This intermediate is used in the Reformatsky synthesis by reaction with an aldehyde or a ketone (Section 19.9).

Although organosodium compounds are so reactive that they can attack the solvent, the corresponding organolithium compounds can be prepared without this problem. They are used extensively. For example, *n*-butyl bromide and lithium form *n*-butyllithium in high yield with pentane as a solvent. Aryl halides such as bromobenzene and chlorobenzene are also reactive toward lithium metal.

$$CH_3CH_2CH_2CH_2\!-\!Br + 2Li \xrightarrow{\text{pentane}} CH_3CH_2CH_2CH_2\!-\!Li + LiBr$$

n-Butyl bromide n-Butyllithium

$$\langle\!\bigcirc\!\rangle\!-\!Br + 2Li \xrightarrow{\text{ether}} \langle\!\bigcirc\!\rangle\!-\!Li + LiBr$$

Bromobenzene   Phenyllithium

Other Organometallic Compounds. Dialkylzinc, dialkylcadmium, and dialkylmercury compounds are conveniently prepared from alkyl halides by first forming the Grignard reagent and subsequently adding zinc chloride, cadmium chloride, or mercuric chloride.

$$CH_3CH_2Cl + Mg \rightarrow CH_3CH_2MgCl$$

Ethyl chloride   Ethylmagnesium
                        chloride

$$\xrightarrow{ZnCl_2} (CH_3CH_2)_2Zn + MgCl_2$$
Diethylzinc

$$\xrightarrow{CdCl_2} (CH_3CH_2)_2Cd + MgCl_2$$
Diethylcadmium

$$\xrightarrow{HgCl_2} (CH_3CH_2)_2Hg + MgCl_2$$
Diethylmercury

The reaction of ethyl chloride and lead (as a sodium–lead alloy) is an important industrial reaction for the preparation of tetraethyllead (Section 4.19).

$$4\,CH_3CH_2Cl + 4\,Pb(Na) \rightarrow (CH_3CH_2)_4Pb + 4\,NaCl + 3\,Pb$$

Tetraethyllead

17.11   Reactions of Halides with Organometallic Compounds

In the preceding sections, it was mentioned that the preparation of an organosodium compound from sodium and an organic halide is complicated by the attack of the highly reactive organosodium product on unreacted halide. The result of this reaction is the coupling of two alkyl halides to yield an alkane.

$$CH_3\!-\!Cl + 2Na \rightarrow CH_3\!-\!Na + NaCl$$

$$CH_3\!-\!Na + CH_3\!-\!Cl \rightarrow CH_3\!-\!CH_3 + NaCl$$

Since the C—Na bond has considerable ionic character (Section 4.19), the carbon in methylsodium acts as the nucleophilic carbanion, and it can displace chloride from methyl chloride in an S_N2-type reaction:

$$CH_3^-Na^+ + CH_3\!-\!Cl \rightarrow CH_3\!-\!CH_3 + Na^+Cl^-$$

This coupling reaction is known as the *Wurtz*† *reaction*, and it is of some limited synthetic

† Adolphe Wurtz. 1817–1884. Born Strasbourg. University of Paris.

utility. *However, such dimerization is more often an unwanted side reaction in the preparation of Grignard reagents.* E2 elimination can accompany the coupling reaction.

$$CH_3CH_2CH_2CH_2^- Na^+ + CH_3CH_2CH_2CH_2Cl \rightarrow CH_3(CH_2)_2CH_2CH_2(CH_2)_2CH_3$$

n-Butylsodium   *n*-Butyl chloride   *n*-Octane (coupling product)

$$+ CH_3CH_2CH=CH_2 + CH_3(CH_2)_2CH_3 + Na^+Cl^-$$

1-Butene   Butane

Elimination products

The reactions of 1,2- or 1,3-dihaloalkanes with magnesium or other metals to form alkenes or cyclopropanes, mentioned in Section 17.10, can be looked upon as intra-molecular Wurtz-type reactions. An initially formed Grignard reagent collapses with displacement of the neighboring bromide. Zinc or sodium can be used in place of magnesium.

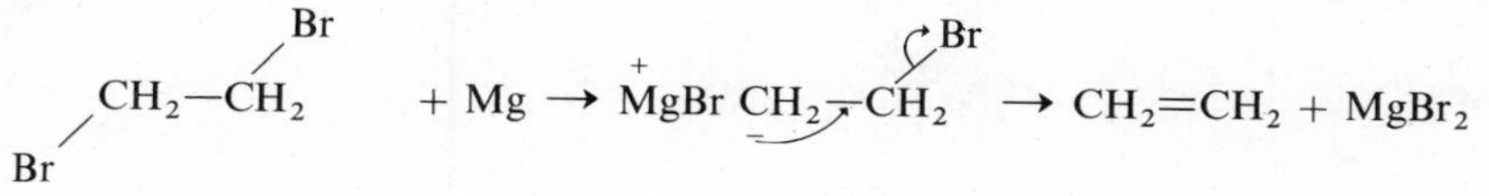

EXERCISE 17.17

Write a reasonable mechanism for the reaction of 1,3-dibromopropane with magnesium to yield cyclopropane.

It is particularly difficult to prepare allylic and benzylic Grignard reagents, because they rapidly displace bromide from unreacted halide in a Wurtz-type reaction.

$$CH_2=CHCH_2-Br + Mg \xrightarrow{ether} CH_2=CHCH_2-MgBr$$

Allyl bromide   Allylmagnesium bromide

$$CH_2=CHCH_2-MgBr + CH_2=CHCH_2-Br \xrightarrow{fast} CH_2=CHCH_2CH_2CH=CH_2$$

1,5-Hexadiene

$$+ MgBr_2$$

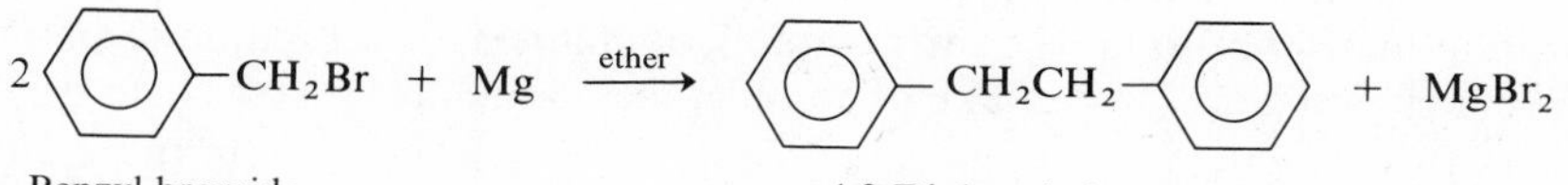

Benzyl bromide   1,2-Diphenylethane

Experimental know-how can minimize this annoying side reaction, however.

A useful coupling reaction of aryl halides is the *Ullmann reaction.* Aryl halides are heated with copper and biaryl compounds are formed.

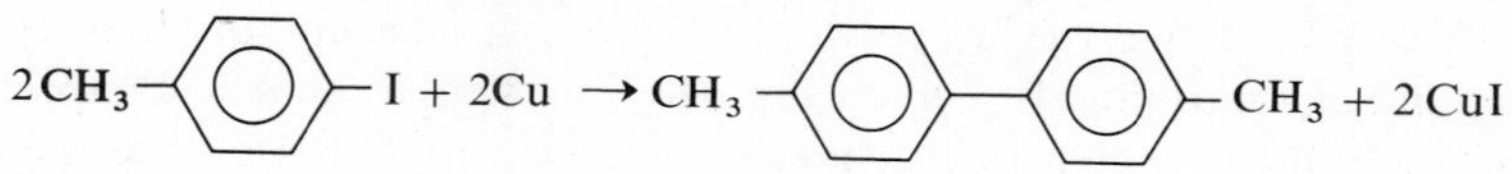

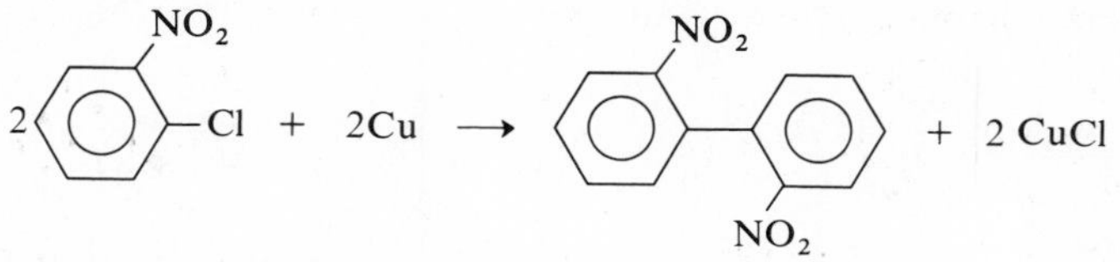

o-Chloronitrobenzene   2,2'-Dinitrobiphenyl

Unstable organocopper compounds are intermediates in this reaction.

17.12   Reduction of Organic Halides

Alkyl halides can be reduced to alkanes by action of an active metal such as zinc, and an acid.

$$CH_3-\underset{\underset{CH_3}{|}}{CH}-Cl + Zn + HCl \rightarrow CH_3CH_2CH_3 + ZnCl_2$$

Isopropyl
chloride   Propane

A more reactive metal will give similar results with a weaker acid.

$$CH_3CH_2CH_2CH_2Br + 2\,Na + EtOH \rightarrow CH_3CH_2CH_2CH_3 + EtONa + NaBr$$

An indirect reduction of a halide to a hydrocarbon occurs if moisture is allowed to come in contact with a Grignard reagent (or other reactive organometallics).

$$CH_3CH_2MgBr + H_2O \rightarrow CH_3CH_3 + MgBr(OH)$$

$$\text{(benzene ring)}-CH_2MgCl + D_2O \rightarrow \text{(benzene ring)}-CH_2D + MgCl(OD)$$

Halides may also be reduced by catalytic hydrogenation.

$$\text{(benzene ring)}-CH_2-Br + H_2 \xrightarrow[OH^-]{Ni} \text{(benzene ring)}-CH_3 + Br^- + H_2O$$

Benzyl bromide   Toluene

$$\text{(cyclohexyl-Br)} + H_2 \xrightarrow[OH^-]{Pt} \text{(cyclohexane)} + Br^- + H_2O$$

17.13   Summary of Synthetic Methods for Organic Halides

In this section are listed the synthetic methods which are generally useful for the preparation of organic halides. Continuing the earlier practice (Chapter 15), all synthetic methods for halides are included here for the sake of completeness and later review. The student should study at this time those methods using reactions already covered in this chapter and previous chapters, specifically Methods 1a, 2a, b, and 3b.

It would also be advisable now to review the synthetic methods for alkenes given in Section 15.17 which have been covered since that time. These are Methods 1a, c, h, and 2a, b on page 340. Some of the problems following this section will test the student's knowledge of these synthetic reactions. If the student is unable to solve a synthetic problem, the place to look for help is the last section of the chapter (except for Chapter 16) which discusses the kind of compound for which a synthesis is wanted; that is, Chapter 15 for unsaturated compounds, Chapter 17 for halides, and so on. This practice will be continued in the next several chapters.

1. Alkyl halides
   a. Addition to alkenes (Sections 15.3–15.4):
      (1) of HX

$$\underset{/}{\overset{\backslash}{C}}=\underset{\backslash}{\overset{/}{C}} + HX \rightarrow -\underset{\underset{H}{|}}{C}-\underset{\underset{X}{|}}{C}-$$

(Carbonium ion mechanism, except for HBr in the presence of peroxide in which case the product is different.)

   (2) of X_2

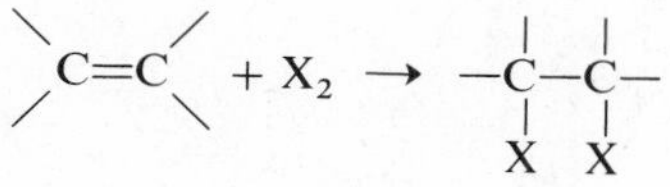

$$\ce{>C=C< + X2 -> -\underset{X}{\overset{|}{C}}-\underset{X}{\overset{|}{C}}-}$$

b. From alcohols (Section 18.3):

   (1) and HX; X = Br, I, in some cases Cl

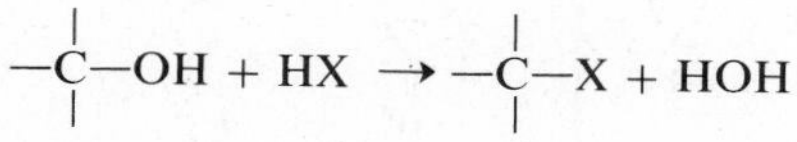

$$\ce{-\overset{|}{\underset{|}{C}}-OH + HX -> -\overset{|}{\underset{|}{C}}-X + HOH}$$

   (2) and PX_3; X = Br, I, in some cases Cl

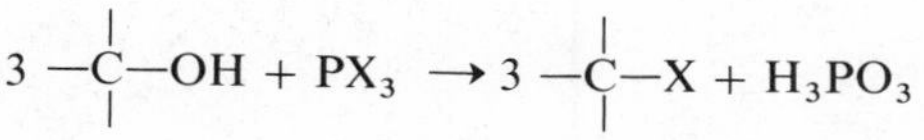

$$\ce{3 -\overset{|}{\underset{|}{C}}-OH + PX3 -> 3 -\overset{|}{\underset{|}{C}}-X + H3PO3}$$

   (3) and $SOCl_2$

$$\ce{-\overset{|}{\underset{|}{C}}-OH + SOCl2 -> -\overset{|}{\underset{|}{C}}-Cl + SO2 + HCl}$$

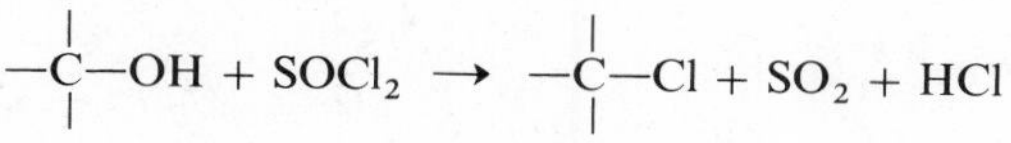

c. From alkanes (Section 23.7)

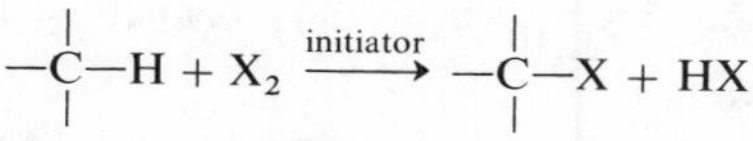

$$\ce{-\overset{|}{\underset{|}{C}}-H + X2 ->[initiator] -\overset{|}{\underset{|}{C}}-X + HX}$$

(Free radical mechanism which usually leads to a mixture of hard-to-separate products.)

d. Hunsdiecker reaction (Section 20.11)

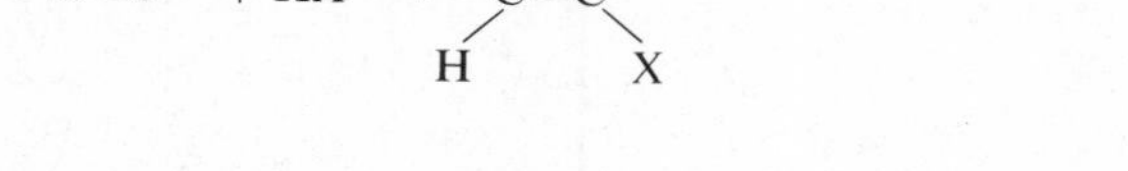

$$\ce{-\overset{|}{\underset{|}{C}}-CO2^- Ag^+ + Br2 -> -\overset{|}{\underset{|}{C}}-Br + CO2 + AgBr ⌄}$$

2. Vinyl halides

a. By addition of HX to alkynes (Section 15.16)

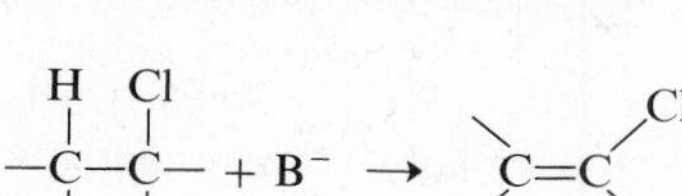

$$\ce{-C#C- + HX -> \underset{H}{\overset{}{C}}=\underset{X}{\overset{}{C}}}$$

b. From dihaloalkanes (Section 17.6)

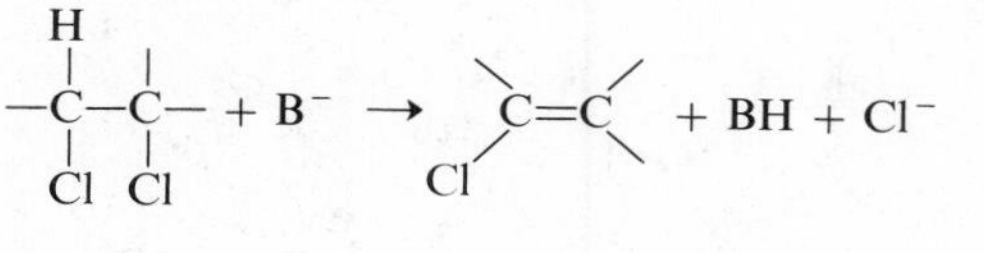

$$\ce{-\underset{\underset{Cl}{|}}{\overset{\overset{H}{|}}{C}}-\overset{\overset{Cl}{|}}{C}- + B^- -> C=C\overset{Cl}{} + BH + Cl^-}$$

$$\ce{-\overset{\overset{H}{|}}{C}-\underset{\underset{Cl}{|}}{\overset{\overset{}{|}}{C}}- + B^- -> \underset{Cl}{C}=C + BH + Cl^-}$$

3. Aryl halides
   a. From diazonium salts via amines (Section 22.7)

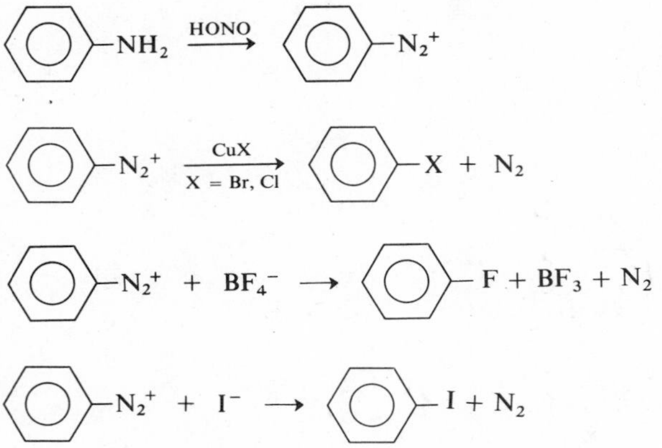

$$C_6H_5-NH_2 \xrightarrow{HONO} C_6H_5-N_2^+$$

$$C_6H_5-N_2^+ \xrightarrow[X = Br, Cl]{CuX} C_6H_5-X + N_2$$

$$C_6H_5-N_2^+ + BF_4^- \longrightarrow C_6H_5-F + BF_3 + N_2$$

$$C_6H_5-N_2^+ + I^- \longrightarrow C_6H_5-I + N_2$$

   b. From aromatic hydrocarbons (Section 16.2)

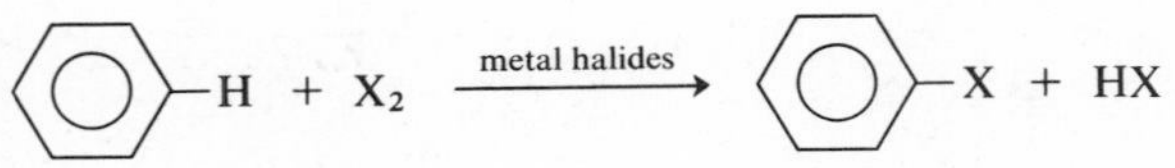

$$C_6H_5-H + X_2 \xrightarrow{\text{metal halides}} C_6H_5-X + HX$$

(The metal halide catalyst may be $AlCl_3$, $FeCl_3$, etc.)

PROBLEMS

1. How would you synthesize $CH_3-C\equiv C-CD_3$ from $CH_3-CH=CH_2$ and CD_3Cl?

2. (a) Give a structure consistent with the following nmr data obtained from a compound of formula $C_4H_8Br_2$:

	Area Integration:
δ 1.9 singlet	3
δ 3.9 singlet	1

   (b) Give a structure consistent with the following nmr data obtained from a compound of formula C_8H_9Br:

	Integration:
δ 2.0 doublet	3
δ 5.15 quartet	1
δ 7.35 multiplet	5

3. Compound A is an intermediate in the synthesis of B from *trans*-2-butene. What are the structures of A and B?

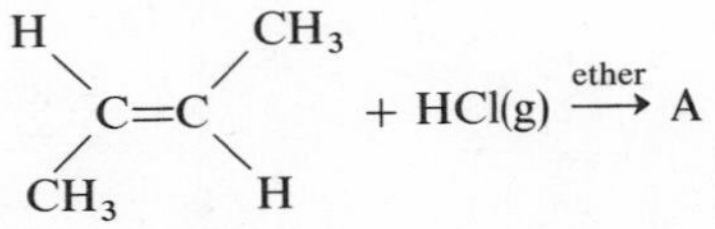

$$C=C \ (\text{H, CH}_3 / \text{CH}_3, \text{H}) + HCl(g) \xrightarrow{\text{ether}} A$$

$$A + CH_3O^-Na^+ \xrightarrow[\substack{\text{cold,} \\ \text{dilute soln.}}]{CH_3OH} B$$

4. When 2-bromo-3-methylbutane is warmed in wet acetone, a compound is formed which gives the infrared and nmr spectra shown. Identify the product and give your interpretation of the spectra in terms of your answer.

5. Predict the *substitution* products:

   (a) $CH_3-Br + HC\equiv C^-Na^+ \longrightarrow$

   (b) 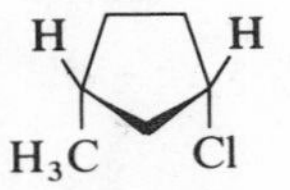 $+ HO^- \longrightarrow$

Infrared spectrum (neat liquid film) of unknown, Problem 4.

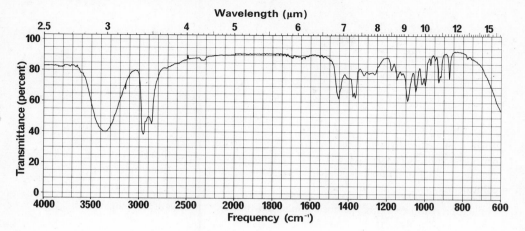

NMR spectrum of unknown, Problem 4.

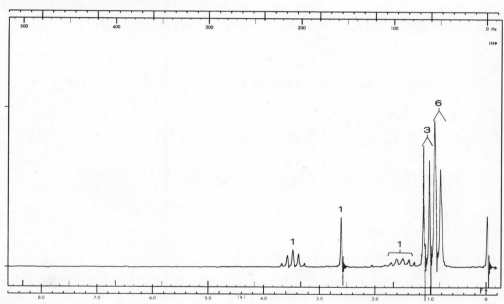

5. (*continued*)

(c) $CH_3-\underset{Br}{\overset{CH_3}{\underset{|}{\overset{|}{C}}}}-\underset{H}{\overset{H}{\underset{|}{\overset{|}{C}}}}-CH_3 + H_2O \xrightarrow{acetone}$

(d) [benzene ring with C bonded to H, Cl, CH₃] $+ CH_3O^- \xrightarrow{CH_3OH}$

(e) [benzene ring with C bonded to H, Cl, CH₃] $\xrightarrow{H_2O}$

(f) [benzene ring with C bonded to H, Cl, CH₃] $+ Br^- \longrightarrow$

(g) OPTIONAL PROBLEM. $CH_2{=}CH{-}CH_2CH_2{-}Cl \xrightarrow{H_2O}$

(h) 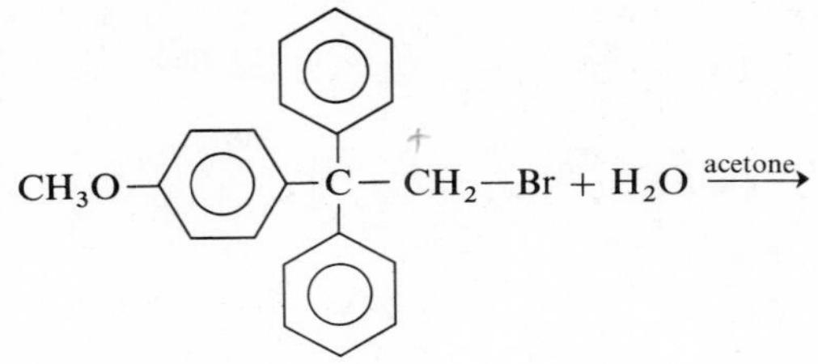 $CH_3O{-}\langle\bigcirc\rangle{-}\overset{+}{C}{-}CH_2{-}Br + H_2O \xrightarrow{\text{acetone}}$

6. When triphenylmethyl chloride, $(C_6H_5)_3CCl$, is placed in benzene in the presence of benzene-soluble $(CH_3CH_2CH_2CH_2)_4N^+ \,{}^*Cl^-$ (with radioactive chloride), chloride exchange occurs at a rate independent of the concentration of the quaternary ammonium chloride. *Explain.*

7. Predict the *relative rates* of the nucleophilic substitution reactions of: (a) ethoxide in ethanol with CH_3Br, $\langle\bigcirc\rangle{-}Br$, CH_3CH_2Br, $CH_3{-}\overset{\underset{\textstyle Br}{|}}{\overset{\textstyle CH_3}{C}}{-}CH_3$,

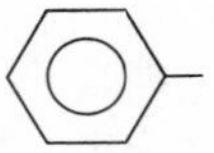

    $CH_2{=}CH{-}CH_2{-}Br$, [bicyclic structure with Br], $CH_3{-}\overset{\underset{\textstyle CH_3}{|}}{\overset{\textstyle CH_3}{C}}{-}CH_2{-}Br$, $CH_2{=}CH{-}Br$,

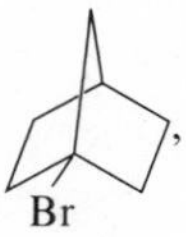

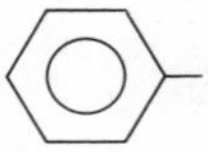

    $\langle\bigcirc\rangle{-}CH_2{-}Br$; (b) ethoxide in ethanol with $CH_3{-}\overset{\overset{\textstyle CH_3}{|}}{CH}{-}Br$, $CH_3{-}\overset{\overset{\textstyle CH_3}{|}}{CH}{-}F$,

    $CH_3{-}\overset{\overset{\textstyle CH_3}{|}}{CH}{-}Cl$, $CH_3{-}\overset{\overset{\textstyle CH_3}{|}}{CH}{-}I$; (c) water in formic acid solution with $\langle\bigcirc\rangle{-}CH_2{-}Br$,

    $O_2N{-}\langle\bigcirc\rangle{-}CH_2Br$, $H_3C{-}\langle\bigcirc\rangle{-}CH_2Br$, $H_3CO{-}\langle\bigcirc\rangle{-}CH_2Br$.

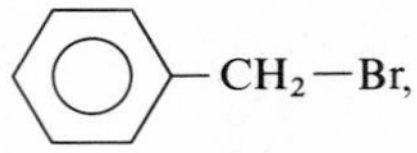

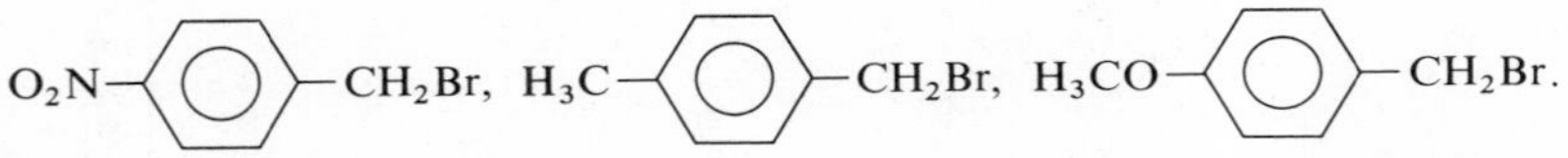

8. Consider the reaction

    $$CH_3CH_2Br + HO^- \rightarrow CH_3CH_2OH + Br^-$$

    (a) What will happen to the rate if the concentration of ethyl bromide is doubled? of hydroxide? Suppose the concentrations are each increased by a factor of 3?
    (b) If the temperature is increased?
    (c) Draw a picture of the transition state for the rate-determining step.
    (d) Sketch an energy diagram for the reaction and label it carefully.

9. Answer Problem 8a–d for the following reaction:

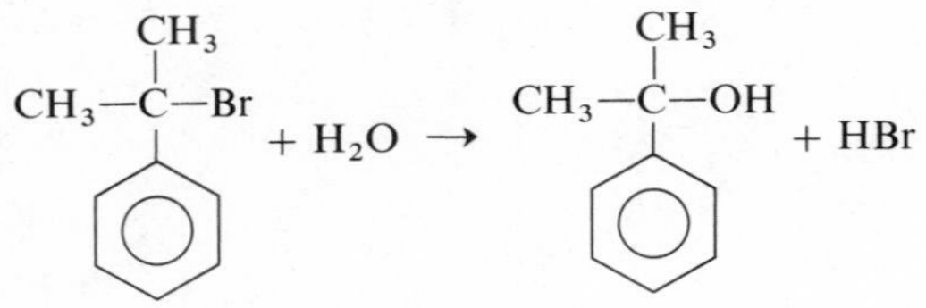

    $CH_3{-}\overset{\overset{\textstyle CH_3}{|}}{\underset{\underset{\textstyle \bigcirc}{|}}{C}}{-}Br + H_2O \rightarrow CH_3{-}\overset{\overset{\textstyle CH_3}{|}}{\underset{\underset{\textstyle \bigcirc}{|}}{C}}{-}OH + HBr$

10. Discuss: (a) ion pair; (b) nonclassical electron delocalization; (c) intramolecular nucleophilic substitution; (d) anchimeric assistance.

11. (a) Discuss the factors which favor α elimination. (b) Discuss briefly the factors which influence whether a β elimination occurs by the E1 mechanism, the E2 mechanism, or the carbanion mechanism.

12.   Predict the *elimination* products:

(a) $CH_3CH_2-CH-CH_3 \xrightarrow[E2]{E1}$
               |
               Br

(b) [structure with H, Br, C₆H₅, CH₃, H] $\xrightarrow[E1]{E2}$

(c) [cyclohexane structure with H, CH₃, Cl, H, (CH₃)₂CH, H, H H] $\xrightarrow[E1]{E2}$

(d) [cyclohexane structure with H, CH₃, H H, (CH₃)₂CH, H, Cl H] $\xrightarrow[E1]{E2}$

13.   When 2-bromo-3-methylbutane is heated with HBr, a compound which gives the nmr
      spectrum shown is formed. What is the product? Fully interpret the nmr spectrum.

NMR spectrum of unknown, Problem 13.

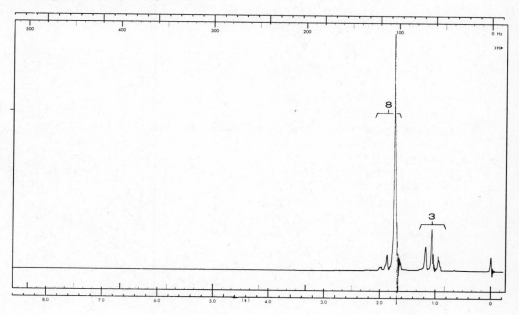

14.   How would you synthesize *meso*-2,3-dihydroxybutane from 2-bromobutane? How would
      you synthesize *dl*-2,3-dihydroxybutane from the same starting material?

15.   Propose a method for synthesizing *p*-nitroaniline from chlorobenzene.

16.   Predict the products:

(a) [structure: Br, H₃C, CH₃, H, Br] + Mg $\xrightarrow{ether}$ (b) $CH_3CH-Cl + Na \longrightarrow$
                                                                              |
                                                                             CH_3

17.   Propose a synthetic route to: (a) $CH_3-\langle\bigcirc\rangle-CH_3$ from $CH_3-\langle\bigcirc\rangle-CH_2Br$;

      (b) $CH_2=CH-CH_2-CH_3$ from allyl chloride and methyl bromide; (c) CH_3CHCH_3
                                                                                    |
                                                                                    D

      from propene and D_2O.

18.   Predict the major products of the following reactions:

(a) 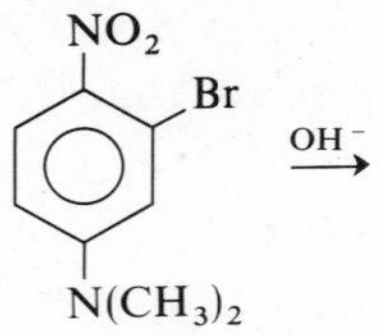 $\xrightarrow{OH^-}$

(b) 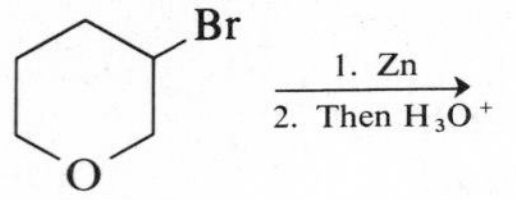 $\xrightarrow[\text{2. Then } H_3O^+]{\text{1. Zn}}$

(c) 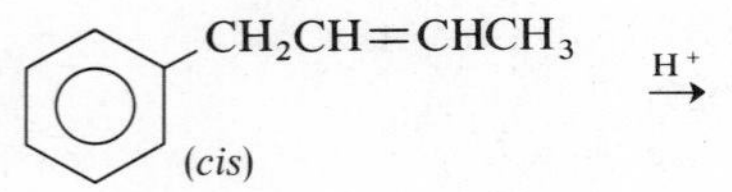 $\xrightarrow{H^+}$

(d) 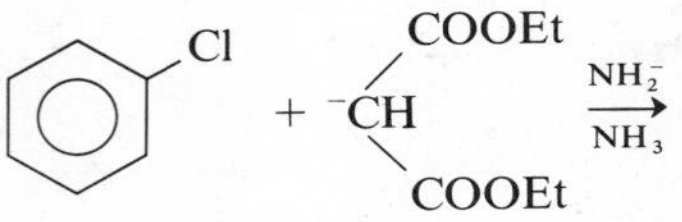 $\xrightarrow[NH_3]{NH_2^-}$

(e) 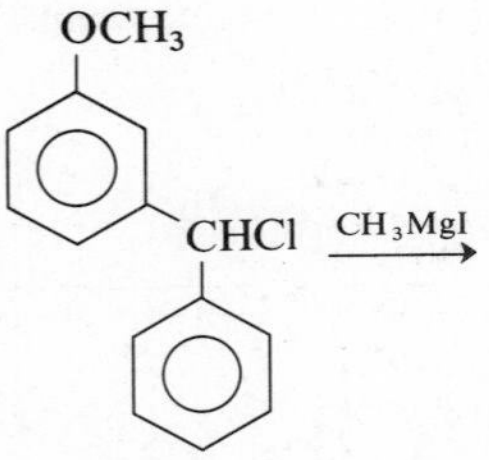 $\xrightarrow{CH_3MgI}$

(f) $Ph-C{\equiv}CH$ $\xrightarrow[\text{2. } CH_3CH_2CH_2Br]{\text{1. } NH_2^-}$

(g)  $+ CHBr_3$ $\xrightarrow{t\text{-BuO}^-}$

19.   Beginning with acetylene and any desired alkyl halides, outline reasonable laboratory syntheses for the following compounds:
(a) $CH_3CH_2CH_2C{\equiv}CH$
(b) $CH_3CH_2CH_2C{\equiv}CCH_2CH_3$
(c) cis-$CH_3CH_2CH_2CH{=}CHCH_2CH_3$
(d) $threo$-$CH_3CH_2CH_2\underset{\underset{HO}{|}}{C}H\underset{\underset{OH}{|}}{C}HCH_2CH_3$
(e) A single optical isomer of $threo$-3,4-heptanediol

20.   Outline syntheses of the following from n-butyl bromide:
(a) 1-Butene   (b) $trans$-2-Butene
(c) cis-2-Butene   (d) 1-Butyne
(e) 2-Butyne   (f) 2-Bromobutane
(g) Valeronitrile   (h) Di-n-butyl sulfide
(i) n-Butyl phenyl ether

21.   A liquid, C_3H_7I, was boiled with a solution of potassium hydroxide in ethyl alcohol and a gas was generated. When the gas was passed into concentrated HI, a liquid was formed. It proved to be C_3H_7I, but the boiling point was not the same as that of the original C_3H_7I. Identify each of the three compounds encountered in this sequence.

22.   A colorless liquid of boiling point less than 50°C sank to the bottom when added to water, but did not mix with it. When it was stirred and gently warmed with dilute sodium hydroxide, it slowly dissolved, and the resulting solution gave a pale yellow precipitate with silver nitrate. When the original substance was boiled with alcoholic potassium hydroxide, a gas was evolved which discharged the color of bromine in carbon tetrachloride solution when it was bubbled through it. What *kind* of substance was the product of the first treatment? What is the most probable structure for the original compound?

23.   Considering the principles of nucleophilic displacement, which of the following reagents would you expect to react with ammonia to form a primary amine?
(a) Isopropyl bromide   (b) 2-Phenyl-2-methyl-1-bromopropane
(c) Propionaldehyde diethyl acetal   (d) 3-Chlorotoluene
(e) 1-p-Tolylcyclohexyl chloride   (f) 2,4,6-Trinitrochlorobenzene
(g) n-Propyl butyrate

24. Give the principal organic products to be expected from the reaction of *n*-butyl bromide with each of the following reagents:
    (a) Warm, aq. NaOH
    (b) Cold, conc. H_2SO_4
    (c) Sodium iodide in acetone
    (d) Benzene and $AlCl_3$
    (e) $C_6H_5-C\equiv CNa$

25. Show how to accomplish the following transformations in a practical way, using equations and specifying essential reagents and conditions:
    (a) 2,2,5,5-Tetramethyl-3-hexene to di-*t*-butylacetylene
    (b) 2-Butene to 2-chloro-2-butene

Optional Problems

1.

2.

CHAPTER 18

REACTIONS OF ALCOHOLS, PHENOLS, AND ETHERS

18.1   Introduction

The structures, properties, and nomenclature of alcohols and ethers were discussed in Sections 4.7 through 4.11, and phenols were examined in Section 11.2.

$$R\!-\!OH \qquad\qquad R\!-\!O\!-\!R \qquad\qquad \text{（◯）}\!-\!OH$$

An alcohol   An ether   Phenol

These pertinent sections should be reviewed, since they form the foundation upon which the understanding of the reactions of these compounds will be built.

Alcohols are usually characterized spectroscopically. In nmr spectra, the electro-negative oxygen causes protons on the neighboring carbon atom to be shifted downfield (Section 5.4). The hydroxyl proton itself has a chemical shift which is concentration-dependent (Section 5.4). The O—H stretching and the C—O stretching in the infrared are quite characteristic (Section 9.2). Phenols show O—H and C—O stretching in the infrared, in addition to bands characteristic of aromatic rings. A simple color test for phenols is also very useful. A drop of dilute $FeCl_3$ solution added to a few drops of a phenol in a solvent (usually ethyl alcohol) gives an intense color, usually blue, green or purple. The test is characteristic of phenols and other stable enols. β-Keto esters, for example, also give the test, whereas simple ketones and esters, as well as alcohols, do not.

Alcohols and ethers are extremely important compounds, both industrially and in the laboratory. Some of their commercial uses have been mentioned in earlier sections. In this chapter, the reactions of these compounds are discussed, with emphasis on their utility for the synthesis of other classes of organic compounds.

The reactions of alcohols can be divided into four types: (1) those in which the O—H bond is cleaved, (2) those in which the C—O bond is cleaved, (3) those in which the oxygen acts as a base, and (4) oxidation. The most important reactions of phenols involve substitution on the aromatic ring (discussed in Sections 16.6 and 16.7), oxidation to quinones (Section 16.9), and O—H cleavage (discussed in this chapter). Ethers are rela-tively inert compounds; the most important reaction they undergo is cleavage of the C—O bond.

18.2   Alkoxides and Phenoxides. Ether Formation

In Section 4.7 it was mentioned that alcohols are weak acids which react with active metals to form alkoxides.

$$2\,CH_3O\!-\!H + 2\,Na \rightarrow 2\,CH_3O^-Na^+ + H_2$$
Methanol   Sodium methoxide

$$2\ CH_3-\underset{\underset{CH_3}{|}}{\overset{\overset{CH_3}{|}}{C}}-O-H + 2\ K \longrightarrow 2\ CH_3-\underset{\underset{CH_3}{|}}{\overset{\overset{CH_3}{|}}{C}}-O^-K^+ + H_2$$

t-Butyl alcohol   Potassium t-butoxide

The relative acidity of alcohols is *tertiary < secondary < primary < methanol*. There-fore, t-butyl alcohol is less acidic than is methanol, and consequently, t-butoxide is a stronger base than methoxide. The major factor in determining the acidities of alkoxides is solvation; the bulky alkyl groups on tertiary and secondary alkoxides prevent them from being solvated as well as primary alkoxides and methoxide, thus making them more reactive toward proton donors.

RELATIVE ACIDITIES OF ALCOHOLS. *Older books often state that the inductive effect is responsible for the greater acidity of methanol compared with that of* t-*butyl alcohol. However, no induction is anticipated from attaching one saturated carbon atom to another. That the solvation explanation is correct is shown by the fact that the difference in acidities of these alcohols is virtually wiped out when the measurements are carried out in dimethyl sulfoxide, which is a poor solvating agent for anions. Recent measurements have shown that* t-butyl alcohol *is more acidic than methanol in the gas phase.*

Other strong bases, such as H^- or NH_2^-, can also be used to generate alkoxides from alcohols.

$$R-O-H + H^- \longrightarrow R-O^- + H_2$$

$$R-O-H + NH_2^- \longrightarrow R-O^- + NH_3$$

Alcohols destroy Grignard reagents in an acid–base reaction, forming alkoxide salts.

$$ROH + R'MgX \longrightarrow R'H + R\overset{-}{O}\overset{+}{M}gX$$

$$CH_3CH_2OH + \langle\bigcirc\rangle-MgBr \longrightarrow \langle\bigcirc\rangle + CH_3CH_2OMgBr$$

Ethanol   Phenylmagnesium   Benzene   Ethoxide salt
            bromide

Grignard reagents behave as carbanions due to the polar nature of the C—Mg bond. It is understandable that they are stronger bases than alkoxides, since the negative charge is better supported by a more electronegative atom.

Phenols are considerably more acidic than alcohols. In fact, phenoxide anion can be prepared simply by reaction of phenol with aqueous sodium hydroxide solution. The greater acidity of a phenol as compared to an alcohol is attributed (page 234) to the greater resonance stabilization of the phenoxide anion than of the phenol. The methyl group in p-cresol destabilizes the anion by its inductive effect, causing p-cresol to be less acidic than phenol (0.7:1) (page 236). A p-nitro group stabilizes the anion by its reson-ance and inductive effects, making p-nitrophenol more acidic than phenol (630:1) (page 236).

$$\langle\bigcirc\rangle-OH + Na^+OH^- \longrightarrow \langle\bigcirc\rangle-O^-Na^+ + HOH$$

Phenol   Sodium phenoxide

Alkoxides and phenoxides are extensively employed for the preparation of ethers in a reaction known as the *Williamson synthesis*. The ethers are formed by an S_N2 displacement by alkoxides on alkyl halides,

$$RO^-M^+ + R'X \longrightarrow RO{-}R' + MX$$

where R' is primary or secondary alkyl; X is I, Br, or Cl. For example:

Potassium *t*-butoxide   Methyl iodide   *t*-Butyl methyl ether

In planning such a synthesis, one must be careful to remember the scope and limitations of S_N2 reactions (discussed in Sections 17.1, 17.2, and 17.6). For example, *t*-butyl methyl ether can easily be prepared from methyl iodide and potassium *t*-butoxide (above). It *cannot* be prepared from sodium methoxide and *t*-butyl bromide, because elimination is the dominant reaction with tertiary alkyl halides.

t-Butyl bromide   Isobutylene

As another example, consider that ethyl phenyl ether can be prepared from phenoxide and ethyl chloride, but not from ethoxide and chlorobenzene. The failure in this case is because of the inertness of chlorobenzene (unsubstituted with para or ortho nitro groups) to nucleophilic displacement (Section 17.8).

Sodium phenoxide   Ethyl chloride   Ethyl phenyl ether

Chlorobenzene   Sodium ethoxide

If the halide, called the *leaving group*, and the alkoxide are in the same molecule, intramolecular displacement may occur with backside S_N2-type attack of the alkoxide on the carbon bearing the halogen. In this manner, *trans*-2-butene oxide can be formed from the reaction of *erythro*-3-bromo-2-butanol with base, and the cis oxide can similarly be formed from the threo halohydrin.

Erythro isomer   *trans*-2-Butene oxide

Threo isomer   *cis*-2-Butene oxide

This method is the second important way to prepare epoxides, the other being the epoxidation of alkenes with peracids (Section 15.10).

EXERCISE 18.1

Suggest a sequence of reactions that would enable one to synthesize *trans*-2-butene oxide from 2-butyne. Repeat for the synthesis of the *cis*-oxide.

Note especially that the alkoxide nucleophile and the leaving halide must have an anti-coplanar geometry for epoxide formation to occur. Because the hydroxyl group and the chlorine atom cannot attain an anti-coplanar relationship in *cis*-2-chlorocyclohexanol, no cyclohexene oxide is formed when this compound reacts with base. For the trans isomer, an anti-coplanar arrangement may be attained if the molecule undergoes ring inversion to the less stable diaxial conformer. Although the concentration of the latter is small, it is in ready equilibrium with the diequatorial conformer. As diaxial conformer undergoes cyclization to cyclohexene oxide, equilibrium is maintained, and eventually all the material is consumed.

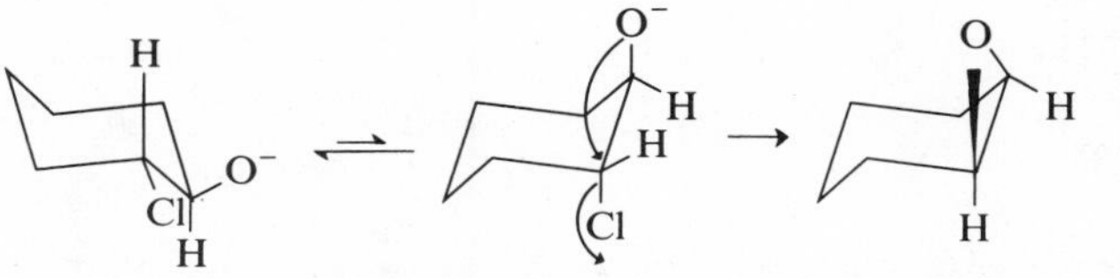

trans-2-Chlorocyclohexanol
(conjugate base)

Cyclohexene oxide

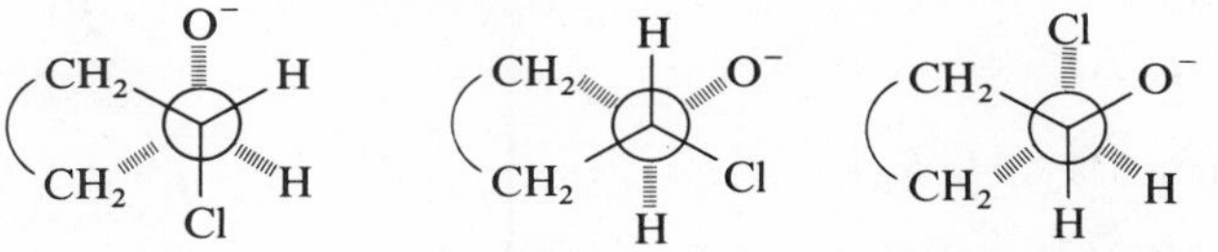

(Anti-coplanar
relationship in
diaxial conformation
of trans isomer)

(Gauche relationship
in the diequatorial
conformation of the
trans isomer)

(Gauche relationship
in the cis isomer)

EXERCISE 18.2

When *cis*-2-chlorocyclohexanol is treated with base, the product is cyclohexanone. Propose a mechanism for this reaction.

Alkoxides and phenoxides are capable of displacing other leaving groups besides halides. For example, methyl phenyl ether (anisole) can be prepared from phenoxide and dimethyl sulfate.

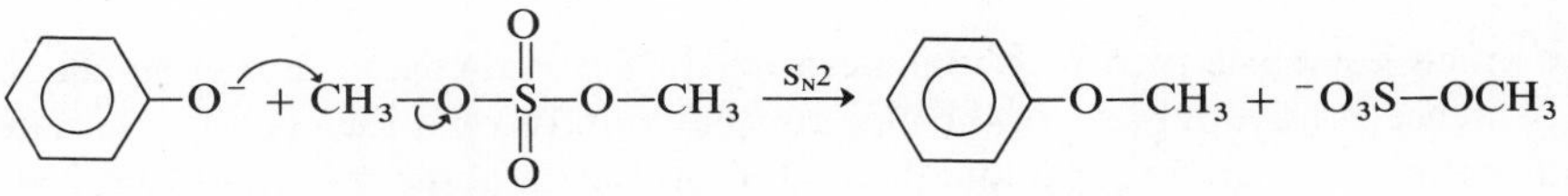

Phenoxide   Dimethyl sulfate   Anisole

Likewise, *n*-butyl ethyl ether can be prepared from ethoxide and *n*-butyl *p*-toluene-sulfonate.

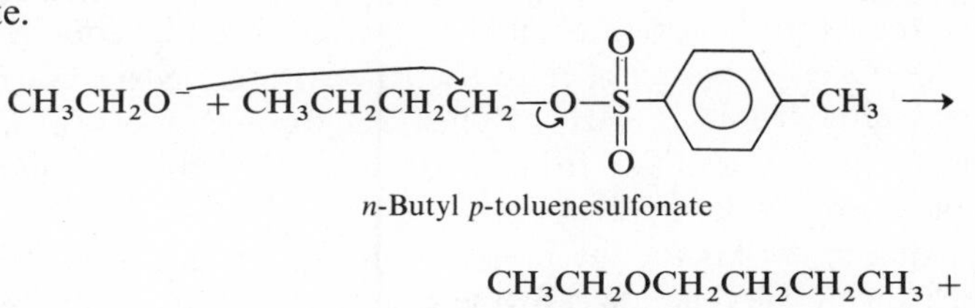

n-Butyl *p*-toluenesulfonate

$$CH_3CH_2OCH_2CH_2CH_2CH_3 + {}^-O_3S \underset{}{\bigcirc} CH_3$$

n-Butyl ethyl ether

Other important reactions of phenoxides involve substitution on the aromatic ring; these were mentioned in Chapter 16.

Acids react with diazomethane to replace the acidic hydrogen with a methyl group (Section 20.4). Phenols, being somewhat acidic, can be methylated by reaction with diazomethane.

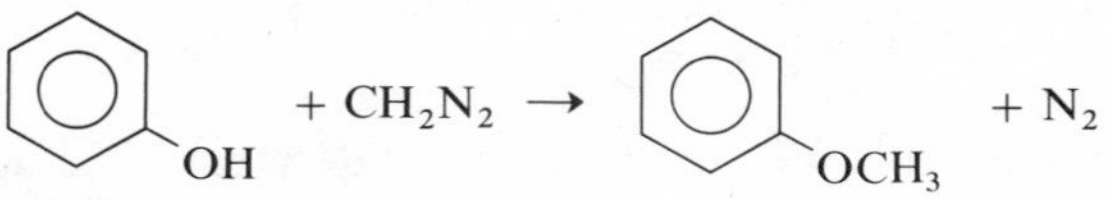

$$\text{(phenol)} + CH_2N_2 \rightarrow \text{(anisole)} + N_2$$

Alcohols are not sufficiently acidic to undergo a similar reaction in the absence of a catalyst. However, if a Lewis acid such as BF_3 is added, the methylation proceeds.

$$ROH + CH_2N_2 \xrightarrow{BF_3} ROCH_3 + N_2$$

The function of the BF_3 is to increase the acidity of the alcohol.

$$R\overset{+}{-}\underset{-BF_3}{O}-H \rightleftharpoons R\underset{-BF_3}{-O} + H^+$$

EXERCISE 18.3

If excess HCl were used as a catalyst in the above reaction instead of BF_3, a different product would be obtained. Explain.

18.3   Conversion of Alcohols to Alkyl Halides

In the preceding section, reactions of alcohols and phenols which depend upon their acidic properties were discussed. An alcohol is also a Lewis base; that is, it can offer a pair of electrons from the oxygen for bond formation with a Lewis acid. The following are examples of reactions of methanol in which it acts as a base:

$$CH_3-\overset{..}{\underset{..}{O}}-H + H-Cl \rightleftharpoons CH_3-\overset{H}{\underset{}{\overset{|}{\overset{+}{O}}}}-H + Cl^-$$

A protonated alcohol

$$CH_3-O-H + ZnCl_2 \rightleftharpoons CH_3-\overset{H}{\underset{+}{\overset{|}{O}}}-\underset{-}{ZnCl_2}$$

Phenols are much less basic than alcohols, because the resonance and inductive effects of the ring decrease the availability of the electron pairs on oxygen for reaction with an acid. (Recall that phenols are more acidic than alcohols for the same reason; pages 234-237).

We often take advantage of complexes formed between alcohols and protons or other Lewis acids. For example, the C—O bond in an alcohol is quite inert to nucleophilic substitution reactions in which the hydroxyl group would be replaced by a nucleophile. This is because breaking the C—O bond would require that the strongly basic ^-OH group be displaced. However, water from $C-\overset{+}{O}H_2$, $Zn(OH)Cl$ from $C-\overset{+}{O}HZnCl$, phosphite from $C-O-P(OR)_2$, and SO_2 and Cl^- from $C-O-S(=O)Cl$ are all good leaving groups and can be replaced by nucleophiles.

Alcohols are important starting materials for the preparation of alkyl halides. The most common method of preparing an alkyl halide is by the reaction of an alcohol with a hydrogen halide. An initial equilibrium is established with formation of the protonated alcohol. This protonated alcohol can then undergo an S_N2 displacement by X^-, or an S_N1 reaction to yield a carbonium ion which is subsequently attacked by X^-. The water from $C{-}^+OH_2$ is the leaving group. Which path a particular alcohol follows (S_N2 or S_N1) depends upon the reaction conditions, carbonium ion stability, steric factors, and other conditions, as were discussed in general for S_N2 and S_N1 reactions in Sections 17.1 –17.3. The accepted mechanisms for the formation of ethyl bromide and *t*-butyl chloride represent typical S_N2 and S_N1 reactions as shown.

S_N2

$$CH_3CH_2{-}OH + H{-}Br \xrightleftharpoons{\text{fast}} CH_3CH_2{-}\overset{+}{O}H_2 + Br^-$$

$$Br^- + CH_3CH_2\overset{\curvearrowleft}{\overset{+}{\underset{}{C}}}OH_2 \xrightarrow[\text{slow}]{S_N2} CH_3CH_2{-}Br + H_2O$$

S_N1

$$CH_3{-}\underset{\underset{CH_3}{|}}{\overset{\overset{CH_3}{|}}{C}}{-}OH + H{-}Cl \xrightleftharpoons{\text{fast}} CH_3{-}\underset{\underset{CH_3}{|}}{\overset{\overset{CH_3}{|}}{C}}{-}\overset{+}{O}H_2 + Cl^-$$

$$CH_3{-}\underset{\underset{CH_3}{|}}{\overset{\overset{CH_3}{|}}{C}}{-}\overset{+}{O}H_2 \xrightleftharpoons[\text{slow}]{S_N1} CH_3{-}\overset{+}{C}\!\!\begin{smallmatrix}CH_3\\ \\ CH_3\end{smallmatrix} + H_2O$$

$$Cl^- + CH_3{-}\underset{\underset{CH_3}{|}}{\overset{\overset{CH_3}{|}}{C}}{}^+ \xrightleftharpoons{\text{fast}} CH_3{-}\underset{\underset{CH_3}{|}}{\overset{\overset{CH_3}{|}}{C}}{-}Cl$$

If an optically active alcohol is used, either racemization or inversion of configuration may result, depending on whether the structure of the alcohol and the conditions favor the S_N1 or the S_N2 mechanism, respectively.

EXERCISE 18.4

Would you expect optically active 1-deuterioethanol to react with HBr and yield 1-deuterioethyl bromide with inversion of configuration, or with racemization? Explain.

Tertiary alcohols in general react rapidly with halogen acids; the secondary alcohols are slower and the primary ones slower still. Phenols do not undergo the reaction at all.

From a practical point of view, one usually prepares a halide as an intermediate in a synthetic sequence, not because one really wants the halide itself. It does not usually matter, therefore, which halogen is involved, and a particular halide is chosen because it is easy to synthesize and will readily undergo the desired subsequent reaction. In practice, bromides are most often used. The bromide can be prepared from almost any alcohol with HBr. If the alcohol is of low molecular weight and fairly soluble in water (up to about six carbon atoms), aqueous HBr is the reagent of choice. For higher alcohols, anhydrous HBr is commonly used.

Alcohols can be readily converted to iodides with HI, but HI is expensive, and sometimes it will reduce the resulting alkyl iodide to a hydrocarbon.

$$RI + HI \rightarrow RH + I_2$$

Iodides rarely offer any advantages over bromides, and hence they are seldom prepared. (When they are, they are usually made from the corresponding alkyl chloride by treatment with sodium iodide; Sections 17.1, 17.2.) Fluorides, on the other hand, cannot be prepared in this way; HF is simply too unreactive.

Allylic and benzylic alcohols, as well as tertiary alcohols, are sufficiently reactive with HCl, that for these particular types, the chlorides are usually prepared in preference to the bromides. It is possible to convert a primary alcohol to a chloride with HCl if a strong Lewis acid such as $ZnCl_2$ is used as a catalyst.

$$n\text{-}C_6H_{13}CH_2OH \xrightarrow[ZnCl_2]{HCl} n\text{-}C_6H_{13}CH_2Cl$$

Such reactions are not often used, however, since carbonium ion rearrangements become serious side reactions in the presence of zinc chloride.

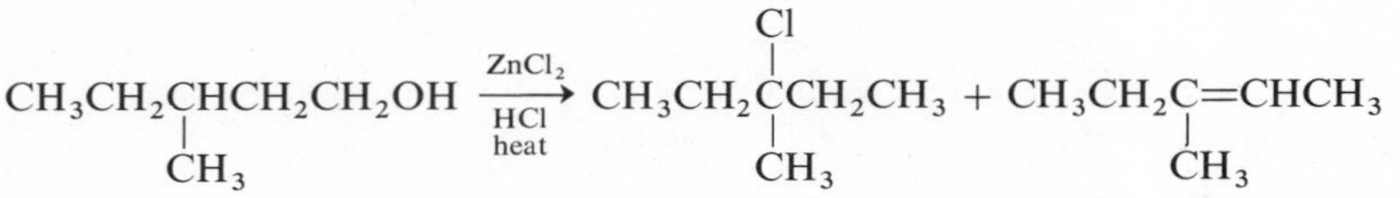

$$CH_3CH_2CHCH_2CH_2OH \xrightarrow[\substack{HCl \\ heat}]{ZnCl_2} CH_3CH_2\overset{Cl}{\underset{CH_3}{\underset{|}{\overset{|}{C}}}}CH_2CH_3 + CH_3CH_2C{=}CHCH_3$$

with CH_3 substituents as shown.

EXERCISE 18.5

Write a mechanism which explains the products obtained from the reaction of 3-methyl-1-pentanol with HCl in the presence of $ZnCl_2$.

EXERCISE 18.6

Predict the product of the following reaction:

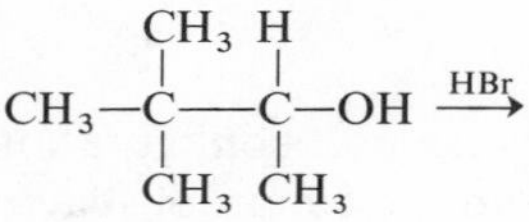

$$CH_3-\overset{CH_3}{\underset{CH_3}{\underset{|}{\overset{|}{C}}}}-\overset{H}{\underset{CH_3}{\underset{|}{\overset{|}{C}}}}-OH \xrightarrow{HBr}$$

Alkyl iodides can be prepared from reaction of alcohols with phosphorus and iodine (i.e., PI_3 formed in situ).

$$6\,R{-}OH + 3\,I_2 + 2\,P \rightarrow 6\,RI + 2\,H_3PO_3$$

Chlorides and bromides can be prepared from inorganic acid halides such as PCl_3, PCl_5, PBr_3. Yields are highest with primary alcohols, and rearrangement is less likely here than with hydrogen halides.

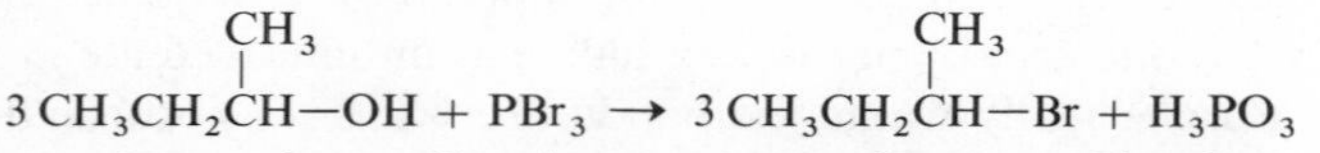

$$3\,CH_3CH_2\overset{CH_3}{\underset{|}{C}}H{-}OH + PBr_3 \rightarrow 3\,CH_3CH_2\overset{CH_3}{\underset{|}{C}}H{-}Br + H_3PO_3$$

| 2-Butanol | Phosphorus tribromide | 2-Bromobutane | Phosphorous acid |

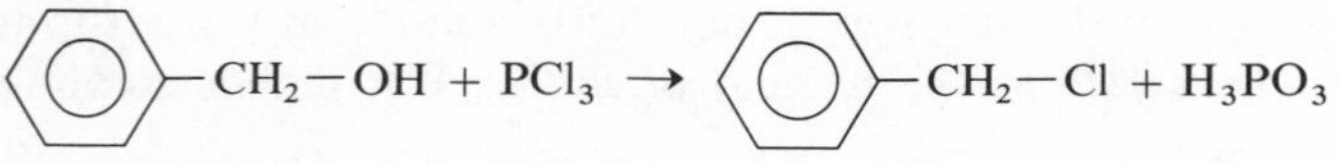

$$\langle\bigcirc\rangle{-}CH_2{-}OH + PCl_3 \rightarrow \langle\bigcirc\rangle{-}CH_2{-}Cl + H_3PO_3$$

| Benzyl alcohol | Phosphorus trichloride | Benzyl chloride |

Since trialkyl phosphites, $P(OR)_3$, are also formed as by-products, it seems clear that esters of the type $R{-}OPX_2$ form first and that these subsequently react with X^-.

$$ROH + PX_3 \rightarrow RO{-}PX_2 + X^- + H^+$$

$$X^- + R\overset{\frown}{-}O-PX_2 \rightarrow R-X + \ ^-OPX_2$$

Trialkyl phosphites arise in the following way:

$$ROPX_2 + ROH \rightarrow (RO)_2PX + HX$$

$$(RO)_2PX + ROH \rightarrow (RO)_3P + HX$$

EXERCISE 18.7

Although the reaction is of limited use because of the expense of PCl_5 and the inefficient utilization of chlorine, the following reaction occurs in good yield:

$$RCH_2OH + PCl_5 \rightarrow RCH_2Cl + POCl_3 + HCl$$

| | Phosphorus | | Phosphorus |
| | pentachloride | | oxychloride |

Propose a mechanism for the reaction.

A useful reagent for converting alcohols to alkyl chlorides is *thionyl chloride*, $SOCl_2$. An intermediate alkyl chlorosulfite formed in the reaction eliminates SO_2 spontaneously, or upon heating.

$$R-O-H + Cl\overset{\overset{O}{\|}}{-S}-Cl \rightarrow R-O-\overset{\overset{O}{\|}}{S}-Cl + H-Cl$$

Thionyl chloride   An alkyl chlorosulfite

$$R-O-\overset{\overset{O}{\|}}{S}-Cl \overset{\Delta}{\rightarrow} R-Cl + SO_2$$

If an amine is added to generate chloride ion from the chlorosulfite, inversion of configuration predominates. In this case, chloride ion displaces the chlorosulfite group in an S_N2 reaction.

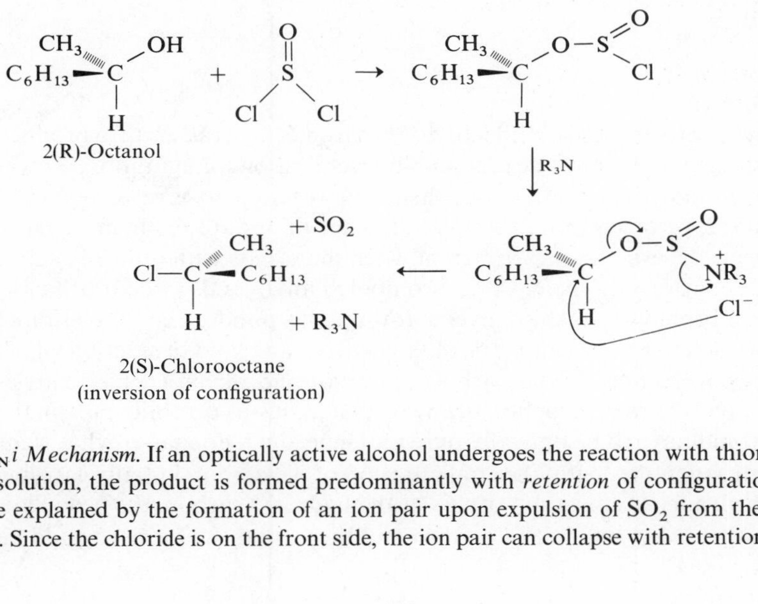

2(R)-Octanol

2(S)-Chlorooctane
(inversion of configuration)

The $S_N i$ Mechanism. If an optically active alcohol undergoes the reaction with thionyl chloride in ether solution, the product is formed predominantly with *retention* of configuration. This result can be explained by the formation of an ion pair upon expulsion of SO_2 from the alkyl chlorosulfite. Since the chloride is on the front side, the ion pair can collapse with retention of configuration.

2(R)-Octanol

$S_N i$ | Et_2O

2(R)-Chlorooctane
(retention of configuration)

Ion pair—solvated back-side

This mechanism is substitution (S), nucleophilic (N), and internal (i), so it is symbolized $S_N i$. An ether must be present to obtain an $S_N i$ reaction from a simple alkyl chlorosulfite. Its function is to stabilize the positive charge developed in the ion pair. In the absence of ether, the $S_N i$ reaction is so slow that the $S_N 2$ reaction is the predominant one, and the product is mostly of inverted configuration. A chlorosulfite which leads to a sufficiently stable carbonium ion, such as α-phenylethyl cation ($Ph-\overset{+}{C}HCH_3$) will give the $S_N i$ reaction in the absence of ether, but not in the presence of excess chloride ion.

Thus, it is possible to exercise a high degree of stereochemical control in the conversion of an alcohol to a chloride by selecting the proper reagents and conditions.

18.4 Neighboring Group Participation

Neighboring group participation (Section 17.4) is sometimes observed in reactions of suitably constituted alcohols. As an example of the stereochemical detection of neighboring group participation, when 2,3-dibromobutane is formed from 3-bromo-2-butanol and HBr, retention of configuration is observed.

2-Bromo-2-butanol, threo dl pair

2,3-Dibromobutane, dl pair

erythro dl pair

meso

The threo isomer gives a threo product, while the erythro isomer gives an erythro product. At first glance this seems to be simply reaction with retention of configuration. This is unusual because we would really expect this particular reaction to give inversion of configuration if it is $S_N 2$, or racemization if it is $S_N 1$. That things are really more complicated than first meets the eye becomes apparent when the results with optically active starting materials are considered. The dl-threo bromoalcohol gives dl-threo dibromide. However, pure d-threo bromoalcohol also gives a dl-threo dibromide. The pure l isomer also gives a dl product. These results cannot be obtained from any kind of reaction which involves only the alcohol center. If the carbon of the bromo alcohol which carries the bromine is never involved in the reaction in any way, since it was optically pure in the starting material it would have to be optically pure in the product, no matter what went on at the hydroxyl carbon. Note that if the configuration of the carbon initially carrying the bromine is retained, and racemization occurs at the hydroxyl carbon, the product is not dl-threo but is rather a 1:1 mixture of erythro and threo, and the former would be optically active.

The only possible interpretation of these facts requires that neighboring group participation occur during the course of the reaction. The reaction is carried out under S_N1 conditions, and we have the following:

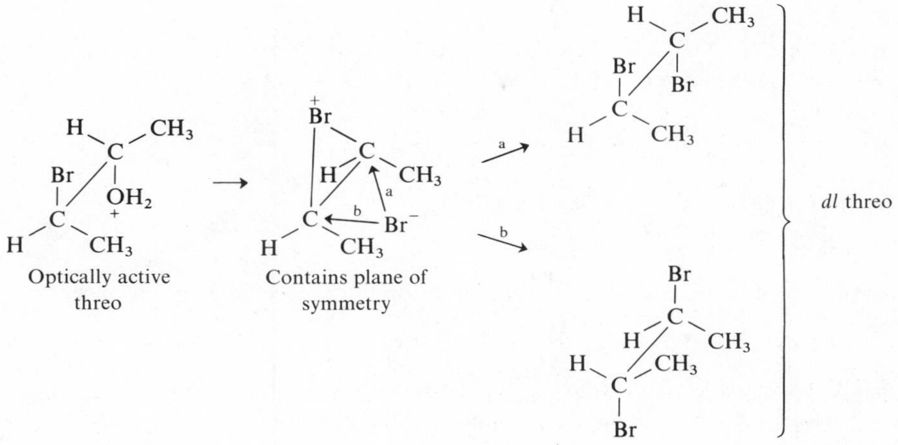

As the water molecule leaves, the neighboring bromine comes in from the backside and forms a cyclic bromonium ion. This ion has a plane of symmetry, and hence we know that we will never get optically active products from it. Attack by bromide ion is now equally probable at either carbon, so we obtain the two molecules shown in equal amounts. Study of these molecules will show that they are enantiomers, and together they constitute the *dl*-threo dibromide that is the actual product.

EXERCISE 18.8

From the reaction of either *d*- or *l-erythro*-2-bromo-3-butanol with HBr, the product is *meso*-2,3-dibromobutane. Show how this product is formed. Is the intermediate bromonium ion dissymmetric?

Note that the original observation was the apparent reaction of these compounds with retention of configuration. Remember that two inversions give a stereochemical result which is indistinguishable from retention (Section 3.6). With neighboring group participation in general, there is an inversion when the neighboring group attacks as the leaving group departs, followed by a second inversion as a nucleophile attacks the reaction center and displaces the neighboring group. The two inversions thus yield retention overall. In the case of the bromo alcohols just discussed, the situation is complicated by the fact that the original reaction center and the center to which the neighboring group was originally attached, become equivalent during the reaction.

These studies on 3-bromo-2-butanol were described and interpreted in 1938 by H. J. Lucas† and S. Winstein,†† and they first called attention to the phenomenon we now refer to as *neighboring group participation*.

Two factors were cited in Section 17.4 as being consistent with neighboring group participation: (1) the absence of an external nucleophile in the rate-determining step; and (2) an unusually large reaction rate. Now we can add (3), a stereochemical result that would not be obtained for the type of reaction under study in the absence of the neighboring group. These three items taken together are the basis on which the presence or absence of neighboring group participation in a given case is inferred.

---

† Howard J. Lucas. 1885–1963. Born Marietta, Ohio. California Institute of Technology.
†† Saul Winstein. 1912–1969. Born Montreal. University of California at Los Angeles.

18.5   Conversion of Alcohols to Esters

Alcohols are converted to carboxylate esters by reaction with carboxylic acids or acid chlorides.

$$R-OH + CH_3\overset{O}{\overset{\|}{C}}OH \overset{H^+}{\rightleftharpoons} RO\overset{O}{\overset{\|}{C}}CH_3 + HOH$$

$$\text{Acetic acid} \qquad \text{Alkyl acetate}$$

$$R-OH + CH_3\overset{O}{\overset{\|}{C}}-Cl \rightarrow RO\overset{O}{\overset{\|}{C}}CH_3 + HCl$$

$$\text{Acetyl chloride}$$

These reactions will be discussed in detail in Section 20.5; specific examples are:

$$CH_3CH_2\overset{O}{\overset{\|}{C}}-OH + CH_3CH_2OH \xrightarrow{H^+} CH_3CH_2\overset{O}{\overset{\|}{C}}-OCH_2CH_3 + H_2O$$

$$\text{Propionic acid} \qquad \text{Ethanol} \qquad\qquad \text{Ethyl propionate}$$

Benzoic acid   Methanol   Methyl benzoate

If an alcohol reacts with nitric acid, an ester of nitric acid can be formed; however, oxidation of the alcohol (Section 18.7) is a serious side reaction. Alkyl nitrates are dangerous compounds, not often used in the laboratory because they can explode upon heating. For example, glyceryl trinitrate (nitroglycerin) is used in *dynamite*, a relatively safe explosive, made essentially by impregnating sawdust with nitroglycerin.

Nobel, the Swedish industrial chemist who invented dynamite, used proceeds from dynamite patents to establish a trust fund. Interest from this fund forms the basis of the Nobel Prizes, which have been awarded annually since 1900.

$$\begin{array}{l} CH_2OH \\ | \\ CHOH \\ | \\ CH_2OH \end{array} + 3\,HNO_3 \xrightarrow{H_2SO_4} \begin{array}{l} CH_2-ONO_2 \\ | \\ CH-ONO_2 \\ | \\ CH_2-ONO_2 \end{array} \xrightarrow[\text{shock}]{\text{heat or}} \tfrac{3}{2}N_2 + 3\,CO_2 + \tfrac{5}{2}H_2O + \tfrac{1}{4}O_2$$

$$\text{Glycerin} \qquad\qquad \text{Nitroglycerin}$$

Sulfonate esters are readily prepared from alcohols or phenols and sulfonyl chlorides in the presence of a base. Alkyl benzenesulfonates and *p*-toluenesulfonates are often employed as alkylating reagents, an example of which was given in Section 18.2. The use

Benzenesulfonyl
chloride   Methyl benzenesulfonate

of dimethyl sulfate as a methylating agent was also discussed in Section 18.2.

Esters of Some Inorganic Acids. Trialkyl phosphates, $(RO)_3P{=}O$, and phosphites, $(RO)_3P$, are esters of phosphoric and phosphorous acid, respectively. They are not prepared directly from the acids, but from the acid chlorides in the presence of an amine.

$$3\ CH_3CH_2OH + \underset{Cl}{\overset{Cl}{Cl-P=O}} + 3\ \bigcirc_N \longrightarrow (CH_3CH_2O)_3P=O + 3\ \bigcirc_{\underset{H}{N+}} Cl^-$$

| Ethanol | Phosphorus oxychloride | Pyridine | Triethyl phosphate | Pyridinium chloride |

$$3\ CH_3CH_2OH + \underset{Cl}{\overset{Cl}{Cl-P}} + 3\ \bigcirc_N \longrightarrow (CH_3CH_2O)_3P + 3\ \bigcirc_{\underset{H}{N+}} Cl^-$$

| Ethanol | Phosphorus trichloride | Pyridine | Triethyl phosphite | Pyridinium chloride |

The most important substance of this type is tricresyl phosphate (TCP), a commonly used gasoline additive and component of hydraulic fluid. The commercial material is made from an inexpensive mixture of cresol isomers.

Dialkyl sulfates and alkyl hydrogen sulfates are di- and monoalkyl esters of sulfuric acid, respectively. They can be prepared by reaction of the alcohol with sulfuric acid. The alcohol is initially protonated by the acid. Since sulfuric acid is a good ionizing solvent, a carbonium ion is often subsequently formed.

$$R-OH + H-O-\overset{\overset{O}{\|}}{\underset{\underset{O}{\|}}{S}}-O-H \rightleftharpoons R-\overset{+}{\underset{H}{O}}-H + {}^-O_3S-OH$$

Sulfuric acid

$$R-\overset{+}{\underset{H}{O}}-H \rightleftharpoons R^+ + H_2O$$

If the carbonium ion reacts with one of the sulfuric acid molecules which is solvating it, an alkyl hydrogen sulfate is formed. Reaction of another carbonium ion with the alkyl hydrogen sulfate leads to a dialkyl sulfate.

$$R^+ + H-O-\overset{\overset{O}{\|}}{\underset{\underset{O}{\|}}{S}}-O-H \rightarrow R-\overset{+}{\underset{H}{O}}-\overset{\overset{O}{\|}}{\underset{\underset{O}{\|}}{S}}-O-H \rightarrow RO-\overset{\overset{O}{\|}}{\underset{\underset{O}{\|}}{S}}-OH + H^+$$

An alkyl hydrogen sulfate

$$R^+ + HO-\overset{\overset{O}{\|}}{\underset{\underset{O}{\|}}{S}}-OR \rightarrow R-\overset{+}{\underset{H}{O}}-\overset{\overset{O}{\|}}{\underset{\underset{O}{\|}}{S}}-OR \rightarrow R-O-\overset{\overset{O}{\|}}{\underset{\underset{O}{\|}}{S}}-OR + H^+$$

A dialkyl sulfate

18.6   Dehydration. Conversion of Alcohols to Alkenes and Ethers

The initial step of the reaction of sulfuric acid with an alcohol is the formation of a protonated alcohol, ROH_2^+. The ultimate products from such reactions are alkenes, ethers, and polymers, as well as alkyl sulfates. These products are formed from the protonated alcohol via an S_N1 ionization to yield a carbonium ion, or an S_N2 displacement by another molecule of alcohol to yield an ether.

Alkene Formation and the Pinacol Rearrangement

Alkenes are formed from the protonated alcohol via E1 elimination.

$$\overset{H}{\underset{|}{\underset{|}{-C}}}\overset{H}{\underset{|}{-\underset{|}{C}}}-\overset{+}{O}H_2 \;\rightleftharpoons\; \overset{H}{\underset{|}{-\underset{|}{C}}}\overset{}{-\underset{|}{C}}^+ + H_2O \;\rightleftharpoons\; \diagup\!\!\!\diagdown C=C\diagdown\!\!\!\diagup + H_3O^+$$

Tertiary alcohols are readily dehydrated to alkenes via the E1 mechanism and they require much lower reaction temperatures than do most primary alcohols. The carbonium ion mechanism for the dehydration of an alcohol to an alkene consists of a series of equilibria and it is the reverse of the acid-catalyzed hydration of an alkene to an alcohol (Section 15.3).

$$R_2CH-COHR_2 \rightleftharpoons R_2C=CR_2 + H_2O$$

The equilibrium can be driven in either direction under proper conditions. Strong acids favor alkene, dilute acid favors alcohol. The temperature is the major controlling factor, however. Low temperatures favor the alcohol, while high temperatures favor the alkene, because of the large increase in entropy upon dehydration (Why?). Since the alkenes and carbonium ions are all in equilibrium, the most stable alkene (Section 7.10) is formed in the largest amount and rearrangements are common. 1-Butanol and 2-butanol, for example, both yield *trans*-2-butene as the major dehydration product.

$$CH_3CH_2CH_2CH_2\overset{+}{O}H_2 + HOSO_3^- \rightleftharpoons CH_3CH_2CH=CH_2 + H_2SO_4 + H_2O$$
Protonated 1-Butanol   1-Butene

$$-H^+ \;\|\; +H^+$$

$$\underset{\underset{+OH_2}{|}}{CH_3CH_2CH-CH_3} \;\underset{+H_2O}{\overset{-H_2O}{\rightleftharpoons}}\; CH_3CH_2\overset{+}{C}H-CH_3$$

Protonated 2-Butanol $\overset{-H^+}{\underset{+H^+}{/\!/}}$ $+H^+ \;\|\; -H^+$

$$\underset{H}{\overset{CH_3}{\diagdown}}C=C\underset{H}{\overset{CH_3}{\diagup}}$$
cis-2-Butene

$$\underset{H}{\overset{CH_3}{\diagdown}}C=C\underset{CH_3}{\overset{H}{\diagup}}$$
trans-2-Butene
(major product)

Neopentyl alcohol and 2-methyl-2-butanol yield 2-methyl-2-butene.

$$CH_3-\underset{\underset{CH_3}{|}}{\overset{\overset{CH_3}{|}}{C}}-CH_2\overset{C^+}{\frown}\overset{+}{O}H_2 \;\rightarrow\; CH_3-\underset{}{\overset{\overset{CH_3}{|}}{C}}-CH_2CH_3 + H_2O$$

Protonated neopentyl
alcohol $S_N1 \;/\!/$ $\|$ E1

$$CH_3-\underset{\underset{+OH_2}{|}}{\overset{\overset{CH_3}{|}}{C}}-CH_2CH_3$$ $$CH_3-\overset{\overset{CH_3}{|}}{C}=CH-CH_3 + H^+$$

Protonated 2-methyl-2-butanol   2-Methyl-2-butene

1,2-Diols (glycols) may undergo rearrangement upon dehydration in acid. The reaction is known as the *pinacol rearrangement*.

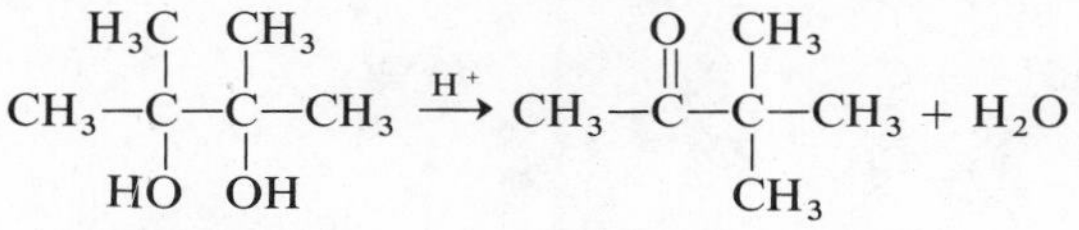

$$
\underset{\substack{\text{2,3-Dimethyl-2,3-}\\\text{butanediol (Pinacol)}}}{CH_3-\underset{\underset{\displaystyle OH}{|}}{\overset{\overset{\displaystyle H_3C\quad CH_3}{|\quad\;|}}{C-C}}-CH_3} \xrightarrow{H^+} \underset{\substack{\text{\textit{t}-Butyl methyl ketone}\\\text{(Pinacolone)}}}{CH_3-\underset{\underset{\displaystyle CH_3}{|}}{\overset{\overset{\displaystyle O\quad CH_3}{\parallel\quad\;|}}{C-C}}-CH_3} + H_2O
$$

A carbonium ion is formed from the protonated diol, followed by a 1,2 shift of a methyl group to give a more stable carbonium ion.

$$
CH_3-\overset{H_3C\;\;CH_3}{\underset{H_2O\;\;\;\;OH}{C-C}}-CH_3 \xrightarrow{-H_2O} CH_3-\overset{H_3C\;\;CH_3}{\underset{\overset{+}{}\;\;OH}{C-C}}-CH_3 \rightarrow CH_3-\overset{CH_3}{\underset{CH_3\;\;O-H}{C-C}}-CH_3 \xrightarrow{-H^+} \text{Product}
$$

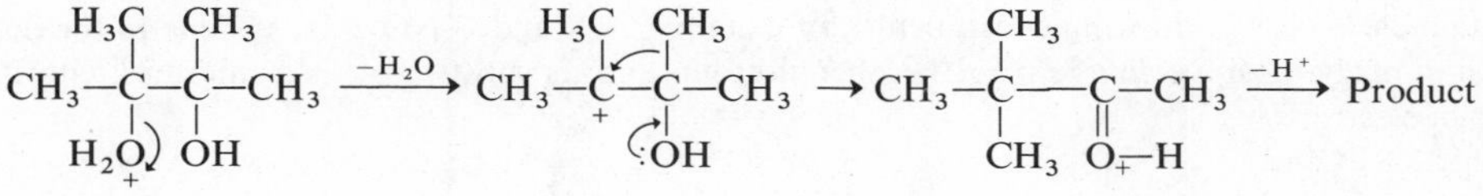

The driving force for this reaction is the conversion of the carbonium ion, with an open sextet of electrons, into the conjugate acid of a ketone—a cation in which each atom has a full octet. The pinacol rearrangement is a special case of a skeletal rearrangement via a carbonium ion, the general term for which is a *Wagner–Meerwein rearrangement* (Section 17.3).

Migratory Aptitudes. In the case of unsymmetrical pinacols, two generalizations may be considered in attempting to deduce the nature of the predominant reaction product: (1) the more stable carbonium ion is formed faster, and (2) migration of an aryl group (with its pair of electrons) is preferred over hydride migration, which is, in turn, preferred over alkyl migration. Thus:

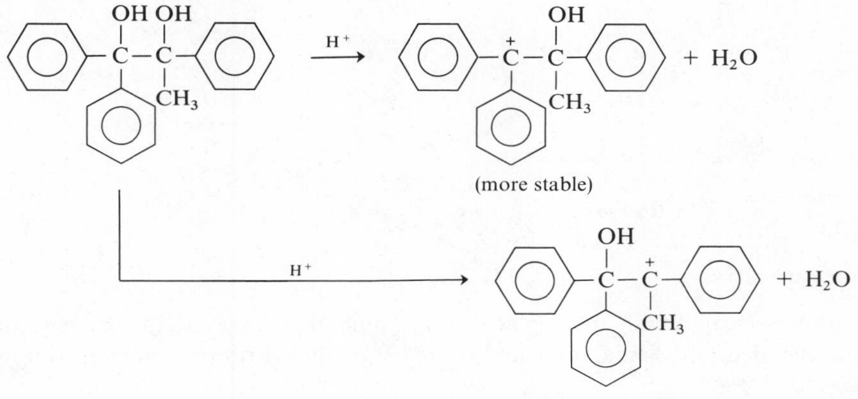

(more stable)

(less stable)

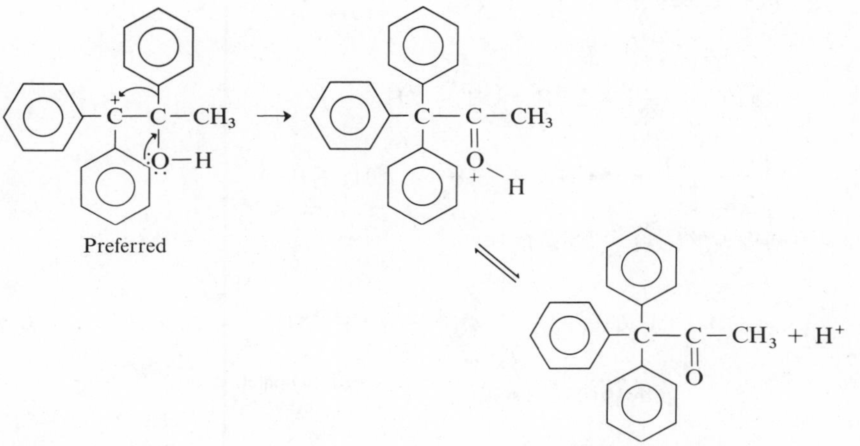

Preferred

The product

Also

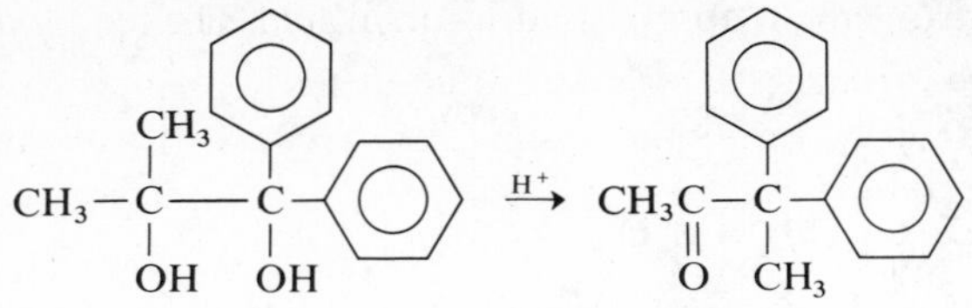

These generalizations are not always completely reliable. The "migratory aptitude" of a group depends to some extent on its environment—the molecule and the stereochemistry in the neighborhood of the reacting center. Migratory aptitude may also change with changes in the reaction conditions.

Aryl groups with substituents which can stabilize positive charge through resonance or inductive effects, for example, p-CH_3O— and CH_3—, migrate in preference to aryl groups which contain electron-withdrawing substituents, for example, —X and —NO_2. This is due to the dispersion of the positive charge over the phenyl group and its substituent as it migrates with its pair of electrons.

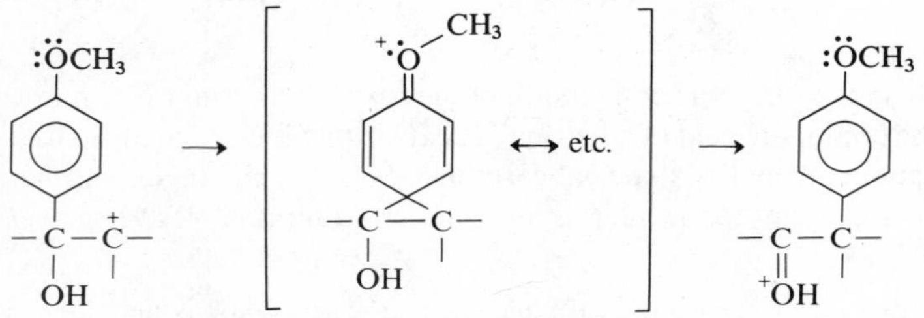

Charge stabilized by OCH_3

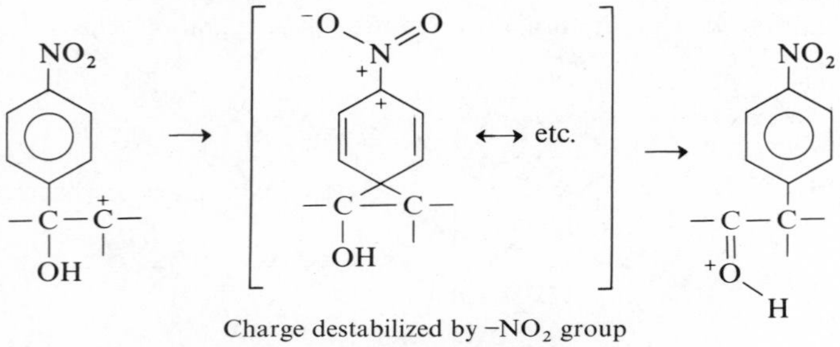

Charge destabilized by —NO_2 group

Ether Formation

If an alcohol is treated with sulfuric acid at a temperature *lower* than that required to dehydrate the alcohol to an alkene, and if excess alcohol is present, dehydration to an ether occurs.

$$2\,R\text{—OH} \xrightarrow{H_2SO_4} R\text{—O—}R + H_2O$$

An alcohol   An ether

$$2\,CH_3CH_2OH \xrightarrow[180°C]{H_2SO_4} 2\,CH_2\text{=}CH_2 + 2\,H_2O$$

$$\xrightarrow[140°C]{H_2SO_4} CH_3CH_2\text{—O—}CH_2CH_3 + H_2O$$

Primary alcohols react via the S_N2 pathway.

Ethyl hydrogen sulfate

Protonated ethyl ether

$$CH_3CH_2\text{—O—}CH_2CH_3$$

$$+ H^+$$

Ditertiary ethers are unstable due to steric crowding of the bulky groups around the oxygen; they are therefore not formed from tertiary alcohols. Secondary alcohols may react via the S_N1 mechanism to yield the corresponding ethers, as shown for the formation of diisopropyl ether from 2-propanol.

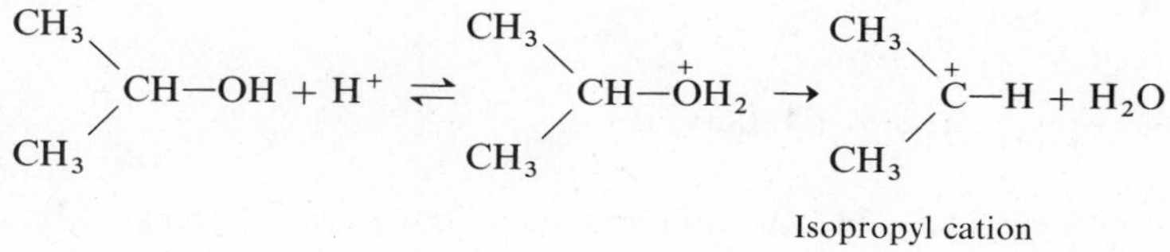

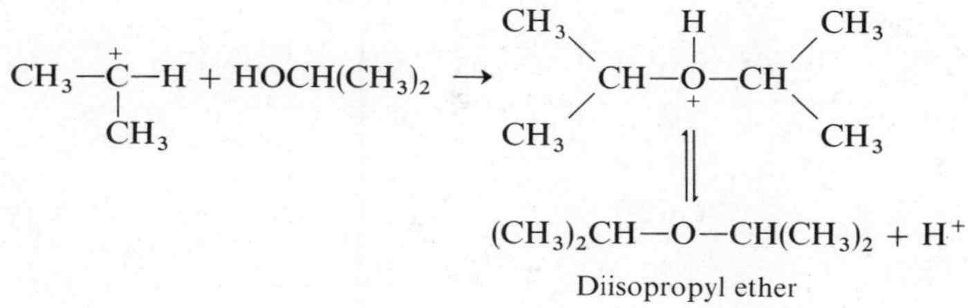

$$CH_3{-}CH{-}OH + H^+ \rightleftharpoons CH_3{-}CH{-}\overset{+}{O}H_2 \rightarrow CH_3{-}\overset{+}{C}{-}H + H_2O$$

Isopropyl cation

$$CH_3{-}\overset{+}{C}{-}H + HOCH(CH_3)_2 \rightarrow CH{-}\overset{+}{O}{-}CH$$

$$(CH_3)_2CH{-}O{-}CH(CH_3)_2 + H^+$$

Diisopropyl ether

If two similar alcohols are mixed in sulfuric acid, three ethers can be formed:

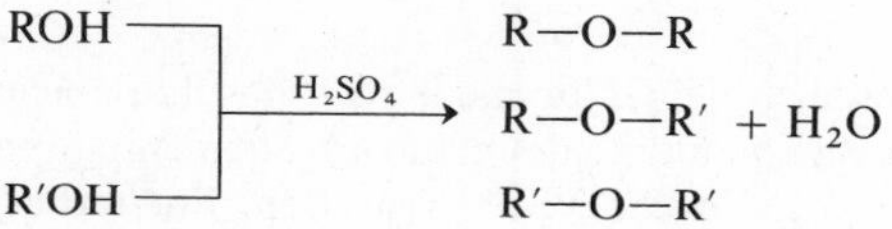

$$\left.\begin{array}{l} ROH \\[4pt] R'OH \end{array}\right\} \xrightarrow{H_2SO_4} \begin{array}{l} R{-}O{-}R \\ R{-}O{-}R' + H_2O \\ R'{-}O{-}R' \end{array}$$

However, if one of the alcohols is *t*-butyl alcohol, only *t*-butyl alkyl ethers are formed due to the rapid formation of the *t*-butyl cation. 2-Methylpropene can be used in place of *t*-butyl alcohol:

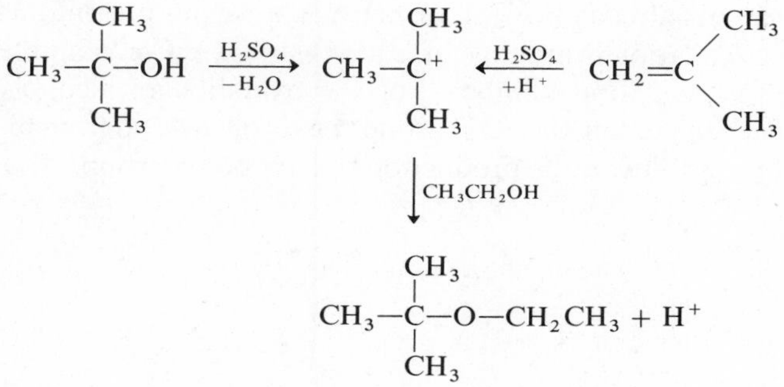

$$CH_3{-}\underset{CH_3}{\overset{CH_3}{C}}{-}OH \xrightarrow[-H_2O]{H_2SO_4} CH_3{-}\underset{CH_3}{\overset{CH_3}{C}}{}^+ \xleftarrow[+H^+]{H_2SO_4} CH_2{=}\overset{CH_3}{\underset{CH_3}{C}}$$

$$\downarrow CH_3CH_2OH$$

$$CH_3{-}\underset{CH_3}{\overset{CH_3}{C}}{-}O{-}CH_2CH_3 + H^+$$

t-Butyl phenyl ether can be prepared by the Williamson synthesis if mild conditions are used.

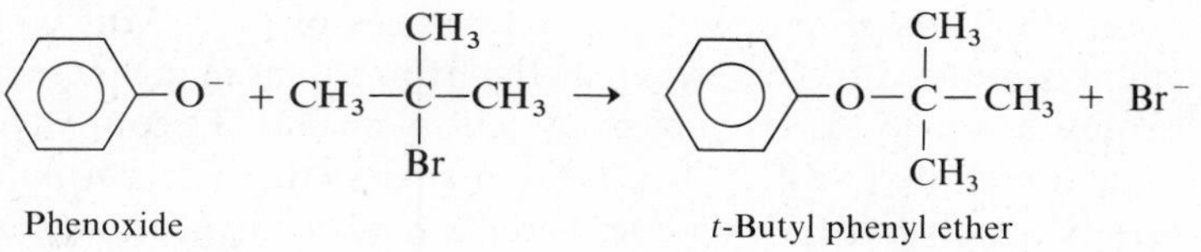

$$\langle\bigcirc\rangle{-}O^- + CH_3{-}\underset{Br}{\overset{CH_3}{C}}{-}CH_3 \rightarrow \langle\bigcirc\rangle{-}O{-}\underset{CH_3}{\overset{CH_3}{C}}{-}CH_3 + Br^-$$

Phenoxide   *t*-Butyl phenyl ether

The reaction proceeds via an S_N1 ionization of the bromide, and the resulting carbonium ion then reacts with the phenoxide.

Cyclodehydration of Diols. Diols can be dehydrated to cyclic ethers. For example, 1,2,4-trihydroxy-butane dehydrates intramolecularly to 3-hydroxytetrahydrofuran.

1,2,4-Trihydroxybutane   3-Hydroxytetrahydrofuran

By carefully controlling conditions and concentrations, 1,4-dioxane can be prepared by a bimolecular condensation of 1,2-ethanediol, followed by cyclization.

1,4-Dioxane

Acid catalysts other than sulfuric acid can be used to dehydrate alcohols. Phosphoric acid, *p*-toluenesulfonic acid, and the solid catalysts silica gel and aluminum oxide are often employed. Other Lewis acids such as $B(OH)_3$, $ZnCl_2$, and BF_3, also catalyze dehydration. For tertiary alcohols, I_2 is an especially useful, mild Lewis acid. It should be emphasized that the role of the acid is a catalytic one, that is, the acid is not consumed in the dehydration.

18.7   Oxidation

The organic chemist associates *oxidation* with a *removal of hydrogen* and formation of a new bond, either between two atoms already present, or between an atom present and oxygen. Another way of viewing oxidation is in terms of *loss of electrons:* For example, oxidation leads to an increase in oxidation number. For the oxidation of alcohols, hydrogen is removed from the carbon bearing the $-OH$ group (α hydrogens) and from the oxygen, the new bond formation resulting in the production of a carbonyl group.

The reaction products may be aldehydes, ketones, or acids.

It can be seen that primary and secondary alcohols may be oxidized; but tertiary alcohols, which have no α-hydrogen atoms, are resistant. In fact, tertiary alcohols can only be oxidized when carbon–carbon bond cleavage occurs subsequent to dehydration.

The most commonly used oxidants for alcohols are derivatives of Cr^{VI}, Mn^{VII}, or Mn^{IV}. Hexavalent chromium is reduced to Cr^{III}, whereas the heptavalent manganese is reduced to Mn^{II} in acidic solution and to MnO_2 in basic or neutral media. The sources of Cr^{VI} are sodium dichromate dihydrate ($Na_2Cr_2O_7 \cdot 2H_2O$) in acid solution or chromic anhydride (CrO_3) in a variety of solvents (in pyridine, *Sarett's reagent*; in acetone and aqueous sulfuric acid, *Jones' reagent*).

It is more difficult to balance organic oxidation–reduction reactions than the student might suspect at this point, and we will postpone this problem until Section 23.2.

Oxidation of alcohols is usually accomplished with chromic acid.

$$H-\overset{|}{\underset{|}{C}}-OH + Cr^{VI} \rightarrow \overset{\diagdown}{\underset{\diagup}{C}}=O + Cr^{III}$$

The first step of the reaction is the formation of a chromate ester.

$$ROH + HO-\overset{O}{\underset{O}{\overset{||}{\underset{||}{Cr}}}}-OH \rightarrow R-O-\overset{O}{\underset{O}{\overset{||}{\underset{||}{Cr}}}}-OH + H_2O$$

Chromic acid   An alkyl
hydrogen chromate

If the ester has an α-hydrogen atom, an elimination can occur.

$$H_2O:\curvearrowright H-\overset{|}{\underset{|}{C}}-O-\overset{O}{\underset{O}{\overset{||}{\underset{||}{Cr}}}}-OH \rightarrow H_3O^+ + \overset{\diagdown}{\underset{\diagup}{C}}=O + {}^-CrO_3H$$

The chromium has now been reduced from an oxidation number of $+6$ to $+4$. H_2CrO_3 is not stable, but undergoes disproportionation with Cr^{VI} to give two molecules of Cr^V. The latter each oxidize a molecule of alcohol, and are in the process converted to Cr^{III}. The α-carbon atom of the alcohol has been oxidized, due to the removal of the attached hydrogen and the formation of a new carbon-to-oxygen bond. Some examples of this method are the oxidations of 2-butanol to 2-butanone and menthol to menthone.

$$CH_3CH_2\overset{|}{\underset{\overset{|}{CH_3}}{CH}}-OH \xrightarrow{H_2CrO_4} CH_3CH_2\overset{O}{\overset{||}{C}}CH_3$$

The aldehydes initially formed from the oxidation of primary alcohols are usually further oxidized to carboxylic acids. The aldehyde is hydrated to a *gem*-diol, which is esterified and oxidized.

$$RCH_2OH + H_2CrO_4 \rightarrow RCH=O$$

$$RCH=O + H_2O \rightleftharpoons R\overset{OH}{\overset{|}{C}H}-OH$$

$$R\overset{OH}{\overset{|}{C}H}-OH + HO-\overset{O}{\underset{O}{\overset{||}{\underset{||}{Cr}}}}-OH \rightleftharpoons R-\overset{OH}{\overset{|}{C}H}-O-\overset{O}{\underset{O}{\overset{||}{\underset{||}{Cr}}}}-OH + H_2O$$

$$R-\overset{OH}{\underset{\underset{H_2O:\curvearrowright}{\overset{|}{\underset{|}{C}}}}{}}-O-\overset{O}{\overset{||}{Cr}}-OH \rightarrow H_3O^+ + R-\overset{OH}{\overset{|}{C}}=O + {}^-CrO_3H$$

For example, caproic acid is the product of the chromic acid oxidation of 1-hexanol.

$$CH_3CH_2CH_2CH_2CH_2CH_2OH + H_2CrO_4 \rightarrow CH_3CH_2CH_2CH_2CH_2\overset{\displaystyle O}{\overset{\displaystyle \|}{C}}-OH$$

If the aldehyde is volatile, it may be possible to distill it from the reaction mixture before it is oxidized to the carboxylic acid; propionaldehyde can be prepared from *n*-propyl alcohol in this way.

$$CH_3CH_2CH_2OH \xrightarrow[\substack{H_2SO_4/H_2O \\ distill}]{Na_2Cr_2O_7} CH_3CH_2CHO$$

This method is restricted, however, to aldehydes containing four carbons or less.

By choosing the oxidizing agent carefully, some degree of selectivity can be introduced in oxidations of alcohols. For example, fairly respectable yields of aldehydes have been obtained from primary alcohols by oxidation with CrO_3 in pyridine. The success of this method has been attributed to the fact that the water concentration under these conditions is kept low, reducing the conversion of the aldehyde to its hydrate and thereby preventing it from further oxidation to acid.

$$CH_3CH=CHCH_2OH \xrightarrow[\substack{pyridine \\ 25°C}]{CrO_3} CH_3CH=CHCHO$$

Benzylic and allylic alcohols are oxidized to the corresponding aldehydes by MnO_2, whereas saturated alcohols are not easily attacked under the same conditions.

$$PhCH_2OH \xrightarrow{MnO_2} Ph\overset{\displaystyle O}{\overset{\displaystyle \|}{C}}-H$$

$$RCH_2OH \xrightarrow{MnO_2} \text{No oxidation}$$

On the other hand, potassium permanganate will oxidize saturated primary alcohols, as well as benzylic and allylic alcohols, all the way to acids.

$$PhCH_2OH \xrightarrow{KMnO_4} PhCOOH$$

$$RCH_2OH \xrightarrow{KMnO_4} RCOOH$$

Jones' reagent (aqueous chromic acid in acetone) is especially valuable for the oxidation of alcohols without affecting a carbon–carbon double bond present in the same molecule.

In strongly acidic media an alcohol may dehydrate to an alkene which is then oxidized. Even tertiary alcohols can be oxidized in this way. Acetone and carbon dioxide, for example, are formed from *t*-butyl alcohol and nitric acid.

$$CH_3-\underset{\underset{\displaystyle CH_3}{|}}{\overset{\overset{\displaystyle CH_3}{|}}{C}}-OH \xrightarrow{HNO_3} [CH_3-\underset{\underset{\displaystyle CH_3}{|}}{C}=CH_2] + H_2O$$

$$\xrightarrow{HNO_3} CH_3-\underset{\underset{\displaystyle CH_3}{|}}{C}=O + CO_2 + H_2O$$

The bond between the carbon atoms bearing the hydroxyl groups in a 1,2-diol is easily cleaved by oxidizing agents. Chromic acid and permanganate oxidize these carbons to their highest oxidation states.

$$
\begin{array}{c}
CH_3 \\
| \\
CHOH \\
| \\
CH_2OH
\end{array}
\xrightarrow{KMnO_4}
\begin{array}{c}
CH_3 \\
| \\
CH=O
\end{array}
+ CH_2=O
\xrightarrow{KMnO_4}
\begin{array}{c}
CH_3 \\
| \\
COOH
\end{array}
+ CO_2
$$

1,2-Propanediol   Acetaldehyde   Formaldehyde   Acetic acid

Periodic acid and lead tetraacetate, in contrast, do not oxidize the initially formed acetaldehyde and formaldehyde further.

$$
\begin{array}{c}
CH_3 \\
| \\
CHOH \\
| \\
CH_2OH
\end{array}
+ HIO_4 \rightarrow CH_3CH=O + CH_2O + HIO_3 + H_2O
$$

[or Pb(OCOCH_3)_4]   [or Pb(OCOCH_3)_2 + 2CH_3COOH]

Since carbonyl compounds are relatively easy to isolate and identify, periodic acid oxidation has been extensively used to determine structures of glycols and polyols, especially the complex natural compounds known as *sugars* (Section 27.5).

EXERCISE 18.9

What conclusions can you draw if the periodic oxidation of a diol occurs and yields: (a) only a single carbonyl compound RR′C=O; (b) two aldehydes: RCHO and R′CHO; (c) formaldehyde and a ketone R_2C=O; (d) only a single compound which contains two carbonyl groups (give an example of a glycol that would give this result).

Mechanism of Glycol Cleavage. An intermediate cyclic ester is formed from a 1,2-diol with lead tetraacetate, and this then undergoes an oxidation–reduction process.

Similar cyclic esters are also believed to be formed (and cleaved) with periodic acid and with potassium permanganate (Section 15.10).

Dehydrogenation of Alcohols. Commercially, primary and secondary alcohols are oxidized catalytically in the presence of copper.

$$
\begin{array}{c}
OH \\
| \\
Ph-CH-CH_3
\end{array}
\xrightarrow[300°C]{Cu}
\begin{array}{c}
O \\
|| \\
Ph-C-CH_3
\end{array}
+ H_2
$$

$$
CH_2=CH-CH_2-OH \xrightarrow[300°C]{Cu} CH_2=CH-CH=O + H_2
$$

This type of reaction is known as *dehydrogenation*.

18.8   Reactions of Ethers

Simple ethers are quite unreactive compounds, and for this reason they are often used as solvents in which to carry out organic reactions. They are inert to bases.

$$CH_3CH_2OCH_2CH_3 \begin{cases} \xrightarrow[CH_3OH]{^-OCH_3} \text{No reaction} \\ \xrightarrow[\text{liq. } NH_3]{NH_2^-} \text{No reaction} \\ \xrightarrow[H_2O]{OH^-} \text{No reaction} \end{cases}$$

Ethers do undergo a few reactions in the presence of acids, mostly under fairly strenuous conditions. Ethers are bases which can enter into equilibria with acids such as sulfuric acid, boron trifluoride, and Grignard reagents (Section 4.19).

$$R-O-R + H-O-\overset{\overset{O}{\|}}{\underset{\underset{O}{\|}}{S}}-O-H \rightleftharpoons R-\overset{\overset{H}{|}}{\overset{+}{O}}-R + \ ^-O_3S-OH$$

An ether   Sulfuric acid   A protonated   Hydrogen
                                 ether   sulfate anion

$$C_2H_5-O-C_2H_5 + BF_3 \rightleftharpoons C_2H_5-\overset{+}{\underset{\underset{^-BF_3}{|}}{O}}-C_2H_5$$

Boron trifluoride
etherate

Trialkyloxonium salts, such as triethyloxonium fluoroborate, can be prepared and isolated.

$$CH_3CH_2I + AgBF_4 + (CH_3CH_2)_2O \rightarrow (CH_3CH_2)_3O^+BF_4^- + AgI$$

Such oxonium salts are useful, exceptionally reactive, alkylating agents. For example:

$$ROH + Et_3O^+BF_4^- \rightarrow ROEt + Et_2O + H^+BF_4^-$$

Cleavage is the most common reaction of ethers.

$$R-O-R' + 2HI \xrightarrow{\text{heat}} RI + R'I + H_2O$$

The acid-catalyzed cleavage of the C—O bond proceeds via an initial protonation of the ether. Depending on the nature of the R groups, the oxonium ion can then undergo either S_N1 cleavage to an alcohol and a carbonium ion:

$$R-\overset{\overset{H}{|}}{\underset{+}{O}}-R \xrightarrow{S_N1} R-OH + R^+$$

or S_N2 attack by a nucleophile with HOR as a leaving group.

$$Z: + R-\overset{\overset{H}{|}}{\overset{+}{O}}-R \xrightarrow{S_N2} Z^+-R + HOR$$

As would be anticipated, primary alkyl groups in the ether favor the S_N2 mechanism, while tertiary alkyl groups favor the S_N1 mechanism. Examples are the cleavages of dimethyl ether and *t*-butyl methyl ether by HI.

$$CH_3-O-CH_3 + H-I \longrightarrow CH_3-\overset{\overset{H}{|}}{\underset{+}{O}}-CH_3 + I^-$$

Dimethyloxonium
iodide

$$I^- + CH_3-\overset{+}{\underset{\underset{H}{|}}{O}}-CH_3 \xrightarrow{S_N2} I-CH_3 + HOCH_3$$

$$\downarrow HI$$

$$ICH_3 + H_2O$$

$$CH_3-O-\overset{\overset{CH_3}{|}}{\underset{\underset{CH_3}{|}}{C}}-CH_3 + H-I \longrightarrow CH_3-\overset{\overset{H}{|}}{\underset{+}{O}}-\overset{\overset{CH_3}{|}}{\underset{\underset{CH_3}{|}}{C}}-CH_3 + I^-$$

t-Butylmethyloxonium
iodide

$$CH_3-\overset{+}{\underset{\underset{HI}{|}}{O}}\overset{\overset{H}{|}}{}-\overset{\overset{CH_3}{|}}{\underset{\underset{CH_3}{|}}{C}}-CH_3 \xrightarrow{S_N1} CH_3OH + \overset{\overset{CH_3}{|}}{\underset{\underset{CH_3}{|}}{\overset{+}{C}}}-CH_3$$

$$CH_3I + H_2O \longleftarrow$$

$$I-\overset{\overset{CH_3}{|}}{\underset{\underset{CH_3}{|}}{C}}-CH_3 \xleftarrow{HI} CH_2=C\overset{CH_3}{\underset{CH_3}{\big\langle}} + HI$$

The alcohols formed in the initial reaction are subsequently converted to the iodides.

Since phenols do not readily undergo nucleophilic substitution, an alkyl phenyl ether is converted by HI to an alkyl iodide and a phenol.

$$\langle\!\langle\bigcirc\rangle\!\rangle-O-CH_3 \xrightarrow[130°C]{57\% HI} \langle\!\langle\bigcirc\rangle\!\rangle-\overset{\overset{H}{|}}{\underset{+}{O}}-CH_3 \quad I^-$$

Anisole   Methylphenyloxonium iodide

$$\langle\!\langle\bigcirc\rangle\!\rangle-\overset{\overset{H}{|}}{\underset{+}{O}}-CH_3 + I^- \longrightarrow \langle\!\langle\bigcirc\rangle\!\rangle-OH + CH_3I$$

Cleavage of ethers also occurs with HBr and with HCl; since these acids are less reactive than HI (because Cl^- and Br^- are poorer nucleophiles than I^-), higher concentrations and temperatures are required for them to be effective.

The cyclic ether *tetrahydrofuran* is cleaved by hydrochloric acid in the presence of zinc chloride to yield 1,4-dichlorobutane, a valuable intermediate for the manufacture of nylon.

$$\overset{\square}{\underset{O}{}} + 2\,HCl \xrightarrow{ZnCl_2} \overset{CH_2-\!\!\!-\!\!\!-CH_2}{\underset{\underset{Cl}{\overset{|}{CH_2}}\quad\underset{Cl}{\overset{|}{CH_2}}}{}} + H_2O$$

1,4-Dichlorobutane

18.9   Reactions of Epoxides

While ethers in general are quite unreactive, epoxides (also called *oxiranes* or *alkene oxides*, Section 15.10), are quite different in their chemical behavior. They react readily with acids, and even with many bases, because of the strain present in the ring. The cleavage reactions (ring openings) of epoxides are extremely useful for synthetic purposes, as can be seen from Table 18.1.

Table 18.1   Ring-Opening Reactions of Ethylene Oxide

1. $H_2C-CH_2 + H_2O \xrightarrow{H^+} CH_2-CH_2$
    $\quad\ \ \backslash\!\diagup\qquad\qquad\qquad\quad |\qquad |$
    $\qquad O\qquad\qquad\qquad\qquad OH\quad OH$

2. $H_2C-CH_2 + CH_3OH \xrightarrow{H^+} CH_2-CH_2$
    $\quad\ \ \backslash\!\diagup\qquad\qquad\qquad\qquad\quad |\qquad\ |$
    $\qquad O\qquad\qquad\qquad\qquad\quad OH\quad OCH_3$

3. $H_2C-CH_2 + CH_3OCH_2CH_2-OH \xrightarrow{H^+} CH_3OCH_2CH_2-O-CH_2CH_2-OH$
    $\quad\ \ \backslash\!\diagup$
    $\qquad O$

4. $H_2C-CH_2 + nH_2C-CH_2 \xrightarrow[\substack{trace \\ H_2O}]{H^+} HOCH_2CH_2{+}OCH_2CH_2{\xrightarrow{}_n}OCH_2CH_2OH$
    $\quad\ \ \backslash\!\diagup\qquad\quad \backslash\ \diagup\qquad\qquad\qquad\qquad\qquad polyethylene\ glycol$
    $\qquad O\qquad\qquad O$

5. $H_2C-CH_2 +$ ⬡$-O^- \rightarrow$ ⬡$-OCH_2CH_2-O^- \xrightarrow{H^+}$
    $\quad\ \ \backslash\!\diagup$
    $\qquad O$

                     ⬡$-OCH_2CH_2OH$

6. $H_2C-CH_2 + CH_3MgBr \longrightarrow CH_3-CH_2CH_2-OMgBr \xrightarrow{H_2O} CH_3CH_2CH_2OH + Mg(OH)Br$
    $\quad\ \ \backslash\!\diagup$
    $\qquad O$

7. $H_2C-CH_2 + NH_3 \longrightarrow CH_2-CH_2$ $[+ NH(CH_2CH_2OH)_2$ and $N(CH_2CH_2OH)_3]$
    $\quad\ \ \backslash\!\diagup\qquad\qquad\qquad\ |\qquad |$
    $\qquad O\qquad\qquad\qquad NH_2\quad OH$

8. $H_2C-CH_2 + CH_3SH \xrightarrow{H^+} CH_2-CH_2$
    $\quad\ \ \backslash\!\diagup\qquad\qquad\qquad\qquad |\qquad\ |$
    $\qquad O\qquad\qquad\qquad\quad CH_3S\quad OH$

9. $H_2C-CH_2 + 2HI \longrightarrow CH_2-CH_2 + H_2O$
    $\quad\ \ \backslash\!\diagup\qquad\qquad\qquad |\qquad |$
    $\qquad O\qquad\qquad\qquad I\qquad I$

10. $H_2C-CH_2 + HCl \longrightarrow CH_2-CH_2$
    $\quad\ \ \backslash\!\diagup\qquad\qquad\qquad\ |\qquad |$
    $\qquad O\qquad\qquad\qquad\ OH\quad Cl$

11. $H_2C-CH_2 + HBr \longrightarrow CH_2-CH_2$
    $\quad\ \ \backslash\!\diagup\qquad\qquad\qquad\ |\qquad |$
    $\qquad O\qquad\qquad\qquad\ OH\quad Br$

12. $4\,H_2C-CH_2 + LiAlH_4 \longrightarrow \left(\begin{matrix}CH_2CH_2\\ |\quad\ |\\ H\quad O\end{matrix}\right)_4 Al^-Li^+ \xrightarrow{2H_2O} 4\,CH_3CH_2OH + LiAlO_2$
    $\quad\ \ \backslash\!\diagup$
    $\qquad\ O$

13. $2\,H_2C-CH_2 + H_2S \longrightarrow CH_2CH_2-S-CH_2CH_2$
    $\quad\ \ \backslash\!\diagup\qquad\qquad\qquad\ |\qquad\qquad\qquad\quad |$
    $\qquad O\qquad\qquad\qquad HO\qquad\qquad\qquad OH$

EXERCISE 18.10

Suggest a mechanism for the reaction of ethylene oxide with H_3O^+ [reaction (1) in Table 18.1].

EXERCISE 18.11

Show by means of a reaction coordinate diagram why reaction (1) in Table 18.1 is so much faster than the analogous reaction of diethyl ether.

The three-membered ring is highly strained and will open under mild conditions, releasing a considerable amount of strain energy. The greater reactivity of epoxides compared with acylic ethers is seen particularly in their reactions with nucleophiles.

For example, ethylene oxide is readily cleaved with methoxide in an S_N2 reaction, whereas diethyl ether does not react. (With very strong bases, e.g., carbanions, diethyl ether slowly undergoes an elimination reaction yielding ethylene.)

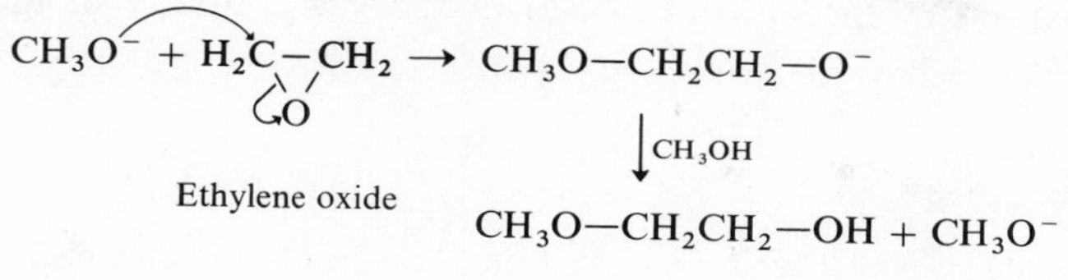

$$CH_3O^- + H_2\overset{\frown}{C}-CH_2 \rightarrow CH_3O-CH_2CH_2-O^-$$
$$\underset{O}{\diagdown}$$

Ethylene oxide

$$\downarrow CH_3OH$$

$$CH_3O-CH_2CH_2-OH + CH_3O^-$$

Orientation in Epoxide Opening. Support for the S_N2 mechanism can be found in the second-order kinetics and in the fact that propylene oxide is opened by attack of the methoxide at the less hindered primary carbon atom.

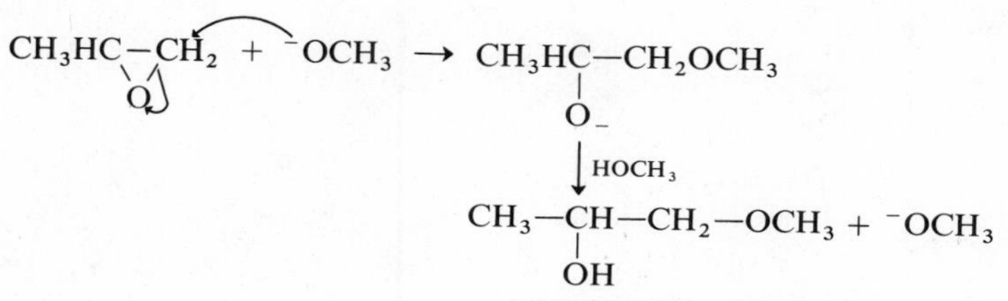

$$CH_3HC-\overset{\frown}{CH_2} + {}^-OCH_3 \rightarrow CH_3HC-CH_2OCH_3$$
$$\underset{O}{\diagdown} \qquad\qquad\qquad \underset{O^-}{|}$$

$$\downarrow HOCH_3$$

$$CH_3-\underset{\underset{OH}{|}}{CH}-CH_2-OCH_3 + {}^-OCH_3$$

1-Methoxy-2-propanol

Propylene oxide reacts under acidic (S_N1) conditions via the more stable secondary carbonium ion.

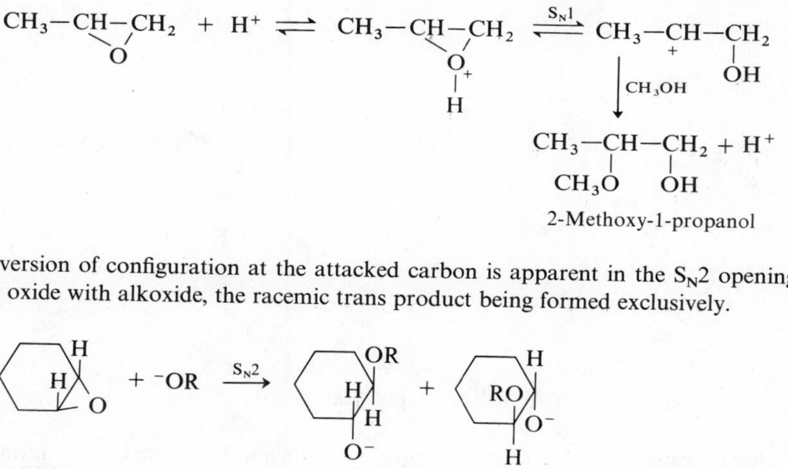

$$CH_3-CH-CH_2 + H^+ \rightleftharpoons CH_3-CH-CH_2 \underset{}{\overset{S_N1}{\rightleftharpoons}} CH_3-\overset{+}{CH}-\underset{\underset{OH}{|}}{CH_2}$$
$$\underset{O}{\diagdown} \qquad\qquad \underset{\underset{H}{|}}{\overset{+}{O}}$$

$$\downarrow CH_3OH$$

$$CH_3-CH-CH_2 + H^+$$
$$\underset{CH_3O}{|} \quad \underset{OH}{|}$$

2-Methoxy-1-propanol

The inversion of configuration at the attacked carbon is apparent in the S_N2 opening of cyclohexene oxide with alkoxide, the racemic trans product being formed exclusively.

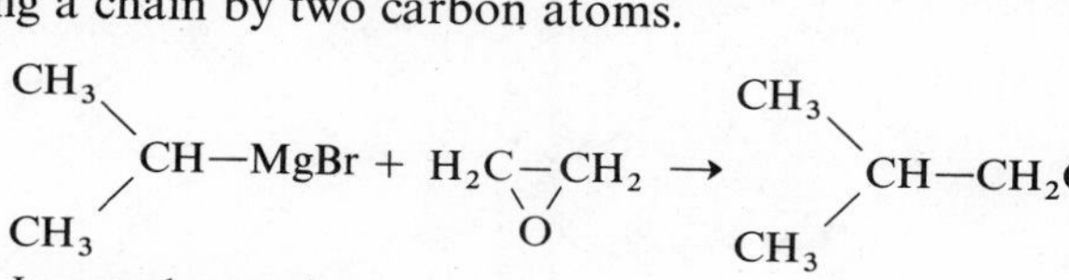

Cyclohexene oxide   *dl*-Trans

The reaction of ethylene oxide with Grignard reagents is a convenient method for extending a chain by two carbon atoms.

Isopropylmagnesium bromide

$$\uparrow Mg, ether$$

$$CH_3\underset{\underset{CH_3}{|}}{CH}-Br$$

$$\uparrow HBr$$

$$CH_3\underset{\underset{CH_3}{|}}{CH}-OH$$

$$\downarrow H_2O$$

$$CH_3\underset{\underset{CH_3}{|}}{CH}CH_2CH_2OH + Mg(OH)Br$$

In this manner 2-propanol can be converted to 3-methyl-1-butanol. The opening proceeds with attack by the nucleophilic carbon of the Grignard reagent on a carbon of the epoxide. Formation of a complex between a magnesium atom (Lewis acid) of the Grignard reagent and the oxygen of the epoxide increases the susceptibility of the epoxide carbon to nucleophilic attack.

18.10   The Claisen Rearrangement

When phenoxide displaces bromide from allyl bromide, two products can be formed, allyl phenyl ether from alkylation on oxygen (O-alkylation) and o-allylphenol from alkylation on carbon (C-alkylation). The course of the reaction depends upon the solvent.

The initial product of C-alkylation is not observed; it rapidly tautomerizes to the aromatic system, o-allylphenol.

If allyl phenyl ether is heated to 200°C, it rearranges to o-allylphenol. The mechanism is intramolecular and cyclic with a new C—C bond forming between the γ carbon and the ring at the same time the C—O bond is breaking.

If radioactive ^{14}C is present at the γ position in the allylic group of allyl phenyl ether, it is found as the carbon atom bonded to the aromatic ring in *o*-allylphenol.

This rearrangement is known as the *ortho-Claisen† rearrangement.* If the ortho position is blocked, so that the dienone cannot reestablish the aromatic system, the migration continues to the para position.

Allyl 2,6-dimethylphenyl ether   A dienone

A dienone   4-Allyl-2,6-dimethylphenol

Analogous rearrangements occur with allyl vinyl ethers (see also Section 15.12).

Allyl vinyl ether   4-Pentenal

These reactions are relatively unusual in that they do not involve any of the standard types of reaction intermediates (carbonium ions, carbenes, etc., see Chapter 12), but rather go directly from reactants to products by the internal shifting of bonding electrons ("valence tautomerism").

18.11   Reactions Involving the Alpha Carbon–Hydrogen Bond

The α hydrogens of aliphatic ethers are readily attacked by free radicals. For example, ethers react with oxygen in a light-catalyzed free-radical reaction to form hydroperoxides.

These compounds are unstable and may explode spontaneously. For this reason, peroxides must be destroyed before ethers can be safely heated and concentrated. Diisopropyl ether reacts particularly rapidly with oxygen.

The common laboratory solvents diethyl ether and tetrahydrofuran can also form dangerous peroxides upon prolonged storage.

† Ludwig Claisen. 1851–1930. Born Cologne. University of Bonn, Owens College (Manchester), Universities of Munich, Aachen, Kiel, Berlin; Godesberg (private laboratory).

Ethers can be halogenated at the α carbon by treatment with chlorine or bromine in the presence of an initiator.

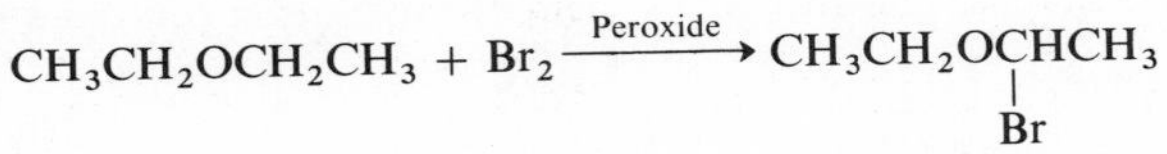

$$CH_3CH_2OCH_2CH_3 + Br_2 \xrightarrow{\text{Peroxide}} CH_3CH_2OCHCH_3$$
$$\underset{Br}{|}$$

These α-halo ethers can be dehydrohalogenated to yield vinyl ethers.

$$CH_3CH_2OCHBrCH_3 \xrightarrow[\text{heat}]{OH^-} CH_3CH_2OCH{=}CH_2$$

18.12 Summary of Synthetic Methods for Alcohols, Phenols, and Ethers

Continuing our earlier practice, we are listing here all of the synthetic methods which are generally useful for the preparations of the kinds of compounds discussed in this chapter: alcohols, ethers, and epoxides. Several of the reactions here are included for later reference and they need not be studied at this time. For alcohols these are the group of reactions under 1c, (1)–(4); under 1d, (1)–(4); and method 1e. For phenols, skip for now methods 2a and 2d. For epoxides, skip reactions under 4b.

The remaining reactions given in this section should be studied at this time. In addition, reactions listed as 1b in Section 15.19 can now be studied, and also the reactions under 1b in Section 17.13. Practice in designing syntheses is the best way to learn these reactions, and the problems which follow this section will include some chosen for this purpose.

1. Alcohols
   a. From alkenes
      (1) (Section 15.3) (hydration)

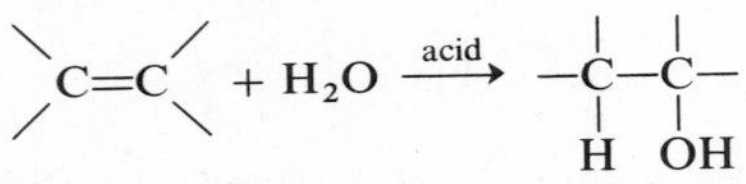

      (2) (Section 15.9) (hydroboration)

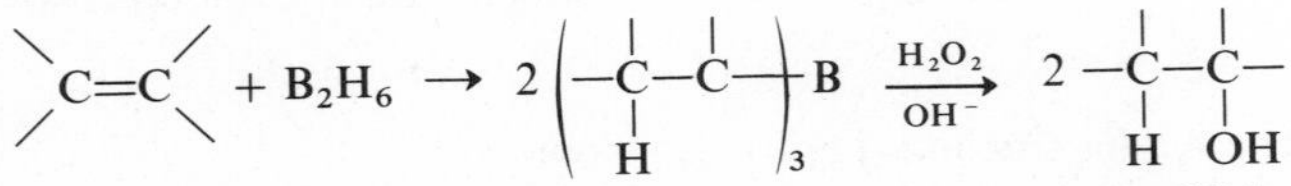

      (3) (Section 15.10)

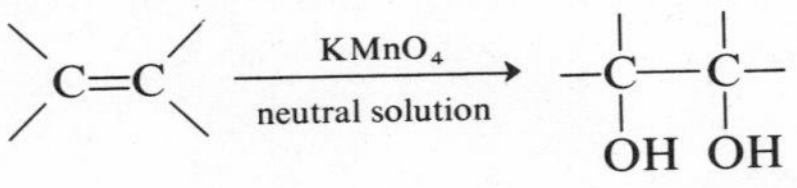

(gives cis diol)

      (4) (Section 15.10)

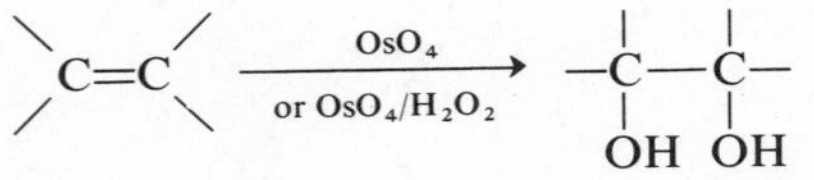

(gives cis diol)

      (5) (Section 15.10)

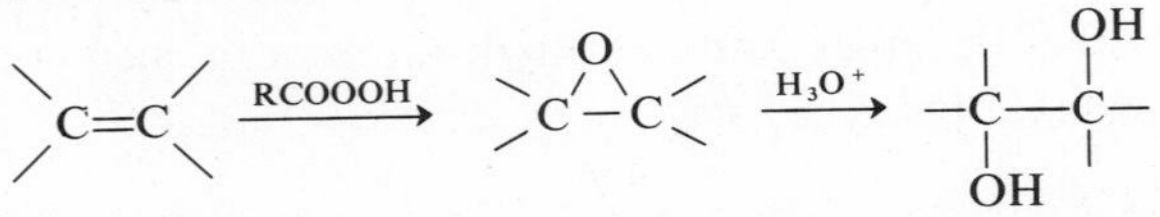

(gives trans diol)

b. From alkyl halides (Sections 17.1, 17.2)
  (1)

$$R-X + HO^- \rightarrow R-OH + X^-$$

c. From Grignard reagents (Section 19.9)
  (1)

$$R-MgX + H_2C=O \rightarrow R-CH_2-O-MgX \xrightarrow{H^+} R-CH_2-OH$$

  (2)

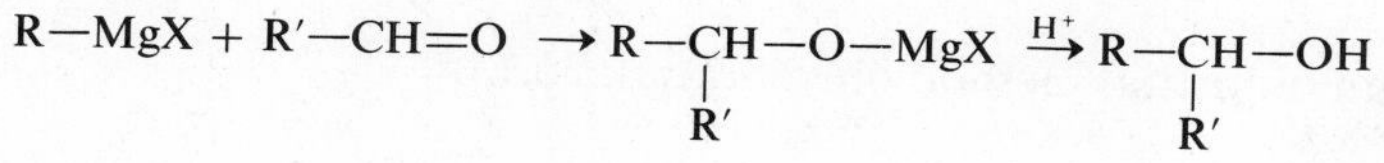

$$R-MgX + R'-CH=O \rightarrow R-\underset{\underset{R'}{|}}{CH}-O-MgX \xrightarrow{H^+} R-\underset{\underset{R'}{|}}{CH}-OH$$

  (3)

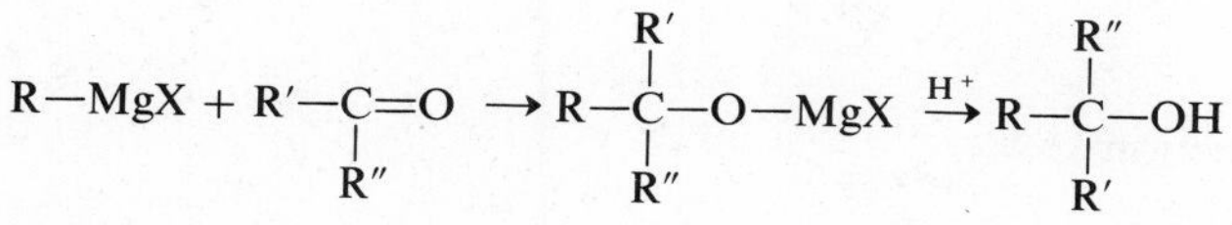

$$R-MgX + R'-\underset{\underset{R''}{|}}{C}=O \rightarrow R-\underset{\underset{R''}{\overset{\overset{R'}{|}}{C}}}{|}-O-MgX \xrightarrow{H^+} R-\underset{\underset{R'}{\overset{\overset{R''}{|}}{C}}}{|}-OH$$

  (4) (Section 20.9)

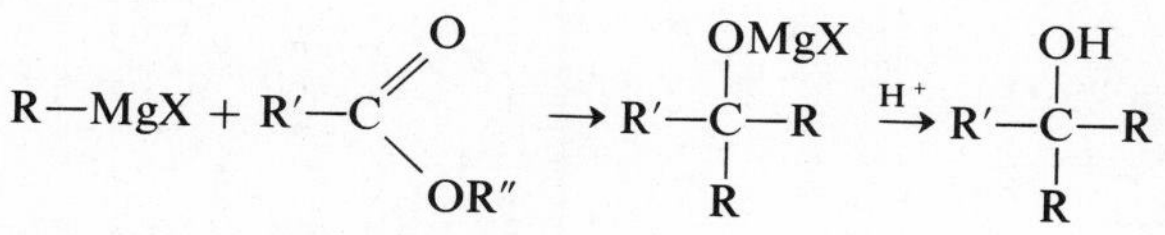

$$R-MgX + R'-\underset{\underset{OR''}{}}{\overset{\overset{O}{\|}}{C}} \rightarrow R'-\underset{\underset{R}{\overset{\overset{OMgX}{|}}{C}}}{|}-R \xrightarrow{H^+} R'-\underset{\underset{R}{\overset{\overset{OH}{|}}{C}}}{|}-R$$

  (5) (Section 18.9)

$$R-MgX + \underset{\underset{O}{\diagdown\diagup}}{H_2C-CH_2} \rightarrow R-CH_2CH_2-OMgX \xrightarrow{H^+} R-CH_2CH_2OH$$

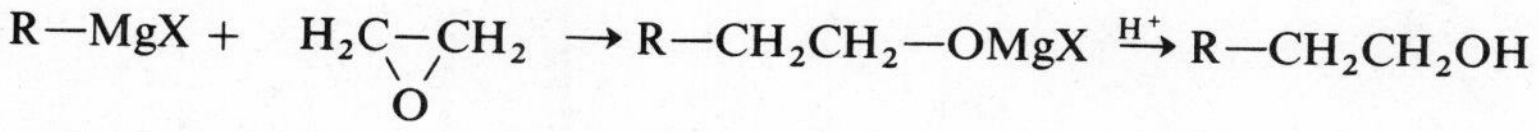

d. By reduction:
  (1) of aldehydes (Section 19.11)

$$RCH=O \xrightarrow{[H]} RCH_2OH \qquad H_2/Pt; NaBH_4 \text{ or } LiAlH_4$$

  (2) of ketones (Section 19.11)

$$R_2C=O \xrightarrow{[H]} R_2CHOH \qquad H_2/Pt; NaBH_4 \text{ or } LiAlH_4$$

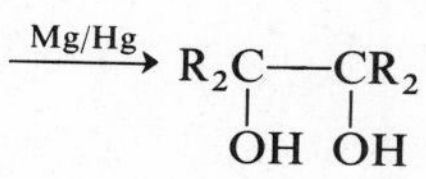

$$\xrightarrow{Mg/Hg} \underset{\underset{OH \quad OH}{|\qquad|}}{R_2C-CR_2}$$

  (3) of carboxylic acids (Section 20.8)

$$RCOOH \xrightarrow{[H]} RCH_2OH \qquad B_2H_6; LiAlH_4$$

  (4) of carboxylic esters (Section 20.8)

$$RCOOR' \xrightarrow{LiAlH_4} RCH_2OH + R'CH_2OH \quad [Na + EtOH \text{ also can be used}]$$

  (5) of epoxide rings (Section 18.9)

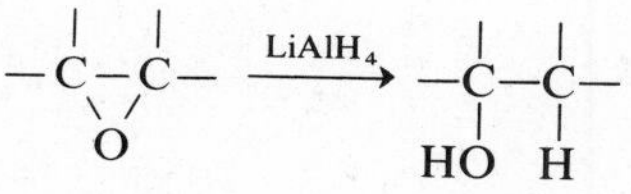

$$-\underset{\underset{O}{\diagdown\diagup}}{C-C}- \xrightarrow{LiAlH_4} -\underset{\underset{HO \quad H}{|\qquad|}}{C-C}-$$

e. From hydrolysis of carboxylic esters (Section 20.6)

$$RCO_2R' \xrightarrow[\text{H}^+ \text{ or OH}^-]{\text{H}_2\text{O}} RCO_2H + HOR$$

2. Phenols†
   a. From arylamines (Section 22.7).

   b. From aryl halides (an industrial method only, Section 35.13)

   c. From arenesulfonates (Section 16.8)

   d. From hydroperoxides (Section 23.1)

3. Ethers
   a. From alcohols:
      (1) and alkyl halides (Sections 17.1–17.3)

$$R-O^- + R'X \rightarrow R-O-R' + X^-$$

      (2) and diazomethane (Section 18.2)

$$ROH + CH_2N_2 \xrightarrow{\text{BF}_3} R-O-CH_3 + N_2$$

      (3) by bimolecular dehydration (Section 18.6)

$$2ROH \xrightarrow{\text{H}^+} R-O-R + H_2O$$

      (4) by addition to alkenes

4. Epoxides
   a. From alkenes:
      (1) and organic peracids (Section 15.10)

† G can be a substituent, for example, H, Br, R.

(2) and alkaline hydrogen peroxide (Section 19.7)

$$\text{C=C} \quad + H_2O_2 \xrightarrow{\;^-OH\;} \quad \text{C} - \text{C}$$

(3) by action of alkali on the corresponding halohydrin (Sections 15.5 and 18.2)

$$\text{C=C} \; + \; X-OH \; \rightarrow \; -\overset{|}{\underset{X}{C}}-\overset{\overset{OH}{|}}{\underset{}{C}}-$$

$$-\overset{\overset{OH}{|}}{\underset{X}{C}}-\overset{|}{\underset{}{C}}- \; + \; KOH \; \rightarrow \; -\overset{O}{\overset{/\backslash}{C-C}}- \; + \; KX \; + \; H_2O$$

b. From aldehydes and ketones (Sections 19.10 and 19.17):
 (1) and dimethyloxosulfonium methylide

$$R_2C{=}O + (CH_3)_2\overset{\overset{O}{\|}}{S}{=}CH_2 \;\rightarrow\; R_2\overset{O}{\overset{/\backslash}{C}}{-}CH_2 + (CH_3)_2S{=}O$$

(2) and dimethylsulfonium methylide

$$R_2C{=}O + (CH_3)_2S{=}CH_2 \;\rightarrow\; R_2\overset{O}{\overset{/\backslash}{C}}{-}CH_2 + (CH_3)_2S$$

(3) and hexamethylphosphorous triamide

$$Ph{-}CHO + [(CH_3)_2N]_3P \;\rightarrow\; Ph{-}\overset{O}{\overset{/\backslash}{HC}}{-}CH{-}Ph + [(CH_3)_2N]_3PO$$

PROBLEMS

1. List the following compounds in order of increasing acidity:

2. Give a structure consistent with the following nmr data obtained from a compound of formula C_7H_8O: $\delta\,3.7$ broad singlet, $A = 1$; $\delta\,4.45$ singlet, $A = 2$; $\delta\,7.25$ singlet, $A = 5$.

3. Compound C, which is seven times more potent than ether as an anesthetic, is synthesized from ethylene via the following series of reactions:

$$CH_2{=}CH_2 \xrightarrow{\;HOCl\;} A \xrightarrow{\;H_2SO_4\;} B \xrightarrow[\;200{-}240°C\;]{\text{fused KOH}} C$$

The nmr and the infrared spectra of C are given. What are the structures of A–C? Interpret the nmr and infrared spectra.

NMR spectrum of compound C, Problem 3.

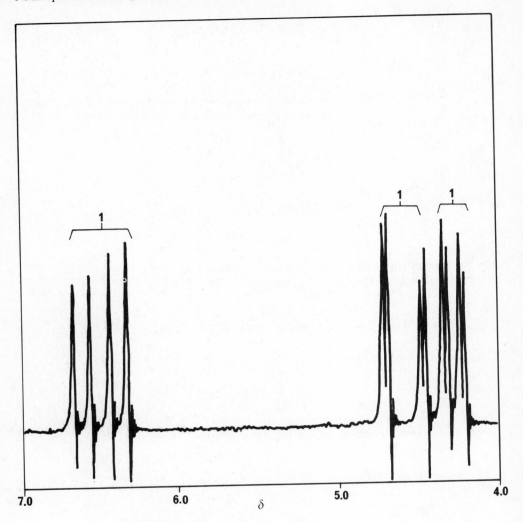

Infrared spectrum of compound C, Problem 3.

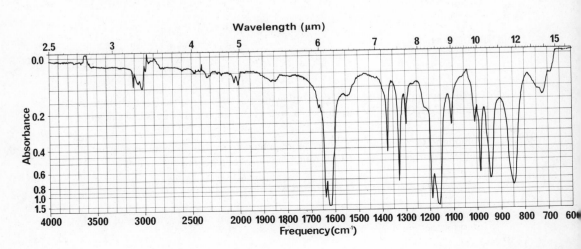

4. How would you carry out the following reactions:

$$CH_3CH_2\underset{\underset{OH}{|}}{C}HCH_3 \rightarrow CH_3CH_2\underset{\underset{Cl}{|}}{C}HCH_3$$

   (a) *Optional Problem.* D isomer → D isomer
   (b) D isomer → L-isomer

5. (a) Outline the mechanism of the following reaction:

$$CH_3CH_2CH_2CH_2OH + HBr \xrightarrow{(H_2O)} CH_3CH_2CH_2CH_2Br + H_2O$$

   (b) Draw a reaction coordinate diagram for the reaction.
   (c) What rate expression is demanded by parts (a) and (b)?
   (d) Repeat (a)–(c) for the following reaction:

$$CH_3CH_2\underset{\underset{CH_3}{|}}{\overset{\overset{CH_3}{|}}{C}}-OH + HBr \xrightarrow{(H_2O)} CH_3CH_2\underset{\underset{CH_3}{|}}{\overset{\overset{CH_3}{|}}{C}}-Br + H_2O$$

6. Outline a synthesis of ethyl tosylate, beginning with ethanol, benzene, and inorganic reagents.

7. Compound A reacted with HIO_4 to give a single compound B. The latter showed a strong absorption band at 1720 cm^{-1}. Compound A, when treated with concentrated sulfuric acid, gave another compound (C). The latter was analyzed and had the formula $C_6H_{12}O$. The nmr spectrum of C showed only two singlets: δ 1.10, $A = 3$; δ 2.05, $A = 1$. What are the structures of A–C?

8. Write a reasonable mechanism for the following reaction:

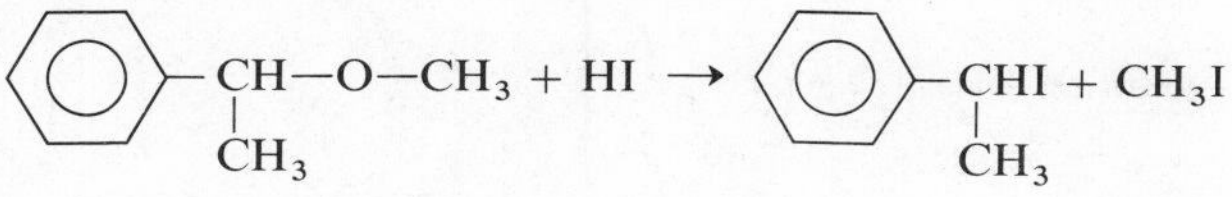

9. Complete the following reactions:

   (a) $CH_2{=}CH{-}\underset{\underset{Cl}{|}}{C}H{-}Cl + C_2H_5O^- \rightarrow$

   (b) $(CH_3)_3COH + CH_3OH \xrightarrow{15\% H_2SO_4}$

   (c) $CH_3\underset{\underset{CH_3}{|}}{C}HCH_2CH_2OH \xrightarrow{HBr}$

   (d) $CH_3\underset{\underset{CH_3}{|}}{C}HCH_2CH_2OH \xrightarrow{PBr_3}$

   (e) $CH_3CH_2\underset{\underset{CH_3}{|}}{C}HCH_2OH \xrightarrow{KMnO_4}$

   (f)

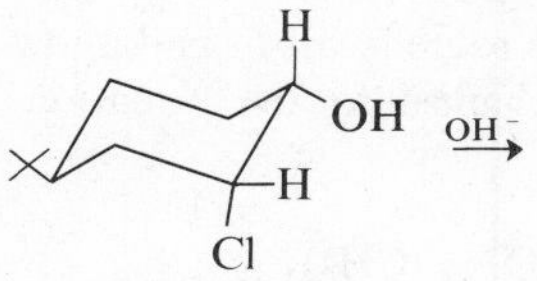

   (g)

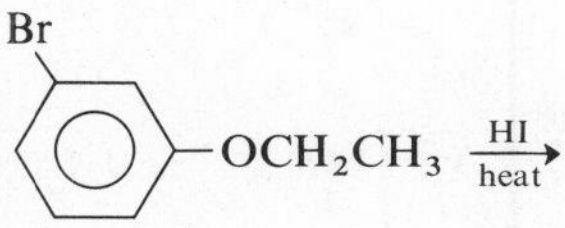

(h) 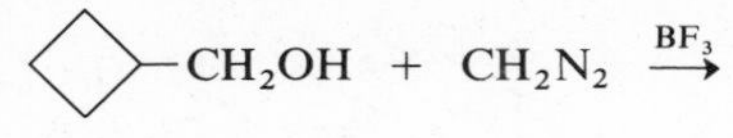 △—CH_2OH + CH_2N_2 $\xrightarrow{BF_3}$

(i) $CH_3CH_2O^-$ + $CH_3O-SO_2-OCH_3$ →

(j) 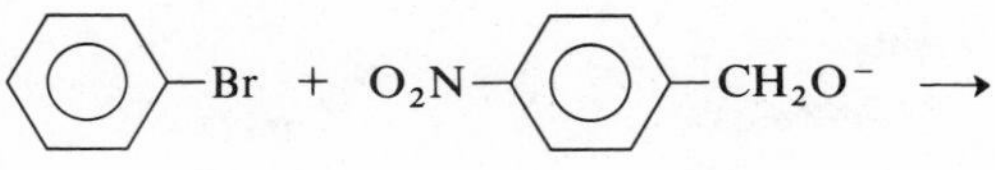 ⟨○⟩—Br + O_2N—⟨○⟩—CH_2O^- →

(k) 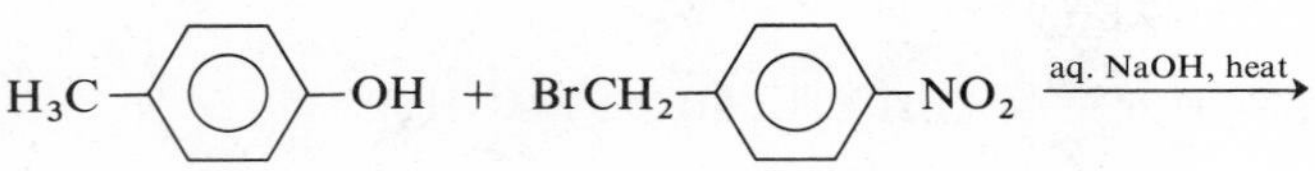 H_3C—⟨○⟩—OH + $BrCH_2$—⟨○⟩—NO_2 $\xrightarrow{aq.\ NaOH,\ heat}$

(l) 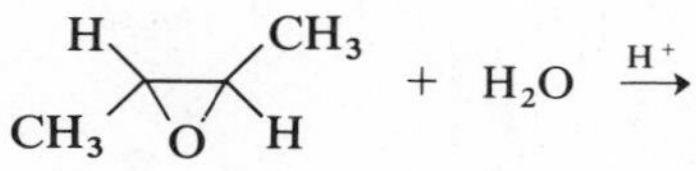 $\underset{CH_3\ \ \ \ O\ \ \ \ H}{\overset{H\ \ \ \ \ \ CH_3}{\triangle}}$ + H_2O $\xrightarrow{H^+}$

(m) 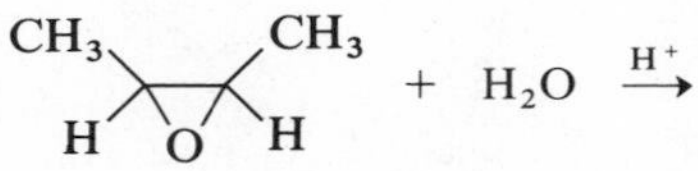 $\underset{H\ \ \ \ O\ \ \ \ H}{\overset{CH_3\ \ \ \ CH_3}{\triangle}}$ + H_2O $\xrightarrow{H^+}$

(n) $CH_2-CH-CH_2$ $\xrightarrow{NaOH}$
        $\underset{Cl\ \ \ \ OH\ \ \ OH}{|\ \ \ \ \ |\ \ \ \ \ |}$

(o) 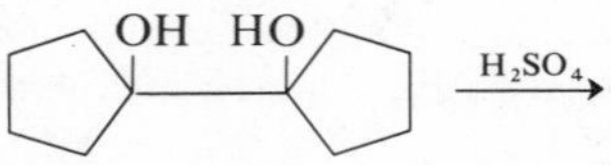 [cyclopentane-OH HO-cyclopentane] $\xrightarrow{H_2SO_4}$

(p) $HOCH_2CH_2CH_2CH_2CH_2Br$ $\xrightarrow{OH^-}$

(q) 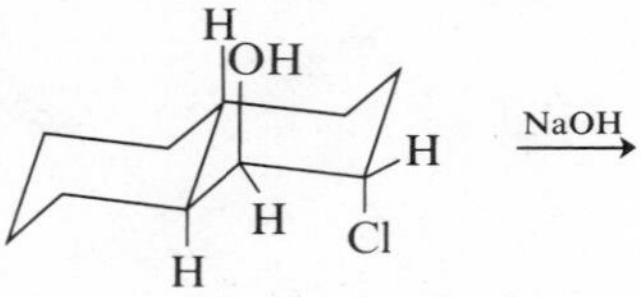 [cyclohexane with H, OH, H, Cl, H substituents] $\xrightarrow{NaOH}$

10. An unknown compound (A) decolorizes a solution of bromine in carbon tetrachloride
     and also decolorizes a solution of cold, dilute, neutral potassium permanganate. When
     A is treated with peroxybenzoic acid, or with Cl_2, H_2O followed by concentrated OH^-,
     compound B is formed. When B is treated with water solution in the presence of acid,
     C is formed. After treatment of C with periodic acid (HIO_4), benzaldehyde and
     acetaldehyde are isolated.
     (a) What are the structures of compounds A–C?
     (b) What would you predict to be formed from C in the presence of sulfuric acid?

11. Suggest reasonable laboratory syntheses of 1-butanol from inorganic reagents and:
     (a) 1-Butene
     (b) n-Butyl bromide
     (c) Ethylene oxide and ethyl bromide
     (d) Ethylene

12. Classify the following reactions as good, fair, or bad synthetic routes for preparation
     of the indicated products under the conditions given. If the route is fair or bad, show
     the product formed by the competing reaction. Give a mechanism for the formation
     of the major product actually formed in each case.

     (a) $(CH_3)_3C-Cl$ + $(CH_3)_3C-O^-Na^+$ $\xrightarrow{50°C}$ $(CH_3)_3C-O-C(CH_3)_3$

     (b) 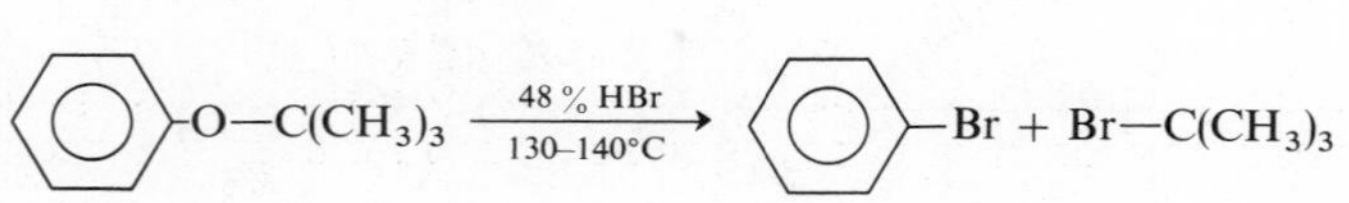 ⟨○⟩—$O-C(CH_3)_3$ $\xrightarrow[130-140°C]{48\%\ HBr}$ ⟨○⟩—Br + $Br-C(CH_3)_3$

(c) CH₃CH₂—CH—CH₂—OH $\xrightarrow{\text{KMnO}_4}$ CH₃CH₂—CH—CH=O

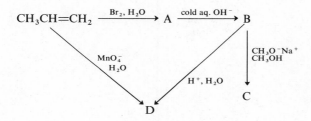

(d) CH₃CH₂ˎˎ╲C╱Br + H₂O $\xrightarrow{25°C}$ HO╲C╱CH₂CH₃ + HBr

(e) (CH₃)₃C—CH—CH₃ $\xrightarrow{\text{conc. H}_2\text{SO}_4}$ (CH₃)₃C—CH=CH₂
         |
         OH

(f) [epoxide structure] $\xrightarrow[\text{CH}_3\text{O}^-\text{Na}^+]{\text{CH}_3\text{OH}}$ CH₃O—CH—CH₂OH

13. What are the structures of A, B, C, and D in the scheme given below? Give the mechanism of the formation of D from B.

CH₃CH=CH₂ $\xrightarrow{\text{Br}_2,\ \text{H}_2\text{O}}$ A $\xrightarrow{\text{cold aq. OH}^-}$ B

          MnO₄⁻
          H₂O   CH₃O⁻Na⁺
                                 CH₃OH

                H⁺, H₂O

          D   C

14. The nmr and infrared spectra of an unknown compound, b.p. 35°, are given. The compound analyzes as follows: 62.0% C, 10.4% H. What is its structure?

NMR spectrum of unknown, Problem 14.

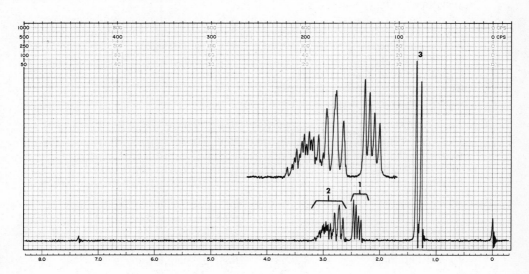

Infrared spectrum of unknown, Problem 14.

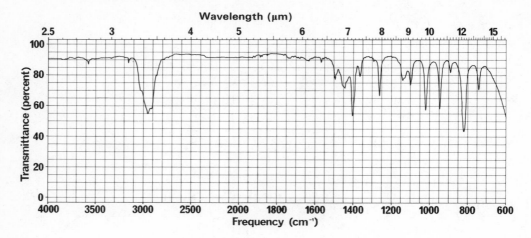

15. How would you carry out the following transformations? (Several steps may be necessary.)

(a)

(b)

$$
(c)\ CH_3CH_2C{\equiv}CH + CH_3CH_2OH \rightarrow CH_3CH_2\overset{\overset{\displaystyle O}{\|}}{C}CH_2CH_2CH_3
$$

16. Explain the following stereochemical facts:

$$
\underset{\underset{C_6H_5}{|}}{CH_3-\underset{\underset{|}{}}{CH}-\overset{\overset{OTs}{|}}{CH}CH_3} \xrightarrow{HOAc} CH_3\underset{\underset{C_6H_5}{|}}{CH}-\overset{\overset{OAc}{|}}{CH}CH_3
$$

D threo   → DL threo
D erythro → D erythro

17. Specify a simple chemical test to distinguish the following pairs of compounds. Give the reagent to be used and the observation that you would make.
    (a) Isopropyl ether and allyl ether
    (b) Ethyl ether and methyl iodide
    (c) n-Butyl ether and n-butyl alcohol
    (d) 1-Methoxy-2-propanol and 1,2-butanediol

18. An attempt to prepare t-butylethylene by heating $(CH_3)_3C-CH-CH_3$ with sulfuric acid did, indeed, produce an olefin of the expected formula C_6H_{12}, but its properties (physical, $\overset{|}{OH}$ spectroscopic) were different from those expected for t-butylethylene. Explain what happened.

19. Which of the following substances will react with sodium ethoxide?
    (a) Water   (b) Propionic acid
    (c) Acetylene   (d) Calcium carbide
    (e) Ammonia   (f) Ethyl ether
    (g) Ethyl bromide   (h) Potassium acetate

20. Give satisfactory synthetic methods for the following:
    (a) Ethyl neopentyl ether from any required alcohol or olefin.
    (b) Isopropyl alcohol from an olefin; from an alkyl halide; by a Grignard reaction.

21. Give the product resulting from treating 2-pentanol with each of the following reagents; if no substantial reaction occurs, say so.
    (a) CrO_3 and warm, aq. H_2SO_4 (b) Aq. NaOH
    (c) Conc. H_2SO_4 at approx. 150°C   (d) H_2/Ni
    (e) KBr, heat   (f) Metallic K
    (g) PI_3

Optional Problem

1. (a) Upon treatment with acid, A (R $= C_2H_5$) yields B and C. Show all steps in these transformations

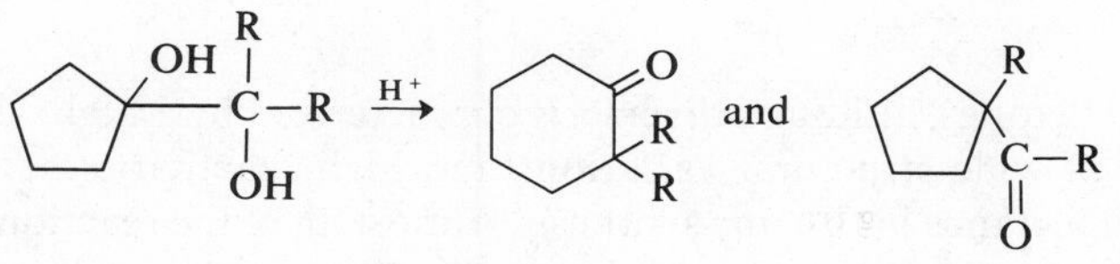

     A   B   C

   (b) Account for the fact that when R $= C_6H_5$, A yields only B.
   (c) Show the most likely steps in the following transformation:

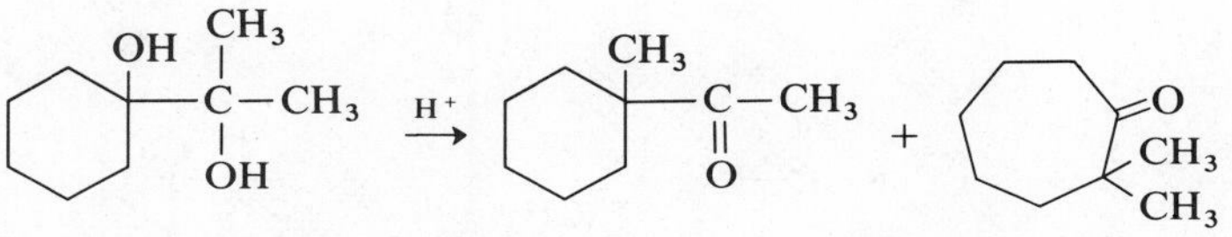

   (d) Predict the products of the pinacol rearrangement of 2,3-diphenyl-2,3-butanediol; of 1,3-diphenyl-1,2-propanediol.

CHAPTER 19

REACTIONS OF ALDEHYDES AND KETONES

The chemistry of aldehydes and ketones, although diverse, is characterized by a high degree of predictability. Because of wide structural variations and high reactivity, these substances are of exceptional importance in organic synthesis. Almost all of the reactions exhibited by aldehydes and ketones may be categorized as either (1) carbonyl addition reactions, (2) reactions of enols or enolates, or (3) oxidation–reduction reactions.

The student is urged to review briefly at this time sections 8.1 through 8.6 on the bonding, structure, and nomenclature of carbonyl compounds.

$$
\underset{\text{Aldehydes}}{R-\overset{\displaystyle O}{\overset{\|}{C}}-H \qquad Ar-\overset{\displaystyle O}{\overset{\|}{C}}-H} \qquad\qquad \underset{\text{Ketones}}{R-\overset{\displaystyle O}{\overset{\|}{C}}-R \qquad \overset{\displaystyle O}{\overset{\|}{\underset{(CH_2)_n}{C}}} \qquad Ar-\overset{\displaystyle O}{\overset{\|}{C}}-R}
$$

19.1 Carbonyl Addition Reactions. Addition of Water

The most characteristic reactions of carbonyl compounds are additions across the carbon–oxygen double bond.

$$
\overset{\diagdown}{\underset{\diagup}{}}C{=}O + AB \longrightarrow B-\overset{|}{\underset{|}{C}}-O-A
$$

In their simplest form, such reactions involve the attack of a nucleophilic species at the carbonyl carbon to give a tetrahedral intermediate in which the oxygen bears a negative charge. This species is subsequently protonated or associated with a Lewis acid to yield the product.

$$
B^- + \overset{\diagdown}{\underset{\diagup}{}}C{=}O \longrightarrow B-\overset{|}{\underset{|}{C}}-O^- \xrightarrow{A^+} B-\overset{|}{\underset{|}{C}}-OA
$$

EXERCISE 19.1

The attack of the nucleophile always occurs at carbon rather than oxygen; this is true when the reaction is kinetically controlled, and it is also true when the reaction is thermodynamically controlled. Explain.

Alternatively, in acid-catalyzed addition reactions, an electrophile first becomes associated with the carbonyl oxygen, thus activating the carbonyl carbon towards subsequent nucleophilic attack.

$$\ce{>C=O + A^+ ->} \quad \ce{>C=\overset{+}{O}-A} \quad \xrightarrow{\text{B}^-} \quad \ce{B-\overset{|}{\underset{|}{C}}-OA}$$

In order to illustrate the factors governing carbonyl addition reactions, we will consider in some detail the addition of water to aldehydes and ketones.

$$120° \; \begin{matrix} R \\ \diagdown \\ C=O \\ \diagup \\ R \end{matrix} \xrightleftharpoons{\ce{H2O}} 109.5° \; \begin{matrix} R \quad OH \\ \diagdown \; \diagup \\ C \\ \diagup \; \diagdown \\ R \quad OH \end{matrix}$$

sp^2 sp^3

The position of equilibrium in such reactions will be influenced both by the bulk and by the electrical nature of the substituent groups.

Note that in the hydrate the substituent groups are in closer proximity (bond angle 109.5°) than in the starting carbonyl compound (bond angle 120°). Thus it would be expected that bulky R groups would suppress product formation.

$$\begin{matrix} H \\ \diagdown \\ C=O \\ \diagup \\ H \end{matrix} \xrightleftharpoons{\ce{H2O}} \begin{matrix} H \quad OH \\ \diagdown \; \diagup \\ C \\ \diagup \; \diagdown \\ H \quad OH \end{matrix}$$

0.01%   99.99%

$$100\% \qquad \xrightleftharpoons{\ce{H2O}} \qquad 0\%$$

In the case of small ring ketones, the addition reaction results in the relief of a certain amount of ring strain. For example, the very labile compound *cyclopropanone* adds water to give a stable hydrate.

$$\triangleright{=}O \qquad \xrightleftharpoons{\ce{H2O}} \qquad \triangleright\hspace{-6pt}\begin{matrix} OH \\ OH \end{matrix}$$

0%   100%

Angle strain at   Angle strain at substituted
carbonyl carbon: $120° - 60° = 60°$ carbon: $109\frac{1}{2}° - 60° = 49\frac{1}{2}°$

Electrical factors may also operate to favor or disfavor the formation of addition products. Factors which stabilize the carbonyl compound over the addition product will, of course, tend to increase the amount of carbonyl compound present at equilibrium, and vice versa. Formaldehyde is almost completely hydrated, whereas acetone is negligibly hydrated at equilibrium. This is largely the result of the stabilizing effect of the electron-releasing methyl groups on the carbonyl double bond (just as alkyl substitution tends to stabilize carbon–carbon double bonds; Sections 7.9 and 7.10). Note that alkyl groups, both by bulk and by electrical effects, increase the stability of the carbonyl form relative to the addition product.

$$\begin{matrix} H \\ \diagdown \; {}^{\delta^+} \; {}^{\delta^-} \\ C=O \\ \diagup \\ H \end{matrix} \qquad\qquad \begin{matrix} CH_3 \\ \diagdown \; {}^{\delta^+} \; {}^{\delta^-} \\ C=O \\ \diagup \\ CH_3 \end{matrix}$$

Formaldehyde   Acetone

In benzaldehyde and similar compounds the carbonyl groups are stabilized by electron delocalization, which is not possible in the addition product; in such compounds only trace amounts of hydrate are present at equilibrium (Table 19.1).

Benzaldehyde

Table 19.1   Hydrate Formation

Carbonyl compound	Approximate percentage of hydrate at equilibrium pH 7, 25°C
CH_2O	100
CH_3CHO	58
CCl_3CHO *chloral*	100
CH_3COCH_3	0
CF_3COCF_3	100
⬡—CHO	0

In compounds such as chloral (trichloroacetaldehyde), the carbonyl form is destabilized by the strongly electronegative halogens.

Chloral   Chloral hydrate

Indeed, the hydrates of chloral and hexachloroacetone are among the few examples of isolable *gem*-diols.

Chloral hydrate is a fast-acting sleep-inducing drug, commonly known as knockout drops. The legendary "Mickey Finn" is the potent and dangerous combination of alcohol and chloral hydrate.

Electric and steric factors not only influence the position of equilibrium in a simple reversible addition reaction to a carbonyl group, but also strongly influence the rate at which addition reactions occur. The transition state for product formation must have some tetrahedral character and some bonding of the nucleophile to carbon. Factors which stabilize or destabilize the addition product relative to the starting materials would therefore be expected to have a similar effect on the relative energy of the transition state leading to the product.

In simple addition reactions, formaldehyde, cyclopropanone, and hexafluoroacetone, for example, should be more reactive (react faster) than acetone, while such compounds as di-*t*-butyl ketone and acetophenone should react more slowly.

The rate of addition of any given molecule AB to a carbonyl compound will vary not only with the structure of the carbonyl compound, but also with the conditions under which the reaction is carried out. In the case of hydration of acetaldehyde, reaction is quite slow at pH 7 but proceeds more rapidly as the pH decreases (rate of addition by mechanism A increases) or increases (rate of addition by mechanism B increases).

Mechanism A

$$
CH_3CHO + H^+ \rightleftharpoons \left[CH_3C \begin{matrix} \overset{+}{O}-H \\ \\ H \end{matrix} \right] \overset{H_2O}{\rightleftharpoons} CH_3\underset{H}{\overset{OH}{C}}-OH + H^+
$$

Mechanism B

$$
CH_3CHO + OH^- \rightleftharpoons \left[CH_3-\underset{H \quad OH}{\overset{O^-}{C}} \right] \overset{H_2O}{\rightleftharpoons} CH_3\underset{H}{\overset{OH}{C}}-OH + OH^-
$$

General Acid–Base Catalysis. A careful study of the hydration of acetaldehyde indicated that both the forward and reverse reactions are catalyzed not only by [H$^+$] or [OH$^-$], but also by proton acids in their un-ionized forms, as well as by weak bases, under conditions of constant pH, [H$^+$], and [OH$^-$]. Such observations are indicative of catalysis via hydrogen-bonded complexes, referred to as *general acid* or *general base catalysis*, (Section 14.5).

General acid catalysis is due to the increased reactivity towards nucleophilic addition of the hydrogen-bonded complex $>$C$=$O - - - HA relative to that of the free carbonyl group, $>$C$=$O.

$$
CH_3CHO + HA \underset{fast}{\overset{fast}{\rightleftharpoons}} \underset{H}{\overset{CH_3}{\diagdown}} C=O\text{- - -}HA \underset{-H_2O,\ slow}{\overset{+H_2O,\ slow}{\rightleftharpoons}}
$$

General   Hydrogen-bonded
acid   complex

$$
\underset{H \quad \overset{+}{O}H_2}{\overset{CH_3 \diagup O^-\text{- - -}HA}{C}} \underset{fast}{\overset{fast}{\rightleftharpoons}} \underset{H \quad OH}{\overset{CH_3 \diagup OH}{C}} + HA
$$

In general base catalysis, the attacking reagent is made more nucleophilic by forming a hydrogen-bonded complex, HO—H - - - B.

$$
HOH + B \underset{fast}{\overset{fast}{\rightleftharpoons}} HO—H\text{- - -}B
$$

Base

$$
B\text{- - -}H—OH + \underset{H}{\overset{CH_3 \diagdown}{C}}=O \underset{slow}{\overset{slow}{\rightleftharpoons}} BH^+ + \underset{H \quad OH}{\overset{CH_3 \diagup O^-}{C}} \underset{fast}{\overset{fast}{\rightleftharpoons}} B + \underset{H \quad OH}{\overset{CH_3 \diagup OH}{C}}
$$

19.2   Addition of Alcohols

Alcohols add to the carbonyl groups of aldehydes and ketones.

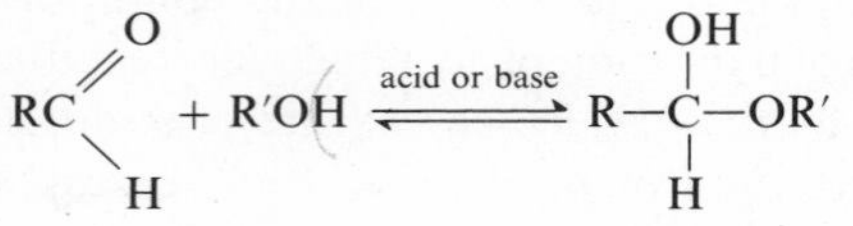

Hemiacetal

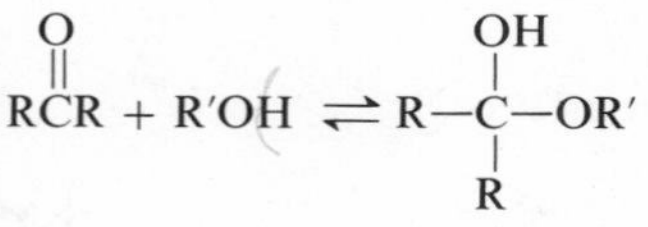

Hemiketal

The formation of simple hemiacetals and hemiketals may be aided by either acid or base catalysis, but generally the hemiacetals and hemiketals are too unstable to be isolated. In the presence of mineral acid, a hemiacetal or hemiketal can react with an additional molecule of alcohol to form an acetal or ketal.

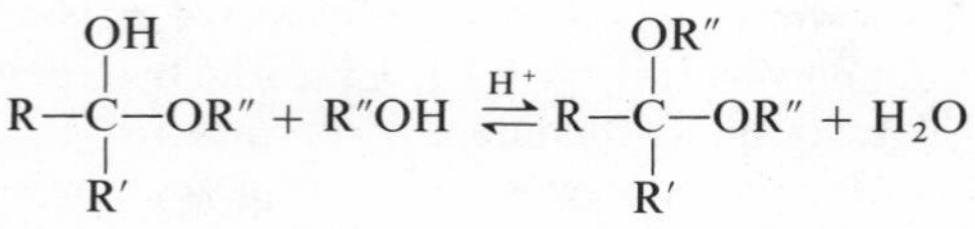

Hemiacetal or   Acetal or
hemiketal   ketal

The conversion of a hemiacetal to an acetal, or of a hemiketal to a ketal, is analogous to the formation of ethers via an S_N1 reaction.

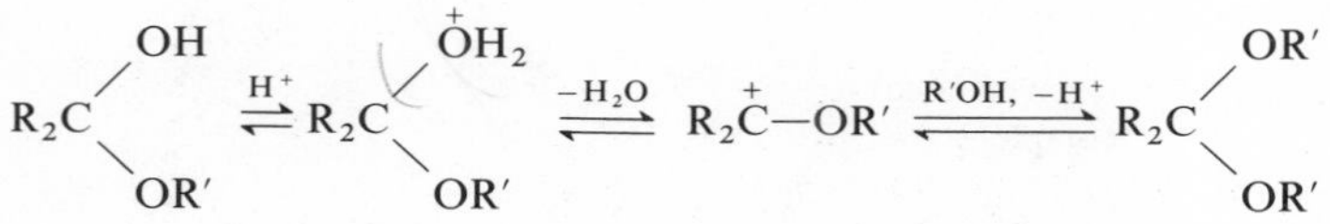

Stabilized
carbonium ion

EXERCISE 19.2

Why do we refer to the intermediate carbonium ion as "stabilized"?

The formation of acetals from aldehydes and simpler alcohols such as ethanol may be facilitated by removal of water from the reaction system. This may be accomplished by azeotropic distillation with benzene (constant boiling mixture, bp 64.6°C, of 7% water, 74% benzene, and 19% ethyl alcohol). Simple ketals cannot be prepared by the direct method because of unfavorable equilibria. Diethyl ketals may often be made by an exchange reaction with ethyl orthoformate; note that in such a reaction no water is formed.

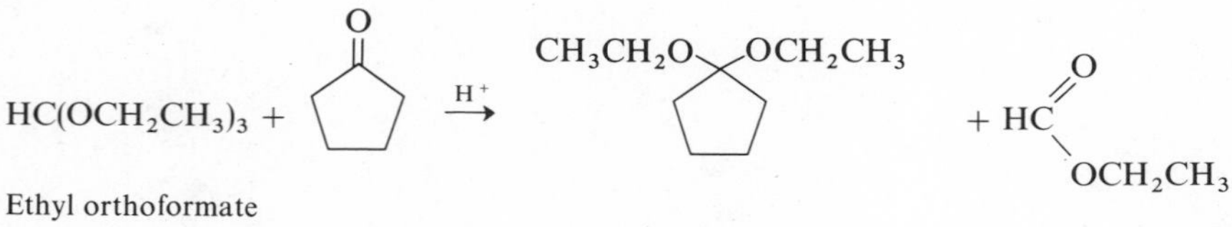

$HC(OCH_2CH_3)_3$ +

Ethyl orthoformate

Cyclic ketals or acetals are readily prepared from ethylene glycol or 1,3-propanediol.

$$CH_3CH_2C\underset{H}{\overset{O}{\diagup}} + HOCH_2CH_2CH_2OH \xrightarrow{H^+} CH_3CH_2CH\underset{O-CH_2}{\overset{O-CH_2}{\diagup}}CH_2 + H_2O$$

$$\text{(cyclohexanone)} + HOCH_2CH_2OH \xrightarrow{H^+} \text{(cyclic acetal)} + H_2O$$

EXERCISE 19.3

Why does the equilibrium of a ketone with ethylene glycol favor the ketal so much more than does the corresponding equilibrium with ethanol and the same ketone?

Acetals and ketals are readily hydrolyzed to their parent carbonyl compounds and alcohols by aqueous acid. The mechanism is exactly the reverse of that of their formation.

EXERCISE 19.4

Write out the mechanism for the hydrolysis of acetone dimethyl acetal by aqueous acid.

Ketals and acetals, however, are very stable toward base. This combination of lability toward acids and stability toward basic reagents makes acetals and ketals useful as "protecting groups"—protecting the aldehydic or ketonic carbonyl from reaction while chemical transformations are carried out elsewhere in the molecule.

Example

Consider the conversion of γ-bromobutyraldehyde to γ-methoxybutyraldehyde.

$$Br-CH_2CH_2CH_2CHO \rightarrow CH_3O-CH_2CH_2CH_2CHO$$

The obvious way to convert a primary aliphatic halide to the corresponding methoxy compound is to carry out a direct displacement of the halogen by methoxide ion.

$$RCH_2Br + CH_3ONa \rightarrow RCH_2OCH_3 + NaBr$$

In the case under consideration, this direct introduction of an alkoxy group cannot be used, since methoxide ion would rapidly effect an aldol-type condensation involving the $-CH_2CHO$ portion of the molecule (Section 19.14). This complication is easily averted by converting the bromo aldehyde (I) to an acetal such as (II) prior to treating it with sodium methoxide.

$$Br-CH_2CH_2CH_2CHO \rightarrow Br-CH_2CH_2CH_2\underset{O}{\overset{O}{\diagdown}} \xrightarrow{NaOMe} CH_3O-CH_2CH_2CH_2\underset{O}{\overset{O}{\diagdown}}$$

$$\text{I} \qquad\qquad\qquad \text{II} \qquad\qquad\qquad\qquad \text{III}$$

$$\downarrow H_3O^+$$

$$CH_3O-CH_2CH_2CH_2CHO$$

$$\text{IV}$$

The resulting methoxy acetal (III) can then be treated with dilute acid to liberate the desired methoxy aldehyde (IV). It should be noted that the ordinary ether function in IV is quite stable to mild acid conditions (Section 18.8).

19.3   Polymerization

The lower aldehydes (but not ketones), undergo polymerization reactions related to acetal formation in the presence of trace amounts of water and acid catalysts. Formaldehyde in water solution polymerizes to a solid, long-chain polymer called *paraformaldehyde*. When heated, this solid material reverts to gaseous formaldehyde, and hence it is a convenient source of pure, anhydrous formaldehyde. When formaldehyde or paraformaldehyde is heated with dilute mineral acid, a cyclic trimer, 1,3,5-trioxane, is formed.

$$(n + 2)CH_2O + H_2O \longrightarrow HOCH_2(OCH_2)_nOCH_2OH$$

Paraformaldehyde

CH$_2$O
(gas)

1,3,5-Trioxane

EXERCISE 19.5

Suggest a mechanism for the polymerization reaction of formaldehyde to paraformaldehyde.

ALDEHYDE POLYMERS. *Very pure formaldehyde may be polymerized in the presence of trace amounts of water to yield a linear polyoxymethylene of the formula* HO$+$CH$_2$O$)_n$OH *with n up to 6000. Depolymerization may be prevented by replacing the end hydrogens ("end-capping") with other groups such as acetyl. The very strong, high-melting thermoplastic known as* Delrin (*du Pont*) *is such a stabilized formaldehyde polymer.*

In the presence of acid, acetaldehyde polymerizes to the cyclic trimer, paraldehyde, *and the cyclic tetramer,* metaldehyde. *The former is occasionally used as a sleep-inducing drug (hypnotic), while the latter is used as an agricultural poison for snails.*

Paraldehyde   Metaldehyde

19.4   Addition of Hydrogen Sulfide and Thiols

Thiols (to be discussed in more detail in Section 26.2) add to carbonyl compounds to form thioacetals and thioketals, in a manner analogous to the formation of acetals and ketals (Section 19.2). Lewis acids, especially boron trifluoride, are very effective catalysts for these additions. The equilibria for the formation of thioacetals and thioketals are usually quite favorable: These substances are not readily hydrolyzed back to carbonyl compounds.

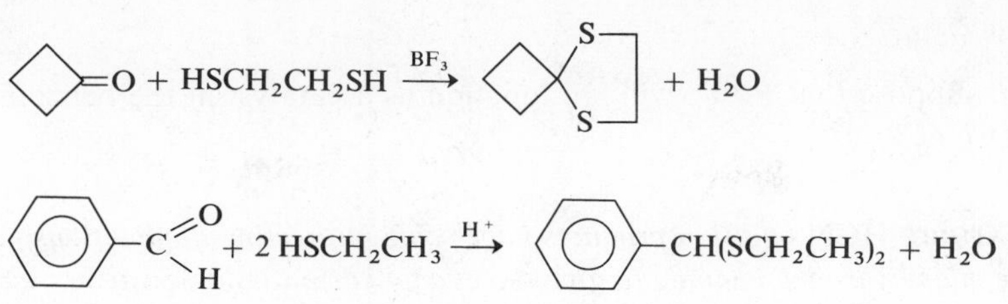

$$\square\!\!=\!\!O + HSCH_2CH_2SH \xrightarrow{BF_3} \text{(dithiane ring)} + H_2O$$

$$C_6H_5-C{\overset{O}{\underset{H}{\big\langle}}} + 2\,HSCH_2CH_3 \xrightarrow{H^+} C_6H_5-CH(SCH_2CH_3)_2 + H_2O$$

Dithiols. In the presence of an acid catalyst, aldehydes and ketones add hydrogen sulfide to form *gem*-dithiols. These substances are somewhat more stable than the corresponding hydrates, although those formed from aldehydes are quite prone to polymerization.

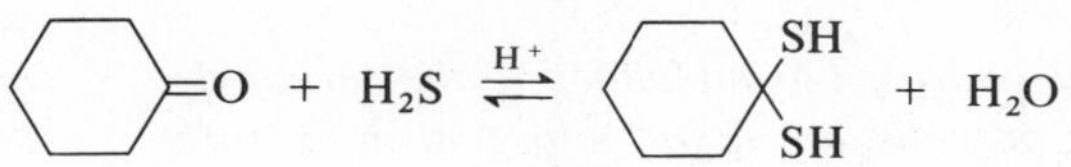

$$\bigcirc\!\!=\!\!O + H_2S \rightleftharpoons \underset{SH}{\overset{SH}{\bigcirc\!\!\big\langle}} + H_2O$$

19.5   Addition of Hydrogen Cyanide and the Benzoin Condensation

Hydrogen cyanide will add to carbonyl compounds, except for highly hindered ones, to give an adduct called a *cyanohydrin*. Cyanide ion is an essential catalyst for the reaction.

$$R_2C\!=\!O + HCN \overset{CN^-}{\rightleftharpoons} \underset{OH}{R_2C\!-\!C\!\equiv\!N}$$

The stoichiometry requires that HCN be added, but the mechanism actually involves cyanide ion as the attacking nucleophile.

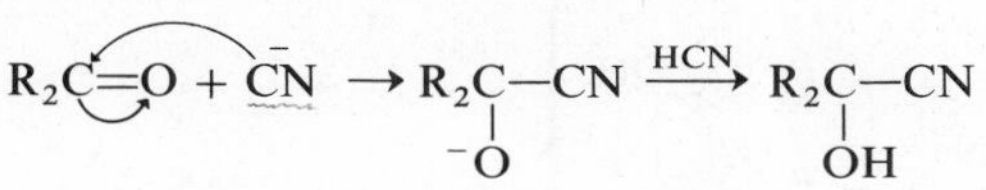

$$R_2C\!=\!O + \,^-CN \rightarrow \underset{^-O}{R_2C\!-\!CN} \xrightarrow{HCN} \underset{OH}{R_2C\!-\!CN}$$

In practice, since HCN is somewhat hazardous to work with, the reaction is run by mixing the carbonyl compound with cyanide ion and then slowly acidifying the solution.

The equilibrium is usually very favorable to cyanohydrin formation. If it is desired to reverse the reaction and to recover the carbonyl compound from the cyanohydrin, this can be done by treating the cyanohydrin with aqueous base. The equilibrium concentration of HCN is then converted to CN^-, and the carbonyl compound is liberated.

In a related reaction, benzaldehyde and other nonenolizable aldehydes undergo a bimolecular reaction to yield α-hydroxy ketones. The reaction, which is specifically catalyzed by cyanide ion, is known as the *benzoin condensation*. The cyanide ion converts the aldehyde to the cyanohydrin, which under basic reaction conditions is transformed into a carbanion stabilized by conjugation with the nitrile. The steps are illustrated below.

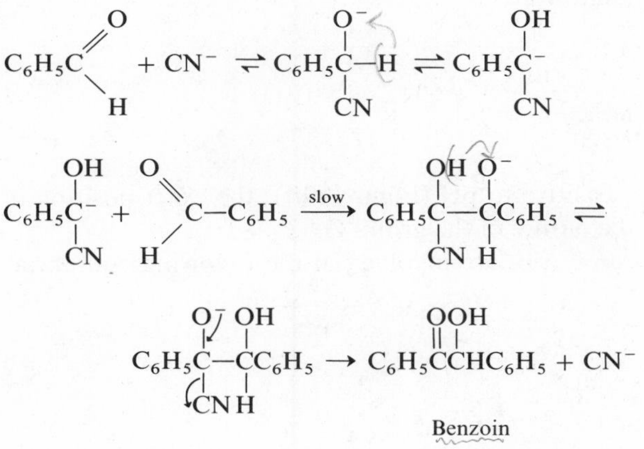

$$C_6H_5C{\overset{O}{\underset{H}{\big\langle}}} + CN^- \rightleftharpoons \underset{CN}{\overset{O^-}{C_6H_5C\!-\!H}} \rightleftharpoons \underset{CN}{\overset{OH}{C_6H_5C^-}}$$

$$\underset{CN}{\overset{OH}{C_6H_5C^-}} + \underset{H}{\overset{O}{C\!-\!C_6H_5}} \xrightarrow{slow} \underset{CN\ H}{\overset{OH\ O^-}{C_6H_5C\!-\!CC_6H_5}} \rightleftharpoons$$

$$\underset{CN\ H}{\overset{O^-\ OH}{C_6H_5C\!-\!CC_6H_5}} \rightarrow \underset{\quad\ H}{\overset{O\ OH}{C_6H_5CCHC_6H_5}} + CN^-$$

Benzoin

EXERCISE 19.6

Why do you suppose that EtO^- will *not* function as a catalyst in the benzoin condensation?

CYANOHYDRINS IN NATURE. *HCN addition products have some interesting applications in nature. Benzaldehyde adds hydrogen cyanide to give the cyanohydrin* mandelonitrile.

$$\underset{\text{CN}}{\overset{\text{H}}{\underset{|}{\overset{|}{C}}}}\text{—OH}$$

This nitrile, either in free form, or with the hydroxyl group added to the carbonyl of a sugar to form an acetal (a glycoside), *provides a way for an organism to store hydrogen cyanide in a nontoxic form. Bitter almonds contain* amygdalin *(a glucoside of mandelonitrile), which makes them unattractive (highly poisonous) food.*

Some animals make use of cyanohydrins in a defensive way. The brightly marked millipede Apheloria corrigata *stores mandelonitrile in defensive glands. When disturbed, the nitrile is mixed with an enzyme which promotes its rapid dissociation. In this way, the millipede is able to produce a very repellent mixture of hydrogen cyanide and benzaldehyde in response to predator attack.*

19.6   Addition of Sodium Hydrogen Sulfite

Sodium hydrogen sulfite (sodium bisulfite) in aqueous solution readily adds to most aldehydes, methyl ketones, and unhindered cyclic ketones.

$$\underset{\diagup}{\overset{\diagdown}{C}}{=}O + NaHSO_3 \rightleftharpoons \underset{SO_3H}{\overset{O^-}{\underset{|}{\overset{|}{C}}}} Na^+ \rightleftharpoons \underset{SO_3^-}{\overset{OH}{\underset{|}{\overset{|}{C}}}} Na^+$$

The crystalline addition products ("*bisulfite addition products*") are often insoluble in the very concentrated aqueous reagent and precipitate. The reaction has occasional utility in the separation and/or purification of carbonyl compounds from mixtures. Washing such a mixture with dilute aqueous sodium hydrogen sulfite will extract the carbonyl compound into the aqueous phase as the addition product. Addition of either aqueous acid or base to the addition product destroys the hydrogen sulfite ion and regenerates the carbonyl compound.

19.7   Condensation with Ammonia and Its Derivatives

Under the influence of acid catalysis, ammonia and a variety of its derivatives condense with carbonyl compounds and eliminate water.

$$\underset{\diagup}{\overset{\diagdown}{C}}{=}O + {:}NH_2G \overset{H^+}{\rightleftharpoons} \underset{NHG}{\overset{\overset{H}{O}H}{\underset{|}{\overset{|}{C}}}} \overset{H^+}{\rightleftharpoons} \underset{G}{\overset{\diagdown}{C}}{=}N + H_2O$$

The rate of such a reaction is quite sensitive to pH (Figure 19.1); the exact position of the rate maximum is dependent on the nature of the group G.

The two reactants, in the presence of acid, are involved in the following equilibria:

$$GNH_2 + H^+ \rightleftharpoons GNH_3^+$$

$$\underset{\diagup}{\overset{\diagdown}{C}}{=}O + H^+ \rightleftharpoons \underset{H}{\overset{\diagdown}{C}}{=}\overset{+}{O}$$

Figure 19.1

Rate of condensation of an ammonia derivative with a carbonyl compound as a function of pH.

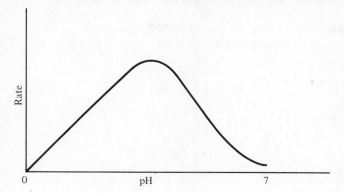

The effective species in the addition reaction are GNH_2 and $>C=\overset{+}{O}H$. The rate of the formation of the adduct will reach a maximum at the pH at which the product of the concentrations of the two species reaches a maximum.

$$\text{Rate of adduct formation} = k[GNH_2][>C=\overset{+}{O}H]$$

In many cases the steps subsequent to the formation of the initial adduct are fast under the conditions employed for the condensation, so that the addition step is rate-controlling for the overall reaction.

$$\overset{\diagdown}{\underset{\diagup}{}}C=O + H^+ \overset{fast}{\rightleftharpoons} \overset{\diagdown}{\underset{\diagup}{}}C=\overset{+}{\underset{H}{O}} \xrightarrow[\text{slow}]{NH_2G}$$

$$\overset{\diagdown}{\underset{\diagup}{}}\underset{\overset{+}{NH_2G}}{\overset{OH}{C}} \overset{fast}{\rightleftharpoons} \overset{\diagdown}{\underset{\diagup}{}}\underset{\overset{..}{NHG}}{\overset{\overset{+}{OH_2}}{C}} \underset{fast}{\overset{-H_2O}{\rightleftharpoons}} \overset{\diagdown}{\underset{\diagup}{}}\underset{G}{\overset{H}{C=\overset{+}{N}}} \overset{-H^+\text{ (fast)}}{\rightleftharpoons} \overset{\diagdown}{\underset{\diagup}{}}C=N\overset{\diagdown}{\underset{G}{}}$$

In a number of other cases adduct formation is the fast step, and dehydration becomes rate-determining. A few rare cases are known in which the reaction can be stopped after the addition step under carefully controlled conditions. For example, the addition product of acetaldehyde and ammonia can be isolated.

$$CH_3C\overset{\overset{\textstyle O}{\diagup}}{\diagdown_H} + NH_3 \rightleftharpoons CH_3\underset{\overset{|}{H}}{\overset{\overset{+}{N}H_3}{C}}-O^- \rightleftharpoons CH_3\underset{\overset{|}{H}}{\overset{\overset{|}{N}H_2}{C}}-OH$$

Acetaldehyde ammonia
mp 97°C

General Acid Catalysis. Such reactions are often subject to general acid catalysis (Section 14.5, 19.1). For example, at constant pH (sodium acetate–acetic acid buffer) reactions of this type may be found to be dependent on the concentration of acetic acid, which activates the carbonyl group by hydrogen-bond association. In such an event, the overall reaction would follow a rate expression of the type

$$\text{Rate} = k[GNH_2][>C=\overset{+}{O}H] + k'[GNH_2][>C=O][HOAc]$$

Ammonia

The condensation of ammonia with the carbonyl group of an aldehyde or ketone is readily reversible. For most ketones, the equilibria involved for the formation of the initial adducts are quite unfavorable. While a few stable adducts of ammonia and aldehydes are known, these initial adducts usually dehydrate to yield imines. The latter are quite reactive and commonly react further.

$$
\underset{H}{\overset{C_6H_5}{\diagup}}C{=}O + NH_3 \rightleftharpoons \underset{H\quad NH_2}{\overset{C_6H_5\quad OH}{\diagup\ \ \diagdown}}C \xrightarrow{-H_2O} \underset{H}{\overset{C_6H_5}{\diagup}}C{=}NH \rightarrow \text{Further products}
$$

An aldimine

Primary and Secondary Amines

Primary amines react with aldehydes and ketones to produce *N*-substituted imines. In contrast to the unsubstituted imines, the *N*-substituted derivatives are usually isolable.

$$
\bigcirc{=}O + (CH_3)_3CNH_2 \longrightarrow \bigcirc{=}N{\diagdown}_{C(CH_3)_3} + H_2O
$$

N-t-Butylcyclohexanimine

$$
\underset{H}{\overset{C_6H_5}{\diagup}}C{=}O + CH_3NH_2 \longrightarrow \underset{H\quad CH_3}{\overset{C_6H_5}{\diagup}}C{=}N + H_2O
$$

N-Methylbenzaldimine

Secondary amines react with aldehydes and ketones to produce *enamines*. These substances are versatile synthetic intermediates (Section 21.3).

$$
\bigcirc{=}O + HN\bigcirc \xrightarrow[-H_2O]{H^+} \bigcirc{-}N\bigcirc
$$

N-(1-Cyclohexenyl)pyrrolidine

Hydroxylamine

Aldehydes and ketones condense with hydroxylamine, usually in an acetic acid–sodium acetate medium, to yield products known as *oximes*.

$$
\underset{CH_3}{\overset{C_6H_5}{\diagup}}C{=}O + NH_2OH \longrightarrow \underset{CH_3\quad OH}{\overset{C_6H_5}{\diagup}}C{=}N + \underset{CH_3}{\overset{C_6H_5\quad OH}{\diagup\ \ \diagdown}}C{=}N
$$

Major   Minor

It is evident that the hydroxyl group of the oxime may be either cis or trans to the phenyl group in the above example. For historical reasons, such isomers are referred to as syn and anti rather than cis and trans. Analogous geometrical isomerism can be shown by *N*-substituted imines.

Hydrazine and Its Derivatives   NH₂NH₂

Hydrazine, with its two primary amino groups, may undergo mono- or dicondensation with aldehydes or ketones.

Acetone hydrazone   Acetone azine

The substituted hydrazines behave in a fashion analogous to hydroxylamine.

Phenylhydrazine   Acetophenone phenylhydrazone

2,4-Dinitrophenylhydrazine   Acetaldehyde 2,4-dinitrophenylhydrazone

Semicarbazide   Cyclobutanone semicarbazone

Oximes, phenylhydrazones, semicarbazones, and particularly 2,4-dinitrophenyl-hydrazones are frequently crystalline solids with characteristic, sharp melting points, and they are quite useful for the isolation and identification of aldehydes and ketones.

19.8   Conversion of Carbonyl Compounds to Halides

A number of reagents can be used to convert an aldehyde or ketone to a *gem*-dihalide. Such reagents are commonly polyhalogen derivatives of phosphorus and sulfur, which react by virtue of the ability of these elements to act as Lewis acids through the expansion of their octets.

Phosphorus pentachloride, which exists in the crystalline state as $PCl_4^+ PCl_6^-$, reacts with aldehydes and ketones in ether solution to produce *gem*-dichlorides.

In the following schematic mechanism, the nucleophilic species involved in shown as chloride, but in actual fact it may be PCl_6^-.

$$PCl_5 \rightleftharpoons PCl_4^+ + Cl^-$$

A similar reaction does not take place with PBr_5, which dissociates readily to $PBr_3 + Br_2$. The carbonyl compound is brominated by the resulting Br_2.

Replacement of the carbonyl oxygen by a *gem*-difluoro group may be achieved with sulfur tetrafluoride, but since this reagent is gaseous and highly toxic, for general laboratory use the preferred reagent is phenylsulfur trifluoride.

19.9 Addition of Organometallic Compounds

One of the most important and versatile synthetic procedures for the generation of new carbon–carbon bonds is the addition of an organometallic reagent across a carbon–heteroatom multiple bond.

$$R-M + \underset{/}{\overset{\backslash}{C}}=Z \longrightarrow R-\underset{|}{\overset{|}{C}}-Z-M$$

M = Li, Mg, etc.   Z = O, N, S

We will study some examples of reactions of this type here, and many more in our study of the chemistry of acids and acid derivatives (Chapter 20).

The initial product of the addition of a Grignard reagent (RMgX, Sections 4.19, 17.10) to an aldehyde or ketone is a complex magnesium alkoxide from which the alcohol may be liberated by the addition of dilute acid.

If the alcohol product is sensitive to strong acids, the hydrolysis may be performed with a solution of ammonium chloride.

Addition of a Grignard reagent to formaldehyde yields a primary alcohol. All other aldehydes add Grignard reagents to yield secondary alcohols, while ketones yield tertiary alcohols. Such reactions are of the utmost importance in the synthesis of a complex alcohol, since by the proper choice of the carbonyl compound and the Grignard reagent, almost any desired alcohol can be prepared.

$$CH_3 \overset{CH_2}{\underset{MgBr}{\overset{|}{C}}} + \enspace \text{(cyclopentanone)} =O \xrightarrow{THF} \xrightarrow{H_3O^+} \text{(cyclopentane ring)} \overset{CH_3}{\underset{OH}{\overset{|}{C}}} CH_2$$

$$CH_3MgI + \text{(phenyl)}\overset{O}{\overset{\|}{C}}CH_2CH_3 \xrightarrow{ether} \xrightarrow{H_3O^+} \text{(phenyl)}\overset{OH}{\underset{CH_3}{\overset{|}{C}}}CH_2CH_3$$

Using the conversion of an alcohol to a bromide with HBr, the formation of the Grignard reagent, and the addition of the Grignard reagent to a carbonyl, one can convert simple alcohols to more complex ones. When these reactions, together with oxidations of alcohols to carbonyl compounds, are used in sequence, it is possible to synthesize reasonably complicated alcohols. The following examples illustrate such syntheses.

Example 1

Prepare $CH_3CH_2CHOHCH_3$ from CH_3CH_2OH.

   The product contains four carbons, the starting material only two. Clearly, two molecules of starting material must be joined together; this is easily done by addition of a Grignard to an aldehyde.

$$CH_3CH_2MgBr + CH_3CHO \rightarrow \xrightarrow{H_3O^+} CH_3CH_2\underset{OH}{\overset{|}{C}HCH_3}$$

The Grignard reagent and acetaldehyde must be prepared from ethanol:

$$CH_3CH_2OH \xrightarrow{HBr} CH_3CH_2Br \xrightarrow[Et_2O]{Mg} CH_3CH_2MgBr$$

and

$$CH_3CH_2OH \xrightarrow[distill]{H_2Cr_2O_7} CH_3CHO$$

Although it is usual to work synthetic problems backwards, as was done here, we write them forwards, as follows:

$$CH_3CH_2OH \xrightarrow{HBr} CH_3CH_2Br \xrightarrow[Et_2O]{Mg} CH_3CH_2MgBr \enspace \searrow$$
$$\xrightarrow{H_2Cr_2O_7, \text{ distill}} CH_3CHO \enspace \nearrow \xrightarrow{H_3O^+} CH_3CH_2\underset{OH}{\overset{|}{C}HCH_3}$$

Example 2

Outline a synthesis of $CH_3\underset{CH_3}{\overset{O}{\overset{\|}{C}H}\overset{|}{C}}CH_3$ from compounds containing not more than three carbons.

   Addition of $CH_3\underset{CH_3}{\overset{|}{C}H}MgBr$ to $H\overset{O}{\overset{\|}{C}}CH_3$ would give us the desired carbon skeleton. (So would addition of CH_3MgBr to $CH_3\underset{CH_3}{\overset{|}{C}H}CHO$, but the latter contains more than three carbons; however, see below.) Thus we can write

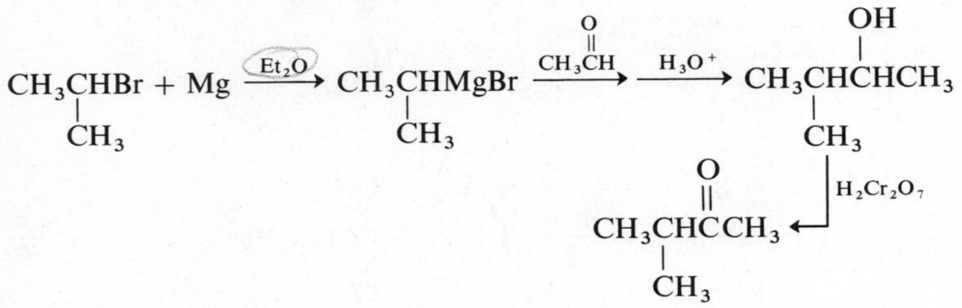

$$CH_3CHBr + Mg \xrightarrow{Et_2O} CH_3CHMgBr \xrightarrow[]{CH_3CH}^{O} \xrightarrow{H_3O^+} CH_3CHCHCH_3$$
$$\underset{CH_3}{|} \qquad \qquad \underset{CH_3}{|} \qquad \qquad \qquad \underset{CH_3}{|} \overset{OH}{|}$$

$$CH_3CHCCH_3 \longleftarrow \Big\downarrow^{H_2Cr_2O_7}$$
$$\underset{CH_3}{|} \overset{\overset{O}{||}}{}$$

An alternative, if we were determined to use CH_3CHCHO as an intermediate,
$$\underset{CH_3}{|}$$

would be

$$CH_3CHBr \xrightarrow[\substack{2.\ H_2C=O \\ 3.\ H_3O^+}]{1.\ Mg} CH_3CHCH_2OH \xrightarrow[distill]{H_2Cr_2O_7} CH_3CHCHO \xrightarrow{CH_3MgBr}$$
$$\underset{CH_3}{|} \qquad \qquad \underset{CH_3}{|} \qquad \qquad \underset{CH_3}{|}$$

$$CH_3CHCHCH_3 \xrightarrow[2.\ H_2Cr_2O_7]{1.\ H_3O^+} CH_3CHCCH_3$$
$$\underset{CH_3}{|}\overset{OMgBr}{|} \qquad \qquad \underset{CH_3}{|}\overset{\overset{O}{||}}{}$$

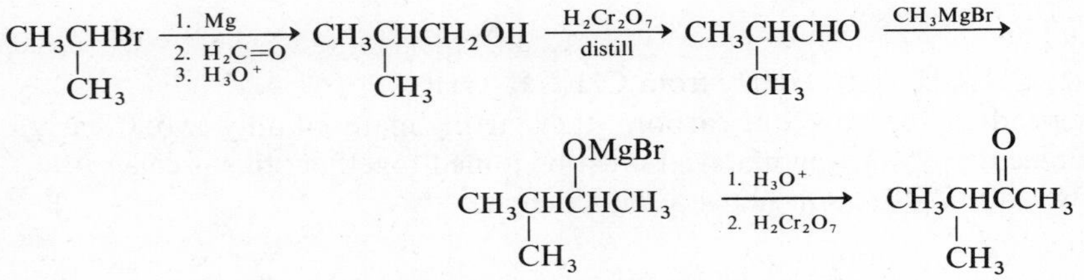

This synthesis is longer and less practical than the earlier one, but it is reasonable.

EXERCISE 19.7

Outline practical laboratory synthesis of the following alcohols from the starting materials mentioned.

(a) 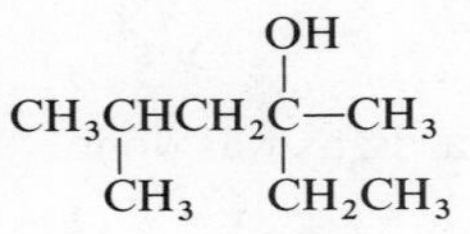 $CH_3CHCH_2\overset{\overset{OH}{|}}{C}-CH_3$ from any alcohols containing four carbons, or less
$\quad\ \ \underset{CH_3}{|}\quad \underset{CH_2CH_3}{|}$

(b) 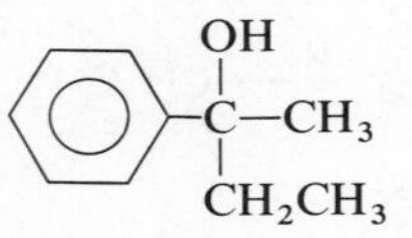 ⬡$-\overset{\overset{OH}{|}}{\underset{\underset{CH_2CH_3}{|}}{C}}-CH_3$ from benzene and two-carbon compounds

(c) $CH_3CH_2CH_2CH_2OH$ from ethylene

(d) 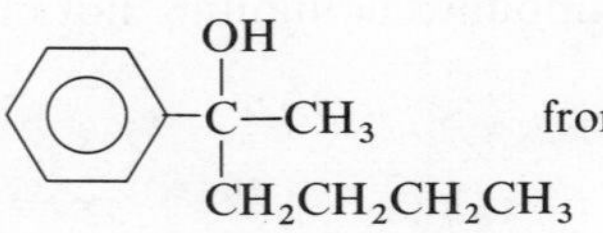 ⬡$-\overset{\overset{OH}{|}}{\underset{\underset{CH_2CH_2CH_2CH_3}{|}}{C}}-CH_3$ from benzene and two-carbon compounds

For simplicity in our discussions, we shall consider the Grignard reagent, prepared in ether or tetrahydrofuran (THF) solution, to have the structure RMgX, and just remember that the magnesium (a Lewis acid) is coordinated with molecules of solvent. The addition of the Grignard reagent to the carbonyl group involves an initial coordination with the magnesium, followed by a slow addition step.

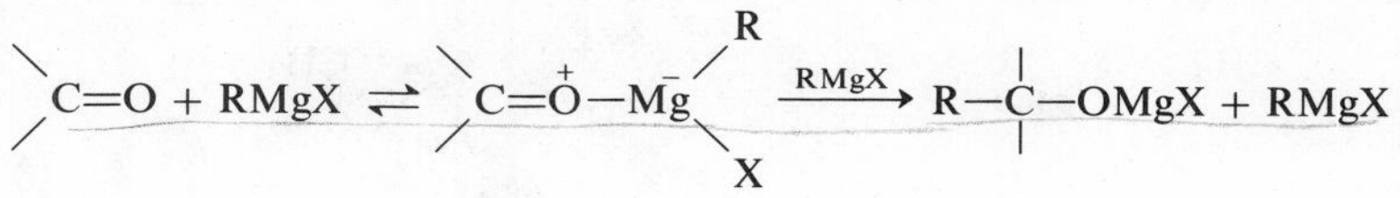

$$\underset{\diagup}{\overset{\diagdown}{C}}=O + RMgX \rightleftharpoons \underset{\diagup}{\overset{\diagdown}{C}}=\overset{+}{O}-\overset{-}{Mg}\underset{X}{\overset{R}{\diagup}} \xrightarrow{RMgX} R-\overset{|}{\underset{|}{C}}-OMgX + RMgX$$

In some cases a cyclic transition state involving two molecules of Grignard reagent has been postulated on the basis of the observed kinetics of the reaction.

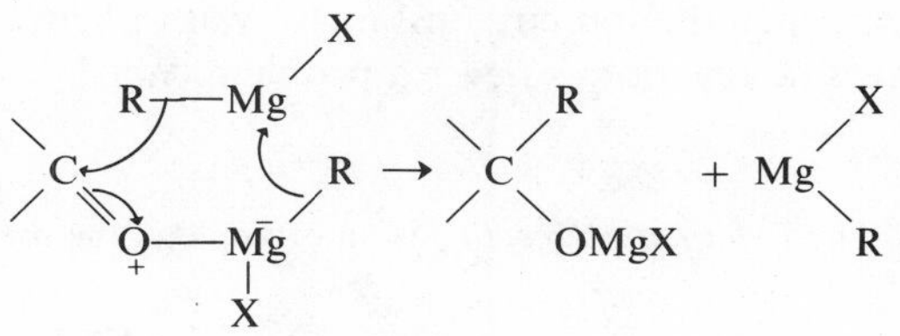

With simple carbonyl compounds and Grignard reagents, high yields of products are usually obtained. Extensive branching of the alkyl groups of either the carbonyl compound or of the Grignard reagent often results in side reactions becoming important or even exclusive. The principal side reactions are reduction and enolization.

Reduction

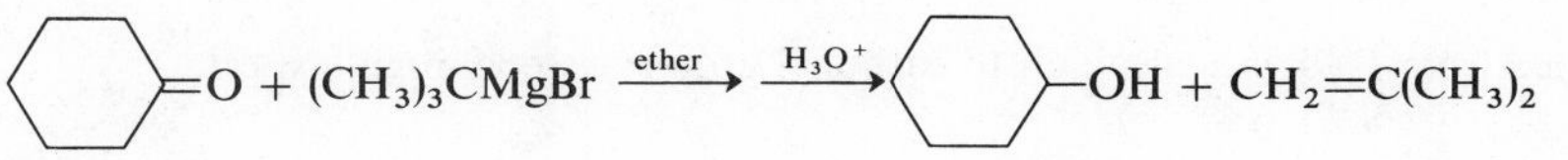

Note that the overall result is the reduction of the ketone to an alcohol. The mechanism of the reduction is as follows:

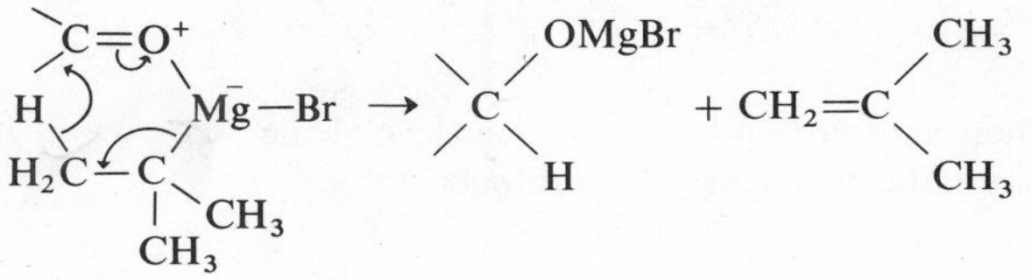

Enolization

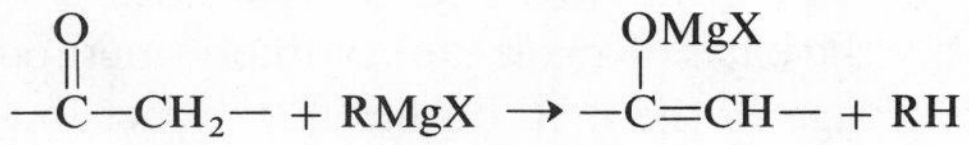

$$\underset{O}{\overset{\parallel}{-C}}-CH_2- + RMgX \rightarrow \underset{OMgX}{\overset{|}{-C}}=CH- + RH$$

In this case the ketone is converted to an enolate salt, which upon hydrolysis merely gives back the starting ketone.

Organosodium and especially organolithium reagents behave in much the same manner as Grignard reagents in addition reactions to aldehydes and ketones. They are, however, much more reactive, and much greater care must be given to their manipulation and use. For routine work, it is usually much more convenient to employ Grignard reagents. The sodium and lithium reagents show much less tendency towards reduction and enolization than do the corresponding Grignard reagents, and they do permit the synthesis of highly hindered alcohols.

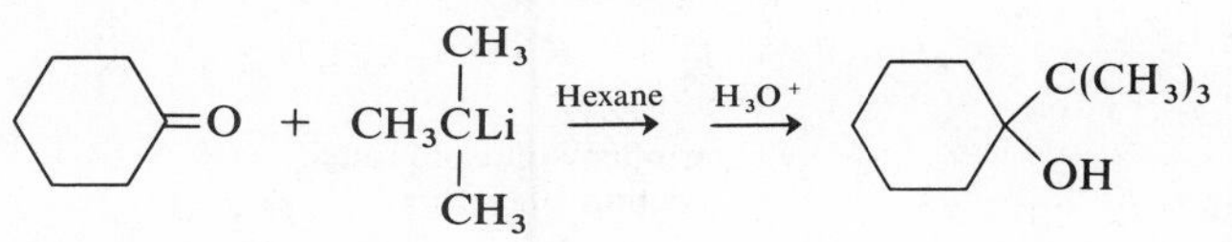

$$CH_3C{-}C{-}CCH_3 + CH_3C{-}Cl + Na \rightarrow CH_3C{-}C{-}CCH_3$$

EXERCISE 19.8

Reduction of a carbonyl group by a Grignard reagent is in some instances a serious side reaction, in others not, depending on circumstances. With phenyl and methyl Grignard reagents, this side reaction is never a problem. Why?

Addition of Other Organometallic Compounds. The *Reformatsky reaction* is an example of the use of an organozinc reagent in synthesis.

$$ClCH_2COOEt + Zn \rightarrow ClZnCH_2COOEt$$

$$R{-}C \underset{CH_3}{\overset{O}{\Big\|}} + ClZnCH_2COOEt \xrightarrow{\ H_3O^+\ } R{-}\underset{CH_3}{\overset{OH}{\underset{|}{C}}}{-}CH_2COOEt$$

Aldehyde or   A simple
ketone   α-haloester

The anions formed from 1-alkynes also add to carbonyl groups, as one might expect.

$$R'{-}C{\equiv}C^- Na^+ + R_2C{=}O \rightarrow R'{-}C{\equiv}C{-}\underset{R}{\overset{R}{\underset{|}{\overset{|}{C}}}}{-}O^- Na^+ \xrightarrow{H^+} R'{-}C{\equiv}C{-}\underset{R}{\overset{R}{\underset{|}{\overset{|}{C}}}}{-}OH$$

Since this reaction forms a new carbon–carbon bond and yields an acetylenic alcohol which can undergo a variety of further transformations, it is useful in synthetic work.

19.10   Addition of Ylides

Phosphorus and sulfur ylides (pages 221, 220), which are generated by reaction of appropriate salts with strong bases, readily condense with aldehydes and ketones. The phosphorus ylides, known as *Wittig reagents*, are the basis of an elegant synthetic method for the preparation of alkenes. The great advantage in the method lies in the fact that no ambiguity exists concerning the location of the double bond in the product.

Step 1: Formation of salt

$$CH_3I + (C_6H_5)_3P \rightarrow (C_6H_5)_3\overset{+}{P}CH_3\ I^-$$

Methyltriphenylphosphonium
iodide

Step 2: Formation of ylide

$$(C_6H_5)_3\overset{+}{P}CH_3\ I^- \xrightarrow[\substack{CH_3SOCH_3 \\ 25^\circ C}]{Na^+\ ^-CH_2SOCH_3} [(C_6H_5)_3P{=}CH_2 \leftrightarrow (C_6H_5)_3\overset{+}{P}{-}\overset{-}{C}H_2]$$

Methylenetriphenylphosphorane
(Section 10.6)

Step 3: Condensation with carbonyl compound

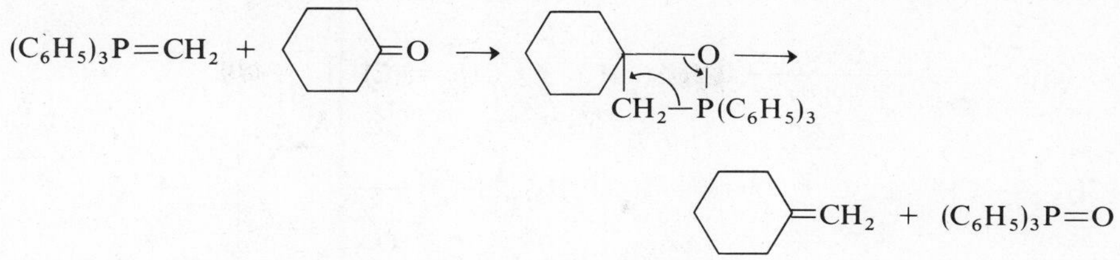

A variety of solvents and base systems have been employed. The most common are methanesulfinylcarbanion (generated by the reaction of sodium hydride with dimethyl sulfoxide) in dimethyl sulfoxide, *n*-butyllithium in ether or tetrahydrofuran, or alkoxides in alcohols. The ylides are generally not isolated; immediately following their generation they are allowed to react with carbonyl compounds in the same reaction flask. The reaction is most often applied with the methylene reagent. Others may be used with almost equal facility, but frequently they give rise to mixtures of *cis*- and *trans*-alkenes.

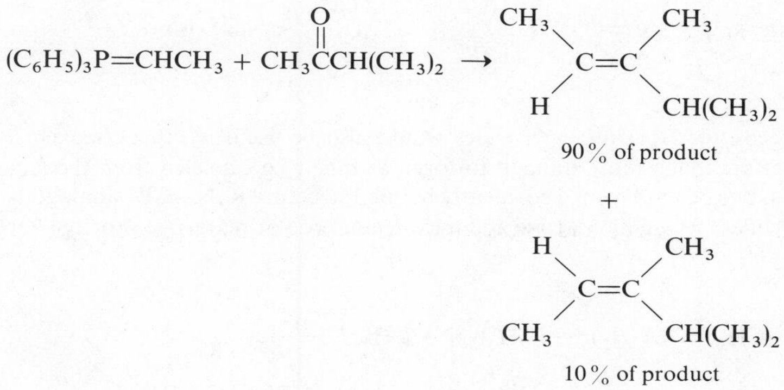

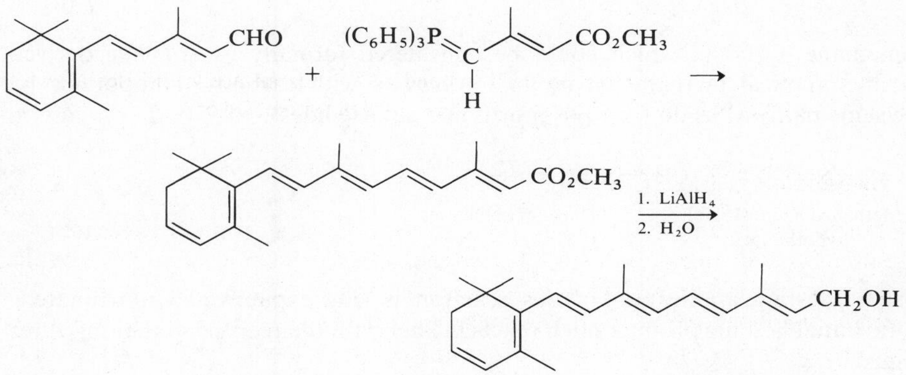

90% of product

+

10% of product

Vitamin A$_2$

EXERCISE 19.9

Outline syntheses of the alkenes shown, using as starting materials in each case an alkyl halide, a carbonyl compound, and triphenylphosphine.

(a)

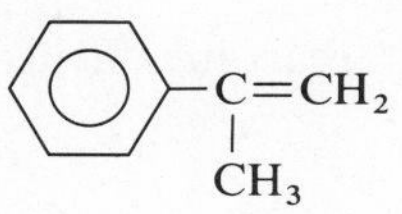

(b) $CH_3CH_2C=CHCH_3$
        |
     CH_2CH_3

(c)

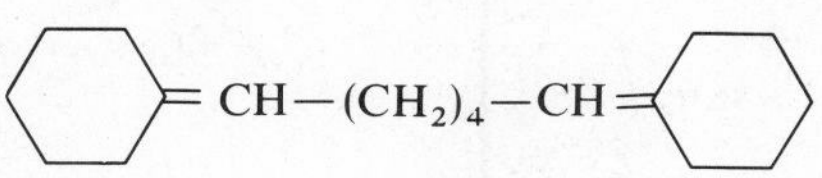

Uses of Sulfur Ylides. Sulfur ylides react with simple aldehydes and ketones to produce oxiranes (epoxides). Some of the more useful sulfur ylides are shown.

$$(CH_3)_3S^+I^- \xrightarrow[CH_3SOCH_3]{Na^+ \, ^-CH_2SOCH_3} [\overset{-}{C}H_2\overset{+}{S}(CH_3)_2 \leftrightarrow CH_2{=}S(CH_3)_2]$$

$$(CH_3)_2\overset{+}{S}=CH_2 + \langle\bigcirc\rangle{-}CHO \rightarrow \langle\bigcirc\rangle{-}HC{-}CH_2 + CH_3SOCH_3$$

By analogy, one might consider that nitrogen ylides would also be useful synthetic reagents. The simple nitrogen ylides are much more difficult to form, as might be expected from the fact that nitrogen cannot expand its octet to form a covalently bonded structure $R_3N{=}CR_2$ analogous to $R_3P{=}CR_2$. Nitrogen ylides are highly reactive and may decompose or rearrange shortly after generation.

$$(CH_3)_4N^+ \, X^- \rightarrow (CH_3)_3\overset{+}{N}{-}\overset{-}{C}H_2 \rightarrow (CH_3)_3N + CH_2{:}$$

$$CH_2{:} \rightarrow CH_2{=}CH_2 + Polymer$$

Diazomethane, CH_2N_2, which could be considered formally as an ylide derived from the hypothetical methanediazonium ion, reacts with carbonyl compounds by much the same pathway as do the phosphorus and sulfur ylides.

$$CH_3{-}\overset{+}{N}{\equiv}N \, X^- \qquad \overset{-}{C}H_2{-}\overset{+}{N}{\equiv}N \leftrightarrow etc.$$

Methanediazonium salt   Diazomethane
(hypothetical)

The most interesting application of this reaction is ring expansion. Unfortunately, some of the initial ketonic product often reacts further with the reagent so that mixtures are obtained.

The mechanism involves a carbonyl addition, followed by either rearrangement or closure of the epoxide ring.

or

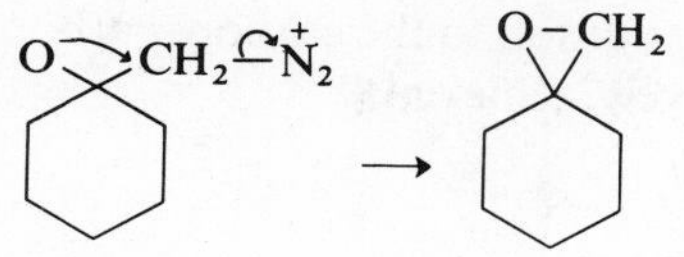

19.11 Reduction to Alcohols

By Complex Metal Hydrides

For usual laboratory-scale operations, complex metal hydrides offer the most convenient method for the reduction of aldehydes and ketones to the corresponding alcohols. The most important of these reagents are lithium aluminum hydride and sodium borohydride. The expense of these reagents usually prohibits their use on a large scale.

Lithium aluminum hydride, a highly reactive, powerful reducing agent, rapidly and efficiently reduces the carbonyl groups of aldehydes, ketones, acids, and acid derivatives as well as a number of other polar functional groupings. It is highly sensitive to moisture and is best handled in ether solution following the conventional procedures employed for Grignard reagents. As in the Grignard synthesis, the reduction of carbonyl compounds gives rise to intermediate metal alkoxides from which the desired products are liberated by mild hydrolysis.

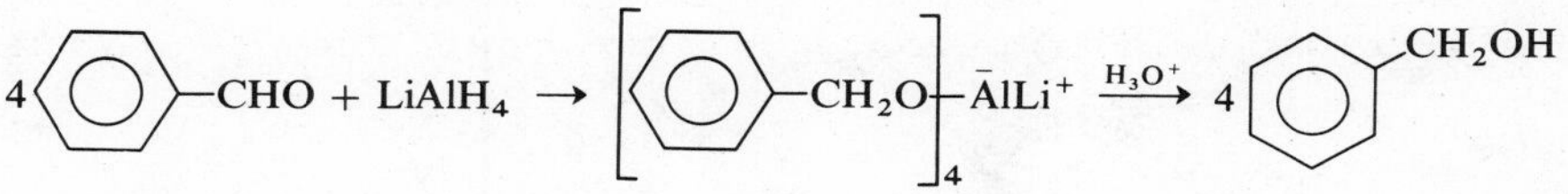

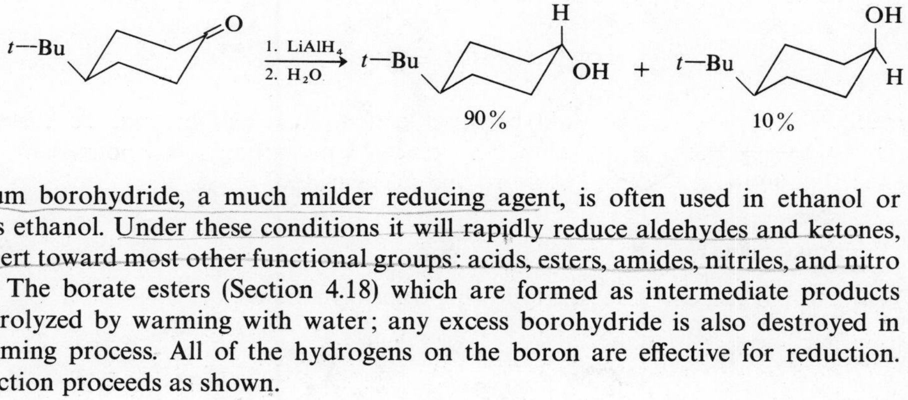

Sodium borohydride, a much milder reducing agent, is often used in ethanol or aqueous ethanol. Under these conditions it will rapidly reduce aldehydes and ketones, but is inert toward most other functional groups: acids, esters, amides, nitriles, and nitro groups. The borate esters (Section 4.18) which are formed as intermediate products are hydrolyzed by warming with water; any excess borohydride is also destroyed in the warming process. All of the hydrogens on the boron are effective for reduction. The reaction proceeds as shown.

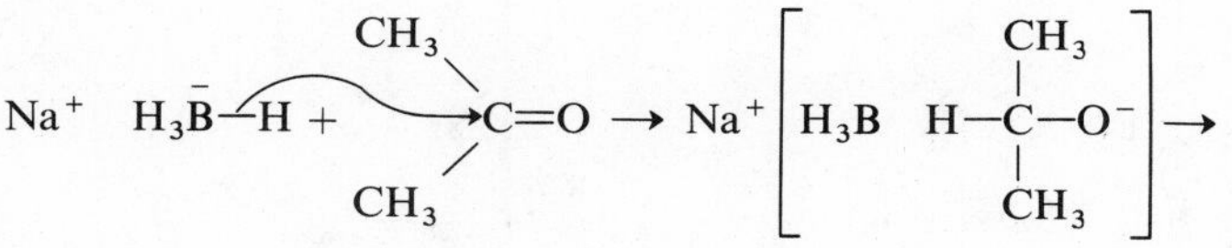

$$Na^+ \quad H_3\bar{B}-OCH(CH_3)_2 \xrightarrow{(CH_3)_2C=O} \rightarrow \rightarrow Na^+\bar{B}[OCH(CH_3)_2]_4$$

$$Na^+ \; {}^-B[OCH(CH_3)_2]_4 \xrightarrow[H_2O, \Delta]{NaOH} NaH_2BO_3 + 4 \; (CH_3)_2CHOH$$

Simple metal hydrides such as sodium hydride or lithium hydride are very poor reducing agents, since the hydride ion is a strong base but a poor nucleophile.

Diborane (B_2H_6), which is used in the hydroboration of alkenes (Section 15.9), will reduce carbonyls and a variety of other polar functional groups. However, the reaction with other functional groups is usually not as rapid as the addition to the carbon–carbon double bond, and often the latter addition may be selectively achieved.

By Catalytic Hydrogenation

For large-scale operations, catalytic hydrogenation affords the most practical method for the reduction of aldehydes and ketones to alcohols. Such reductions may be carried out in inert solvents or in pure liquids, employing finely divided Ni, Pd, or Pt catalysts. The latter is usually a superior catalyst for addition of hydrogen to a carbon–heteroatom double bond. In certain instances, soluble coordination complexes of noble metal compounds may be used to advantage as catalysts. Hydrogenation of the carbonyl group of an aldehyde or ketone is much slower than hydrogenation of a carbon–carbon double bond. It is not usually possible to catalytically reduce a carbonyl group in the presence of a double bond without concomitant saturation of the double bond.

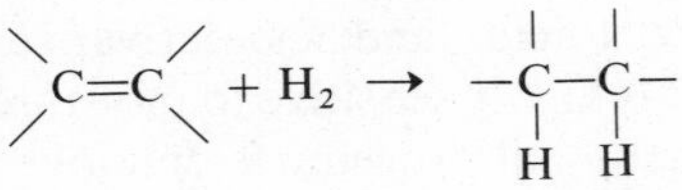

$$\ce{C=C} + H_2 \rightarrow \quad \ce{-C-C-} \quad \Delta H = -30\,\text{kcal}$$

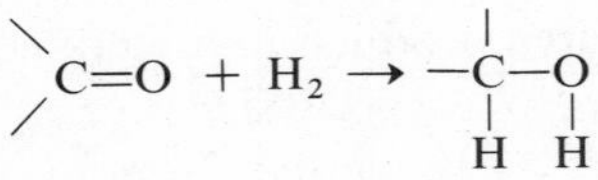

$$\ce{C=O} + H_2 \rightarrow \quad \ce{-C-O} \quad \Delta H = -12\,\text{kcal}$$

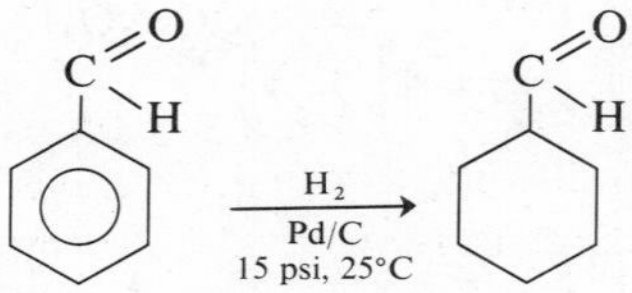

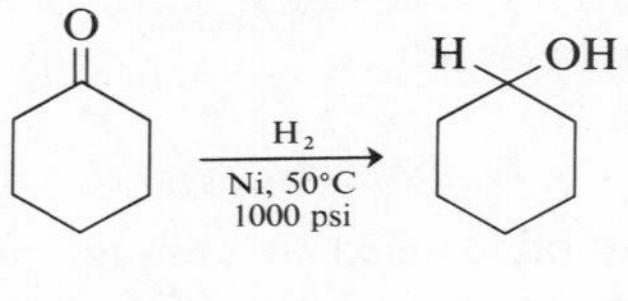

EXERCISE 19.10

How would you carry out the following transformations?

(a)

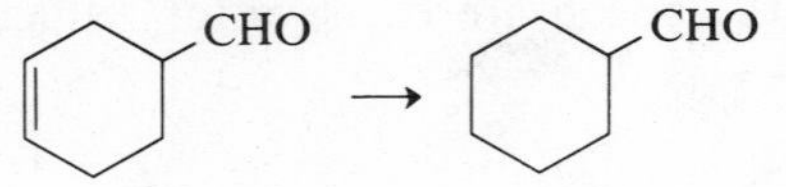

(b)

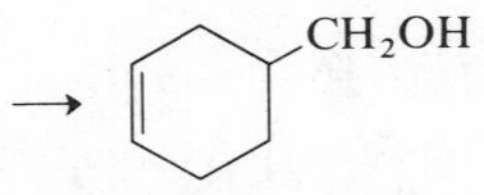

(c)

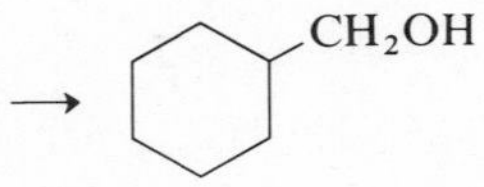

Dissolving Metal Reductions

For previous discussion of dissolving metal reductions see Section 16.10.

Ketones may be reduced in high yield with sodium in alcohol, and this was a favorite method of the early chemists. Although such reductions have now largely been replaced by reductions using metal hydrides or catalytic methods, the procedure may occasionally offer stereochemical advantage in that the more stable alcohol is ordinarily the major product.

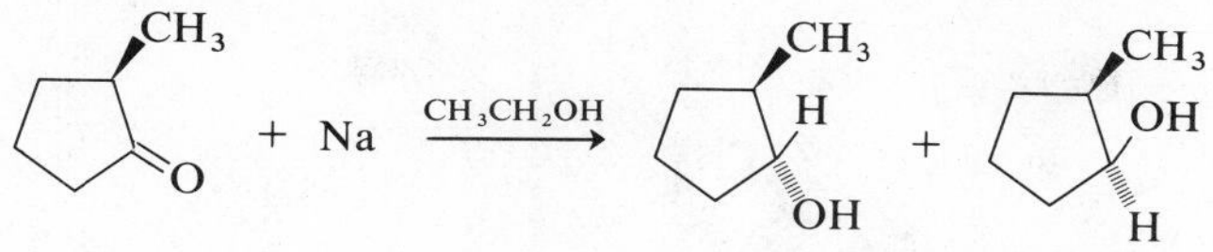

trans, major   *cis*, minor

Such reductions are believed to follow the course outlined below:

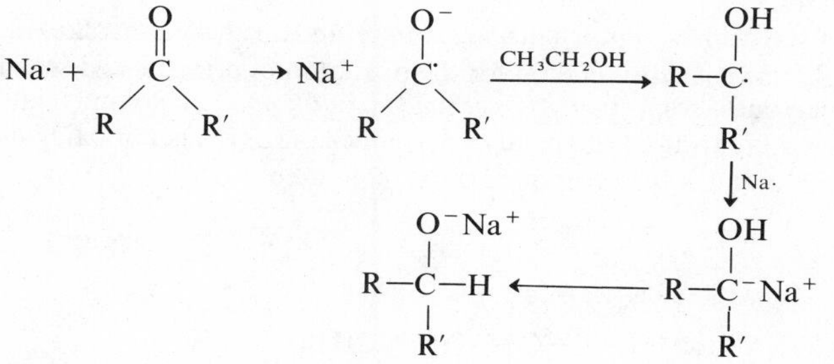

The anion radical is an intermediate which exists in solution long enough to detect. The metal salts of such anion radicals are called *ketyls*. They are often colored. If benzophenone is converted to the ketyl with sodium, for example, the ketyl concentration is sufficient to give the solution a beautiful blue color.

Sodium in alcohol or liquid ammonia is also capable of reducing esters, acetylenes, and conjugated olefins. Simple alkenes are inert to these conditions. The reduction of simple aliphatic aldehydes under these conditions often proceeds in poor yield because of competing condensation reactions (Section 19.14).

The reduction of ketones with metals in the absence of protonic solvents leads to coupling of the intermediate anion radicals. This process (known as *bimolecular reduction*) is particularly efficient when magnesium amalgam is employed.

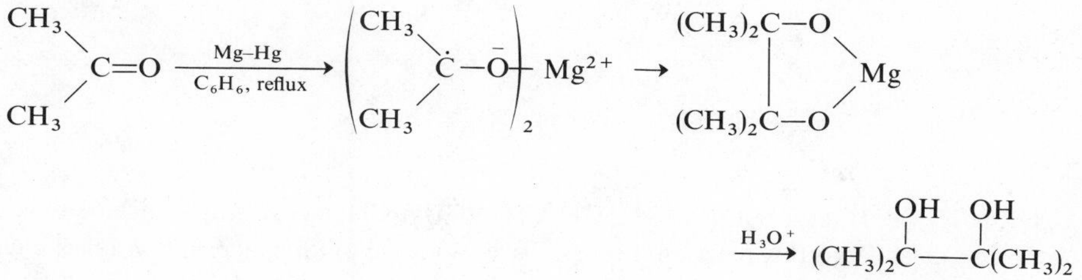

Pinacol

Hydride Transfer from Alkoxides. Hydride transfer can occur from a primary or secondary alkoxide to a carbonyl compound to yield another alkoxide and another carbonyl compound. The process is reversible.

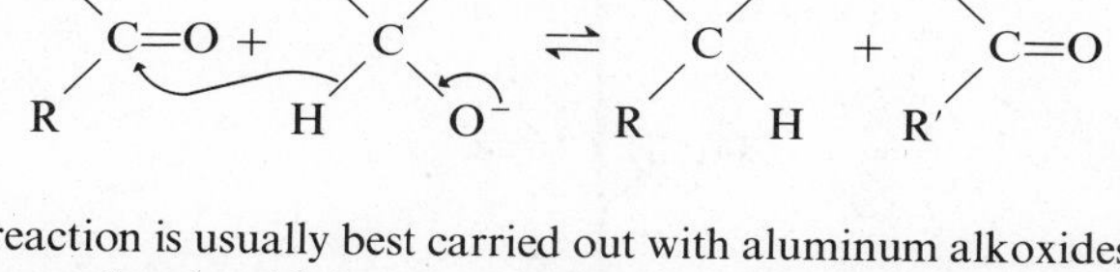

The reaction is usually best carried out with aluminum alkoxides. Apparently the aluminum atom acting as a Lewis acid site can coordinate with the acceptor carbonyl and help promote the hydride transfer.

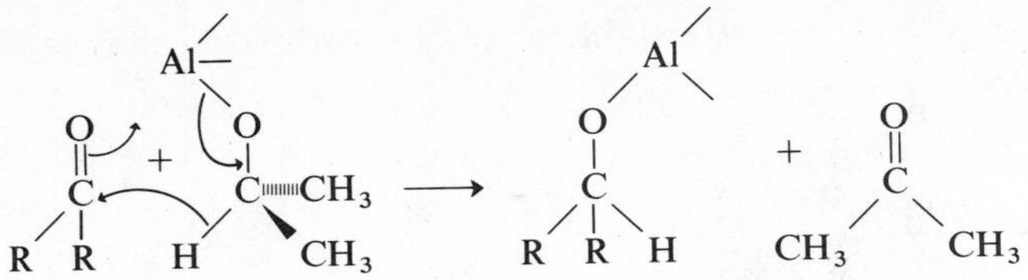

A reagent of practical utility in performing such reductions (known as *Meerwein–Ponndorf–Verley reductions*) is the commercially available *aluminum isopropoxide*. With this reagent, a reduction may be driven to completion by distillation of the acetone as it is formed. Since such reactions are reversible, in cases where geometrical isomers can be formed the thermodynamically more stable product usually predominates.

With the use of a large excess of a hydride acceptor, such as acetone, and an aluminum alkoxide, the reaction can be useful as a mild and selective method for the oxidation of primary and secondary alcohols to aldehydes and ketones, respectively (*Oppenauer oxidation*). The commercially available aluminum *t*-butoxide is frequently used as a catalyst. Cyclohexanone is a better oxidizing agent for this purpose than acetone, and it is the compound most often used.

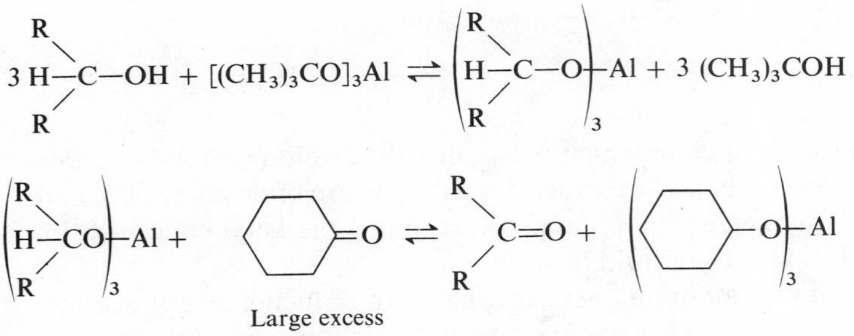

Large excess

From a mechanistic standpoint, the above reactions are closely related to the *Cannizzaro reaction* in which aldehydes without alpha hydrogens undergo self-oxidation–reduction in the presence of strong alkali.

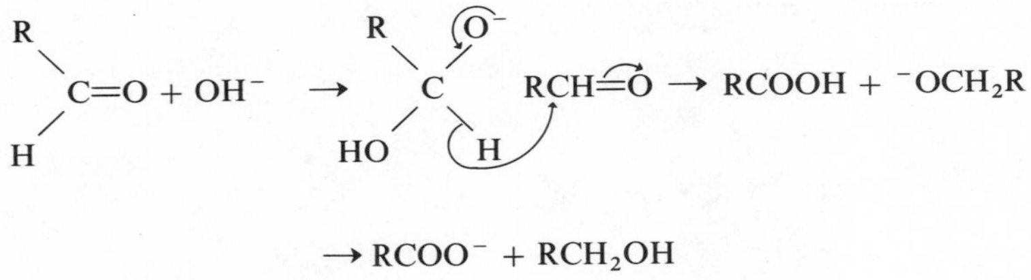

$$\rightarrow RCOO^- + RCH_2OH$$

$R = C_6H_5$, $(CH_3)_3C$, H, etc., but not CH_3, CH_3CH_2, $(CH_3)_2CH$, etc. Aldehydes which have α hydrogens do not undergo this reaction, because base-catalyzed aldol condensation takes place (Section 19.14) so much more readily.

19.12   Reduction to Hydrocarbons

Clemmensen Reduction

The carbonyl group of a ketone can be reduced to a methylene group with zinc amalgam and hydrochloric acid.

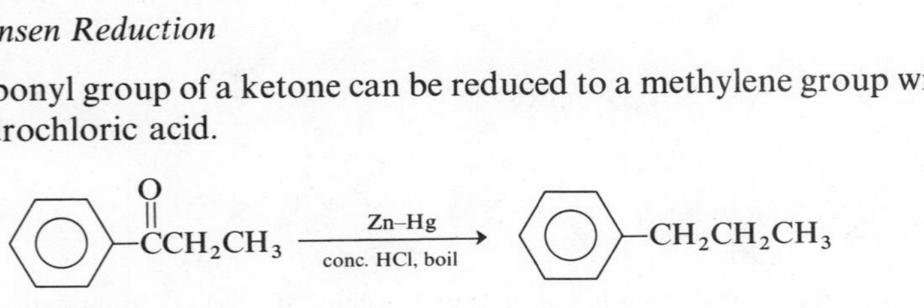

Wolff–Kishner Reduction

Aldehydes and ketones are reduced to hydrocarbons in the presence of excess hydrazine and strong base at elevated temperatures. Diethylene glycol ($HOCH_2CH_2OCH_2CH_2OH$, bp 245°C) is a convenient solvent for the reaction. The water formed during the reaction lowers the boiling point of the mixture, so the reaction is ordinarily driven to completion by distilling out the water.

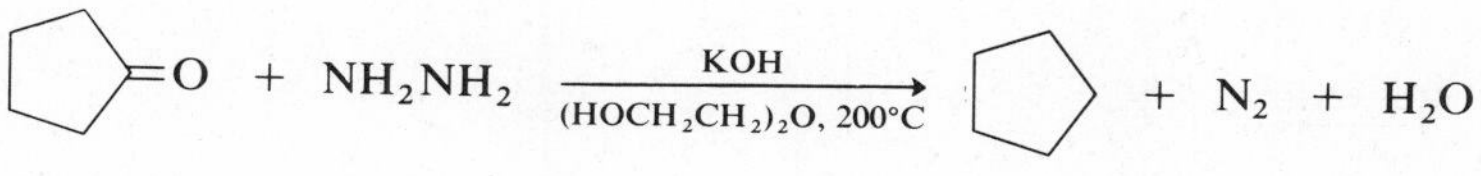

The initial step of the reaction is the formation of the hydrazone, which rearranges and decomposes in the presence of strong base. The usual mechanism is shown below:

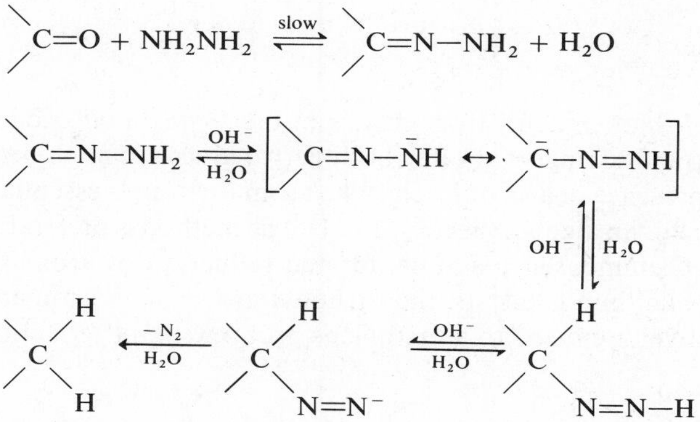

The reaction can be carried out at a lower temperature in the presence of a sufficiently strong base. For example, if the preformed hydrazone is added to a suspension of potassium *t*-butoxide in dimethyl sulfoxide, since the alkoxide is a much stronger base when not hydrogen-bonded to solvent, the reaction is rapid at room temperature.

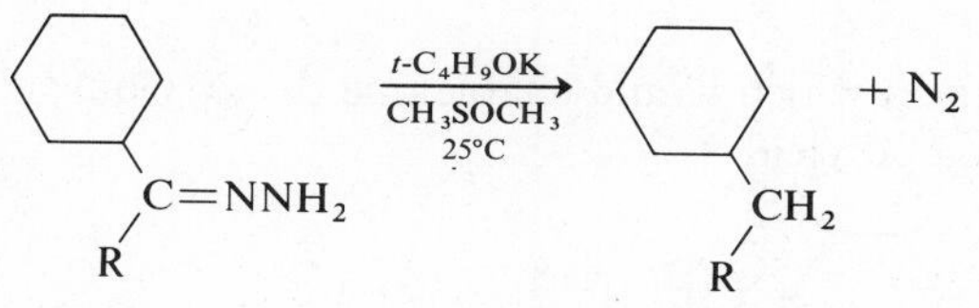

Miscellaneous Methods

A number of finely divided metal catalysts (of the type used in catalytic hydrogenation) when saturated with hydrogen, have the ability to strip sulfur from organic molecules, forming hydrocarbons and metal sulfides. This type of reaction is often troublesome during catalytic hydrogenations; even a trace amount of an organic sulfur compound may poison (render inactive) the metal catalyst. Occasionally such *desulfurization* reactions may be used to synthetic advantage.

$$R—S—R + Ni(H_2) \longrightarrow 2\,RH + NiS$$

Aldehydes and ketones readily condense with thiols to form thioacetals and thioketals (page 478). Desulfurization of these materials converts the original carbonyl site to a methylene group. Owing to its effectiveness and relatively low cost, Raney nickel is almost always used for desulfurization.

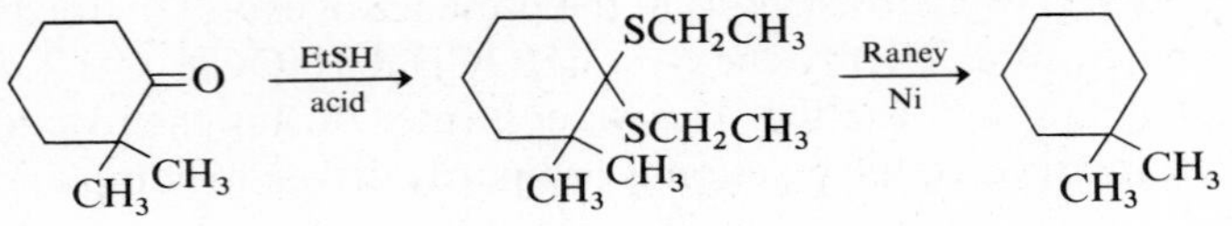

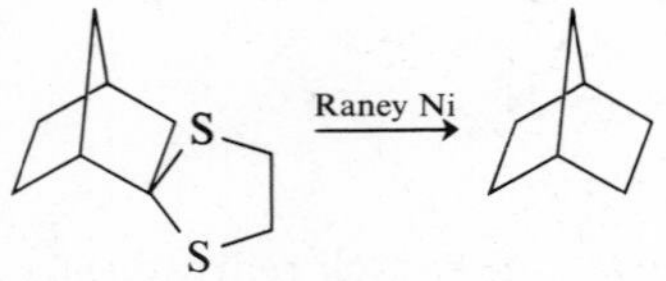

The cleavage of a bond by means of hydrogen is termed *hydrogenolysis*.

$$R-Z + H_2 \xrightarrow{\text{cat.}} R-H + HZ$$

In each of the above reactions of thioketals, hydrogenolysis of the C—S bond occurs.

Carbonyl groups adjacent to aromatic rings may often be directly reduced to methylene groups by hydrogenolysis in the presence of a strong acid. The aromatic ring is essential; if it is not present, the reduction yields an alcohol (Section 19.11). The method is preferable to either the Wolff–Kishner or Clemmensen reactions for the reduction of aromatic carbonyls to methylenes. With palladium catalysts, the carbonyl group of an aromatic aldehyde or ketone may be selectively reduced to a methylene group without reduction of an aliphatic carbonyl group.

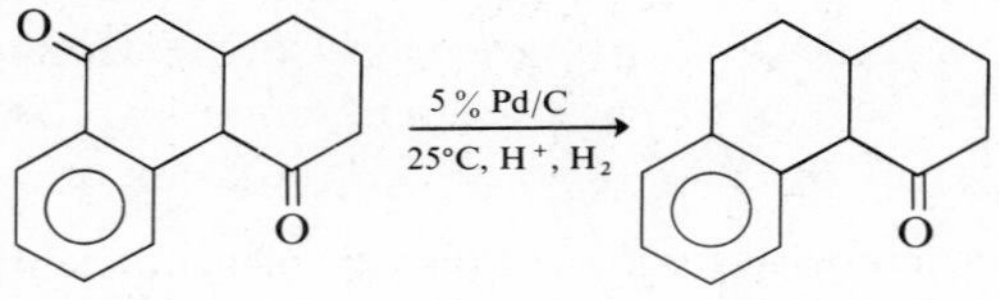

Such reactions probably depend upon the formation of a carbonium ion from the intermediate benzyl alcohol.

EXERCISE 19.11

List five different reaction sequences which would enable one to carry out the following transformation in good yield:

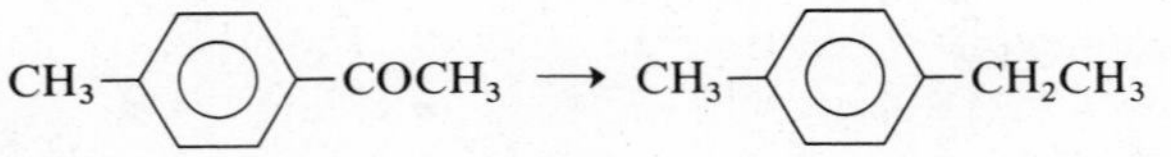

Reduction of a carbonyl group to a methylene group may also be achieved in a step-wise manner by employing conventional procedures previously discussed.

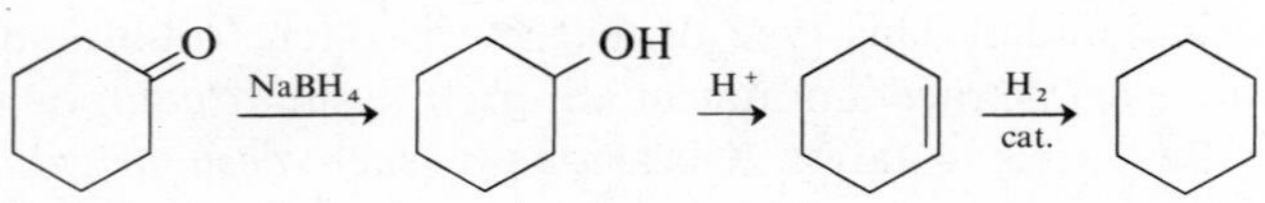

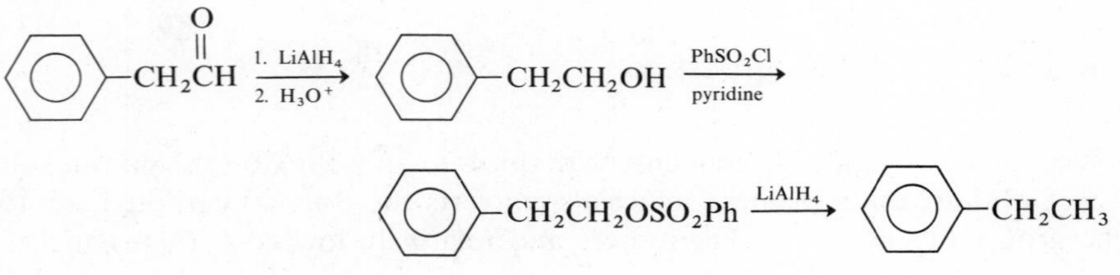

$$
\underset{\underset{CH_3}{|}}{CH_3CHCH_2CH_2}\overset{\overset{O}{\|}}{CH} \xrightarrow{LiAlH_4} \underset{\underset{CH_3}{|}}{CH_3CHCH_2CH_2CH_2OH}
$$

$$
\downarrow{HBr}
$$

$$
\xrightarrow{H_2O} \underset{\underset{CH_3}{|}}{CH_3CHCH_2CH_2CH_2MgBr} \xleftarrow{Mg} \underset{\underset{CH_3}{|}}{CH_3CHCH_2CH_2CH_2Br}
$$

$$
\downarrow
$$

$$
\underset{\underset{CH_3}{|}}{CH_3CHCH_2CH_2CH_3}
$$

19.13 Halogenation

The halogenation of the carbon adjacent to an enolizable ketone occurs according to the scheme shown.

$$
\underset{\underset{|}{\overset{\overset{H}{|}}{-C}}-\overset{\overset{O}{\|}}{C}-}{} + X_2 \xrightarrow[\text{or base}]{\text{acid}} \underset{\underset{|}{\overset{\overset{X}{|}}{-C}}-\overset{\overset{O}{\|}}{C}-}{} + HX
$$

The reaction is accelerated by the addition of either acids or bases. Indeed, it has been found that the rate of halogenation of a ketone is proportional to the concentrations of ketone and of added acids (general acid catalysis, see Sections 14.5, 19.1), but is independent of the concentration or identity of the halogen (chlorine, bromine, or iodine). Clearly then, the transition state for the rate-controlling step does not involve the halogen. Since this kind of reaction occurs in acid solution, we may assume that the intermediate involved is not an enolate ion but rather is the enol form of the ketone. (At this point, the student may wish to review Section 8.3: keto–enol tautomerism.) The slow step of the reaction, since it cannot involve halogen, must be the formation of the enol. The mechanism must then be as follows:

$$
\underset{\overset{|}{H}}{\overset{|}{-C}}-C=O \underset{\text{fast}}{\overset{\overset{HB}{}}{\rightleftharpoons}} \underset{\overset{|}{H}}{\overset{|}{-C}}-C=\overset{+}{O}H \underset{}{\overset{\text{slow}}{\rightleftharpoons}} \underset{/}{\overset{\backslash}{C}}=\overset{|}{C}-OH
$$
$$
\text{enol}
$$

$$
\underset{/}{\overset{\backslash}{C}}=\overset{|}{C}-OH + Br_2 \xrightarrow{\text{fast}} \underset{\underset{Br}{|}/}{\overset{\backslash}{C}}-\overset{|}{C}=\overset{+}{O}H + Br^- \underset{}{\overset{\text{fast}}{\rightleftharpoons}} \underset{\underset{Br}{|}/}{\overset{\backslash}{C}}-\overset{|}{C}=O + HBr
$$

If such a mechanism is correct, then halogenation of an optically active ketone should proceed at a rate identical to the rate of acid-catalyzed racemization under the same conditions, since formation of the enol is also the step which destroys the asymmetry of the α carbon. It has been found that the rates of bromination, iodination, and racemization of phenyl *sec*-butyl ketone are identical, within experimental error.

$$
\underset{\underset{CH_3}{|}}{CH_3CH_2-\overset{\overset{H}{|}}{C}-\overset{\overset{O}{\|}}{C}-C_6H_5} \xrightarrow[\text{slow}]{H^+} \underset{\underset{CH_3}{}}{\overset{CH_3CH_2}{}}\underset{\underset{C_6H_5}{}}{\overset{OH}{}}C=C \xrightarrow[\text{fast}]{X_2} \underset{\underset{CH_3}{|}}{CH_3CH_2CXCC_6H_5}\overset{\overset{O}{\|}}{}
$$

Optically active

$$
\downarrow{H^+ \text{ fast}}
$$

$$
\underset{\underset{CH_3}{|}}{CH_3CH_2CHCC_6H_5}\overset{\overset{O}{\|}}{}
$$

Racemic

In base-promoted halogenation of ketones, the rates are again found to be entirely independent of the concentration and identity of the halogen. (We use the term *promoted* rather than *catalyzed* since base is stoichiometrically consumed in the overall reaction.) In such reactions, the first and rate-controlling step is the removal of a proton from the α carbon to give the enolate, which is then rapidly consumed in subsequent fast steps.

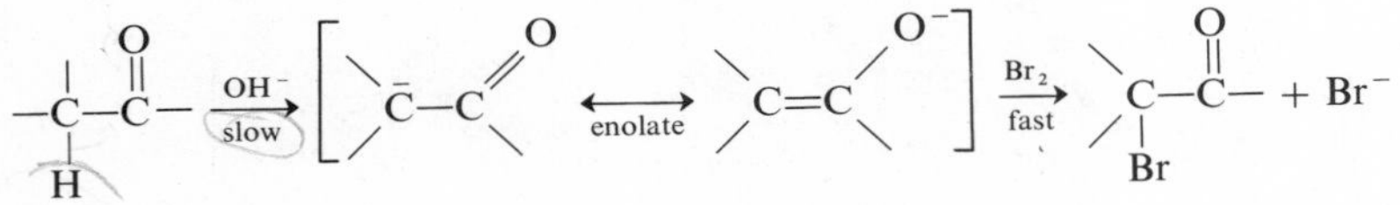

Returning to the acid-catalyzed reaction, let us consider the orientation of the halogen in the product obtained from the halogenation of an unsymmetrical ketone, such as methyl ethyl ketone. We find that halogenation occurs almost exclusively on the more substituted α carbon. It seems reasonable that an enol containing a more highly substituted carbon–carbon double bond will be more stable (Section 7.10) and would be formed preferentially.

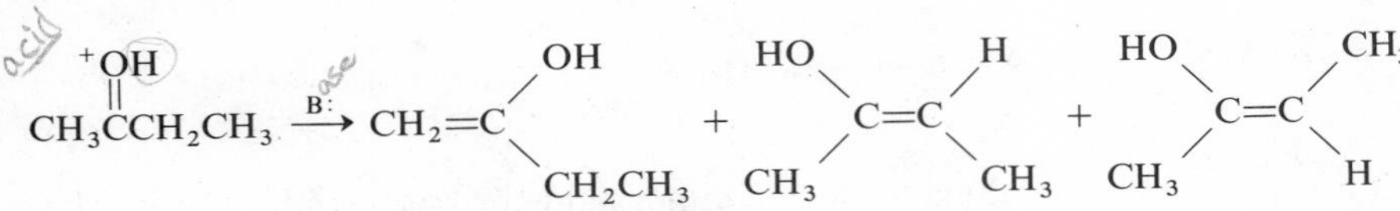

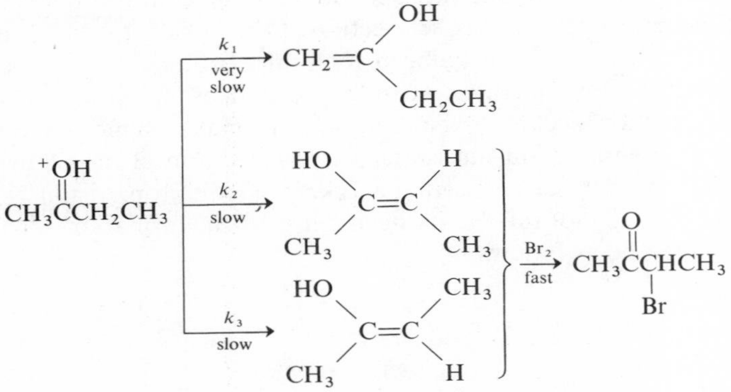

$$k_1 \ll k_2 \simeq k_3$$

The picture changes when we examine base-catalyzed reactions. The principal resonance forms for the two enolates derived from methyl ethyl ketone are shown below:

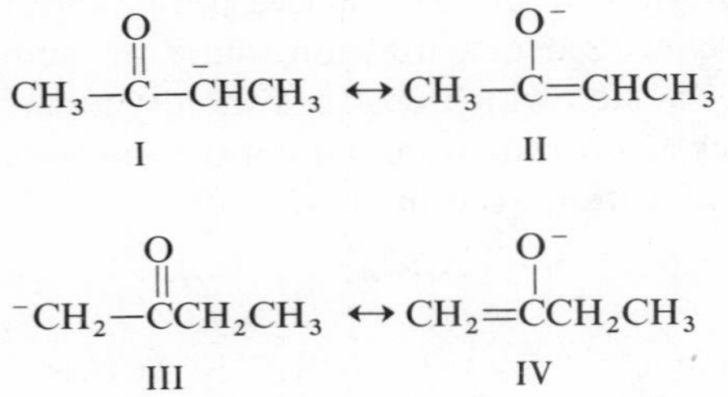

Based upon the ability of the methyl group to release electron density, structure I should be less stable than structure III (recall that a primary carbanion is more stable than a secondary). On the other hand, it might be anticipated that II, which contains the more highly substituted double bond, would be more stable than IV. The actual situation appears to be delicately balanced. In general it is found that the less substituted enolate is formed more rapidly but may or may not predominate at equilibrium. In halogenation reactions, equilibration between enolates is never achieved, owing to the rapid consumption of the enolate by the halogen. In base-promoted halogenation, then, substitution always occurs at the less substituted α carbon, just the opposite of what is observed for the acid-catalyzed halogenation.

$$CH_3CCH_2CH_3 \xrightarrow[Br_2]{OH^-} BrCH_2CCH_2CH_3$$

The introduction of an α-halogen substituent with its strong electron-withdrawing effect should enhance the stability and rate of formation of the enolate. Thus the product of the base-promoted bromination of acetone, even in the presence of a large excess of acetone, is the unsymmetrical tribromo compound. The initially formed bromoacetone is more readily brominated than acetone, and the dibromo compound is still more readily brominated.

$$CH_3CCH_3 \xrightarrow[\substack{OH^- \\ slow}]{Br_2} CH_3CCH_2Br \xrightarrow[\substack{OH^- \\ fast}]{Br_2} CH_3CCHBr_2$$

$$\xrightarrow[\substack{OH^- \\ faster}]{Br_2}$$

$$CH_3CCBr_3$$

In the presence of hydroxide ion, such trihalomethyl ketones are usually cleaved to form acids and trihalomethanes (haloforms).

$$CH_3CCBr_3 \xrightarrow{OH^-} CH_3-C-CBr_3 \longrightarrow CH_3C + {}^-CBr_3 \longrightarrow CHBr_3 + CH_3COO^-$$
$$\qquad\qquad\qquad\quad OH \qquad\qquad\quad OH$$

This reaction, known as the *haloform reaction*, depends on the stability of the trihalomethyl anions. The reaction has occasional utility in the preparation of an acid from the corresponding methyl ketone or from compounds which can be oxidized to a methyl ketone by the combination of base and halogen.

$$\triangleright\!-\!\overset{O}{\overset{\|}{C}}\!-\!CH_3 \xrightarrow[\substack{2.\ H_3O^+}]{1.\ Br_2,\ OH^-,\ H_2O} \triangleright\!-\!COOH + CHBr_3$$
$$\qquad\qquad\qquad\qquad\qquad\qquad 85\%$$

$$(CH_3)_2C\!=\!CHCCH_3 \xrightarrow[\substack{2.\ H_3O^+}]{1.\ Cl_2,\ OH^-,\ H_2O} (CH_3)_2C\!=\!CHCOOH + CHCl_3$$
$$\qquad\qquad\qquad\qquad\qquad\qquad\qquad 50\%$$

$$\overset{OH}{\underset{CHCH_3}{\bigcirc}} \xrightarrow[\substack{2.\ H_3O^+}]{1.\ I_2,\ NaOH,\ H_2O} \overset{COOH}{\bigcirc} + CHI_3$$

Sodium hypochlorite (NaOCl) is usually used to carry out the haloform reaction on a synthetic scale, because it is cheap and the chloroform is easy to remove from the product. For analytical purposes, sodium hypoiodite is the preferred reagent. Iodoform is a yellow solid, easy to identify, and because the atomic weight of iodine is so high, a large amount of iodoform is produced from a small amount of methyl ketone.

Ketones substituted by halogen in the position α to the carbonyl group are highly reactive toward bimolecular nucleophilic substitution. Such substances react very rapidly with even mediocre nucleophiles such as acetate ion; for example,

$$
\underset{\text{α-Chloroacetophenone}}{\text{C}_6\text{H}_5\text{—}\overset{\overset{\text{O}}{\|}}{\text{C}}\text{—CH}_2\text{Cl}} + {}^-\text{O}\text{—}\overset{\overset{\text{O}}{\|}}{\text{C}}\text{—CH}_3 \xrightarrow{\text{fast}} \underset{\text{Phenacyl acetate}}{\text{C}_6\text{H}_5\text{—}\overset{\overset{\text{O}}{\|}}{\text{C}}\text{—CH}_2\text{O}\overset{\overset{\text{O}}{\|}}{\text{C}}\text{CH}_3}
$$

LACHRYMATORS. *Chlorination of acetophenone gives α-chloroacetophenone, also known as phenacyl chloride. This substance is a relatively harmless but very potent lachrymator (tear gas) which is widely used in law enforcement. It is also a component of the chemical weapon known as MACE. Apparently irritation by such substances is due to alkylation of nucleophilic sites on membranes and, in part, to the hydrogen halide produced on hydrolysis. Most volatile halogen compounds which are highly reactive towards nucleophilic substitution are potent lachrymators. Examples include α-bromoacetophenone, chloroacetone, 1,3-dichloroacetone, benzyl chloride, and allyl bromide.*

19.14   Aldol Additions

The addition of enols or enolates to carbonyl functions constitutes a large and very important group of organic reactions. When the addition occurs at the carbonyl group of an aldehyde or ketone, the reaction is known as *aldol addition*. Such additions are usually achieved by base catalysis, as exemplified by the self-condensation of acetaldehyde.

$$
\text{CH}_3\text{CHO} + \text{OH}^- \rightleftharpoons \text{CH}_2\text{=C}\overset{\text{O}^-}{\underset{\text{H}}{}} + \text{H}_2\text{O}
$$

$$
\underset{\text{H}}{\text{CH}_3\text{C}}\overset{\text{O}}{} + \text{CH}_2\text{=C}\overset{\text{O}^-}{\underset{\text{H}}{}} \rightleftharpoons \underset{\text{H}}{\text{CH}_3\overset{\text{O}^-}{\text{C}}\text{CH}_2\text{—}\overset{\overset{\text{O}}{\|}}{\text{CH}}} \underset{\text{base}}{\overset{\text{H}_2\text{O}}{\rightleftharpoons}} \underset{\underset{\text{H}}{\text{Acetaldol}}}{\text{CH}_3\overset{\text{OH}}{\text{C}}\text{CH}_2\text{CHO}}
$$

Addition of the enolate to form a carbon–oxygen bond is thermodynamically unfavorable.

$$
\text{CH}_3\text{CHO} + \text{CH}_2\text{=C}\overset{\text{O}^-}{\underset{\text{H}}{}} \rightleftharpoons \text{CH}_3\overset{\text{O}^-}{\text{CHOCH=CH}_2}
$$

Simple aldols are reasonably stable in base, but they dehydrate in acid.

$$
\underset{}{\text{CH}_3\overset{\text{OH}}{\text{CH}}\text{—CH}_2\text{CHO}} \xrightarrow{\text{H}^+} \underset{\text{Crotonaldehyde}}{\text{CH}_3\text{CH=CHCHO}} + \text{H}_2\text{O}
$$

The aldol condensation itself can be catalyzed by acid, so the easiest preparation of crotonaldehyde from acetaldehyde is by treatment with acid.

$$2\,CH_3CHO \xrightarrow{H^+} CH_3CH\!=\!CHCHO + H_2O$$

EXERCISE 19.12

Outline laboratory syntheses of the following compounds from any one-carbon or two-carbon compounds plus benzene.

(a) 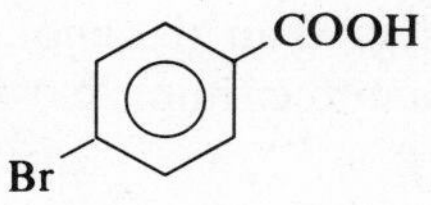 Br–C6H4–COOH

(b) $CH_3\underset{\underset{CH_3}{|}}{CH}\overset{\overset{O}{\|}}{C}OH$

(c) $CH_3CH_2CH_2CH_2\overset{\overset{O}{\|}}{C}CH_3$

Note that it is the α carbon of one molecule which condenses with the carbonyl carbon of the second molecule.

$$2\,CH_3CH_2CHO \xrightarrow{OH^-} CH_3CH_2\underset{\underset{CH_3}{|}}{\overset{\overset{OH}{|}}{CH}}CHCHO$$

$CH_3CH = C\overset{O^-}{\underset{H}{}}$

The aldol condensation involving a ketone as a carbonyl component is unfavorable under conditions of basic catalysis.

$$2\,CH_3\overset{\overset{O}{\|}}{C}CH_3 \underset{OH^-}{\rightleftharpoons} CH_3-\overset{\overset{O}{\|}}{C}-CH_2-\overset{\overset{OH}{|}}{\underset{\underset{CH_3}{|}}{C}}-CH_3$$

Diacetone alcohol

The equilibrium between acetone and diacetone alcohol lies about 95% toward acetone. Diacetone alcohol can be prepared from acetone in good yield, however, by allowing the equilibrium to be established, then removing the base catalyst. The low-boiling acetone can then be distilled away from the diacetone alcohol. The poor yield that would be obtained in the reaction is overcome by automatically recycling the recovered acetone with the aid of a device called a *Soxhlet extractor*.

Diacetone alcohol is easily dehydrated by a mild acid to the α,β-unsaturated ketone, which has the odd name mesityl oxide.

$$CH_3-\overset{\overset{OH}{|}}{\underset{\underset{CH_3}{|}}{C}}-CH_2\overset{\overset{O}{\|}}{C}-CH_3 \xrightarrow{I_2} \overset{CH_3}{\underset{CH_3}{}}C\!=\!CH-\overset{\overset{O}{\|}}{C}-CH_3$$

Mesityl oxide, 85% yield

EXERCISE 19.13

From the bond-energy data in Section 13.2, calculate which of the following reactions is more favorable:

$$2\,CH_3CHO \rightarrow CH_3-\overset{\overset{OH}{|}}{CH}CH_2CHO$$

$$2\,CH_3CHO \rightarrow CH_3-\overset{\overset{OH}{|}}{\underset{\underset{H}{|}}{C}}-O-CH\!=\!CH_2$$

While the equilibrium between a ketone and its aldol is unfavorable, if the condensation is carried out in acid, a good yield of the α,β-unsaturated ketone can be obtained directly.

$$2\ CH_3-\underset{\underset{O}{\|}}{C}-CH_3 \xrightarrow{H^+} \underset{CH_3}{\overset{CH_3}{\diagdown}}C=CH-\underset{\underset{O}{\|}}{C}-CH_3$$

The reaction mechanism for the acid-catalyzed aldol condensation is formally similar to that for the base-catalyzed reaction, except that the enol rather than the enolate is one of the reacting species, and the protonated carbonyl rather than the simple carbonyl is the other.

$$CH_3-\underset{\underset{O}{\|}}{C}-CH_3 + H^+ \rightleftharpoons CH_3-\underset{\overset{+}{O}H}{\overset{\|}{C}}-CH_3 \underset{B}{\rightleftharpoons} CH_3\underset{OH}{\overset{|}{C}}=CH_2$$

$$\underset{enol}{CH_3-\underset{\underset{|}{:OH}}{C}=CH_2} + \underset{\underset{CH_3}{|}}{\overset{+}{\overset{\overset{+}{O}H}{\|}}C}-CH_3 \underset{protonated\ carbonyl}{\rightleftharpoons} CH_3-\underset{\overset{+}{O}H}{\overset{\|}{C}}-CH_2-\underset{\underset{CH_3}{|}}{\overset{OH}{\overset{|}{C}}}-CH_3 \xrightarrow{-H^+}$$

$$CH_3-\underset{\underset{O}{\|}}{C}-CH_2-\underset{\underset{CH_3}{|}}{\overset{OH}{\overset{|}{C}}}-CH_3$$

$$CH_3-\underset{\underset{O}{\|}}{C}-CH_2-\underset{\underset{CH_3}{|}}{\overset{OH}{\overset{|}{C}}}-CH_3 \xrightarrow{H^+} CH_3-\underset{\underset{O}{\|}}{C}-CH-\underset{\underset{H}{\cdot}\ \underset{CH_3}{|}}{\overset{+}{\overset{\overset{+}{O}H_2}{C}}}-CH_3 \rightarrow$$

$$B-$$

$$H_2O + CH_3-\underset{\underset{O}{\|}}{C}-CH=C\underset{CH_3}{\overset{CH_3}{\diagup}}$$

The student should carefully compare the base-catalyzed and acid-catalyzed aldol condensation, because (as we will see later) this parallelism is a fundamental property of carbonyl compounds and will be met with repeatedly.

EXERCISE 19.14

In terms of thermodynamics, why does the aldol condensation of acetone proceed to a considerable extent in acid solution but not in basic solution?

Mixed aldol additions are most successful when one member readily forms an enolate and the other member has a carbonyl which is highly susceptible to additions. Formaldehyde and benzaldehyde are especially suited for use as the carbonyl component in mixed aldol condensation, since they are readily susceptible to addition and do not form enolates.

$$CH_3\underset{\underset{O}{\|}}{C}CH_3 + CH_2O \xrightarrow{B:} CH_3\underset{\underset{O}{\|}}{C}CH_2CH_2OH$$

Aldol reactions of benzaldehyde are usually successful only under conditions that effect the dehydration of the initial aldol. In simple condensation reactions of benzaldehyde and related substances, the α,β-unsaturated carbonyl compounds which are obtained usually have the more stable stereochemistry. Condensations may occur at all available α-methylene positions.

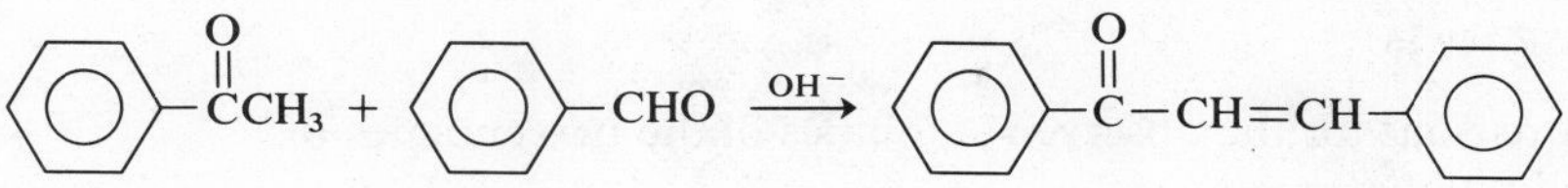

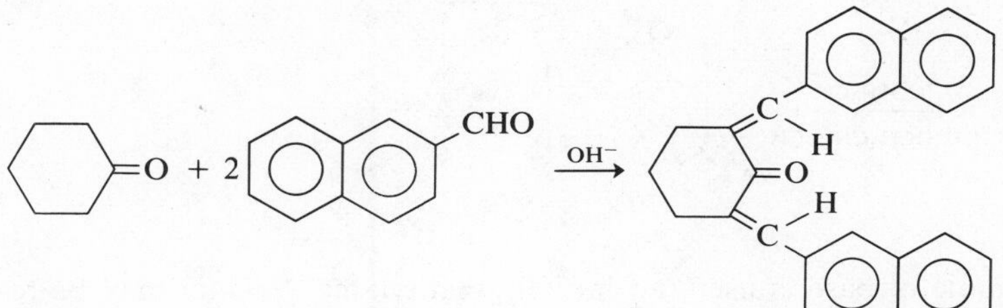

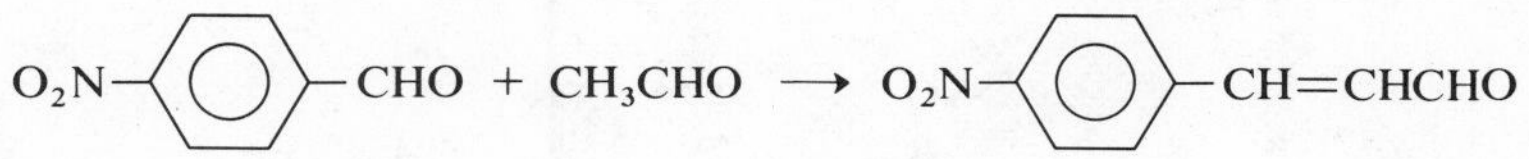

Mixed aldol additions with formaldehyde must be run under carefully controlled conditions to prevent polyaddition from occurring—all hydrogens may be replaced.

The Crossed Cannizzaro Reaction. The condensation of formaldehyde and acetaldehyde in the presence of calcium hydroxide yields the intermediate tris(hydroxymethyl)acetaldehyde, which under the reaction conditions undergoes a "crossed Cannizzaro" reaction (see page 494) with formaldehyde to yield *pentaerythritol*. Pentaerythritol is important in the plastics and polymer industries. As the tetranitrate (PETN) it is a useful high explosive.

$$CH_3CHO + CH_2O \xrightarrow{Ca(OH)_2} (HOCH_2)_3CCHO \xrightarrow[OH^-]{CH_2O} (HOCH_2)_4C + HCOO^-$$

Pentaerythritol

EXERCISE 19.15

Write a mechanism for the reaction of acetaldehyde and formaldehyde to give pentaerythritol.

19.15 Alkylation of Enolates

Ketones with enolizable hydrogens can be quantitatively converted to enolates by treatment with powerful bases in aprotic solvents (Table 19.2). Under such conditions aldehydes tend to polymerize.

Table 19.2 | Commonly Used Strong Bases and Solvents

Bases	NaNH$_2$, KNH$_2$, NaH, LiH, (CH$_3$CH$_2$)$_2$NLi, (C$_6$H$_5$)$_3$CNa, (CH$_3$)$_3$COK
Solvents	Ether, Benzene, Toluene, 1,2-Dimethoxyethane

Enolates are effective nucleophiles in S_N2 reactions, but owing to complications the reactions are of very limited synthetic utility. One complication is that mixtures of *C*-alkylation products are usually obtained. Let us examine the methylation of 2-methylcyclohexanone. The equilibrium composition for solutions of potassium enolates of 2-methylcyclohexanone in 1,2-dimethoxyethane is approximately 70–30.

EXERCISE 19.16

Suggest reasons for the observed stabilities of the two enolates of 2-methylcyclohexanene.

Even though only 1 mole of base is used, an initially methylated product may be re-converted to an enolate by an exchange reaction with another enolate. As a result, complex mixtures may be formed.

In general, simple alkylation reactions are synthetically useful only when alkylation of all of the available sites is desired.

Useful methods for controlling alkylations of ketones have been developed, but they are somewhat complicated and will be discussed in subsequent chapters.

Intramolecular alkylations often proceed in excellent yield, especially when the entropy of ring closure is favorable (the chain not too long).

The Favorskii Rearrangement. An intriguing example of intramolecular alkylation is provided by the *Favorskii rearrangement.* Treatment of an α-halo ketone with hydroxide ion causes a rearrangement of the carbon skeleton to provide a carboxylate salt.

The reaction proceeds through a transient cyclopropanone, which is readily opened by base.

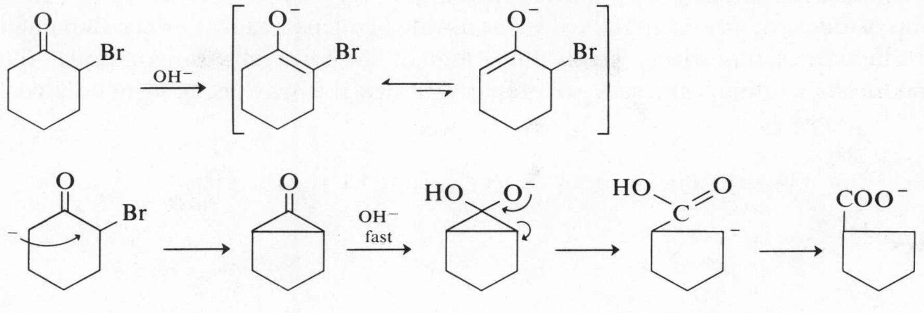

EXERCISE 19.17

Write the mechanism of the following reaction:

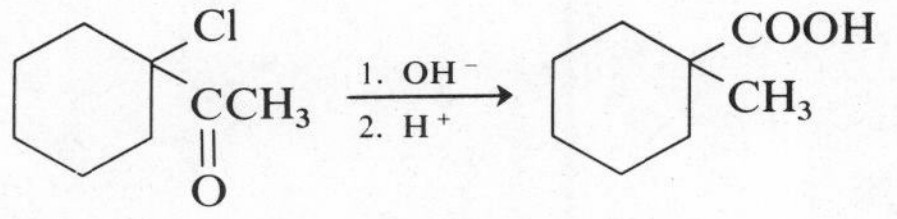

Enolates are *ambident nucleophiles*; in simple alkylation reactions products of both *C*- and *O*-alkylation may result. (*Ambident* is derived from Latin words *ambo* and *dent*, meaning *both teeth*; i.e., two different points of attack.)

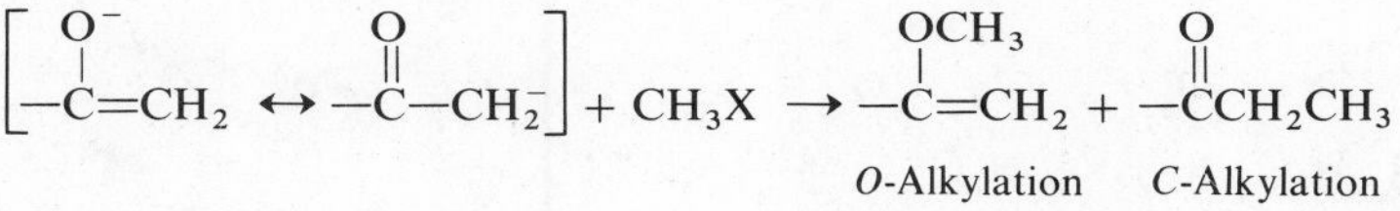

In contrast to aldol addition reactions, *O*-alkylation is not readily reversible, although it is less favorable than alkylation on carbon. (Note that *C*-alkylation results in a compound containing a carbon–oxygen double bond, whereas *O*-alkylation results in a product containing a carbon–carbon double bond.) The $C=O$ bond is unusually strong, and its formation is thermodynamically favorable (Section 13.2). The extent to which *O*-alkylation occurs depends on the reactivity of the alkylating reagent (kinetic control). With highly reactive alkylating agents (such as $ROCH_2Cl$, α-halo ketones, and acid chlorides), the transition state will resemble the reactants, with the charge on the enolate portion concentrated more on oxygen than carbon. With less reactive alkylating agents (such as RCH_2Br), the transition state will tend to resemble the products, and *C*-alkylation corresponds to the more stable product.

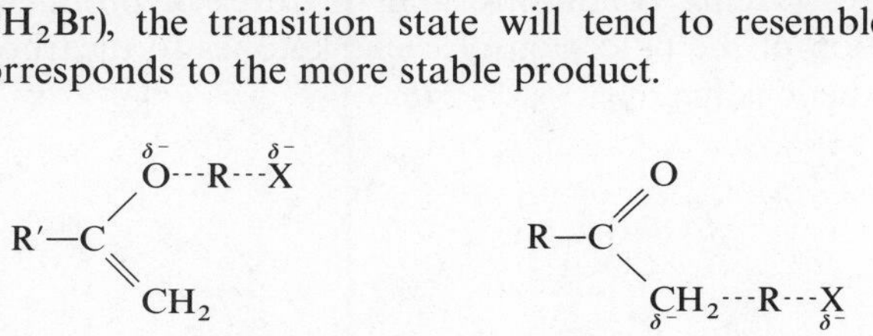

Transition state for *O*-alkylation   Transition state for *C*-alkylation

O-Alkylation is not usually a serious problem with simple carbonyls. It becomes more of a problem with β-diketones and related compounds which form stable enols.

19.16   Oxidation of Aldehydes and Ketones

Aldehydes are among the most readily oxidized classes of organic compounds. They are converted to carboxylic acids by numerous oxidizing agents, including not only the usual reagents such as permanganate and dichromate, but also relatively weak oxidizing agents such as silver and cupric ions.

Oxidation of aldehydes by ammoniacal silver nitrate (Tollens' reagent) is accompanied by the production of free silver, which plates out in the form of a mirror under the proper conditions. Ordinary mirrors are prepared in just this way, using formaldehyde.

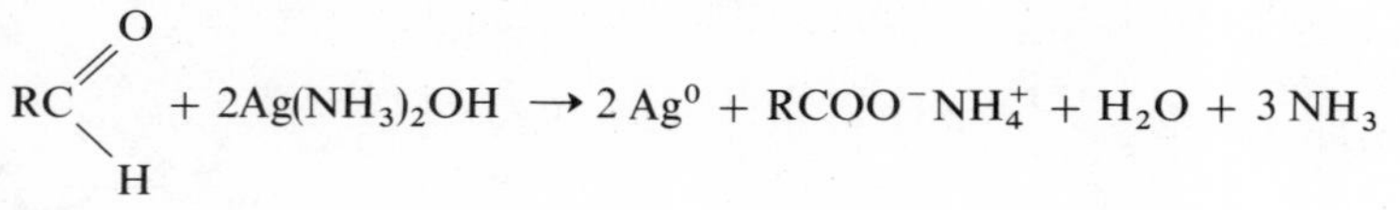

$$RC\overset{O}{\underset{H}{\diagup}} + 2Ag(NH_3)_2OH \rightarrow 2\,Ag^0 + RCOO^-NH_4^+ + H_2O + 3\,NH_3$$

Oxidation of Aldehydes. In the presence of a radical initiator, the oxidation of aldehydes by oxygen occurs readily, even at room temperature. Depending on the reaction conditions, either acids or peracids may be obtained.

Initiation

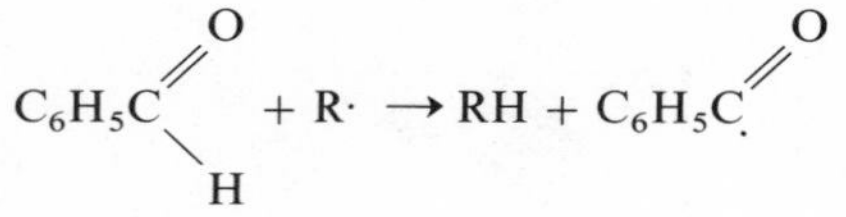

$$C_6H_5C\overset{O}{\underset{H}{\diagup}} + R\cdot \rightarrow RH + C_6H_5C\overset{O}{\underset{\cdot}{\diagup}}$$

Propagation

$$C_6H_5C\overset{O}{\underset{\cdot}{\diagup}} + O_2 \rightarrow C_6H_5C\overset{O}{\underset{OO\cdot}{\diagup}}$$

$$C_6H_5C\overset{O}{\underset{OO\cdot}{\diagup}} + C_6H_5C\overset{O}{\underset{H}{\diagup}} \rightarrow C_6H_5C\overset{O}{\underset{OOH}{\diagup}} + C_6H_5C\overset{O}{\underset{\cdot}{\diagup}}$$

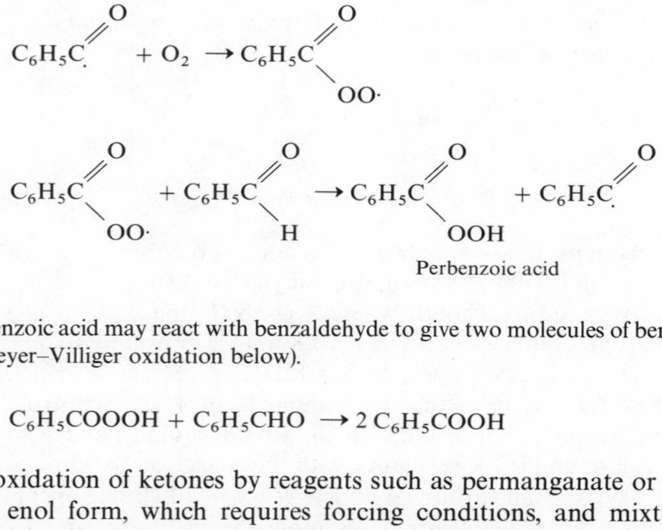

Perbenzoic acid

Perbenzoic acid may react with benzaldehyde to give two molecules of benzoic acid (see discussion of Baeyer–Villiger oxidation below).

$$C_6H_5COOOH + C_6H_5CHO \rightarrow 2\,C_6H_5COOH$$

The oxidation of ketones by reagents such as permanganate or dichromate proceeds via the enol form, which requires forcing conditions, and mixtures of products are usually formed. With the exception of the oxidation of cyclic ketones to dicarboxylic acids, the reaction is of little synthetic value.

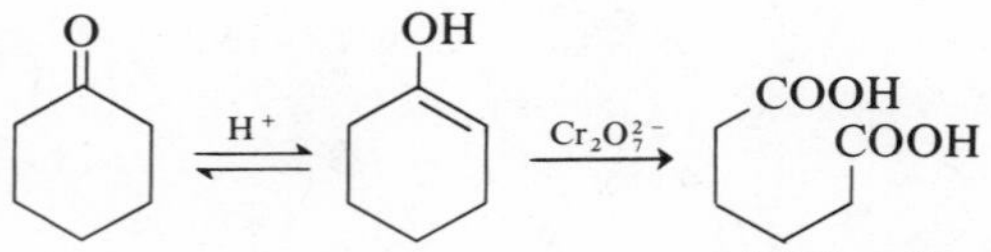

Adipic acid

Aldehydes and ketones containing a methylene group adjacent to the carbonyl may be oxidized to dicarbonyl compounds by selenium dioxide. The reagent is both expensive and toxic.

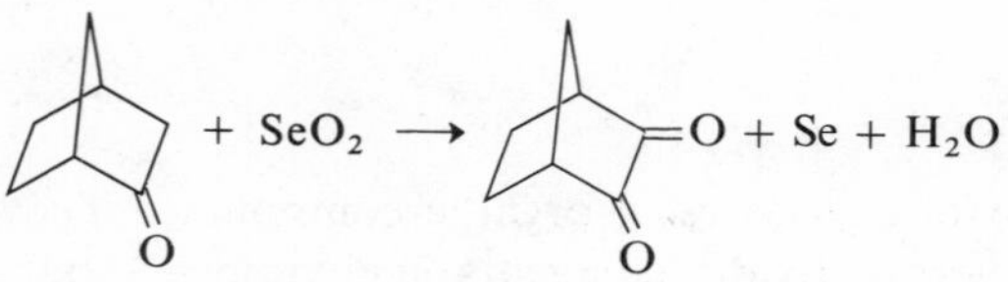

$$\text{C}_6\text{H}_5\!-\!\overset{\overset{\textstyle O}{\|}}{\text{C}}\text{CH}_3 + \text{SeO}_2 \rightarrow \text{C}_6\text{H}_5\!-\!\overset{\overset{\textstyle O}{\|}}{\text{C}}\text{CHO} + \text{Se} + \text{H}_2\text{O}$$

In a reaction known as the *Baeyer†–Villiger oxidation*, ketones may be converted to esters by reaction with peracids. Cyclic ketones yield lactones. The commonly used peracids for such oxidations include perbenzoic, *m*-chloroperbenzoic, peracetic, and trifluoroperacetic acid.

$$\text{PhCOCH}_3 \xrightarrow{\;\text{CH}_3\text{CO}_3\text{H}\;} \text{Ph}\!-\!\text{O}\!-\!\overset{\overset{\textstyle}{}}{\text{C}}(\text{CH}_3)\!=\!\text{O}$$

$$\text{cyclohexanone} \xrightarrow[\substack{\text{CHCl}_3 \\ 25°\text{C}}]{\;\text{C}_6\text{H}_5\text{CO}_3\text{H}\;} \text{lactone} \quad 71\%$$

The reaction is catalyzed by acid and involves an addition of the peracid to the carbonyl group of the ketone.

$$\underset{R^*}{\overset{R}{\diagdown}}\text{C}=\text{O} + R'\text{CO}_3\text{H} \rightleftharpoons \;\; \underset{R^*}{\overset{R}{\diagdown}}\text{C}\underset{\text{O}\!-\!\overset{\overset{\textstyle O}{\|}}{\text{O}}\text{CR'}}{\overset{\ddot{\text{O}}\text{H}}{\diagup}} \;\; \xrightarrow[\text{slow}]{H^+} \;\; R\!-\!\overset{\overset{\textstyle +\text{OH}}{\|}}{\text{C}}\text{OR}^* + R'\text{COO}^-$$

Whereas the rearrangement step of the reaction is believed to be concerted, as shown, if we look at it stepwise, it will be clear that the oxygen to which the R group migrates (the *migration terminus*) is electron deficient in the transition state, and the reaction is in an electronic sense closely analogous both to the carbonium ion rearrangement such as that observed with neopentyl compounds (Section 17.3) and to the pinacol rearrangement (Section 18.6).

$$\underset{R}{\overset{R}{\diagdown}}\text{C}\underset{\text{O}\!-\!\text{O}\!-\!\overset{\overset{\textstyle O}{\|}}{\text{C}}\!-\!R}{\overset{\text{OH}}{\diagup}} \;\rightarrow\; \underset{R}{\overset{R}{\diagdown}}\text{C}\underset{\text{O}_+}{\overset{\ddot{\text{O}}\text{H}}{\diagup}} \;+\; {}^-\text{O}\!-\!\overset{\overset{\textstyle O}{\|}}{\text{C}}R$$

The group that migrates in the Baeyer–Villiger reaction does so with retention of configuration. With unsymmetrical ketones, the following "migratory aptitudes" have been noted.

t-Alkyl > *sec*-Alkyl > Phenyl > *n*-Alkyl > Methyl

Thus in the overall reaction, oxygen would be inserted in the following ketones as shown by the arrow.

$$\text{cyclopropyl}\!-\!\overset{\overset{\textstyle O}{\|}}{\text{C}}\text{CH}_3 \qquad \text{Ph}\!-\!\overset{\overset{\textstyle O}{\|}}{\text{C}}\!-\!\text{CH}_2\text{CH}_3 \qquad \text{CH}_3\text{CH}_2\!-\!\overset{\overset{\textstyle O}{\|}}{\text{C}}\!-\!\text{CH}_3$$

† Adolph von Baeyer. 1835–1917. Born Berlin. Universities of Strasbourg and Munich. Nobel Prize 1905.

EXERCISE 19.18

Predict the products of the reactions of the ketones shown with perbenzoic acid.

(a) [structure: 2-methylcyclohexanone]

(b) [structure: benzophenone with OCH₃ substituent]

(c) [structure: bicyclic diketone]

19.17   α,β-Unsaturated Aldehydes and Ketones

A carbonyl group and a carbon–carbon double bond in conjugation act as a single functional group. The electronic structure of such substances may be represented by the following resonance forms:

[resonance structures of α,β-unsaturated carbonyl system]

The most significant changes in the chemical properties of α,β-unsaturated carbonyl functions relative to isolated carbonyl and carbon–carbon double bonds is a modification of the reactivity of the carbon–carbon double bond. The addition of electrophilic reagents such as bromine is greatly retarded. Such additions can be made to occur only under vigorous conditions and with prolonged reaction times.

[reaction scheme: C=C–C=O with Br₂, heat, slow → C–C–C=O with Br Br]

On the other hand, the ease of nucleophilic addition to the carbon–carbon double bond is greatly enhanced. The nucleophile (Z) attacking an α,β-unsaturated carbonyl system may become attached to either the carbonyl carbon (simple addition) or to the β carbon (conjugate addition).

[reaction scheme]

Simple addition   Conjugate addition

1,4-Addition may occur with α,β-unsaturated carbonyl compounds, as it does with dienes (Section 15.11). In this case, however, the initial adduct is an enol, which quickly tautomerizes to the ketone. Whether addition to an α,β-unsaturated carbonyl compound occurs at the $>$C=O or $>$C=C$<$, or whether a mixture is obtained, depends on steric and electronic factors in both the carbonyl compounds and in the nucleophilic reagent, as well as upon the reaction conditions.

Like simple additions to carbonyl groups, conjugate addition may be achieved either by base (or direct nucleophilic) or acid catalysis.

Base-catalyzed conjugate addition of HZ

$$HZ + OH^- \rightleftharpoons Z^- + H_2O$$

[reaction scheme showing 1,4 Addition and tautomerization to Z–C–CH₂–C=O]

1,4 Addition

Acid-catalyzed conjugate addition of HZ

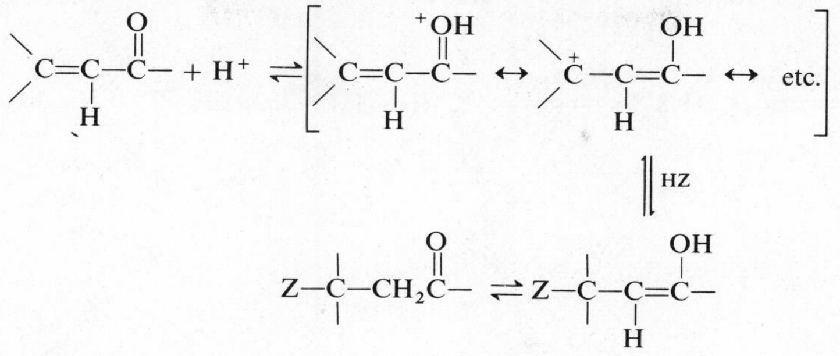

$$\text{C=C–C– + H}^+ \rightleftharpoons \left[\text{C=C–C–} \leftrightarrow \text{C–C=C–} \leftrightarrow \text{etc.} \right]$$

$$\Updownarrow \text{HZ}$$

$$\text{Z–C–CH}_2\text{C–} \rightleftharpoons \text{Z–C–C=C–}$$

Addition of H—X, H—O, H—S, *and* H—N

Hydrogen halides add readily to the carbon–carbon double bonds of α,β-unsaturated aldehydes and ketones. In the example shown below, note that the chloride adds to the β carbon, contrary to the classical Markovnikov rule. However, consideration of the mechanism of addition reveals that addition has occurred in the usual manner, so as to form the more stable intermediate.

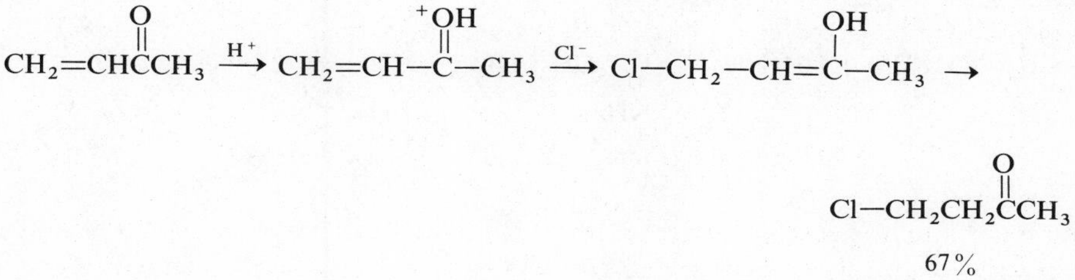

$$\text{CH}_2\text{=CHCCH}_3 \xrightarrow{\text{H}^+} \text{CH}_2\text{=CH–C–CH}_3 \xrightarrow{\text{Cl}^-} \text{Cl–CH}_2\text{–CH=C–CH}_3 \rightarrow$$

$$\text{Cl–CH}_2\text{CH}_2\text{CCH}_3$$

$$67\%$$

The acid- or base-catalyzed addition of water to an α,β-unsaturated carbonyl compound may occur. However, the initial aldol product is usually not stable to the reaction conditions and may revert to starting materials, or it may undergo a reverse (retrograde) aldol reaction.

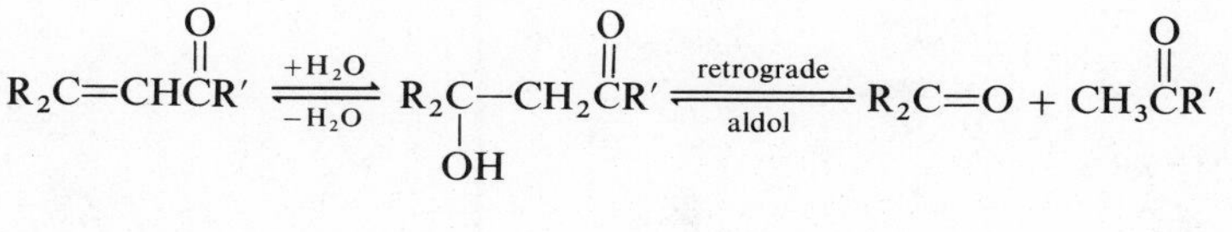

$$\text{R}_2\text{C=CHCR'} \underset{-\text{H}_2\text{O}}{\overset{+\text{H}_2\text{O}}{\rightleftharpoons}} \text{R}_2\text{C–CH}_2\text{CR'} \underset{\text{aldol}}{\overset{\text{retrograde}}{\rightleftharpoons}} \text{R}_2\text{C=O + CH}_3\text{CR'}$$

$$\overset{|}{\underset{\text{OH}}{}}$$

EXERCISE 19.19

Predict what principal product will be obtained when $(\text{CH}_3)_2\text{COHCH}_2\text{COCH}_3$ is treated with aqueous sodium hydroxide.

The addition of alkaline hydrogen peroxide is interesting in that an epoxide is formed.

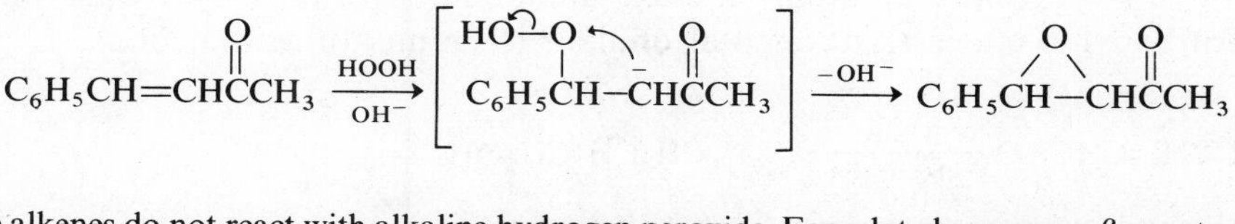

$$\text{C}_6\text{H}_5\text{CH=CHCCH}_3 \xrightarrow[\text{OH}^-]{\text{HOOH}} \left[\text{HO–O} \quad \text{C}_6\text{H}_5\text{CH–CHCCH}_3 \right] \xrightarrow{-\text{OH}^-} \text{C}_6\text{H}_5\text{CH–CHCCH}_3$$

Simple alkenes do not react with alkaline hydrogen peroxide. For related reasons, α,β-unsaturated ketones do not readily form epoxides upon treatment with peracids. Why?

The conjugate addition of an alcohol is usually best achieved under acidic conditions. A small amount of base is commonly used to catalyze the conjugate addition of a thiol.

In many cases no catalyst is necessary to cause the addition of an amine. A number of illustrative examples of such reactions are given below.

$$C_6H_5SH \xrightleftharpoons{NaOCH_3 \text{ (trace)}} C_6H_5S^- \xrightleftharpoons{\overset{O}{\overset{\|}{CH_2=CH_2CH}}} C_6H_5SCH_2-CH=\overset{O^-}{\overset{|}{CH}}$$

$$\downarrow C_6H_5SH$$

$$C_6H_5SCH_2CH_2\overset{O}{\overset{\|}{CH}}$$

$$RCH=CH\overset{O}{\overset{\|}{C}}CH_3 \xrightarrow{NaHSO_3} R\overset{}{\underset{SO_3Na}{\overset{|}{CH}}}CH_2\overset{O}{\overset{\|}{C}}CH_3 \xrightleftharpoons[OH^-]{NaHSO_3} R\overset{}{\underset{SO_3Na}{\overset{|}{CH}}}CH_2\overset{OH}{\underset{SO_3Na}{\overset{|}{C}}}CH_3$$

$$\underset{\text{(pyrrolidine)}}{NH} + C_6H_5CH=CH\overset{O}{\overset{\|}{C}}C_6H_5 \rightarrow C_6H_5\overset{}{\underset{\overset{+}{N}H}{\overset{|}{CH}}}CH=\overset{O^-}{\overset{|}{C}}C_6H_5 \rightarrow C_6H_5\overset{}{\underset{N}{\overset{|}{CH}}}CH_2\overset{O}{\overset{\|}{C}}C_6H_5$$

$$CH_2=CHCHO + NH_2NH_2 \rightarrow \overset{}{\underset{\overset{|}{NH}}{\overset{}{CH_2CH_2CHO}}} \rightarrow$$

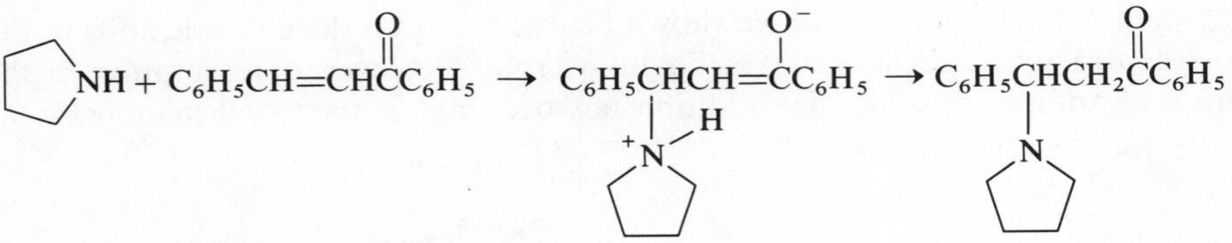

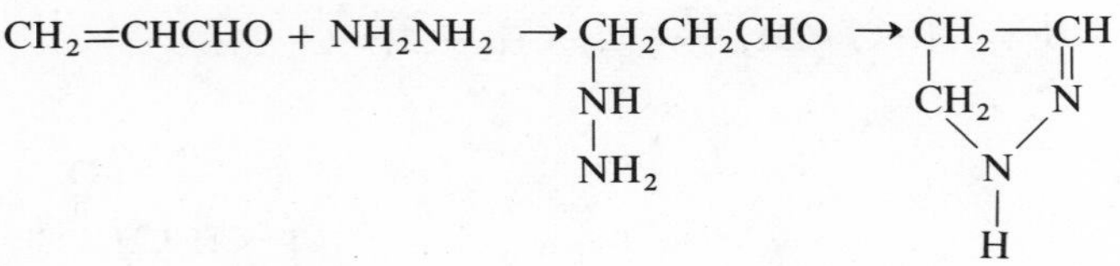

EXERCISE 19.20

Predict the products of the following reactions:

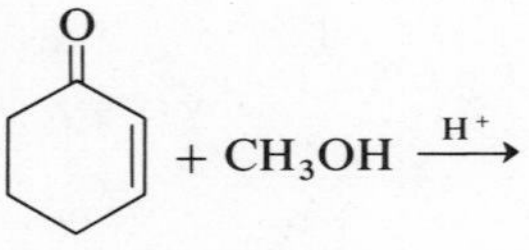

(a) 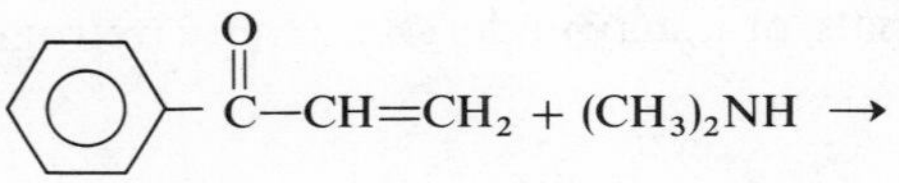 $C_6H_5-\overset{O}{\overset{\|}{C}}-CH=CH_2 + (CH_3)_2NH \rightarrow$

(b) (cyclohexenone) $+ CH_3OH \xrightarrow{H^+}$

(c) $C_6H_5-CH=CH-\overset{O}{\overset{\|}{C}}-C_6H_5 + NH_2NH_2 \rightarrow$

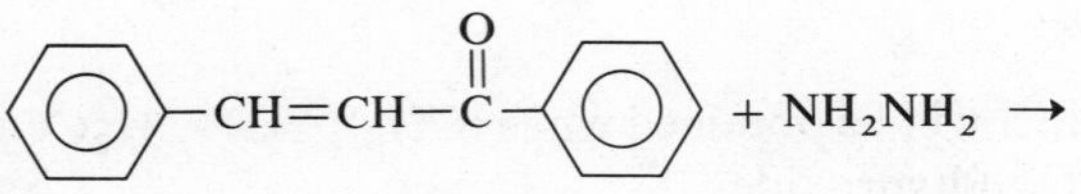

Reduction of α,β-Unsaturated Aldehydes and Ketones

Depending on the reaction conditions, lithium aluminum hydride may reduce an unsaturated carbonyl to either a saturated alcohol, or to an unsaturated alcohol.

$$C_6H_5CH=CHCHO \xrightarrow[\substack{\text{ether, 25°C} \\ \text{2. } H_2O}]{\text{1. LiAlH}_4} C_6H_5CH_2CH_2CH_2OH$$

$$C_6H_5CH=CHCHO \xrightarrow[\substack{\text{added to aldehyde,} \\ \text{ether, } -10°C \\ \text{2. } H_2O}]{\text{1. LiAlH}_4} C_6H_5CH=CHCH_2OH$$

On the other hand, sodium borohydride almost never attacks the carbon–carbon double bond.

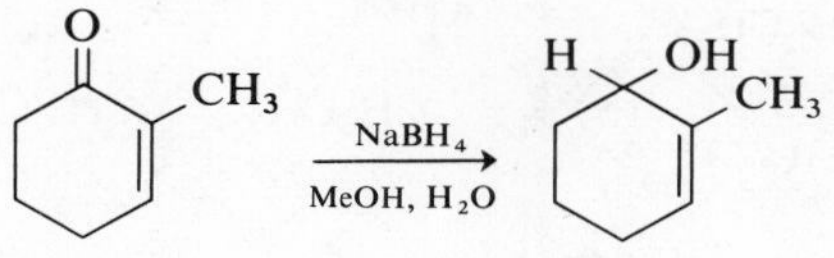

Although dissolving metal systems are ineffective in reducing simple olefins, double bonds conjugated with carbonyl groups are readily reduced. When sodium amalgam is employed, the reaction may be stopped at the intermediate stage.

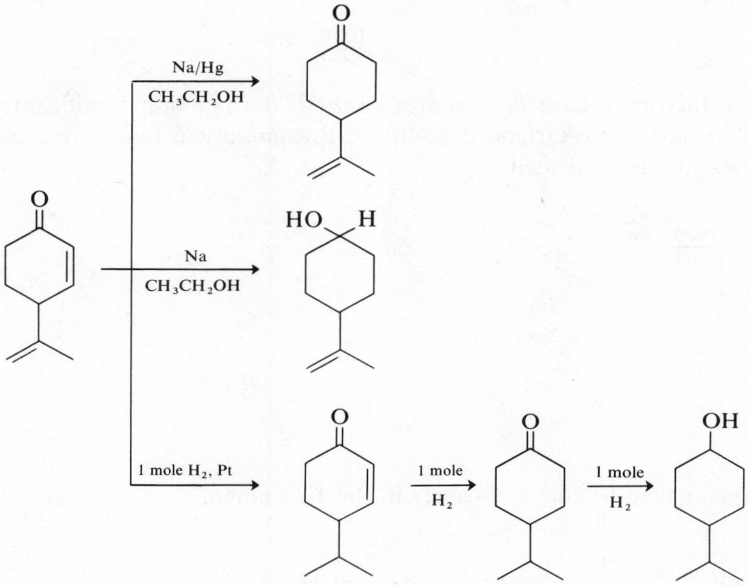

Addition of Hydrogen Cyanide

The base-catalyzed addition of hydrogen cyanide typically proceeds at the carbonyl carbon of an α,β-unsaturated aldehyde, but it will usually give the product of conjugate addition with an α,β-unsaturated ketone.

$$CH_3CH{=}CHCHO \xrightarrow[\text{aq. }H_2SO_4]{\text{NaCN(xs)}} CH_3CH{=}CHCHCN$$

(with OH on the CH)

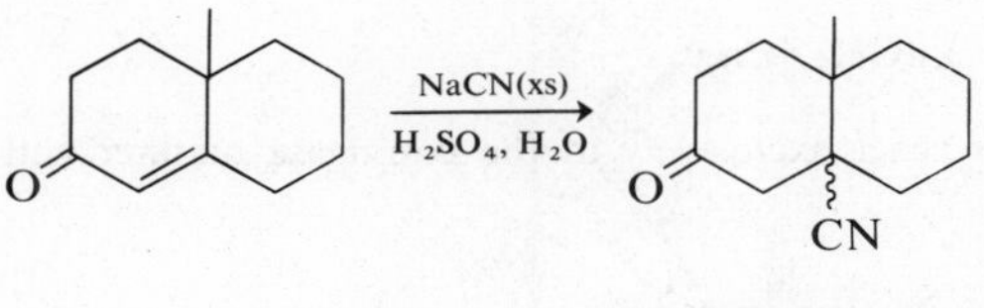

Mixture of Isomers

Addition of Organometallic Reagents

Grignard reagents may also add in the simple or conjugate manner; the reaction course is profoundly affected by steric factors. In the examples below, note the dramatic effect of the introduction of an additional methyl group on the ketone.

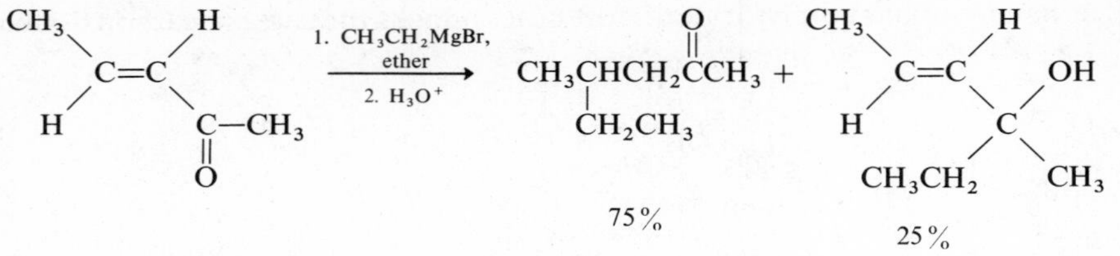

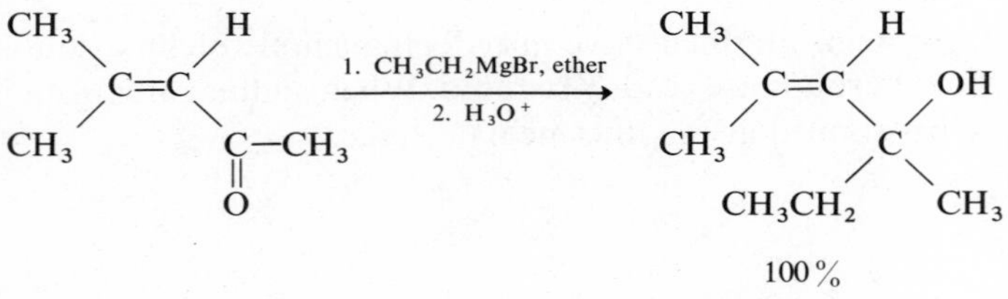

75%

25%

100%

The addition of a catalytic amount of a cuprous salt to the reaction significantly increases the amount of conjugate Grignard addition. Presumably, a highly reactive transient organocopper species is formed.

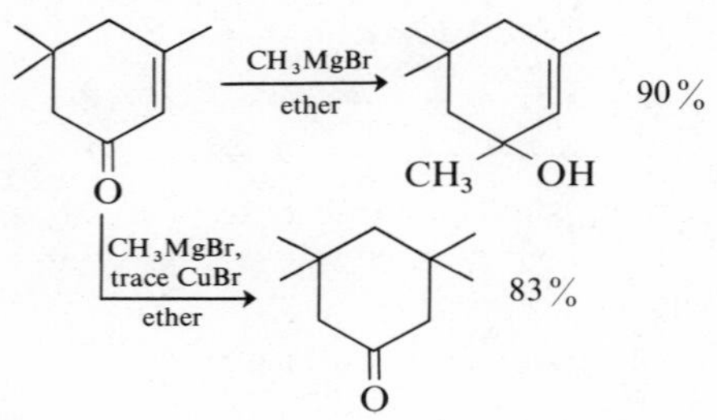

90%

83%

Organolithium reagents tend to add exclusively in the 1,2 manner.

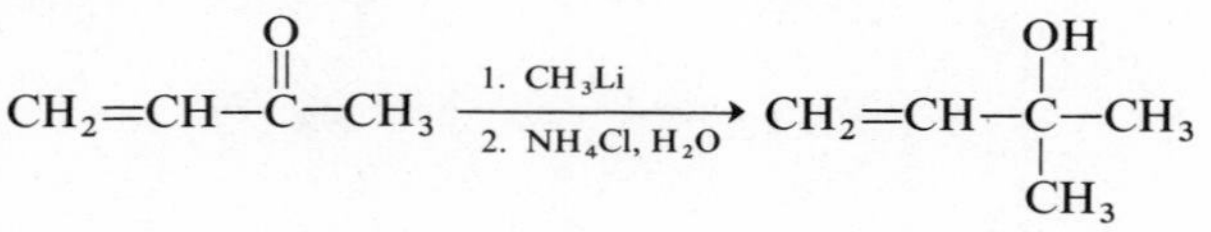

$$CH_2{=}CH{-}\overset{\overset{\displaystyle O}{\|}}{C}{-}CH_3 \xrightarrow[\text{2. NH}_4\text{Cl, H}_2\text{O}]{\text{1. CH}_3\text{Li}} CH_2{=}CH{-}\underset{\underset{\displaystyle CH_3}{|}}{\overset{\overset{\displaystyle OH}{|}}{C}}{-}CH_3$$

From a preparative point of view, if 1,2 addition is wanted, the organolithium compound is ordinarily used. If conjugate addition is wanted, cuprous salt is used as a catalyst, along with the Grignard reagent.

Organocopper Compounds. Alkyl and aryl lithium compounds react with an equivalent of cuprous iodide to produce insoluble polymeric organocopper compounds.

$$RLi + CuI \longrightarrow (RCu)_n + LiI$$

Addition of a second equivalent of organolithium reagent produces the soluble lithium dialkylcopper reagents, for example, lithium dimethylcopper.

$$CH_3Li + CuI \xrightarrow{\text{ether}} (CH_3Cu)_n \xrightarrow[\text{ether}]{\text{CH}_3\text{Li}} Li(CH_3)_2Cu$$

Lithium dimethylcopper and related reagents react exclusively in the conjugate manner with α,β-unsaturated carbonyl compounds.

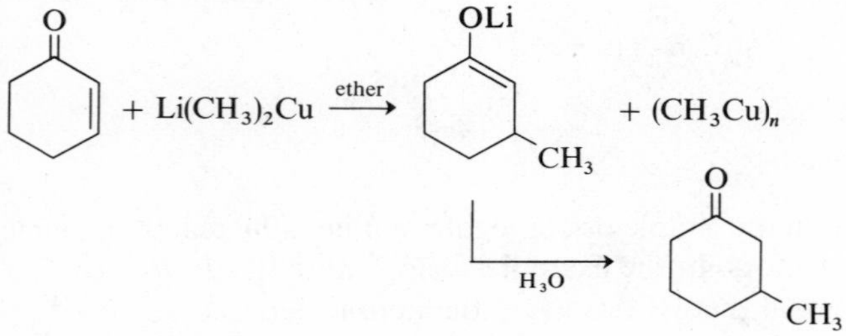

These reagents react very sluggishly or not at all with saturated ketones, esters, etc. They do, however, react with a variety of other functional groups, for example,

$$CH_3CH_2CH_2CH_2Br \xrightarrow{Li(CH_3)_2Cu} CH_3CH_2CH_2CH_2CH_3$$

$$C_6H_5I \xrightarrow{Li(CH_3)_2Cu} C_6H_5CH_3$$

$$RCOCl \xrightarrow{Li(CH_3)_2Cu} RCOCH_3$$

Condensation with Ylides

The Wittig reagents condense in a simple 1,2 manner with unsaturated carbonyl compounds.

Whether the sulfur ylides condense to give oxiranes or cyclopropanes appears to be mainly a function of the nature of the ylide. In general, dimethylsulfonium methylide yields oxiranes, whereas dimethyloxosulfonium methylide gives cyclopropyl ketones.

Michael† Addition Reactions

Enolates and related carbon nucleophiles may combine with α,β-unsaturated carbonyl compounds in the conjugate manner. An example is the addition of acetophenone to benzalacetophenone.

† Arthur Michael. 1853–1942. Born Buffalo, New York. Tufts and Harvard Universities.

Similar conjugate additions of an enolate may occur with α,β-unsaturated esters, nitriles, nitro compounds, and sulfones. This type of reaction, although discovered by Claisen, was first extensively studied by Michael and is generally called the *Michael reaction*. Such reactions are usually run with catalytic amounts of a base such as sodium hydroxide, sodium ethoxide, or an amine. Some examples are given below.

Ring compounds can often be made either through double Michael additions

or by Michael additions followed by intramolecular aldol condensations.

Such reactions are extremely useful for synthesis of complex molecules; such applications will be discussed in detail in Section 34.1.

EXERCISE 19.21

Write the detailed mechanisms of the previous five reactions.

19.18   Summary of Synthetic Methods for Aldehydes

Continuing our usual practice, this section summarizes for review purposes useful synthetic methods which are available for the preparation of aldehydes. Section 19.19 gives similar information for ketones.

Most of the synthetic methods for aldehydes have been covered in previous chapters. Those which have not yet been discussed (Methods 2 and 3) utilize carboxylic acids or their derivatives as starting materials, and these will be covered in Chapter 20. A study of these particular reactions may be postponed until Chapter 20 is covered.

General Methods

1. Oxidation of primary alcohols (Section 18.7)

$$RCH_2OH \xrightarrow{[O]} RCHO$$

   a. With Cr^{VI}.
   b. With "active MnO_2" for allylic and benzylic alcohols only.
2. Partial reduction of acid derivatives (Section 20.8).
   a. Rosenmund reduction of acid chlorides

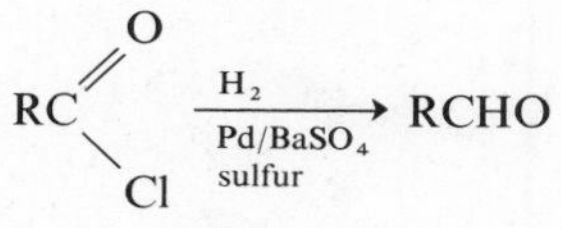

$$RC\underset{Cl}{\overset{O}{\big\backslash}} \xrightarrow[\substack{Pd/BaSO_4 \\ sulfur}]{H_2} RCHO$$

   b. Hydride reductions

$$RCN \xrightarrow{Al(i\text{-}Bu)_2H} \xrightarrow{H_3O^+} RCHO$$

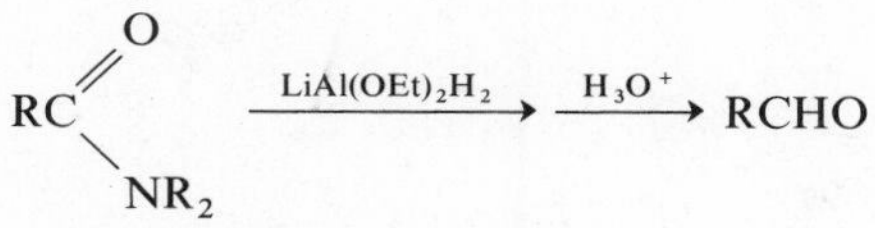

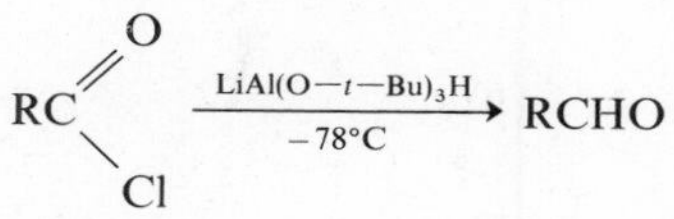

$$RC\underset{NR_2}{\overset{O}{\big\backslash}} \xrightarrow{LiAl(OEt)_2H_2} \xrightarrow{H_3O^+} RCHO$$

$$RC\underset{Cl}{\overset{O}{\big\backslash}} \xrightarrow[-78°C]{LiAl(O-t-Bu)_3H} RCHO$$

3. Reactions of organometallic reagents (Section 20.9).
   a. Grignard reagents and ethyl orthoformate

$$RMgX + HC(OCH_2CH_3)_3 \rightarrow RCH(OCH_2CH_3)_2 \xrightarrow{H_3O^+} RCHO$$

   b. Addition of organometallic compounds to dimethylformamide

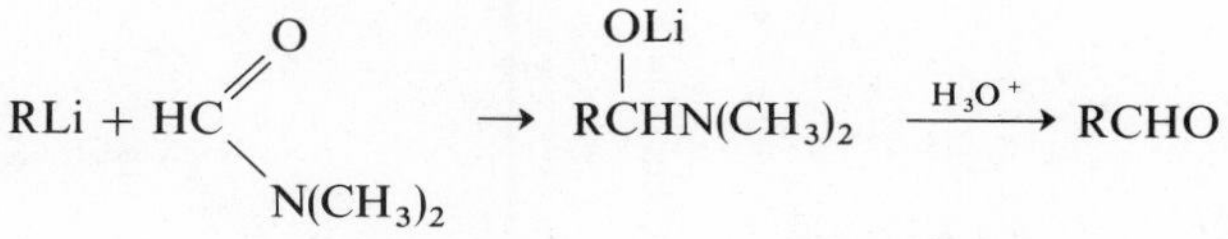

$$RLi + HC\underset{N(CH_3)_2}{\overset{O}{\big\backslash}} \rightarrow RCH\overset{OLi}{\underset{}{\big|}}N(CH_3)_2 \xrightarrow{H_3O^+} RCHO$$

4. Formylation of aromatic compounds. (These reactions are mostly of the Friedel–Crafts type. They are of limited use.)

   a. Gattermann–Koch reaction

$$ArH + CO + HCl \xrightarrow[Cu_2Cl_2]{AlCl_3} ArCHO$$

   b. Gattermann reaction

$$ArH + HCN + HCl \xrightarrow{ZnCl_2} \xrightarrow{H_3O^+} ArCHO$$

c. Reimer–Tiemann reaction

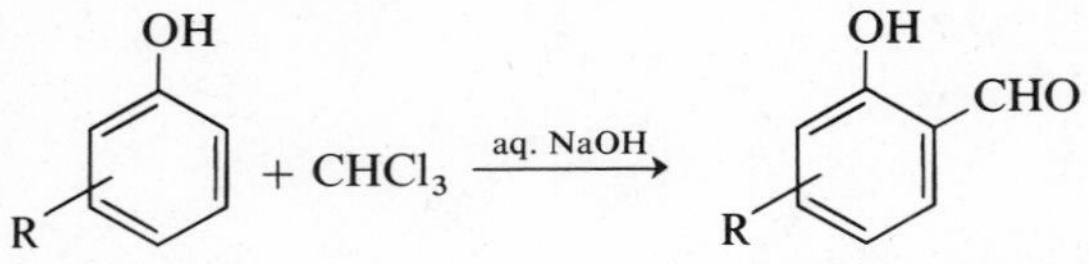

(Phenols) + $CHCl_3$ $\xrightarrow{\text{aq. NaOH}}$ o-Hydroxybenzaldehydes (salicylaldehydes)

d. Dimethylformamide–phosphoryl chloride reagent

$$HCON(CH_3)_2 + POCl_3 \rightarrow (CH_3)_2\overset{+}{N}{=}C\overset{O-POCl_2}{\underset{H}{\diagdown}}\quad Cl^-$$

$$ArH + (CH_3)_2\overset{+}{N}{=}C\overset{OPOCl_2}{\underset{H}{\diagdown}}\quad Cl^- \xrightarrow{H_2O} ArCHO$$

Incidental Methods

1. Ozonolysis of alkenes (Section 15.10).

$$RCH{=}CHR' \xrightarrow[\text{2. Zn, H}_2\text{O}]{\text{1. O}_3} RCHO + R'CHO$$

2. Oxidative cleavage of glycols (Section 18.7).

$$\underset{\underset{HO\ \ OH}{|\ \ \ |}}{RCHCHR'} \xrightarrow[\text{H}_2\text{O}]{\text{NaIO}_4} RCHO + R'CHO$$

3. Hydrolysis of aldehyde derivatives.

Acetals (Section 19.2)
Sodium hydrogen sulfite addition compounds (Section 19.6)
Oximes
Hydrazones
Enamines } (Section 19.7)
Imines, etc. } $\xrightarrow{H_3O^+}$ RCHO

19.19 Summary of Synthetic Methods for Ketones

As usual, the student will find it helpful to review at this time each of the methods below which have been covered previously, in Chapters 15–18. Methods for which references are given to later chapters need not be studied at this time, as they are included for later review.

1. Oxidation of secondary alcohols (Section 18.7).

$$R_2CHOH \xrightarrow{[O]} R_2C{=}O$$

a. $Na_2Cr_2O_7/H_2SO_4$.
b. CrO_3/pyridine.
c. With active MnO_2, for allylic and benzylic alcohols only.
d. With CH_3SOCH_3, dicyclohexylcarbodiimide, H_3PO_4 (Section 26.6).

2. Acetoacetic ester synthesis (Section 20.15).

$$RX + CH_3\overset{\overset{\displaystyle O}{\|}}{C}CH_2COOCH_2CH_3 \xrightarrow[\substack{CH_3CH_2OH \\ 2.\ H_3O^+}]{1.\ NaOCH_2CH_3} CH_3\overset{\overset{\displaystyle O}{\|}}{C}CH_2R$$

3. Carbonylation of alkylboranes (Section 15.9).

$$(CH_3)_2CH\overset{\overset{\displaystyle CH_3}{|}}{\underset{\underset{\displaystyle CH_3}{|}}{C}}-BH_2 \xrightarrow[2.\ R'CH=CH_2]{1.\ RCH=CH_2} (CH_3)_2CH\overset{\overset{\displaystyle CH_3}{|}}{\underset{\underset{\displaystyle CH_3}{|}}{C}}-B\overset{CH_2CH_2R}{\underset{CH_2CH_2R'}{}} \xrightarrow[H_2O]{CO}$$

$$(CH_3)_2CH\overset{\overset{\displaystyle CH_3}{|}}{\underset{\underset{\displaystyle CH_3}{|}}{C}}-\overset{}{\underset{\underset{\displaystyle OH}{|}}{B}}-\overset{\overset{\displaystyle CH_2CH_2R}{|}}{\underset{\underset{\displaystyle OH}{|}}{C}}-CH_2CH_2R' \xrightarrow[NaOAc]{H_2O_2} \overset{RCH_2CH_2}{\underset{R'CH_2CH_2}{}}C{=}O$$

4. Friedel–Crafts acylation (Sections 16.5 and 20.10).

$$ArH + RC\overset{\overset{\displaystyle O}{\|}}{\underset{\underset{\displaystyle Cl}{}}{}} \xrightarrow{AlCl_3} Ar\overset{\overset{\displaystyle O}{\|}}{C}R + HCl$$

5. Hydration of acetylenes (Section 15.16).

$$RC{\equiv}CH \xrightarrow[aq.\ H_2SO_4]{HgSO_4} R\overset{\overset{\displaystyle O}{\|}}{C}CH_3$$

6. Addition of organometallic reagents to acids and derivatives (Section 20.9).

$$RC\overset{\overset{\displaystyle O}{\|}}{\underset{\underset{\displaystyle Cl}{}}{}} + R'_2Cd \rightarrow \xrightarrow{H_3O^+} R-\overset{\overset{\displaystyle O}{\|}}{C}-R'$$

R' = primary alkyl or aryl only

$$RC\overset{\overset{\displaystyle O}{\|}}{\underset{\underset{\displaystyle OH}{}}{}} + 2\ CH_3Li \xrightarrow{-78°C} \xrightarrow{H_3O^+} R\overset{\overset{\displaystyle O}{\|}}{C}CH_3$$

$$RC{\equiv}N + R'MgX \rightarrow \xrightarrow{H_3O^+} R\overset{\overset{\displaystyle O}{\|}}{C}R'$$

$$R-\overset{\overset{\displaystyle O}{\|}}{C}-NR_2 + R'MgX \rightarrow \xrightarrow{H_3O^+} R-\overset{\overset{\displaystyle O}{\|}}{C}-R'$$

$$R-C(OEt)_3 + R'MgX \rightarrow \xrightarrow{H_3O^+} R-\overset{\overset{\displaystyle O}{\|}}{C}-R' \quad \text{(Section 21.4).}$$

7. Rearrangement of hydroperoxides (Section 23.1).

$$\langle\!\bigcirc\!\rangle-\overset{\overset{\displaystyle CH_3}{|}}{\underset{\underset{\displaystyle CH_3}{|}}{C}}-H + O_2 \rightarrow \langle\!\bigcirc\!\rangle-\overset{\overset{\displaystyle CH_3}{|}}{\underset{\underset{\displaystyle CH_3}{|}}{C}}-OOH \xrightarrow{H_3O^+}$$

$$(CH_3)_2CO + \langle\!\bigcirc\!\rangle-OH$$

8. Reduction of acyloins (Section 20.17).

$$2\,RCOOCH_2CH_3 \xrightarrow{Na} R\overset{\overset{\displaystyle O}{\|}}{C}\overset{\overset{\displaystyle OH}{|}}{C}HR \xrightarrow[HOAc]{Zn} R\overset{\overset{\displaystyle O}{\|}}{C}CH_2R$$

Acyloin

9. Condensation of esters with methanesulfinyl carbanion (Section 26.6)

$$R\overset{\overset{\displaystyle O}{\|}}{C}{-}OCH_3 \;+\; {}^-CH_2SCH_3 \;\rightarrow\; R{-}\overset{\overset{\displaystyle O}{\|}}{C}{-}CH_2SCH_3 \xrightarrow{Al/Hg} R\overset{\overset{\displaystyle O}{\|}}{C}CH_3$$

Incidental Methods

1. Rearrangement of 1,2-glycols (pinacol rearrangement) (Section 18.6).

$$\underset{\underset{\displaystyle HO\quad OH}{|\quad\;|}}{R_2C{-}CR_2} \xrightarrow[acid]{strong} R_3C\overset{\overset{\displaystyle O}{\|}}{C}R$$

2. Thermal decarboxylation of carboxylate salts (Section 20.17).

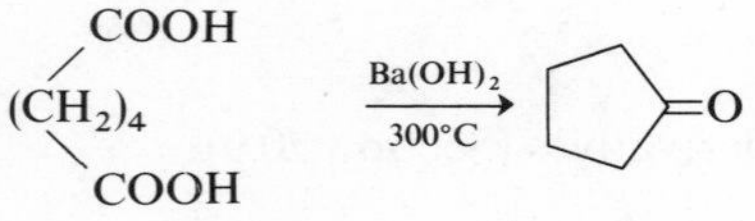

$$(CH_2)_4\overset{\nearrow COOH}{\underset{\searrow COOH}{}} \xrightarrow[300°C]{Ba(OH)_2} \bigcirc\!\!=\!\!O$$

3. Ozonolysis of alkenes (Section 15.10).

$$R_2C{=}CR_2' \xrightarrow{[O]} R_2C{=}O + O{=}CR_2'$$

4. Oxidative cleavage of glycols (Section 18.7).
   a. NaIO$_4$ plus catalytic amount of KMnO$_4$.
   b. NaIO$_4$ plus catalytic amount of OsO$_4$.

5. Hydrolysis of ketone derivatives (Sections 19.2, 19.6, 19.7).

$$\left.\begin{array}{l}\text{Ketals}\\ \text{Oximes}\\ \text{Enamines}\\ \text{Imines, etc.}\end{array}\right\} \xrightarrow{H_3O^+} \overset{R}{\underset{R}{}}\!\!C{=}O$$

PROBLEMS

1. Write structures for the following compounds:
    (a) Isobutyraldehyde
    (b) *p*-Chloroacetophenone
    (c) 2-Hexanone
    (d) 2,2,6-Trimethylcyclohexanone
    (e) Ethyl isopropyl ketone
    (f) 4-Methoxybenzaldehyde
    (g) Methyl vinyl ketone
    (h) *trans*-3-Penten-2-one

2. The infrared and nmr spectra of compound A, which has the formula C$_{10}$H$_{12}$O, are reproduced here. Suggest the structure of compound A.

Infrared spectrum of compound A, Problem 2.

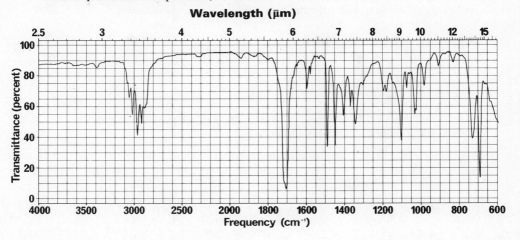

NMR spectrum of compound A, Problem 2.

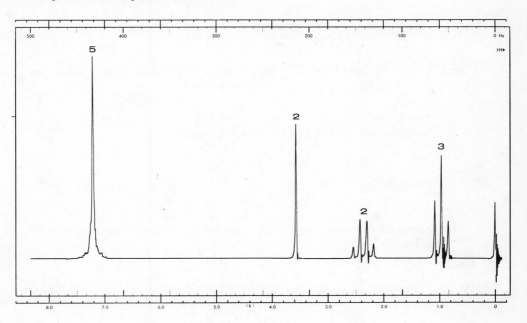

3. The addition of hydrogen cyanide to carbonyl compounds is a readily reversible reaction.

$$\text{C=O} + \text{HCN} \rightleftharpoons \text{C}\begin{smallmatrix}\text{OH}\\\text{CN}\end{smallmatrix}$$

Indicate in each case which of the following would be expected to contain more cyanohydrin at equilibrium in the above reaction. Indicate your reasoning.

(a) H_2CO or CH_3COCH_3

(b) CH_3COCH_3 or CH_3COCCl_3

(c) ⬡—CHO or ⬡—C(=O)—CH₃

(d) ⬠=O or ⬜=O

4.   The infrared spectrum of compound B, $C_6H_{10}O$, is reproduced. On the basis of the spectrum choose the correct structure from the following possibilities:

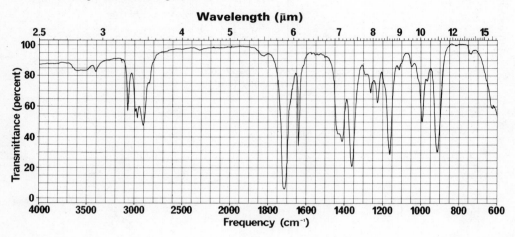

Infrared spectrum of compound B, Problem 4.

5.   (a) Predict the rate expression for the following reaction.

$$\begin{matrix} \diagdown \\ \diagup \end{matrix} C{=}O + Z^- \rightarrow \begin{matrix} \diagdown \\ \diagup \end{matrix} C \begin{matrix} Z \\ O^- \end{matrix}$$

   (b) Arrange the following pairs of compounds in order of *expected reactivity* with Z^-. Explain.

   (a) $(CH_3)_3C{-}\overset{\overset{\displaystyle O}{\|}}{C}{-}H$ and $CH_3{-}\overset{\overset{\displaystyle O}{\|}}{C}{-}H$

   (b) Ⓟ$-\overset{\overset{\displaystyle O}{\|}}{C}{-}H$ and $CH_3{-}\overset{\overset{\displaystyle O}{\|}}{C}{-}H$

   (c) $ClCH_2{-}\overset{\overset{\displaystyle O}{\|}}{C}{-}H$ and $CH_3{-}\overset{\overset{\displaystyle O}{\|}}{C}{-}H$

6.   Suggest reagents for the conversion of 3-pentanone to:
   (a) Triethylcarbinol
   (b) 2,3-Pentanedione
   (c) 3,4-Diethyl-3,4-hexanediol
   (d) 3,3-Difluoropentane
   (e) 3-Pentanol
   (f) Pentane
   (g) 2,2-Diethyl-1,3-dioxane
   (h) 3,4-Diethyl-2-hexene
   (i) 2,2-Diethyloxirane
   (j) 2,2-Dibromo-3-pentanone

7.   Suggest a method for the conversion of:

   (a) [structure: cyclopentanone] to [structure: cyclobutane-COOH]   (Optional problem)

(b) 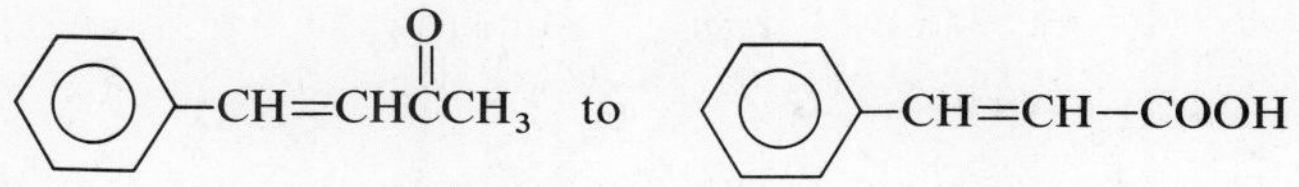 [structure] $-CH=CHCCH_3$ to [structure] $-CH=CH-COOH$

(c) 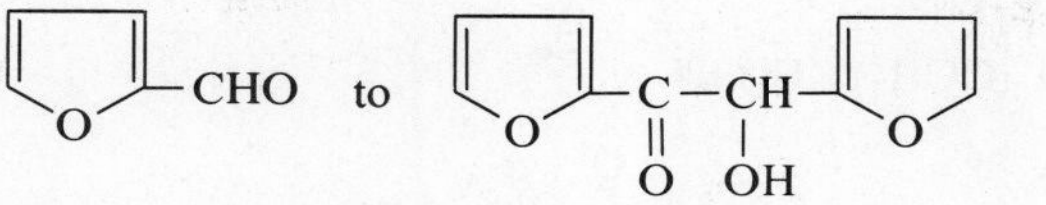 [structure] $-CHO$ to [structure] $C-CH-$ [structure] (with O and OH below)

(d) $R-OH$ to $R-CH_2-OH$ (Homologation)

(e) 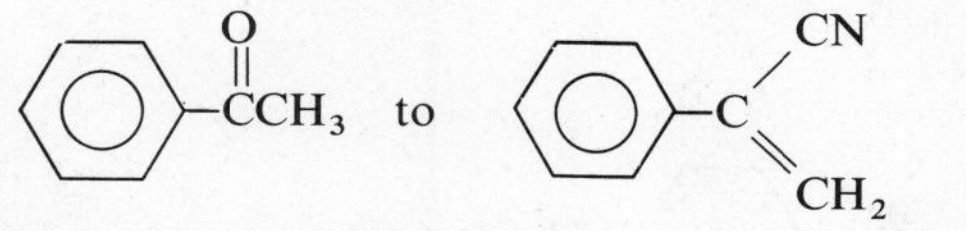 [structure] $-CCH_3$ to [structure] C with CN and CH_2

8. Using acetone and methyl iodide as the only sources of carbon atoms, devise a synthesis of each of the following:

    (a) $(CH_3)_3COH$ (b) $(CH_3)_3CCOOH$

    (c) $(CH_3)_2C=CHC(CH_3)_2$ (with OH above the CH)   (d) $(CH_3)_2C=C(CH_3)_2$

9. 2-Cyclohexenone is available commercially for $84 per 100 g. Illustrate how 2-cyclo-hexenone could be converted to:

    (a) 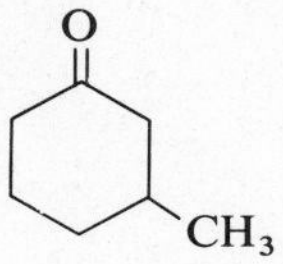 [structure with O and CH$_3$]

    (b) 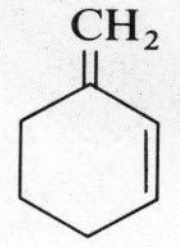 [structure with CH$_2$]

    (c) 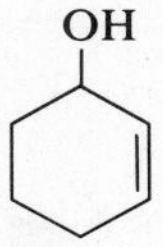 [structure with OH]

    (d) 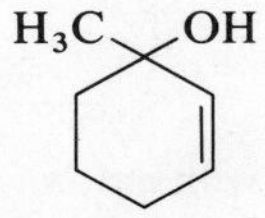 [structure with H$_3$C and OH]

    (e) 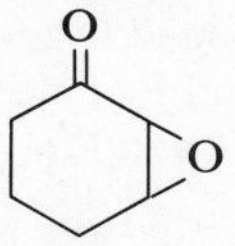 [structure with O and O]

    (f) 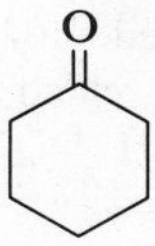 [structure with O]

10. Suggest mechanisms for each of the following reactions:

    (a) 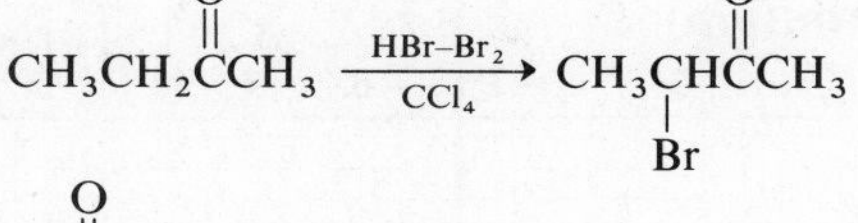 $CH_3CH_2CCH_3$ $\xrightarrow[CCl_4]{HBr-Br_2}$ CH_3CHCCH_3 (with O above, Br below)

    (b) 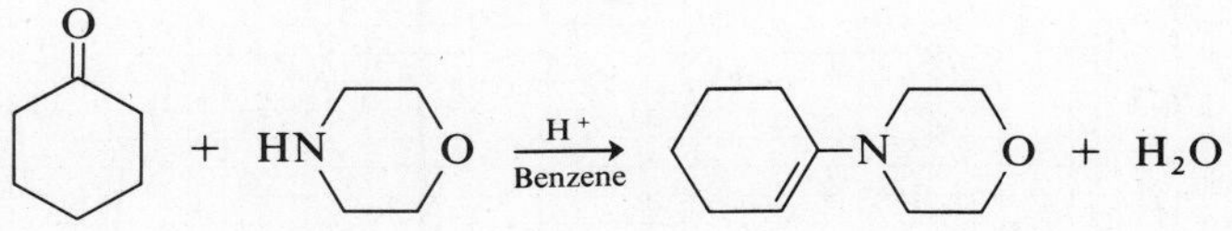 [structure] $+ HN$ [ring with O] $\xrightarrow[Benzene]{H^+}$ [structure] $-N$ [ring with O] $+ H_2O$

    (c) 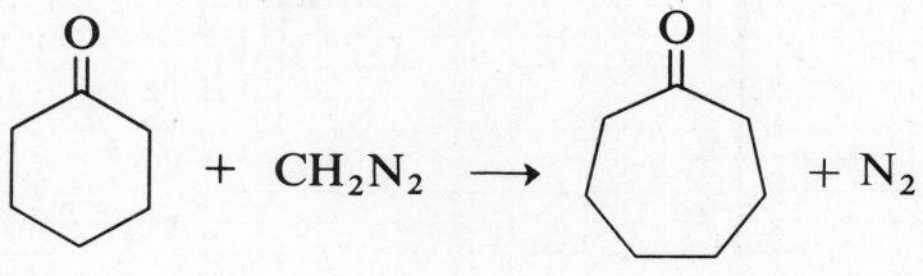 [structure with O] $+ CH_2N_2 \longrightarrow$ [structure with O] $+ N_2$

    (d) 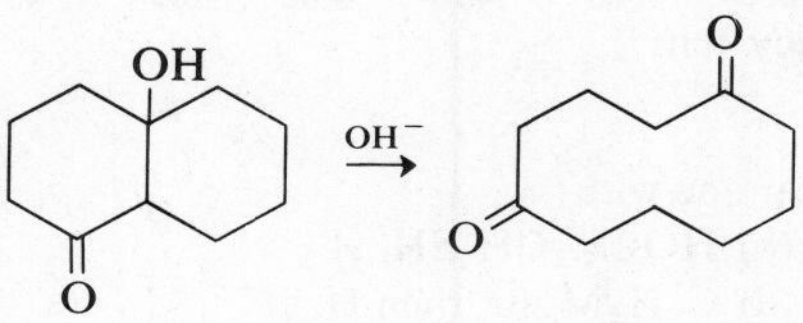 [structure with OH and O] $\xrightarrow{OH^-}$ [structure with two O]

(e) $\begin{array}{c} CH_3 \\ \\ CH_3 \end{array} C{=}O + HSCH_2CH_2OH \xrightarrow{BF_3} \begin{array}{c} CH_3 \quad S{-}CH_2 \\ \quad C \\ CH_3 \quad O{-}CH_2 \end{array} + H_2O$

(f) $H_2O + CH_2O \rightarrow HOCH_2(OCH_2)_nCH_2OH$

(g) $\underset{\text{Ph}}{\bigcirc}\overset{O}{\overset{\|}{C}}CH_2CH_2CH_2Br \xrightarrow{OH^-} \underset{\text{Ph}}{\bigcirc}\overset{O}{\overset{\|}{C}}\triangleleft$

(h) $CH_3CHO + O_2 \rightarrow CH_3COOH$

(i) $\underset{\underset{H}{N}}{\bigcirc} + CH_2{=}CHCCH_3 \xrightarrow{H^+} \underset{N}{\bigcirc}CH_2CH_2\overset{O}{\overset{\|}{C}}CH_3$

(j) $3\,CH_3COCH_3 \xrightarrow{\text{strong } H^+}$ [1,3,5-trimethylbenzene]

(k) [4-methyl-2-cyclobutenone structure] $\xrightarrow{OH^-} CH_3\overset{O}{\overset{\|}{C}}CH_2\overset{O}{\overset{\|}{C}}CH_3$

(l) [cyclohexanone] $+ LiAlH_4 \rightarrow \left(\underset{H}{\bigcirc}{-}O{-} \right)_4 AlLi$

11. Compound C upon treatment with chromic anhydride/pyridine reagent gave a new compound D. The infrared spectrum of compound D is shown below. Compound D reverted to compound C when treated with sodium borohydride. Compound D and 2,4-dinitrophenylhydrazine reagent yielded a yellow crystalline compound E of melting point 142°C which analyzed for $C_{11}H_{12}N_4O_4$. Write structures for C, D, and E.

Infrared spectrum of compound D, Problem 11.

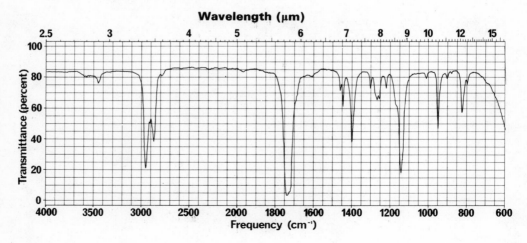

12. Write equations for the reaction of cyclopentanone with:
(a) $H_2^{18}O$, H^+ (b) $HOCH_2CH_2SH$, H^+
(c) $NaBH_4$ (d) C_6H_5MgBr, then H_3O^+

(e) PhCOOOH
(g) Cl_2 + HCl
(i) CH_3Li, then NH_4Cl
(k) $(C_6H_5)_3P{=}CH_2$
(m) CrO_4^{2-}, H^+, heat

(f) NH_2OH
(h) $NH_2NHCONH_2$
(j) $(CH_3)_3CMgCl$
(l) Zn(Hg)/HCl

13. Write the structures of the products of the principal reaction, if any, of propionaldehyde with:
   (a) Absolute alcohol and dry HCl
   (b) Phenylhydrazine
   (c) Tollens' reagent
   (d) HCN + CN^-
   (e) Butadiene
   (f) Lithium aluminum hydride

14. Write each step, including all essential reagents and conditions, for converting acetophenone into:
   (a) Ethylbenzene
   (b) Diphenylmethylcarbinol
   (c) Styrene

15. A water-soluble liquid, bp about 60°C, shows strong absorption at 1720 cm^{-1} in the infrared. Its nmr spectrum shows a doublet at δ 9.5 (1H), a complex multiplet at δ 2.6 (1H), and a doublet at δ 1.1 (6H). Write a structure consistent with these data.

16. A water-soluble liquid did not react with Tollens' reagent, but did react with hydroxylamine. It could be identified by two observations: (1) treatment with iodine and NaOH solution gave a yellow precipitate of iodoform; (2) treatment with hydrogen and a catalyst produced an alcohol that could not be resolved into optically active forms by any method. What was it?

CHAPTER 20

REACTIONS OF CARBOXYLIC ACIDS
AND THEIR DERIVATIVES

The carboxyl group is one of the most common functional groups. The chemistry of the carboxyl group includes reactions involving (1) removal of the acidic proton by a base; (2) attack by the carboxyl group or the carboxylate ion acting as a nucleophile upon other substrates; (3) attack of another nucleophile on the carbonyl portion of the carboxyl group; and (4) attack of a base upon an α hydrogen, activated by the carbonyl group of the carboxylic acid or derivative. Furthermore, combinations of these types of reactions are common.

$$
\begin{array}{c}
\overset{\displaystyle \overset{..}{\underset{..}{O}}:}{\underset{\underset{\displaystyle B:}{\overset{\displaystyle |}{\underset{\displaystyle \textcircled{4}}{H}}}{\cdots C \cdots \overset{\textcircled{2}}{C} \cdots \overset{..}{\underset{..}{O}} \cdots H \overset{\textcircled{1}}{\leftarrow} :B}}}
\end{array}
$$

:Z = nucleophile

20.1   Simple Acid–Base Reactions

A simple acid–base reaction—salt formation—occurs when a carboxylic acid comes in contact with an organic or inorganic base. Triethylamine, an organic base, will react with a carboxylic acid to give the triethylammonium salt of the acid. The reaction is reversible.

$$
\begin{array}{ccc}
& C_2H_5 & C_2H_5 \\
\parallel & / & + / \\
R-\overset{O}{\overset{\parallel}{C}}-O-H + :N-C_2H_5 & \rightleftharpoons R-CO_2^- + HN-C_2H_5 \\
& \backslash & \backslash \\
& C_2H_5 & C_2H_5
\end{array}
$$

The strong inorganic base, sodium hydroxide, also reacts to form a salt.

$$
R-\overset{O}{\overset{\parallel}{C}}-\overset{..}{O}-H + :\overset{Na^+}{\overset{..}{O}}H^- \rightleftharpoons R-CO_2^- + Na^+ + H_2O
$$

Salt

The equilibrium is more on the side of the salt in this case because sodium hydroxide is a stronger base than triethylamine. The stronger the acid or the stronger the base, the more the equilibrium favors the salt. A useful and common method of measuring acid strength is to use hydroxide ion as a common base in a comparison of acids, and to make a determination of the pH at which the concentrations of the acid and its anion are exactly equal. This is done by titrating the acid with NaOH to exactly 50% neutralization and determining the pH at this point with a pH meter. The higher this pH, the weaker is the acid.

20.2   Inductive Effect and Acid Strength

Trichloroacetic acid is about 15,000 times more acidic than acetic acid. The inductive effect of the chlorine-to-carbon bond, $C \rightarrow Cl$ (Section 19.1) is responsible for this difference. It results in a small positive charge on the carbon to which it is attached, which in turn induces a smaller positive charge on the adjacent atom. This inductive effect stabilizes the carboxylate ion of trichloroacetic acid compared to the carboxylate ion of acetic acid by reducing the amount of negative charge that must be accumulated in the carboxylate group.

$$CH_3-\overset{O}{\overset{\|}{C}}-O-H + \bar{O}H \rightleftharpoons \left[CH_3-\overset{O}{\overset{\|}{C}}-O^- \leftrightarrow CH_3-\overset{O^-}{\overset{|}{C}}=O \right] + H_2O$$

$$\overset{Cl}{\underset{Cl}{Cl\leftarrow C}}\leftarrow\overset{O}{\overset{\|}{C}}-O-H + \bar{O}H \rightleftharpoons \left[\overset{Cl}{\underset{Cl}{Cl\leftarrow C}}\leftarrow\overset{O}{\overset{\|}{C}}-O^- \leftrightarrow \overset{Cl}{\underset{Cl}{Cl\leftarrow C}}\leftarrow\overset{O^-}{\overset{|}{C}}=O \right] + H_2O$$

The inductive effect decreases rapidly with distance, as shown by a comparison of α-, β-, and γ-chlorobutyric acids with butyric acid itself. In the α position, one chlorine increases the acidity about nine times. In the β position, the effect of the chlorine is reduced, giving a sixfold increase in acidity, and in the γ position, one chlorine only doubles the strength of the acid.

$$CH_3CH_2\overset{Cl}{\overset{|}{C}}H\overset{O}{\overset{\|}{C}}-OH > CH_3\overset{Cl}{\overset{|}{C}}HCH_2\overset{O}{\overset{\|}{C}}-OH > ClCH_2CH_2CH_2\overset{O}{\overset{\|}{C}}-OH >$$

Relative   9   6   2
acid
strengths

$$CH_3CH_2CH_2\overset{O}{\overset{\|}{C}}-OH$$
1

EXERCISE 20.1

List in order of increasing acid strength:

$$\underset{NO_2}{\overset{|}{CH_2}}CH_2COOH, \quad CH_3\underset{NO_2}{\overset{|}{CH}}COOH, \quad CH_3\underset{Cl}{\overset{|}{CH}}COOH, \quad CH_3CH_2COOH$$

20.3   Resonance Effect and Acid Strength

The effect of resonance is also important in determining acid strength. *p*-Nitrobenzoic acid is about six times stronger than benzoic acid, while *p*-methoxybenzoic acid is only one-half as strong. The ability of the nitro group to attract electrons from the benzene ring results in a positive charge on the carbon atom adjacent to the carboxyl group, which in turn induces a positive charge on the carboxyl carbon, stabilizing the corresponding carboxylate ion by reducing the electron density about the oxygens (Section 16.6).

The effect in *p*-methoxybenzoic acid is opposite to that in *p*-nitrobenzoic acid. The methoxyl group is able to donate electrons to the benzene ring and build up negative charge in the carbonyl group of the acid. This additional negative charge tends to hold the proton, and it also tends to increase the negative charge in the carboxyl group of the carboxylate ion. The larger the negative charge in the carboxylate ion, the more it will attract a proton from water to reverse the initial acid–base reaction.

The resonance effect cannot operate in a saturated system: Methoxyacetic acid, for example, is stronger than acetic acid, owing solely to the electron-withdrawing inductive effect of the methoxy group.

20.4   Carboxylate as a Nucleophile

The carboxylate ion is a very good nucleophile for attack on carbon.

To achieve such a displacement reaction on carbon, the organic acid is first deliberately converted to a sodium, ammonium, or organic amine salt. The salt is chosen so as to be soluble in the reaction mixture. The classical identification of carboxylic acids involves the preparation of the easily crystallizable phenacyl esters by this reaction.

Phenacyl bromide   Phenacyl ester

Carboxylate ion also acts as a nucleophile in the reaction of a carboxylic acid with diazomethane.

$$RCOOH + CH_2N_2 \longrightarrow RCOOCH_3 + N_2$$

Diazomethane, CH_2N_2, is a yellow gas (see Section 22.4) which is extremely reactive toward proton acids. The reaction with a carboxylic acid takes place in two steps. The first step is the transfer of an acidic proton to a base.

However, this acid–base reaction generates a good nucleophile (the carboxylate ion) and a substrate to which is attached the best known leaving group, nitrogen (N_2). The second reaction step is the formation of a new carbon-to-oxygen bond, along with the only by-product, nitrogen. The reaction proceeds under mild conditions in excellent yield and is particularly useful for converting an expensive acid to its methyl ester. The scope of the reaction of organic acids with diazo compounds is broad: Almost any organic acid, either aromatic or aliphatic, will react smoothly under mild conditions to give an excellent yield of ester. The fact that the only by-product is nitrogen makes this one of the cleanest synthetic organic reactions.

20.5   Reactions of Carboxylic Acids to Yield Acid Derivatives

Acid chlorides, anhydrides, ketenes, esters, and amides are often referred to as *acid derivatives*, since they are both readily prepared from acids and readily converted to acids. Nitriles are sometimes also considered to be acid derivatives; their chemistry will be considered mainly in the following chapter (Section 21.4).

Preparation of Acid Halides

The reaction of a carboxylic acid with thionyl chloride yields an acid chloride, sulfur dioxide, and hydrogen chloride. The reaction proceeds by initial attack of the carboxylic acid on the sulfur atom with elimination of hydrogen chloride. The resulting intermediate is not stable and loses sulfur dioxide to give the acid chloride.

$$
(Ar)R-\overset{\overset{\textstyle O}{\|}}{C}-O-H + \underset{\underset{\textstyle Cl}{|}}{\overset{\overset{\textstyle Cl}{|}}{S}}=O \;\longrightarrow\; R-\overset{\overset{\textstyle O}{\|}}{\underset{\underset{\textstyle Cl^{-}}{\uparrow}}{C}}-O-\overset{\overset{\textstyle O}{\|}}{S}-Cl + HCl
$$

$$
\downarrow
$$

$$
R-\overset{\overset{\textstyle O}{\|}}{C}-Cl + SO_2
$$

This reaction has broad applicability, although other functional groups in the same molecule which would react with hydrogen chloride may interfere.

Alternative reagents for the conversion of a carboxylic acid to the corresponding acid chloride are phosphorus trichloride and phosphorus pentachloride. With thionyl chloride, the by-products are both gases. With the phosphorus halides, the by-products are either nonvolatile phosphorous acid or the volatile liquid phosphorus oxychloride (bp 105°C). The latter may be difficult to separate from the acid chloride if the boiling points of the two are similar.

$$
3\; R-\overset{\overset{\textstyle O}{\|}}{C}-OH + PCl_3 \;\longrightarrow\; 3\; R-\overset{\overset{\textstyle O}{\|}}{C}-Cl + H_3PO_3
$$

$$
R-\overset{\overset{\textstyle O}{\|}}{C}-OH + PCl_5 \;\longrightarrow\; R-\overset{\overset{\textstyle O}{\|}}{C}-Cl + POCl_3 + HCl
$$

EXERCISE   20.2

Suggest a mechanism for the reaction of acetic acid with phosphorus pentachloride.

Acid halides other than chlorides are known, but they are of little importance.

Preparation of Acid Anhydrides

Acid anhydrides can be prepared by the reaction of an acid chloride with a carboxylate ion.

$$R-\overset{\overset{O}{\|}}{C}-Cl + \overset{-}{O}-\overset{\overset{O}{\|}}{C}-R \rightarrow R-\overset{\overset{O}{\|}}{C}-O-\overset{\overset{O}{\|}}{C}-R + Cl^-$$

The reaction proceeds smoothly under mild conditions, and it illustrates the nucleophilic attacking power of carboxylate ion as well as the reactivity of the carbonyl group of an acid chloride. The scope of the reaction is broad, including aromatic and aliphatic acids. The yields are excellent, and the most serious limitation stems from the fact that unsymmetrical anhydrides are unstable and disproportionate easily.

Formally speaking, an anhydride is derived from two molecules of acid by loss of one molecule of water. A *ketene*, the most reactive of the acid derivatives, is similarly derived from one molecule of an acid by the loss of one molecule of water. A general ketene synthesis consists of allowing a tertiary amine, usually triethylamine, to react with an acid chloride containing at least one hydrogen on the α-carbon atom. The most reactive ketenes cannot be isolated from this reaction, since they easily undergo secondary reactions, which will not be discussed here.

$$(C_2H_5)_3N: + (C_6H_5)_2C-C\overset{\overset{O}{\diagup\diagup}}{\underset{Cl}{\diagdown}} \rightarrow (C_6H_5)_2C=C=O + \overset{+}{H}N(C_2H_5)_3 \; Cl^-$$
$$\underset{H}{}$$
$$ketene$$

Ketene. The simplest member of the group, known simply as ketene, can be made in the laboratory by passing acetone vapor through a tube heated to 750°C.

$$CH_3\overset{\overset{O}{\|}}{C}-CH_3 \xrightarrow{750°C} CH_2=C=O + CH_4$$

Commercially, acetic acid is dehydrated at high temperatures with a catalyst to give ketene for use in preparing acetic anhydride.

Preparation of Esters

Simple esters are usually prepared in the laboratory by allowing a mixture of a carboxylic acid and an alcohol to react in the presence of a mineral acid catalyst. The reaction is often referred to as *Fischer esterification*.

$$CH_3-C\overset{\overset{O}{\diagup\diagup}}{\underset{OH}{\diagdown}} + C_2H_5OH \overset{H^+}{\rightleftharpoons} CH_3-C\overset{\overset{O}{\diagup\diagup}}{\underset{OC_2H_5}{\diagdown}} + H_2O$$

The reaction comes to equilibrium with appreciable amounts of the starting materials remaining. Often the carboxylic acid is the more valuable starting material, and methyl or ethyl alcohol is the other component. One then simply uses a large excess of the alcohol to shift the equilibrium to the right. In most other cases, the water can be removed from the reaction by azeotropic distillation with a suitable solvent, such as benzene, thereby driving the reaction to completion.

The mechanism of the Fischer esterification involves a number of steps.

The reaction is acid-catalyzed, the function of the strong acid being to convert the carboxylic acid to its conjugate acid. The carbonyl group of the latter undergoes nucleophilic attack by the oxygen of the alcohol, which gives the protonated species shown. Proton transfers are very rapid between oxygen atoms, and the next species shown is formed by removing a proton from the oxygen next to R′ and adding a proton to another oxygen. The electrons can then shift as shown, and a water molecule is ejected, giving the conjugate acid of the ester, which loses a proton to form the ester.

There are a number of alternative methods for preparing esters, and each is useful under certain circumstances. The more useful of these methods are listed.

The reaction of an acid with diazomethane (or with other diazo compounds) is an excellent method, but hazardous except on a very small scale (Section 20.4). Ketenes react with alcohols to give esters, but the reaction is of limited usefulness because of the limited availability of ketenes.

The reaction of an acid chloride with an alcohol is satisfactory. This reaction is used when it is desired to convert a valuable alcohol to an ester, usually the acetate. Most often the reaction is carried out in pyridine, which forms a salt with the HCl generated and prevents the solution from becoming acidic. An anhydride can be used in place of an acid chloride in a similar way. Acetic anhydride is the only anhydride which is cheap enough for this purpose and it ordinarily is used instead of acetyl chloride; the acid chloride is used in most other cases.

Transesterification is the term applied to the reaction of an ester with an alcohol to yield a different ester.

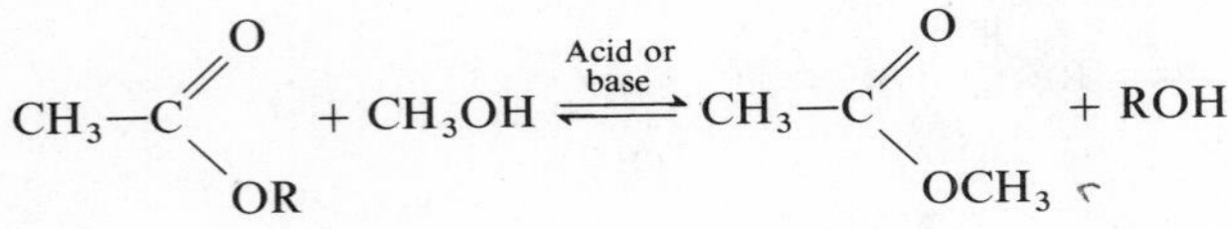

$$CH_3-C\underset{OR}{\overset{O}{\diagdown}} + CH_3OH \underset{base}{\overset{Acid\ or}{\rightleftharpoons}} CH_3-C\underset{OCH_3}{\overset{O}{\diagdown}} + ROH$$

Transesterification is catalyzed by acids as well as by bases. The mechanism of acid-catalyzed transesterification is closely analogous to that of the Fischer esterification. Alkyl titanates, $(RO)_4Ti$, are exceptionally powerful catalysts for transesterification and are used industrially.

EXERCISE 20.3

Suggest a mechanism for the following reaction:

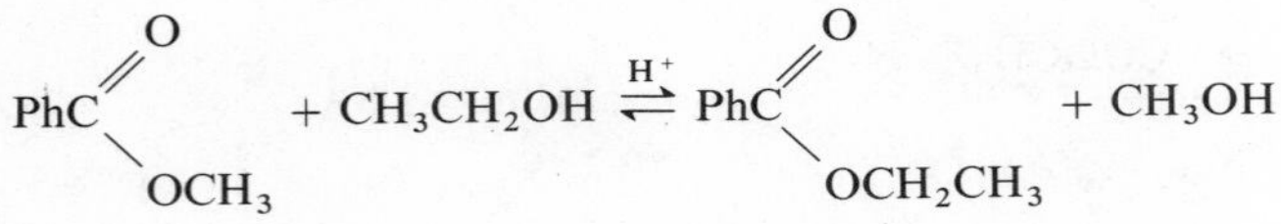

$$PhC\underset{OCH_3}{\overset{O}{\diagdown}} + CH_3CH_2OH \overset{H^+}{\rightleftharpoons} PhC\underset{OCH_2CH_3}{\overset{O}{\diagdown}} + CH_3OH$$

With only rare exceptions, aliphatic and aromatic acids can be converted to esters by all of the methods discussed above. There are limitations on the alcohols that are satisfactory in these reactions, however. Primary and secondary alcohols can generally be used in esterifications of all kinds. Tertiary alcohols cannot be esterified in the presence of acids because they are easily converted to carbonium ions, which then undergo elimination or other reactions.

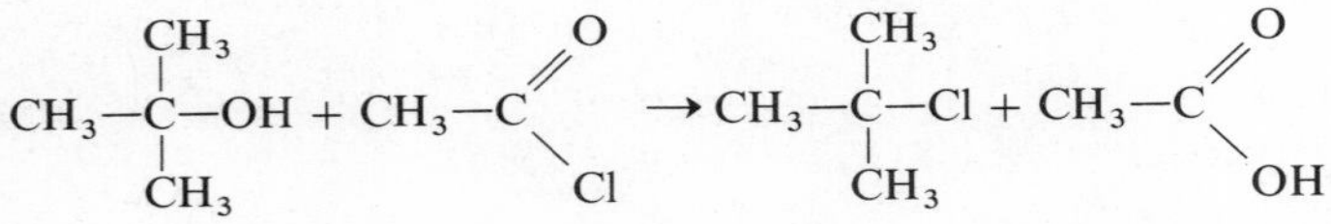

$$CH_3-\underset{CH_3}{\overset{CH_3}{\underset{|}{C}}}-OH + CH_3-C\underset{Cl}{\overset{O}{\diagdown}} \rightarrow CH_3-\underset{CH_3}{\overset{CH_3}{\underset{|}{C}}}-Cl + CH_3-C\underset{OH}{\overset{O}{\diagdown}}$$

Esterification of tertiary alcohols with acid chlorides is generally successful under basic conditions, however:

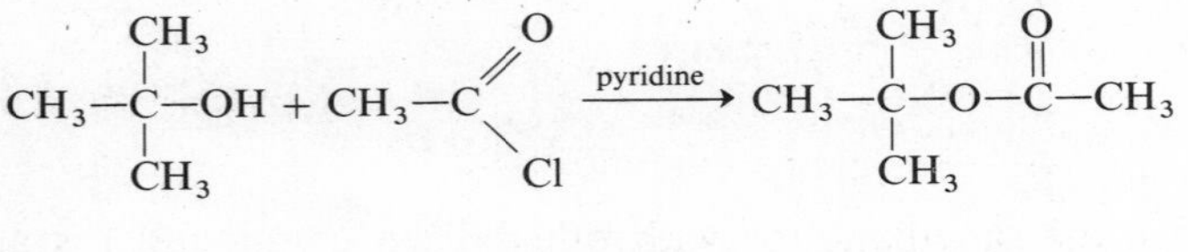

$$CH_3-\underset{CH_3}{\overset{CH_3}{\underset{|}{C}}}-OH + CH_3-C\underset{Cl}{\overset{O}{\diagdown}} \overset{pyridine}{\longrightarrow} CH_3-\underset{CH_3}{\overset{CH_3}{\underset{|}{C}}}-O-\overset{O}{\overset{||}{C}}-CH_3$$

or

$$CH_3-\underset{CH_3}{\overset{CH_3}{\underset{|}{C}}}-O^- + CH_3-C\underset{Cl}{\overset{O}{\diagdown}} \rightarrow CH_3-\underset{CH_3}{\overset{CH_3}{\underset{|}{C}}}-O-\overset{O}{\overset{||}{C}}-CH_3 + Cl^-$$

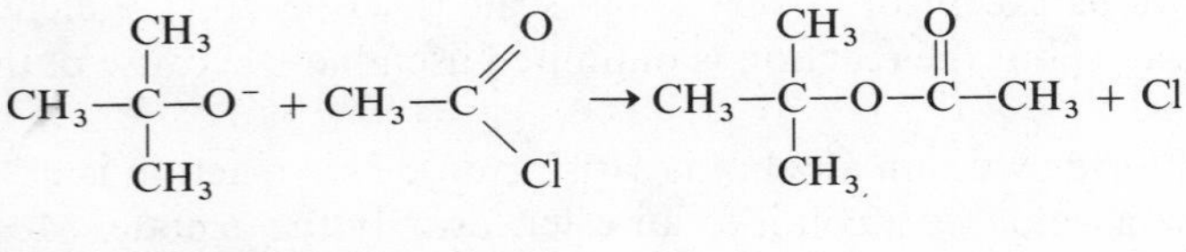

Preparation of Amides and Nitriles

All of the acid derivatives discussed so far react with ammonia, primary amines, and secondary amines to give amides. Excess ammonia serves as a convenient acid scavenger. In reactions with primary or secondary amines, a tertiary amine is usually added for the same purpose. The amides produced do not ordinarily undergo further acylation due to their low basicity (see also Section 21.1, Acylation).

$$R-\overset{\displaystyle O}{\underset{\displaystyle Cl}{C}} + 2\,NH_3 \rightarrow R-\overset{\displaystyle O}{\underset{\displaystyle NH_2}{C}} + \overset{+}{N}H_4\,Cl^-$$

$$R-\overset{\displaystyle O}{\underset{\displaystyle Cl}{C}} + NH_2R' + R''_3N \rightarrow R-\overset{\displaystyle O}{\underset{\displaystyle NHR'}{C}} + R''_3\overset{+}{N}HCl^-$$

$$R-\overset{\displaystyle O}{\underset{\displaystyle Cl}{C}} + NHR'_2 + R''_3N \rightarrow R-\overset{\displaystyle O}{\underset{\displaystyle NR'_2}{C}} + R''_3\overset{+}{N}HCl^-$$

$$H_2C=C=O + NH_3 \rightarrow CH_3-\overset{\displaystyle O}{\underset{\displaystyle NH_2}{C}}$$

$$R-\overset{\displaystyle O}{\underset{\displaystyle OCH_3}{C}} + NH_3 \rightarrow R-\overset{\displaystyle O}{\underset{\displaystyle NH_2}{C}} + HOCH_3$$

$$R-\overset{\displaystyle O}{\underset{\displaystyle OH}{C}} + NH_3 \rightarrow R-\overset{\displaystyle O}{\underset{\displaystyle O^-\overset{+}{N}H_4}{C}} \xrightarrow{\Delta} R-\overset{\displaystyle O}{\underset{\displaystyle NH_2}{C}} + H_2O$$

$$\begin{array}{c} R-\overset{\displaystyle O}{\underset{\displaystyle O}{C}} \\ \big| \\ R-\underset{\displaystyle O}{\overset{\displaystyle }{C}} \end{array} + 2\,NH_3 \rightarrow R-\overset{\displaystyle O}{\underset{\displaystyle NH_2}{C}} + R-CO_2^-\overset{+}{N}H_4$$

With a ketene, only 1 mole of ammonia is needed and no by-product is formed. With an acid chloride, 2 moles of ammonia are needed, and the by-product is ammonium chloride. With an acid anhydride, the by-product is the ammonium salt of 1 mole of the orginal carboxylic acid, and again, 2 moles of ammonia are required.

In contrast to these reactions, which are rapid and essentially complete, the reaction of an ester with ammonia is quite slow and is seldom of preparative importance.

With the parent acid, the first reaction with ammonia is formation of a salt which is stable at room temperature. If the salt is isolated and heated well above 100°C, water is driven out as water vapor or steam, and the amide is formed.

$$R-\overset{\displaystyle O}{\overset{\|}{C}}-OH + NH_3 \rightarrow R-\overset{\displaystyle O}{\overset{\|}{C}}-O^-\overset{+}{N}H_4 \xrightarrow{\Delta} R\overset{\displaystyle O}{\overset{\|}{C}}-NH_2 + H_2O$$

Further dehydration of such an unsubstituted amide gives a nitrile (organic cyanide). Generally a chemical dehydrating agent such as phosphorus oxychloride or pentoxide or thionyl chloride is used, but large-scale or commercial processes utilize pyrolysis at temperatures of about 250°C.

$$R-\overset{\displaystyle O}{\overset{\|}{C}}-NH_2 + SOCl_2 \rightarrow RC\equiv N + SO_2 + 2HCl$$

$$R-\overset{\overset{\displaystyle O}{\|}}{C}-NH_2 \xrightarrow{250°C} RC\equiv N + H_2O$$

Nitriles can also be made by the displacement of a halide using cyanide ion as discussed in Section 17.1 and given in Table 17.1.

$$RX + NaCN \rightarrow RCN + NaX$$

Reactions of nitriles will be discussed in Section 21.4.

Organic amines with at least one hydrogen on the nitrogen atom will react with carboxylic acids equally as well as ammonia to give N-substituted amides. Tertiary amines, with no hydrogen on nitrogen, cannot be converted to amides; thus, they are conveniently used as scavengers for acid in the reaction of an expensive organic amine with an acid chloride or an acid anhydride. The reaction would otherwise use two equivalents of expensive amine and result in only one equivalent of the product.

Reactions of amides will be discussed in Section 21.5.

20.6   Hydrolysis of Acid Derivatives. Saponification

All of the derivatives of acids can be forced to react with water to regenerate the parent acid. The reactivity scale toward water can be correlated with the predicted reactivity of the carbonyl group ($>C=O$) of the acid derivatives.

Reactivity towards water

$$\overset{\diagdown}{\underset{\diagup}{}}C=C=O > R-\overset{\overset{\displaystyle O}{\|}}{C}-Cl > R\overset{\overset{\displaystyle O}{\|}}{C}-O-\overset{\overset{\displaystyle O}{\|}}{C}R > R\overset{\overset{\displaystyle O}{\|}}{C}-OR > R\overset{\overset{\displaystyle O}{\|}}{C}-NH_2$$

The relative reactivities of the compounds RCOZ can best be understood in terms of the following resonance forms:

$$R-\overset{\overset{\displaystyle O}{\diagup\diagdown}}{\underset{\ddot{Z}}{C}} \leftrightarrow R-\overset{\overset{\displaystyle O^-}{\diagup}}{\underset{\ddot{Z}}{\overset{+}{C}}} \leftrightarrow R-\overset{\overset{\displaystyle O^-}{\diagup}}{\underset{Z^+}{C}}$$

$$\quad\quad I \quad\quad\quad\quad II \quad\quad\quad\quad III$$

What appears to be a nonbonding electron pair on Z (in resonance form I) occupies a *p* orbital parallel to the *p* orbitals which make up the π bond of the carbonyl group. The electron pair from Z is thus delocalized into the carbonyl group, as indicated by resonance form III. The more this form contributes to the hybrid, the less positive charge is present on the carbonyl carbon, and the less reactive the carbonyl is toward nucleophilic attack. A less electronegative element (N) is more willing to share its electrons than a more electronegative one (O), or a still more electronegative one (Cl). The center oxygen of the anhydride has to share its electrons with two carbonyls, so it contributes less electron density to either one of them than does the ester oxygen. Ketene has no corresponding resonance form. It is in addition strained and unhindered, so it is not surprising that it is the most reactive compound of the group.

Ketenes and anhydrides react smoothly with water under mild conditions to give the parent acid with no by-product. Acid chlorides also react smoothly, but generate a mole of hydrogen chloride. Esters and amides react with water to give the parent acid only in the presence of strong acid or strong base (or, biologically, in the presence of enzymes).

$$R-\overset{\overset{\displaystyle O}{\|}}{C}-NH_2 + H_2O \xrightarrow{H^+} R\overset{\overset{\displaystyle O}{\|}}{C}-OH + \overset{+}{N}H_4$$

$$R-\overset{\overset{\displaystyle O}{\|}}{C}-NH_2 + H_2O \xrightarrow{\text{OH}^-} R-\overset{\overset{\displaystyle O}{\|}}{C}-O^- + NH_3$$

$$R-\overset{\overset{\displaystyle O}{\|}}{C}-OCH_3 + H_2O \xrightarrow[\underset{\text{OH}^-}{\text{or}}]{\text{H}^+} R\overset{\overset{\displaystyle O}{\|}}{C}-OH + HOCH_3$$

Strong acid can be used in catalytic amounts for the hydrolysis of esters (reverse of Fischer esterification), but one equivalent plus a catalytic amount is necessary for amides since the by-product ammonia destroys 1 mole of acid by salt formation. Strong base cannot be used in catalytic amounts in either case, since the resulting carboxylic acid destroys 1 mole of base by salt formation.

EXERCISE 20.4

Write a detailed mechanism for the hydrolysis of an ester in acid solution.

The reaction of esters with strong base, called *saponification*, is involved in the preparation of soap, and is one of the oldest organic reactions known. The reaction mechanism has been investigated in great detail.

In the earliest days of organic chemistry, the efforts of chemists were directed at learning what products could be obtained from chemical reactions. The first studies aimed at finding out what went on during the course of a reaction were carried out by Wilhelm Ostwald.† He measured rates of hydrolysis of esters as early as 1883.

Inspection of the starting materials and products suggests that there are two fundamentally different kinds of mechanisms by which saponification might proceed; the first involves breaking of the acyl C—O bond, and the second breaking of the O—C alkyl bond.

Acyl cleavage

$$R-\overset{\overset{\displaystyle O}{\|}}{C}\{-OCH_3 \xrightarrow{\text{OH}^-} R-\overset{\overset{\displaystyle O}{\|}}{C}-OH + {}^-OCH_3 \tag{1}$$

Alkyl cleavage

$$R-\overset{\overset{\displaystyle O}{\|}}{C}-O-\{CH_3 \xrightarrow{\text{OH}^-} R-\overset{\overset{\displaystyle O}{\|}}{C}-O^- + CH_3OH \tag{2}$$

In order to try to decide which of these mechanisms is correct, we might look at the kinetics of the reaction. The rate expression for the saponification is $-d[\text{ester}]/dt = k[\text{ester}][\text{OH}^-]$. This means that the transition state for the reaction contains the elements of one molecule of ester and one molecule of hydroxide ion. The rate-determining step could be either an attack by the hydroxide ion on the ester, or there could be an equilibrium step in which the ester and hydroxide ion react to form a complex, and the decomposition of this complex might be rate-determining. The reaction is quite irreversible, because whether it goes by mechanism (1) or by mechanism (2), carboxylate salts are the reaction products: directly if mechanism (2) is correct and by a subsequent acid–base reaction if mechanism (1) is correct. The carboxylate ion is very stable and does not react with alcohol to give back ester.

---

† Wilhelm Ostwald. 1853–1932. Universities of Riga (Latvia) and Leipzig. Nobel Prize, 1909.

If mechanism (1) is correct, this would seem to be, in its most simple form, an S_N2 type of displacement of methoxide by hydroxide attack on the carbonyl carbon.

$$R-\overset{\overset{\displaystyle O}{\|}}{\underset{\underset{\displaystyle -OH}{\curvearrowleft}}{C}}-OCH_3 \xrightarrow{\text{slow}} R-\overset{\overset{\displaystyle O}{\|}}{C}-OH + {}^-OCH_3 \xrightarrow{\text{fast}} R-\overset{\overset{\displaystyle O}{\|}}{C}-O^- + CH_3OH$$

The first step would be rate-determining, and hence the reaction would follow second-order kinetics. If reaction (2) describes the correct mechanism, the kinetics also would be second order. Therefore, kinetics cannot distinguish between mechanisms (1) and (2).

$$R-\overset{\overset{\displaystyle O}{\|}}{C}-O\overset{\curvearrowright}{} CH_3 + {}^-OH \rightarrow R-\overset{\overset{\displaystyle O}{\|}}{C}-O^- + CH_3OH$$

The question of which carbon-to-oxygen bond is broken was settled by labeling the alkoxyl oxygen with ^{18}O. The label appears in the alcohol product and not in the acid salt, proving that the oxygen-to-carbonyl-carbon bond is broken and that mechanism (1) is in fact the one usually followed.

$$R-\overset{\overset{\displaystyle O}{\|}}{C}-{}^{18}OCH_3 \rightarrow R-\overset{\overset{\displaystyle O}{\|}}{C}-O^- + CH_3\,{}^{18}OH$$

While mechanism (1) holds in simple cases, there are some important reactions in which the mechanism of hydrolysis is one of attack on the alkoxyl carbon. For example, because of hindrance at the carbonyl group the methyl ester of *mesitoic acid* is unreactive under ordinary saponification conditions. When the reaction is forced, attack occurs on the methyl carbon (mechanism 2).

Methyl mesitoate

EXERCISE 20.5

Methyl mesitoate does not react with sodium ethoxide in ethanol, but after very prolonged refluxing it does. What are the products?

This change of mechanism from an attack on the carbonyl carbon to a displacement on the alcohol carbon can be understood by considering the carboxylate as a leaving group. As the strength of the carboxylic acid is increased by substitution, the carboxylate anion becomes more stable and, thus, a better leaving group in the displacement reaction.

X, Y = strong electron-withdrawing groups ($-NO_2$, $-C{\equiv}N$, etc.)

One important result of the change to an S_N2 mechanism is that the configuration of the alkoxyl carbon will be inverted. If inversion of an alkoxyl carbon is desired for a particular synthesis, an acid even stronger than a carboxylic acid is used to form the ester, when possible. Methanesulfonic acid and toluenesulfonic acid are such strong acids; they are readily available as starting materials in the form of the acid or the acid chloride and their esters are saponified easily.

$$CH_3\overset{O}{\underset{O}{\overset{\|}{\underset{\|}{S}}}}-O-CH_3 + {}^-OH \rightarrow CH_3\overset{O}{\underset{O}{\overset{\|}{\underset{\|}{S}}}}-O^- + CH_3OH$$

After it was determined that in ordinary saponification the initial attack of hydroxide is on the carbonyl carbon (mechanism 1), the next question was whether the reaction involves a direct (concerted) substitution, as shown previously, (page 534), or whether it is really an addition–elimination sequence, which would be suggested by the fact that additions to carbonyls occur easily (the addition of alcohol to an aldehyde to give a hemiacetal, for example, Section 19.2).

$$R-\overset{O}{\overset{\|}{C}}-O-CH_3 + {}^-OH \rightleftharpoons R-\underset{OH}{\overset{O^-}{\overset{|}{\underset{|}{C}}}}-O-CH_3 \rightarrow R-\overset{O}{\overset{\|}{C}}-OH + {}^-OCH_3$$

$$\downarrow$$

$$R-\overset{O}{\overset{\|}{C}}-O^- + HOCH_3$$

When the carbonyl oxygen in an ester was labeled with ${}^{18}O$, exchange with ${}^{16}O$ in the water solvent occurred, providing good evidence that the reaction is *not* a direct displacement. This experiment was carried out by M. Bender,[†] who treated the labeled ester with base and allowed the reaction to proceed only part way to completion. The ester which had not yet saponified was then recovered, and the ${}^{18}O$ content was measured. If saponification were a simple displacement reaction, the unreacted ester would still contain the same concentration of ${}^{18}O$ which it had before the reaction. In fact, the ${}^{18}O$ concentration was found to be much smaller than this. The two-step addition–elimination mechanism nicely accounts for the ${}^{18}O$ exchange, however.

Addition–elimination

$$R-\overset{{}^{18}O}{\overset{\|}{\underset{{}^-OH}{C}}}-OCH_3 \rightleftharpoons R-\underset{OH}{\overset{{}^{18}O^-}{\overset{|}{\underset{|}{C}}}}-OCH_3 \rightleftharpoons R-\underset{O^-}{\overset{{}^{18}OH}{\overset{|}{\underset{|}{C}}}}-OCH_3 \rightleftharpoons R-\overset{O}{\overset{\|}{C}}OCH_3 + {}^{18}OH^-$$

The addition–elimination mechanism, rather than the direct displacement mechanism, is commonly used to explain similar reactions with other acid derivatives such as acid chlorides, anhydrides, nitriles, and amides.

$$R-\overset{O}{\overset{\|}{C}}-Cl + {}^-OH \rightarrow R-\underset{OH}{\overset{O^-}{\overset{|}{\underset{|}{C}}}}-Cl \rightarrow R-\overset{O}{\overset{\|}{C}}-OH + Cl^-$$

20.7 Acid-Catalyzed Hydrolysis

In basic hydrolysis of an acid derivative, hydroxide ion attacks the carbonyl carbon. In acidic hydrolysis, water is the best nucleophile available, and it attacks an ester very

---

† Myron L. Bender. Born 1924, St. Louis, Missouri. Illinois Institute of Technology, Northwestern University.

slowly. If, however, the ester is protonated prior to the attack, then the hydrolysis becomes rapid. The mechanism of acid hydrolysis in a simple case is summarized in the equations shown.

As indicated in the previous section, the hydrolysis of esters in simple cases follows an addition–elimination mechanism; this mechanism is similar in either acidic or basic solution. In acid solution, as in basic solutions, other mechanisms also may occur in special cases. If the alcohol portion of the ester is one which forms a reasonably stable carbonium ion, a common reaction mechanism in acidic solvent is S_N1, analogous to the S_N2 reaction which is found in basic solution. These reactions are, of course, facilitated by a good leaving group, a tosylate or p-nitrobenzoate derivative of the alcohol, for example.

In acid hydrolysis, as in base hydrolysis, if the carbonyl is hindered to the approach of the weak nucleophile water, and the transition to the more bulky tetrahedral intermediate is unfavorable, the reaction may proceed by yet another mechanism. For example, acid hydrolysis of the methyl ester of mesitoic acid requires very strong acid and follows an alternative reaction path.

20.8   Reduction

Among the reactions of acids and acid derivatives which proceed by nucleophilic attack on the carbonyl, two classes of reagents other than those containing heteroatoms such as —N:, :O:, :Cl: are widely used. Suitable metal hydrides react with the formation of carbon-to-hydrogen bonds and give products of reduction. Organometallic reagents react to form new carbon-to-carbon bonds.

The most important metal hydride reagent is lithium aluminum hydride, which provides the equivalent of hydride ion, a powerful base.

The carboxyl group is usually reduced by lithium aluminum hydride. The acidic hydrogen first reacts to liberate hydrogen gas. The carbonyl group of the carboxylate ion is then attacked by the AlH_4^- ion, and the group is reduced all the way to the primary alkoxide. The overall reaction is

$$4RCOOH + 3LiAlH_4 \longrightarrow 4H_2 + (RCH_2O)_4AlLi \xrightarrow{H_3O^+} 4RCH_2OH$$

The reaction probably goes through an intermediate aldehyde, which is rapidly reduced further.

EXERCISE   20.6

Write a detailed mechanism for the reduction of acetic acid to ethanol by $LiAlH_4$.

Sometimes the salt of the acid formed initially ($RCOO\overset{-}{Li}\overset{+}{Al}H_3$) is insoluble and precipitates, preventing the reduction. In such cases, the acid may be converted to an ester, which is easily reduced with $LiAlH_4$.

$$4\ R—C\overset{\displaystyle O}{\underset{\displaystyle OCH_2CH_3}{\big\backslash}} + 2\ LiAlH_4 \longrightarrow (R—CH_2—O)_4AlLi + (CH_3CH_2O)_4AlLi$$

$$\downarrow H_3O^+$$

$$4\ RCH_2OH + 4\ CH_3CH_2OH$$

Although all four hydrogens are potentially usable as hydride ion, an excess of lithium aluminum hydride is generally used. This excess is decomposed at the end of the reaction, usually by the addition of alcohol or ethyl acetate, and the alkoxide salt is acidified before the reaction is worked up.

Acid chlorides and anhydrides react smoothly with $LiAlH_4$ to give the corresponding primary alcohols.

Attempts to stop the reduction at the intermediate aldehyde stage are not successful with $LiAlH_4$. A search for a less active hydride led to the discovery that lithium tri-*t*-butoxy-aluminum hydride often specifically allows the reduction to be stopped at the aldehyde stage if the reaction is carried out at dry ice temperature ($-78°C$).

An older method to accomplish the same transformation involves catalytic reduction of the acid chloride using a partially poisoned catalyst (*Rosenmund reduction*).

Acid derivatives containing nitrogen are reduced with $LiAlH_4$ to amines. Nitriles and amides derived from ammonia give primary amines. Amides derived from primary and secondary amines give secondary and tertiary amines, respectively.

The reduction of either a nitrile or an *N,N*-dialkyl amide can sometimes be stopped at the aldehyde stage by using specific aluminum hydride reagents.

Sodium dissolving in alcohol constitutes a reagent which reduces aliphatic esters to alcohols, and has been used to prepare long-chain alcohols from vegetable oils in the detergent industry. This type of reduction fails with esters of aromatic acids. (See Section 19.11.)

$$n\text{-}C_{17}H_{35}-\overset{\displaystyle O}{\overset{\|}{C}}-OCH_3 \xrightarrow{\text{Na–EtOH}} n\text{-}C_{17}H_{35}-CH_2OH + CH_3OH$$

Esters react with sodium metal in the absence of a proton source to give bimolecular reduction products called *acyloins*.

$$2\,CH_3-\overset{\displaystyle O}{\underset{\displaystyle OEt}{C}} + 4\,Na \rightarrow CH_3-\overset{Na^+\ ^-O}{\underset{}{C}}=\overset{O^-Na^+}{\underset{}{C}}-CH_3 \xrightarrow{H_3O^+} CH_3-\overset{\displaystyle O}{\overset{\|}{C}}-\overset{\displaystyle OH}{\underset{}{C}H}-CH_3$$

Acetoin
(an acyloin)

The reaction takes place on the surface of the metal and is rather analogous to the bimolecular reduction of ketones to pinacols (Section 19.11). The reaction is of limited use with simple molecules, but has been a very important key step in the synthesis of many large-ring compounds (Sections 20.17 and 34.2).

> *Catalytic Reduction of Esters.* Since lithium aluminum hydride is expensive, large-scale industrial reactions generally use other reagents. Esters can be hydrogenated to primary alcohols, but only at high temperatures and at high pressures of hydrogen in the presence of copper chromite catalyst.
>
> $$CH_3(CH_2)_{10}\overset{\displaystyle O}{\overset{\|}{C}}-OCH_3 + H_2 \xrightarrow[\text{175°C; 5000 psi}]{CuO\cdot CuCr_2O_4} CH_3(CH_2)_{10}CH_2OH + HOCH_3$$
>
> Methyl laurate   Lauryl alcohol

20.9 Reaction with Organometallic Reagents

Certain organometallic reagents react with acid derivatives by attack at the carbonyl group to form carbon-to-carbon bonds in a manner similar to that observed with aldehydes and ketones (Section 19.9). The most common reagent is the Grignard reagent, although alkyl and aryl lithium compounds are coming into widespread use. Grignard reagents react with esters to give tertiary alcohols. The equivalent of the carbanion R^- is available to attack the carbonyl.

The first intermediate is not stable and the ions CH_3O^- and MgX^+ are eliminated. The resulting ketone reacts faster than the starting ester with the Grignard reagent, and the product is therefore always a tertiary alcohol in which two R groups are identical.

$$2\,CH_3CH_2MgBr + CH_3-\underset{\displaystyle CH_3}{\overset{\displaystyle}{C}H}-\overset{\displaystyle O}{\overset{\|}{C}}-OCH_3 \rightarrow CH_3-\underset{\displaystyle CH_3}{\overset{\displaystyle}{C}H}-\underset{\displaystyle CH_2CH_3}{\overset{\displaystyle OH}{C}}-CH_2CH_3$$

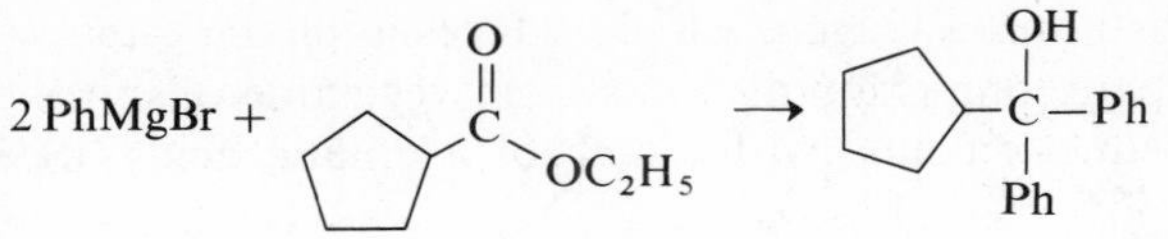

$$2\ PhMgBr\ +\ \underset{cyclopentyl}{\ce{C(=O)OC2H5}}\ \longrightarrow\ \underset{cyclopentyl}{\ce{C(OH)(Ph)(Ph)}}$$

EXERCISE 20.7

If an excess of a Grignard reagent RMgX is added to diethyl carbonate, what is the product?

EXERCISE 20.8

If an excess of a Grignard reagent is added to ethyl formate, what is the product?

EXERCISE 20.9

Complete the following equation:

$$\underset{\underset{1\ mole}{}}{\overset{\overset{O}{\|}}{CH_3C}-OEt}\ +\ \underset{1\ mole}{CH_3MgX}\ \longrightarrow$$

An excellent method for the preparation of ketones involves the reaction of a nitrile or an *N,N*-dialkyl amide with a Grignard reagent. In contrast to the reaction with esters, the first addition intermediate is stable at the temperature of refluxing ether. Addition of mineral acid then forms the ketone (also see method 3b, page 515).

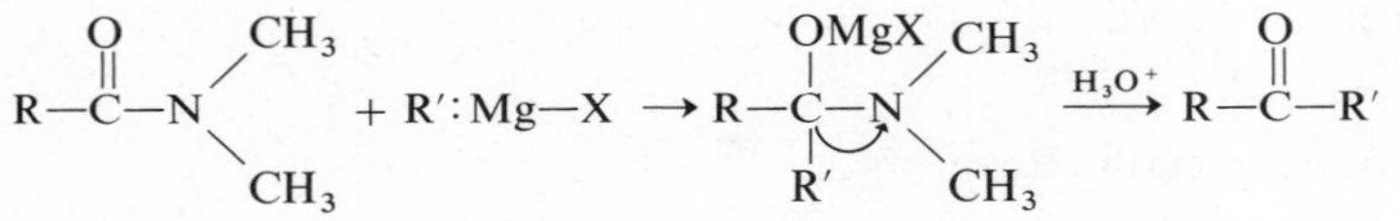

Stable until
acidified

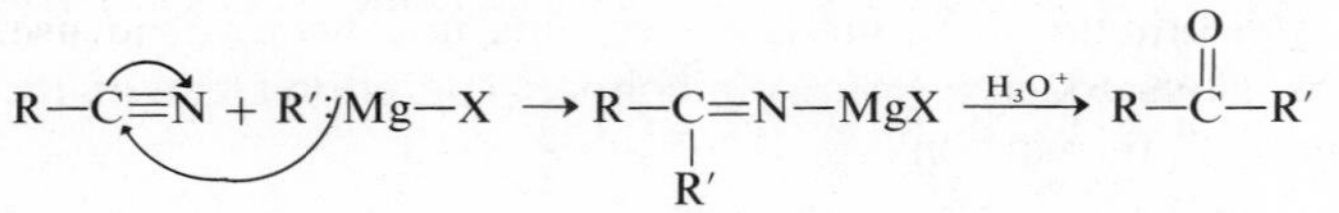

An *N,N-dialkyl* amide must be employed in this ketone synthesis. Amides which have at least one relatively acidic hydrogen on the nitrogen atom generally form an insoluble salt with the Grignard reagent, which will react no further.

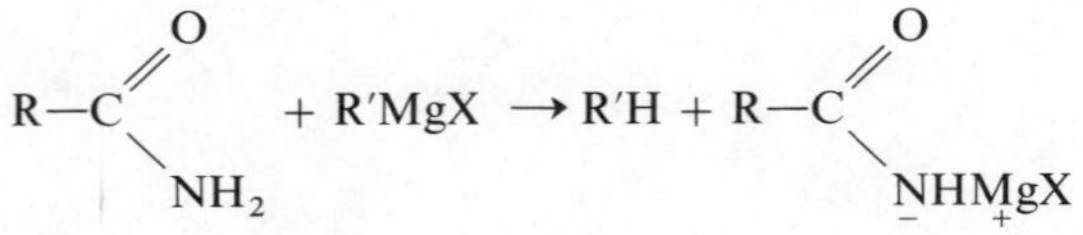

The reaction of ortho esters with Grignard reagents is discussed in Section 21.4.

Acids react with Grignard reagents extremely rapidly to give hydrocarbon and the magnesium halide salt of the acid. The latter is generally insoluble and precipitates, and further reaction is prevented. On the other hand, a lithium alkyl adds to the carbonyl group of a carboxylic acid. The important feature of this reaction is that the intermediate formed after one addition of the reagent to the carboxylate salt is reasonably stable and after treatment with an acid, the ketone is usually obtained in good yield.

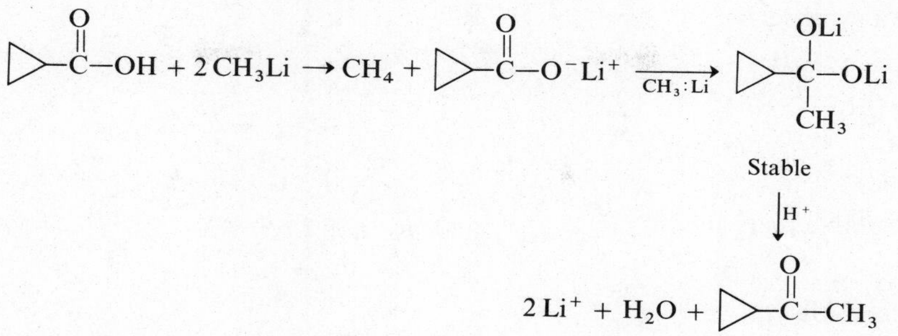

Stable

$$2 Li^+ + H_2O + \quad \overset{O}{\underset{||}{\triangleright\!-\!C}}\!-\!CH_3$$

Since conversion of acids or acid derivatives to ketones is an important synthetic procedure, the above reaction is useful.

Dialkyl (or diaryl) cadmiums react with acid chlorides to yield ketones. This is another practical way to prepare a ketone from an acid.

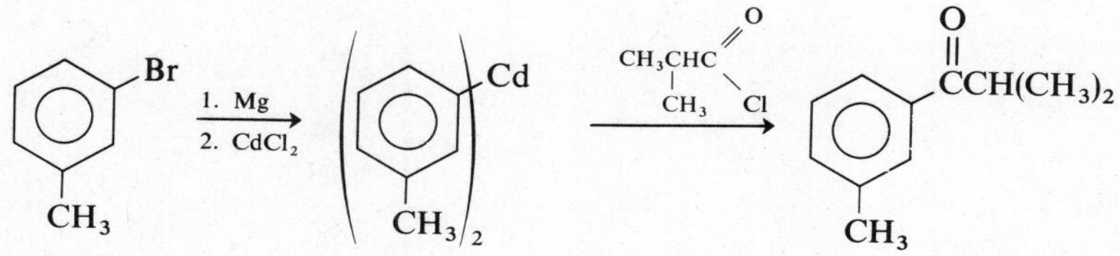

$$CH_3CH_2CH_2CH_2Br \xrightarrow[\text{2. CdCl}_2]{\text{1. Mg}} (CH_3CH_2CH_2CH_2)_2Cd$$

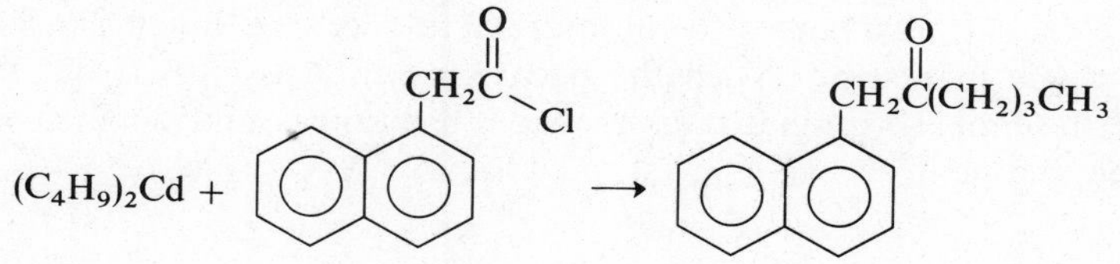

A limitation is that only *primary* alkyl and aryl cadmium reagents can be used. Secondary and tertiary alkyl cadmium compounds spontaneously decompose to give free radicals, which undergo various other reactions.

20.10   Friedel–Crafts Acylation

Acid chlorides will react with carbon-to-carbon double bonds in the presence of the powerful Lewis acid, aluminum chloride. With aromatic compounds, the reaction provides an excellent synthesis of aromatic ketones.

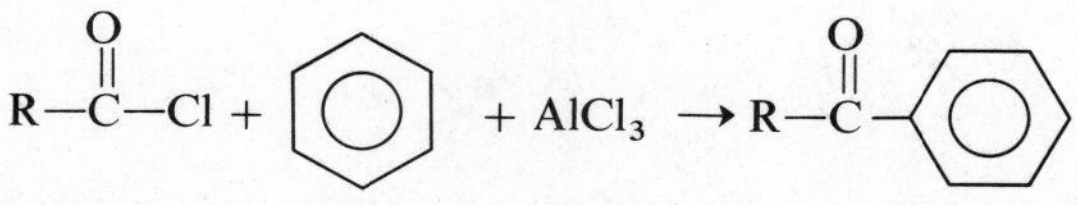

The mechanism involves generation of an acylium ion, which then attacks the aromatic ring in an electrophilic aromatic substitution (Section 16.5). With an olefin in place of an arene, an initial chloro ketone can usually be isolated, but it easily loses hydrogen chloride.

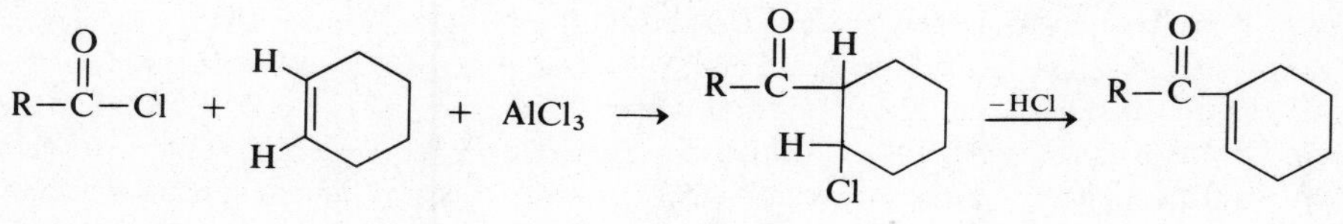

EXERCISE 20.10

Outline a synthesis of

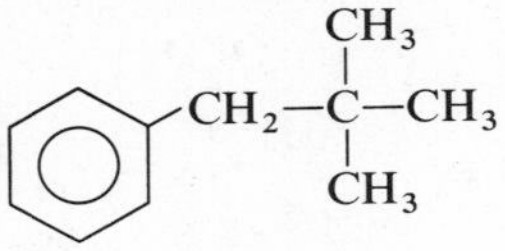

from available materials.

20.11   Decarboxylation

Although ordinary carboxylic acids are stable to over 200°C, carboxylic acids which have a multiple bond in the β, γ position undergo smooth loss of carbon dioxide at temperatures between 100° and 200°C to give a decarboxylated product. In the case of β-keto acids, the acid-catalyzed decarboxylation usually proceeds readily even at 50–60°C. The enol form of a ketone is the initial reaction product.

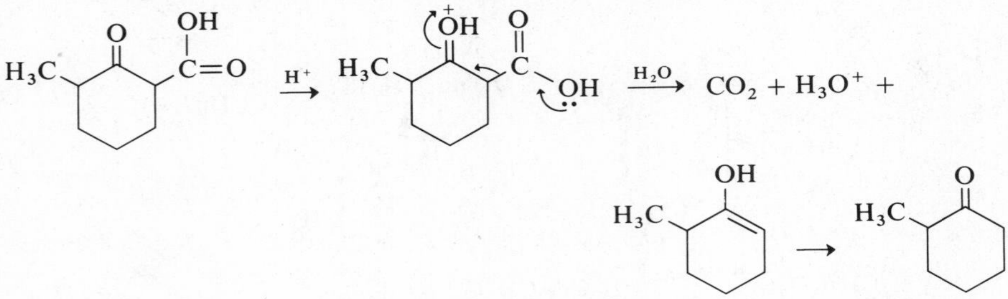

The enol intermediate quickly rearranges to the more stable ketone, but it can be trapped in a useful synthetic maneuver. When the decarboxylation is carried out in the presence of bromine, the enol is brominated faster than it rearranges, and is therefore converted to an α-bromo ketone.

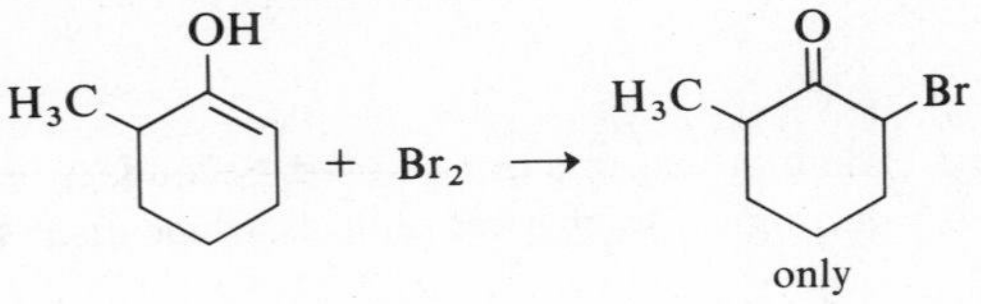

This bromo ketone cannot be prepared in a practical way by bromination of the ketone itself. Such bromination gives a mixture which is difficult to separate.

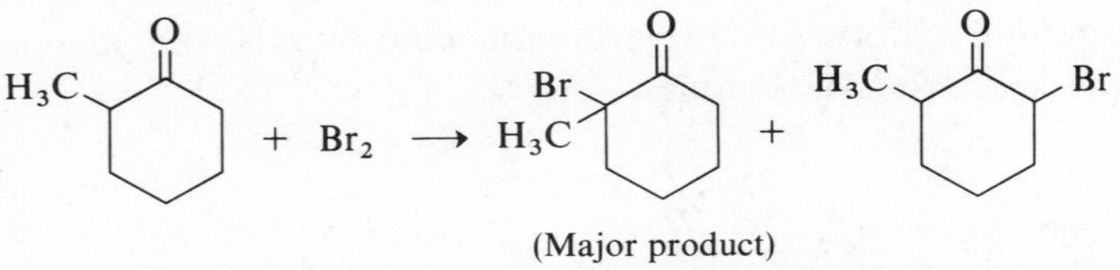

In addition to β-keto acids, the following types of compounds undergo decarboxylation and give the compounds shown after tautomerization of the corresponding enol-like intermediates.

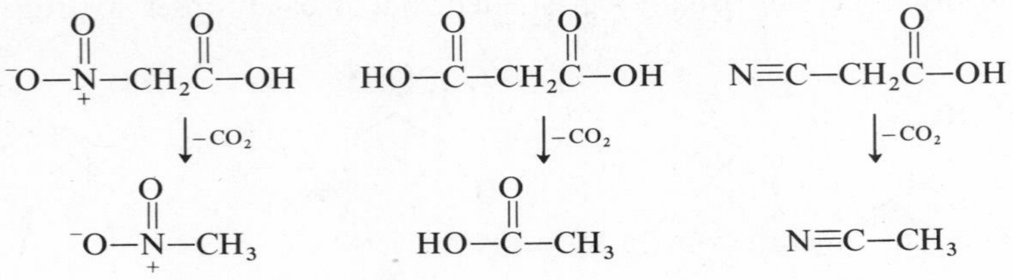

Decarboxylation of a β,γ-unsaturated acid is interesting because the product corresponding to the enol is simply a stable alkene.

β,γ-Unsaturated acid   Alkene

Decarboxylative Elimination. Whereas the acid proton is necessary for the facile thermal decarboxylation of β,γ-unsaturated acids, the carboxylate ion is required for a related reaction, which is referred to as a *decarboxylative elimination*. In addition to the ion, a good leaving group in the β position is necessary.

This reaction has been used for the stereospecific synthesis of alkenes. An anti-coplanar relationship is required for such a reaction.

EXERCISE 20.11

Outline a synthesis of *cis-β-bromostyrene* from cinnamic acid (PhCH=CHCOOH). Which isomer of the acid is required, cis or trans?

Another decarboxylation useful in synthesis is the *Hunsdiecker reaction* of the silver salt of a carboxylic acid with bromine in dry chloroform.

$$R-\overset{\overset{O}{\parallel}}{C}-OAg + Br_2 \xrightarrow{\text{dry } CCl_4} \left[R-\overset{\overset{O}{\parallel}}{C}-O-Br \right] \rightarrow R-Br + CO_2$$

Mechanism of the Hunsdiecker Reaction. Occasionally the same reaction can be effected by heating the acid and bromine with mercuric oxide, but the yield is very sensitive to experimental conditions. These reactions probably involve free-radical intermediates similar to those formed in the decomposition of diacylperoxides.

$$R-\overset{\overset{O}{\parallel}}{C}-O-Br \rightarrow R-\overset{\overset{O}{\parallel}}{C}-O\cdot + Br\cdot \rightarrow CO_2 + R\cdot \xrightarrow{Br_2} RBr$$

$$R-\overset{\overset{O}{\parallel}}{C}-O-O-\overset{\overset{O}{\parallel}}{C}-R \rightarrow 2\,R\overset{\overset{O}{\parallel}}{C}-O\cdot \rightarrow CO_2 + R\cdot$$
$$\xrightarrow{Br_2} RBr + Br\cdot$$

One further type of product can be formed during a decarboxylation reaction. The *Kolbe electrolysis* of the sodium salts of acids gives hydrocarbons.

$$R-\overset{\overset{O}{\parallel}}{C}-O^- \rightarrow R-\overset{\overset{O}{\parallel}}{C}-O\cdot + e^- \quad \text{(anode)}$$

$$R-\overset{\overset{O}{\parallel}}{C}-O\cdot \rightarrow R\cdot + CO_2$$

$$R\cdot + \cdot R \rightarrow R-R$$

Sodium hydroxide and hydrogen are formed at the cathode.

The conversion of amides and azides to amines of one less carbon atom amounts to a decarboxylation, and useful reactions which will lead to this result will be discussed in Sections 21.5 and 22.9. The decarboxylation of an ordinary acid via a heavy metal salt proceeds via a keto acid intermediate and is discussed in Section 20.17.

20.12   α-Halo Acids. The Hell–Volhard–Zelinsky Reaction

Reaction of acid derivatives can occur at the α carbon. Such reactions may be base-catalyzed and proceed via the enolate ion (to be discussed later), or they may be acid-catalyzed and proceed via the enol. One such reaction is the substitution of an α hydrogen by chlorine or bromine using phosphorus or a phosphorus halide as a catalyst (Hell–Volhard–Zelinsky reaction).

Carboxylic acids themselves have a negligible enol content, and they do not react with halogen as aldehydes and ketones do, even in the presence of acid. Acid chlorides, on the other hand, are faintly enolic. A little phosphorus catalyzes the α-halogenation of an acid. The phosphorus reacts with halogen to give phosphorus pentahalide, which converts some acid to acid halide. The enol of the latter is then halogenated. By interchange reactions, the halogenated acid halide gives the halogenated acid, and more acid halide is generated. The process continues until all of the acid has been halogenated.

The α hydrogens can be selectively replaced, one at a time.

The reaction can be stopped at the mono-, di-, or trisubstituted stage by using the proper amount of halogen. Chlorine and bromine are equally useful for such halogenations.

The α-halo acids are excellent synthetic intermediates. The halogen can be substituted by reaction with a variety of reagents such as hydroxide, alkoxide, ammonia, and amines.

$$CH_3CH-CH_2-CH-C\overset{O}{\underset{OH}{\diagdown}} \xrightarrow{\text{1. NH}_3} CH_3-CHCH_2-CH-COO^- \quad NH_4^+$$

with CH_3 and Br substituents on the left structure, and CH_3 and NH_2 substituents on the right.

An α-amino acid
(constituent of proteins,
Chapter 29)

$$\xrightarrow[\text{2. H}^+]{\text{1. CH}_3O^-} CH_3-CHCH_2CH-COOH$$

with CH_3 and OCH_3 substituents.

One of the most important nucleophiles for replacement of the halogen at the α carbon is cyanide ion.

$$^-CN \quad Cl-CH_2COOH \rightarrow \underset{COOH}{\overset{CN}{\underset{|}{CH_2}}} \xrightarrow[\text{H}^+]{\underset{\text{HOEt}}{\text{H}_2\text{O}}} \underset{COOC_2H_5}{\overset{COOC_2H_5}{\underset{|}{CH_2}}} \quad (+ \; NH_4^+)$$

(as Na salt) · Diethyl malonate

Diethyl malonate is a very useful synthetic intermediate and will be taken up in the next section.

EXERCISE 20.12

The amino acid *alanine* (α-aminopropionic acid) is one of the basic building blocks of living systems. How would you synthesize *dl*-alanine from propionic acid?

20.13 Malonic Ester Synthesis

With the simplest α-chloro acid, chloroacetic acid, cyanide ion gives cyanoacetic acid, which can be converted into diethyl malonate (malonic ester). Ethyl chloroacetate can be used in place of the carboxylic acid to give cyanoacetic ester. Both malonic ester and cyanoacetic ester have hydrogen atoms which are activated by two powerful electron withdrawing groups, and these hydrogens are only a little less acidic than those of β-diketones (Section 8.2). Malonic ester can be used as the starting point in a very useful sequence of steps, which are collectively called the *malonic ester synthesis*. Cyanoacetic ester can be used in a similar way.

The objective is to convert RBr into RCH_2COOH; that is, to increase the length of a carbon chain by two and end up with a carboxylic acid. The procedure is as follows:

$$\underset{COOC_2H_5}{\overset{COOC_2H_5}{\underset{|}{CH_2}}} \xrightarrow{\text{Na}^+\text{OC}_2\text{H}_5} \text{Sodiomalonic ester} \xrightarrow{\text{RBr}} \cdots$$

$$RCH_2COOH \xleftarrow[-CO_2]{\Delta} R-CH\overset{COOH}{\underset{COOH}{\diagup}}$$

with OH^- or H_3O^+ conditions.

Further, since there are two acidic hydrogens on malonic ester, it can be alkylated twice using the same or two different alkyl halides. This allows the following type of overall transformation (in several steps):

$$R-Br + R'-Br \rightarrow R-\underset{R'}{\overset{}{\underset{|}{CH}}}-COOH$$

The details of such a synthesis are shown.

$$CH_2(COOEt)_2 \xrightarrow[\text{2. R—Br}]{\text{1. EtO}^-} RCH(COOEt)_2 \xrightarrow[\text{2. R'—Br}]{\text{1. EtO}^-} RR'C(COOEt)_2$$

$$\downarrow \begin{array}{c} H_3O^+ \\ \Delta \end{array}$$

$$RR'CHCOOH$$

As the preceding sequences show, while it is not possible to carry out directly the transformation R—Br + $CH_3COOH \rightarrow$ R—CH_2COOH or R'—Br + RCH_2COOH $\rightarrow RR'CHCOOH$, we can in fact accomplish these operations by first putting on an extra carboxyl (i.e., using malonic ester) and then taking it off (decarboxylation).

EXERCISE 20.13

A method for extending a carbon chain by two and ending up with an alcohol was discussed earlier. R—Br $\rightarrow$R—CH_2CH_2OH. How was it done? (Section 18.9.)

$$R\text{-}Mg\text{-}Br \qquad \overset{CH_2\text{-}CH_2}{\underset{O}{\triangle}}$$

Using very strong bases, certain carboxylic acids have recently been converted to dianions which can be directly alkylated. The reaction is of limited value and fails for acetic and propionic acids.

$$R—CH_2COOH \rightarrow R—\overset{-}{CH}—COO^- \xrightarrow{R'X} \overset{R}{\underset{R'}{\diagup}}CH—COO^-$$

A typical synthesis by this method is shown below.

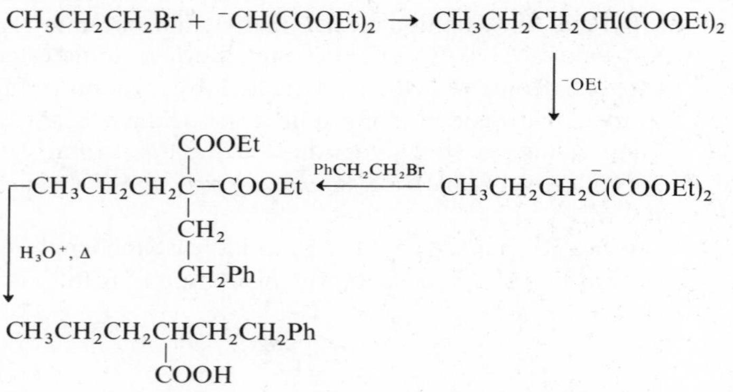

$$CH_3CH_2CH_2Br + \ ^-CH(COOEt)_2 \rightarrow CH_3CH_2CH_2CH(COOEt)_2$$

$$\downarrow ^-OEt$$

$$\begin{array}{c} COOEt \\ | \\ \lceil CH_3CH_2CH_2C—COOEt \xleftarrow{PhCH_2CH_2Br} CH_3CH_2CH_2\overset{-}{C}(COOEt)_2 \\ | \\ CH_2 \\ | \\ H_3O^+, \Delta \quad CH_2Ph \end{array}$$

$$\begin{array}{c} CH_3CH_2CH_2CHCH_2CH_2Ph \\ | \\ COOH \end{array}$$

EXERCISE 20.14

Outline preparations of the following compounds using the malonic ester synthesis.

(a) $CH_3CH_2CH_2CH_2CH_2COOH$

(b) $\begin{array}{c} CH_3CH_2CHCH_2CH_3 \\ | \\ COOH \end{array}$

(c) $\begin{array}{c} CH_3—CH—CH_2COOH \\ | \\ CH_3 \end{array}$

A Side Reaction in Malonic Ester Alkylation. Dialkylation of malonic ester is a side reaction when monoalkylation is desired. This side reaction can be understood by considering the reaction after half the alkylation has occurred. The initial carbanion and the alkylated product are present in equal concentrations, and an acid–base reaction will occur.

$$
\underset{}{C_2H_5O-\overset{\overset{\displaystyle O}{\|}}{C}-\underset{\displaystyle }{C}H-\overset{\overset{\displaystyle O}{\|}}{C}-OC_2H_5} \qquad C_2H_5O-\overset{\overset{\displaystyle O}{\|}}{C}-\underset{\underset{\displaystyle H}{|}}{C}H-\overset{\overset{\displaystyle O}{\|}}{C}-OC_2H_5
$$

$$
+ \qquad\qquad\qquad \rightleftharpoons \qquad\qquad +
$$

$$
C_2H_5O-\overset{\overset{\displaystyle O}{\|}}{C}-\underset{\underset{\displaystyle R}{|}}{\overset{\overset{\displaystyle H}{|}}{C}}-\overset{\overset{\displaystyle O}{\|}}{C}-OC_2H_5 \qquad C_2H_5O-\overset{\overset{\displaystyle O}{\|}}{C}-\underset{\underset{\displaystyle R}{|}}{\overset{}{C}}-\overset{\overset{\displaystyle O}{\|}}{C}-OC_2H_5
$$

Insofar as the new carbanion is formed, it can be involved in another alkylation reaction to give dialkyl by-product. Although the new carbanion will be more basic from the effect of R, it is not necessarily more nucleophilic toward carbon, and it certainly is more hindered than its competitor. In practice, a small amount of dialkyl by-product is almost always formed, however.

20.14   The Claisen Condensation

When ethyl acetate is treated with sodium ethoxide, it is largely converted to the sodium salt of ethyl acetoacetate.

$$
2CH_3-\overset{\overset{\displaystyle O}{\|}}{C}-OEt + {}^-OEt \overset{ether}{=\!=\!=} CH_3-\overset{\overset{\displaystyle O}{\|}}{C}-\overset{-}{C}H-\overset{\overset{\displaystyle O}{\|}}{C}-OEt + EtOH
$$

Ethyl acetoacetate (salt)

The reaction is general for esters which contain at least two α-hydrogens and is referred to as the *Claisen condensation*.

$$
RCH_2-\overset{\overset{\displaystyle O}{\|}}{C}-OEt + EtO^- \rightleftharpoons RCH_2-\overset{\overset{\displaystyle O}{\|}}{C}-\underset{\underset{\displaystyle R}{|}}{\overset{}{C}}-\overset{\overset{\displaystyle O\,\cdot}{\|}}{C}-OEt + EtO^-
$$

Esters in which at least one hydrogen is present on the carbon *alpha* to the carbonyl group are weakly acidic and can be converted into the corresponding resonance-stabilized anions by reaction with a strong base.

$$
\underset{(base)}{B{:}}{\overset{\frown}{\;}}H-\underset{\underset{\displaystyle R}{|}}{\overset{\overset{\displaystyle R}{|}}{C}}-\overset{\overset{\displaystyle O}{\|}}{C}-OR' \rightarrow B-H + \left[\underset{}{R_2\overset{-}{C}}-C\overset{\diagup O}{\diagdown OR'} \leftrightarrow R_2C{=}C\overset{\diagup O^-}{\diagdown OR'} \right]
$$

Many bases of sufficient strength to remove the alpha hydrogen are unsuitable in practice for producing ester anions, since they can also attack the ester carbonyl and bring about destruction of the ester. Hydroxide ion, for example, brings about the irreversible saponification of the ester. On the other hand, the alkoxide ion corresponding to the alkoxy group of the ester is an ideal base for anion formation, since its attack upon the ester carbonyl is a reversible process which does not destroy the ester. This reaction is illustrated for ethyl acetate and ethoxide ion.

$$
CH_3-\overset{\overset{\displaystyle O}{\|}}{C}-O-C_2H_5 + {}^-OC_2H_5 \rightleftharpoons CH_3-\underset{\underset{\displaystyle OC_2H_5}{|}}{\overset{\overset{\displaystyle O^-}{|}}{C}}-OC_2H_5
$$

The only observable reaction starts when the base attacks the α hydrogen, producing an enolate ion.

$$H\overset{\frown}{-}CH_2-\overset{\overset{\displaystyle O}{\|}}{C}-OC_2H_5 \rightleftharpoons \left[\bar{C}H_2-\overset{\overset{\displaystyle O}{\|}}{C}-OC_2H_5 \leftrightarrow CH_2=\overset{\overset{\displaystyle O^-}{|}}{C}-OC_2H_5\right]+ HOC_2H_5$$
$$\overset{\displaystyle}{\underset{\displaystyle \bar{O}C_2H_5}{}}$$

The enolate is both a new base and a nucleophile. As a base, it can attack the proton of ethanol to reverse the acid–base reaction. As a nucleophile, it can attack another ester carbonyl carbon to give the usual tetrahedral carbon adduct, which will lose ethoxide ion to give a β-keto ester. Up to the formation of the tetrahedral intermediate, the reaction is closely parallel to the aldol condensation (Section 19.14).

$$C_2H_5O-\overset{\overset{\displaystyle O}{\|}}{C}-CH_2 + CH_3\overset{\overset{\displaystyle O}{\|}}{C}-OC_2H_5 \rightleftharpoons CH_3\overset{\overset{\displaystyle O^-}{|}}{\underset{\underset{\displaystyle OC_2H_5}{|}}{C}}-CH_2\overset{\overset{\displaystyle O}{\|}}{C}-OC_2H_5$$

$$CH_3\overset{\overset{\displaystyle O}{\|}}{C}-\bar{C}H-\overset{\overset{\displaystyle O}{\|}}{C}-OC_2H_5 \underset{EtO^-}{\overset{EtOH}{\rightleftharpoons}} CH_3\overset{\overset{\displaystyle O}{\|}}{C}-CH_2-\overset{\overset{\displaystyle O}{\|}}{C}-OC_2H_5$$

Loss of ethoxide from the tetrahedral intermediate yields a β-keto ester, which is called *ethyl acetoacetate* or sometimes *acetoacetic ester*. It has hydrogen atoms activated by two carbonyl groups, and they are clearly much more acidic than the α hydrogens of the starting ester. The newly formed alkoxide would then convert most of this ester to its anion, the driving force for the overall reaction being the production of the weakest acid and the weakest base.

Not counting the reversible equilibrium of alkoxide attack on carbonyl, four successive delicately balanced equilibria are established when sodium ethoxide is added to ethyl acetate. The beauty of the sequence for the organic chemist is that he can drive the series of equilibria to completion in the forward direction by distilling the alcohol, or in the backward direction by adding a large excess of alcohol.

For 2 moles of ethyl acetate, 1 mole of sodium ethoxide is used and 1 mole of alcohol is formed. After all the alcohol is distilled and the reactions driven to the right, the product is the sodium salt of the β-keto ester. Generally, the reaction is finished by addition of a proton in the form of a weak acid, and then isolation of the product as the keto ester.

$$2\,CH_3\overset{\overset{\displaystyle O}{\|}}{C}-OC_2H_5 + {}^-OC_2H_5 \rightleftharpoons CH_3\overset{\overset{\displaystyle O}{\|}}{C}-\bar{C}H-\overset{\overset{\displaystyle O}{\|}}{C}-OC_2H_5 + HOC_2H_5$$

$$\Big\downarrow {\scriptstyle CH_3COOH}$$

$$CH_3COCH_2COOC_2H_5$$

If the keto ester is dissolved in a large excess of alcohol and a catalytic amount of sodium ethoxide or other strong base is added (either deliberately or inadvertently) the keto ester will be smoothly converted to starting ester.

$$CH_3\overset{\overset{\displaystyle O}{\|}}{C}-CH_2\overset{\overset{\displaystyle O}{\|}}{C}-OC_2H_5 + HOC_2H_5 \xrightarrow[EtOH]{\substack{strong\\base}} 2\,CH_3\overset{\overset{\displaystyle O}{\|}}{C}-OC_2H_5$$

EXERCISE 20.15

What product do you expect when ethyl propionate (2 moles) is treated with sodium ethoxide (1 mole) in ethanol? Write the mechanism of the reaction.

20.15 Alkylation of β-Keto Esters. The Acetoacetic Ester Synthesis

The β-keto esters, of which acetoacetic ester is the simplest example, are very useful chemical intermediates for the synthesis of ketones and carboxylic acids. The *acetoacetic ester synthesis* can be used to prepare substituted acetic acids just as the *malonic ester synthesis* is used (Section 20.13). In addition, the acetoacetic ester synthesis can be used to prepare methyl ketones. Both variations of the synthesis start with the alkylation of acetoacetic ester.

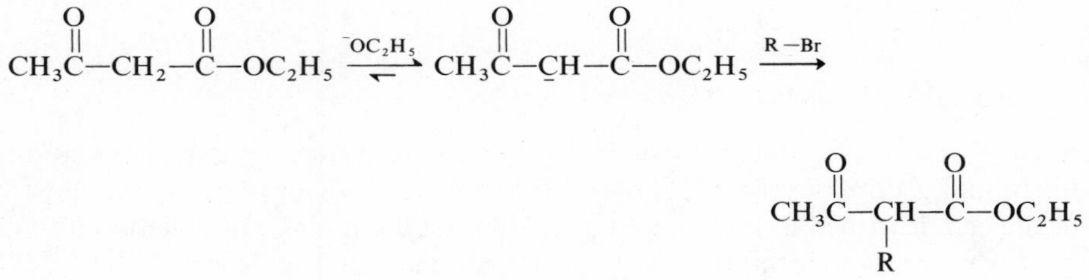

Although the β-keto esters are isolated and stored as such, the sodium salts are the key intermediates for the alkylation reactions. Such a salt, written as the carbanion, reacts with an alkylating agent to give substitution of an alkyl group on carbon as shown above.

O-Alkylation. Two main problems accompany the acetoacetic ester synthesis. If the alkylating reagent is extremely reactive, such as benzyl chloride, a significant amount of *O*-alkylation occurs.

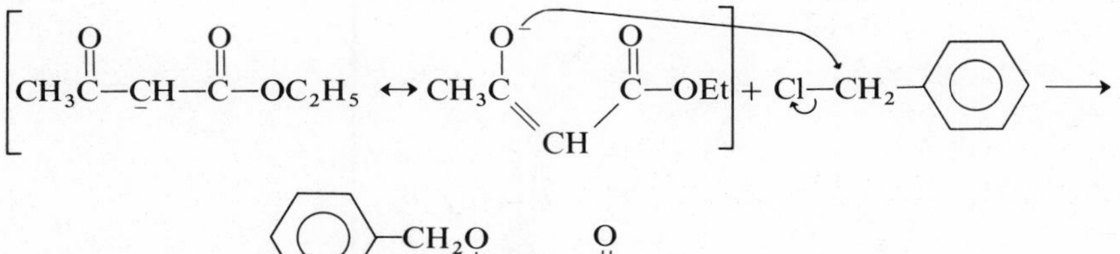

The second problem is dialkylation, which was previously discussed for the malonic ester synthesis (Section 20.13).

After isolation, the new substituted β-keto ester can be used to synthesize either of two different types of compounds.

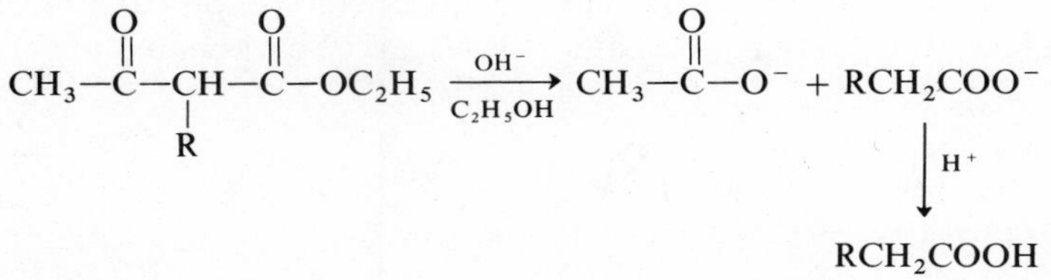

Acid Cleavage

Treatment with a catalytic amount of base and a large excess of alcohol would be expected to start the reversal of the four successive equilibria which formed the parent. The products would be two esters, $CH_3COOC_2H_5$ and $RCH_2COOC_2H_5$. Since the corresponding parent acids are often desired rather than the esters, enough hydroxide can be added to saponify the esters in the original reaction, and the products can be isolated as acids.

Ketone Cleavage

If the new β-keto ester is hydrolyzed with acid, the reversal of the Claisen condensation does not take place. The first reaction product is the β-keto acid, which upon heating undergoes decarboxylation to give a ketone. This is the second useful type of product which can be formed from the β-keto ester.

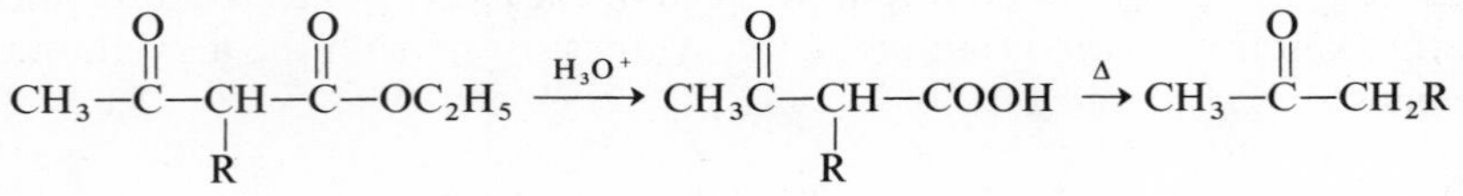

$$CH_3-\overset{\overset{O}{\|}}{C}-\overset{}{\underset{\underset{R}{|}}{CH}}-\overset{\overset{O}{\|}}{C}-OC_2H_5 \xrightarrow{H_3O^+} CH_3\overset{\overset{O}{\|}}{C}-\underset{\underset{R}{|}}{CH}-COOH \xrightarrow{\Delta} CH_3-\overset{\overset{O}{\|}}{C}-CH_2R$$

20.16   Preparative Methods for Carboxylic Acids

The fact that the carboxyl group is one of the most common, most stable, and most studied of the functional groups is reflected in the numerous methods of preparation, most of which have been described in previous chapters. Before discussing polyfunctional acids, a review of the common methods of preparation of carboxylic acids is in order.

Oxidation

A carboxylic acid is often the first really stable product of an oxidation reaction. Primary alcohols, aldehydes, alkylbenzenes, and olefins with at least one hydrogen on the double bond are oxidized to carboxylic acids.

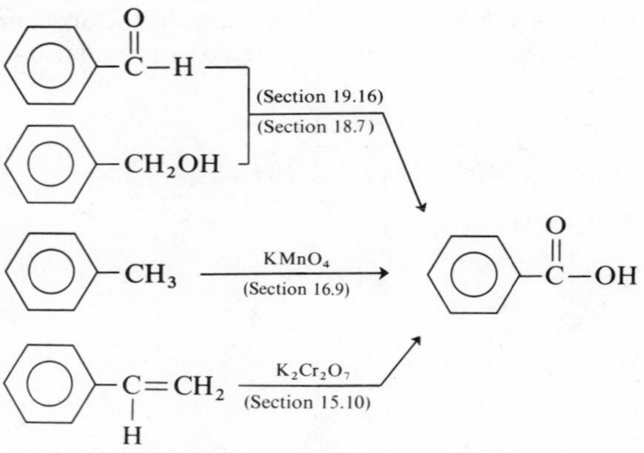

Carbonation of an Organometallic Reagent

An important method for the preparation of carboxylic acids is treatment of an organo-metallic compound with carbon dioxide. Grignard reagents can be prepared from ordinary primary, secondary, or tertiary halides, and in turn can be carbonated in good yields.

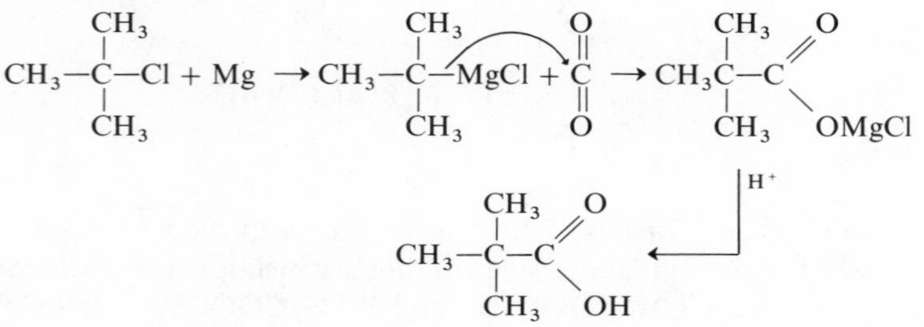

Organolithium compounds also can be carbonated readily.

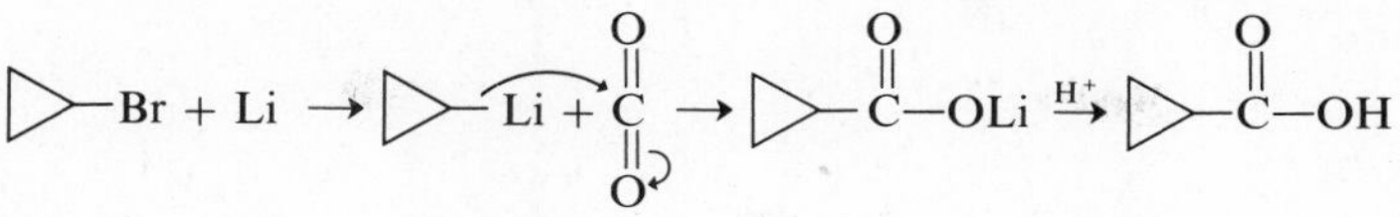

Carbonylation of Stable Carbonium Ions

Stable carbonium ions that are generated under reversible conditions can be "trapped" by carbon monoxide to give acylium ions, $R-C\overset{+}{=}O$. Reaction with water will furnish a carboxylic acid.

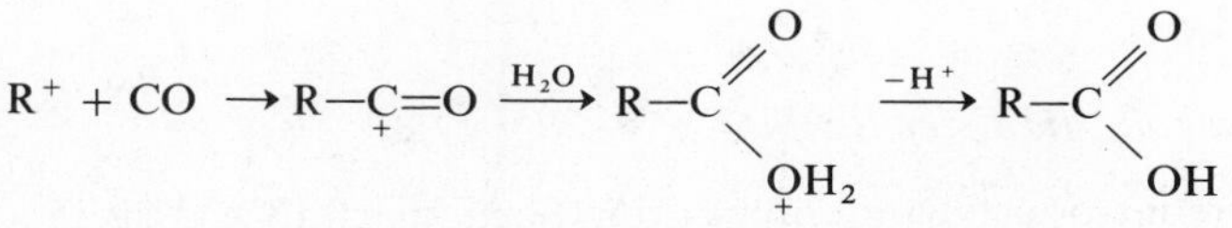

The carbonium ions can be produced from several precursors: alkenes, alcohols, and even saturated hydrocarbons containing a tertiary hydrogen (Sections 23.3, 23.5). In some cases an alkene is treated with an acid catalyst (usually H_2SO_4) and carbon monoxide under pressure and at moderate temperatures, followed by the addition of water.

$$CH_2=CH_2 \xrightarrow[CO]{H^+} CH_3CH_2\overset{+}{C}=O \xrightarrow{H_2O} CH_3CH_2COOH$$

Carbonylation by formic acid is a rapid and simple method for preparing carboxylic acids. In the presence of concentrated sulfuric acid, formic acid is dehydrated to carbon monoxide and water, providing both reagents for the synthesis.

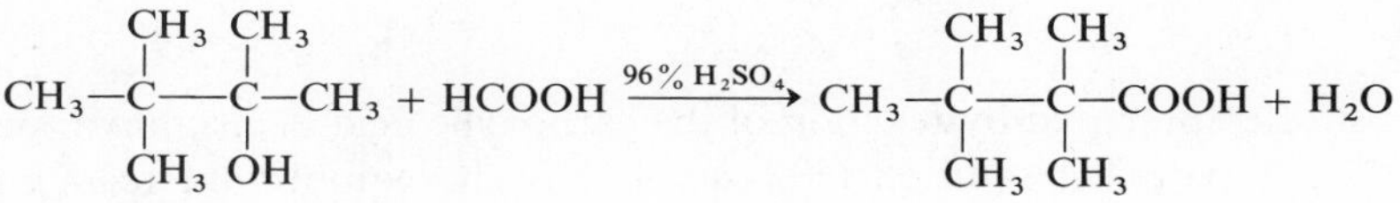

EXERCISE 20.16

Write a mechanism for the above reaction.

When primary and secondary alcohols are used as the carbonium ion precursors, rearrangement usually takes place.

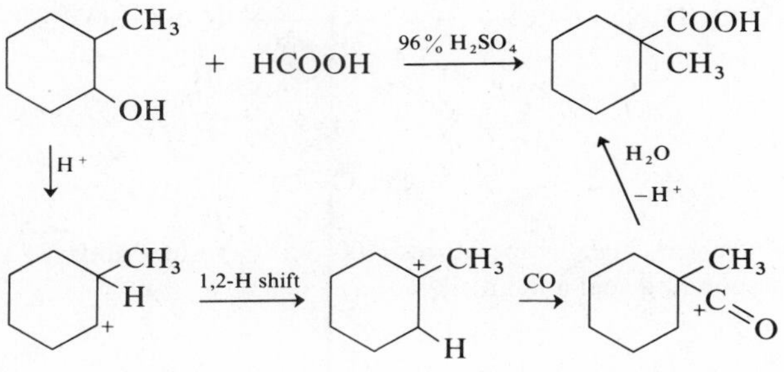

Carbonylation. The protonation of an aldehyde or ketone leads to a relatively stable carbonium ion $(R_2C\overset{+}{=}OH)$, which can be carbonylated. For example, glycolic acid is made by the condensation of formaldehyde, carbon monoxide, and water in the presence of sulfuric acid at 165°C.

$$H_2C=O + CO \xrightarrow[H_2O]{H_2SO_4} HOCH_2COOH$$

Hydrolysis of Acid Derivatives

All of the acid derivatives except the nitrile are generally prepared from the acid, so hydrolysis of an acid derivative is not usually a practical method for preparation of an acid. Nitriles can be prepared by dehydration of an amide (Section 20.5), or by nucleophilic displacement of a leaving group from carbon by cyanide ion (Table 17.1). A limitation on the synthetic usefulness of this displacement results from the fact that cyanide is a strong base, and the side reaction to form olefin may be serious. Primary halides react well, secondary halides vary from poor to fair, and tertiary halides that can dehydrohalogenate give only olefin.

Acetoacetic, Malonic, and Cyanoacetic Ester Synthesis

These multistep syntheses were introduced and discussed in Sections 20.13 and 20.15.

Other Methods

Methyl ketones can be oxidized to an acid and haloform using halogen and hydroxide (the *haloform reaction*, Section 19.13).

Organic peracids react with ketones to give esters by the *Baeyer–Villiger oxidation* (Section 19.16).

Peracids are most often prepared by reaction of the carboxylic acid or its anhydride with aqueous hydrogen peroxide solution (30% or 90%). The equilibrium reaction shown has been established.

$$RCOOH + H_2O_2 \rightleftharpoons RCOOOH + H_2O$$

The chain length of an acid can be extended by one carbon atom using the *Arndt–Eistert reaction* (to be discussed in Section 22.8).

Ester Pyrolysis. Tschugaev Reaction. At very high temperatures (400–500°C), esters undergo a pyrolysis reaction and yield the corresponding acid and an alkene.

While this is a preparation of an acid in a formal sense, in a practical sense it is part of a sequence which converts an alcohol to an olefin. Such reactions go in high yield and are carried out by dropping the ester into a tube packed with glass beads and heated at the desired temperature. The ester is immediately volatilized, and the gaseous products are expelled from the other end of the tube. Esters of stronger acids, such as trichloroacetic, cleave at much lower temperatures.

If a xanthate ester (Section 26.8) is used in place of a carboxylic acid ester, a similar reaction takes place at about 150°C. (*Tschugaev reaction*).

$$CH_3-S-\overset{\overset{\displaystyle S}{\|}}{C}-O-CH_2CH_2R' \xrightarrow{\Delta} CH_3SH + COS + CH_2{=}CH_2R'$$

Since xanthate esters are easily obtained from alcohols (Section 26.8), the esterification–pyrolysis sequence is a method for the conversion of an alcohol to an olefin. In contrast to most other eliminations, these ester pyrolyses are cis eliminations, and they proceed via cyclic transition states.

$$H_3C-\underset{\overset{\displaystyle \downarrow}{H}}{S}\cdots\overset{\overset{\displaystyle S}{\|}}{C}\cdots O \longrightarrow CH_3SH + COS + R'CH{=}CH_2$$

20.17   Polyfunctional Acids and Their Derivatives

The synthesis and reactions of polyfunctional compounds are often orders of magnitude more complicated than the synthesis and reactions of compounds with one functional group. However, as the science of organic chemistry has progressed, chemists have discovered how to protect one functional group from being destroyed while assaulting another. Additionally, chemists have discovered new reagents that are more selective for reaction at one functional group while not reacting with others. In this section polyfunctional acids will be briefly discussed in the order of introduction of the functional groups in the earlier chapters. Discussion of the important *amino acids* will be reserved until Chapter 29.

Unsaturated Acids

Selective oxidation of one unsaturated site in preference to another is generally useful only if one of the sites is aromatic.

Most of the other methods for preparation of carboxylic acids listed in Section 20.16 are applicable with an appropriate starting material containing unsaturation. For example, the hypohalite oxidation of methyl ketones is satisfactory with unsaturated ketones.

Unsaturated halides, including vinyl halides, may be converted to unsaturated acids in the usual way by carbonation of a Grignard or lithium derivative. These reactions always proceed with retention of configuration, as shown.

$$\underset{H}{\overset{CH_3}{\diagdown}}C=C\underset{Cl}{\overset{H}{\diagup}} + Li \rightarrow \underset{H}{\overset{CH_3}{\diagdown}}C=C\underset{Li}{\overset{H}{\diagup}} \xrightarrow[2.\ H_3O^+]{1.\ CO_2} \underset{H}{\overset{CH_3}{\diagdown}}C=C\underset{CO_2H}{\overset{H}{\diagup}}$$

$$\underset{H}{\overset{CH_3}{\diagdown}}C=C\underset{H}{\overset{Cl}{\diagup}} + Li \rightarrow \underset{H}{\overset{CH_3}{\diagdown}}C=C\underset{H}{\overset{Li}{\diagup}} \xrightarrow[2.\ H_3O^+]{1.\ CO_2} \underset{H}{\overset{CH_3}{\diagdown}}C=C\underset{H}{\overset{CO_2H}{\diagup}}$$

Compounds which contain isolated carbonyl groups and isolated double bonds show the usual reactions of the separate functions: the two groups react independently. An α,β-unsaturated or conjugated acid may often undergo conjugate addition (Michael addition), analogous to the similar reactions of carbonyl compounds (Section 19.17).

$$H_2C=CH-\overset{O}{\overset{\|}{C}}-OH + HCl \rightarrow H_2C=CH-\overset{\overset{+}{\overset{\frown}{C}OH}}{\overset{\|}{C}}-OH$$
$$Cl^-$$

$$ClCH_2CH_2\overset{O}{\overset{\|}{C}}-OH \xleftarrow{\text{tautomerize}} \left[ClH_2C-CH=\overset{OH}{\overset{|}{C}}-OH \right]$$
$$\text{(enol)}$$

$$CH_2=CH-C\diagdown_{OR}^{O} \begin{cases} \xrightarrow[\text{or } R_2N^-]{R_2NH} R_2NCH_2CH_2\overset{O}{\overset{\|}{C}}-OR \\[2mm] \xrightarrow[(OH^-)]{HOH} HOCH_2CH_2\overset{O}{\overset{\|}{C}}-OR \\[2mm] \xrightarrow{^-CH(\overset{O}{\overset{\|}{C}}OC_2H_5)_2} \underset{C_2H_5O\overset{C}{\overset{\|}{O}}}{\overset{C_2H_5O\overset{C}{\overset{\|}{O}}}{}}CHCH_2CH_2\overset{O}{\overset{\|}{C}}-OR \end{cases}$$

$$PhCH=CHCO_2C_2H_5 + KCN \xrightarrow{C_2H_5OH} \underset{\overset{|}{C}\equiv N}{Ph-CHCH_2COOC_2H_5} \xrightarrow{H_3O^+}$$

$$\underset{Ph}{\overset{|}{HOOCCHCH_2COOH}}$$

Acids which are β, γ- or γ, δ-unsaturated react with strong acid to give lactones by ring closure, and react with strong base to give α,β-unsaturated acids by rearrangement.

$$CH_2=CHCH_2CH_2\overset{O}{\overset{\|}{C}}-OH \underset{}{\overset{H^+}{\rightleftharpoons}} CH_3\overset{+}{C}HCH_2CH_2\overset{O}{\overset{\|}{C}}-\ddot{O}H \rightarrow \underset{H_3C}{}\overset{}{\diagup}\overset{}{O}\diagdown_O$$

$$CH_2=CHCH_2\overset{O}{\overset{\|}{C}}-OH \xrightarrow{^-OH} CH_3CH=CH-\overset{O}{\overset{\|}{C}}-OH \text{ (as salt)}$$

α,β-Unsaturated acid derivatives are the most important and useful unsaturated acid derivatives; they can be made from α-halo acids by dehydrohalogenation, or from α-hydroxy or β-hydroxy derivatives by dehydration.

Halo Acids

Dehydrohalogenation of an α-halo acid gives the unsaturated acid.

From α,β-unsaturated acids, β-halo acids can be prepared by the addition of HX (see preceding section).

γ-, δ-, and ω-Halo acids can be prepared from dihalides. Chloro alcohols are useful starting materials.

$$Cl(CH_2)_nOH \xrightarrow{HBr} Cl(CH_2)_nBr \xrightarrow{CN^-} Cl(CH_2)_nC{\equiv}N \xrightarrow[H_3O^+]{heat} Cl(CH_2)_n\overset{\displaystyle O}{\overset{\|}{C}}{-}OH$$

If the chloro alcohol is not available, a dichloride or dibromide can be used, but the yield is poorer. (Why?)

Alcoholic, Phenolic, and Alkoxy Acids

α-Hydroxy acids are best made by the cyanohydrin synthesis.

$$R{-}\overset{\displaystyle O}{\overset{\|}{C}}{-}H + HCN \xrightarrow{CN^-} R{-}\overset{\displaystyle OH}{\underset{\displaystyle H}{\overset{\displaystyle |}{\underset{\displaystyle |}{C}}}}{-}C{\equiv}N \xrightarrow[H_2O]{H^+} R{-}\overset{\displaystyle |}{\underset{\displaystyle OH}{CH}}{-}\overset{\displaystyle O}{\overset{\|}{C}}{-}OH$$

Some hydroxy acids are found in nature and are of biological importance. The most significant of these is *lactic acid* (α-hydroxypropionic acid), which is the acidic constituent of sour milk, and which is also an important muscle metabolite. Another common hydroxy acid is *citric acid*, the sour component of citrus fruit and also an important biochemical intermediate.

$$CH_3{-}\underset{\displaystyle OH}{\overset{\displaystyle |}{CH}}{-}COOH \qquad HOOCCH_2{-}\underset{\displaystyle OH}{\overset{\displaystyle COOH}{\overset{\displaystyle |}{\underset{\displaystyle |}{C}}}}{-}CH_2COOH$$

Lactic acid   Citric acid

Whereas γ-hydroxy and δ-hydroxy acids are easily converted to lactones, α-hydroxy acids do not similarly form α-lactones. An α-lactone would contain a highly strained three-membered ring, and such a lactone has never been isolated (it is believed that they are intermediates in certain reactions, however). The α-hydroxy acid instead prefers to form a dimeric lactone, known as a *lactide*.

A lactide

The β-hydroxy acids behave like their β-halo analogs. Upon dehydration, often just by heating, they revert to the unsaturated acids.

Reformatsky Reactions. Sometimes β-hydroxy acids can be prepared by means of the Reformatsky reaction (Section 19.9).

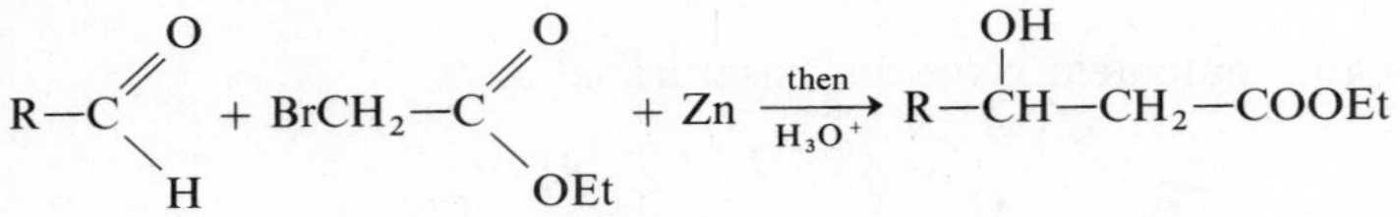

Often the hydroxy ester dehydrates to the α,β-unsaturated ester during the reaction or during the work-up.

The γ- and δ-hydroxy acids readily give lactones by intramolecular esterification. Heat will accomplish the conversion without the necessity for acid catalysis. In fact, the cyclization is usually spontaneous, and the free hydroxy acids are rarely isolable as such.

EXERCISE 20.17

Predict the product of the following reaction:

$$HOCH_2CH_2CH_2CH_2CH_2COOH \xrightarrow[\Delta]{H^+}$$

Kolbe Reaction. Phenols can be carbonated to give phenolic acids. The reaction is known as the *Kolbe reaction* (note that there is another reaction called *Kolbe electrolysis*, Section 20.11). The sodium salt of the phenol is treated with carbon dioxide under pressure.

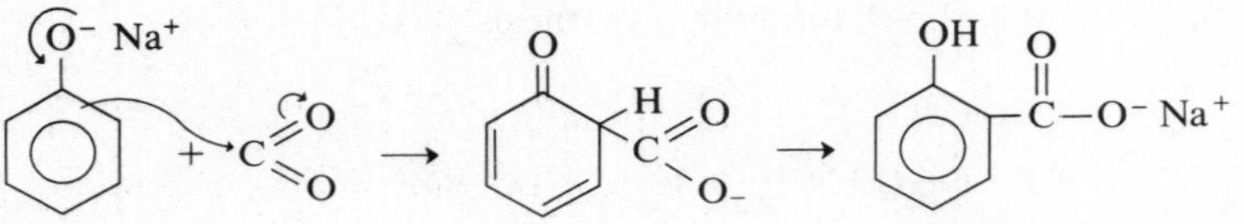

Sodium salicylate

Acetylation of salicylic acid gives aspirin, acetylsalicylic acid.

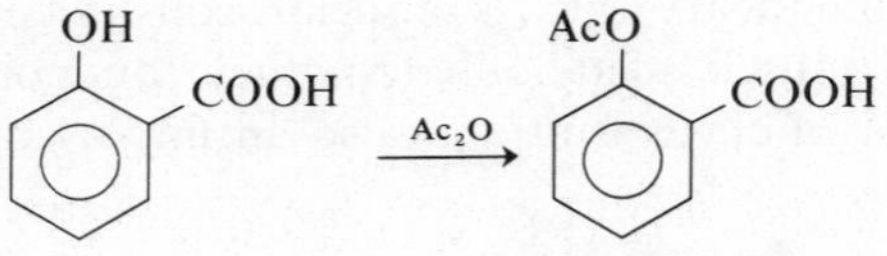

Aspirin

Keto Acids and Diacids

The simple and important keto acid derivative, acetoacetic ester, has been discussed in some detail (Sections 20.14 and 20.15). Ethyl oxalate has no active α-hydrogen atoms and has very reactive carbonyl groups. It can take part in a mixed ester condensation to give a diketo ester, which upon heating loses carbon monoxide to give a β-keto ester.

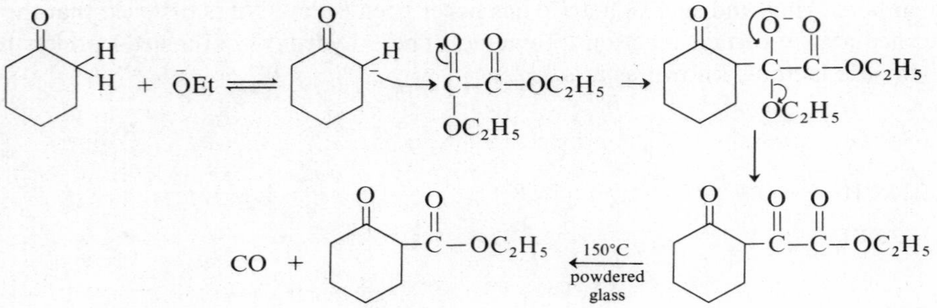

An α-keto acid can be prepared from the corresponding acid chloride and cuprous cyanide, followed by hydrolysis of the resulting α-keto cyanide.

$$CH_3{-}\overset{\underset{\displaystyle \|}{O}}{C}{-}Cl + CuCN \rightarrow CH_3{-}\overset{\underset{\displaystyle \|}{O}}{C}{-}C{\equiv}N \xrightarrow{H^+} CH_3\overset{\underset{\displaystyle \|}{O}}{C}{-}\overset{\underset{\displaystyle \|}{O}}{C}{-}OH$$

Pyruvic acid

Pyruvic acid is an important biochemical intermediate; it is involved in the metabolism of sugar to produce energy.

Carbonic acid is the simplest of the dicarboxylic acids, in the sense that its single carbonyl group serves to activate two hydroxyl groups. Carbonic acid is in facile equilibrium with carbon dioxide and water. At atmospheric pressure and room temperature, the equilibrium favors carbon dioxide and water.

Many stable derivatives of carbonic acid, such as phosgene, ethyl chlorocarbonate, diethyl carbonate, and urea, are commercially available and useful compounds.

$$H{-}O{-}\overset{\underset{\displaystyle \|}{O}}{C}{-}O{-}H \rightleftharpoons H{-}O{-}H + CO_2$$

Carbonic acid

$$Cl{-}\overset{\underset{\displaystyle \|}{O}}{C}{-}Cl \qquad C_2H_5O{-}\overset{\underset{\displaystyle \|}{O}}{C}{-}Cl \qquad C_2H_5O{-}\overset{\underset{\displaystyle \|}{O}}{C}{-}OC_2H_5 \qquad H_2N{-}\overset{\underset{\displaystyle \|}{O}}{C}{-}NH_2$$

Phosgene   Ethyl chlorocarbonate   Diethyl carbonate   Urea
(Ethyl chloroformate)

Oxalic acid is commercially available from the reaction of sodium formate with sodium hydroxide at high temperature.

$$HC{-}ONa + NaOH \xrightarrow{\Delta} HO{-}\overset{\underset{\displaystyle \|}{O}}{C}{-}\overset{\underset{\displaystyle \|}{O}}{C}{-}OH \text{ (as salt)} + H_2$$

Malonic acid is commercially available via chloroacetic acid and ethyl cyanoacetate (Section 20.13).

Succinic acid is made from the hydrogenation of maleic acid, a polyfunctional compound with one double bond and two carboxyl groups which is made in large tonnage lots from the catalytic oxidation of benzene. Maleic acid is converted to the thermodynamically more stable trans isomer, known as fumaric acid, upon heating with aqueous mineral acid. Dehydrogenation of succinic acid to fumaric acid by the enzyme *succinic dehydrogenase* is a biochemical process of some importance.

Maleic   Maleic acid (*cis*)   Succinic acid
anhydride

Glutaric and adipic acids are made by the oxidation of cyclopentanone and cyclohexanone, respectively.

The aromatic dicarboxylic acid, phthalic acid, is made commercially by oxidation of either naphthalene or *o*-xylene.

EXERCISE 20.18

Draw a picture of the σ framework of phthalic anhydride, show all the 2*p* orbitals which make up the π system, and indicate the number of electrons contributed by each p orbital.

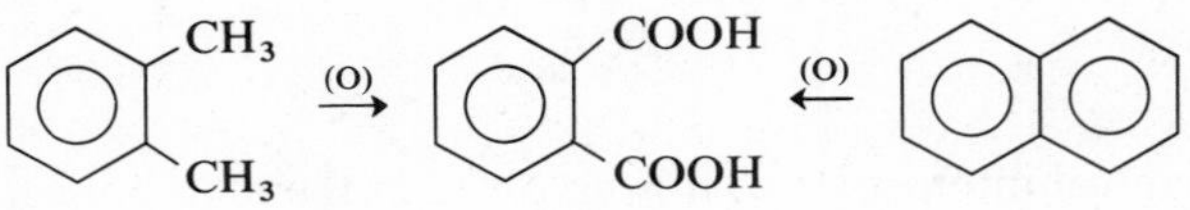

Carbonic, oxalic, and malonic acids undergo decarboxylation at room temperature, 140°C, and 150°C, respectively. Oxalic acid gives formic acid as the other product, and malonic acid gives acetic acid.

Succinic, glutaric, maleic, and phthalic acids all give a stable intramolecular anhydride when heated with acetic anhydride. Formation of a relatively unstrained five- or six-membered ring is the key requirement.

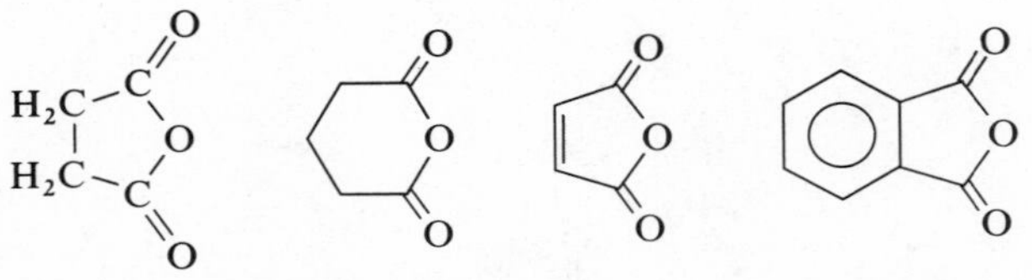

| Succinic anhydride | Glutaric anhydride | Maleic anhydride | Phthalic anhydride |

EXERCISE 20.19

What product do you expect from the following reaction?

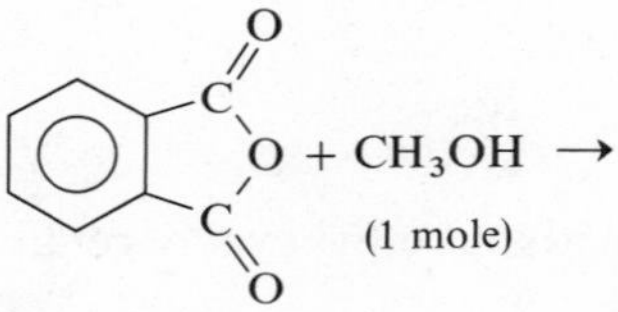

The yield of the product is essentially quantitative. Write a mechanism for the reaction.

When an ester of adipic or pimelic acid is treated with a strong base, an intramolecular Claisen-type condensation (called a *Dieckmann cyclization*) occurs, yielding a β-keto ester containing a five- or six-membered ring. Larger diesters yield polymers under ordinary conditions.

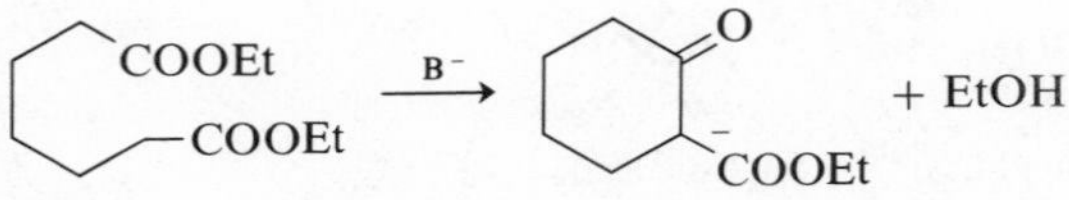

It is also possible to cyclize the free acids (by pyrolysis of certain heavy metal salts). Under these circumstances, the intermediate β-keto acid decarboxylates, and a cyclic ketone is isolated. Many different heavy metals have been utilized. Barium, calcium, manganese, and thorium have proven to be the most useful. As usual, five- and six-membered rings are formed in high yields. The strained medium rings are formed in yields of the order of 1–2%, and very large rings are formed in yields of a few percent. The reaction is of some historical interest, because it was used in the first successful synthesis of large ring compounds (Ruzicka,† 1926). In its simplest form, this reaction was the first commercial source of acetone, from pyrolysis of calcium acetate (hence the name "acetone").

$$(CH_2)_n \begin{matrix} COOH \\ COOH \end{matrix} \xrightarrow[\text{metal oxide catalyst}]{\Delta} (CH_2)_n \, C=O + H_2O$$

Esters react with sodium in hydrocarbon (aprotic) solvents to form *acyloins*, or α-ketols (Section 20.8).

$$RC \overset{O}{\underset{OEt}{\diagdown}} \xrightarrow{Na} R-\overset{O}{\overset{\|}{C}}-\overset{OH}{\overset{|}{CH}}-R$$

The reaction is of particular importance because it is an excellent way to prepare in high yield medium- and large-ring compounds not otherwise easily accessible (Section 34.2).

$$(CH_2)_8 \begin{matrix} COOEt \\ COOEt \end{matrix} \xrightarrow{Na} (CH_2)_8 \begin{matrix} CHOH \\ | \\ C=O \end{matrix} \xrightarrow[H^+]{Zn-Hg} (CH_2)_9 \, C=O$$

Two other cyclic derivatives of dicarboxylic acids are important: succinimide and phthalimide. Each is made from the cyclic anhydride by reaction with ammonia, followed by heating.

Succinimide   Phthalimide

One acyl group substituted for a hydrogen atom of ammonia or of an amine largely removes the pair of electrons from nitrogen and converts the basic amine to a neutral amide. A second carbonyl group increases the positive charge on nitrogen to the extent that the remaining hydrogen in an imide is weakly acidic (about like phenol). The effect of each acyl group attached to ammonia is thus to increase the acidity by approximately 10^5.

Basic   Neutral   Acidic

20.18   Summary of Synthetic Methods for Acids

As in previous chapters, summarized here are the preparative methods useful for the compounds discussed in this chapter. Methods 1–12 should be familiar and should be reviewed. The other methods need not be studied at this time, but are included here for later reference.

† Leopold Ruzicka. Born 1887, Vukova, Yugoslavia. Utrecht; Eidgenoessische Technische Hochschule, Zurich. Nobel Prize, 1939.

1. Hydrolysis of acid chlorides, anhydrides, esters, amides, etc. (Section 20.6)

$$RC\overset{\displaystyle O}{\underset{\displaystyle X}{\diagup}} + H_2O \xrightarrow{\text{catalyst}} RC\overset{\displaystyle O}{\underset{\displaystyle OH}{\diagup}}$$

2. Carbonation of organometallic derivatives of primary, secondary, tertiary, aliphatic, and aromatic chlorides, bromides, and iodides (Section 20.16)

$$R{-}X + Mg \rightarrow RMgX \xrightarrow{CO_2} RC\overset{\displaystyle O}{\underset{\displaystyle OMgX}{\diagup}} \rightarrow RC\overset{\displaystyle O}{\underset{\displaystyle OH}{\diagup}}$$

$$R{-}X + Li \rightarrow RLi \xrightarrow{CO_2} RC\overset{\displaystyle O}{\underset{\displaystyle OLi}{\diagup}} \rightarrow RC\overset{\displaystyle O}{\underset{\displaystyle OH}{\diagup}}$$

3. Oxidation of primary alcohols or aldehydes (Sections 18.7 and 19.16)

$$RC\overset{\displaystyle O}{\underset{\displaystyle H}{\diagup}} \xrightarrow{[O]} RC\overset{\displaystyle O}{\underset{\displaystyle OH}{\diagup}}$$

$$RCH_2OH \xrightarrow{[O]} RC\overset{\displaystyle O}{\underset{\displaystyle OH}{\diagup}}$$

4. Haloform reaction of methyl ketones (Section 19.13)

$$RC\overset{\displaystyle O}{\underset{\displaystyle CH_3}{\diagup}} + NaOCl \rightarrow RC\overset{\displaystyle O}{\underset{\displaystyle CCl_3}{\diagup}} \xrightarrow[\text{2. } H^+]{\text{1. } {}^-OH} RC\overset{\displaystyle O}{\underset{\displaystyle OH}{\diagup}} + CHCl_3$$

5. Baeyer–Villiger oxidation of ketones (Section 19.16)

$$R{-}\overset{\displaystyle O}{\overset{\|}{C}}{-}R + R'{-}C\overset{\displaystyle O}{\underset{\displaystyle O{-}OH}{\diagup}} \rightarrow RC\overset{\displaystyle O}{\underset{\displaystyle OR}{\diagup}} \rightarrow R'C\overset{\displaystyle O}{\underset{\displaystyle OH}{\diagup}}$$

6. Oxidation of olefins (Section 15.10)

$$\overset{\displaystyle R}{\underset{\displaystyle H}{}}C{=}C\overset{\displaystyle R'}{\underset{\displaystyle H}{}} \xrightarrow{[O]} RC\overset{\displaystyle O}{\underset{\displaystyle OH}{\diagup}} + R'C\overset{\displaystyle O}{\underset{\displaystyle OH}{\diagup}}$$

7. Acid cleavage in the acetoacetic ester synthesis (Section 20.15)

$$R{-}\overset{\displaystyle COOC_2H_5}{\underset{\displaystyle H \quad COCH_3}{\overset{\diagup}{C}}} \xrightarrow[\text{NaOH}]{\text{strong}} RCH_2C\overset{\displaystyle O}{\underset{\displaystyle OH}{\diagup}}$$

8. Chain lengthening by the Arndt–Eistert reaction (Sections 20.16, 22.8)

$$RC\overset{O}{\underset{OH}{}} \xrightarrow{SOCl_2} RC\overset{O}{\underset{Cl}{}} \xrightarrow{CH_2N_2} RC\overset{O}{\underset{CHN_2}{}} \xrightarrow{Ag_2O} RCH{=}C{=}O \xrightarrow{H_2O} RCH_2C\overset{O}{\underset{OH}{}}$$

9. Decarboxylation of a substituted malonic acid (Sections 20.13, 24.6)

$$RCH\overset{COOH}{\underset{COOH}{}} \rightarrow RCH_2COOH$$

10. Oxidation of certain secondary alcohols or ketones (Section 19.16)

$$\bigcirc{-}OH \xrightarrow{HNO_3} HO\overset{O}{\overset{\|}{C}}{-}(CH_2)_4{-}\overset{O}{\overset{\|}{C}}OH$$

11. Side-chain oxidation of aromatic hydrocarbons (Section 16.9)

$$\bigcirc{-}R \xrightarrow{[O]} \bigcirc{-}\overset{O}{\underset{OH}{\overset{\|}{C}}}$$

12. Cyanohydrin synthesis on aldehydes and methyl ketones (Section 19.5)

$$R{-}C\overset{O}{\underset{H}{}} + HCN \rightarrow R{-}\underset{OH}{\overset{}{CH}}{-}CN \xrightarrow{H_3O^+} R{-}\underset{OH}{\overset{}{CH}}C\overset{O}{\underset{OH}{}}$$

13. Strecker amino acid synthesis on aldehydes and methyl ketones.

$$RC\overset{O}{\underset{H}{}} + NH_4CN \rightarrow R{-}\underset{NH_2}{\overset{}{CH}}CN \rightarrow R{-}\underset{NH_2}{\overset{}{CH}}\overset{O}{\overset{\|}{C}}OH$$

14. Cannizzaro reaction on aromatic aldehydes and formaldehyde (Section 19.11)

$$2\,RC\overset{O}{\underset{H}{}} + NaOH \rightarrow RCH_2OH + RC\overset{O}{\underset{OH}{}}$$

15. Kolbe reaction (Section 20.17)

$$\underset{}{\overset{ONa}{\bigcirc}} + CO_2 \xrightarrow[\text{pressure}]{\text{heat}} \overset{OH}{\underset{}{\bigcirc}}{-}\overset{O}{\underset{ONa}{\overset{\|}{C}}}$$

20.19   Summary of Synthetic Methods for Acid Derivatives

In this section the preparative methods for acid derivatives are summarized, and all of these methods should be studied at this time.

1. Acid halides (Section 20.5)

$$RC\underset{OH}{\overset{O}{<}} + SOCl_2 \rightarrow RC\underset{Cl}{\overset{O}{<}} + SO_2 + HCl$$

2. Acid anhydrides and ketones (Section 20.5)

$$RC\underset{Cl}{\overset{O}{<}} + RC\underset{O^-Na^+}{\overset{O}{<}} \rightarrow R-\overset{O}{\overset{\|}{C}}-O-\overset{O}{\overset{\|}{C}}-R$$

3. Esters (Section 20.5)

$$R-C\underset{OH}{\overset{O}{<}} + HOR' \xrightarrow{H^+} RC\underset{OR'}{\overset{O}{<}} + H_2O$$

$$R-C\underset{OH}{\overset{O}{<}} + CH_2N_2 \rightarrow RC\underset{OCH_3}{\overset{O}{<}} + N_2$$

$$RC\underset{Cl}{\overset{O}{<}} + HOR' \rightarrow RC\underset{OR'}{\overset{O}{<}} + HCl$$

$$\begin{array}{c} R-\overset{O}{\overset{\|}{C}} \\ R-\overset{O}{\underset{\|}{C}} \end{array}\hspace{-1em}O + HOR' \rightarrow R-C\underset{OR'}{\overset{O}{<}} + RC\underset{OH}{\overset{O}{<}}$$

$$RC\underset{OR'}{\overset{O}{<}} + HOR'' \xrightarrow{H^+} RC\underset{OR''}{\overset{O}{<}} + HOR'$$

4. Amides and nitriles (Section 20.5)

$$R-\overset{O}{\overset{\|}{C}}-O-\overset{O}{\overset{\|}{C}}-R + 2\,HNR_2 \rightarrow RC\underset{NR_2}{\overset{O}{<}} + R-C\underset{O^-}{\overset{O}{<}} R_2\overset{+}{N}H_2$$

$$RC\!\!\overset{\displaystyle O}{\underset{\displaystyle Cl}{\diagdown}} + 2\,HNR_2 \longrightarrow RC\!\!\overset{\displaystyle O}{\underset{\displaystyle NR_2}{\diagdown}} + R_2\overset{+}{N}H_2\ Cl^-$$

$$RC\!\!\overset{\displaystyle O}{\underset{\displaystyle OCH_3}{\diagdown}} + HNR_2 \longrightarrow RC\!\!\overset{\displaystyle O}{\underset{\displaystyle NR_2}{\diagdown}} + HOCH_3$$

$$RC\!\!\overset{\displaystyle O}{\underset{\displaystyle OH}{\diagdown}} + NH_3 \longrightarrow RC\!\!\overset{\displaystyle O}{\underset{\displaystyle O^-}{\diagdown}}\ NH_4^+ \overset{\Delta}{\longrightarrow} RC\!\!\overset{\displaystyle O}{\underset{\displaystyle NH_2}{\diagdown}} + H_2O$$

$$R\!\!-\!\!C\!\!\overset{\displaystyle O}{\underset{\displaystyle NH_2}{\diagdown}} + SOCl_2 \longrightarrow RC\!\!\equiv\!\!N + SO_2 + HCl$$

$$R\!\!-\!\!X + NaCN \longrightarrow RC\!\!\equiv\!\!N + NaX$$

PROBLEMS

1. Which of each of the following pairs will be the stronger acid? Why?

    (a) $CH_3\!\!-\!\!\underset{\underset{\displaystyle Cl}{|}}{CH}\!\!-\!\!COOH$ $Cl\!\!-\!\!\underset{\underset{\displaystyle Cl}{|}}{C}HCOOH$

    (b) [benzene ring]—COOH   [benzene ring with Cl]—COOH

    (c) O_2NCH_2—[benzene ring]—OH $O_2NCH_2CH_2$—[benzene ring]—OH

    (d) $HOOC\!\!-\!\!COOH$ $HOOC\!\!-\!\!CH_2\!\!-\!\!COOH$

2. Give two examples of reactions in which carboxylate ion participates as a nucleophile.

3. Write the reagents and equations to convert benzoic acid to (a) the acid chloride; (b) the anhydride; (c) the amide; (d) the methyl ester; and (e) the nitrile.

4. Arrange the compounds shown in order of increasing reactivity toward ethanol. Explain.

    $$CH_3\!\!-\!\!C\!\!\overset{\displaystyle O}{\underset{\displaystyle OCH_3}{\diagdown}} \qquad CH_3\!\!-\!\!C\!\!\overset{\displaystyle O}{\underset{\displaystyle Cl}{\diagdown}} \qquad CH_3\!\!-\!\!C\!\!\overset{\displaystyle O}{\underset{\displaystyle N(CH_3)_2}{\diagdown}} \qquad [benzene ring]\!\!-\!\!C\!\!\overset{\displaystyle O}{\underset{\displaystyle N(CH_3)_2}{\diagdown}}$$

5. A compound (A) had the formula $C_{11}H_{14}O_2$, and it reacted and dissolved when heated in aqueous base. Extraction of the aqueous solution gave a compound (B), C_7H_8O. The nmr spectrum of B showed three singlets at δ 3.7, 4.4, and 7.2, with areas of 1, 2, and 5 respectively. When B was refluxed with aqueous $KMnO_4$, another compound (C) was isolated. The latter had the formula $C_7H_6O_2$ and showed strong bands at 1690 and 2800–3300 cm^{-1} (broad) in the infrared. When the basic aqueous solution from the original treatment of A was acidified, an evil-smelling compound (D) could be extracted which had the formula $C_4H_8O_2$. It showed three peaks in the nmr, a singlet at δ 11 (area, 1), a doublet at δ 1.1 (area, 6), and a heptet at δ 2.4 (area, 1). What are the structures of A, B, C, and D?

6. Starting with diphenylacetic acid, outline a synthesis of diphenylketene. Write the product of the reaction of diphenylketene with (a) water; (b) aniline; (c) phenol; (d) methyl alcohol; and (e) diphenylacetic acid.

7. Explain the difference in the reaction mechanism and in the products formed when hydroxide ion attacks an acetate or a tosylate ester.

8. Predict products and give a reasonable mechanism for the reaction.

(a) $CH_3-\overset{O}{\overset{\|}{C}}-OCH_3 + CH_3CH_2OH \overset{H^+}{\rightleftharpoons}$

(b) $CH_3\underset{CH_3}{\overset{}{\underset{|}{CH}}}-\overset{O}{\overset{\|}{C}}-Cl + CH_3CH_2OH \longrightarrow$

(c)

(d) $CH_2=CHCH_2CH_2CO_2H \xrightarrow{HOBr} BrCH_2$

(Just give the mechanism for this one.)

(e) $CH_3-\underset{CH_3}{\overset{CH_3}{\underset{|}{\overset{|}{C}}}}-\overset{O}{\overset{\diagup\!\!\diagup}{C}}\diagdown_{OH} \xrightarrow[\text{2. heat}]{\text{1. } NH_3}$

(f) $HO-\overset{O}{\overset{\|}{C}}-\underset{CH_3}{\overset{CH_3}{\underset{|}{\overset{|}{C}}}}-C\equiv N \xrightarrow{200°C}$

9. Give the product of the reaction of excess lithium aluminum hydride with each of the following:

(a) $R_2CHCOOH$ (b) $R_2CHCOOCH_3$

(c) $R_2CHCONH_2$ (d) $R_2CH\overset{O}{\overset{\|}{C}}-N$

(e) $R_2CHC\equiv N$ (f) $R_2C=C=O$

10. A compound, A, containing only carbon, hydrogen, and oxygen, was insoluble in aqueous base, but on heating in base yielded a new compound, B, which was also insoluble in aqueous base. Compound B was found to have the formula $C_5H_{12}O_2$ and its nmr spectrum is shown.

NMR spectrum of compound B, Problem 10.

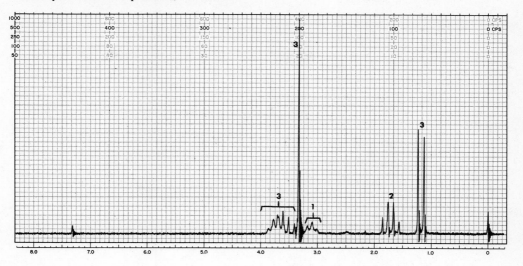

When the aqueous basic solution was made acidic, a new crystalline compound, C, could be filtered from the solution. Compound C was found to have the formula $C_7H_6O_2$ and its infrared spectrum is shown.

Infrared spectrum (chloroform solution) of compound C, Problem 10.

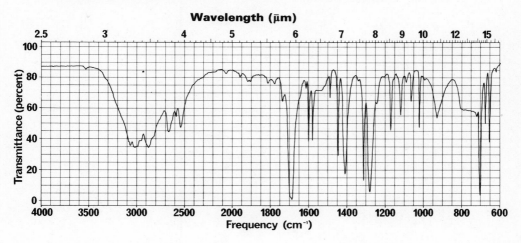

What are the structures of A, B, and C.

11.   Give the product of the reaction of each of the following starting materials with excess phenylmagnesium bromide, followed by acid hydrolysis:

(a) Ph—C(=O)—O—Ph

(b) CH_3—C(=O)—O—Ph

(c) Ph—C(=O)—N⟨morpholine⟩O

(d) Ph—C(=O)—NH_2

(e) Ph—C≡N

12. Complete the following:

(a) $CH_3CH_2\underset{\underset{CH_3}{|}}{CH}-C\overset{O}{\underset{OH}{\diagdown}}$ + Br_2 $\xrightarrow{PBr_3}$

(b) $PhCOOC_2H_5 + CH_3COOC_2H_5 \xrightarrow[\text{2. } H^+]{\text{1. } C_2H_5O^-}$

(c) [cyclohexene ring]—COOH $\xrightarrow{\Delta}$

(d) $Ph\!\!-\!\!\underset{\underset{H}{|}}{\overset{\overset{Cl}{|}}{C}}\!\!-\!\!\underset{\underset{H}{|}}{\overset{\overset{COOH}{|}}{C}}\!\!-\!\!CH_3 \xrightarrow{\Delta}$

(e) $CH_3(CH_2)_{16}-C\overset{O}{\underset{OAg}{\diagdown}}$ $\xrightarrow{Br_2}$

13. Explain the fact that the hydrolysis of acetoacetic ester can yield acetic acid or acetone, depending on the conditions employed.

14. Outline syntheses of the following compounds from the specified starting materials plus benzene, toluene, malonic ester, acetoacetic ester and any other compounds containing four carbons or less.

(a) $CH_3CH_2\underset{\underset{CH_2CH_3}{|}}{CH}-\overset{\overset{O}{||}}{C}-CH_3$ (without using acetoacetic ester)

(b) $(CH_3)_2C{=}CH-\overset{\overset{O}{||}}{C}-CH_3$

(c) $CH_3-\underset{\underset{CH_3}{|}}{\overset{\overset{CH_3}{|}}{C}}-CH_2CH_2-O-\overset{\overset{O}{||}}{C}-CH_3$

(d) $Ph-CH_2-\overset{\overset{O}{||}}{C}-\underset{\underset{Ph}{|}}{CH}\overset{\overset{O}{||}}{C}-OCH_2CH_3$

(e) $CH_3-\overset{\overset{O}{||}}{C}-\underset{\underset{CH_2CH_2CH_3}{|}}{CH}-CH_2CH_2CH_2CH_3$ (from acetoacetic ester)

(f) $CH_3CH_2CH_2CH_2-N\overset{\diagup CH_3}{\diagdown CH_3}$ (from butyric acid)

(g) $CH_3CH_2CH_2-\overset{\overset{O}{||}}{C}-CH_2CH_2CH_2CH_3$ (from butyric acid only)

15. Compound A ($C_4H_6O_2$) was oxidized with ammonical silver nitrate to B, which on pyrolysis yielded acetone as the only organic product. From these data write the structures of A and B.

16. An unknown acid, $C_8H_{12}O_4$, is either (a) 1-methylcyclopentane-*cis*-1,3-dicarboxylic acid, (b) 1-methylcyclopentane-*trans*-1,3-dicarboxylic acid, (c) *trans*-2-methylcyclopentane-*cis*-1,3-dicarboxylic acid, or (d) 2-methylcyclopentane-1,1-dicarboxylic acid. If it is found to form a mono ester when heated with ethanol and sulfuric acid, which structure(s) would be indicated? If, on the other hand, it is converted into a neutral substance, $C_8H_{10}O_3$, by gentle warming with acetic anhydride, what structure(s) would be indicated? If the acid lost carbon dioxide on heating to about 150°C, which structure(s) would be indicated? If the acid resisted bromination by the Hell-Volhard-Zelinsky procedure, which structure(s) would be indicated? If the compound was optically inactive, and all attempts at resolution failed totally, what structure(s) would be indicated?

17. An acidic liquid reacts with thionyl chloride to form a new liquid which contains chlorine and has a biting odor. When the new liquid is warmed with the dry sodium salt of the original substance, a third liquid, free of chlorine, is formed; it reacts with ethanol to form a fourth liquid, having a sickly sweet odor. Treatment of this last substance with lithium aluminum hydride produces *only* ethanol. Write appropriate structures for each organic substance.

18. When a mixture of *p*-ethylbenzoic acid and *o*-chlorobenzoic acid (both insoluble in water) is shaken with sodium formate solution, one dissolves and the other is left behind. Explain this result. What would have happened if sodium carbonate solution had been used? If sodium trichloroacetate had been used?

19. When a certain fat is boiled with sodium hydroxide solution, it takes 189–190 g for complete reaction with 1 mole of the alkali. What must be the average number of carbon atoms in the soap molecules produced?

CHAPTER 21

REACTIONS OF ORGANIC NITROGEN COMPOUNDS
I. AMINES AND RELATED COMPOUNDS

Organic nitrogen compounds undergo a vast number of seemingly unrelated reactions. Much of this diversity is due to the large number of nitrogen-containing functional groups which exist, and to the variation in electronic structure of the nitrogen atom in these functional groups. A complete discussion of this enormous and fascinating area of organic chemistry is impossible in an introductory text. We will limit ourselves to the important reactions of the most significant types of organic nitrogen compounds.

For the sake of convenience the reactions of nitrogen compounds will be presented in two parts. This chapter will be devoted to the chemistry of amines and related compounds, all of which contain a single nitrogen atom bound to carbon. Chapter 22 will deal with functional groups having nitrogen–nitrogen or nitrogen–oxygen bonds.

21.1   Amines

The chemistry of amines is dominated by their basicity and nucleophilic nature, which in turn result from the presence of the unshared electron pair on the nitrogen atom.

Salt Formation

Simple aliphatic amines, whether primary, secondary, or tertiary, are all stronger bases than ammonia, and they readily form water-soluble salts with mineral acids. Amines bearing one aryl group on the nitrogen, such as aniline, are much less basic but still form salts with dilute aqueous mineral acids. Diarylamines are very weak bases and are insoluble in aqueous acid; triarylamines are neutral compounds. (See Section 11.3 for a review of the factors influencing the basicity of aryl amines.)

Alkylation

Amines react with alkylating agents such as alkyl halides to give alkyl ammonium salts containing the new alkyl substituent. The reaction occurs with nucleophilic displacement of a halide ion from the alkyl halide by the lone pair of electrons on the nitrogen atom.

$$R_3N: + R—X \rightarrow R_4N^+ X^-$$

The alkylation of an unhindered primary or secondary amine with a reactive halide is usually not a practical synthetic method for the following reason. The initially formed secondary or tertiary ammonium salt is converted in part to the corresponding free amine by excess amine reagent, and the product may then undergo further alkylation, as the following equations show.

$$C_2H_5NH_2 + CH_3I \rightarrow C_2H_5\overset{+}{N}H_2\ I^-$$
$$\underset{\underset{\displaystyle CH_3}{|}}{}$$

$$C_2H_5\overset{+}{N}H_2\ I^- + C_2H_5NH_2 \rightleftharpoons C_2H_5NH + C_2H_5\overset{+}{N}H_3\ I^-$$
$$\underset{CH_3}{|} \qquad\qquad\qquad \underset{CH_3}{|}$$

$$C_2H_5NH + CH_3I \rightarrow C_2H_5-\overset{\overset{\displaystyle CH_3}{|+}}{N}H\ I^-$$
$$\underset{CH_3}{|} \qquad\qquad\qquad \underset{CH_3}{|}$$

$$C_2H_5-\overset{\overset{\displaystyle CH_3}{|+}}{N}H\ I^- + C_2H_5NH_2 \rightleftharpoons C_2H_5-\overset{\overset{\displaystyle CH_3}{|}}{N} + C_2H_5\overset{+}{N}H_3\ I^-$$
$$\underset{CH_3}{|} \qquad\qquad\qquad\qquad \underset{CH_3}{|}$$

$$C_2H_5N(CH_3)_2 + CH_3I \rightarrow C_2H_5\overset{+}{N}(CH_3)_3\ I^-$$

Alkylation is useful for the conversion of tertiary amines to quaternary ammonium salts, sometimes for the conversion of a halide to a primary amine (since a large excess of ammonia can be used), and in other special cases, but it is not the method of choice for the preparation of secondary and tertiary amines.

The elimination of HX from the alkylating agent to give an olefin can be a serious side reaction with such compounds as β-phenylethyl halides; t-alkyl halides give almost entirely olefins. Indeed, tertiary amines are often purposely used to carry out such elimination reactions.

$$C_6H_5-CH_2-CH_2-Br + R_3N \xrightarrow[\text{(minor)}]{\text{(major)}} \begin{array}{l} C_6H_5-CH=CH_2 + R_3\overset{+}{N}H\ Br^- \\[4pt] C_6H_5-CH_2-CH_2-\underset{+}{N}R_3\ Br^- \end{array}$$

Acylation

Primary and secondary amines react very readily with acid halides to give amides (Section 20.5). The reaction takes place by the addition of the nucleophilic nitrogen of the amine to the carbonyl carbon, followed by elimination of hydrogen halide. An amide is far less basic than the corresponding amine, because of electron withdrawal from the nitrogen both by induction and by resonance. A consequence of the low basicity of amides is that they do not readily undergo further acylation by acid halides; consequently, only one acyl group is introduced into a primary amine under ordinary reaction conditions.

The *Schotten–Baumann* procedure is a simple method of acylation in which an amine can be quantitatively converted into an amide. A mixture of the amine, cold aqueous base, and an excess of acyl halide is stirred or shaken together, preferably in the presence of a solvent. The aqueous base (usually NaOH or, better, Na_2CO_3) acts as the scavenger for the HX produced. The success of the method is due to the generally high nucleophilicity of amines, which compete successfully with hydroxide ion and water in attacking the acyl halide carbonyl group.

$$(CH_3)_2CHCOCl + HN\bigcirc \xrightarrow[\text{(cold)}]{H_2O,\ NaOH} (CH_3)_2CHCO-N\bigcirc$$

Tertiary amines are also commonly used as acid scavengers in the reaction of an acid halide with a primary or secondary amine. The tertiary amine most often used for this purpose is the aromatic base pyridine, which is readily available commercially.

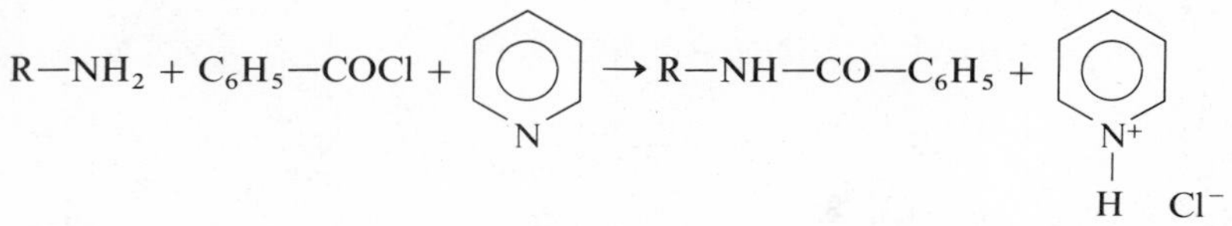

$$R-NH_2 + C_6H_5-COCl + \underset{\text{Pyridine}}{\bigcirc_N} \rightarrow R-NH-CO-C_6H_5 + \underset{\substack{\text{Pyridinium chloride}}}{\bigcirc_{\overset{+}{N}}\overset{|}{\underset{H \quad Cl^-}{}}}$$

Superficially, tertiary amines appear not to react with acyl halides, since they can be recovered unchanged after treatment with an acyl halide, followed by work-up with aqueous base. In reality, they react to form salts, $R'-CO-NR_3^+X^-$, which are themselves very effective acylating agents and which are hydrolyzed rapidly by water.

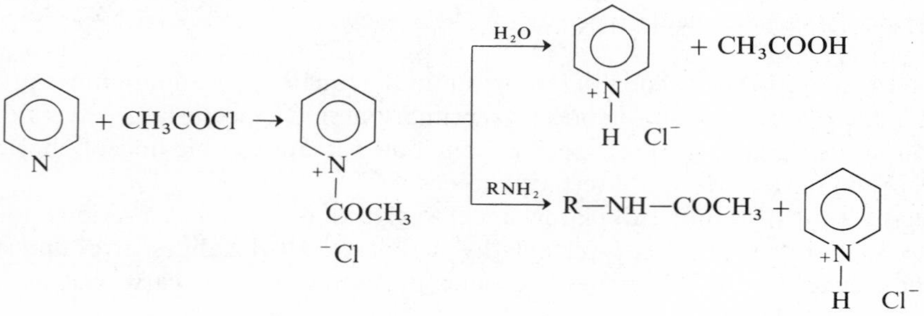

$$\bigcirc_N + CH_3COCl \rightarrow \underset{\substack{COCH_3 \\ {}^-Cl}}{\bigcirc_{\overset{+}{N}}} \begin{cases} \xrightarrow{H_2O} \underset{\substack{H \quad Cl^-}}{\bigcirc_{\overset{+}{N}}} + CH_3COOH \\ \xrightarrow{RNH_2} R-NH-COCH_3 + \underset{\substack{H \quad Cl^-}}{\bigcirc_{\overset{+}{N}}} \end{cases}$$

Primary and secondary amines also react with acid anhydrides to give amides. As with acyl halides, either two equivalents of the amine or one equivalent of amine and one of an acid scavenger base are usually employed for complete reaction to take place. This reaction is most often carried out with the inexpensive and convenient acetylating agent *acetic anhydride*, which is ordinarily used together with pyridine as a scavenger base.

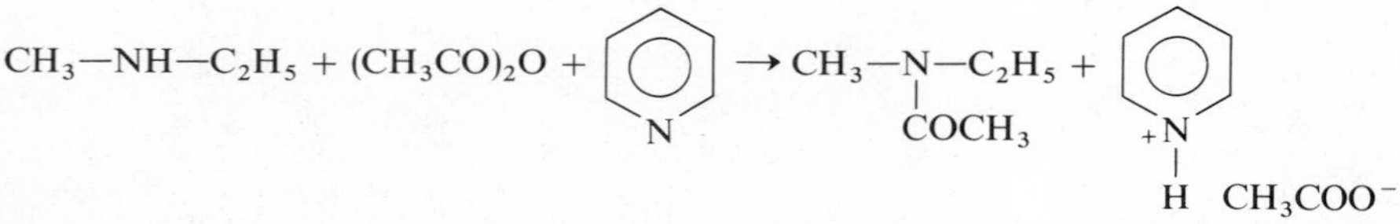

$$CH_3-NH-C_2H_5 + (CH_3CO)_2O + \bigcirc_N \rightarrow CH_3-\underset{\substack{COCH_3}}{\overset{|}{N}}-C_2H_5 + \underset{\substack{H \quad CH_3COO^-}}{\bigcirc_{\overset{+}{N}}}$$

It should be noted that cyclic anhydrides, such as phthalic anhydride, give only a monoamide of a dicarboxylic acid when treated with a primary or secondary amine.

$$\underset{\substack{CO}}{\bigcirc_{CO}^{\diagup CO}} O + 2\,(CH_3)_2NH \rightarrow \underset{\substack{COO^- \; H_2\overset{+}{N}(CH_3)_2}}{\bigcirc^{\diagup CON(CH_3)_2}} \xrightarrow{H^+} \underset{\substack{COOH}}{\bigcirc^{\diagup CON(CH_3)_2}}$$

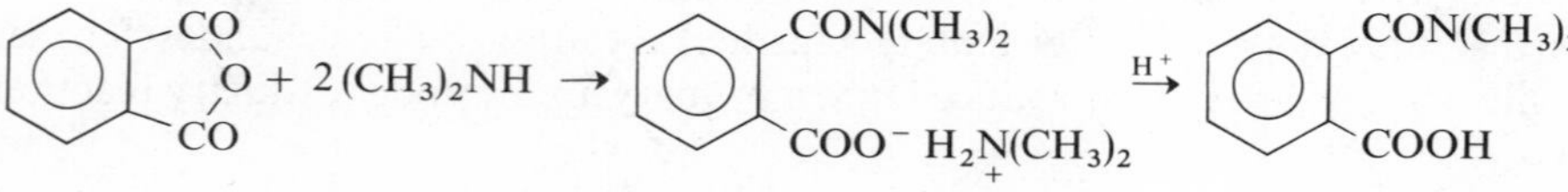

EXERCISE 21.1

What will be the major product of the reaction of 4-nitrophthalic anhydride with *n*-butylamine? Explain.

Isocyanates from Primary Amines. The reaction of excess phosgene ($COCl_2$, carbonyl chloride) with primary amines is somewhat unusual. The initially produced carbamoyl chloride ($R-NH-COCl$) readily loses HCl and is converted into an isocyanate ($R-N=C=O$). This reaction is illustrated by the conversion of 2,4-diaminotoluene into toluene-2,4-diisocyanate, which is an important starting material in the manufacture of polyurethan plastic foams (Section 25.2).

Sulfonylation

The acid chlorides of sulfonic acids react with primary and secondary amines to give sulfonamides; this reaction forms the basis of the classical *Hinsberg test* for distinguishing among primary, secondary, and tertiary amines. When a primary amine is shaken with benzenesulfonyl chloride and excess cold aqueous NaOH, the resulting clear solution contains the sodium salt of an *N*-substituted sulfonamide; acidification of the solution gives a precipitate of the nonbasic free sulfonamide. The unusual acidity of sulfonamides of the type RSO_2NHR' is due to the powerful electron-withdrawing inductive effect of the sulfonyl group ($-SO_2-$).

$$RNH_2 + C_6H_5SO_2Cl \xrightarrow[H_2O]{NaOH} C_6H_5SO_2NHR \xrightarrow{NaOH} C_6H_5SO_2NR\ Na^+$$

Water soluble

$$C_6H_5SO_2\underset{Na^+}{NR} \xrightarrow[H_2O]{H^+} C_6H_5SO_2NHR \downarrow$$

Precipitate

The reaction of a secondary amine with benzenesulfonyl chloride yields an *N,N*-disubstituted sulfonamide which precipitates immediately from the basic reaction mixture, and which is soluble in neither base nor acid.

$$R_2NH + C_6H_5SO_2Cl \xrightarrow[H_2O]{NaOH} C_6H_5SO_2NR_2 \downarrow$$

Precipitate

Tertiary amines, of course, are recovered unchanged under the conditions of the Hinsberg test. They probably do react with sulfonyl halides to give quaternary sulfonamide intermediates of the type $RSO_2^+NR_3\ X^-$, but these would be highly reactive sulfonylating agents, and would be hydrolyzed very rapidly by water. Indeed, as with acyl halides, the reaction of a primary or secondary amine with a sulfonyl halide is often carried out preparatively in pyridine solution, so that the pyridine may serve as an acid scavenger.

To apply the Hinsberg test, the amine is shaken with benzenesulfonyl chloride and cold aqueous alkali. If a homogeneous solution results, the amine is primary; if an insoluble material is present, the amine is either secondary (and the insoluble material is the secondary sulfonamide) or tertiary (and the insoluble material is unreacted amine). To differentiate between the secondary and tertiary amines, the insoluble material is acidified. A tertiary amine will form a salt and dissolve, while the secondary sulfonamide, being neutral, remains as an insoluble material.

SUCARYL. *Primary and secondary amines react vigorously with chlorosulfonic acid* ($Cl—SO_3H$) *to give salts of substituted sulfamic acids* ($R—NH—SO_3H$ *or* $R_2N—SO_3H$). *The sodium salt of cyclohexylsulfamic acid was widely used as a sweetener for low-calorie beverages under the name of "Sucaryl" until it was banned by the federal government as a potential health hazard.*

Cl—SO$_3$H + 3 ⬡—NH$_2$ ⟶

⬡—NH$_3$Cl$^-$ + ⬡—NH—SO$_3^-$ ⬡—NH$_3^+$

(several steps)

⬡—NH—SO$_3^-$Na$^+$

Sucaryl

Nitrosation

The reaction of amines with nitrous acid is a complex subject which is of both great theoretical and practical importance. The nitrosation of amines is usually carried out by adding aqueous $NaNO_2$ to a cold aqueous solution of the amine in dilute mineral acid; a small amount of free amine in equilibrium with the protonated amine is the reacting species. The nitrous acid, which is an unstable compound, is always generated in the cold reaction mixture as it is used. The actual nitrosating reagent is the nitrosonium ion (NO^+), formed by the protonation of nitrous acid followed by loss of water.

$$HNO_2 + H^+ \rightleftharpoons H_2NO_2^+ \rightleftharpoons H_2O + NO^+$$

Secondary Amines. Secondary amines, both aliphatic and aromatic, react with nitrous acid to give yellow, neutral nitrosamines ($R_2N—NO$).

$$C_6H_5—NH—CH_3 + HNO_2 \rightarrow C_6H_5—\underset{\underset{NO}{|}}{N}—CH_3$$

The nonbasic character of nitrosamines is due to electron withdrawal by the nitroso group, which acts in a manner analogous to the carboxyl group in carboxamides. These compounds are, in fact, amides of nitrous acid.

$$R_2N—N{=}O \leftrightarrow R_2\underset{+}{N}{=}N—O^-$$

Tertiary Amines. It has often been stated in textbooks that aliphatic tertiary amines do not react with nitrous acid. In reality such amines react in a complex way in weakly acid solution. The reaction is of limited importance.

> *Reaction of Aliphatic Tertiary Amines with Nitrous Acid.* The initially formed nitrosammonium ion ($R_3N^+—NO$) appears to undergo rapid elimination of the unstable inorganic species *nitroxyl* (HNO), which is detectable as N_2O. The initial organic product in the reaction with a tertiary amine is an *immonium ion* ($R_2N^+{=}CHR'$) which hydrolyzes to an aldehyde and a secondary amine. Finally, nitrosation of the secondary amine yields a *nitrosamine*.
>
> $$(CH_3)_2N—CH_2C_6H_5 + HNO_2 \rightarrow (CH_3)_2\overset{+}{\underset{\underset{NO}{|}}{N}}—CH_2C_6H_5$$
>
> $$\rightarrow HNO + (CH_3)_2\overset{+}{N}{=}CHC_6H_5$$

$$2\,HNO \rightarrow H_2N_2O_2 \rightarrow H_2O + N_2O$$

$$(CH_3)_2\overset{+}{N}{=}CHC_6H_5 + H_2O \rightarrow (CH_3)_2\overset{+}{N}H_2 + C_6H_5{-}CHO$$

$$(CH_3)_2NH + HNO_2 \rightarrow (CH_3)_2{-}NO + H_2O$$

Aromatic tertiary amines such as *N,N*-dimethylaniline are nitrosated rapidly in the aromatic ring, the position para to the amino substituent being attacked by NO^+.

$$(CH_3)_2N{-}\langle\bigcirc\rangle + HNO_2 \longrightarrow (CH_3)_2N{-}\langle\bigcirc\rangle{-}NO$$

p-Nitroso-*N,N*-dimethylaniline

EXERCISE 21.2

Write the complete mechanism for the preceding reaction.

Primary Amines. The products of the reaction of cold nitrous acid with primary amines are quite varied and are dependent upon the nature of the organic substituent attached to the amino group.

The overall reaction of primary aromatic amine with nitrous acid in cold aqueous mineral acid solution is the conversion of the amine to an arenediazonium salt ($Ar{-}N_2^+X^-$). This process is known as *diazotization*, and it is of great synthetic utility in view of the wealth of chemical transformations which diazonium salts undergo (Section 22.7). The overall reaction is exemplified by the conversion of aniline to benzenediazonium chloride.

$$C_6H_5{-}NH_2 + HCl + HNO_2 \xrightarrow{(0-5°C)} C_6H_5{-}N_2^+\,Cl^- + 2\,H_2O$$

Note the resonance stabilization of the benzenediazonium ion.

$$\langle\bigcirc\rangle{-}\underset{+}{N}{\equiv}N \longleftrightarrow {+}\langle\bigcirc\rangle{=}\underset{+}{N}{=}\underset{-}{N} \longleftrightarrow \langle\bigcirc\rangle{=}\underset{+}{N}{=}\underset{-}{N}$$

The diazotization of aniline takes place in three steps: (a) nitrosation of the amino group to yield a nitrosamine; (b) tautomerization of the nitrosamine to a hydroxyazo compound; and (c) reaction of the latter with a proton to give the diazonium ion.

$$C_6H_5{-}NH_2 \xrightarrow[\text{(a)}]{HNO_2} C_6H_5{-}NH{-}NO \xrightarrow[\text{(b)}]{} C_6H_5{-}N{=}N{-}OH \xrightarrow[\text{(c)}]{H^+} C_6H_5{-}N_2^+$$

Aliphatic primary amines react with nitrous acid to give mixtures which can contain alcohols, olefins, cyclopropanes, and even halides if halide ion is present; often the original carbon skeleton is rearranged in the products. The exact nature and proportion of products formed depends very much on the structure of the amine and the specific nitrosation conditions used.

$$CH_3CH_2CH_2NH_2 \xrightarrow{HNO_2} CH_3CH_2CH_2{-}N_2^+ \xrightarrow[H_2O]{-N_2} \begin{cases} CH_3CH_2CH_2{-}OH \\[4pt] CH_3{-}\underset{\underset{OH}{|}}{CH}{-}CH_3 \\[8pt] CH_3{-}CH{=}CH_2 \\[4pt] \overset{\displaystyle CH_2}{\underset{H_2C{-}CH_2}{\diagup\diagdown}} \end{cases}$$

Mechanism of Nitrous Acid Deamination. The products obtained from *n*-propylamine, for example, can all be explained by assuming the initial formation of the *n*-propyldiazonium ion, a structure which has no resonance stabilization and which has not been directly detected. It presumably decomposes immediately with the loss of molecular nitrogen. It seems logical that the free *n*-propyl cation is then formed and that this reactive species is the precursor of all of the observed products. It can also be argued that the products obtained may be formed directly from the lower-energy diazonium ion in reactions which are concerted with the loss of nitrogen. Clearly, the products suggest that the mechanism has a strong similarity to the Wagner–Meerwein rearrangement of carbonium ions (Section 17.3). Recent research tends to favor the concerted decomposition mechanism.

Certain cyclic amines can undergo either ring expansion or ring contraction reactions on treatment with nitrous acid. For example, aminomethylcyclopentane gives, in addition to olefins, a mixture of alcohols in which cyclohexanol predominates. (This reaction is called the *Demyanov ring expansion*. A related ring expansion was discussed in Section 19.10.)

(Percentages refer to percent of the alcohol fraction isolated.)

The reaction of *trans*-2-phenylcyclohexylamine with nitrous acid illustrates the importance of stereochemical factors in the decomposition of diazonium ion intermediates. Ring contraction takes place predominantly, since this reaction involves an S_N2-type displacement of the diazonium group by a carbon–carbon bond of the cyclohexane skeleton which is anti to the leaving group. The seemingly simpler displacement of the diazonium group by the adjacent benzylic hydrogen, which also yields a stable benzyl type of carbonium ion, is not observed; such a reaction is stereochemically unfavored since the hydrogen in question is cis to the departing diazonium group.

Reaction with Aldehydes and Ketones

Primary and secondary amines add readily and reversibly to the carbonyl groups of most aldehydes and ketones to give α-hydroxyamines, also called *carbinolamines*.

$$R_2NH + R_2'C{=}O \rightleftharpoons R_2N{-}\underset{\underset{\displaystyle }{|}}{\overset{\overset{\displaystyle OH}{|}}{C}}R_2'$$

The carbinolamines derived from primary amines usually undergo spontaneous dehydration, particularly in the presence of an acid catalyst, to give substituted *imines*, frequently referred to as *Schiff bases*.

$$R-N=CH-R \qquad\qquad R-N=CR_2$$

An aldimine   A ketimine

The imines derived from primary aromatic amines and aromatic aldehydes are the best known members of the group, since they form easily and usually crystallize well.

$$C_6H_5-CHO + C_6H_5NH_2 \rightarrow C_6H_5-CH=N-C_6H_5 + H_2O$$

Benzalaniline

Carbonyl compounds containing at least one α hydrogen react with secondary amines when water is removed concomitantly to give compounds known as *enamines*, which contain a basic nitrogen directly attached to an olefinic carbon ($R_2NCR=CR_2$). As we shall see later (Section 21.3), enamines are useful intermediates for synthetic purposes.

Pyrrolidine

EXERCISE 21.3

Write the mechanism of the preceding reaction.

Some further reactions of aldehydes and ketones with amines will be discussed under the reactions of amines. These are some of the many reactions in which imines are first formed, but then are converted into secondary products in the reaction mixture.

Ring Substitution in Aromatic Amines

Aromatic substitution reactions of aromatic amines form an important part of their chemistry. These reactions have already been discussed in Chapter 16.

Oxidation

All types of amines are easily oxidized. The course of the reaction is quite variable and depends very much on the structure of the amine, as well as on the specific oxidizing agent used. Only the oxidation of tertiary amines is of major interest.

Aliphatic tertiary amines, as well as dialkylanilines, are oxidized by hydrogen peroxide or peracids under mild conditions with the formation of tertiary amine oxides, $R_3N^+-O^-$. Note that the nitrogen atom is oxidized in this reaction.

$$C_6H_5-N(CH_3)_2 + H_2O_2 \rightarrow C_6H_5-\overset{+}{N}(CH_3)_2 + H_2O$$
$$\underset{O^-}{|}$$

N,N-Dimethylaniline *N*-oxide

Oxidation at Carbon. Mercuric acetate oxidizes tertiary amines having an α hydrogen to immonium ions, which can readily lose a β proton to yield enamines. Note that the initial attack of mercury on the molecule is actually at the nitrogen atom.

$$(CH_3)_2N-CH_2CH_2-C_6H_5 + Hg(OAc)_2 \rightarrow (CH_3)_2\overset{+}{N}-CHCH_2-C_6H_5$$

$$(CH_3)_2N-CH=CH-C_6H_5 \xleftarrow{-H^+} (CH_3)_2\overset{+}{N}=CH-CH_2-C_6H_5 + :Hg + HOAc$$

Oxidation of Secondary Amines. Aliphatic secondary amines, like their tertiary amine analogs, are oxidized readily by hydrogen peroxide. The initially produced secondary amine oxides cannot be isolated, however, since they immediately tautomerize to *N,N*-dialkylhydroxylamines (R_2N-OH).

N-Hydroxypiperidine

Oxidation of Primary Amines. The oxidation of primary aliphatic amines usually produces a mixture of products: imines, enamines, nitriles, and so on. It is rarely a reaction of preparative interest.

The oxidation of primary aromatic amines can also give very complex products. For example, mild chromic acid oxidation of aniline gives a polymer known as "aniline black," which finds use as a dye. More vigorous chromic acid oxidation of aniline yields benzoquinone.

$$\text{Aniline black} \xleftarrow{CrO_3} C_6H_5NH_2 \xrightarrow{CrO_3} O=\!\!\!\!\bigcirc\!\!\!\!=O$$

Peracids often oxidize the amino group of aromatic primary amines to a nitro group without attack on the aromatic nucleus. Peracetic acid (CH_3CO_3H) and pertrifluoroacetic acid (CF_3CO_3H) are the most useful reagents for this reaction.

$$H_3C-\bigcirc-NH_2 \xrightarrow{RCOOOH} H_3C-\bigcirc-NO_2$$

N-*Chlorination*

Aliphatic primary and secondary amines react rapidly with a solution of hypochlorous acid (HOCl) or, more conveniently, *t*-butyl hypochlorite (*t*-BuOCl). *N*-Chloroamines or *N,N*-dichloroamines are formed, depending upon the amount of chlorinating agent used.

$$R-NH_2 \xrightarrow{HOCl} R-NHCl \xrightarrow{HOCl} R-NCl_2$$

N-Chloroamines undergo elimination of HCl with alkoxides to give imines. They are also easily converted back into the parent amines by reducing agents.

Conversion to Isocyanides

Isocyanides are formed when primary amines are heated with a mixture of chloroform and a strong base such as KOH.

$$C_6H_5NH_2 + CHCl_3 + 3\,KOH \rightarrow C_6H_5NC + 3\,KCl + 3\,H_2O$$
Phenyl isocyanide

This reaction, which has been known for over a century, has been used as a qualitative test for primary amines; the formation of volatile isocyanides is readily noted by their characteristic, nauseating odor.

The mechanism of this transformation is apparent on the basis of modern theory. Chloroform and strong base are a known source of the transient intermediate dichlorocarbene (CCl_2); attack of the amine nitrogen on the carbene, followed by loss of HCl, yields the isocyanide.

$$CHCl_3 \xrightarrow{\text{KOH}} CCl_2 \xrightarrow{\text{R—NH}_2} R\overset{+}{\underset{}{-}}NH_2\overset{-}{\underset{}{-}}CCl_2 \xrightarrow{\text{KOH}} R-NC$$

Like CO, isocyanides have no simple classical valence-bond structure, but the following resonance contributors may be written: $[R-N{=}C \leftrightarrow R-\overset{+}{N}{\equiv}C^-]$.

21.2   Quaternary Ammonium Salts

Substitution of all four hydrogens of the ammonium ion (NH_4^+) by alkyl (or aryl) groups gives a *quaternary ammonium ion* (R_4N^+). Such an ion, unlike an amine, has no basic properties since no unshared electrons remain on the nitrogen atom. Quaternary ammonium salts, $R_4N^+X^-$, are completely ionic structures; the hydroxides ($R_4N^+OH^-$) are as strongly basic as NaOH and KOH. The reactions of quaternary ammonium compounds bear little relation, therefore, to those of amines.

The Hofmann Elimination

Quaternary ammonium hydroxides in which one of the substituent groups on the nitrogen atom bears at least one β hydrogen decompose on heating with the formation of a tertiary amine and an olefin. The reaction, which has been known since 1851, is called the *Hofmann elimination*.† The simplest example of this reaction is the pyrolysis of trimethylethylammonium hydroxide. The required hydroxide is readily prepared from the corresponding halide salt by reaction with wet silver oxide.

$$2\,(CH_3)_3\overset{+}{N}{-}CH_2CH_3\,I^- + Ag_2O + H_2O \rightarrow 2\,AgI{\downarrow} + 2(CH_3)_3\overset{+}{N}{-}CH_2CH_3 \quad OH^-$$

$$(CH_3)_3\overset{+}{N}{-}CH_2{-}CH_2{-}H \quad OH \xrightarrow{\text{heat}} (CH_3)_3N + CH_2{=}CH_2 + H_2O$$

Considerable evidence exists which indicates that the Hofmann elimination usually takes place by a *concerted* reaction, as shown above. In this respect, the reaction is quite analogous to the elimination of HX from alkyl halides to give olefins. There is one important difference between these two olefin-forming reactions, however. Dehydrohalogenation tends to follow the so-called *Saytzev rule* and yields the *most substituted* olefin (Section 17.5). The Hofmann elimination, on the other hand, tends to yield the *least substituted* olefin as the major reaction product.

---

† August W. von Hofmann. 1818–1892. Born Giessen, Germany. University of Bonn, Royal College of Chemistry, London, and University of Berlin.

R—CH$_2$—CH—CH$_3$
       |
     $^+$N(CH$_3$)$_3$

⟶ OH$^-$

R—CH$_2$—CH=CH$_2$
Hofmann type, least substituted
olefin formed

R—CH$_2$—CH—CH$_3$
       |
       X

⟶ OH$^-$

R—CH=CH—CH$_3$
Saytzev type, most substituted
olefin formed

Several explanations have been offered to account for the change in orientation from Saytzev rule control (most highly substituted alkene favored) in E1 reactions and E2 dehydrohalogenations to Hofmann rule control (least highly substituted alkene favored) in eliminations of trimethylammonium (and dimethylsulfonium) compounds. It has been established that dehydrohalogenation and the Hofmann elimination are both subject to kinetic control, in contrast to the dehydration of an alcohol with acid, which is ordinarily subject to thermodynamic control (Section 18.6). Electronic effects seem to be the most important cause for the difference in orientation caused by changes in the leaving group. In E1 reactions and in E2 reactions of halides and tosylates, the double bond is almost completely formed in the transition state. The transition state of lowest energy will, therefore, be the one which leads to the thermodynamically more stable (usually the most highly substituted) alkene (Saytzev rule).

H
|
CH$_3$—C——CH—CH$_3$ ⟶
| |
CH$_3$ Br

[CH$_3$CH—CH⋯CH$_2$ ← H←:B]‡
         |
        CH$_3$ Br
Higher energy

↓

[CH$_3$—C ⋯ CHCH$_3$ ← B:→H]‡ ⟶
         |
        CH$_3$ Br
Lower energy

CH$_3$
   \
    C=CHCH$_3$
   /
CH$_3$
Preferred alkene
(Saytzev rule)

For E2 reactions of ionium compounds the tertiary amine and sulfide groups are poorer leaving groups, and the relative acidities of the β-hydrogen atoms control orientation. Electron-donating alkyl groups reduce the acidity of the hydrogen at carbons to which they are connected. Thus, β hydrogens attached to the least substituted β carbons are preferentially removed, giving the least highly substituted alkene (Hofmann rule).

CH$_3$
 |
CH$_3$→C—CH—CH$_3$ $\xrightarrow[\text{heat}]{^-\text{OH}}$
 | |
 H $^+$N(CH$_3$)$_3$↑

CH$_3$
   \
    CH—CH=CH$_2$
   /
CH$_3$
Preferred alkene
(Hofmann rule)

Less acidic
β hydrogen

More acidic
β hydrogens

Steric effects cannot be overlooked as a contributing factor toward determining orientation in elimination reactions. In addition, base strength and solvent effects also play a significant part.

The Saytzev and Hofmann rules are no longer valid when one of the β carbons bears a substituent which makes anion formation easier at that position.

$$C_6H_5-CH_2-CH_2-\overset{+}{N}(C_2H_5)_3 \overset{\Delta}{\rightarrow} C_6H_5-CH=CH_2 + N(C_2H_5)_3 + H_2O$$

$$OH^-$$

Compounds containing a basic nitrogen atom in a ring can be degraded to nitrogen-free olefins by a sequence of repeated methylation and Hofmann elimination reactions. This process, sometimes called "exhaustive methylation" of an amine, is illustrated below using *N*-methylpiperidine. This kind of sequence has been used for structure determination.

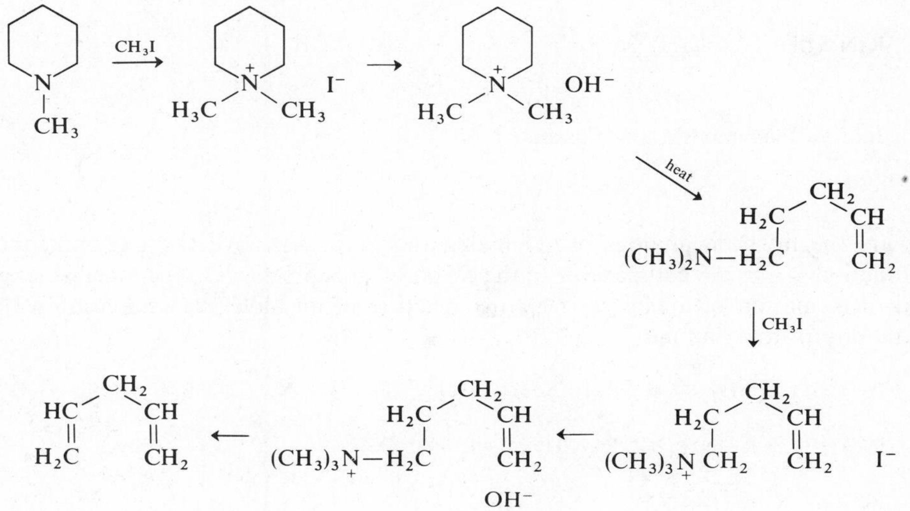

It may be noted that reactions of the S_N1 or $E1$ type do not occur with simple amines or ammonium salts as they do with simple alcohols. Acid will not bring about the elimination of ammonia and the formation of an olefin from a simple amine.

$$RCH_2CH_2NH_2 \overset{H^+}{\not\rightarrow} RCH=CH_2 + NH_3$$

This can be understood by realizing that the ionization of an amine (as its ammonium salt)

$$R_3C-\overset{+}{N}H_3 \rightleftharpoons R_3\overset{+}{C} + :NH_3$$

requires breaking a C—N bond, which is much stronger than a C—O bond (*Table 13.1*). Alternatively, the ammonia can be regarded as so basic that the above equilibrium is shifted so far to the left that such a reaction simply does not proceed.

Displacement of an N-*Alkyl Group.* A side reaction in the Hofmann elimination is the displacement of a tertiary amine and formation of an alcohol. This reaction involves attack by hydroxide ion on a carbon *alpha* to the positive nitrogen. This path assumes major proportions when the Hofmann elimination requires attack of hydroxide ion on a highly hindered β hydrogen, as in 3,3-dimethyl-butyltrimethylammonium hydroxide, and is, of course, the only reaction when there is no β hydrogen, as in benzyltrimethylammonium hydroxide.

$$(CH_3)_3C-CH-CH_2-\overset{+}{N}(CH_3)_3 \rightarrow (CH_3)_3C-CH=CH_2 + N(CH_3)_3 + H_2O$$

Minor product, 20%

Hindered attack

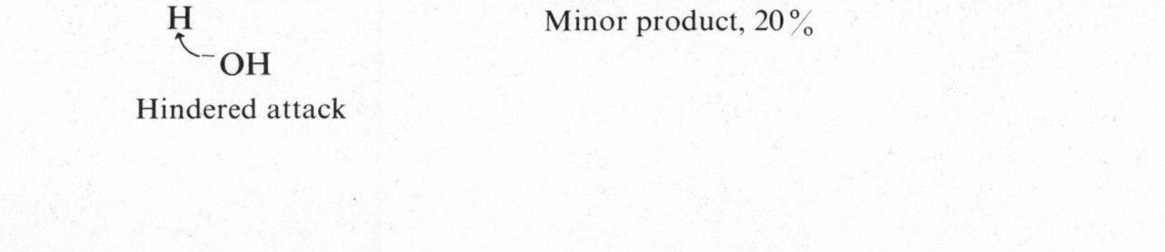

$$(CH_3)_3C-CH_2-CH_2-\overset{+}{N}(CH_3)_2 \rightarrow (CH_3)_3C-CH_2-CH_2-N(CH_3)_2 + CH_3OH$$

with the CH_3 group and ^-OH shown:

Unhindered displacement   Major product

There are occasions when one would like to convert a quaternary salt to a tertiary amine; the Hofmann elimination then becomes the undesired side reaction. The reagent of choice for this reaction is one which is an excellent nucleophile but a weak base. Thiophenoxide ion is such a reagent and gives high yields of amines.

$$R_3\overset{+}{N}-CH_3\ I^- + C_6H_5-S^-Na^+ \rightarrow R_3N + C_6H_5-SCH_3 + NaI$$

21.3   Imines, Isocyanates, and Enamines

Imines

Imines are the nitrogen analogs of aldehydes and ketones; all of them contain the imino function $>C=N-$, comparable to the carbonyl group $>C=O$. The most general method of formation of an imine is by the reaction of an aldehyde or ketone with ammonia or a primary amine.

$$R-CHO + NH_3 \rightleftharpoons R-CH=NH + H_2O \qquad R_2CO + NH_3 \rightleftharpoons R_2C=NH + H_2O$$

$$R-CHO + R-NH_2 \rightleftharpoons R-CH=N-R + H_2O$$

$$R_2CO + R-NH_2 \rightleftharpoons R_2C=NR + H_2O$$

The most characteristic reaction of an imine is the ready hydrolysis to a carbonyl compound and ammonia (or an amine); the reaction is acid-catalyzed, and generally proceeds rapidly in aqueous mineral acid.

$$(C_6H_5)_2C=NH + H_2O + HCl \rightarrow (C_6H_5)_2C=O + NH_4Cl$$

Polymerization of Simple Imines. The simpler imines derived from ammonia are so unstable that they are known only as reactive intermediates. Thus, acetaldimine trimerizes readily, and formaldimine has not been isolated, for it rapidly undergoes self-condensation with loss of ammonia to give an unusual compound known as hexamethylenetetramine.

$$CH_3CHO + NH_3 \rightleftharpoons CH_3-CH=NH + H_2O \qquad \bigg| \qquad CH_2O + NH_3 \rightleftharpoons CH_2=NH + H_2O$$

$$3CH_3CH=NH \rightarrow$$

Acetaldimine trimer

$$6\,CH_2=NH \rightarrow 2\,NH_3 +$$

$(CH_2)_6N_4$

Hexamethylenetetramine

Imines are readily reduced to amines by such varied reducing agents as sodium borohydride, hydrogen and Raney nickel, and formic acid. Such reduction reactions, coupled with the condensation of the amine and carbonyl compound, and from which the imines are never isolated, afford mild methods of alkylating a primary amine.

$$CH_3NH_2 + O=C(CH_3)_2 \rightleftharpoons CH_3N=C(CH_3)_2 + H_2O$$
$$\downarrow {\scriptstyle H_2/Ni}$$
$$CH_3NH-CH(CH_3)_2$$

Secondary amines are similarly alkylated via immonium salt intermediates

$$CH_3-NH-CH_2CH_3 + O{=}CHPh$$

$$\big\updownarrow$$

$$\underset{\overset{|}{CH_2CH_3}}{CH_3-\overset{+}{N}{=}CHPh} \xrightarrow[H_2]{Ni} \underset{\overset{|}{CH_2CH_3}}{CH_3-N-CH_2Ph}$$

An immonium ion

A great advantage of this type of reaction over alkylation with an alkyl halide is that over-alkylation with the formation of quaternary salts cannot take place.

The methylation of a primary or secondary amine to a tertiary amine by a mixture of formic acid and formaldehyde is particularly useful; it is referred to as the *Eschweiler–Clark reaction*. An immonium salt is the intermediate, formic acid acting as a reducing agent by a hydride transfer mechanism.

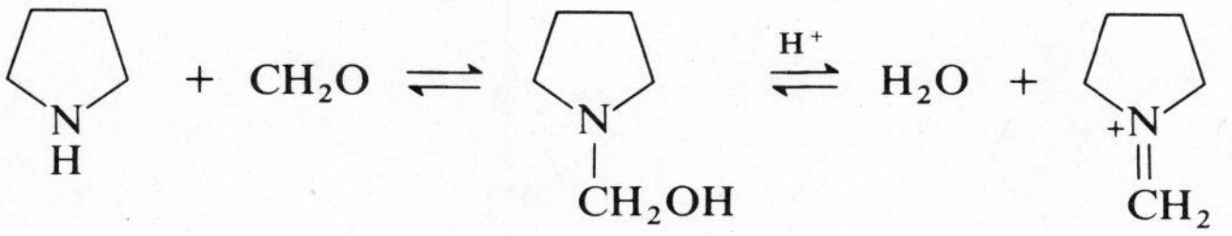

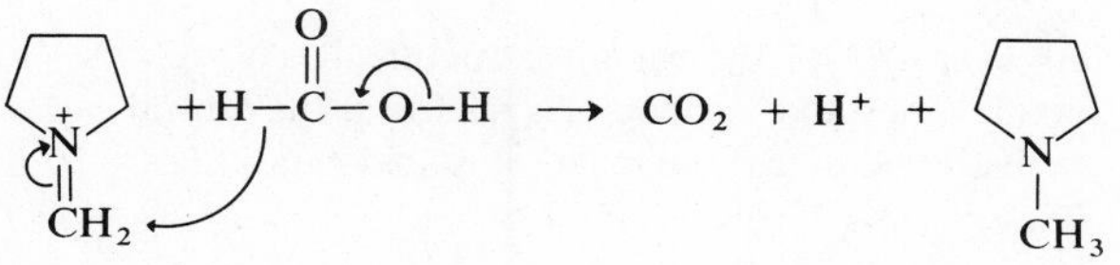

Similarly

$$(CH_3)_3C-NH_2 + 2\,CH_2O + 2\,HCOOH \rightarrow (CH_3)_3C-N(CH_3)_2 + 2\,H_2O + 2\,CO_2$$

The *Mannich reaction* is a very general reaction which takes place between an amine, an aldehyde (or ketone), and a highly nucleophilic carbon atom. The reaction may be viewed as the addition of a nucleophilic carbon to an immonium ion intermediate. Formaldehyde and dimethylamine are the most commonly employed aldehyde and amine components; the third component is usually a ketone (reacting as the enol), a phenol or one of certain heterocyclic compounds containing the enamine structure.

Example 1

$$C_6H_5-CO-CH_3 + CH_2O + HN(CH_3)_2 + HCl \rightarrow$$

$$C_6H_5-CO-CH_2-CH_2-\overset{\overset{\textstyle H}{|}}{\underset{+}{N}}(CH_3)_2 \quad Cl^-$$

Mechanism

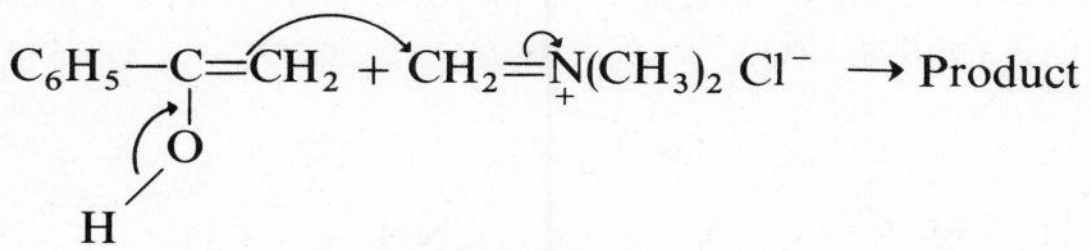

Enol of ketone   Immonium ion

Example 2

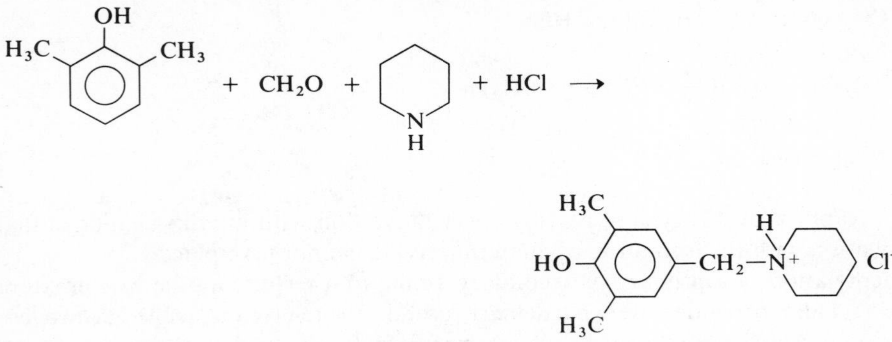

Mechanism

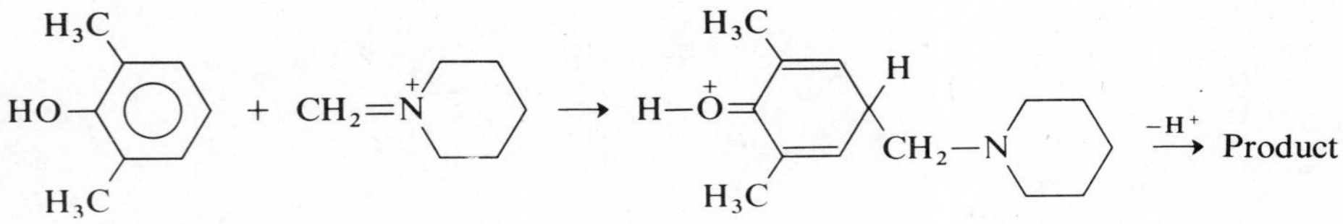

Carbodiimides. These are a special class of imines of the general structure R—N=C=N—R; they are formally diimines of carbon dioxide. They add nucleophiles readily at the central carbon atom. For example, water adds to give substituted ureas; the reaction is acid-catalyzed.

$$C_6H_5\text{—N=C=N—}C_6H_5 \xrightarrow{H^+} (C_6H_5\text{—N=}\underset{+}{C}\text{—NH—}C_6H_5) \xrightarrow{H_2O}$$

$$C_6H_5\text{—NH—CO—NH—}C_6H_5$$

N,N′-Diphenylurea

Carbodiimides can be prepared by dehydration of ureas, the reverse of the preceding reaction (Section 21.6). Carboxylic acids add to carbodiimides under very mild conditions. The products are highly reactive acylating agents and react easily with primary or secondary amines to give amides and the urea corresponding to the carbodiimide used. This reaction sequence has seen much use in recent years in the synthesis of peptides from amino acids (see Section 29.9). Dicyclohexylcarbodiimide is the reagent commonly employed.

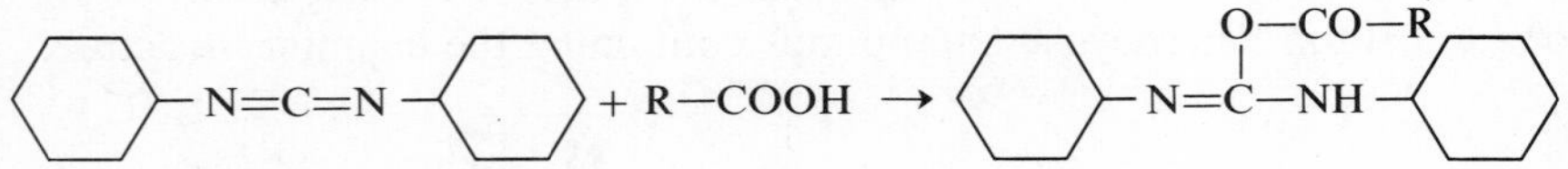

(not isolated)

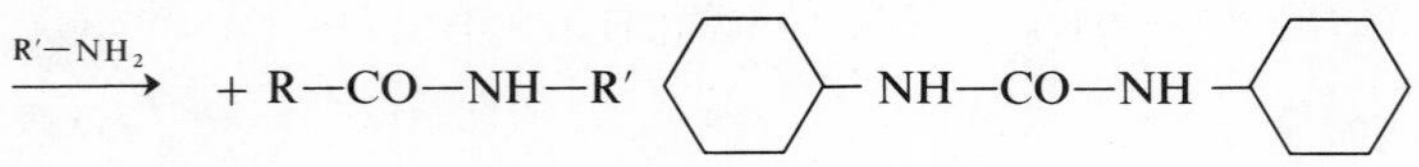

Isocyanates

Isocyanates have the general structure R—N=C=O (abbreviated RNCO) and therefore contain a carbon atom which forms part of both an imino group and a carbonyl group. Formally, they are monoimines of carbon dioxide.

The unsaturated carbon of an isocyanate is readily attacked by a variety of nucleophiles. Grignard reagents, amines, and alcohols give amides, ureas, and urethans, respectively.

$$C_6H_5\text{—NCO} + CH_3MgBr \rightarrow C_6H_5\text{—}\underset{\text{MgBr}}{N}\text{—}\overset{O}{\overset{\|}{C}}\text{—}CH_3 \xrightarrow[H_2O]{H^+} C_6H_5NH\text{—}\overset{O}{\overset{\|}{C}}\text{—}CH_3$$

$$C_6H_5-NCO + CH_3NH_2 \rightarrow C_6H_5-NH-\overset{\overset{\displaystyle O}{\|}}{C}-NH-CH_3$$

N-Phenyl-N'-methylurea

$$C_6H_5-NCO + C_2H_5OH \rightarrow C_6H_5-NH-\overset{\overset{\displaystyle O}{\|}}{C}-OC_2H_5$$

Ethyl N-phenylcarbamate
(N-Phenylurethan)

The latter type of reaction is of great industrial importance, since urethan polymers are obtained when polyols react with diisocyanates.

Isocyanates react readily with water. The initially formed carbamic acid loses carbon dioxide spontaneously to give a primary amine which can usually be intercepted as a salt if acid is present; under nonacidic conditions the amine reacts immediately with unchanged isocyanate to give a symmetrically substituted urea.

$$R-NCO + H_2O \rightarrow R-NH-COOH \xrightarrow{-CO_2} R-NH_2 \xrightarrow{H^+} R-NH_3^+$$

$\downarrow$ R—NCO

$$R-NH-CO-NH-R$$

Isothiocyanates. Isothiocyanates are the sulfur analogs of isocyanates and have the general structure $R-N=C=S$. Allyl isothiocyanate ($CH_2=CH-CH_2-NCS$) occurs in natural mustard oil and is the principal flavoring component of mustard.

Enamines

Enamines are the nitrogen analogs of enols and have the general structure $R_2C=CR-NR_2$. Looked at in a different way, they are tertiary amines in which one of the substituents is a vinyl or substituted vinyl group. In the absence of special stabilizing structural features, enamines bearing a hydrogen on the nitrogen are not stable and tautomerize to imines.

A tertiary enamine: A primary   An imine
stable   enamine:
(cannot tautomerize)   *unstable*

The enamine system ($C=C-N$) forms a conjugated system in which the carbon atom β to nitrogen has considerably higher electron density than an ordinary olefinic carbon and is therefore unusually nucleophilic.

$$R_2C=\overset{\overset{\displaystyle R}{|}}{\underset{\cdot\cdot}{C}}-NR_2 \leftrightarrow R_2\overset{-}{C}-\overset{\overset{\displaystyle R}{|}}{C}=\overset{+}{N}R_2$$

Enamines are fairly stable to hydrolysis in the absence of acid, but are hydrolyzed rapidly by aqueous acid to carbonyl compounds and secondary amine salts.

$$(CH_3)_2C=CH-N(C_2H_5)_2 \xrightarrow[H_2O]{H^+} (CH_3)_2\overset{\overset{\displaystyle }{\underset{\underset{\displaystyle H}{|}}{C}}}{C}-CH=\overset{+}{N}(C_2H_5)_2 \xrightarrow{H_2O}$$

$$(CH_3)_2CH-CHO + H_2\overset{+}{N}(C_2H_5)_2$$

Enamines react readily with acyl chlorides and with alkyl halides which are highly reactive in S_N2 reactions (e.g., allyl chloride, benzyl chloride, α-halo carbonyl derivatives, and methyl iodide) to give mostly *C-alkylation products*. These products, which are immonium salts, are rapidly hydrolyzed by water to give α-alkyl or α-acyl carbonyl compounds; enamines derived from ketones give the best results. Since enamines are readily prepared from ketones and secondary amines, this reaction sequence is extremely useful for the synthesis of many types of α-substituted ketones. Enamines derived from pyrrolidine usually give particularly goods results.

Unfortunately, alkyl halides of ordinary reactivity give only small amounts of *C*-alkylation products with enamines and large amounts of *N*-alkylation products. Hydrolysis of the latter gives back the unalkylated ketone from which the starting enamine was prepared.

It may be that enamines react with halides of all types to give N-alkylation initially and that C-alkylation is successful only in those cases where N-alkylated products undergo either an inter- or an intramolecular transfer of the alkyl group from nitrogen to carbon.

21.4   Nitriles

Organic cyanides (nitriles) are practically neutral compounds and do not form salts with aqueous acids. In general, reactions of nitriles can be separated into the reactions of the cyano group ($-C\equiv N$) and the reactions of anions of nitriles which have α hydrogens (R_2CH-CN). In addition, α,β-unsaturated nitriles undergo reactions analogous to those of α,β-unsaturated carbonyl compounds.

Additions to the Cyano Group

The cyano group, like the carbonyl group, is polarized so that the carbon atom is the positive end of the dipole and the hetero atom is the negative end. Additions to the cyano group are therefore similar in many ways to carbonyl additions.

$$R-C\equiv N: \;\leftrightarrow\; R-\overset{+}{C}=\overset{..}{\underset{-}{N}}:$$

The best known and most widely used reaction of nitriles is their hydrolysis to carboxylic acids (Section 20.6). This reaction takes place in the presence of either strong acid or strong base; in both cases, amides are the first reaction products, but they cannot be isolated unless their rate of hydrolysis is lower than that of the original nitrile.

Alkaline hydrolysis

$$R-C\equiv N + OH^- \rightarrow R-C\begin{smallmatrix}N^-\\||\\\\OH\end{smallmatrix} \xrightarrow{H_2O} R-C\begin{smallmatrix}NH\\||\\\\OH\end{smallmatrix} \rightarrow R-C\begin{smallmatrix}NH_2\\|\\\\O\end{smallmatrix} \rightarrow R-COONa$$

Acid hydrolysis

$$R-C\equiv N + H^+ \rightarrow R-\overset{+}{C}=NH \xrightarrow{H_2O} R-C\begin{smallmatrix}NH\\||\\\\{}^+OH_2\end{smallmatrix} \rightarrow R-C\begin{smallmatrix}NH_2\\|\\\\O\end{smallmatrix} \rightarrow R-COOH$$

EXERCISE 21.4

Write the mechanisms for the acidic and basic hydrolyses of benzonitrile.

The hydrolysis of aromatic nitriles can sometimes be stopped at the amide stage; this partial hydrolysis is accomplished by dissolving the nitrile in concentrated sulfuric acid and then pouring the acid solution onto ice.

$$C_6H_5CN \xrightarrow{H_2SO_4} C_6H_5\overset{+}{C}=NH \xrightarrow[0°C]{H_2O} C_6H_5CONH_2$$

The acid alcoholysis of nitriles provides an interesting parallel to acid hydrolysis. The reaction of a nitrile with dry hydrogen chloride and 1 mole of alcohol affords the hydrochloride of an *imidate ester* (the imino analog of an ordinary ester, sometimes referred to as an *imino ether*). These imidate esters are excellent synthetic intermediates for the preparation of *ortho esters*, ordinary esters, amides, and alkyl halides. Imidate ester salts react with water at room temperature to give ordinary esters in excellent yield. Reaction with excess alcohol provides the best method for the preparation of an ortho ester (the ketal of an ordinary ester). Heating above the melting point smoothly pyrolyzes an imidate ester hydrochloride and provides an excellent yield of the amide plus the alkyl chloride. The amide is formed by clean inversion of configuration at the center to which the chlorine becomes attached.

$$
C_6H_5CN \xrightarrow[C_2H_5OH]{HCl} C_6H_5\overset{\overset{\displaystyle NH_2^+\ Cl^-}{\|}}{C}-OC_2H_5 \xrightarrow{C_2H_5OH} C_6H_5C(OC_2H_5)_3
$$

$$\xrightarrow{H_2O} C_6H_5COOC_2H_5$$

Ethyl benzimidate   Ethyl orthobenzoate
hydrochloride

$$C_6H_5CONH_2 + C_2H_5Cl \xleftarrow{\Delta}$$

The reaction of an ortho ester with a Grignard reagent is a useful synthetic reaction for the preparation of ketones and ketals.

$$
R-C(OEt)_3 + R'MgX \rightarrow R-\overset{\overset{\displaystyle OEt}{|}}{\underset{\underset{\displaystyle OEt}{|}}{C}}-R' \xrightarrow{H_3O^+} R-\overset{\overset{\displaystyle O}{\|}}{C}-R'
$$

Nitriles are alkylated on nitrogen by tertiary alcohols in sulfuric acid solution. This reaction (known as the *Ritter reaction*), yields amides, which on hydrolysis afford *t*-alkyl amines. The reaction can indeed be carried out starting with any alcohol (or alkene) which can act as a source of a fairly stable carbonium ion. It should be noted that compounds such as *t*-butylamine, which cannot be prepared from *t*-butyl chloride and ammonia (elimination occurs exclusively), are readily synthesized by the Ritter reaction.

$$
(CH_3)_3C-OH \xrightarrow{H_2SO_4} (CH_3)_3C^+ \xrightarrow{CH_3CN} CH_3-\underset{+}{C}=NC(CH_3)_3 \underset{\downarrow H_2O}{}
$$

$$
(CH_3)_3C-NH_2 \xleftarrow[\Delta]{OH^-} CH_3CO-NH-C(CH_3)_3
$$

Grignard reagents add to the cyano group of most nitriles to give salts of ketimines. Since the ketimine salts are readily hydrolyzed to ketones, this reaction can often serve as a convenient ketone synthesis. For practical purposes, the reaction is not useful with nitriles containing a *very* active hydrogen α to the cyano group, since such compounds can react with Grignard reagents to give carbanions.

and

But

$$RMgBr + C_6H_5CH_2CN \rightarrow R-H + C_6H_5-\overset{-}{C}H-CN\ \overset{+}{M}gBr$$

The reduction of nitriles to primary amines can be carried out in a number of ways. The most commonly used methods are catalytic reduction in the presence of Raney nickel and ammonia, and chemical reduction by lithium aluminum hydride or by metallic sodium and alcohol.

$$CH_3CH_2-CN \xrightarrow[\text{EtOH,NH}_3]{\text{Ni, H}_2} CH_3CH_2CH_2NH_2$$

$$C_6H_5-CH_2CN \xrightarrow[\text{Et}_2O]{\text{LiAlH}_4} \xrightarrow{\text{H}_2O} C_6H_5CH_2CH_2NH_2$$

Reactions of Nitriles Having α Hydrogens

Nitriles which have at least one hydrogen on the carbon atom bearing the cyano group react with strong bases to form anions. These anions are quite analogous in structure to the enolates derived from aldehydes and ketones.

$$R-CH_2-C\equiv N \xrightarrow{B^-} [R-\underset{|}{C}H-C\equiv N \leftrightarrow R-CH=C=N^-]$$

Nitrile anions are good nucleophiles and readily undergo alkylation on carbon rather than nitrogen. (The few exceptions to this rule which are known are caused by exceptional steric hindrance.) More than one alkyl group can be introduced if excess alkyl halide and base are employed; indeed, monoalkylation of most nitriles is impractical.

$$CH_3CH_2CN \xrightarrow[\text{NH}_3]{\text{NaNH}_2} CH_3\overset{-}{C}H-CN \xrightarrow{C_2H_5I} CH_3-\overset{C_2H_5}{\underset{|}{C}H}-CN \xrightarrow[\text{2. C}_2\text{H}_5\text{I}]{\text{1. NaNH}_2} CH_3-\overset{C_2H_5}{\underset{C_2H_5}{\overset{|}{\underset{|}{C}}}}-CN$$

The nitrile group itself can be attacked by a nitrile anion to give an imine or enamine from which a β-keto nitrile results on mild hydrolysis. This reaction has been particularly useful for the preparation of five- and six-membered rings; such ring formation is known as the *Thorpe cyclization.*

EXERCISE 21.5

Write the mechanism of the Dieckmann cyclization (Section 20.17) and compare it with that of the Thorpe cyclization.

Under special (high-dilution) conditions, this reaction can be used to give good yields of rings containing 12 or more atoms (Section 34.2).

Reactions of α,β-Unsaturated Nitriles

α,β-Unsaturated nitriles contain the conjugated system $C=C-C\equiv N$, which is very similar in its general properties to the α,β-unsaturated carbonyl system $C=C-C=O$. By far the most important member of this series is *acrylonitrile*, $CH_2=CH-CN$, an extremely important starting material in the manufacture of synthetic fibers (Section 25.3). Acrylonitrile readily undergoes Michael-type reactions with many types of nucleophiles. For example, it reacts with ethylene glycol as follows:

$$HOCH_2CH_2OH + 2CH_2=CHCN \xrightarrow{OH^-}$$

$$N\equiv C-CH_2CH_2-O-CH_2CH_2-O-CH_2CH_2-C\equiv N$$

Cyanoethylation. Cyclohexanone will react with 4 moles of acrylonitrile in the presence of base; the introduction of acrylonitrile units into an "active methylene" compound is sometimes referred to as "cyanoethylation."

α,β-Unsaturated nitriles are usually good dienophiles in the Diels–Alder reaction (Section 15.12); the electron-withdrawing cyano group activates the olefinic system towards reaction with most dienes (i.e., electron-rich dienes). As might be expected, tetracyanoethylene is one of the most reactive dienophiles known.

Tetracyanoethylene

21.5   Amides

In this section, we will describe and compare the reactions of the most important types of amides, insofar as these reactions occur at nitrogen. (The carbonyl reactions of amides were discussed in Chapter 20.)

Alkylation on Nitrogen

Both sulfonamides and imides (but not carboxamides) which have a hydrogen on the nitrogen atom are completely converted to anions by sodium hydroxide. Carboxamides, while more acidic than ketones, may be converted to anions by more powerful bases such as NaH or $NaNH_2$. These anions are good nucleophiles and react with primary or secondary alkyl halides to give N-alkyl derivatives. This sequence constitutes a preparative method for secondary amines when followed by hydrolysis (see page 593).

$$C_6H_5-SO_2-NH-CH_3 \xrightarrow{\text{NaOH}} C_6H_5-SO_2-\underset{\text{\_}}{N}-CH_3 \ Na^+ \xrightarrow{C_2H_5I}$$

$$C_6H_5-SO_2-\overset{C_2H_5}{\underset{|}{N}}-CH_3$$

Gabriel Synthesis. Alkylation of the readily prepared phthalimide forms the basis of the Gabriel synthesis of primary amines. In this procedure, potassium phthalimide is alkylated with an alkyl halide; dimethylformamide is the best solvent for this reaction. The resulting N-alkylphthalimide is often resistant to ordinary hydrolysis conditions, but reacts readily with hydrazine to give phthalhydrazide and a primary amine. The advantage of the Gabriel synthesis is that it is an indirect means of carrying out the transformation $RX \rightarrow RNH_2$ without the formation of secondary or tertiary amine by-products.

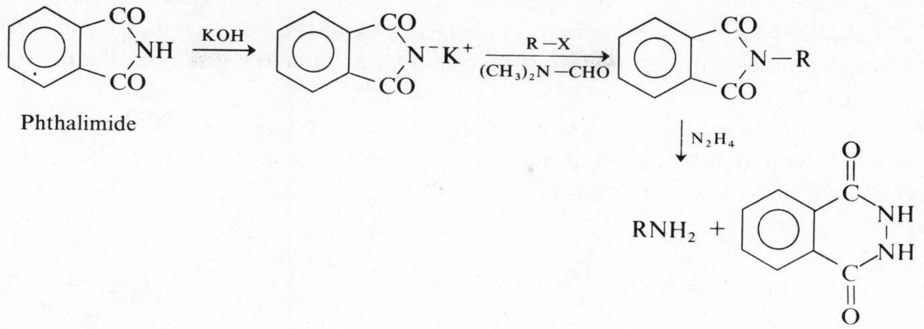

Phthalimide

EXERCISE 21.6

Will the Gabriel synthesis be useful for the preparation of *t*-butylamine? Explain.

Reaction with Nitrous Acid

Both sulfonamides and carboxamides having a free amino group react with nitrous acid (though sometimes sluggishly) to give sulfonic and carboxylic acids, respectively. The mechanism of the reaction is presumed to involve unstable diazonium intermediates.

$$R-CO-NH_2 \xrightarrow{HNO_2} R-COOH + N_2 \quad (\text{via } R-CO-N_2^+)$$

$$R-SO_2-NH_2 \xrightarrow{HNO_2} R-SO_3H + N_2$$

EXERCISE 21.7

Neopentylamine reacts with nitrous acid to give rearranged products, while pivalamide [$(CH_3)_3CCONH_2$] reacts under similar conditions to give pivalic acid. Can you interpret this difference in terms of the intermediate carbonium ions? (*Hint:* See page 358.)

Urea (carbamide) is often used as a scavenger for unwanted excess nitrous acid in reaction mixtures, since it gives only gaseous reaction products and water.

$$H_2N-CO-NH_2 + 2\,HNO_2 \rightarrow 2\,N_2 + HO-\overset{\overset{\displaystyle O}{\|}}{C}-OH + 2\,H_2O$$

$$H_2CO_3 \rightarrow CO_2 + H_2O$$

Monosubstituted amides react with nitrous acid to give *N*-nitroso derivatives, which are useful as precursors of diazoalkanes. The syntheses of two diazomethane precursors are shown below. The synthesis of *N*-nitroso-*N*-methylurea is particularly interesting since it shows the preferential reaction of nitrous acid with the substituted (i.e., most basic) amide nitrogen. The starting material, *N*-methylurea, is made by a reaction analogous to Wöhler's classical synthesis of urea from ammonium cyanate.

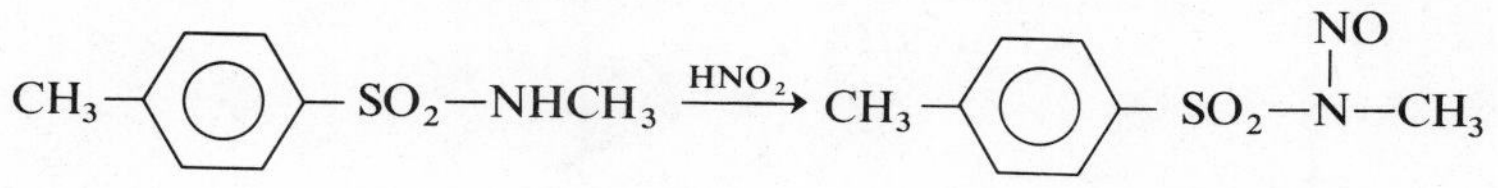

(Diazald)

$$CH_3\overset{+}{N}H_3\,NCO^- \xrightarrow[\Delta]{H_2O} CH_3-NH-CO-NH_2 \xrightarrow{HNO_2} CH_3-\underset{\underset{\displaystyle NO}{|}}{N}-CO-NH_2$$

From CH_3NH_2,
KCNO and acid

N-Nitroso-*N*-
methylurea

Halogenation on Nitrogen

All types of amides which have a hydrogen on the amide nitrogen react readily with hypohalites (usually generated in the reaction mixture from the halogen and base). The resulting N-halo amides form salts with aqueous alkali if a hydrogen remains on the amide nitrogen.

N-Bromosuccinimide is obtained when an aqueous solution of succinimide is treated with bromine and an equivalent of base. As described elsewhere (Section 23.7), this compound is a valuable allylic brominating agent.

$$\underset{\text{Succinimide}}{\left[\begin{array}{l}\text{CO}\\\text{NH}\\\text{CO}\end{array}\right.} + Br_2 + NaHCO_3 \xrightarrow{H_2O} \underset{\text{N-Bromosuccinimide}}{\left[\begin{array}{l}\text{CO}\\\text{N—Br}\\\text{CO}\end{array}\right.} + NaBr + CO_2 + H_2O$$

EXERCISE 21.8

Suggest a mechanism for the preceding reaction.

N-Halo derivatives of unsubstituted carboxamides are key intermediates in the *Hofmann degradation*, a simple laboratory method for the conversion of amides to amines having one less carbon atom (hence the term degradation). The overall reaction simply involves the reaction of an amide with bromine in the presence of three equivalents of alkali.

$$R—CO—NH_2 + Br_2 + 3\,NaOH \xrightarrow{H_2O} R—NH_2 + 2\,NaBr + NaHCO_3 + H_2O$$

The steps in the Hofmann degradation can be written formally as follows:

1. An N-bromo amide is produced.

$$R—CONH_2 + Br_2 + NaOH \rightarrow R—CO—NHBr + NaBr + H_2O$$

2. The N-bromo amide forms a sodium salt.

$$R—CO—NHBr + NaOH \rightarrow R—CO—\underline{N}—Br\ Na^+$$

3. The sodium salt loses NaBr to form a very unstable nitrene (monovalent nitrogen) intermediate.

$$R—CO—\underline{N}—Br\ Na^+ \rightarrow NaBr + [R—CO—N]$$

4. The nitrene immediately rearranges to an isocyanate by migration of the substituent R. Since the group R migrates with the electron pair of the original R-to-CO bond, an optically active group R* migrates with complete *retention* of its configuration.

$$R^*—\overset{\overset{\text{O}}{\|}}{C}—\ddot{N}: \rightarrow R^*—\ddot{N}=C=O$$

Actually, no proof that the nitrene is a discrete *intermediate* has ever been obtained, and the available evidence strongly indicates that steps 3 and 4 are actually concerted.

$$R—\overset{\overset{\text{O}}{\|}}{C}—N—Br \rightarrow O=C=N—R + Br^-$$

5. The isocyanate reacts with base (Section 21.3) to give an amine via a carbamate salt.

$$R-NCO + OH^- \rightarrow R-NH-COO^- \xrightarrow[\Delta]{OH^-} CO_3^{2-} + R-NH_2$$

Ureas ($R-NH-CO-NH-R$) are often major by-products in the Hofmann degradation, since they are formed by addition of the amine to unhydrolyzed isocyanate. If the entire Hofmann degradation is carried out in dry methanol, ureas are not formed and the product is a urethan ($R-NH-COOCH_3$), which can be hydrolyzed to the amine in a separate step.

EXERCISE 21.9

Acid azides undergo a reaction (called the *Curtius rearrangement*) which has a certain mechanistic similarity to the Hofmann degradation.

$$R-C\underset{N_3}{\overset{O}{\big|}} \xrightarrow{heat} R-N=C=O \xrightarrow{H_2O} RNH_2 + CO_2$$

Suggest a mechanism for this reaction.

Reaction with Inorganic Nonmetal Halides

Unsubstituted carboxamides ($RCONH_2$) are dehydrated to nitriles when heated with PCl_5, $POCl_3$, or $SOCl_2$ (page 531).

$$CH_3O-\langle\bigcirc\rangle-CONH_2 + SOCl_2 \xrightarrow{\Delta} CH_3O-\langle\bigcirc\rangle-CN + SO_2 + 2HCl$$

Substituted amides undergo an interesting conversion into a nitrile and an alkyl halide when heated with PCl_5 or PBr_5. This process, known as the *von Braun reaction*, affords an indirect means of replacing a nitrogen atom by a halo substituent; it is particularly effective when the acyl group of the amide is benzoyl. Compounds known as *imidoyl halides* are intermediates in these reactions. Note the use of an *N,N*-disubstituted amide in the second example.

$$CH_3CH_2CH_2CH_2-NH_2 \xrightarrow{C_6H_5COCl} n\text{-Bu}-NH-CO-C_6H_5$$

(n-Bu$-NH_2$) $\Delta \downarrow PCl_5$

$$CH_3-CH_2-CH_2-CH_2-N\overset{+}{\equiv}C-C_6H_5 \xleftarrow{} n\text{-Bu}-N=C\underset{Cl}{\overset{C_6H_5}{\big<}}$$

Cl^- (with arrow)

$\downarrow$

n-Bu$-Cl$ + $N\equiv C-C_6H_5$ An imidoyl chloride

$$HN\langle\bigcirc\rangle \xrightarrow{C_6H_5COCl} C_6H_5-CO-N\langle\bigcirc\rangle \xrightarrow[\Delta]{PBr_5} C_6H_5CN +$$

$$\begin{array}{c} Br \\ | \\ CH_2-CH_2 \\ \diagdown \\ \qquad CH_2 \\ \diagup \\ CH_2-CH_2 \\ | \\ Br \end{array}$$

Vilsmeier–Haack Synthesis. The reaction of an *N*-formyl derivative of a secondary amine and POCl$_3$ with a reactive aromatic compound affords a convenient method of directly introducing an aldehyde group into the aromatic compound. This reaction proceeds by way of the cation of an imidoyl chloride.

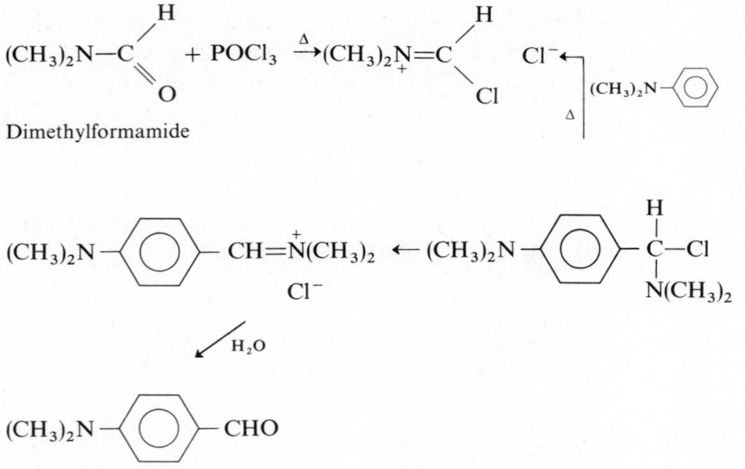

21.6   Summary of Synthetic Methods for Amines and Related Compounds

As usual, any reactions which have not yet been discussed in the text need not be studied at this time. They are indicated by reference to a section number in the next chapter (22).

1. Primary amines
    a. Alkylation
        (1) Section 21.1 (usually poor method)

$$R-X + NH_3 \text{ (excess)} \rightarrow R-NH_2$$

        (2) Ritter reaction, Section 21.4

$$R_3C-OH + R'-CN \xrightarrow{H_2SO_4} R_3C-NH-COR' \xrightarrow{H_3O^+} R_3C-NH_2$$

        (3) Gabriel synthesis, Section 21.5

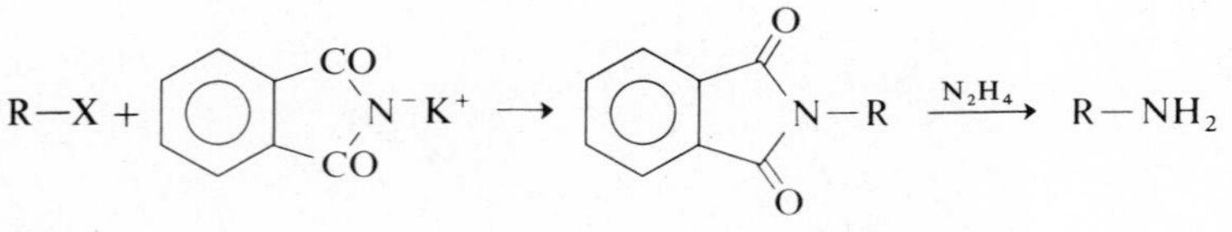

    b. Reduction

$$R-NO_2 \rightarrow R-NH_2 \quad \text{(Pt or Pd + H}_2\text{, SnCl}_2 \text{ or Fe + H}^+\text{, Section 22.1)}$$

$$R-N_3 \rightarrow R-NH_2 \quad \text{(Pt + H}_2\text{, SnCl}_2\text{, or LiAlH}_4\text{, Section 22.9).}$$

$$R_2C=NOH \rightarrow R_2CH-NH_2 \quad \text{(Na + EtOH, Ni + H}_2 + NH_3\text{, Section 22.3)}$$

$$\left.\begin{array}{l} R-CN \rightarrow R-CH_2NH_2 \\ R-CONH_2 \rightarrow R-CH_2NH_2 \end{array}\right] \text{—(LiAlH}_4\text{, Section 20.8)}$$

    c. Amide hydrolysis

$$R-CO-NH-R' \rightarrow R'-NH_2 \quad \text{(H}^+ \text{ or OH}^- \text{ and H}_2\text{O, Section 20.16)}$$

d. Rearrangements
   (1) Hofmann degradation, Section 21.5

$$R-CONH_2 \rightarrow R-NH_2$$

   (2) Curtius rearrangement, Section 22.9

$$R-CON_3 \rightarrow R-NH_2$$

2. Secondary amines
   a. Alkylation

$$R-X + R'-NH_2 \rightarrow R-NH-R' \quad \text{(usually a poor method, Section 21.1)}$$

$$R-NH_2 \rightarrow C_6H_5SO_2-NH-R \xrightarrow{R'-X} C_6H_5SO_2-N\begin{array}{c} R \\ \diagdown \\ R' \end{array} \rightarrow R-NH-R'$$

   b. Reductive alkylation

$$R-NH_2 + O{=}CR'_2 \rightarrow R-NH-CHR'_2 \quad \text{(H}_2 + \text{Ni, or NaBH}_4\text{, Section 21.3)}$$

   c. Reduction

$$R-CO-NH-R' \xrightarrow{\text{LiAlH}_4} R-CH_2-NH-R' \quad \text{(Section 20.8)}$$

3. Tertiary amines
   a. Alkylation

$$R_2NH + R'-X \rightarrow R_2N-R' \quad \text{(only fair method, Section 21.1)}$$

   b. Reductive alkylation

$$RNH_2 + CH_2O + HCOOH \rightarrow RN(CH_3)_2 \quad \text{(Section 21.3)}$$

$$R_2NH + CH_2O + HCOOH \rightarrow R_2N-CH_3$$

   c. Reduction

$$R-CO-NR'_2 \xrightarrow{\text{LiAlH}_4} R-CH_2-NR'_2 \quad \text{(Section 20.8)}$$

4. Quaternary ammonium salts

$$R_3N + R'X \rightarrow R_3\overset{+}{N}-R' \, X^- \quad \text{(Section 17.1)}$$

5. Imines (Many simple imines are unstable toward hydrolysis; imines are encountered mostly as reaction intermediates, Sections 19.7 and 21.3.)

$$Ar-NH_2 + Ar-CHO \rightarrow Ar-CH{=}N-Ar$$

$$RC{\equiv}N + R'MgX \rightarrow RR'C{=}NMgX \xrightarrow{H_2O} RR'C{=}NH \quad \text{(Easily isolable as long as R and R' are not both small alkyl groups)}$$

6. Carbodiimides

$$R-CO-NH-CO-R \rightarrow R-C=N=C-R \quad \text{(tosyl chloride or COCl}_2 \text{ in pyridine)}$$

$$2R-NCO \xrightarrow{Ph_3P} R-N=C=N-R + Ph_3PO$$

7. Isocyanates

$$R-CON_3 \xrightarrow{\Delta} R-NCO \quad \text{(Section 22.9)}$$

8. Enamines

$$R_2CH-CO-R + R'_2NH \xrightarrow[-H_2O]{H^+} R_2C=C\begin{smallmatrix} R \\ \\ NR'_2 \end{smallmatrix} \quad \text{(Section 21.3)}$$

9. Cyanides

$$R-X \xrightarrow{NaCN} R-CN \quad \text{(Section 17.1)}$$

$$R-CH=NOH \rightarrow R-CN \quad \text{(SOCl}_2\text{, POCl}_3 \text{ or Ac}_2O, \text{ Section 22.3)}$$

$$R-CONH_2 \rightarrow R-CN \quad \text{(SOCl}_2\text{, POCl}_3\text{, or P}_2O_5, \text{ Section 21.5)}$$

$$Ar-N_2^+ \xrightarrow[NaCN]{CuCN} Ar-CN \quad \text{(Section 22.7)}$$

10. Isocyanides

$$R-NH_2 + CHCl_3 + KOH \rightarrow R-NC \quad \text{(Section 21.1)}$$

$$R-NH-CHO \rightarrow R-NC \quad \text{(POCl}_3 \text{ in pyridine)}$$

11. Amides
    a. Carboxamides

$$R-COO^- NH_4^+ \longrightarrow R-CONH_2 \quad \text{(Section 20.5)}$$

$$\left.\begin{array}{l} R-COCl \\ (R-CO)_2O \\ R-CO-OR' \end{array}\right\} \begin{array}{l} \xrightarrow{NH_3} R-CONH_2 \\ \xrightarrow{R'NH_2} R-CONHR' \quad \text{(Section 20.5)} \\ \xrightarrow{R'_2NH_2} R-CONR'_2 \end{array}$$

$$R-CN \xrightarrow[H_2O]{H_2SO_4} R-CONH_2 \quad \text{(Section 21.4)}$$

$$R_3C-OH + R'-CN \xrightarrow{H_2SO_4} R_3C-NH-CO-R' \quad \text{(Section 21.4)}$$

$$R-NCO + R'-OH \rightarrow R-NH-CO-OR' \quad \text{(a carbamate or urethan, Section 21.3)}$$

$$R-NCO + R'MgX \rightarrow \xrightarrow{H_3O^+} RNHCOR' \quad \text{(Section 21.3)}$$

$$R-NH_2 + R'NCO \rightarrow R-NH-CO-NHR' \quad \text{(a urea, Section 21.3)}$$

b. Imides (Sections 21.5, 20.5)†

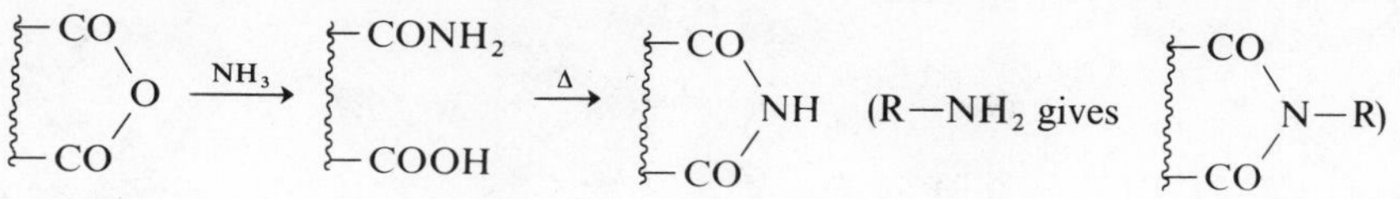

c. Sulfonamides (Section 21.1)

PROBLEMS

1. Complete the following:

   (a) $CH_3CH_2-\underset{\underset{CH_3}{|}}{N}-Ph + CH_3I \rightarrow$

   (b)

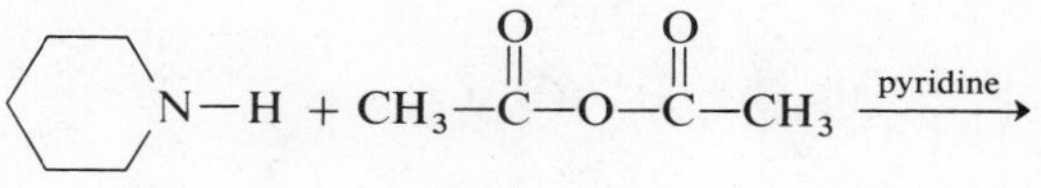

   (c)

   (d)

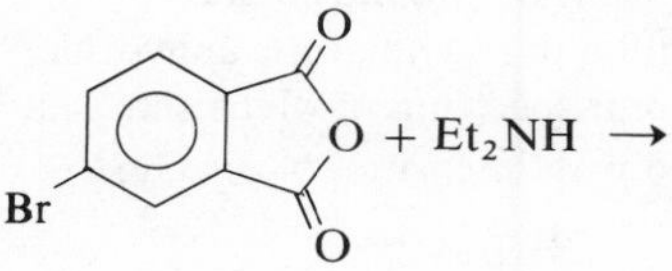

2. Explain how the Hinsberg test can be used to distinguish primary, secondary, and tertiary amines.

3. Which of the following sets of products would you predict from the following reaction? Why?

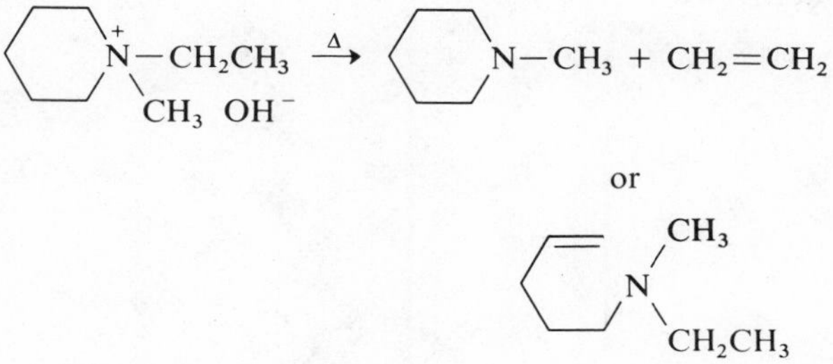

   or

4. Complete the following:

   (a)

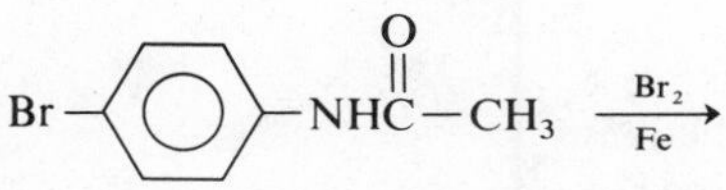

† The wavy line indicates the attachment of unspecified groups, usually comprising a ring, as in succinimide, phthalimide, and so on.

(b) $t\text{-Bu}-CH_2-\overset{\overset{\displaystyle CH_3}{|}}{\underset{\underset{\displaystyle CH_3}{|}}{\overset{+}{N}}}-CH_2-CH_3 \quad \overset{\Delta}{\longrightarrow}$

$\qquad\qquad\qquad OH^-$

(c) $CH_3CH_2CH_2CH_2NH_2 \xrightarrow[\text{HCOOH}]{\text{H}_2\text{CO}}$

(d) $Ph-\overset{\overset{\displaystyle O}{\|}}{C}-CH_3 + CH_3CHO + NHMe_2 \longrightarrow$

(e) 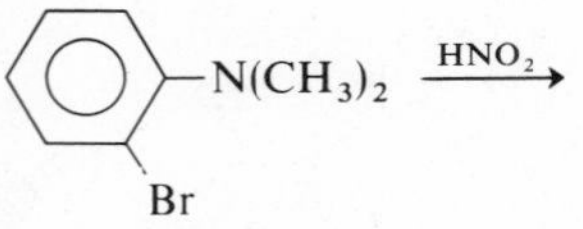 ⟨benzene ring⟩$-N(CH_3)_2 \xrightarrow{\text{HNO}_2}$ with Br substituent

(f) *Optional Problem.* ⟨benzene ring⟩$-\overset{\overset{\displaystyle CH_3}{|}}{\underset{\underset{\displaystyle CH_3}{|}}{\overset{+}{N}}}-CH_3 + OH^- \overset{\Delta}{\longrightarrow}$

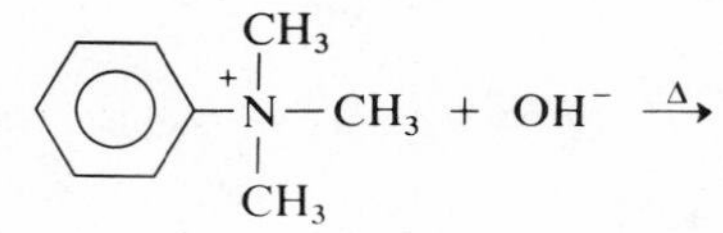

5. Outline syntheses for the following from available materials:

(a) 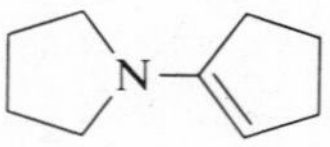 ⟨pyrrolidine–cyclopentene structure⟩

(b) 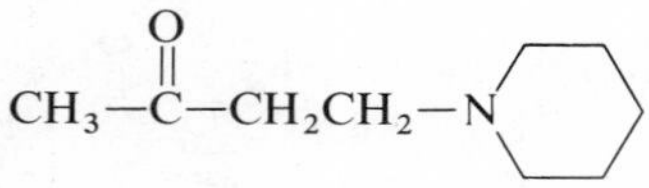 $CH_3-\overset{\overset{\displaystyle O}{\|}}{C}-CH_2CH_2-N$⟨piperidine ring⟩

(c) ⟨cyclohexene⟩ from ⟨cyclohexyl ring with⟩ $N(CH_3)_2$

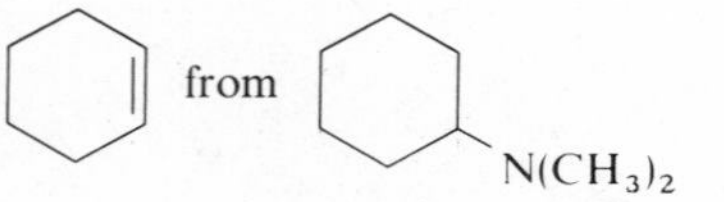

(d) $(CH_3)_3C-NH_2$

6. A colorless basic liquid C_7H_9N (A) reacts immediately with sodium nitrite in cold dilute sulfuric acid to give a neutral yellow oil (B). Reaction of A with acetic anhydride in pyridine solution gives a neutral white solid (C), the nmr spectrum of which shows a singlet at δ 1.9, a singlet at δ 3.5, and a multiplet at δ 7.3 with intensities of $1:1:1.67$, respectively. Assign structures to A, B, and C.

7. Write mechanisms for the following transformations:

(a) $Ph-C\equiv N \xrightarrow[\text{EtOH}]{\text{HCl}} Ph-\overset{\overset{\displaystyle OEt}{|}}{\underset{\underset{\displaystyle OEt}{|}}{C}}-OEt$

(b) $Ph-\overset{\overset{\displaystyle O}{\diagup}}{C}\diagdown_{NH_2} \xrightarrow[\text{OH}^-]{\text{Br}_2} Ph-NH_2$

(c) $R-\overset{\overset{\displaystyle O}{\diagup}}{C}\diagdown_{NH_2} + HNO_2 \longrightarrow RCOOH + N_2$

8. Define and give a specific example of the following reactions:
(a) Eschweiler–Clark reaction
(b) Thorpe reaction
(c) Mannich reaction
(d) Hofmann elimination
(e) Hofmann degradation
(f) Reductive amination

9. Write the detailed mechanism of the following Hofmann degradation.

    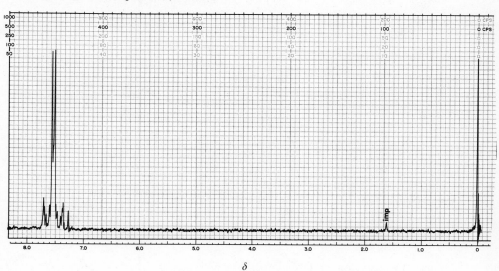

    Which of the intermediates you have drawn are actual isolable compounds, as opposed to transient species?

10. How would you carry out the following synthesis:

    $$Ph-C{\equiv}N \rightarrow Ph-\underset{\underset{OEt}{|}}{\overset{\overset{OEt}{|}}{C}}-CH_2CH_2CH_3$$

11. A neutral compound C_7H_4NCl (A) gave the nmr spectrum shown.

    NMR spectrum of compound A, Problem 11.

    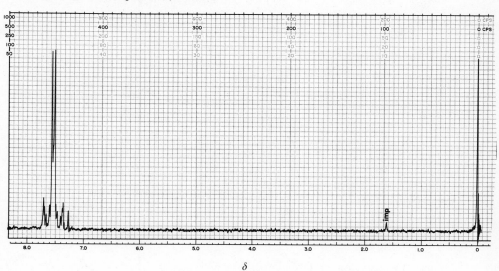

    Reaction of A with $LiAlH_4$ afforded a basic product C_7H_8NCl (B), a solution of which in cold dilute H_2SO_4 reacted immediately with sodium nitrite to give a neutral substance C_7H_7OCl (C). After the original compound (A) was refluxed with 30% aqueous KOH and the resulting solution was acidified, an acidic solid $C_7H_5O_2Cl$ (D) was obtained. Write structures for compounds A–D.

12. How could tetramethylammonium chloride be distinguished from dimethylethyl-ammonium chloride by a simple chemical test?

13. Considering the relative strengths of bases, which of the following is more basic than ethylamine?
    (a) Diethylamine   (b) Ammonia
    (c) Sodium acetate   (d) *m*-Toluidine
    (e) Potassium *t*-butoxide   (f) Sulfanilamide

14. Illustrate the following processes by means of equations; be sure to include essential reagents and conditions.
    (a) Conversion of an amide to a primary amine of one less carbon atom
    (b) Conversion of an amide to a primary amine of the same number of carbon atoms
    (c) Conversion of an amide to a primary amine of one more carbon atom

15. Which of the following reagents will react significantly with the compound given, under ordinary laboratory conditions?
    (1) Ammonia with—aniline hydrochloride
    　　　　　　　　　cyclohexylamine hydrochloride
    　　　　　　　　　acetamide
    　　　　　　　　　diethylamine
    　　　　　　　　　p-nitrophenol
    　　　　　　　　　m-chlorotoluene
    (2) *N,N*-Dimethylaniline with—aqueous bromine
    　　　　　　　　　　　　　　　ammonium chloride
    　　　　　　　　　　　　　　　benzoyl chloride
    　　　　　　　　　　　　　　　warm, aq. NaOH
    　　　　　　　　　　　　　　　ethyl bromide
    　　　　　　　　　　　　　　　nitrous acid
    　　　　　　　　　　　　　　　ethyl acetate

16. Give simple, easily observable chemical tests for distinguishing between the following pairs of compounds, and state the observation you would expect to make in each case.
    (a) *N*-Methylaniline and *o*-toluidine
    (b) *m*-Chloroaniline and *m*-chloroacetanilide
    (c) Tributylammonium chloride and tetrabutylammonium chloride
    (d) *p*-Nitrophenol and *p*-nitro-*N,N*-dimethylaniline

Optional Problems

1. Write a mechanism for the following reaction:

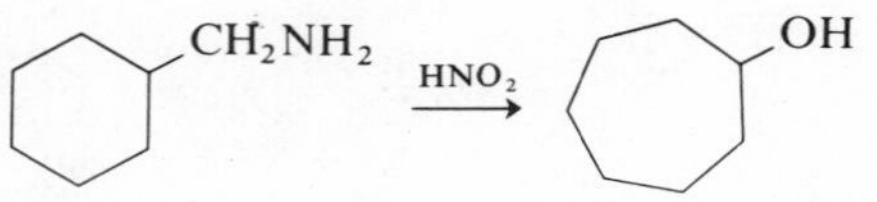

2. How would you carry out the following reaction?

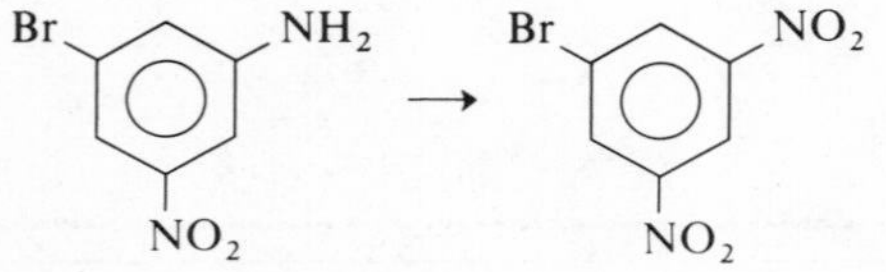

3. Suggest a mechanism for the following reaction:

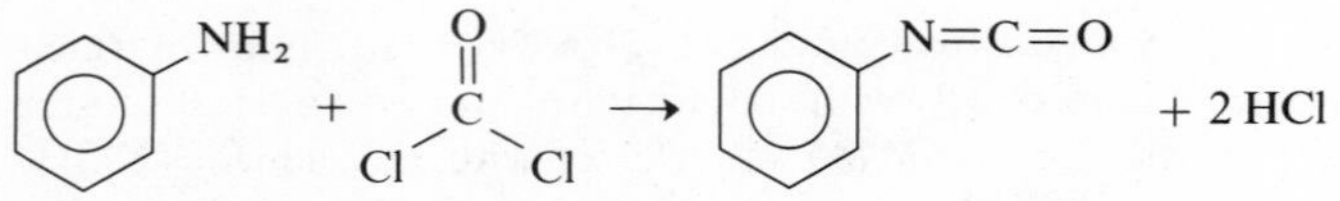

4. Complete the following:

(a) Ph—N—CH$_2$Ph + HNO$_2$ →
    　　|
    　　CH$_3$

(b) 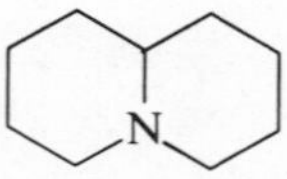 + Hg(OAc)$_2$ →

　　　　　　H
　　　　　　|
(c) CH$_3$—CH—N—CH$_3$ + H$_2$O$_2$ →
　　　　　|
　　　　　CH$_3$

(d) 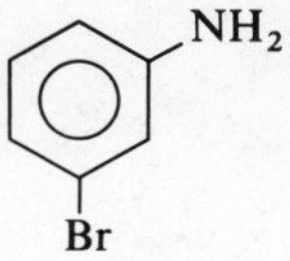 + F₃C—COOOH →

(e)  CH₃——NH₂ + HCCl₃ + OH⁻ →

5. Illustrate by means of equations the preparation of cyclopentylamine using the Gabriel phthalimide method.

CHAPTER 22

REACTIONS OF ORGANIC NITROGEN COMPOUNDS II. COMPOUNDS CONTAINING NITROGEN–NITROGEN OR NITROGEN–OXYGEN BONDS

Chapter 21 was concerned with the reactions of amines and related compounds. In this chapter we will first consider classes of compounds containing a single nitrogen atom which is bound to one or more oxygen atoms (Sections 22.1–22.3). Then compounds containing two or more nitrogens within a single functional group will be examined. These include N-nitroso compounds, hydrazine derivatives, azo compounds, diazonium salts, diazo compounds, and hydrazoic acid derivatives (Sections 22.4–22.9).

22.1 Nitro Compounds

The reactions of nitro compounds can be conveniently divided into those characteristic of the nitro group ($-NO_2$) itself, and those characteristic of enolizable nitro compounds (i.e., compounds having at least one hydrogen on the carbon α to the nitro group). First we will consider the very important aromatic nitro compounds, which, since they contain no α hydrogens, undergo mainly reactions of the nitro group itself. We will then consider a few of the very interesting (and sometimes quite complex) reactions of enolizable aliphatic nitro compounds.

Aromatic Nitro Compounds

By far the most important reaction of aromatic nitro compounds is their reduction to aromatic amines. The simple two-step sequence of direct nitration of an aromatic compound, followed by reduction, affords the simplest and most practical general synthesis of aromatic amines.

$$C_6H_6 \xrightarrow[H_2SO_4]{HNO_3} C_6H_5-NO_2 \xrightarrow{[6H]} C_6H_5-NH_2$$

The reduction of aromatic nitro compounds to amines is one of the most studied of all organic reactions, and a great number of reagents have been found to be suitable for the conversion. Among these are hydrogen in the presence of a catalyst (Ni, Pt, or Pd); iron, tin, or zinc with mineral acid; stannous chloride and hydrochloric acid; hydrazine in the presence of a Pd catalyst; sodium dithionite ($Na_2S_2O_4$); sodium and ammonium sulfides and polysulfides; chromous chloride; and ferrous hydroxide. Catalytic reduction and stannous chloride reduction are most commonly used in the laboratory. Commercially, iron is the favored reagent; scrap iron or pig iron can be used, and only a catalytic amount of acid is needed. The overall reaction is

$$4 C_6H_5-NO_2 + 9 Fe + 4 H_2O \rightarrow 4 C_6H_5-NH_2 + 3 Fe_3O_4$$

The reduction of the nitro group to the amino group involves reduction of a nitrogen atom from its highest oxidation state to its lowest oxidation state. When a nitro compound is reduced in the absence of strong acid, reduction products of intermediate oxidation level can sometimes be isolated; more often, these intermediates undergo further condensations to give bimolecular reaction products. The general reduction scheme, due to F. Haber (1898), is shown for nitrobenzene. With the exception of the highly reactive *nitrosobenzene*, all of the compounds in this scheme can be isolated from the reaction mixtures, using specific experimental conditions for each desired product. (Nitrosobenzene can be prepared by oxidation of N-phenylhydroxylamine.)

Haber reduction scheme

$$C_6H_5-NO_2 \xrightarrow{[H]} C_6H_5-NO \xrightarrow{C_6H_5NH_2} C_6H_5-N=N-C_6H_5 \xrightarrow{[H]}$$

Nitrosobenzene   Azobenzene

$$C_6H_5-NH-NH-C_6H_5$$
Hydrazobenzene

$$C_6H_5-NH_2 \xleftarrow{[H]} C_6H_5-NHOH \xrightarrow{C_6H_5NO} C_6H_5-N=\overset{+}{N}-C_6H_5 \quad C_6H_5-NH_2$$
$$\underset{O^-}{|}$$

Aniline N-Phenylhydroxylamine   Azoxybenzene   Aniline

Selective Reductions of Nitrobenzene. N-Phenylhydroxylamine is conveniently prepared by reducing nitrobenzene with zinc dust in the presence of aqueous ammonium chloride; the zinc is converted to zinc oxide in this reaction.

$$C_6H_5-NO_2 \xrightarrow[H_2O, NH_4Cl]{Zn} C_6H_5-NHOH$$

In alkaline solution, reduction of nitrobenzene with zinc yields hydrazobenzene as the major product.

$$2\,C_6H_5-NO_2 \xrightarrow[H_2O, C_2H_5OH]{Zn, NaOH} C_6H_5-NH-NH-C_6H_5$$

Azoxybenzene is readily prepared by heating nitrobenzene with sodium arsenite.

$$2\,C_6H_5-NO_2 \xrightarrow[NaOH, H_2O]{As_2O_3} C_6H_5-N=\overset{+}{N}-C_6H_5$$
$$\underset{O^-}{|}$$

Special Properties of Aromatic Nitro Compounds. A methyl substituent ortho or para to an aromatic nitro group will condense with reactive carbonyl compounds in the presence of a strong base. These reactions are due to the ability of the nitro group to stabilize a benzyl carbanion by resonance interaction.

(as Na salt)

Polynitro aromatic compounds form crystalline, sharp-melting, colored addition products with polynuclear aromatic hydrocarbons. These addition products are *charge-transfer complexes* (Section 7.17); they are often used to purify and characterize hydrocarbons. The following nitro compounds are those most often employed for this purpose.

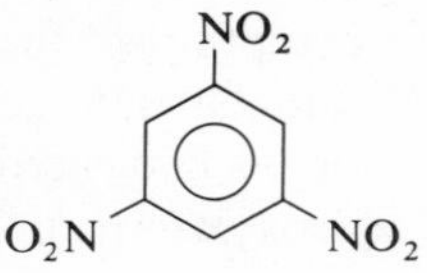

| 1,3,5-Trinitrobenzene | Picric acid (2,4,6-Trinitrophenol) | 2,4,7-Trinitrofluorenone |

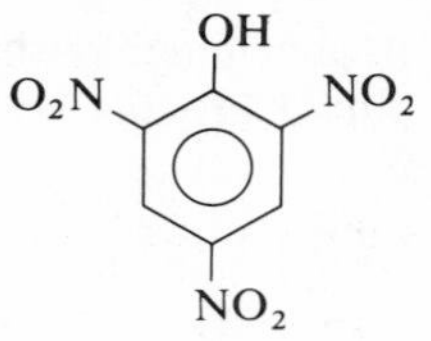

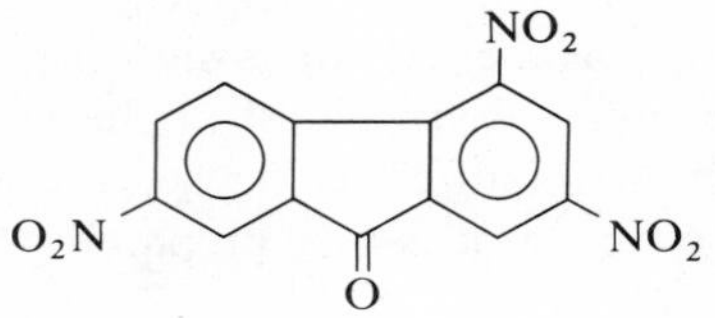

Aliphatic Nitro Compounds

Like aromatic nitro compounds, nitroalkanes are readily reduced to amines by a variety of reducing agents.

$$R-CH_2NO_2 \xrightarrow{[H]} R-CH_2NH_2$$

Nitroalkanes having at least one hydrogen on the carbon atom α to the nitro group are reasonably acidic and form anions readily. Thus, nitromethane dissolves in aqueous sodium hydroxide to give sodium methylenenitronate (Section 12.3).

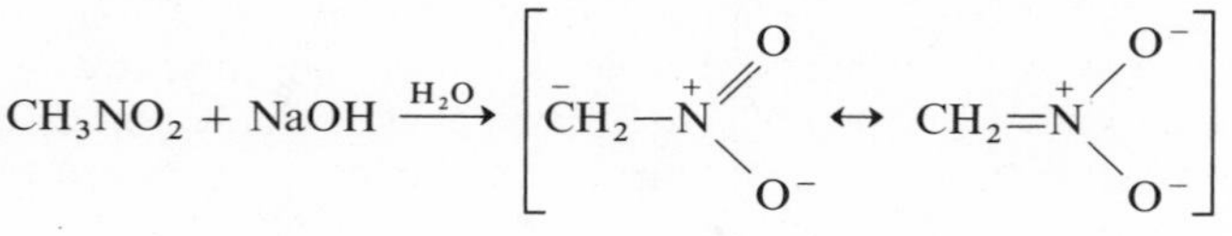

Methylenenitronate anion

Careful neutralization of a solution of a nitronate anion affords a *nitronic acid*, sometimes known as an *aci*-nitro compound. Nitronic acids, which are tautomers of nitro compounds, are generally more stable than the enols of carbonyl compounds, with which they may be compared. Thus, neutralization of the sodium salt of phenyl-nitromethane yields the crystalline benzylidenenitronic acid (mp 84°C), which only slowly tautomerizes back to the oily nitro compound.

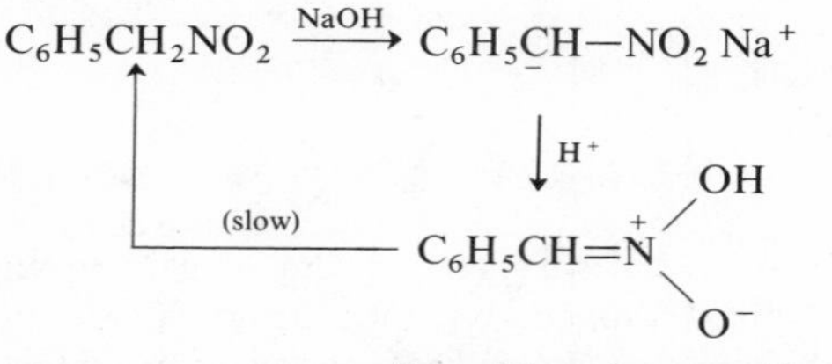

Benzylidenenitronic acid

In contrast, nitronate anions attack the carbonyl groups of aldehydes and ketones to form a new carbon–carbon bond in an aldol-type reaction. Either a β-hydroxynitro compound or an α,β-unsaturated nitro compound results, depending upon conditions and structures of the starting materials.

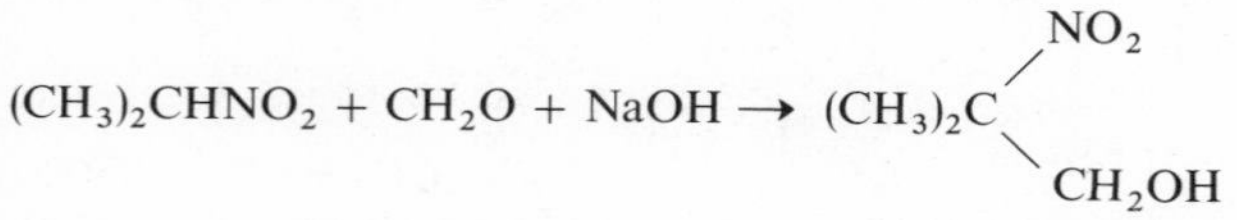

$$C_6H_5CHO + CH_3NO_2 + NaOH \rightarrow C_6H_5-CH=CH-NO_2$$

β-Nitrostyrene

The Nef Reaction. The reaction of nitronate anions with excess cold mineral acid does not give the nitronic acid, but rather a carbonyl compound and nitrous oxide. This process (known as the *Nef reaction*) is believed to proceed by way of the interesting path shown below. Note the intermediate formation of nitroxyl (NOH) as the source of N_2O.

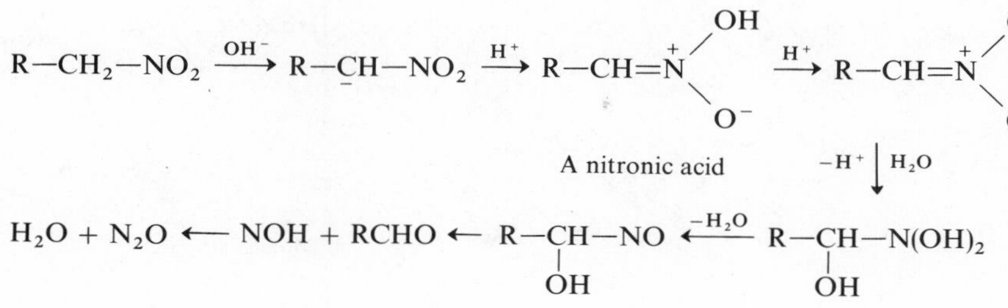

$$R-CH_2-NO_2 \xrightarrow{OH^-} R-\underset{-}{C}H-NO_2 \xrightarrow{H^+} R-CH=\overset{+}{N}\overset{OH}{\underset{O^-}{\big\langle}} \xrightarrow{H^+} R-CH=\overset{+}{N}\overset{OH}{\underset{OH}{\big\langle}}$$

A nitronic acid $\qquad \underset{-H^+}{\overset{}{\Big\downarrow}}\, H_2O$

$$H_2O + N_2O \longleftarrow NOH + RCHO \longleftarrow R-\underset{OH}{\underset{|}{C}H}-NO \xleftarrow{-H_2O} R-\underset{OH}{\underset{|}{C}H}-N(OH)_2$$

22.2 Nitroso Compounds

The most characteristic reaction of *C*-nitroso compounds is their tendency to undergo reversible dimerization; the monomers are blue or green (due to the $-NO$ group), whereas the dimers are essentially colorless. Nitroso dimers have been shown to be *N,N'*-dioxides of azo compounds. Some are cis dimers and some are trans dimers; they are resonance-stabilized structures, as shown.

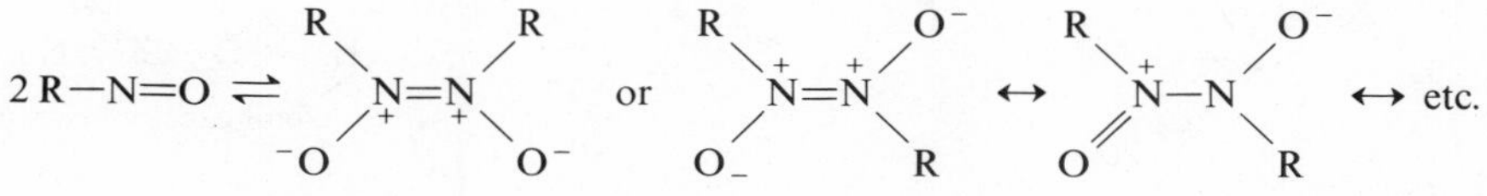

$$2\,R-N=O \rightleftharpoons \overset{R}{\underset{-O}{\big\backslash}}\underset{+}{N}=\underset{+}{N}\overset{R}{\underset{O^-}{\big/}} \quad \text{or} \quad \overset{R}{\underset{O_-}{\big\backslash}}\underset{+}{N}=\underset{+}{N}\overset{O^-}{\underset{R}{\big/}} \longleftrightarrow \overset{R}{\underset{O}{\big\backslash}}N=\underset{+}{N}\overset{O^-}{\underset{R}{\big/}} \longleftrightarrow \text{etc.}$$

cis-Nitroso dimer $\qquad$ *trans*-Nitroso dimer

Some Properties of Aromatic Nitroso Compounds. The position of equilibrium between nitroso monomers and dimers depends partially on temperature and physical state. Thus, nitroso-benzene is mainly the cis dimer in the solid state; it dissociates partially in acetic acid to give a pale green solution and dissociates to a considerable degree on melting to give an emerald green liquid.

$$2\,C_6H_5-NO \underset{68°C}{\overset{20°C}{\rightleftharpoons}} (C_6H_5NO)_2$$
$$\text{mp } 80°C$$

p-Nitrosodimethylaniline is a green solid which is entirely monomeric in the solid state. In this case, the substituent on the ring interacts electronically with the nitroso group.

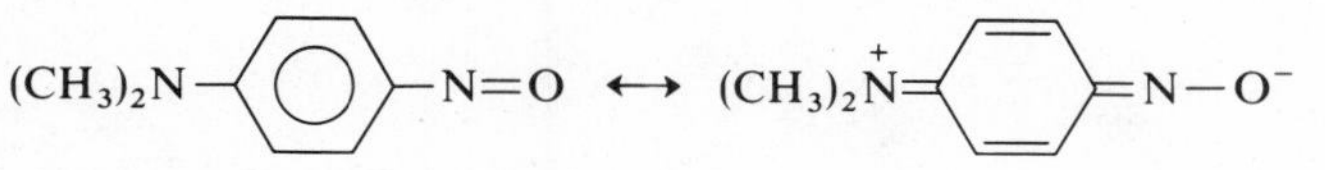

$$(CH_3)_2N-\langle\bigcirc\rangle-N=O \longleftrightarrow (CH_3)_2\overset{+}{N}=\langle\bigcirc\rangle=N-O^-$$

p-Nitrosodimethylaniline forms a bright yellow hydrochloride which is no longer a true nitroso compound, since protonation has taken place on oxygen to give a benzoquinone oxime derivative. Reaction of this salt with alkali, however, regenerates the green free base.

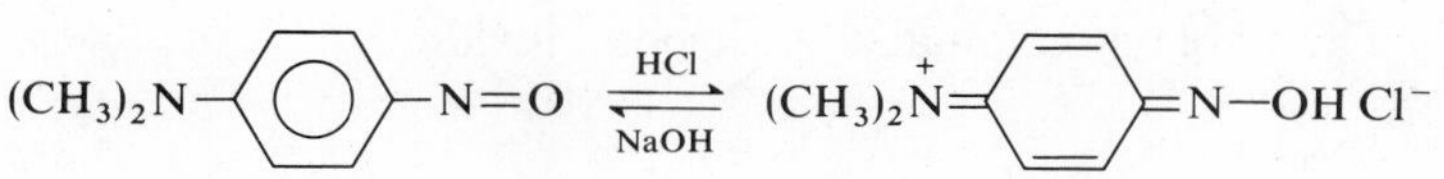

$$(CH_3)_2N-\langle\bigcirc\rangle-N=O \underset{NaOH}{\overset{HCl}{\rightleftharpoons}} (CH_3)_2\overset{+}{N}=\langle\bigcirc\rangle=N-OH\ Cl^-$$
$$\text{Green} \qquad\qquad\qquad\qquad \text{Yellow}$$

p-Nitrosophenol is in tautomeric equilibrium with *p*-benzoquinone monooxime in solution; indeed, the quinone form predominates to the extent of over 85%.

$$HO-\langle\bigcirc\rangle-NO \rightleftharpoons O=\langle\bigcirc\rangle=NOH$$

Azo compounds are formed when aromatic nitroso compounds react with primary aromatic amines in acetic acid solution. Notice that unsymmetrical azo compounds can be prepared by this reaction.

$$C_6H_5-NO + H_2N-\bigotimes-Br \xrightarrow{HOAc} \left[C_6H_5-\underset{\underset{OH}{|}}{N}-NH-\bigotimes-Br \right] \xrightarrow{-H_2O}$$

$$\bigotimes-N=N-\bigotimes-Br$$

Aliphatic nitroso compounds which bear at least one hydrogen on the carbon α to the nitroso group are isomerized rapidly and irreversibly by acid or base to oximes. This reaction is an essential step in the acid- or base-catalyzed "oximination" of active methylene compounds by alkyl nitrites.

$$C_6H_5-CO-CH_3 + n\text{-}Bu-O-NO \xrightarrow{HCl} C_6H_5-CO-CH_2-NO \xrightarrow{HCl}$$

n-Butyl nitrite

Intermediate nitroso compound: not isolable

$$C_6H_5-CO-CH=NOH$$

α-Oximinoacetophenone

EXERCISE 22.1

Predict the product formed by the reaction of diethyl malonate with sodium ethoxide and ethyl nitrite in ethanol solution. Write a mechanism for the formation of this product.

22.3   Compounds Derived from Hydroxylamine

A great number of classes of organic compounds may be derived from hydroxylamine (NH_2OH) by substitution, condensation, or both. For example, a recent monograph lists no less than 54 possible hydroxylamine derivatives of carboxylic acids, none of which is of sufficient general interest to warrant mention in this text. Our discussion will be limited to the most important reactions of oximes, alkyl and aryl hydroxylamines, and N-oxides.

Oximes

The oximes are by far the most important organic derivatives of hydroxylamine. They are readily prepared by the direct reaction of hydroxylamine with aldehydes and ketones.

Oximes are amphoteric compounds. They are very weak bases, forming salts only with concentrated mineral acids. More important, they are also weak acids; they generally dissolve in aqueous alkali and are reprecipitated by carbon dioxide.

$$\underset{Cl^-}{\overset{OH}{\underset{H}{R_2C=\overset{+}{N}}}} \xleftarrow[H_2O]{conc.\ HCl} R_2C=NOH \xrightarrow[CO_2,\ H_2O]{NaOH} R_2C=N-O^-\ Na^+$$

The reduction of an oxime to a primary amine is a generally useful reaction which may be carried out under a variety of reducing conditions. Catalytic reduction using hydrogen and Raney nickel, or chemical reduction using zinc and acetic acid or lithium aluminum hydride, is satisfactory. Note the use of an oxime intermediate in the conversion of a ketone to an amine.

Oxidation of oximes yields nitro compounds by way of nitronic acid intermediates; peroxytrifluoroacetic acid is an excellent reagent for this conversion.

A nitronic acid

Oximes are hydrolyzed to carbonyl compounds and hydroxylamine salts when heated with aqueous mineral acids. In some cases, hydrolysis is difficult because of reversibility of oxime formation; addition of formaldehyde greatly facilitates hydrolysis by combining with the liberated hydroxylamine to give a particularly stable oxime.

The oximes of aldehydes (aldoximes) are easily dehydrated to nitriles by a variety of reagents, such as acetic anhydride or thionyl chloride. Oxime esters are undoubtedly intermediates in this reaction, which affords a convenient method for converting an aldehyde to a nitrile by an elimination reaction.

The oximes of ketones (ketoximes) undergo an overall rearrangement to amides when heated with certain inorganic reagents, followed by treatment with water. This reaction is known as the *Beckmann rearrangement*, and it has been the subject of an enormous amount of study. The reagents most often used to carry out the Beckmann rearrangement are sulfuric acid, polyphosphoric acid, PCl_5, and $SOCl_2$. A simple but important example of this reaction is the rearrangement of cyclohexanone oxime to caprolactam, an intermediate in the manufacture of a synthetic fiber, nylon 6 (Section 25.2).

The mechanism of the Beckmann rearrangement involves: (a) formation of an ester of the oxime, (b) migration of the alkyl or aryl group which is trans (or anti) to the oxime ester function, with loss of an anion from nitrogen, (c) recombination of the resulting anion and carbonium ion to give an enol-type derivative of an amide, and (d) hydrolysis of this enol derivative to an amide on treatment with water on work-up. As expected from this mechanism, an alkyl group migrates with retention of configuration if the migrating carbon is asymmetric.

Acetophenone oxime (*anti* isomer) → Inorganic oxime ester → $CH_3-\overset{+}{C}=N-C_6H_5$ + $OPCl_3$ + Cl^-

$$CH_3-\overset{\displaystyle O}{\overset{\|}{C}}-NH-C_6H_5 \xleftarrow[(d)]{H_2O} CH_3-\underset{\displaystyle Cl}{C}=N-C_6H_5$$

Acetanilide

EXERCISE 22.2

Write a mechanism for the rearrangement of acetophenone oxime to acetanilide using sulfuric acid as the catalyst.

The oximes of aromatic ketones can often be obtained in both syn and anti forms; each isomer gives a different amide on rearrangement. Separate isomers of aliphatic ketoximes have rarely been isolated. The stereospecificity of the Beckmann rearrangement has been used to determine the configuration of oximes of both types. Phosphorus pentachloride is a particularly good reagent for this purpose; sulfuric acid is much less useful, since it can cause equilibration of syn and anti oxime isomers before rearrangement, thus giving a mixture of amides as the final product.

Anti isomer (R_1 = larger group) → $R_2-CO-NH-R_1$

Syn isomer (R_1 = larger group) → $R_1-CO-NH-R_2$

The Beckmann Fragmentation. When one of the substituents R of an oxime corresponds to a relatively stable carbonium ion R^+, fragmentation can take place in a process sometimes known as a *Beckmann fragmentation.* The most useful case of this reaction is the cleavage of an α-oximino ketone which takes place in aqueous alkali on stirring with benzenesulfonyl chloride. The products are a nitrile and an acid (or a cyano acid) and the intermediate is the benzenesulfonate ester of the oxime.

$$C_6H_5-CO-\underset{\underset{\displaystyle OH}{N}}{\overset{\|}{C}}-C_6H_5 \xrightarrow[C_6H_5SO_2Cl]{NaOH, H_2O} C_6H_5-\overset{\displaystyle O}{C}-\underset{\underset{\displaystyle O-SO_2C_6H_5}{N}}{C}-C_6H_5 \longrightarrow$$

$$C_6H_5COOH + C_6H_5CN$$

(as Na salt)

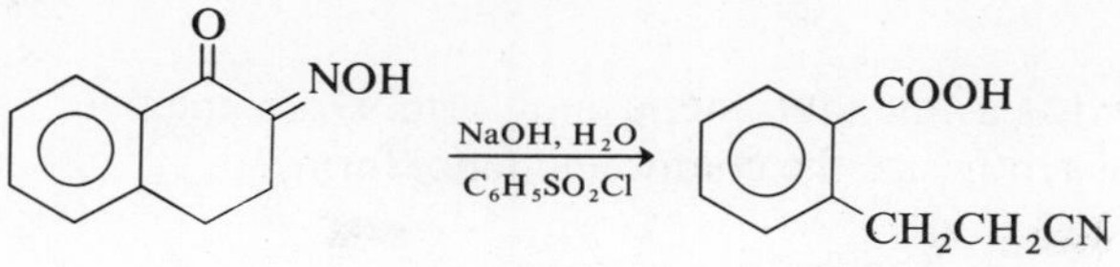

(as Na salt)

α-Oximino ketones react with chloramine (NH_2Cl) in alkaline solution to give α-diazo ketones; the unstable chloramine is generated in the reaction mixture from ammonia and sodium hypochlorite. This unusual transformation, known as the *Forster reaction*, affords a simple synthesis of α-diazo ketones.

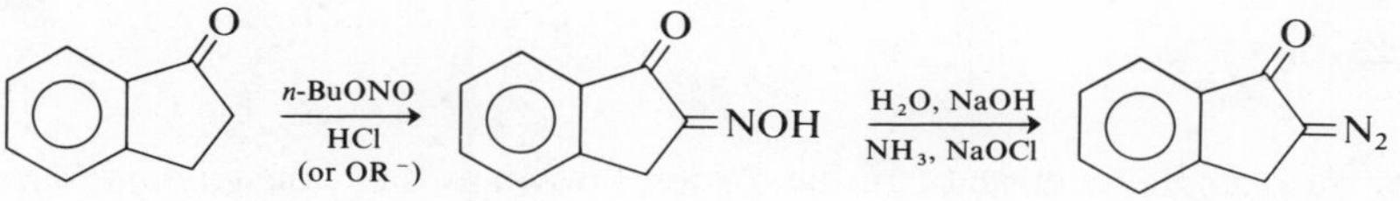

Hydroxylamines

Both *O*-substituted hydroxylamines ($R—ONH_2$) and *N*-substituted hydroxylamines ($RNHOH$ and R_2NOH) are known; the *N*-substituted are the more important group. This brief discussion will be limited to a few important reactions of *N*-phenylhydroxylamine, the most easily prepared and most thoroughly studied member of the group.

N-Phenylhydroxylamine is oxidized rapidly to nitrosobenzene by cold aqueous ferric chloride or chromic acid. This reaction affords the most practical synthesis of nitrosobenzene.

$$C_6H_5—NHOH \xrightarrow[H_2O,\ 5°C]{CrO_3} C_6H_5—NO$$

(as dimer)

The condensation of *N*-phenylhydroxylamine with an aldehyde gives a *nitrone*. This type of reaction illustrates a very general nitrone synthesis.

$$C_6H_5CHO + C_6H_5NHOH \rightarrow \left[\begin{array}{c} C_6H_5—CH—N—C_6H_5 \\ \quad\ \ | \quad\ | \\ \quad\ \ OH\ \ OH \end{array} \right] \rightarrow C_6H_5—CH{=}\overset{+}{N}—C_6H_5$$
$$\underset{O^-}{|}$$

C,N-Diphenylnitrone

In contrast to *N*-alkylhydroxylamines, which are acid-stable, *N*-phenylhydroxylamine undergoes an unusual rearrangement in aqueous sulfuric acid to give *p*-aminophenol; the rearrangement has been shown to be intermolecular by [18]O labeling experiments.

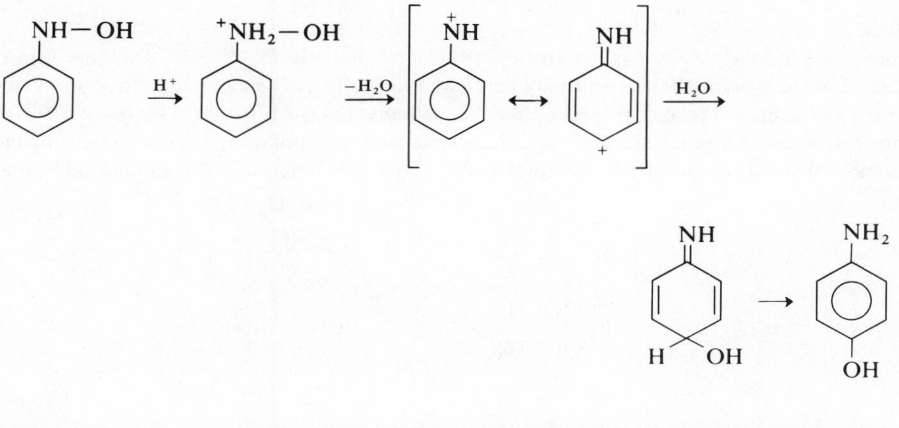

The intermediate cation can pick up a base other than water under appropriate circumstances. For example, the reaction of *N*-phenylhydroxylamine with HF leads to *p*-fluoroaniline as a major product.

EXERCISE 22.3

Nitrosomethane actually exists as the tautomeric enol form. Draw the two structures. How would you synthesize the compound (enol form)?

N-Oxides

Tertiary amine oxides (Section 21.1) are in reality the dipolar ions ($R_3\overset{+}{N}$—O^-) corresponding to *N,N,N*-trialkylhydroxylamines. They are generally viewed as tertiary amine derivatives, since they are easily formed from tertiary amines by mild oxidation and can be reduced back to tertiary amines by a number of reagents, such as PCl_3 or hydrogen and palladium.

$$R_3N \underset{PCl_3}{\overset{H_2O_2}{\rightleftharpoons}} R_3\underset{+}{N}\text{—}\underset{-}{O}$$

The most important single reaction of amine oxides, known as the *Cope elimination*, is closely related to the Tschugaev reaction (Section 20.16). It can serve as an excellent *alkene* synthesis when one of the substituents on the nitrogen atom bears a β hydrogen which is within bonding distance of the negative oxygen.

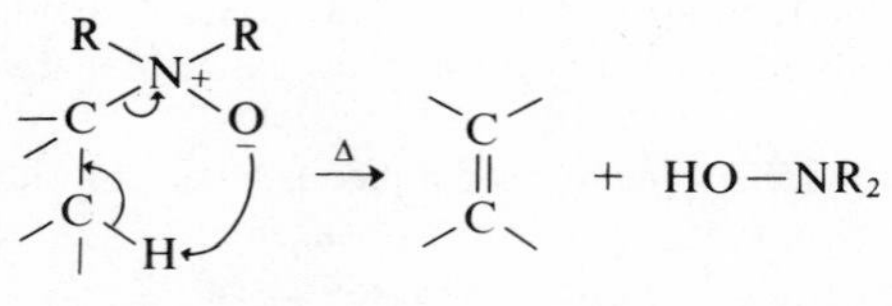

Amine oxide   Olefin   Dialkylhydroxylamine
(syn transition state
necessary)

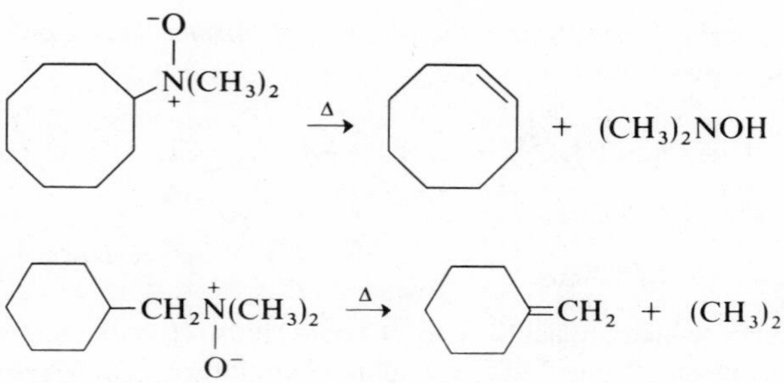

Nitrones. 1,3-Dipolar Additions. Nitrones ($R_2C{=}\overset{\overset{O^-}{|}}{\underset{+}{N}}{-}R \leftrightarrow R_2\overset{+}{C}{-}\overset{\overset{O^-}{|}}{N}{-}R$) are unsaturated analogs of tertiary amine oxides and may be viewed formally as *N*-oxides of imines or *N*-alkyl derivatives of oximes. These compounds, like diazoalkanes (page 617) and azides (page 619), can be thought of as 1,3-dipolar species; the addition of such compounds to unsaturated linkages represents a general reaction for the synthesis of heterocyclic compounds (1,3-dipolar additions).

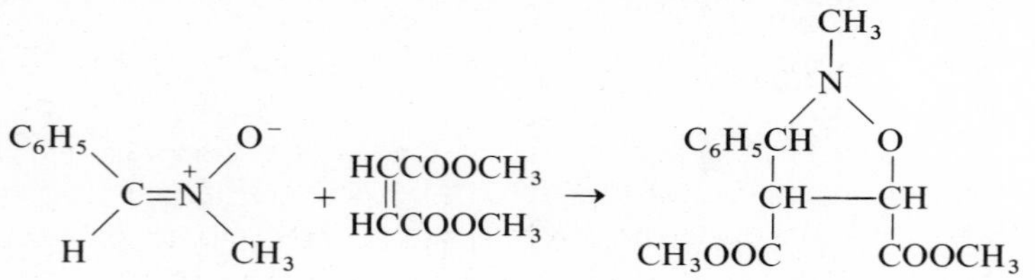

A number of functional groups other than nitrones can also undergo 1,3-dipolar addition reactions. These other functional groups are relatively exotic, and no other 1,3-dipolar additions will be encountered in this text.

22.4   *N*-Nitroso Compounds

The most important reaction of the *N*-nitroso derivatives of secondary amines is reduction of the nitroso group to an amino group. Zinc and acetic acid, or lithium aluminum hydride are generally useful reagents in this reaction, which yields substituted hydrazines.

$$(CH_3)_2N—NO \xrightarrow{\text{Zn, HOAc}} (CH_3)_2N—NH_2$$

Dimethylnitrosamine   *N*,*N*-Dimethylhydrazine

 N-Alkyl-*N*-nitrosoamides (Section 21.5) are cleaved by alkali to give diazoalkanes. The very useful organic reagent diazomethane (CH_2N_2) is most conveniently prepared by this reaction, a mechanism for which is given below. Among the most used starting materials for the synthesis of diazomethane are *N*-methyl-*N*-nitrosourea and *N*-methyl-*N*-nitroso-*p*-toluenesulfonamide (Diazald).

An alkyl
diazotate

$$CH_2N_2 \longleftarrow \overline{CH_2}—N≡N—\overline{O}H$$

$$H_3C—\langle O \rangle—SO_2—N—CH_3 \xrightarrow[\text{H}_2\text{O}]{\text{NaOH}} CH_2N_2 + H_3C—\langle O \rangle—SO_3^-Na^+$$

EXERCISE 22.4

Write a mechanism for the reaction of *N*-methyl-*N*-nitroso-*p*-toluenesulfonamide with base given above.

22.5   Derivatives of Hydrazine

We can divide hydrazine derivatives into (a) C—N derivatives, substituted hydrazines of all types; and (b) C=N derivatives, hydrazones, which are imino compounds derived from hydrazine or substituted hydrazines.

Substituted Hydrazines

Substituted hydrazines having a free amino group condense with aldehydes and ketones to give substituted hydrazones, some of which are used commonly as solid crystalline derivatives of aldehydes and ketones. 2,4-Dinitrophenylhydrazine is the most useful and versatile of these hydrazines, since it gives colored, high-melting, and stable hydrazones (Section 19.7). Semicarbazide (Section 19.7) has also seen considerable use in qualitative organic analysis. Phenylhydrazine played a very important role in the development of carbohydrate chemistry (Section 27.4).

 Hydrazines are generally quite easily oxidized by a variety of oxidizing agents, such as cupric ion, ferric ion, mercuric oxide, periodate ion, ferricyanide ion, sodium hypohalites, and even molecular oxygen. Hydrazine itself is readily oxidized by the same reagents to diimide, which immediately disproportionates to hydrazine and nitrogen.

$$2\,H_2N—NH_2 \xrightarrow{[O]} [2\,HN=NH] \rightarrow H_2N—NH_2 + N_2$$

Diimide

The sodium salt of *p*-toluenesulfonylhydrazine (tosylhydrazine) decomposes on heating to yield sodium *p*-toluenesulfinate and diimide; the diimide which is produced can be intercepted by an olefin as it is generated (Section 15.2). In this way, tosylhydrazine can function indirectly as an olefin-reducing reagent.

$$H_3C-\langle\bigcirc\rangle-SO_2-NH-NH_2 + NaOH \xrightarrow{\Delta} H_3C-\langle\bigcirc\rangle-SO_2^-Na^+ + [HN=NH]$$

$$\downarrow CH_2=CH-CH_2OH$$

$$N_2 + CH_3-CH_2-CH_2OH$$
(99 % yield)

The oxidation of *N,N'*-disubstituted hydrazines yields the stable, disubstituted diimides, better known as *azo compounds*. Azo compounds of many varieties are best prepared in this way.

$$CH_3-NH-NH-CH_3 \xrightarrow{HOCl} CH_3-N=N-CH_3$$
   Hydrazomethane   Azomethane

$$EtO_2C-NH-NH-CO_2Et \xrightarrow{HNO_3} EtO_2C-N=N-CO_2Et$$
N,N'-Dicarbethoxyhydrazine   Ethyl azodicarboxylate

Monoacyl hydrazines (hydrazides of acids) react smoothly with nitrous acid in aqueous acid solution to give acyl azides. This reaction is quite analogous to diazotization of an aromatic amine.

$$C_6H_5-CO-NHNH_2 \xrightarrow[NaNO_2]{HCl, H_2O} C_6H_5-CO-N_3$$
   Benzhydrazide   Benzoyl azide

N-N'-Diaryl hydrazines (hydrazobenzene and its analogs) readily undergo a remarkable isomerization in aqueous acid solution. This reaction, which has been the object of much practical and theoretical study, is known as the *benzidine rearrangement*. The simplest and the most important example is the rearrangement of hydrazobenzene to benzidine (4,4'-diaminobiphenyl), an important intermediate in the manufacture of azo dyes. The rearrangement has been proven to be intramolecular, proceeding through a sandwich-type transition state in which the two benzene rings lie over each other; both the monocation and the dication of hydrazobenzene can undergo rearrangement.

$$C_6H_5-NH-NH-C_6H_5 \xrightarrow{H^+}$$
   Hydrazobenzene

Benzidine

Hydrazones

Hydrazones are the monoimines of the hydrazine series and have the general structure $>C=N-NR_2$. Hydrolysis with aqueous acid breaks down hydrazones into the hydrazines and carbonyl compounds from which they are derived. The ease of such hydrolysis varies considerably with the structure of the molecule, particularly with the basicity of the hydrazine portion.

Unsubstituted hydrazones react with strong bases to give nitrogen and hydrocarbons. This reaction, known as the *Wolff–Kishner reduction*, was discussed in Section 19.12. Unsubstituted hydrazones are generally not stable to storage and may even be difficult to isolate, owing to the ease with which they disproportionate into hydrazine and an azine.

$$2\,R_2C{=}N{-}NH_2 \rightleftharpoons R_2C{=}N{-}N{=}CR_2 + H_2NNH_2$$

Mild oxidation of unsubstituted hydrazones by HgO or MnO_2 in an inert solvent yields diazo compounds.

Fluorenone hydrazone   9-Diazofluorene

Fischer Indole Synthesis. Phenylhydrazones react with strong acids in the absence of water to give *indoles*. This reaction, known as the *Fischer indole synthesis*, will be discussed further in Section 28.5.

Acetophenone   2-Phenylindole
phenylhydrazone

22.6   Azo Compounds

Azo compounds ($R{-}N{=}N{-}R$) have no appreciable basic properties. The aromatic azo compounds (R = aryl) are highly colored, stable compounds, which have been much used as cheap dyestuffs for over a century. (See Section 22.7 for further details.) Bright orange azobenzene is typical of the aromatic azo compounds. Azobenzene is very stable thermally and shows no tendency to lose nitrogen on heating. It is rather stable to oxidation, but peracids oxidize it to azoxybenzene. It is reduced to hydrazobenzene by a number of mild reducing agents (e.g., zinc and alkali).

Reduction with hydrogen and platinum results in N—N bond cleavage with the formation of aniline. Ordinary azobenzene has the trans configuration; ultraviolet irradiation converts it to the higher energy *cis*-azobenzene. *cis*-Azobenzene may be isolated in crystalline form, but it readily isomerizes to the common trans isomer.

Aliphatic azo compounds decompose on heating, with the formation of nitrogen and two radicals. In solution, such radicals are generated in close proximity in a "solvent cage" and have a great tendency to give dimers as major products. The compound shown below, known as azoisobutyronitrile (AIBN), can be stored satisfactorily in solid form, but decomposes slowly in solution to give radicals. It has found considerable use as an initiator for radical chain reactions.

$$
\underset{\text{Azoisobutyronitrile}}{\overset{\text{CN}}{\underset{|}{(CH_3)_2C}}-N=N-\overset{\text{CN}}{\underset{|}{C(CH_3)_2}}} \rightarrow N_2 + 2\,\overset{\text{CN}}{\underset{|}{(CH_3)_2C\cdot}}
$$

The AIBN is obtained by the following synthesis:

$$
2(CH_3)_2CO + NH_2NH_2 + 2\,HCN \rightarrow \underset{\overset{|}{C\equiv N}}{(CH_3)_2C}-NH-NH-\underset{\overset{|}{C\equiv N}}{C(CH_3)_2}
$$

$$\downarrow \text{HgO}$$

AIBN

Azo compounds having electron-withdrawing substituents act as dienophiles in the Diels–Alder reaction. Ethyl azodicarboxylate is the best known compound of this type.

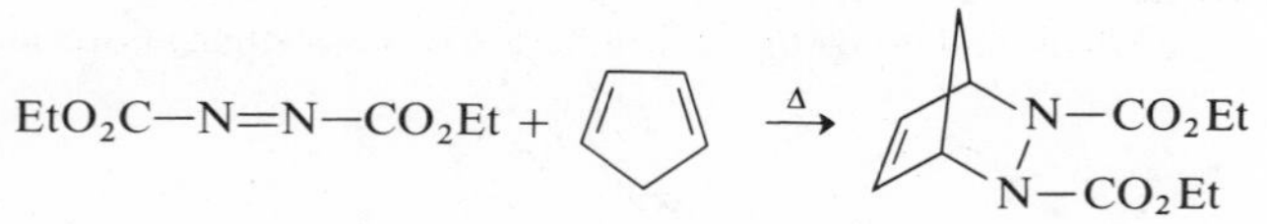

$$
EtO_2C-N=N-CO_2Et + \text{(cyclopentadiene)} \xrightarrow{\Delta} \text{(bicyclic product)}\, \overset{N-CO_2Et}{\underset{N-CO_2Et}{}}
$$

22.7   Aromatic Diazonium Salts

Aromatic diazonium salts ($Ar-N_2^+X^-$) are highly reactive compounds which serve as intermediates in the synthesis of a wide variety of aromatic structural types. Diazonium salts are prepared by treating cold solutions of aromatic amines in aqueous acid with sodium nitrite; the solutions are generally used immediately in the next reaction without isolation of the diazonium salts, most of which are dangerously explosive in the solid state. The reactions of diazonium salts will be divided into those in which nitrogen is lost during the reaction and those in which the two nitrogen atoms of the diazonium group are retained. Diazotizations of aromatic amines are usually carried out in dilute HCl or H_2SO_4, but we shall ignore the anions of diazonium salts in our discussion except where they play a special role in the reaction. Amine precursors will, on the other hand, be indicated, to emphasize the overall structural change from amine to product.

Reactions in Which the Diazonium Group Is Lost

Many useful reactions are known in which a diazonium cation $Ar-N_2^+$ is converted to a product $Ar-G$ with the loss of nitrogen.

Replacement by H. The reaction of a diazonium cation with certain reducing agents, particularly hypophosphorous acid (H_3PO_2), results in the replacement of the diazonium group by hydrogen. Aryl radicals ($Ar\cdot$) are believed to be intermediates. As in the case shown below, this reaction is useful in the preparation of compounds which cannot be made by direct aromatic substitution.

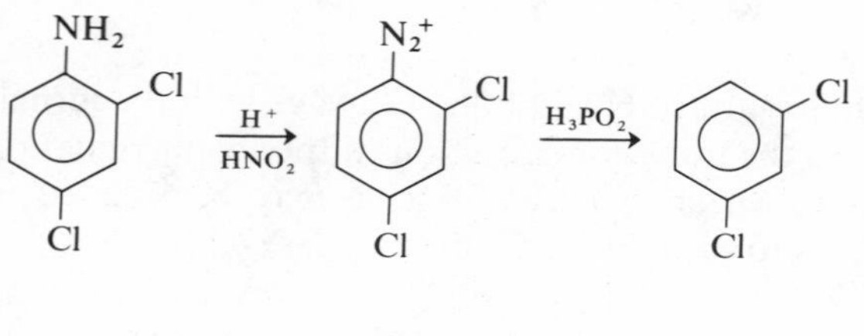

Replacement by OH. Heating an aqueous acid solution of a diazonium cation causes the liberation of nitrogen and the formation of a phenol. Aryl cations (Ar^+) are intermediates in this process. Note the use of this reaction in the example below for the conversion of the readily available *m*-nitroaniline into the otherwise difficult to obtain *m*-nitrophenol.

Replacement by I. Solutions of diazonium cations react readily with aqueous sodium iodide to give aryl iodides. This reaction is the most useful method of preparing aryl iodides, including iodobenzene.

$$C_6H_5-NH_2 \rightarrow C_6H_5-N_2^+ \xrightarrow{NaI} C_6H_5-I$$

Replacement by F. Aqueous HBF_4 (or HPF_6) precipitates diazonium cations as the relatively insoluble diazonium salts $(Ar-N_2^+ BF_4^-$ or $Ar-N_2^+ PF_6^-)$. Unlike most diazonium salts, these can be dried and handled safely in the solid state; on gentle heating in the absence of solvent they decompose to give aryl fluorides. This decomposition (known as the *Schiemann reaction*) is the most general method known for the synthesis of aromatic fluoro compounds.

$$C_6H_5-NH_2 \rightarrow C_6H_5-N_2^+ \xrightarrow{HBF_4} C_6H_5-N_2^+ BF_4^- \xrightarrow[\text{state}]{\text{solid}} C_6H_5-F + BF_3 + N_2$$

Replacement by Cl, Br, or CN. The Sandmeyer Reaction. The diazonium group can be replaced by chloride, bromide, or cyanide. These replacements proceed only in the presence of the corresponding cuprous salts as catalysts, and it is probable that the species $CuCl_2^-$, $CuBr_2^-$, and $Cu(CN)_2^-$ are the actual reagents.

Replacement by Aryl. The Gomberg–Bachmann Reaction. The decomposition of a diazonium salt in the presence of aqueous sodium acetate with a liquid aromatic (e.g., benzene) as a second phase serves as a method of replacing the diazonium group by an aryl substituent. The reaction mechanism is rather complex and is believed to involve a radical chain process.

Generation of Benzyne Intermediates. The dipolar ion, *o*-diazoniobenzoate ("*o*-benzenediazonium carboxylate") is a crystalline solid which can be prepared by nonaqueous diazotization of anthranilic acid. Although it is extremely explosive when dry, it decomposes smoothly in ethylene dichloride solution with the generation of the reactive intermediate benzyne (Section 17.9). The benzyne can be trapped by reagents such as iodine or cyclopentadiene; in the absence of a trapping agent the unusual aromatic hydrocarbon *biphenylene* is formed in fair yield.

Replacement by N_3. Diazonium salts react readily with sodium azide (NaN_3) to give aryl azides. This reaction has been shown by isotopic labeling to proceed by way of very unstable intermediates, pentazoles and diazoazides, having the remarkable structural feature of five nitrogens linked together.

Unstable pentazole
intermediate

$C_6H_5-N_3 + N_2$
Phenyl azide

Reactions Proceeding Without Loss of Nitrogen

The most important reactions of this type are (a) reduction to hydrazines and (b) coupling to electron-rich aromatic rings such as phenols and aromatic amines to give azo compounds.

Reduction to Hydrazines. The diazonium group is reduced to a hydrazine function by either stannous chloride or sodium bisulfite. The bisulfite reduction actually yields an *N*-sulfonic acid, which is easily hydrolyzed to the hydrazine by aqueous acid. The useful reagent *phenylhydrazine* is thus easily prepared starting from aniline.

$$C_6H_5-NH_2$$
$$\downarrow$$

$$C_6H_5-NH-NH_2 \xleftarrow[\text{HCl}]{\text{SnCl}_2} C_6H_5-N_2^+ \xrightarrow{2\,\text{NaHSO}_3} C_6H_5-NH-NH-SO_3H$$
(as a salt)
$$\Big\downarrow \text{H}^+,\text{H}_2\text{O}$$

$$C_6H_5-NH-NH_2$$
(as a salt)

Diazonium Coupling Reaction. Diazonium salts attack aromatic amines and phenoxides, preferably at the para position, to give azo compounds. Mechanistically, the reaction is simply the attack of a weak electrophile ($R-N_2^+$) on a highly electron-rich aromatic species ($Ar-NR_2$ or $Ar-O^-$). This reaction, which has been known for over a century, is known as "coupling," and thousands of azo compounds have been made by this method for use as dyestuffs. The simplest examples of the coupling reaction are shown.

Phenolic coupling

$$C_6H_5-N_2^+ \;+\; \langle\bigcirc\rangle-O^- \;\longrightarrow\; \langle\bigcirc\rangle-N{=}N-\langle\bigcirc\rangle-OH$$

p-Hydroxyazobenzene

Amine coupling

$$C_6H_5-N_2^+ \;+\; \langle\bigcirc\rangle-N(CH_3)_2 \xrightarrow{\text{NaOAc}} \langle\bigcirc\rangle-N{=}N-\langle\bigcirc\rangle-N(CH_3)_2$$

p-Dimethylaminoazobenzene
(Butter Yellow)

The coupling of benzenediazonium ion with aniline affords a crystalline yellow compound, diazoaminobenzene, by coupling at the nitrogen atom of the amine. When diazoaminobenzene is warmed with aniline and aniline hydrochloride for some time, it appears to rearrange to the stable *p*-aminoazobenzene. In reality, this "rearrangement" involves dissociation of the unstable but kinetically favored *N*-coupling product (diazoaminobenzene) to form aniline and $C_6H_5N_2^+Cl^-$, and slow recombination of the latter to the stable, thermodynamically favored *C*-coupling product (*p*-aminoazobenzene).

$$C_6H_5N_2^+ + C_6H_5-NH_2 \xrightarrow[\text{H}_2\text{O}]{\text{NaOAc}} C_6H_5-N{=}N-NH-C_6H_5$$

Diazoaminobenzene

$$\Delta \Big\updownarrow C_6H_5NH_2, C_6H_5NH_3^+Cl^-$$

$$C_6H_5N_2^+Cl^- + C_6H_5NH_2$$

$$\downarrow$$

$$\langle\bigcirc\rangle-N{=}N-\langle\bigcirc\rangle-NH_2$$

p-Aminoazobenzene

EXERCISE 22.5

Draw a reaction coordinate diagram showing the diazoaminobenzene and
p-aminoazobenzene syntheses discussed above.

AZO DYES. *Most commercially used azo dyes have relatively complex structures. For one
thing, at least one sulfonic acid group is generally present to impart water solubility.
Furthermore, simple azobenzene derivatives are all yellow or orange-yellow. Deeper
shades of color, as well as better fastness to light and washing, result from the use of
more highly conjugated azo compounds. The practical syntheses of a host of naphthol-,
naphthylamine-, and aminonaphtholsulfonic acids have been worked out over the past
century; these compounds (which often have quaint industrial names) are the working
tools of the azo dyestuff industry, together with benzidine and its derivatives. A few of
these dye intermediates are shown below, together with a few structures of more complex
azo dyes.*

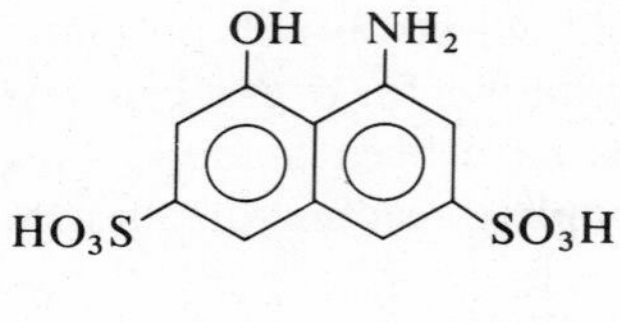

H-acid 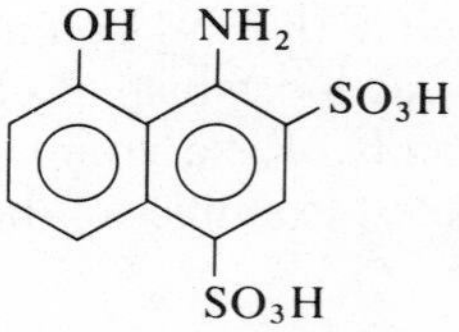   Chicago acid 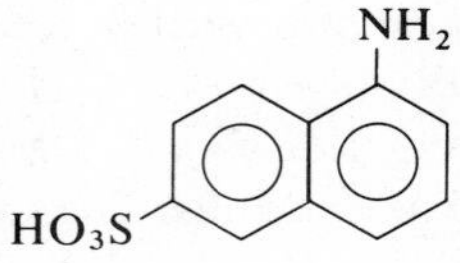   Cleve's acid

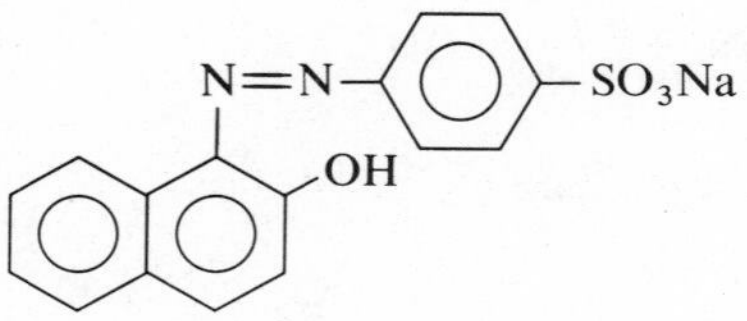

Orange II
(introduced in 1876)

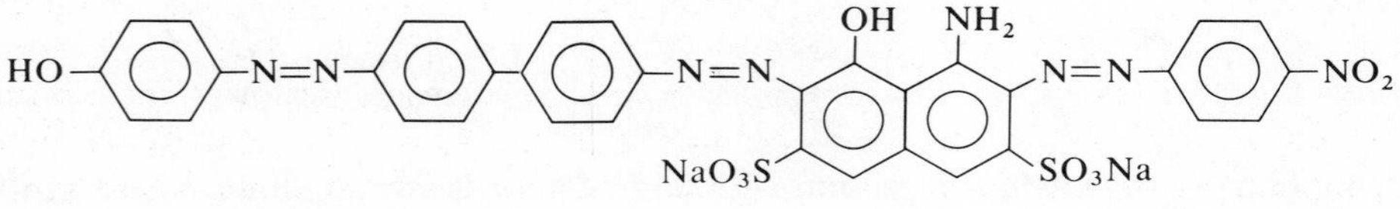

Diamine Green B
(introduced in 1891)

A true dye is adsorbed by the fiber being dyed, while a simple pigment is not. Polar
substituents such as $-SO_3Na$ and $-OH$ play an essential role in holding the dye molecule onto the surface of a polar fiber (such as wool, cotton, nylon) by hydrogen bonding.

Substituents known as *auxochromes* can deepen the color of an azo compound by
increasing conjugation. The most common auxochromes are the groups $-NR_2$, $-NHR$,
$-NH_2$, $-OH$, halogen, and $-OR$, all of which have an unshared electron pair which can
participate in resonance interaction with the azo system.

For example, Butter Yellow can be partially represented by a quinonoid contributor.

One might guess that in acid Butter Yellow would give a yellow solution similar to that of
azobenzene, because of protonation of the auxochrome group. Actually, Butter Yellow
in acid gives a bright red solution due to protonation of the azo group and formation of

the completely quinonoid salt, as shown.

EXERCISE 22.6

Outline a synthesis of Orange II from β-naphthol and sulfanilic acid. How would you synthesize β-naphthol from naphthalene?

EXERCISE 22.7

Many common pH indicators are azo dyes, for example Congo Red, which is red in basic or neutral solution, and blue in acid solution. The neutral (red) form of the dye is shown.

Congo Red

Suggest a structure for the blue form of the dye, assuming that it is a dication.

22.8   Diazoalkanes

Diazoalkanes may be considered as alkanediazonium ylides, as is apparent by writing a dipolar resonance contributor as follows: $R_2C{=}N_2 \leftrightarrow R_2C{=}\!\!-N_2^+$. In general, substituents which stabilize carbanions will stabilize the diazoalkane structure. Consequently, the unstabilized parent compound diazomethane (CH_2N_2) is an explosive (and very poisonous) yellow gas which can be handled safely only in dilute solution. In contrast, the stabilized α-diazoketones ($R{-}CO{-}CN_2{-}R$) are often stable crystalline solids melting well over 100°C. In the following brief discussion we will consider first a few reactions of diazomethane, the most important member of the series as well as a typical unstabilized diazoalkane. We will then consider a few reactions of the α-diazo-ketones, the most important group of stabilized diazo compounds.

Reactions of Diazomethane

Diazomethane is destroyed very rapidly by mineral acids in a reaction which proceeds through the intermediate formation of the methanediazonium ion.

$$CH_2N_2 + HCl \rightarrow CH_3N_2^+ \xrightarrow{Cl^-} N_2 + CH_3Cl$$

Recall that diazomethane reacts with carboxylic acids to give methyl esters (Section 20.4), and with phenols and alcohols to give methyl ethers (Section 18.2), by analogous reactions.

Diazomethane reacts with acid chlorides to give terminal α-diazoketones. This reaction essentially involves an attack by the anionic carbon of diazomethane upon the carbonyl group of the acid chloride. Since an equivalent of HCl is produced, two equivalents of diazomethane must be used, one of which serves merely as an acid scavenger.

A tertiary amine can also serve the function of trapping the acid formed.

$$C_6H_5-COCl + CH_2N_2 \rightarrow C_6H_5-CO-CHN_2 + HCl \xrightarrow{R_3N} R_3\overset{+}{N}HCl^-$$

α-Diazoacetophenone

$$\downarrow CH_2N_2$$

$$CH_3Cl + N_2$$

Diazomethane loses nitrogen in the absence of acids to generate the simplest carbene, methylene (CH_2:). The reaction is promoted by light, heat, and certain catalysts such as cuprous chloride. Of the many reactions of methylene which can take place depending upon experimental conditions and the substrate present, only the addition to unsaturated compounds is illustrated here (compare Section 15.13).

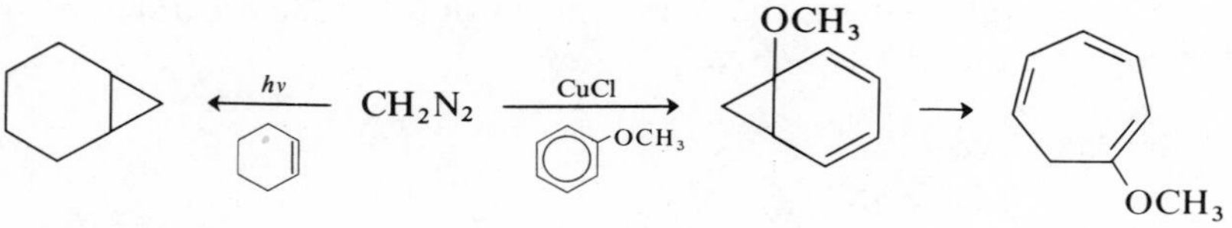

EXERCISE 22.8

What product is obtained from reaction of diazomethane with each of the following: (a) benzoyl chloride; (b) p-bromobenzoic acid; (c) m-hydroxy-benzoic acid.

Reactions of α-Diazoketones

The most important reaction of the readily prepared α-diazoketones is rearrangement with loss of nitrogen. This reaction, known as the *Wolff rearrangement*, generally involves loss of nitrogen to give a ketocarbene which rearranges to a ketene.

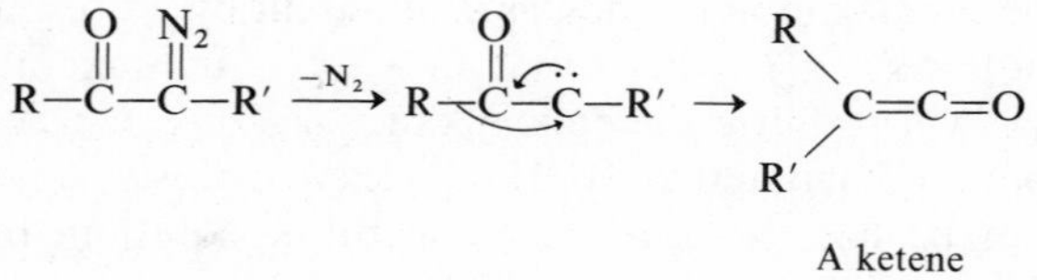

A ketene

The *Arndt–Eistert* synthesis is a method of converting an acid RCOOH to a homo-logous acid RCH_2COOH in which the Wolff rearrangement is the key step. The usual scheme used is outlined below. Note the use of silver oxide as a catalyst for the Wolff rearrangement.

$$R-COOH \rightarrow R-COCl \xrightarrow{CH_2N_2} R-CO-CHN_2 \xrightarrow[EtOH]{Ag_2O} [R-CO-CH]$$

$$\downarrow$$

$$R-CH_2COOH \xleftarrow{hydrolysis} R-CH_2-COOEt \xleftarrow{EtOH} R-CH=C=O$$

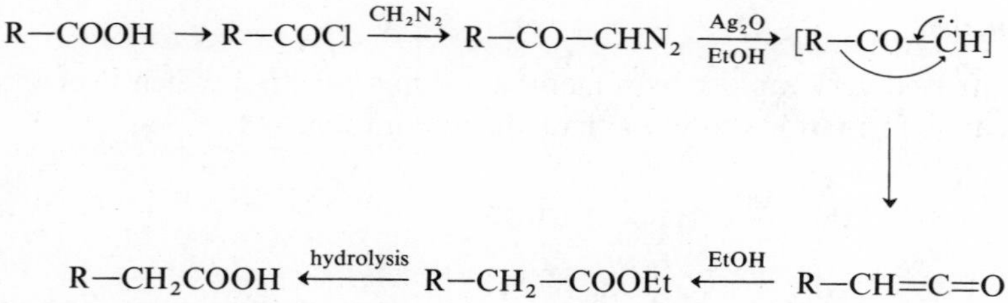

EXERCISE 22.9

The Arndt–Eistert synthesis is a convenient way to carry out the trans-formation $RCOOH \rightarrow RCH_2COOH$. What is a more convenient way to carry out the transformation $RCH_2OH \rightarrow RCH_2CH_2OH$?

Cyclic α-diazoketones often undergo the Wolff rearrangement smoothly only photo-chemically, producing ring-contracted products. As in the example below, this method of ring contraction may succeed in cases where all other ring contraction methods fail.

Benzocyclobutenecarboxylic acid

RING EXPANSIONS AND RING CONTRACTIONS. *Any reaction which involves rearrangement of the carbon skeleton of a molecule can in principle be used for ring expansion or ring contraction. Thus*

will give a ring contraction if C_2 and C_3 are connected in a ring, and it will give ring expansion if C_1 and C_2 are tied together via a ring. If the ring expansion/contraction is thermodynamically favorable, such as a seven-membered ring contracting to a six-membered ring, any rearrangement (such as a Wagner–Meerwein) is likely to succeed. When a cyclic compound is being converted to another with an increase in ring strain, the reaction must be sufficiently exothermic to overcome this additional energy requirement.

22.9   Azides

In contrast to the dangerously explosive hydrazoic acid (HN_3), organic azides are usually safe to handle in the pure state except for those of low molecular weight (e.g., CH_3CON_3). Alkyl azides ($R{-}N_3$), aryl azides ($Ar{-}N_3$), acyl azides ($R{-}CON_3$), and sulfonyl azides ($R{-}SO_2N_3$) are all known.

Alkyl azides can be reduced to primary amines by a number of reagents, for example, platinum and hydrogen, zinc and acid, or $LiAlH_4$. Since alkyl azides are readily pre-pared from alkyl halides or alkyl sulfonates and NaN_3, this reaction offers a useful method for obtaining primary amines free from secondary and tertiary amines.

$$R{-}X \xrightarrow{NaN_3} R{-}N_3 \xrightarrow{Pt,\ H_2} R{-}NH_2 + N_2 \uparrow$$

$$R{-}O{-}SO_2R' \underset{}{\overset{\displaystyle\int NaN_3}{}}$$

Acyl azides lose nitrogen to give isocyanates when heated in an inert solvent. This reaction, known as the *Curtius rearrangement*, is closely related to the Hofmann degrada-tion of amides (Section 21.5) and has been used frequently as an alternative to the latter reaction. In fact, the Curtius rearrangement is usually the preferable procedure, since the final product can be isolated in good yield as either isocyanate, urethan, or acid. The reaction sequence from carboxylic acid to products is outlined below.

$$R{-}COOH$$
$$\downarrow$$
$$R{-}COCl \xrightarrow{NaN_3} R{-}CON_3 \begin{cases} \xrightarrow[\Delta]{inert\ solvent} R{-}N{=}C{=}O \\ \xrightarrow[\Delta]{ROH} R{-}NH{-}COOR \\ \xrightarrow[\Delta]{HOAc,\ H_2O} R{-}NH_2 \end{cases}$$

The rearrangement step in the Curtius reaction is the same as that postulated in the Hofmann degradation and, consequently, the stereochemistry of the migrating group **R** is retained.

$$R-CO-N_3 \xrightarrow{\Delta} N_2 + R-\overset{\overset{\textstyle O}{\|}}{C}\overset{\frown}{N} \rightarrow O=C=N-R$$

The *Schmidt reaction* is a modification of the Curtius rearrangement in which the carboxylic acid is converted to the amine without the necessity of isolating the azide.

$$R-COOH \xrightarrow[\substack{\text{warm, } H_2SO_4 \\ \text{conc.}}]{NaN_3} RNH_2 + N_2 + CO_2$$

It has the advantage of experimental simplicity compared to the Hofmann and Curtius rearrangements.

> **EXERCISE 22.10**
>
> What is the best method (easiest method that gives a pure product in good yield) for carrying out the following transformation?
>
> $$R-CH_2-Br \rightarrow R-CH_2-NH_2$$

22.10   Summary of Synthetic Methods for Compounds with Nitrogen-Containing Functional Groups

1. Amine oxides

$$R_3N \rightarrow R_3\overset{+}{N}-O^- \qquad (H_2O_2 \text{ or } RCO_3H, \text{ Section 22.3})$$

2. Nitrones

$$R-NHOH + R-CHO \rightarrow R-\overset{+}{\underset{\underset{\textstyle O^-}{|}}{N}}=CH-R \qquad (\text{Section 22.3})$$

3. *N*-Nitroso compounds

$$R_2NH \xrightarrow{HNO_2} R_2N-NO \qquad (\text{Section 21.1})$$

4. Hydrazine derivatives

$$Ar-\overset{+}{N_2} \xrightarrow{[H]} Ar-NHNH_2 \qquad (\text{Section 22.7})$$

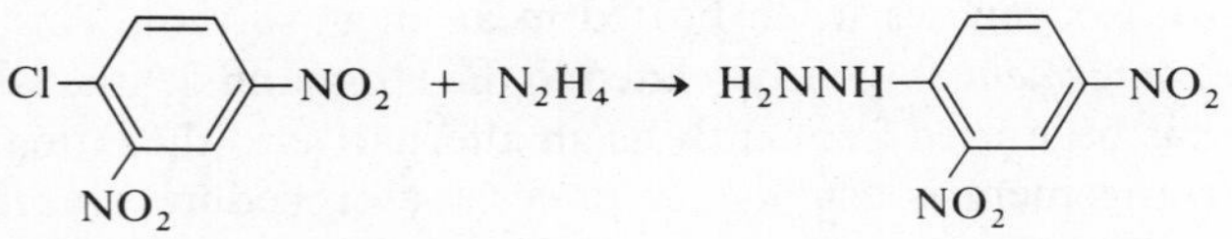

$$Cl\langle\text{C}_6H_3\rangle{-}NO_2 + N_2H_4 \rightarrow H_2NNH\langle\text{C}_6H_3\rangle{-}NO_2 \quad (\text{Section 17.8})$$

(with NO$_2$ substituents)

$$R-CONHNH_2 \xrightarrow{LiAlH_4} R-CH_2NHNH_2$$

$$Ar-NO_2 \xrightarrow{Zn}{OH^-} Ar-NHNH-Ar \qquad (\text{Section 22.1})$$

$$R-N=N-R \xrightarrow{Zn}{OH^-} R-NH-NH-R \qquad (\text{Sections 22.1, 22.6})$$

$$R-COOR' + N_2H_4 \rightarrow R-CONHNH_2 \qquad \substack{(\text{Compare amide formation from esters,} \\ \text{Section 20.5})}$$

$$R-SO_2Cl + N_2H_4 \rightarrow R-SO_2NHNH_2 \qquad \text{(Compare Section 26.7)}$$

$$R-NHNH_2 + R_2CO \rightarrow R-NH-N=CR_2 \qquad \text{(R = alkyl, aryl, acyl, or sulfonyl;}$$
$$\text{Section 19.7)}$$

5. Azo compounds

$$R-NHNH-R \rightarrow R-N=N-R \qquad \text{(NaOCl, Br}_2\text{, HNO}_3 \text{ or H}_2\text{O}_2\text{, Section 22.5)}$$

$$ArN_2^+ \xrightarrow{Ar'-H} Ar-N=N-Ar' \qquad \text{(Ar'}-H = \text{a phenol or amine, Section 22.7)}$$

6. Diazonium salts

$$Ar-NH_2 + HNO_2 \rightarrow Ar-N_2^+ \qquad \text{(Sections 21.1, 22.7)}$$

7. Diazoalkanes

$$\underset{\underset{NO}{|}}{CH_3-N-CONH_2} \quad \text{or} \quad \underset{\underset{NO}{|}}{C_7H_7SO_2-N-CH_3} \xrightarrow{\text{base}} CH_2N_2 \qquad \text{(Section 22.4)}$$

$$R_2C=N-NH_2 \rightarrow R_2C=N_2 \qquad \text{(HgO or MnO}_2\text{, Section 22.5)}$$

$$\underset{\underset{NOH}{\|}}{R-C-CO-R} \rightarrow \underset{\underset{N_2}{\|}}{R-C-CO-R} \qquad \text{(NH}_2\text{Cl, Section 22.3)}$$

8. Azides

$$R-X \xrightarrow{NaN_3} R-N_3 \qquad \text{(Sections 17.1, 22.9)}$$

$$R-COCl \xrightarrow{NaN_3} R-CON_3 \qquad \text{(Section 22.9)}$$

$$R-CONHNH_2 \xrightarrow{HNO_2} R-CON_3 \qquad \text{(Section 22.5)}$$

$$ArN_2^+ \xrightarrow{HN_3} ArN_3 + N_2 \qquad \text{(Section 22.7)}$$

PROBLEMS

1. Complete the following:

   (a) $PhCHO + CH_3CH_2NO_2 \xrightarrow{NaOH}$

   (b) ⟨○⟩—N=N—⟨○⟩—NH₂ + C₆H₅NO $\xrightarrow{HOAc}$

   (c) O_2N—⟨○⟩—$C{\underset{NOH}{\overset{CH_3}{<}}}$ $\xrightarrow[\text{Zn}]{HOAc}$

2. Write the structures and name all of the compounds which have the nitrogen in inter-mediate oxidation states between nitrobenzene and aniline.

3.   Suggest mechanisms for the following reactions:
      (a) Oximation of cyclohexanone with butyl nitrite.

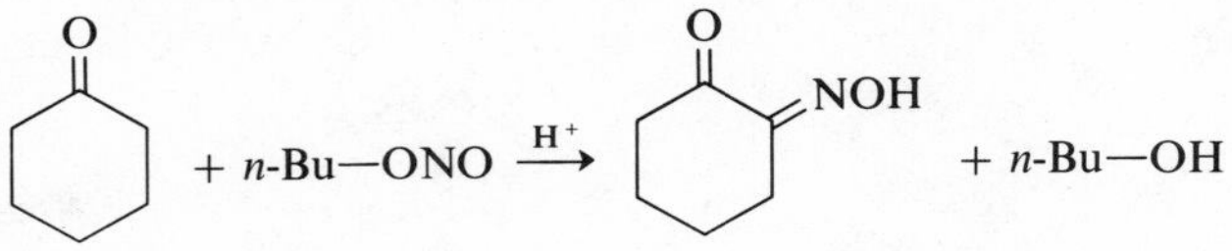

$$\text{(cyclohexanone)} + n\text{-Bu}\text{—ONO} \xrightarrow{\text{H}^+} \text{(2-oximinocyclohexanone, NOH)} + n\text{-Bu}\text{—OH}$$

      (b) Rearrangement of cyclohexanone oxime to caprolactam

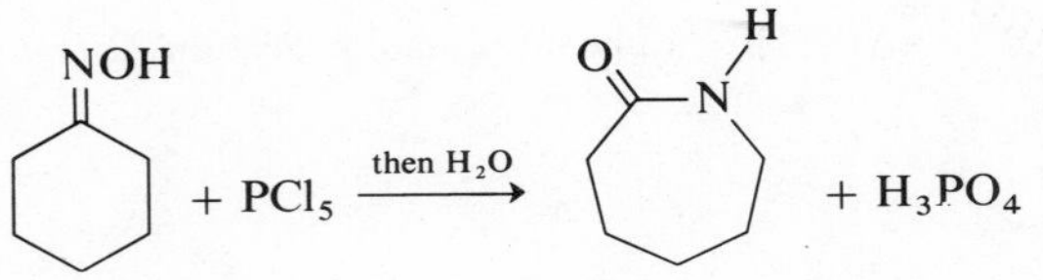

$$\text{(cyclohexanone oxime, NOH)} + \text{PCl}_5 \xrightarrow{\text{then H}_2\text{O}} \text{(caprolactam)} + \text{H}_3\text{PO}_4$$

4.   Predict the products of the following reactions:

      (a) 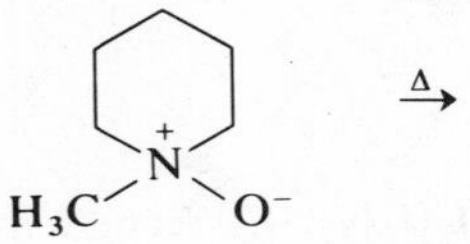   (N-methylpiperidine N-oxide) $\xrightarrow{\Delta}$

      (b) 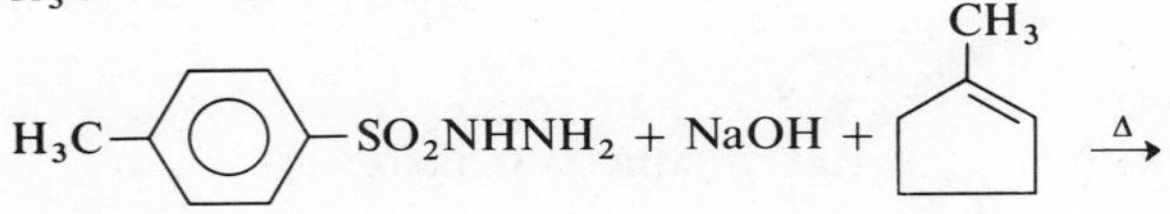 H_3C—⟨aryl⟩—SO_2NHNH_2 + NaOH + (1-methylcyclopentene) $\xrightarrow{\Delta}$

      (c) $\text{CH}_2{=}\text{CH}{-}\text{CH}{=}\text{CH}_2$ + (4-phenyl-1,2,4-triazoline-3,5-dione) $\longrightarrow$

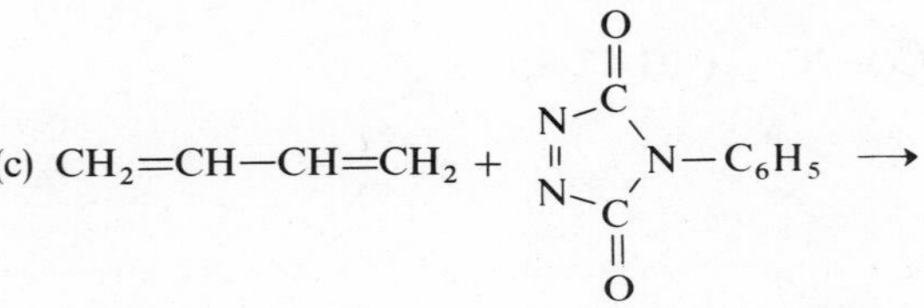

5.   Show how the Arndt–Eistert synthesis can be used to carry out the following conversion:

$$\text{CH}_3\text{—}\underset{\underset{\text{CH}_3}{|}}{\overset{\overset{\text{CH}_3}{|}}{\text{C}}}\text{—COOH} \rightarrow \text{CH}_3\text{—}\underset{\underset{\text{CH}_3}{|}}{\overset{\overset{\text{CH}_3}{|}}{\text{C}}}\text{—CH}_2\text{COOH}$$

6.   Show how the following conversion can be carried out using (a) the Hofmann rearrangement, (b) the Curtius rearrangement, and (c) the Schmidt reaction.

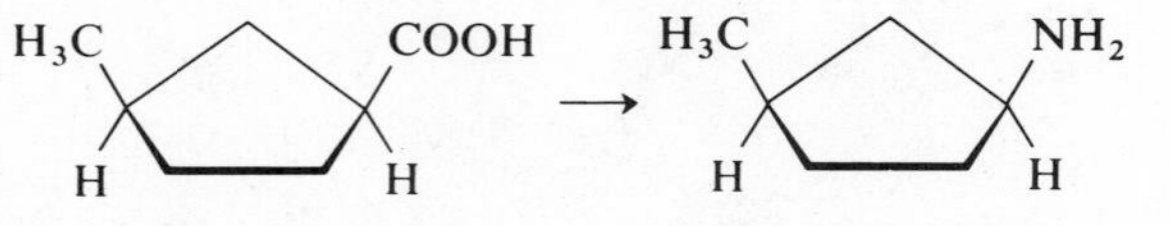

$$\text{(cis-3-methylcyclopentanecarboxylic acid, COOH)} \longrightarrow \text{(cis-3-methylcyclopentylamine, NH}_2\text{)}$$

7.   Show how the following conversions can be carried out.

      (a) 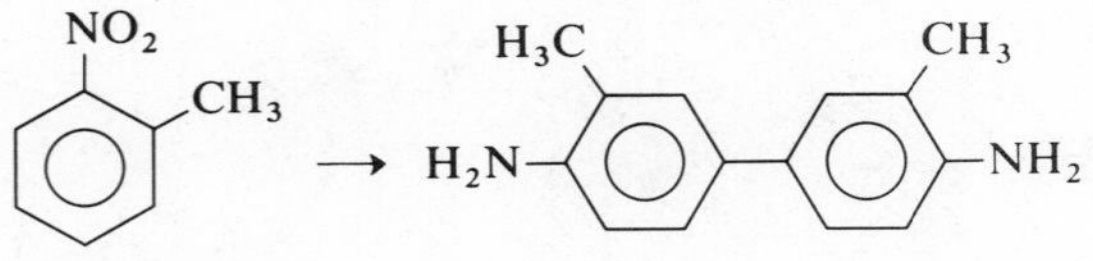 (2-methylnitrobenzene, NO$_2$, CH$_3$) $\longrightarrow$ H_2N—(biphenyl, H$_3$C, CH$_3$)—NH_2

      (b) CH_3O—⟨aryl⟩—NH_2 $\longrightarrow$ CH_3O—⟨aryl⟩—COOH

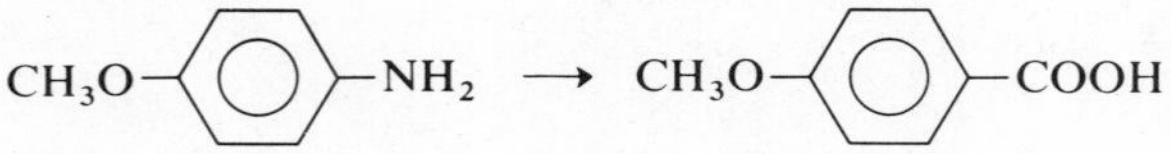

      (c) $(\text{CH}_3)_2\text{NH} \rightarrow (\text{CH}_3)_2\text{N}\text{—NH}_2$

(d) 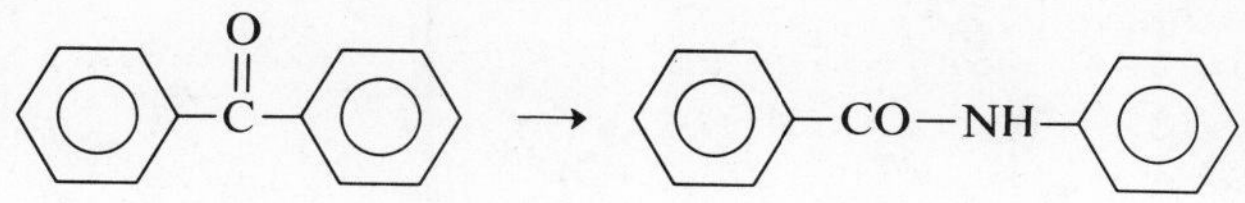 →

(e) 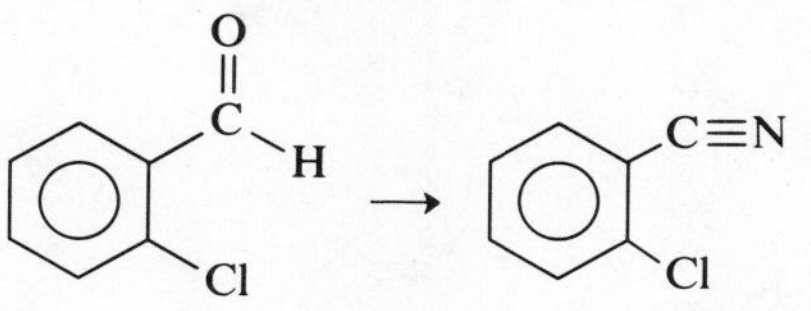 →

(f) 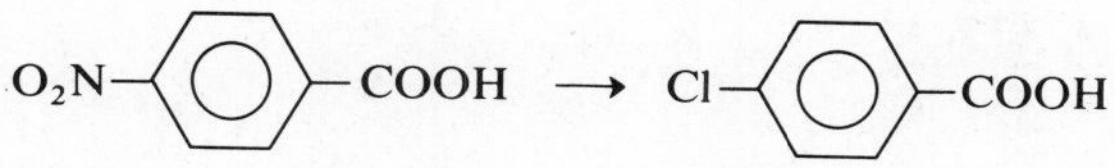 O_2N—⟨benzene⟩—COOH → Cl—⟨benzene⟩—COOH

(g) C_6H_5—CO—CH_2CH_3 → C_6H_5—CO—$\underset{\underset{N_2}{\|}}{C}$—$CH_3$

8. Outline syntheses of the following compounds, starting with *m*-nitroaniline (plus anything else).

(a)

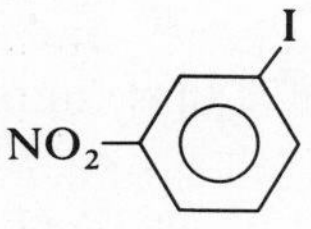

(b)

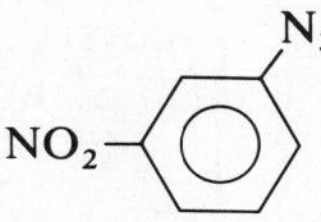

(c)

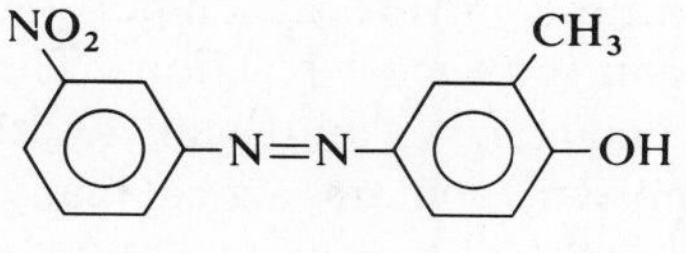

(d)

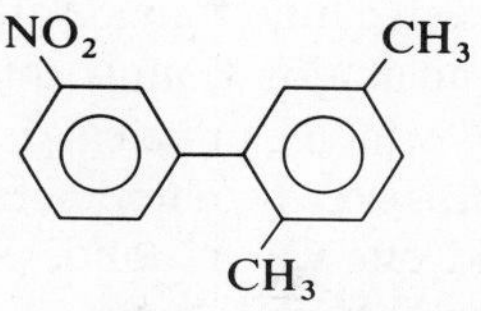

9. A compound A has the molecular formula C_7H_4BrClO. Treatment of A with diazomethane gave B, which upon heating with silver oxide and water was converted to another compound C, $C_8H_7BrO_2$. The nmr spectrum of C is as follows: $\delta\,2.7$ singlet, $A = 2$; $\delta\,7.0$ multiplet, $A = 4$; $\delta\,12.0$ singlet, $A = 1$. What are the structures of compounds A, B, and C?

10. Write equations for the reaction of *m*-methoxybenzenediazonium chloride with the following:
    (a) Hot, dil. H_2SO_4
    (b) Hypophosphorous acid
    (c) *m*-Cresol (as its sodium salt)
    (d) Sodium iodide
    (e) Cuprous cyanide
    (f) *m*-Toluidine

Optional Problem

1. Suggest a mechanism for the following reaction:

$$(C_6H_5)_3C-\underset{\underset{N}{\|}\,\underset{OH}{\diagdown}}{C}-C_6H_5 \xrightarrow{H^+} (C_6H_5)_3COH + C_6H_5CN$$

CHAPTER 23

REACTIONS OF ALKANES
AND CYCLOALKANES

Crude petroleum, of which ten million barrels is produced every day in the United States, is composed mainly of alkanes (see Table 3.3). In Chapters 2 and 3, the bonding, nomenclature, conformational analysis, and stereochemistry of alkanes and cyclo-alkanes were discussed. In this chapter, we will discuss the reactions of these important compounds.

Most of the reactions considered so far in this book, indeed most of the reactions of organic chemistry, involve functional groups. The saturated hydrocarbon portion of the molecule undergoes no major change during the course of most reactions. There are few *selective* reactions which can be carried out on an alkane or on the alkyl portion of most molecules, and this is easy to understand. If a molecule contains a great many C—H and C—C bonds, and one C—Y bond, the C—Y bond will usually undergo a certain number of reactions which are selective, that is, which do not affect the C—C and C—H bonds. It is much more difficult to select one particular C—H or C—C bond for reaction. Competing reactions will occur at many or all of the other C—H or C—C bonds. Among the reactions of alkanes discussed in the following sections are some in which selectivity is possible, and others in which it is neither necessary nor desirable.

23.1   Oxidation

When alkanes and cycloalkanes are ignited in the presence of oxygen, they burn, producing carbon dioxide, water, and heat. For example, the heat of combustion of methane, the principal component of natural gas, is 213 kcal/mole.

$$CH_4(g) + 2\,O_2(g) \rightarrow CO_2(g) + 2\,H_2O(g) + 213.0\ kcal/mole$$

The importance of the oxidation of hydrocarbon fuels to the economic and political stability (and instability) of the world is well known to everyone. The oxidation of hydrocarbons in engines and furnaces is rarely complete; if insufficient oxygen is present, large amounts of carbon monoxide, a health hazard, are produced.

On a laboratory scale, complete oxidation of hydrocarbons, and of other organic compounds, is used in chemical analysis for determination of empirical formulas (Section 2.2). The use of the heats of combustion to determine strain in hydrocarbons was discussed in Sections 3.5 and 13.2.

The oxidation of alkanes, in either complete combustion to CO_2 and H_2O or in less complete oxidation reactions which yield intermediate products, is highly exothermic. However, initiation by heat, light or chemical catalysis is required. The mechanism of oxidation undoubtedly involves the formation and reactions of *free-radical* species (Section 12.4). Oxygen in its ground state is unusual in that it is a diradical, that is, it has two unpaired electrons. Since it is a diradical, oxygen can *abstract* a hydrogen atom from an alkane, producing a hydroperoxy radical and an alkyl radical:

Hydrogen abstraction

$$-\overset{|}{\underset{|}{C}}{:}H + \cdot\ddot{O}{:}\ddot{O} \longrightarrow -\overset{|}{\underset{|}{C}}\cdot \;+\; H{:}\ddot{O}{:}\ddot{O}\cdot$$

Alkyl Hydroperoxy
radical radical

If more than one type of hydrogen atom is available for abstraction, the most stable radical will be formed preferentially. For example, benzyl and allyl radicals form in preference to tertiary, secondary, primary, and methyl radicals (Section 12.4).

In a subsequent step the alkyl radical can react with oxygen to produce a peroxy radical

$$-\overset{|}{\underset{|}{C}}\cdot + \cdot\ddot{O}{-}\ddot{O}\cdot \longrightarrow -\overset{|}{\underset{|}{C}}{-}\ddot{O}{-}\ddot{O}\cdot$$

A peroxy radical

and the peroxy radical can further react with alkane to form an organic peroxide and an alkyl radical:

$$-\overset{|}{\underset{|}{C}}{-}\ddot{O}{-}\ddot{O}\cdot + -\overset{|}{\underset{|}{C}}{:}H \longrightarrow -\overset{|}{\underset{|}{C}}{-}\ddot{O}{-}\ddot{O}{-}H + -\overset{|}{\underset{|}{C}}\cdot$$

An alkyl An alkyl
hydroperoxide radical

The alkyl radical then reacts with oxygen to form another peroxy radical. A new alkyl radical is produced for each one that reacts, until no alkane remains. The student will recognize that such a process is a *chain reaction*, and that it should show the characteristic features of this type of reaction (Section 15.7). The net reaction of the chain sequence is the combination of an alkane and oxygen to form an alkyl hydroperoxide.

$$-\overset{|}{\underset{|}{C}}{-}H + O_2 \longrightarrow -\overset{|}{\underset{|}{C}}{-}\ddot{O}{-}\ddot{O}{-}H$$

Organic hydroperoxides are very reactive compounds. The oxygen–oxygen bond is labile, and it readily cleaves homolytically.

Homolytic cleavage

$$-\overset{|}{\underset{|}{C}}{-}\ddot{O}{-}\ddot{O}{-}H \longrightarrow -\overset{|}{\underset{|}{C}}{-}\ddot{O}\cdot + \cdot\ddot{O}{-}H$$

Further reaction gives complicated mixtures of products.

Compounds which can form stable radicals (benzylic, allylic, or tertiary) usually will react with oxygen at room temperature, the experimental procedure being simply to bubble air through the liquid. Compounds which can form only rather unstable radicals (primary or secondary) do not ordinarily undergo reaction except at high temperatures or in the presence of an initiator. By controlling the reaction conditions, it is possible in some cases to isolate the intermediate hydroperoxides. For example, isopropylbenzene (cumene) forms a tertiary benzylic radical; cumyl hydroperoxide can be isolated at low temperatures:

$$
\underset{\substack{\text{Isopropylbenzene}\\ \text{(cumene)}}}{
\text{C}_6\text{H}_5\overset{\overset{\text{CH}_3}{|}}{\underset{\underset{\text{CH}_3}{|}}{C}}{-}H}
\;+\; O_2 \longrightarrow
\underset{\text{Cumyl hydroperoxide}}{
\text{C}_6\text{H}_5\overset{\overset{\text{CH}_3}{|}}{\underset{\underset{\text{CH}_3}{|}}{C}}{-}\ddot{O}{-}\ddot{O}{-}H}
$$

The oxidation of aromatic side chains is an important synthetic reaction; it was discussed in some detail in Section 16.9.

EXERCISE 23.1

Both *cis-* and *trans*-decalin form the same hydroperoxide on reaction with oxygen. Suggest a structure.

Cumyl Hydroperoxide Rearrangement. The oxidation of cumene to its hydroperoxide and the subsequent acid-catalyzed rearrangements of the hydroperoxide constitute a commercially important process for the synthesis of phenol and acetone.

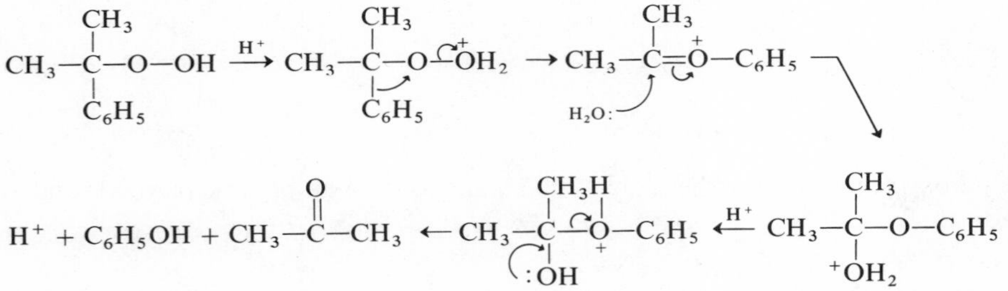

Singlet Oxygen. We have seen that reactions of triplet oxygen (oxygen in its ground state, Figure 23.1) are free-radical in nature and, although highly exothermic, need the typical initiation by heat, light, or a chemical catalyst. Oxygen can be excited to a *singlet* state of higher energy in which the electrons on the highest-energy occupied orbital are spin-paired.

Figure 23.1
The molecular orbital diagram of O_2, showing the triplet nature of the ground state.
(The $2p\pi^*$ electrons are unpaired.)

States of O_2	Occupancy of highest orbitals, $2p\pi^*$	Energy above ground state
First excited state (singlet)	↑↓ —	22 kcal/mole
Ground state (triplet)	↑ ↑	0

| Valence orbitals of oxygen atom | Valence orbitals of oxygen molecule | Valence orbitals of oxygen atom |

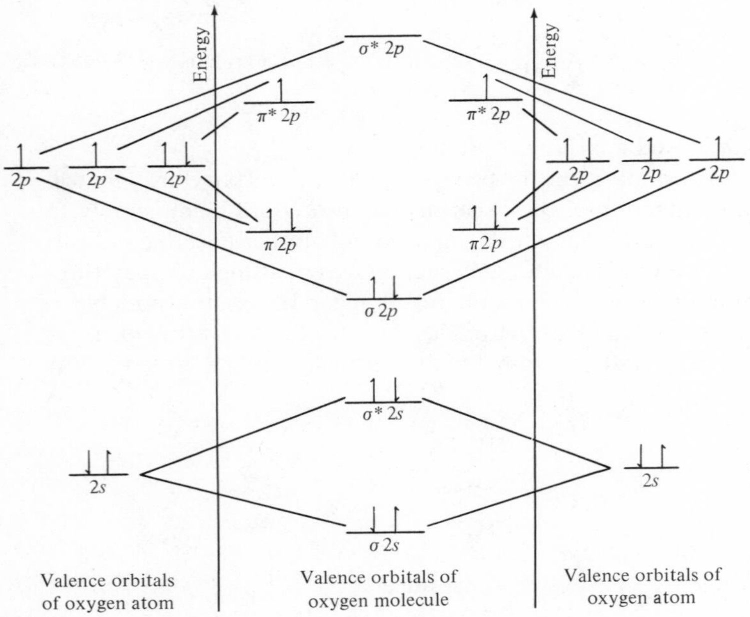

EXERCISE 23.2

Explain why the singlet oxygen is an excited state and a triplet is the ground state, with reference to Figure 23.1.

Singlet oxygen can be viewed as a reactive dienophile which can undergo Diels–Alder reactions (Section 15.12) with suitable dienes. For example, singlet oxygen forms an unstable peroxide with cyclohexadiene in 20% yield, and a very low yield of an addition product with anthracene.

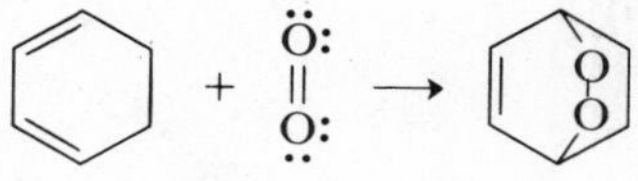

(singlet)

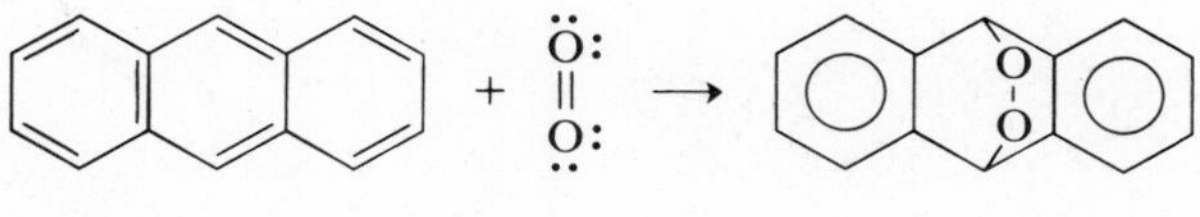

EXERCISE 23.3

Ascaridole, a naturally occurring peroxide from chenopodium oil, is formed from α-terpinene and singlet oxygen. Suggest a structure for ascaridole.

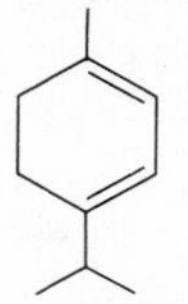

α-Terpinene

Singlet oxygen reacts with alkenes to form α,β-unsaturated hydroperoxides. A mechanism which is consistent with the experimental results is a concerted addition of singlet oxygen to the alkene accompanied by a double-bond shift.

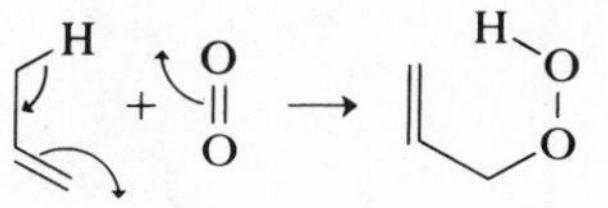

Tetramethylethylene, for example, gives a 60% yield of 3-hydroperoxy-2,3-dimethyl-1-butene. Reduction of the hydroperoxide produces 3-hydroxy-2,3-dimethyl-1-butene.

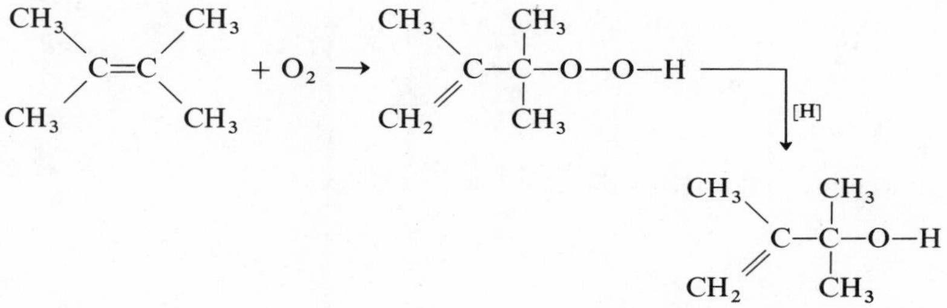

23.2   Balancing Organic Reduction–Oxidation (Redox) Equations

Before we can really study any equilibrium or chemical reaction, we must know exactly what the equilibrium or reaction is—in other words, we must be able to write the balanced equation for the process. Most organic reactions can be balanced by inspection. Only the reduction–oxidation reactions present problems sufficiently serious to merit discussion. For balancing inorganic redox reactions there are a great many methods which may be successfully employed. For the corre-sponding organic reactions, the only method which has been found to be practical is the *method of half-reactions*. There are at least three variants of this method which have been used, in which [O], [H], or e^- are the imaginary components of the half-reaction. Each way is equally artificial; however, each way can be made to work. The student should feel free to use whichever method he prefers. We will describe a method which makes use of [H], and suggest that unless the student already has command of one of the other methods, he utilize this method.

First, it is necessary to write the half-reaction for (a) the compound being oxidized and (b) the compound being reduced. Then three steps are followed in order to balance each half reaction.

1. Balance the charge, using H^+ if in acid solution, or using OH^- if in basic solution.
2. Balance the oxygen with H_2O.
3. Balance the hydrogen with [H].

Then the half-reactions must be added together as usual.

All of this is best illustrated by means of an example. Consider the following:

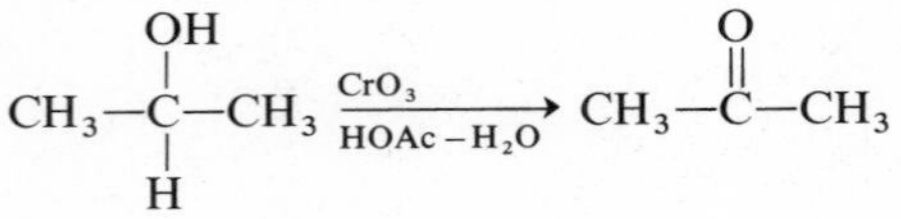

$$\underset{\underset{H}{|}}{\overset{\overset{OH}{|}}{CH_3-C-CH_3}} \xrightarrow[\text{HOAc}-H_2O]{\text{CrO}_3} \underset{}{\overset{\overset{O}{\|}}{CH_3-C-CH_3}}$$

Chromium trioxide has chromium in the +6 state, and the product is chromic ion (+3). The solution is acidic. The (unbalanced) half reactions then are

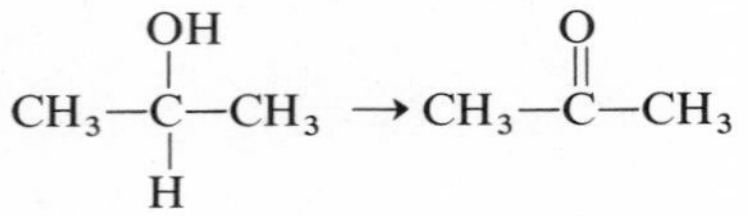

$$\underset{\underset{H}{|}}{\overset{\overset{OH}{|}}{CH_3-C-CH_3}} \rightarrow \overset{\overset{O}{\|}}{CH_3-C-CH_3}$$

and

$$CrO_3 \rightarrow Cr^{3+}$$

Taking these in order, first balance with respect to charge; the first half-reaction is found to be balanced as it stands. Adding protons balances the second half-reaction with respect to charge.

$$CrO_3 + 3H^+ \rightarrow Cr^{3+}$$

Next balance with respect to oxygen:

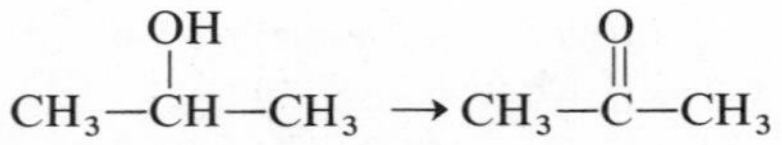

$$\underset{}{\overset{\overset{OH}{|}}{CH_3-CH-CH_3}} \rightarrow \overset{\overset{O}{\|}}{CH_3-C-CH_3} \qquad \text{(ok as is)}$$

$$CrO_3 + 3H^+ \rightarrow Cr^{3+} \qquad \text{(have to add water)}$$

$$CrO_3 + 3H^+ \rightarrow Cr^{3+} + 3H_2O$$

Finally balance hydrogens by adding [H] as shown below:

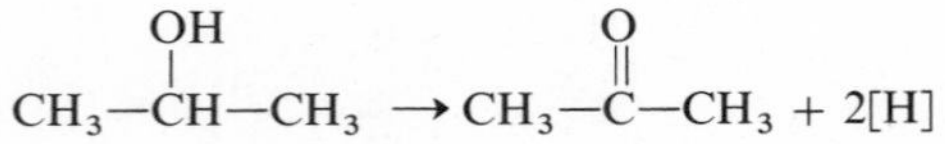

$$\underset{}{\overset{\overset{OH}{|}}{CH_3-CH-CH_3}} \rightarrow \overset{\overset{O}{\|}}{CH_3-C-CH_3} + 2[H]$$

$$3[H] + CrO_3 + 3H^+ \rightarrow Cr^{3+} + 3H_2O$$

Now we have the two balanced half-reactions. We must multiply them and then add them in such a way as to cancel the artificial [H]; that is, multiply the top one by 3, and the bottom one by 2:

$$3CH_3-\overset{\overset{\displaystyle OH}{|}}{CH}-CH_3 \rightarrow 3CH_3-\overset{\overset{\displaystyle O}{||}}{C}-CH_3 + 6[H]$$

$$6[H] + 2CrO_3 + 6H^+ \rightarrow 2Cr^{3+} + 6H_2O$$

then add:

$$3CH_3-\overset{\overset{\displaystyle OH}{|}}{CH}-CH_3 + 2CrO_3 + 6H^+ \rightarrow 3CH_3-\overset{\overset{\displaystyle O}{||}}{C}-CH_3 + 2Cr^{3+} + 6H_2O$$

Then we may check to see that both sides of the equation contain the same number of carbons, chromiums, charges, oxygens, and hydrogens, and thus be sure that we have correctly balanced the equation.

As another example, consider the following reaction:

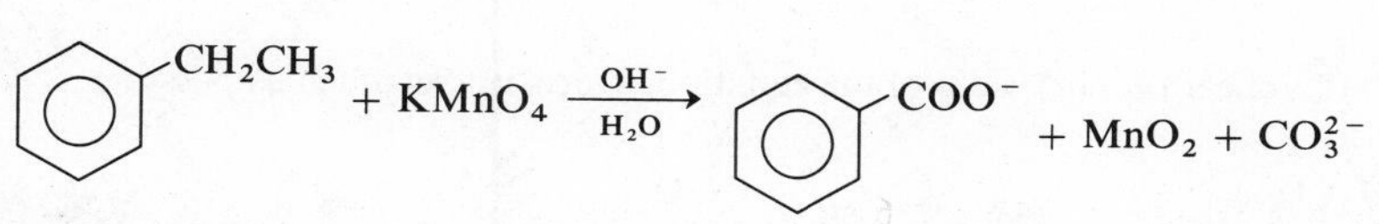

Ethylbenzene is oxidized by potassium permanganate to the salt of benzoic acid and carbonate, while the $+7$ manganese is reduced to $+4$ manganese dioxide. Proceeding as before, the unbalanced half-reactions are

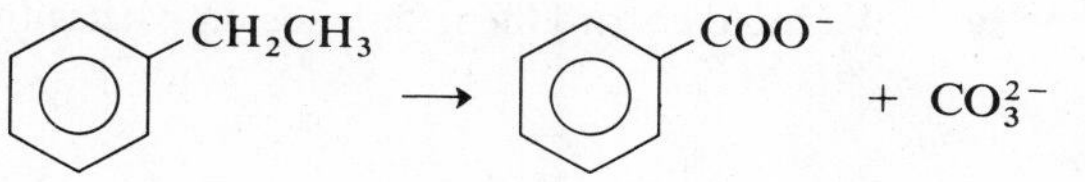

and

$$KMnO_4 \rightarrow K^+ + MnO_2$$

Now if we balance charge (with OH^- since this is a basic solution), these become

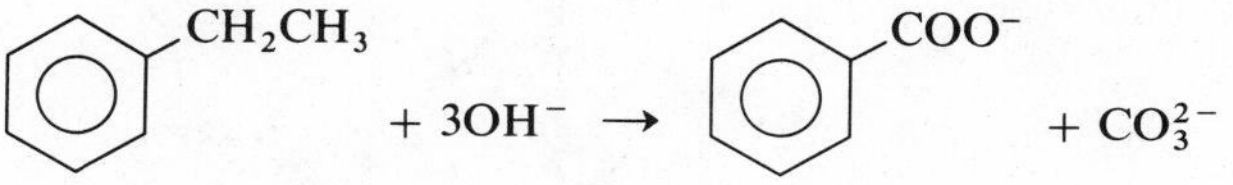

$$KMnO_4 \rightarrow K^+ + MnO_2 + OH^-$$

Next balance oxygen with water:

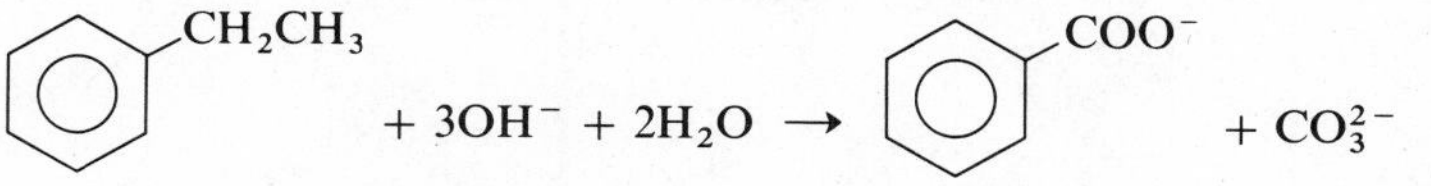

$$KMnO_4 \rightarrow K^+ + MnO_2 + OH^- + H_2O$$

and finally, balance hydrogen with [H]

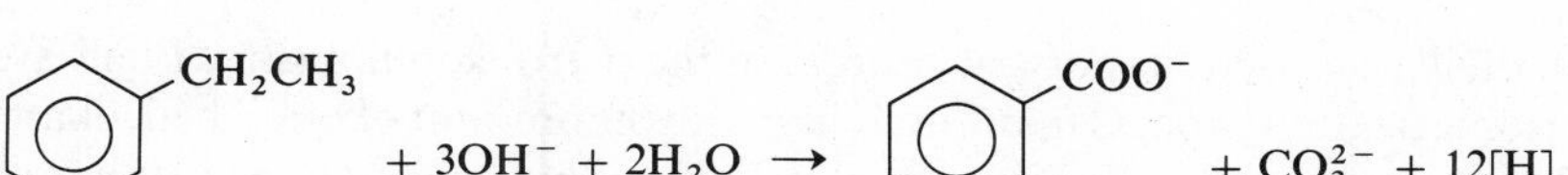

$$KMnO_4 + 3[H] \rightarrow K^+ + MnO_2 + OH^- + H_2O$$

Multiply the last reaction by 4, and add:

$$\text{C}_6\text{H}_5\text{CH}_2\text{CH}_3 + 3\text{OH}^- + 2\text{H}_2\text{O} \rightarrow \text{C}_6\text{H}_5\text{COO}^- + \text{CO}_3^{2-} + 12[\text{H}]$$

$$4\text{KMnO}_4 + 12[\text{H}] \rightarrow 4\text{K}^+ + 4\text{MnO}_2 + 4\text{OH}^- + 4\text{H}_2\text{O}$$

$$\text{C}_6\text{H}_5\text{CH}_2\text{CH}_3 + 3\text{OH}^- + 2\text{H}_2\text{O} + 4\text{KMnO}_4 \rightarrow \text{C}_6\text{H}_5\text{COO}^-$$
$$+ \text{CO}_3^{2-} + 4\text{K}^+ + 4\text{MnO}_2 + 4\text{OH}^- + 4\text{H}_2\text{O}$$

Since water and OH⁻ appear on both sides of the equation, cancel out as much as possible:

$$\text{C}_6\text{H}_5\text{CH}_2\text{CH}_3 + 4\text{KMnO}_4 \rightarrow \text{C}_6\text{H}_5\text{COO}^- + \text{CO}_3^{2-} + 4\text{K}^+ + 4\text{MnO}_2$$
$$+ \text{OH}^- + 2\text{H}_2\text{O}$$

The potassium ions are also common to both sides. We could discard them, or associate each with an anion:

$$\text{C}_6\text{H}_5\text{CH}_2\text{CH}_3 + 4\text{KMnO}_4 \rightarrow \text{C}_6\text{H}_5\text{COOK} + \text{K}_2\text{CO}_3 + 4\text{MnO}_2$$
$$+ \text{KOH} + 2\text{H}_2\text{O}$$

These examples should make it clear that trial-and-error methods for balancing such equations will not suffice. The method described may seem laborious. It is. But it works and is the easiest method for dealing with equations of this type.

23.3 Isomerization

It is well known in the petroleum field that the more highly branched an alkane is, the higher compression it will stand without spontaneous ignition (i.e., no "knocking"). It will thus allow use of a more efficient, higher compression piston. The petroleum industry compares gasoline performance with that of *n*-heptane, which is arbitrarily given an *octane number* of zero, and with 2,2,4-trimethylpentane, which is given an octane number of 100.

$$\text{CH}_3\text{CH}_2\text{CH}_2\text{CH}_2\text{CH}_2\text{CH}_2\text{CH}_3 \qquad \text{CH}_3-\overset{\overset{\displaystyle \text{CH}_3}{|}}{\underset{\underset{\displaystyle \text{CH}_3}{|}}{\text{C}}}-\text{CH}_2-\overset{\overset{\displaystyle \text{CH}_3}{|}}{\text{CH}}-\text{CH}_3$$

n-Heptane
(octane number = 0)

2,2,4-Trimethylpentane
(octane number = 100)

Isomerization of alkanes is an important process in the petroleum industry. Fuels are subjected to an isomerization process in order to increase the amount of branched alkane present, and thus to better their performance in automobile engines. A catalyst is required for such isomerization; aluminum chloride or aluminum bromide is commonly employed. Also, a small amount of alkyl halide, or alkene and hydrogen halide, must be present in order for the catalyst to produce an initial carbonium ion.

$$HCl + AlCl_3 \rightleftharpoons H^+AlCl_4^-$$

$$H^+AlCl_4^- + \diagup C{=}C\diagdown \rightleftharpoons -\underset{H}{\overset{|}{C}}-\overset{|}{\underset{|}{C}}{}^+ + AlCl_4^-$$

The carbonium ion abstracts a hydride ion from a molecule of alkane, for example, *n*-butane.

$$R^+ + CH_3CH_2CH_2CH_3 \rightleftharpoons R{-}H + CH_3\overset{+}{C}HCH_2CH_3$$

 *n*-Butane *sec*-Butyl cation

The *sec*-butyl cation then rearranges to the *t*-butyl cation via a 1,2-methyl shift, followed by a 1,2-hydride shift.

$$CH_3\overset{+}{C}HCH_2CH_3 \rightleftharpoons CH_3{-}\underset{\overset{|}{CH_3}}{\overset{|}{CH}}{-}CH_2^+ \rightleftharpoons CH_3{-}\underset{\overset{+}{}}{\underset{|}{\overset{|}{C}}}{-}CH_3$$

 *sec*-Butyl cation Isobutyl cation *t*-Butyl cation

It may be noted that primary carbonium ions are generated only with extreme difficulty, and it seems likely that even though we may formally interpret a reaction as proceeding through such an intermediate, the migration or rearrangement reaction written as a following step is probably most often concurrent with the generation of the ion.

The force driving the equilibrium to the *t*-butyl cation is the greater stability of the tertiary carbonium ion compared to that of the primary or secondary carbonium ion (Section 12.2). The rearrangement is propagated when a *t*-butyl cation abstracts a hydride from *n*-butane.

$$CH_3CH_2CH_2CH_3 + CH_3{-}\underset{\overset{+}{}}{\underset{|}{\overset{|}{C}}}{-}CH_3 \rightleftharpoons CH_3\overset{+}{C}HCH_2CH_3 + CH_3{-}\underset{\overset{|}{H}}{\overset{|}{C}}{-}CH_3$$

 *n*-Butane *sec*-Butyl Isobutane

 cation

 ⇅

 etc.

Since the isomerization involves a series of equilibria, the composition of the product mixture reflects the relative thermodynamic stabilities of the isomers. Therefore the same equilibrium mixture is obtained from either n-*butane or isobutane; at 150°C there is approximately four times as much isobutane as* n-*butane formed.*

The $C_{10}H_{16}$ *hydrocarbons provide an interesting example of the influence of thermodynamic stability upon the products formed. All known* $C_{10}H_{16}$ *hydrocarbons are isomerized by aluminum halides to* adamantane, *an especially stable, highly symmetrical compound with a diamond-type structure (page 43).*

EXERCISE 23.4

When perhydroazulene is treated with $AlCl_3/HCl$, it is largely isomerized to decalin. Suggest a mechanisn for the transformation. What is the driving force for the reaction?

23.4   Cracking

If alkanes are heated at high temperatures in the absence of oxygen, they fragment into smaller, more highly branched alkanes and alkenes. For example, n-hexane is degraded mainly into methane, ethylene, propene, butene, and butadiene.

$$CH_3(CH_2)_4CH_3 \xrightarrow{\Delta} \begin{cases} H_2 + CH_2{=}CHCH_2CH_2CH_2CH_3\ (+\ isomers) \\ CH_4 + CH_2{=}CHCH_2CH_2CH_3\ (+\ isomers) \\ CH_3CH_3 + CH_2{=}CHCH_2CH_3\ (+\ isomers) \\ CH_2{=}CH_2 + CH_3CH_2CH_2CH_3 \\ CH_2{=}CHCH_3 + CH_3CH_2CH_3 \\ etc. \end{cases}$$

In the petroleum industry this process is known as *thermal cracking*, and it is used to produce gasoline from higher-boiling hydrocarbon fractions. The mechanism proceeds by the formation and fragmentation of radicals.

A catalyst such as chromia-alumina is employed in catalytic cracking. In this case, carbonium ions are probably involved in the formation of branched alkanes and alkenes.
In spite of its immense importance to the petroleum industry, cracking of alkanes has found little utility on a small, laboratory scale. The main reason is that simple alkenes are commercially available at relatively low expense. Another reason is that in the cracking process complex mixtures are formed, from which the desired product must be isolated, often in low yield.

23.5   Alkylation

The petroleum industry has developed a process for combining small alkanes and alkenes into larger, highly branched hydrocarbons which can serve as gasoline. For example, isobutane obtained from n-butane by isomerization (Section 23.3) is used to prepare 2,2,4-trimethylpentane (the standard having an octane rating of 100). First isobutane is converted to isobutylene by heating at a high temperature in the presence of a suitable catalyst. Hydrogen gas is eliminated.

$$\underset{\underset{H}{|}}{\overset{\overset{CH_3}{|}}{CH_3{-}C{-}CH_3}} \xrightarrow[\text{heat}]{\text{catalyst}} \underset{}{\overset{\overset{CH_3}{|}}{CH_3{-}C{=}CH_2}} + H_2$$

Isobutylene is then combined with isobutane at a low temperature in the presence of a strong acid, such as sulfuric acid, which acts as a catalyst. The overall reaction which occurs is alkylation to give 2,2,4-trimethylpentane.

$$\underset{\underset{CH_3}{|}}{\overset{\overset{CH_3}{|}}{CH_3{-}C{-}H}} + \underset{}{\overset{\overset{CH_3}{|}}{CH_2{=}C{-}CH_3}} \xrightarrow{H_2SO_4} \underset{\underset{CH_3}{|}\ \ \ \ \underset{H}{|}}{\overset{\overset{CH_3}{|}\ \ \ \ \overset{CH_3}{|}}{CH_3{-}C{-}CH_2{-}C{-}CH_3}}$$

The sulfuric acid catalyst and the alkene form a carbonium ion, in this case the t-butyl cation, in the first step of the reaction:

$$\underset{}{\overset{\overset{CH_3}{|}}{CH_2{=}C{-}CH_3}} + H_2SO_4 \rightleftharpoons \underset{\overset{+}{}}{\overset{\overset{CH_3}{|}}{CH_3{-}C{-}CH_3}} + HSO_4^-$$

Reaction of the t-butyl cation and another molecule of alkene produces a carbonium ion with eight carbons:

$$\underset{\underset{CH_3}{|}}{\overset{\overset{CH_3}{|}}{CH_3{-}\overset{+}{C}}} + \underset{}{\overset{\overset{CH_3}{|}}{CH_2{=}C{-}CH_3}} \rightleftharpoons \underset{\underset{CH_3}{|}}{\overset{\overset{CH_3}{|}\ \ \ \ \overset{CH_3}{|}}{CH_3{-}C{-}CH_2{-}\overset{+}{C}{-}CH_3}}$$

2,2,4-Trimethylpentane is then formed by hydride transfer from isobutane:

$$(\text{excess}) \quad CH_3{-}\underset{\underset{\displaystyle CH_3}{|}}{\overset{\overset{\displaystyle CH_3}{|}}{C}}{-}H + CH_3{-}\underset{\underset{\displaystyle CH_3}{|}}{\overset{\overset{\displaystyle CH_3}{|}}{C}}{-}CH_2{-}\overset{\overset{\displaystyle CH_3}{|}}{\underset{+}{C}}{-}CH_3 \rightleftharpoons$$

$$CH_3{-}\underset{\underset{\displaystyle CH_3}{|}}{\overset{\overset{\displaystyle CH_3}{|}}{C}}{}^+ + CH_3{-}\underset{\underset{\displaystyle CH_3}{|}}{\overset{\overset{\displaystyle CH_3}{|}}{C}}{-}CH_2{-}\underset{\underset{\displaystyle H}{|}}{\overset{\overset{\displaystyle CH_3}{|}}{C}}{-}CH_3$$

In order to favor this last step and to keep the dimethylneopentylcarbonium ion from reacting with more alkene, an excess of isobutane is employed. The *t*-butyl cation formed in this step then reacts with isobutylene to continue the *chain process*. *t*-Butyl cation and the excess of isobutane are in equilibrium, but the products and reactants are the same, so no net result is observed.

$$CH_3{-}\underset{\underset{\displaystyle CH_3}{|}}{\overset{\overset{\displaystyle CH_3}{|}}{C}}{}^+ + H{-}\underset{\underset{\displaystyle CH_3}{|}}{\overset{\overset{\displaystyle CH_3}{|}}{C}}{-}CH_3 \rightleftharpoons CH_3{-}\underset{\underset{\displaystyle CH_3}{|}}{\overset{\overset{\displaystyle CH_3}{|}}{C}}{-}H + {}^+\underset{\underset{\displaystyle CH_3}{|}}{\overset{\overset{\displaystyle CH_3}{|}}{C}}{-}CH_3$$

Alkylation represents big business to the petroleum industry. In this manner, low molecular weight hydrocarbons obtained from the cracking process are converted to intermediate molecular weight, highly branched alkanes (called *alkylates*) for use in improving the octane rating of gasolines.

23.6 Dehydrogenation and Hydrogenolysis

Cycloalkanes and cycloalkenes containing one or more six-membered rings can usually be converted to the corresponding benzenoid derivatives by heating to a high temperature with a platinum or palladium catalyst. This reaction is known as *dehydrogenation*, and it is the reverse of *hydrogenation* (Sections 11.1, 15.2), which usually is carried out at much lower temperatures.

EXERCISE 23.5

In thermodynamic terms, why is a hydrogenation reaction often favored at low temperature, while the reverse reaction, dehydrogenation, is favored at much higher temperature?

When a quaternary carbon forms part of the ring structure, a benzenoid ring cannot be produced, except by the elimination of an alkyl substituent. In such cases sulfur or selenium are often superior to the noble metals as dehydrogenation agents (being converted to H_2S or H_2Se), although such reactions usually give poor yields, and rearranged products are sometimes obtained.

Dehydrogenation has often been successfully employed in the laboratory as a means of determining the structures of unknown compounds. For example, the basic ring structure of cholesterol, a compound of great biological importance and a cause of hardening of arteries in humans, was determined with considerable difficulty, and a key step in the work was dehydrogenation with selenium.

Cholesterol is the most common member of a group of compounds called the steroids. *These important compounds will be discussed in some detail in Sections 30.6 and 30.7.*

The products obtained, chrysene and methylcyclopentanophenanthrene, were clues to the structure of the cholesterol molecule and provided essential information which ultimately allowed the total structure to be determined.

Cholesterol

Chrysene
(rearrangement product)

Methylcyclopentanophenanthrene

Note that in the course of the dehydrogenation of cholesterol the eight-carbon side chain has been removed. This is the result of *hydrogenolysis*, the rupture of C—C bonds to give alkanes. In this case the hydrogen is derived directly from the dehydrogenation reaction.

Isomerization has been used to determine the relative stabilities of fused ring systems. For example, *trans*-decalin has been found to be 2.7 kcal/mole lower in enthalpy (*more stable*) than *cis*-decalin in the liquid phase; this was done by establishing equilibrium over a palladium catalyst and directly measuring the ratio of the isomers.

$$\Delta H^\circ = +2.7 \text{ kcal/mole}$$

The equilibration proceeds via a dehydrogenation and rehydrogenation sequence and is carried out in a closed system so that hydrogen does not escape. Heats of combustion have also been used to determine relative stabilities of cycloalkanes. For the decalins, heats of combustion gave the same value for ΔH° as was found by direct equilibration.

Commercial Dehydrogenation of Alkanes. Dehydrogenation of *alkanes* to *alkenes* is a drastic reaction which is of no importance in the laboratory. An industrially important example of such a dehydrogenation of an alkane was given in the previous section, that is, the formation of 2-methylpropene and hydrogen from 2-methylpropane. See also Section 35.2.

Due to the great stability of aromatic systems, alkanes containing six or more carbons can be dehydrogenated to arenes. For example, toluene is produced from *n*-heptane by heating the latter in the presence of a catalyst such as platinum or alumina:

$$CH_3(CH_2)_5CH_3 \xrightarrow[\substack{\text{heat,} \\ \text{high pressure} \\ (-H_2)}]{\text{catalyst}} \left[\text{CH}_3\text{-cyclohexene} \right] \longrightarrow \text{toluene} + 3H_2$$

n-Heptane   Methylcyclohexane   Toluene

23.7   Halogenation

A number of reactions discussed in this chapter are *chain reactions* (Section 15.7); that is, large amounts of products are formed after initiation by a small amount of a radical or carbonium ion species. The three steps in a chain reaction are *initiation, propagation,* and *termination.*

The chlorination of methane, for example, proceeds as follows:

Initiation

$$Cl_2 \longrightarrow 2Cl\cdot$$

Propagation

$$Cl\cdot + CH_4 \longrightarrow Cl-H + CH_3\cdot$$

$$CH_3\cdot + Cl_2 \longrightarrow CH_3Cl + Cl\cdot$$

Termination

$$CH_3\cdot + Cl\cdot \longrightarrow CH_3-Cl$$

Free-radical halogenations can be *initiated* by light. A quantum of light or any other form of radiant energy possesses a frequency which depends upon its energy ($E = h\nu$). If light of the proper frequency strikes a halogen molecule, the light can be absorbed and the halogen–halogen bond cleaved to give two radicals.

$$F_2 + 37\,\text{kcal/mole} \xrightarrow{h\nu} 2F\cdot$$

$$Cl_2 + 58\,\text{kcal/mole} \xrightarrow{h\nu} 2Cl\cdot$$

$$Br_2 + 46\,\text{kcal/mole} \xrightarrow{h\nu} 2Br\cdot$$

$$I_2 + 36\,\text{kcal/mole} \xrightarrow{h\nu} 2I\cdot$$

In the first of the two *propagation* steps the halogen radical attacks the alkane (illustrated for methane):

$$CH_4 + F\cdot \longrightarrow HF + CH_3\cdot + 33\,\text{kcal/mole}$$

$$CH_4 + Cl\cdot \longrightarrow HCl + CH_3\cdot + 1\,\text{kcal/mole}$$

$$CH_4 + Br\cdot + 15\,\text{kcal/mole} \longrightarrow HBr + CH_3\cdot$$

$$CH_4 + I\cdot + 31\,\text{kcal/mole} \longrightarrow HI + CH_3\cdot$$

Since the attack of either Br· or I· on methane is an endothermic reaction, the reverse reactions (attack of $CH_3\cdot$ on HBr and HI) are exothermic and energetically more favorable. As a result, methane cannot be brominated or iodinated in this way without many more acts of initiation and a higher temperature than is required for chlorination. If a weaker C—H bond than that found in methane is present, for example, a benzylic C—H bond, bromination may be energetically favorable and will then occur.

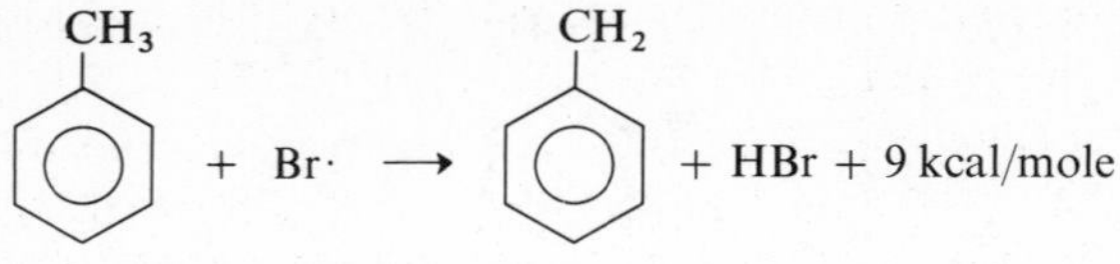

Benzyl radical

The chain reaction is continued in the transfer step by a subsequent attack of the methyl or benzyl radical on a molecule of halogen.

$$CH_3\cdot + F_2 \rightarrow CH_3F + F\cdot + 60\,kcal/mole$$

$$CH_3\cdot + Cl_2 \rightarrow CH_3Cl + Cl\cdot + 24\,kcal/mole$$

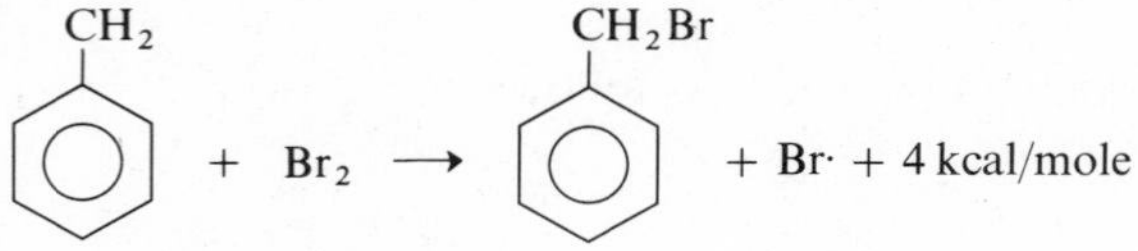

In this step, an alkyl halide is formed as a product and more halogen radical is produced, which can in turn attack methane or toluene as described above. Thus, the formation of a small amount of halogen radical in the initiation step starts a chain reaction in which a product of one propagation reaction is the reactant for another, and so on.

The chain reaction is *terminated* by the coupling of two radicals.

$$Cl\cdot + Cl\cdot \rightarrow Cl_2$$

$$CH_3\cdot + Cl\cdot \rightarrow CH_3Cl$$

$$CH_3\cdot + CH_3\cdot \rightarrow CH_3-CH_3$$

As long as the concentration of radicals is low, propagations are more likely to occur than terminations; it is statistically unlikely that two radicals will collide.

The propagation step of the chain reaction of halogen atoms with methane can be summarized in terms of the *chain length*, that is, the number of molecules halogenated as the result of initiation by a single halogen atom. Because the rate-determining propagation step in chlorination has a low activation energy (both steps are exothermic), the chain length is long (about 10,000). For bromination hydrogen abstraction is endothermic by 15 kcal/mole, there is a sizable activation energy, and the chain length is only 100. For iodination, hydrogen abstraction is endothermic by 31 kcal and the chain length is about zero.

The halogen atom can undergo either of two reactions.

$$X\cdot + CH_4 \rightarrow HX + CH_3\cdot$$

$$X\cdot + X\cdot \rightarrow X_2$$

For iodine the activation energy for the first reaction is so high that the second occurs preferentially, even though the concentration of I· is low and renders this reaction statistically improbable.

Free-radical fluorination of methane occurs even without initiation by light. The requirement of only 4 kcal/mole for the reaction of methane with fluorine suggests that initiation can also occur by the following reaction:

$$CH_4 + F_2 + 4\,kcal/mole \rightarrow CH_3\cdot + HF + F\cdot$$

EXERCISE 23.6

Chlorination of cyclopentane leads to how many isomeric dichlorocyclopentanes? Name them and draw their structures.

To predict what the products of halogenation of an alkane will be, both the stability of the alkyl radicals and the selectivity of the halogen radical must be considered.

The C—H bonds whose cleavage will lead to the formation of the most stable radicals are attacked preferentially by halogen radicals. As has been discussed in earlier chapters, the relative reactivities of alkanes are tertiary > secondary > primary, and the relative stabilities of radicals are tertiary > secondary > primary.

Since Br· is so much less reactive than Cl· with respect to attack on C—H bonds, bromination is much more selective than chlorination. At high temperatures, a chlorine atom reacts with almost any hydrogen in the molecule with which it collides and substitution becomes more random.

For example, consider the halogenation of isobutane. Both tertiary or primary radicals may be formed.

$$CH_3-\underset{\underset{H}{|}}{\overset{\overset{CH_3}{|}}{C}}-CH_3 + X· \rightarrow CH_3-\overset{\overset{CH_3}{|}}{\underset{·}{C}}-CH_3 + CH_3-\overset{\overset{CH_3}{|}}{C}H-CH_2· + HX$$

tertiary   primary   A tertiary radical   A primary radical

Free-radical bromination of isobutane at 300°C gives 2-bromo-2-methylpropane almost exclusively.

$$CH_3-\underset{\underset{H}{|}}{\overset{\overset{CH_3}{|}}{C}}-CH_3 + Br_2 \xrightarrow{300°C} CH_3-\underset{\underset{Br}{|}}{\overset{\overset{CH_3}{|}}{C}}-CH_3 + HBr$$

2-Bromo-2-methylpropane

The combination of the selectivity of bromine and the greater stability of the *t*-butyl radical explain this result.

In contrast, chlorination gives both possible products. This is as would be expected for the far less selective chlorine atom. On a statistical basis the yield of 1-chloro-2-methylpropane would be predicted to be nine times that of 2-chloro-2-methylpropane, for there are nine primary hydrogens and one tertiary hydrogen. However, the yields are found experimentally to be in the ratio 2:1.

$$CH_3-\underset{\underset{H}{|}}{\overset{\overset{CH_3}{|}}{C}}-CH_3 + Cl_2 \xrightarrow{300°C} CH_3-\overset{\overset{CH_3}{|}}{C}H-CH_2-Cl + CH_3-\underset{\underset{Cl}{|}}{\overset{\overset{CH_3}{|}}{C}}-CH_3$$

1-Chloro-2-methylpropane   2-Chloro-2-methylpropane

Experimental yield : 2 to 1
Statistical prediction : 9 to 1

The amount of 2-chloro compound is greater than statistics alone would indicate because of the greater stability of the tertiary radical from which it is formed.

In terms of transition-state theory (Section 14.4), the position of attack of Cl· on propane, for example, depends on the relative reactivities of primary vs. secondary hydrogen atoms, and on a statistical factor, i.e. entropy (Section 13.1).

$$\Delta G^{\ddagger} = \Delta H^{\ddagger} - T\Delta S^{\ddagger}$$

Thus, the free energy of activation ($\Delta G^{\ddagger}$) depends on the relative reactivities of the hydrogens (corresponding to $\Delta H^{\ddagger}$, the enthalpy difference), and on the relative numbers of primary and secondary hydrogen atoms present (corresponding to $\Delta S^{\ddagger}$, the entropy difference). For propane the statistical factor is $3:1$:

$$CH_3CH_2CH_3 \quad \text{Six primary H}$$
$$\text{Two secondary H}$$

If a secondary hydrogen had the same reactivity as a primary one, chlorination of propane would yield three times as much propyl chloride as isopropyl chloride. Actually, the chlorination yields equal amounts of the two chlorides, and attack of Cl· on the secondary hydrogen atoms of propane is therefore approximately three times faster than predicted from the statistical factor alone. This means that secondary hydrogen atoms are three times more reactive toward Cl· than are primary hydrogen atoms.

EXERCISE 23.7

From the data on page 637, what are the relative reactivities toward Cl· of primary and tertiary hydrogens?

Rearrangements of free radicals are much less common than those of the corresponding carbonium ions. Thus, the free-radical chlorination of neopentane yields neopentyl chloride.

$$CH_3-\underset{\underset{CH_3}{|}}{\overset{\overset{CH_3}{|}}{C}}-CH_3 + Cl_2 \rightarrow CH_3-\underset{\underset{CH_3}{|}}{\overset{\overset{CH_3}{|}}{C}}-CH_2-Cl + HCl$$

Neopentyl chloride

$$\left(\text{no} \quad CH_3-\underset{\underset{Cl}{|}}{\overset{\overset{CH_3}{|}}{C}}-CH_2CH_3 \right)$$

2-Chloro-2-methylbutane

Phenyl migrations can occur in radicals with a C_6H_5 group on the carbon adjacent to the radical, but to a lesser extent than in the corresponding carbonium ions.

$$C_6H_5-\underset{\underset{CH_3}{|}}{\overset{\overset{CH_3}{|}}{C}}-CH_2\cdot \rightarrow \cdot\underset{\underset{CH_3}{|}}{\overset{\overset{CH_3}{|}}{C}}-CH_2C_6H_5$$

It is difficult to stop free-radical halogenations at the monosubstituted stage. For example, the chlorination of methane gives various amounts of methylene chloride, chloroform, and carbon tetrachloride, in addition to methyl chloride.

$$CH_4 + Cl_2 \xrightarrow{h\nu} CH_3Cl + CH_2Cl_2 + CHCl_3 + CCl_4$$

Methyl   Methylene   Chloro-   Carbon
chloride   chloride   form   tetrachloride

A large excess of alkane favors the monohalogenated product. For example, if twice as much methane as chlorine is used, methyl chloride is formed in 62% yield and chloroform in 7% yield; if methane and chlorine are used in a one-to-one ratio, only 37% methyl chloride is formed, while chloroform is found in 19% yield. Although chlorination is a rather indiscriminate process, it is sometimes useful, for example, for the preparation of cleaning solvents, which are mixtures of chlorinated hydrocarbons. In this case separation of the mixture is unnecessary.

Initiators other than light can be used. Free-radical reactions can be initiated thermally or with small amounts of peroxides, azo compounds, or alkyl nitrates, or by electrolysis, as well as by other methods.

$$Cl_2 \xrightarrow{\text{heat}} 2Cl\cdot$$

$$R-O-O-R \rightarrow 2RO\cdot$$

$$R-N=N-R \rightarrow 2R\cdot + N_2$$

$$RO-NO_2 \rightarrow RO\cdot + NO_2$$

$$RCO_2^- \xrightarrow{-e^-} RCO_2\cdot \rightarrow R\cdot + CO_2$$

A radical-chain reaction can be *inhibited* by the presence of reagents which react with alkyl radicals to form less reactive radicals. Iodine is such a reagent, the iodine radical being less reactive than the carbon radical.

Phenols and aromatic amines are effective inhibitors of radical reactions. Hydroquinone is widely used as an antioxidant and to prevent polymerization of sensitive compounds. It functions by reacting with radicals to form a more stable radical.

These radicals then disproportionate to form a mixture of quinone and hydroquinone. The latter two compounds form a static charge-transfer complex called *quinhydrone* (which can be isolated as a dark crystalline solid), thus terminating the chain reaction.

A specific reagent for effecting the allylic bromination of alkenes is *N*-bromosuccinimide (NBS). It is a free-radical reaction, and peroxides or light are used as initiators. The active brominating agent is thought to be Br_2, which is liberated at low concentration by reaction of NBS with HBr (the other reaction product).

Halogenation at a benzylic carbon is a useful process for the preparation not only of halides, but also of carbonyl compounds. The rate of each successive halogenation is slower than the one before it, so all of the reactions shown proceed in good yield.

Benzyl chloride → Benzal chloride → Benzotrichloride → CH₂OH, CHO, COOH products

Nitration of alkanes occurs in the gas phase at 400°C via a radical mechanism. Mixtures of products are obtained, and the reaction is not useful in the laboratory (but it is used industrially).

EXERCISE 23.8

Predict the product that will result when *p*-xylene is treated with 4 moles of Cl_2, and the product is hydrolyzed.

23.8   Special Reactions of Small-Ring Hydrocarbons

Cyclopropane is much more reactive than other cycloalkanes, owing to the release of strain energy when the ring is opened (Section 3.5). Cyclobutane is less reactive than cyclopropane, and cycloalkanes with larger rings react for the most part in a manner similar to acyclic hydrocarbons. Ordinarily, the carbon–carbon bonds of alkanes and cycloalkanes are not cleaved by hydrogen in the presence of a catalyst. Small rings do undergo hydrogenolysis, however. Cyclopropane itself, for example, is hydrogenolyzed at 120°C in the presence of a nickel catalyst, or at 25°C over platinum.

$$\underset{H_2C-CH_2}{\overset{CH_2}{\diagup\diagdown}} + H_2 \xrightarrow{Ni, 120°C} CH_3-CH_2-CH_3$$

Cyclobutane can be similarly hydrogenolyzed to *n*-butane, but it requires a much higher temperature. Larger ring cycloalkanes do not add hydrogen except under very drastic conditions (Section 23.6).

EXERCISE 23.9

Both ethylcyclobutane and cyclohexane can be converted in part to *n*-hexane by hydrogenolysis in the presence of a catalyst. Which one will react at the lower temperature? Show why this is so with the aid of a reaction coordinate diagram.

Free-radical halogenations of cycloalkanes in general follow the same routes as halogenations of alkanes. Cyclopropane, chlorine, and ultraviolet light yield cyclopropyl chloride.

$$\underset{H_2C-CH_2}{\overset{CH_2}{\diagup\diagdown}} + Cl_2 \xrightarrow{hv} \underset{H_2C-CH-Cl}{\overset{CH_2}{\diagup\diagdown}} + HCl \quad \left(\begin{array}{c} + \text{ some 1,1-dichloro-} \\ \text{cyclopropane} \end{array}\right)$$

Cyclopropyl chloride

Bromine (in the presence of a catalyst) and iodine, on the other hand, *add* to cyclopropane rather than substitute a hydrogen.

$$\underset{\text{1,3-Dibromopropane}}{H_2C-CH_2} \xrightarrow{}$$

$$\underset{\substack{\text{CH}_2 \\ H_2C-CH_2}}{} + Br_2 \xrightarrow{AlBr_3} \underset{\substack{\text{CH}_2 \\ H_2C \qquad CH_2 \\ | \qquad | \\ Br \qquad Br}}{} \quad \left(\begin{array}{l} \text{+ some 1,1- and 1,2-} \\ \text{dibromocyclopropane} \end{array} \right)$$

1,3-Dibromopropane

Cyclobutane and other cycloalkanes, however, are not opened by these reagents. Some other special reactions of cyclopropane are

$$\underset{\substack{\text{CH}_2 \\ H_2C-CH_2}}{} + HBr \xrightarrow{H_2O} CH_3CH_2CH_2Br$$

$$\underset{\substack{\text{CH}_2 \\ H_2C-CH_2}}{} + H_2O \xrightarrow{H_2SO_4} CH_3CH_2CH_2OH$$

(in $D_2SO_4-D_2O$, D appears on α, β and γ carbons)

$$\underset{\substack{\text{CH}_2 \\ H_2C-CH_2}}{} + PhH \xrightarrow{HF} PhCH_2CH_2CH_3$$

23.9   Methylene Insertion

In Section 22.8 we saw that methylene, a carbene, is formed from diazomethane by the action of light, heat, or catalysts such as cuprous chloride.

$$\underset{\text{Diazomethane}}{CH_2N_2} \xrightarrow[\text{CuCl}]{h\nu, \Delta, \text{ or}} \underset{\text{Methylene}}{CH_2 + N_2}$$

The two different electronic structures of carbenes were discussed in Section 12.5.

When methylene is generated from diazomethane in the presence of an alkane or a cycloalkane, it *inserts* into a carbon–hydrogen bond.

Insertion

$$\underset{}{-\overset{|}{\underset{|}{C}}-H} + CH_2 \xrightarrow[h\nu]{CH_2N_2} -\overset{|}{\underset{|}{C}}-CH_2-H$$

The insertion is nearly random, that is, completely *unselective*. For example, methylene reacts with *n*-pentane to form a mixture of isomeric hexanes, the composition of which reflects a complete lack of selectivity, the 12 hydrogens of the pentane molecule behaving as shown.

$$12\ CH_3CH_2\underset{\substack{| \\ H}}{C}H\underset{\substack{| \\ H}}{C}H_2-H + 12\ CH_2 \xrightarrow[h\nu]{CH_2N_2} 6\ CH_3CH_2CH_2CH_2CH_2-CH_2-H$$

$$+ 4\ CH_3CH_2CH_2\underset{\substack{| \\ CH_2 \\ | \\ H}}{C}HCH_3 + 2\ CH_3CH_2\underset{\substack{| \\ CH_2 \\ | \\ H}}{C}HCH_2CH_3$$

In this reaction methylene is highly reactive and is presumably in the singlet spin state with the unshared electrons paired.

Reactions of methylene can be more selective if it is "cool," that is, in the triplet state with the unshared electrons unpaired. How "hot" or "cool" methylene is depends on experimental conditions, such as the reagent from which it is generated, the wavelength of light used, and whether the reaction is in the liquid or gas phase. For example, when diazomethane is photolyzed in the presence of propane in the gas phase, nearly random amounts of *n*-butane and isobutane are formed. However, when argon is added (so the "hot" methylene can lose energy through collisions), the yield of isobutane is increased, indicating a preferred insertion into a secondary versus a primary C—H bond by the "cooled" methylene.

23.10   Summary of Synthetic Methods for Alkanes and Cycloalkanes

1. Alkanes

a. From natural gas or petroleum: Most alkanes are obtained from natural gas and petroleum sources. The natural alkanes are also transformed into synthetic alkanes by the cracking, isomerization, and alkylation procedures described in this chapter.

b. From alkenes:

(1) By hydrogenation with hydrogen and a catalyst (Section 15.2)

$$\begin{array}{c}\diagdown \\ \diagup\end{array}C=C\begin{array}{c}\diagup \\ \diagdown\end{array} + H_2 \xrightarrow{\text{Pt, Pd, or Ni}} \begin{array}{c} | \quad | \\ -C-C- \\ | \quad | \\ H \quad H \end{array}$$

(2) By hydroboration and hydrolysis of the resulting trialkylboranes (Section 15.9)

$$6 \begin{array}{c}\diagdown \\ \diagup\end{array}C=C\begin{array}{c}\diagup \\ \diagdown\end{array} + B_2H_6 \longrightarrow 2\left(\begin{array}{c} | \quad | \\ -C-C- \\ | \quad | \\ H \end{array}\right)_3 B$$

$$\left(\begin{array}{c} | \quad | \\ -C-C- \\ | \quad | \\ H \end{array}\right)_3 B + 3\,H_2O \xrightarrow{H^+} 3 \begin{array}{c} | \quad | \\ -C-C-H \\ | \quad | \\ H \end{array} + B(OH)_3$$

With D_2O this procedure can be used for placing deuterium in specific positions in an alkane.

$$\left(\begin{array}{c} | \quad | \\ -C-C- \\ | \quad | \\ H \end{array}\right)_3 B + 3\,D_2O \xrightarrow{D^+} \begin{array}{c} | \quad | \\ -C-C-D \\ | \quad | \\ H \end{array} + B(OD)_3$$

c. From alkyl halides (Section 17.12):

(1) by reduction via the Grignard reagent

$$\begin{array}{c} | \\ -C-X \\ | \end{array} + Mg \longrightarrow \begin{array}{c} | \\ -C-MgX \\ | \end{array}$$

$$\begin{array}{c} | \\ -C-MgX \\ | \end{array} + H_2O \longrightarrow \begin{array}{c} | \\ -C-H \\ | \end{array} + HOMgX$$

or

$$\begin{array}{c} | \\ -C-MgX \\ | \end{array} + D_2O \longrightarrow \begin{array}{c} | \\ -C-D \\ | \end{array} + DOMgX$$

(2) by a bimolecular reduction with metallic sodium (the Wurtz reaction, Section 17.11)

$$2 \begin{array}{c} | \\ -C-X \\ | \end{array} + 2\,Na \longrightarrow \begin{array}{c} | \quad | \\ -C-C- \\ | \quad | \end{array} + 2\,NaX$$

(3) by reduction with zinc and a hydrohalic acid (Section 17.12)

$$\begin{array}{c} | \\ -C-X \\ | \end{array} + Zn + HX \longrightarrow \begin{array}{c} | \\ -C-H \\ | \end{array} + ZnX_2$$

(4) by the action of bases on quaternary phosphonium salts (Section 33.11)

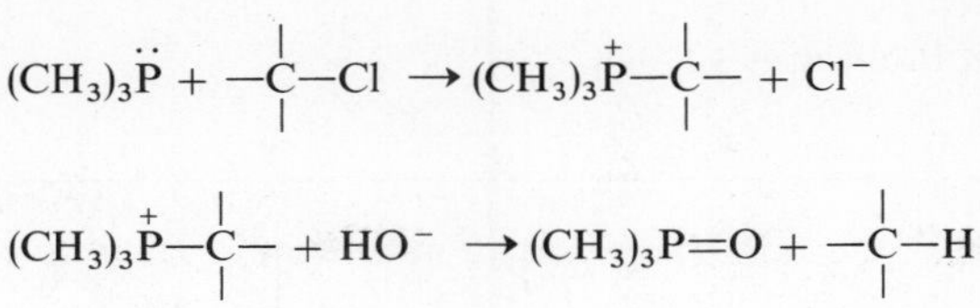

$$(CH_3)_3\overset{..}{P} + -\overset{|}{\underset{|}{C}}-Cl \rightarrow (CH_3)_3\overset{+}{P}-\overset{|}{\underset{|}{C}}- + Cl^-$$

$$(CH_3)_3\overset{+}{P}-\overset{|}{\underset{|}{C}}- + HO^- \rightarrow (CH_3)_3P{=}O + -\overset{|}{\underset{|}{C}}-H$$

d. From ketones (Section 19.12)

$$-\overset{|}{\underset{\overset{\|}{O}}{C}}- \rightarrow -CH_2-$$

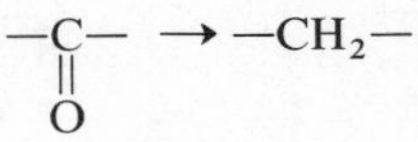

2. Cycloalkanes

a. From petroleum. Various six- and five-membered ring cycloalkanes are available in petroleum.

b. From cycloalkenes (see Method 1b, above, for reactions):
   (1) by hydrogenation of cycloalkenes (Section 15.2)
   (2) by hydroboration of cycloalkenes and hydrolysis of the tricycloalkylborons (Section 15.9)

c. From arenes by hydrogenation (Section 16.10)

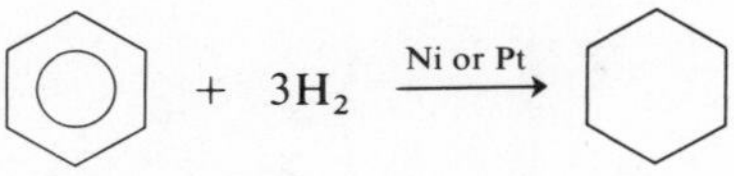

$$\text{benzene} + 3H_2 \xrightarrow{\text{Ni or Pt}} \text{cyclohexane}$$

d. From dihalides (Section 17.11)

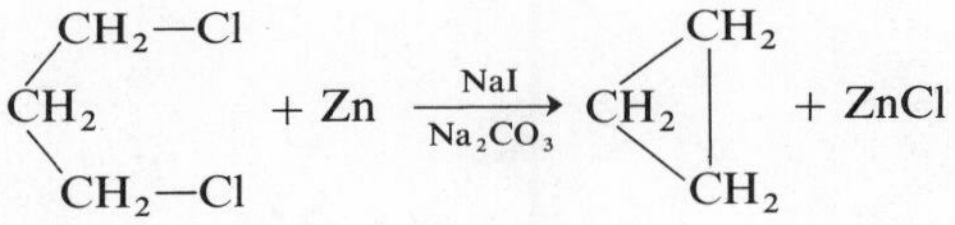

$$\begin{array}{c} CH_2-Cl \\ CH_2 \\ CH_2-Cl \end{array} + Zn \xrightarrow[Na_2CO_3]{NaI} \begin{array}{c} CH_2 \\ CH_2 \\ CH_2 \end{array} + ZnCl$$

e. From ketones (Section 19.12)

$$(CH_2)_n \quad C{=}O \rightarrow (CH_2)_n \quad CH_2$$

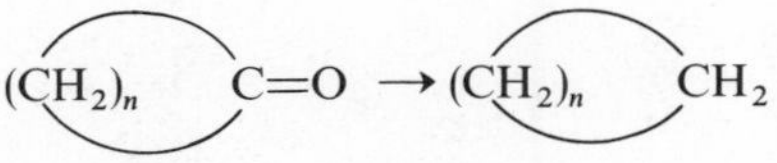

f. From addition of carbenes to alkenes and cycloalkanes (Section 15.13)

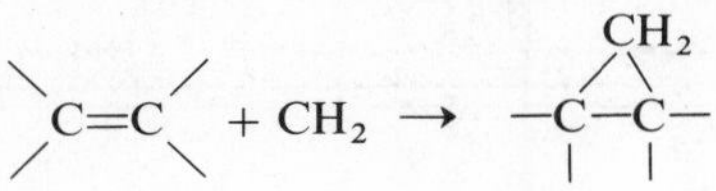

$$\overset{\diagdown}{\diagup}C{=}C\overset{\diagup}{\diagdown} + CH_2 \rightarrow -\overset{|}{\underset{|}{C}}-\overset{|}{\underset{|}{C}}- \text{ (with } CH_2 \text{ bridge)}$$

PROBLEMS

1. Olefinic bonds will migrate under dehydrogenation conditions. For example, when 2,5-dimethyl-1,5-hexadiene is heated to 250°C in the presence of an aluminum oxide–chromium oxide catalyst, an isomer results. The nmr spectrum of the isomer is given on the next page.
   What is the structure of the isomer? Interpret the spectrum.

2. What is the structure of the C_8H_{10} compound for which the nmr spectrum is given on the next page? Interpret the spectrum.

3. Explain (in terms of resonance forms) the following stability order:

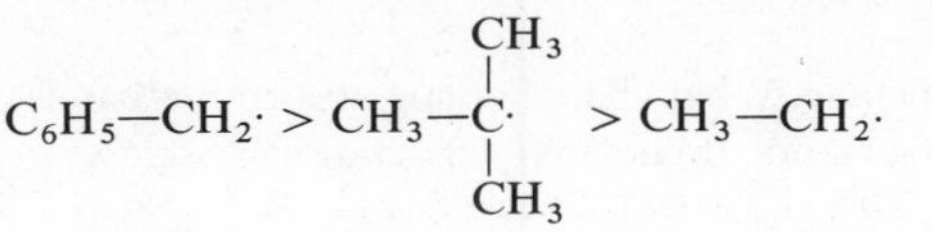

$$C_6H_5-CH_2 \cdot > CH_3-\overset{\overset{\textstyle CH_3}{|}}{\underset{\underset{\textstyle CH_3}{|}}{C}}\cdot > CH_3-CH_2 \cdot$$

NMR spectrum of unknown isomer, Problem 1.

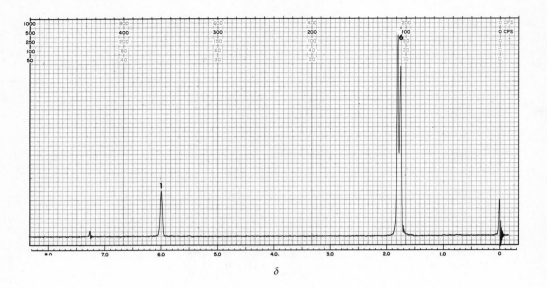

NMR spectrum of unknown, Problem 2.

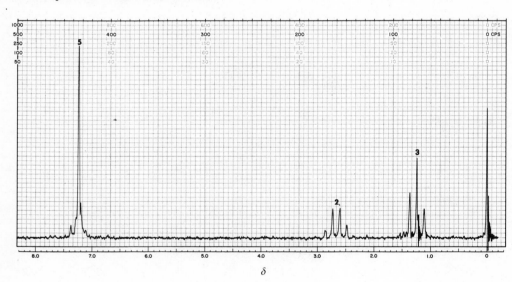

4.   Outline laboratory syntheses of the following compounds from ethanol, methanol, and benzene.

(a) $CH_3-CHCH_2CH_2CH_3$
                 |
                 CH_3

(b) $Ph-CH_2CH_2CH_3$
                CH_3

(c) $CH_3-CH-CH-CH_3$
               | |
             CH_3 CH_3

(d) $CH_3-\overset{\displaystyle CH_3}{\underset{\displaystyle CH_3}{\overset{|}{\underset{|}{C}}}}-CH_2CH_3$

5.   The figure gives the infrared spectrum of octane. What characteristic absorption bands would appear if this were oxidized to (a) 1-octanol, (b) octanal, (c) octanoic acid, (d) 2-octanone, (e) 1-octene, (f) 1-octyne?

Infrared spectrum of *n*-octane as a neat liquid film.

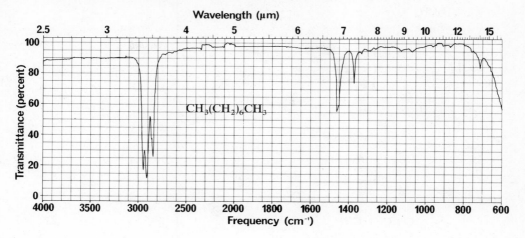

6. For the reaction

$$CH_3-CH_3 + Cl_2 \xrightarrow{(PhCOO)_2}$$

(a) write the reactions for the initiation;
(b) write the reactions for the propagation;
(c) write the reactions for the termination.

7. The relative rates of reactions of hydrogen are 4.5, 3.0, and 1.0 for tertiary, secondary, and primary, respectively, in the following reaction:

$$R-H + Cl_2 \xrightarrow{h\nu} R-Cl + HCl$$

The chlorination of isopentane leads to four different monochlorides. What percentage of each isomer is formed?

8. Suggest a mechanism for the following reaction:

$$2 \bigcirc\!\!-CH_3 + (CH_3-\overset{\overset{\displaystyle O}{\|}}{C}-O-)_2 \xrightarrow{\Delta} \bigcirc\!\!-CH_2-CH_2-\!\!\bigcirc$$

$$+ 2\,CH_4 + 2\,CO_2$$

9. Complete the following:

(a) $CH_3CH{=}CH_2 + Cl_2 \xrightarrow[\text{dark}]{\text{cold}}$

(b) $CH_3CH{=}CH_2 + Cl_2\ (1\ \text{mole}) \xrightarrow{600°C}$

(c) $\bigcirc\ +\ \underset{\overset{\displaystyle\|}{O}}{\overset{\overset{\displaystyle O}{\|}}{}}N{-}Br \xrightarrow{\text{peroxide}}$

(d) $\overset{\displaystyle CH_2}{H_2C\!\!-\!\!CH_2} \xrightarrow{H_3O^+}$

(e) $\begin{matrix} H_2C-CH_2 \\ | \qquad | \\ H_2C-CH_2 \end{matrix} \xrightarrow[h\nu]{Cl_2}$

(f) 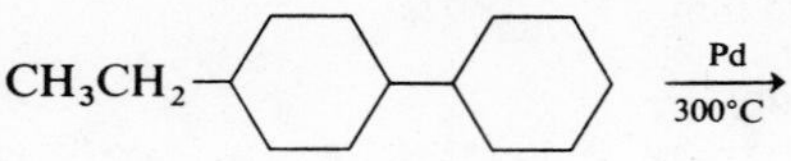 CH_3CH_2—⬡—⬡ $\xrightarrow[300°C]{Pd}$

(g) 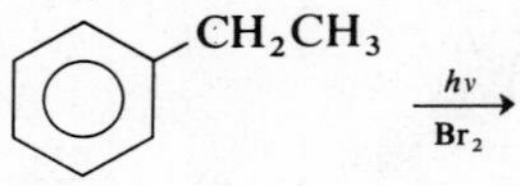   ⬡CH_2CH_3 $\xrightarrow[Br_2]{hv}$

(h) 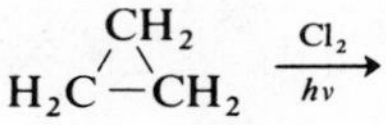 $H_2C\overset{CH_2}{\underset{CH_2}{\triangle}}$ $\xrightarrow[hv]{Cl_2}$

(i) 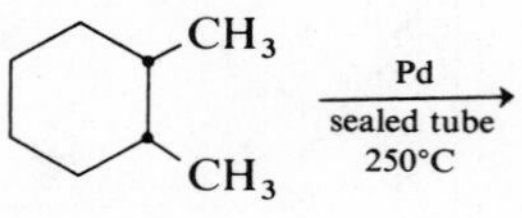   ⬡$\overset{CH_3}{\underset{CH_3}{}}$ $\xrightarrow[\substack{sealed\ tube\\250°C}]{Pd}$

(j) 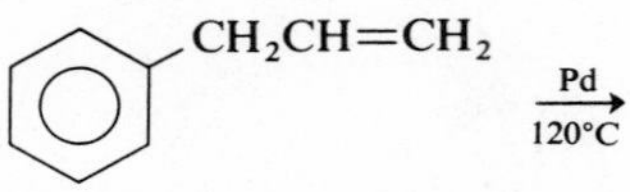   ⬡$CH_2CH=CH_2$ $\xrightarrow[120°C]{Pd}$

10.   3,3-Diethylheptane is inert to bromine in sunlight, but 3,4-diethylheptane reacts, albeit slowly. What is the product to be expected of the latter compound? What is the reason for the difference in reactivity between the two hydrocarbons?

Optional Problems

1.   Write balanced equations for the following reactions:

(a) 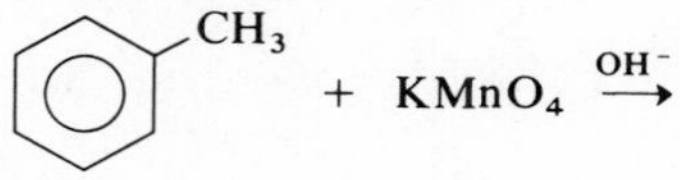   ⬡CH_3 $+$ $KMnO_4$ $\xrightarrow{OH^-}$

(b) 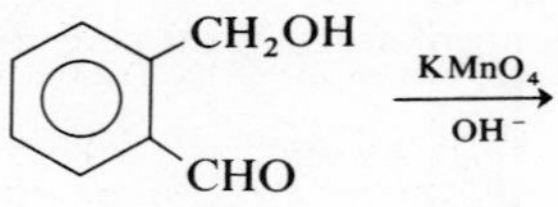   ⬡$\overset{CH_2OH}{\underset{CHO}{}}$ $\xrightarrow[OH^-]{KMnO_4}$

(c) 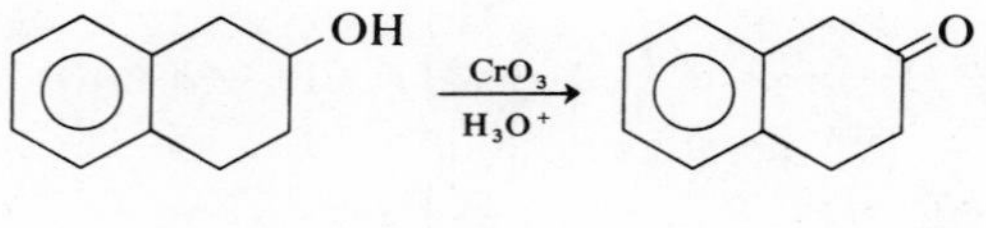   ⬡⬡OH $\xrightarrow[H_3O^+]{CrO_3}$ ⬡⬡O

(d) 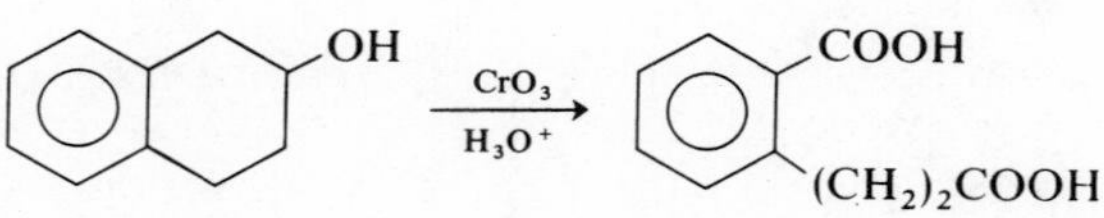   ⬡⬡OH $\xrightarrow[H_3O^+]{CrO_3}$ ⬡$\overset{COOH}{\underset{(CH_2)_2COOH}{}}$

(e) 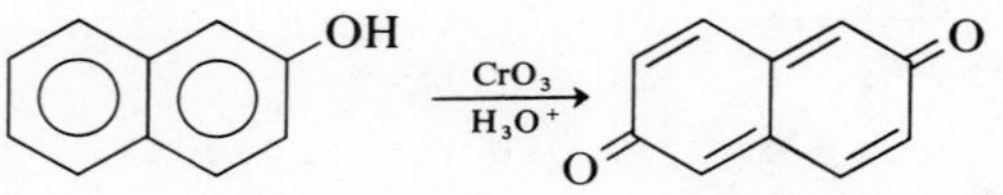   ⬡⬡OH $\xrightarrow[H_3O^+]{CrO_3}$ O⬡⬡O

2.   How many stereoisomers of perhydroanthracene are there? Which of these are optically active?

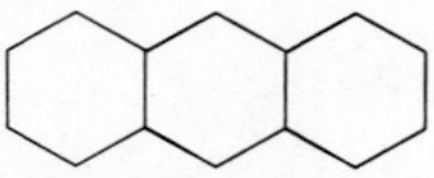

⬡⬡⬡

Perhydroanthracene

CHAPTER 24

INTRODUCTION TO THE PHILOSOPHY AND PRACTICE OF ORGANIC SYNTHESIS

24.1 General Considerations

The earlier chapters of this book have presented the main outlines of the structural and electronic theory of organic chemistry. This theory, though it is still constantly under refinement, forms a mighty edifice of knowledge, which now enables us to correlate logically the physical and chemical properties of organic compounds. A good background in organic chemical theory is invaluable in helping to predict whether a specific organic reaction is likely to take place. In this regard, however, it functions somewhat like the rules of grammar in language: It tells us better what cannot be done than exactly what can be done or, especially, how best to do it. The organic chemist who wishes to convert one compound into another must have a good general knowledge of organic reactions. Furthermore, he will rely heavily upon the details of the enormous experimental literature of organic chemistry which has been accumulated over the past century. If he wants to convert compound A into compound Z, and if his general knowledge of theory and reactions suggests that this conversion should be possible in a one-step operation, he will probably search the chemical literature to see exactly how this conversion has been carried out in the past. He will then choose what seems to be the best known procedure and will often try to make logical improvements in the reaction conditions. Quite possibly he will find that no chemist has previously recorded the conversion of A into Z, but that ample analogy for this general type of conversion exists. He will then devise a procedure based upon the same reaction of some closely analogous compound A′ which contains the same reactive functional group as A.

Most of the time it is not possible to prepare a specific organic compound Z from an available starting material A by any single reaction. Indeed, most organic structures which we can write on paper will represent compounds which cannot be prepared in any *single* reaction from *any* known starting material. This is not really surprising, since an infinite number of organic structures can be written, while only about three million are known compounds, and of these, only a few thousand can be purchased at any price. If the structure of an unknown compound Z does not violate the basic tenets of theory, however, it will always be possible to devise a synthesis of it from known and available starting materials. Depending upon the complexity of Z, the nature of the available starting materials, and the ingenuity of the chemist, such a synthesis can involve anything from putting together two obvious reaction steps, to creating an intellectual masterpiece of 20 or more perfectly planned sequential operations.

The art of organic synthesis serves many important purposes. The theoretical organic chemist must synthesize unusual compounds to test his theories. The natural products chemist, who is concerned with determining the structures of complex naturally occurring organic compounds, still considers the total synthesis of a natural product from simple precursors by known reactions as chemical proof of its structure. The syntheses of such complex natural products as cholesterol, morphine, and chlorophyll have not only led to the discovery of many new synthetic reactions of general utility, but have also been instrumental in the development and refinement of chemical theories. Last but not least, much of the technology of the modern world relies upon the synthetic organic chemist as the source of new and improved drugs, plastics, dyes, detergents, insecticides, and other products. Our ability to predict the usefulness of a new organic structure before it is actually prepared is still relatively rudimentary, particularly in regard to its possible medicinal utility. For this reason, many practically-minded large chemical companies continually carry out research on the synthesis of all types of new, complex, and exotic organic compounds.

In order to learn something about the practice of organic synthesis, the student should first review the individual reactions which he has learned in previous chapters. These reactions *must* be at his fingertips as practical tools. If they are not, he will soon find himself in the position of a person who tries to play a game of chess before learning the allowed movements of each of the different pieces on the board.

The sections entitled "Summary of Synthetic Methods," which are at the ends of Chapters 15 and 17 through 23, are convenient reference sources for individual synthetic steps which the student may have forgotten. The student might find it desirable to do Exercise 24.1 at this point. If he is not able to answer most of these questions correctly, the need for review is clearly indicated.

EXERCISE 24.1

What reagents or reactions are necessary to carry out the following transformations?

(a) $\underset{\overset{\displaystyle O}{\|}}{R-C-R} \rightarrow R-CH_2-R$

(b) $\underset{R}{\overset{R}{>}}C=O \rightarrow \underset{R}{\overset{R}{>}}C\underset{O-CH_2}{\overset{O-CH_2}{<}}$

(c) $R-CH_2OH \rightarrow R-CH_2CH_2OH$

(d) $R-COOH \rightarrow R-CH_2COOH$

(e) $R-CH_2OH \rightarrow R-CH_2CH_2CH_2OH$

(f) $R-NH_2 \rightarrow R-N(CH_3)_2$

(g) $R-C\underset{OH}{\overset{O}{<}} \rightarrow R-C\underset{OCH_3}{\overset{O}{<}}$

(h) $R-C\underset{NH_2}{\overset{O}{<}} \rightarrow R-C\underset{OH}{\overset{O}{<}}$

(i) $R-C\underset{OH}{\overset{O}{<}} \rightarrow R-C\equiv N$

(j) $R-C\underset{N(CH_3)_2}{\overset{O}{<}} \rightarrow \underset{\overset{\displaystyle O}{\|}}{R-C-R'}$

(k) $R-C\equiv C-H \rightarrow R-C\equiv C-R'$

24.2 Simple Functional Group Transformations of Aliphatic Compounds

The simplest kind of organic synthesis is that in which no change occurs in the carbon skeleton. In other words, no carbons are gained or lost, no carbons are rearranged to new positions, and no rings are made or broken. This type of synthesis involves reactions such as oxidations and reductions, displacement reactions, and eliminations. Some examples are given below from the butane and the cyclohexane series.

Example 1

Convert butyric acid into *n*-butylamine.

$$CH_3CH_2CH_2CO_2H \rightarrow CH_3CH_2CH_2CH_2NH_2$$

Simple inspection shows that the carbonyl group of the butyric acid must vanish at some time in the overall process. Reduction of the carbonyl of a carboxyl group or of an acid derivative can be accomplished by only one obvious practical method, LiAlH$_4$ reduction. We can first of all consider route A, involving reduction of the acid as the first step.

(*A*)

$$CH_3CH_2CH_2CO_2H \xrightarrow{\text{LiAlH}_4} CH_3CH_2CH_2CH_2OH$$

n-Butyl alcohol

We must now convert a primary alcohol, R—OH, to the amine R—NH$_2$. The most obvious route,

$$R-OH \xrightarrow{\text{HBr}} R-Br \xrightarrow{\text{NH}_3} R-NH_2$$

is usually unacceptable, because further alkylation of the amine by the halide will take place. On the other hand, the conversion R—Br → R—NH$_2$ can be carried out in this case indirectly, either by way of the azide R—N$_3$ or by way of the Gabriel synthesis. Actually, the alkyl bromide can often be replaced to advantage by the tosylate (*p*-toluenesulfonate) of the alcohol. Route A is thus expanded as follows:

$$CH_3CH_2CH_2COOH \xrightarrow{\text{LiAlH}_4} \textit{n}\text{-Bu}-OH$$

A different approach, giving a more practical solution to the problem, involves reduction of the original carboxyl carbonyl in the *last* step. This is possible, since we know that amides are reduced to amines by LiAlH$_4$; the preliminary conversion of the acid to its amide *via* the acid chloride is straightforward.

(*B*)

$$\textit{n}\text{-Pr}-CO_2H \xrightarrow{\text{PCl}_3} \textit{n}\text{-Pr}-COCl \xrightarrow{\text{NH}_3} \textit{n}\text{-Pr}-CONH_2 \xrightarrow{\text{LiAlH}_4} \textit{n}\text{-Pr}-CH_2NH_2$$

EXERCISE 24.2

Specify alternative reagents and conditions which would allow the steps in routes A and B of Example 1 to be carried out in good yield.

Example 2

Convert *n*-butylamine into 1-butyne.

$$CH_3CH_2CH_2CH_2-NH_2 \rightarrow CH_3CH_2C\equiv CH$$

The desired alkyne can be prepared easily from the corresponding alkene (1-butene) by addition of bromine to the double bond, followed by elimination of two moles of HBr. Conversion of a primary amine to an olefin cannot, however, be carried out by direct elimination of ammonia. The problem is easily solved by exhaustive methylation of the amine to the corresponding trimethylammonium hydroxide, followed by a Hofmann elimination of trimethylamine.

$$H_2N-CH_2CH_2CH_2CH_3 \xrightarrow[\text{base}]{\text{excess } CH_3I} (CH_3)_3\overset{+}{N}-CH_2CH_2CH_2CH_3 \xrightarrow{\Delta}$$

$$OH^-$$

$$CH_2=CH-CH_2CH_3$$

$$\downarrow Br_2$$

$$HC\equiv CCH_2CH_3 \xleftarrow[NH_3]{NaNH_2} \underset{\underset{Br}{|} \quad \underset{Br}{|}}{CH_2-CH-CH_2CH_3}$$

Example 3

Convert 2-bromobutane into 1,2,3-tribromobutane.

$$\underset{\underset{Br}{|}}{CH_3CHCH_2CH_3} \rightarrow \underset{\underset{Br}{|}\ \underset{Br}{|}}{BrCH_2CHCHCH_3}$$

Carbon atoms C-1 and C-3 are not activated by the bromo substituent at C-2; for this reason, direct bromination of 2-bromobutane is not a practical route to the desired tribromide. Clearly all three carbons, C-1, C-2, and C-3, must become either *part* of a functional group in a key intermediate or must be *activated* by such a functional group. 2-Butene, easily prepared from the starting material by elimination of HBr, can function as such an intermediate, since C-1 is an allylic methyl group and therefore capable of undergoing allylic bromination. Addition of bromine to the olefinic bond of the resulting 1-bromo-2-butene gives the desired tribromide.

$$\underset{\underset{Br}{|}}{CH_3CHCH_2CH_3} \xrightarrow{t\text{-BuOK}} \left\{ \begin{array}{c} CH_3CH=CHCH_3 \\ + \\ CH_2=CH-CH_2-CH_3 \end{array} \right\} \xrightarrow{} \left\{ \begin{array}{c} Br-CH_2CH=CHCH_3 \\ + \\ CH_2=CH-\underset{\underset{Br}{|}}{CH}-CH_3 \end{array} \right\}$$

$$\downarrow Br_2$$

$$Br-CH_2-\underset{\underset{Br}{|}}{CH}-\underset{\underset{Br}{|}}{CH}-CH_3$$

Example 4

Convert butyraldehyde into 2-butanone.

$$CH_3CH_2CH_2CHO \rightarrow CH_3CH_2COCH_3$$

The overall reversal of the oxidation levels of C-1 and C-2 which is required can be carried out easily if an intermediate is used in which C-1 and C-2 are part of a common unsaturated function. Either 1-butene or 1-butyne can serve admirably as such a key intermediate, an oxygen function at C-2 being subsequently introduced by hydration. The unsaturation can be introduced from C-1 originally by an elimination reaction. It should be noted that partial isomerization of 1-butene to 2-butene will occur under acidic conditions, but since both of these alkenes hydrate to give the same alcohol, the mixture can be used directly. The alkene and alkyne pathways are illustrated.

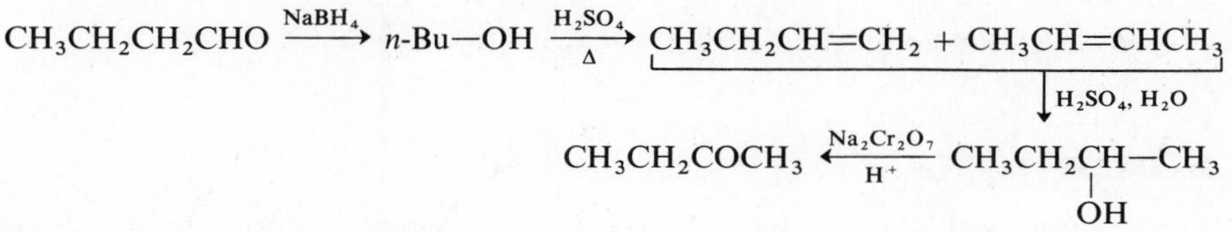

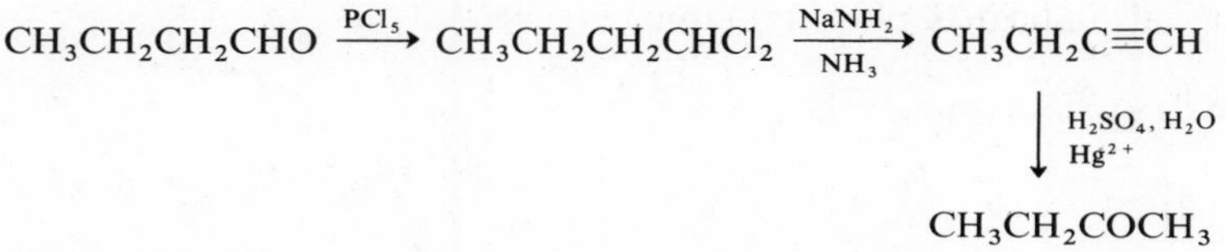

$$CH_3CH_2CH_2CHO \xrightarrow{NaBH_4} n\text{-Bu}-OH \xrightarrow[\Delta]{H_2SO_4} CH_3CH_2CH=CH_2 + CH_3CH=CHCH_3$$

$$\downarrow H_2SO_4, H_2O$$

$$CH_3CH_2COCH_3 \xleftarrow[H^+]{Na_2Cr_2O_7} CH_3CH_2CH-CH_3$$
$$\qquad\qquad\qquad\qquad\qquad\qquad\quad |$$
$$\qquad\qquad\qquad\qquad\qquad\qquad\quad OH$$

$$CH_3CH_2CH_2CHO \xrightarrow{PCl_5} CH_3CH_2CH_2CHCl_2 \xrightarrow[NH_3]{NaNH_2} CH_3CH_2C\equiv CH$$

$$\downarrow \begin{array}{l} H_2SO_4, H_2O \\ Hg^{2+} \end{array}$$

$$CH_3CH_2COCH_3$$

Example 5

Convert cyclohexene into cyclohexene-1-*d*.

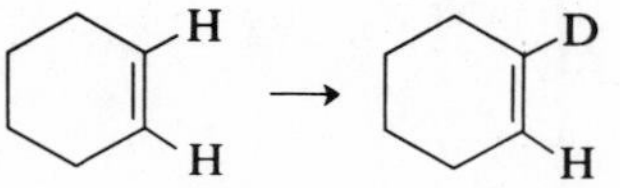

This problem illustrates the synthesis of a simple compound which is labeled specifically with deuterium in one position. Compounds of this type have found much use in nmr studies and in elucidating the fragmentation patterns obtained by mass spectrometry.

The desired cyclohexene has one olefinic deuterium atom in the molecule, all other hydrogens being ordinary hydrogen (protium). This compound could be obtained by loss of water from cyclohexanol-1-*d*. *Acid* dehydration cannot be used, however, since it would lead to loss of the deuterium atom as shown below.

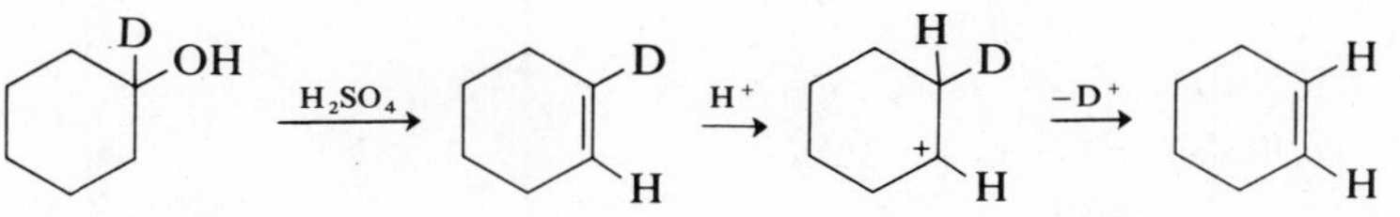

The desired dehydration can be achieved under nonacidic conditions, however, by preparing the tosylate of the alcohol and treating it with a strong *base*.

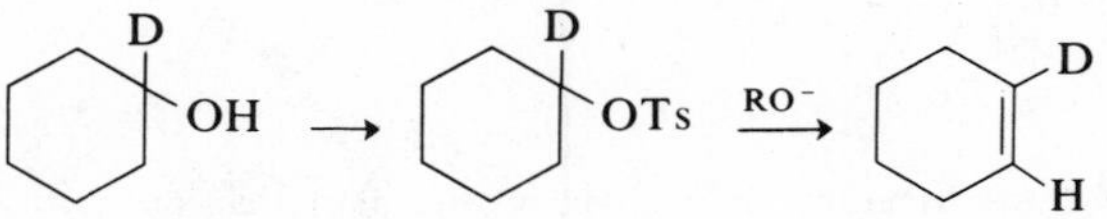

The cyclohexanol-1-*d* can be prepared from the commercially available lithium aluminum deuteride ($LiAlD_4$) by reaction with cyclohexanone. Still working backwards, the problem now resolves itself into the initial conversion of ordinary cyclohexene to cyclohexanone; clearly cyclohexanol, formed by hydration of the olefin, is the final missing intermediate. The entire synthesis has now evolved as follows:

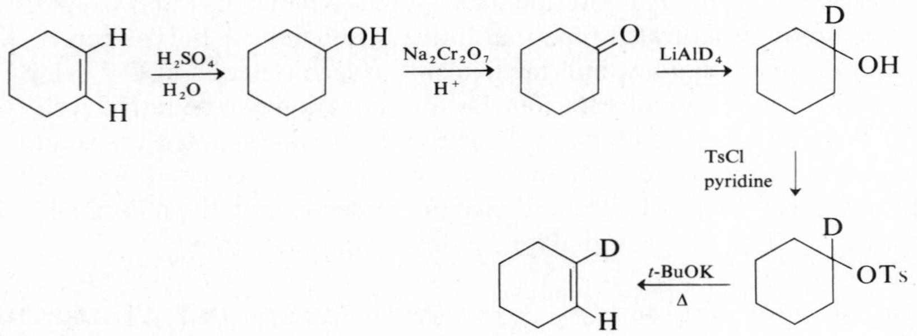

EXERCISE 24.3

Outline practical laboratory syntheses of the following compounds from the starting materials indicated, plus inorganic reagents.

(a) $(CH_3)_2CH{-}CHO \rightarrow (CH_3)_2CH{-}CH_2NH_2$

(b)

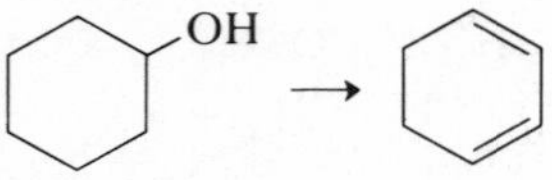

(c)

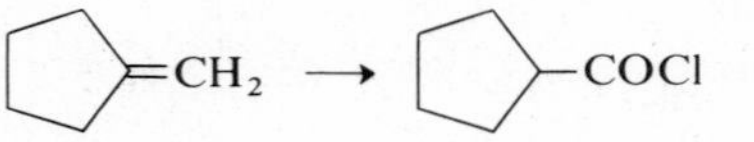

24.3   Extending or Shortening a Carbon Chain by One Atom

In this section, we will consider the synthetic usefulness of a few of the simple reactions which lead to the increase or decrease of a carbon chain at an already functionalized site. If a particular carbon atom of a chain in a simple molecule is functionalized in the form of a halide, alcohol, aldehyde, or ketone, it is usually possible to *add* to the function one carbon atom in the form of cyanide ion or carbon dioxide. Since cyano and carboxyl groups are reduced readily by lithium aluminum hydride, the incorporation of these functions is indirectly equivalent to the introduction of a $-CH_2NH_2$ or $-CH_2OH$ group. These conversions are summarized below. (The student should mentally supply any reagents or conditions necessary for each transformation shown in the remainder of the chapter.)

The Grignard Acid Synthesis†

Alkene $--\rightarrow$ ROH
$\downarrow$
$\llcorner----\rightarrow$ RX $\rightarrow$ RMgX $\rightarrow$ RCOOH $--\rightarrow$ RCH$_2$OH

---

† A dashed arrow ($--\rightarrow$) is used to represent a transformation which might involve more than one step.

Acids by the Nitrile Synthesis

Alkene $--\rightarrow$ ROH $\rightarrow$ ROTs

$\llcorner$ $----\rightarrow$ RX $\longrightarrow$ RCN $\rightarrow$ RCOOH $--\rightarrow$ RCH$_2$OH

$\downarrow$

RCH$_2$NH$_2$

Acids by the Cyanohydrin Synthesis

$$\text{RCH}_2\text{OH} \dashrightarrow \text{RCHO} \rightarrow \text{R}\overset{\text{OH}}{\underset{|}{\text{C}}}\text{HCN} \rightarrow \text{R}\overset{\text{OH}}{\underset{|}{\text{C}}}\text{H—COOH} \dashrightarrow \text{R}\overset{\text{OH}}{\underset{|}{\text{C}}}\text{H—CH}_2\text{OH}$$

Perhaps the two simplest reactions for the *removal* of a single carbon are the haloform reaction of a methyl ketone, and the degradation of a carboxylic acid to an amine by either the Schmidt, Curtius, or Hofmann methods. These conversions are summarized below; the reactions shown by dotted arrows indicate a few obvious extensions of these changes into longer synthetic schemes.

The Haloform Degradation

$$\text{RCH}{=}\text{CH}_2 \dashrightarrow \text{R}\overset{}{\underset{\underset{\text{OH}}{|}}{\text{—CHCH}_3}} \rightarrow \text{R—COCH}_3 \rightarrow \text{R—COOH} \rightarrow \text{R—CH}_2\text{OH}$$

$\downarrow$

R—CHO

The Acid-to-Amine Degradation

$$\text{R—CH}_2\text{OH} \rightarrow \text{R—COOH} \rightarrow \text{R—NH}_2 \rightarrow \text{R—N(CH}_3)_2 \rightarrow \textit{Alkene}$$

A few examples are given to illustrate the use of some of these reaction sequences.

Example 1

Convert cyclohexene into cyclohexanecarboxylic acid.

The carboxyl group of the product represents a new carbon atom added to the starting olefin. Regardless of whether it is introduced by the Grignard route or by the nitrile route, its precursor is a halide such as cyclohexyl bromide, which may be obtained from cyclohexene by addition of hydrogen bromide. Since cyclohexyl bromide is a secondary halide, one may assume that its conversion to the nitrile would be accompanied by a substantial amount of elimination to cyclohexene; consequently, the Grignard route would be expected to be preferable in this case.

Example 2

Convert methylenecyclopentane into β-(cyclopentyl)ethylamine.

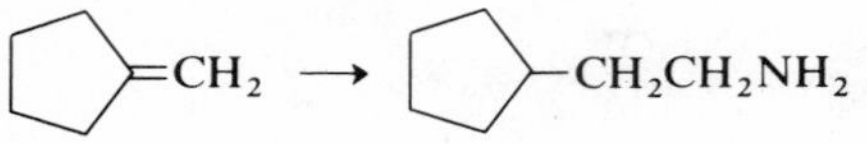

The carbon bearing the amino group must be added to the molecule in the course of the synthesis, along with the amino group itself. Since the unit $-CH_2NH_2$ represents the reduced $-CN$ function, our problem resolves itself into the question of how to prepare cyclopentylmethyl cyanide. This compound can be made easily enough from the corresponding bromide, which, however, is not the normal Markovnikov addition product of HBr to methylenecyclopentane. It should be possible, however, to obtain this compound by the peroxide-catalyzed addition of HBr to this olefin. An alternate and perhaps more reliable way of achieving an anti-Markovnikov addition to methylenecyclopentene would be by hydroboration of the olefin, followed by alkaline H_2O_2 oxidation. The resulting cyclopentylmethanol can then be converted to the desired nitrile either via the corresponding bromide or via its tosylate.

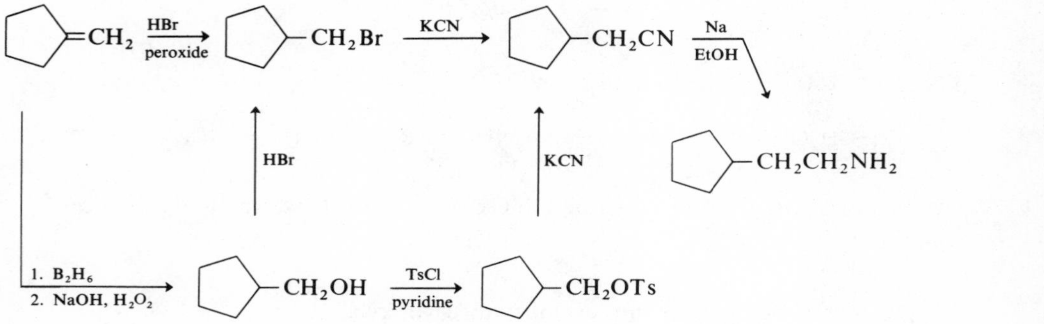

Example 3

Convert 4,4-dimethylcyclohexanemethanol into 4,4-dimethylcyclohexene.

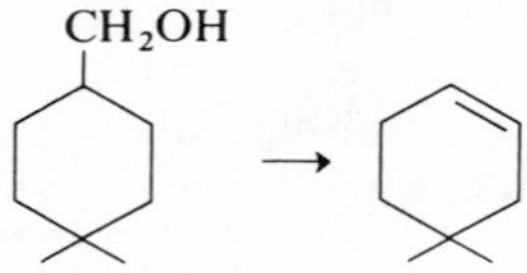

The removal of the $-CH_2OH$ group can be carried out best if it is first oxidized to the more readily lost carboxyl function. The resulting acid, $R-CO_2H$, can be converted to the amine $R-NH_2$ by any of three related procedures (Schmidt, Curtius, or Hofmann); since the molecule contains no functional group sensitive to sulfuric acid, the Schmidt method is simplest. Methylation of the resulting amine easily yields the dimethylamine which can be further degraded to the desired *alkenes* by either the Hofmann or the Cope elimination.

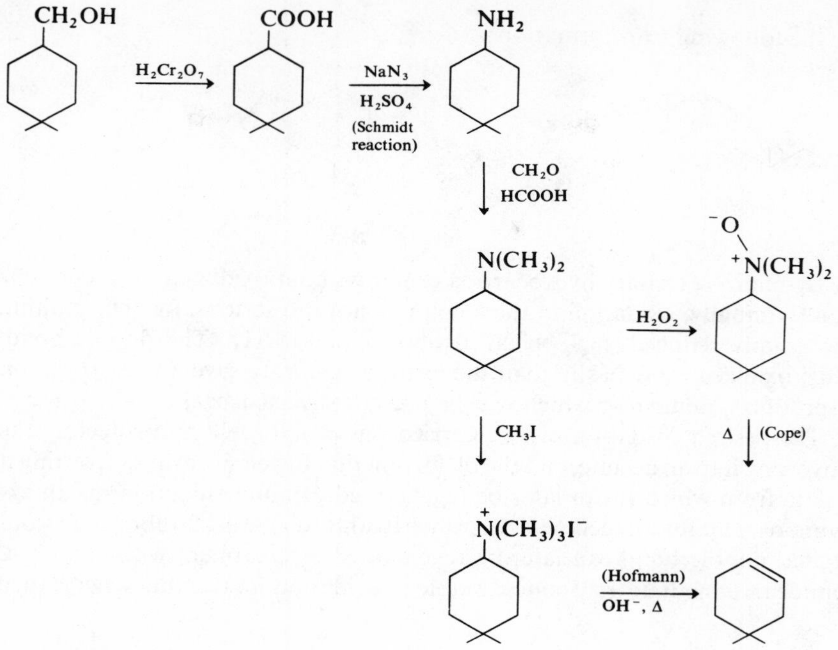

EXERCISE 24.4

Outline practical laboratory syntheses for the following transformations:

(a) Ph—CH₂OH → Ph—CH—COOH
                        |
                        OH

(b) $(CH_3)_2CH—OH \rightarrow (CH_3)_2CH—COOCH_3$

(c)

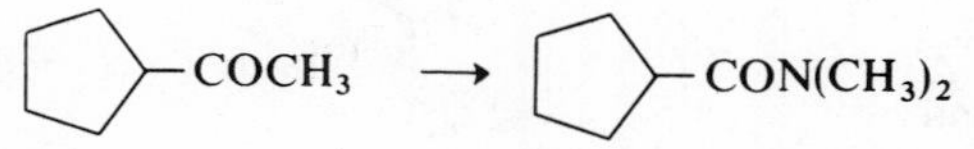

24.4   The Protecting Group Concept

We will now consider how some otherwise difficult or impossible transformations can be achieved by use of a *protecting group*.

The presence of several functional groups in a molecule can greatly complicate the design of a synthesis. Serious problems arise if a molecule contains two or more functions which react indiscriminately with the same reagent. For instance, oxidizing agents such as $KMnO_4$ and CrO_3 will attack olefinic double bonds as well as primary and secondary alcohol groups, aldehyde groups, and other functions.

The following reaction takes place in about 15 % yield and accomplishes a change that would otherwise be very difficult to bring about.

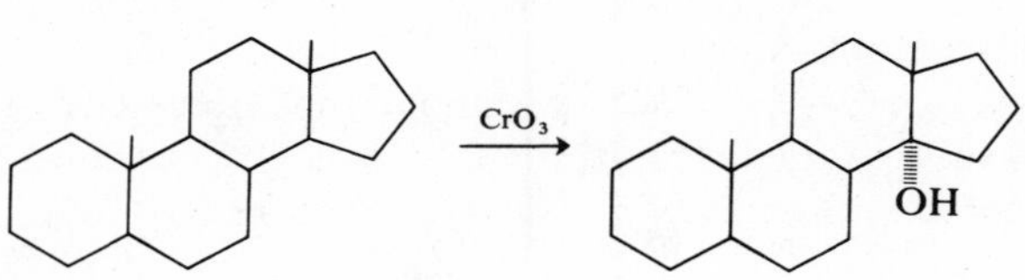

Now consider the following transformation:

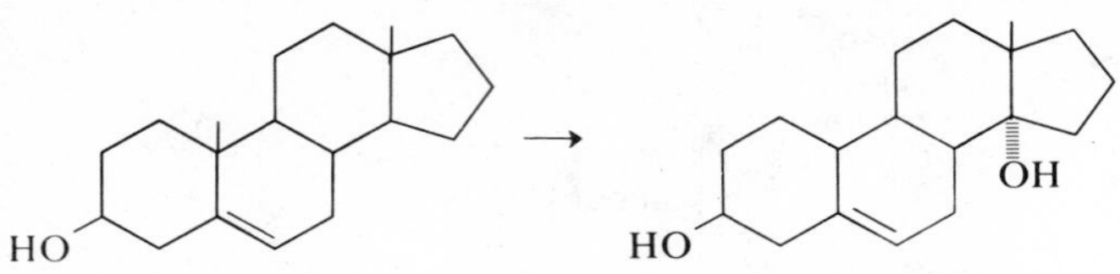

It is necessary to oxidize a tertiary hydrocarbon center without oxidizing the alcohol or the double bond. Actually, oxidation of the alcohol is not too serious, for the resulting ketone can be readily reduced back to an alcohol with LiAlH$_4$. The double bond, however, will be oxidized more easily than the tertiary center, to give allylic oxidation and cleavage products, neither of which can be easily converted back to the original double bond. The desired oxidation can be carried out in fair yield by protecting the alcohol by converting it to an acetate, and the olefin function by temporarily converting it to an inert system from which it can later be regenerated. Bromine functions as an excellent protecting reagent for an olefinic bond, since it adds to give a 1,2-dibromide from which the original double bond can later be regenerated by treatment with zinc dust. The 1,2-dibromide intermediate is, of course, stable to oxidation. This actual scheme then is as follows:

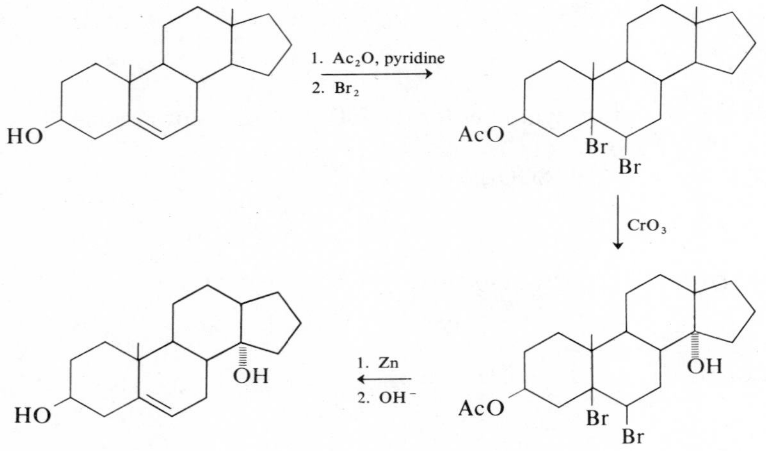

With the development of a number of new selective reagents and conditions for carrying out oxidations during the last several years, this particular kind of protection has become of reduced importance, but it is still of some use in cases such as the one described.

In contrast to the reactive alcohol and carbonyl compounds from which they are derived, acetals and ketals are simply special types of ethers. Like ordinary ethers, they are quite stable to strong bases, Grignard reagents, complex hydrides, and oxidizing agents. Unlike ordinary ethers, however, they are easily decomposed by dilute acid into the alcohol and carbonyl components from which they were originally derived. It is not surprising, therefore, that acetals and ketals can serve to protect alcohol, aldehyde, or ketone functions in a variety of reactions. The original function can later be recovered by acid hydrolysis of the ketal after need for the protection has past. Ethylene glycol is the most common reagent for protecting carbonyls of aldehydes and ketones.

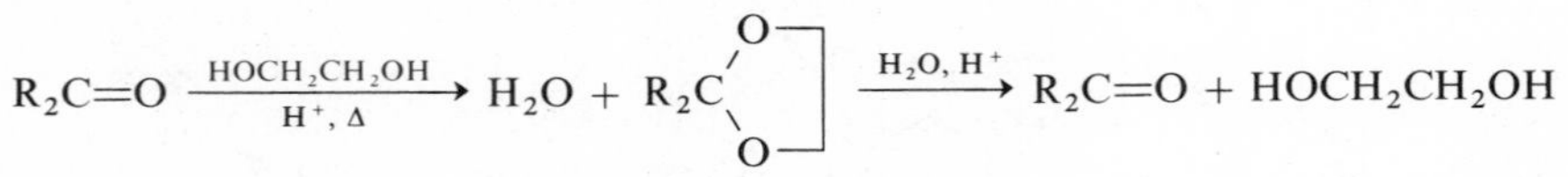

(Water separator)   An ethylene
ketal

The commercially available enol ether *dihydropyran* is the reagent of choice for protecting an alcoholic hydroxyl group; addition of an alcohol to dihydropyran takes place in the presence of a catalytic amount of acid, and the product is an acetal.

Dihydropyran   A tetrahydropyranyl ether

Example 1

Convert methyl 5-ketohexanoate to 2-hydroxy-2-methyl-6-heptanone.

$$CH_3-\overset{O}{\underset{\|}{C}}-CH_2CH_2CH_2COOCH_3 \;\rightarrow\; CH_3\overset{O}{\underset{\|}{C}}-CH_2CH_2CH_2\overset{OH}{\underset{CH_3}{\underset{|}{C}}}-CH_3$$

Obviously it is only necessary to add methyl Grignard to the ester group. However, it is impossible to add a Grignard reagent to an ester function in the presence of a more reactive ketonic carbonyl group without concurrent addition to the ketone. This problem may be circumvented by the use of a ketal as a protecting group.

$$CH_3-\overset{O}{\underset{\|}{C}}-CH_2CH_2CH_2COOCH_3 \;\xrightarrow[\;(-H_2O)\;]{HOCH_2CH_2OH \atop H^+}\;$$

$$\begin{array}{c} CH_2-CH_2 \\ O \quad \backslash \;\; O \\ CH_3-\overset{}{C}-CH_2CH_2CH_2COOCH_3 \end{array}$$

1. CH_3MgBr
2. H_3O^+

$$CH_3\overset{O}{\underset{\|}{C}}CH_2CH_2CH_2\overset{OH}{\underset{|}{C}}(CH_3)_2$$

Example 2

Convert 1-hydroxy-4-bromobutane into 1-acetoxy-4-(trimethylsilyl)butane.

$$HOCH_2CH_2CH_2CH_2Br \;\rightarrow\; CH_3COOCH_2CH_2CH_2CH_2Si(CH_3)_3$$

The obvious method for the replacement of bromine by the trimethylsilyl group is the reaction of a Grignard reagent with the commercially available trimethylchlorosilane, as shown.

$$R-Br \;\rightarrow\; R-MgBr \;\xrightarrow{(CH_3)_3SiCl}\; R-Si(CH_3)_3$$

It is quite impossible, however, to convert a bromo alcohol such as (I) into a Grignard reagent. This is because Grignard reagents react with alcoholic hydroxyl groups. In other words, the Grignard function (RMgX) and the alcohol function (ROH) are *incompatible functional groups* and cannot exist together in the same molecule without either intramolecular or intermolecular reactions taking place. The highly reactive Grignard function is indeed incompatible with most other functional groups (e.g., R_2NH, all types of carbonyls, RCN). For this reason, we cannot take the obvious alternative approach to our problem of acetylating I and then converting the bromo ester (II) into a Grignard reagent. On the other hand, bromo alcohol (I) will add readily to dihydropyran in the presence of an acid catalyst (e.g., p-toluenesulfonic acid) to give a tetrahydropyranyl ether (III) which can be easily converted into a Grignard reagent (IV). Reaction of this Grignard reagent with trimethylchlorosilane yields the silicon-containing acetal (V) which is cleaved by dilute acid to give alcohol (VI). Finally, reaction of VI with acetic anhydride in pyridine gives the desired ester (VII).

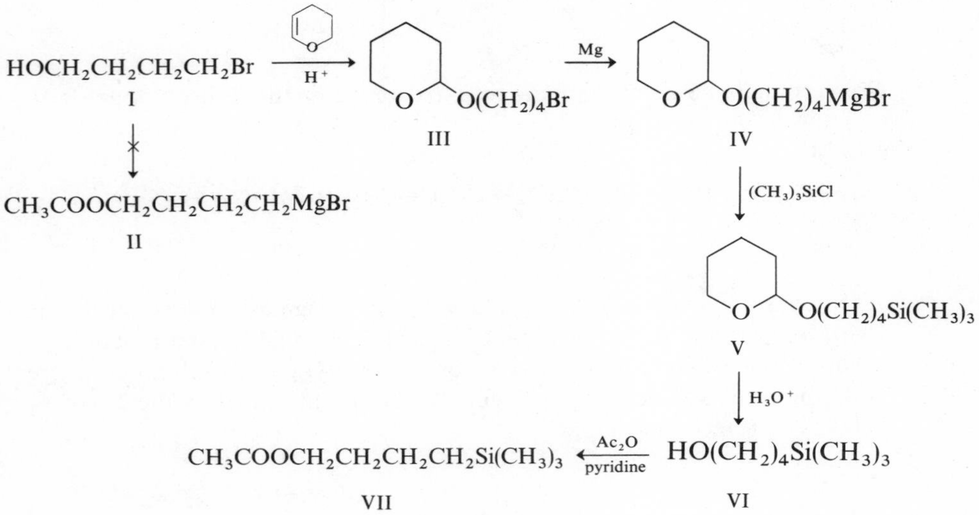

EXERCISE 24.5

Outline reasonable laboratory syntheses which will accomplish the following transformations:

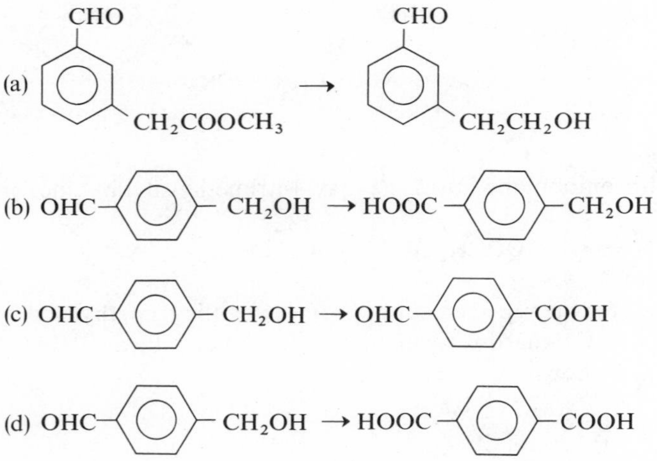

24.5   Simple Functional Group Transformations of Aromatic Compounds. Addition of a Side Chain by the Friedel–Crafts Synthesis

In general, the introduction of functional substituents into an aromatic ring and the interconversion of aromatic substituents requires the use of reactions different from those which have been found most useful with simple aliphatic and alicyclic compounds. For example, aliphatic halides, particularly bromides, are much used in synthesis because most of them undergo nucleophilic displacement reactions with a variety of nucleophilic reagents. Aromatic bromides, on the other hand, are quite inert to this type of displacement, except in special cases in which the halogen is "activated" by a strong electron-withdrawing group in the ortho or para position (see Section 17.8). The use of aromatic bromides is therefore largely confined to the preparation of aryl Grignard reagents, bearing in mind that the reactive Grignard function of Ar—MgBr is incompatible with most other common functional groups on the aromatic ring, with the exception of alkyl and aryl groups, ether substituents, and meta and para halogens (except iodine).

The most versatile substituent in aromatic synthesis is the primary amino group. This group is readily introduced into the aromatic ring by way of nitration followed by reduction of the resulting nitro compound. The amino group is useful in activating the aromatic nucleus toward further substitution. Furthermore, after diazotization it may be replaced by any of a number of other substituents, including H, OH, CN, F, Cl, Br, and I. Replacement of NH_2 by H, which at first seems to be a useless reaction synthetically, actually makes possible the synthesis of many compounds having an unusual orientation of substituents. In such syntheses, the aromatic amino group is introduced for its directing effect and then removed after it has served this function.

By far the most common method of attaching an alkyl chain to an aromatic ring involves the use of the Friedel–Crafts acylation reaction, followed by reduction of the resulting ketone. For reasons discussed in one of the examples below, direct alkylation can be a much more complex and, therefore, less generally useful reaction.

Example 1

Devise practical syntheses of both *m*-aminobenzoic acid and *p*-aminobenzoic acid from toluene.

The obvious approach in both cases is to try to derive the carboxyl group from the methyl group of toluene by oxidation, and to introduce the amino group by way of a nitration reaction followed by reduction. Which isomer of aminobenzoic acid we obtain will depend upon the order in which the necessary chemical operations are carried out. Direct introduction of one nitro group into toluene yields a separable mixture of the liquid *o*-nitrotoluene and the solid *p*-nitrotoluene. Chromic acid oxidation of *p*-nitrotoluene gives *p*-nitrobenzoic acid, which is easily reduced either catalytically or by stannous chloride to *p*-aminobenzoic acid. The apparently alternate approach of reducing *p*-nitrotoluene to *p*-toluidine and oxidizing the latter to *p*-aminobenzoic acid is not possible. This is because the aromatic nucleus of an aryl amine such as *p*-toluidine is much more easily attacked by oxidizing agents than is an alkyl side chain attached to it; complex polynuclear dyes, quinones, and ring cleavage products are formed.

Similar reasoning indicates that *m*-aminobenzoic acid is accessible not by the oxidation of *m*-toluidine, but rather by the reduction of *m*-nitrobenzoic acid. The latter should be formed in the oxidation of *m*-nitrotoluene, but *m*-nitrotoluene is obtained only in trace amounts by the nitration of toluene. The problem is solved very simply by first oxidizing the *o,p*-directing methyl group of toluene. The resulting benzoic acid has a carboxyl group which will direct an incoming nitro group into the *m*-position to give *m*-nitrobenzoic acid.

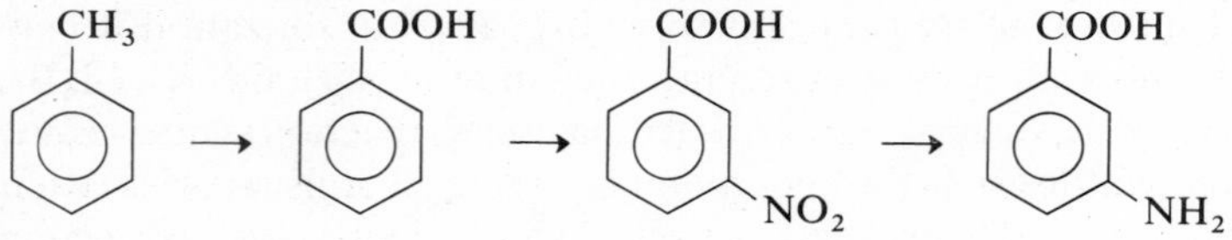

Example 2

Convert benzene into 1,3,5-tribromobenzene.

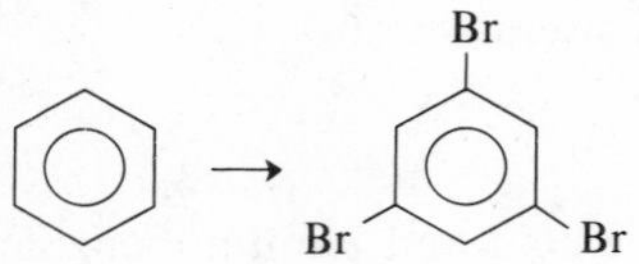

At first glance, this seems to be a simple problem in direct aromatic substitution. Closer analysis shows that this is not the case, since bromine is an *o, p*-directing substituent. Indeed, the major tribromobenzene which should be formed by direct vigorous bromination of benzene is 1,2,4-tribromobenzene. The bromines will only enter the ring meta to each other if a powerful *o,p*-directing group such as hydroxyl or amino is already present. The amino group of aniline serves this function admirably. After the bromines have entered in the desired all-meta arrangement, the amino group is readily removed by diazotization followed by reduction of the diazonium function with H_3PO_2. The initial conversion of benzene to aniline is, of course, trivial.

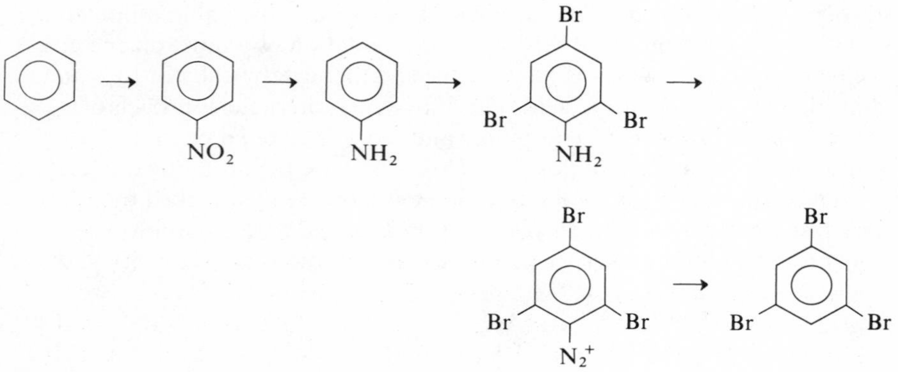

Example 3

Convert *p*-toluidine into *m*-toluidine.

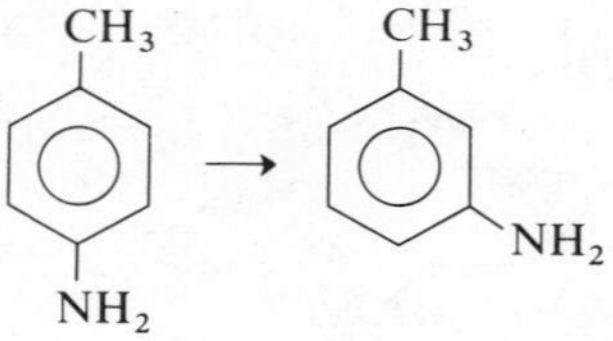

The direct migration of the 4-amino group into the 3 position is, of course, impossible. The original 4-amino substituent must undergo removal at some point via the diazonium salt, and the 3-amino group must be introduced at some point, probably as a nitro function. A key intermediate still having a 4-amino group but having a potential 3-amino group is 4-amino-3-nitrotoluene. Deamination of the latter by way of the diazonium salt yields *m*-nitrotoluene, which on reduction with iron, stannous chloride, or hydrogen yields *m*-toluidine. In view of the ease of oxidation of aromatic amines by nitric acid, as well as their presence in part as *m*-directing cations in strong acid, nitration of *p*-toluidine is best carried out indirectly. Thus, acetylation of *p*-toluidine yields *p*-acetamidotoluene, a compound in which the activating influence of the amino group has been moderated. Nevertheless, the acetamido group is still a stronger activating group than a methyl group, and 4-acetamido-3-nitrotoluene is the major product formed on nitration. Hydrolysis of the latter with hydrochloric acid yields, after basification, 4-amino-3-nitrotoluene. The entire sequence of reactions is outlined below.

Example 4

Convert benzene into *p*-nitro-*n*-propylbenzene.

It is clear that the nitro goup in the product is introduced at some stage by nitration, and the three carbons of the *n*-propyl side chain by some kind of Friedel–Crafts reaction. The nitro group cannot be introduced first, since nitrobenzene is so deactivated that it will not undergo Friedel–Crafts reactions; in addition, if it did react to introduce some other group which was later converted to the propyl group, the latter would have to appear meta to the nitro group, since the latter is always *m*-directing. On the other hand, *p*-nitro-*n*-propylbenzene should be the major product of the mononitration of *n*-propylbenzene. The seemingly obvious solution of the direct Friedel–Crafts alkylation of benzene by *n*-propyl chloride and aluminum chloride is illusory (Section 16.5). The initially formed *n*-propyl cation rearranges to the more stable isopropyl cation faster than it reacts with benzene, and isopropylbenzene is the major reaction product; diisopropylbenzenes are also formed because alkyl benzenes are *more reactive* than benzene in electrophilic substitution reactions. Both polysubstitution and side-chain rearrangement are eliminated by introducing the three-carbon fragment as an *acyl* group. Thus, Friedel–Crafts *acylation* of benzene with propionyl chloride and aluminum chloride yields propiophenone (phenyl ethyl ketone); only one acyl group enters the ring because of the deactivating effect of the carbonyl group of the initial product. Reduction of the carbonyl group of propiophenone by amalgamated zinc and acid (*Clemmensen reduction*), or by hydrazine and strong base (*Wolff–Kishner reaction*), or by hydrogen and palladium, yields *n*-propyl-benzene. The reaction sequence is outlined below.

Example 5

Suggest a practical synthesis of 3,3′-dimethyl-4,4′-difluorobiphenyl starting from a simple and cheap aromatic hydrocarbon (benzene, toluene, or a xylene).

The fluoro substituents provide the key to this problem, since we know that aromatic fluoro compounds can usually be prepared only by way of diazonium fluoborates (*Schiemann reaction*). In this case, the required diazonium intermediate is derived from 3,3′-dimethyl-4,4′-diaminobiphenyl, a simple alkylated analog of benzidine (4,4′-diaminobiphenyl). Like benzidine itself, the desired diamine should be formed easily by the so-called *benzidine rearrangement* reaction, the required starting material being 2,2′-dimethyl-hydrazobenzene. The latter compound should be readily prepared from *o*-nitrotoluene by reduction with zinc and alkali. *o*-Nitrotoluene is obtained easily (along with *p*-nitrotoluene) from toluene by direct nitration. The entire synthesis is outlined below.

Example 6

Synthesize the azo dye *Orange II* starting from benzene and naphthalene.

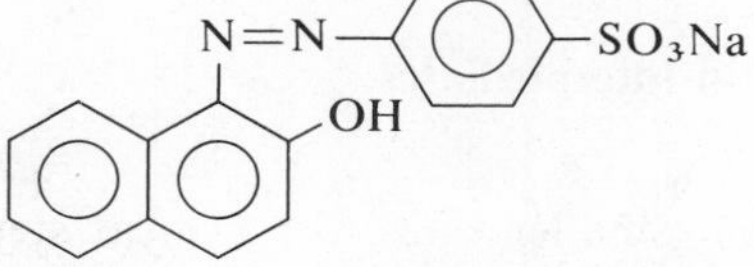

Orange II is an azo compound containing a phenolic function ortho to the azo linkage. This fact suggests that it can be prepared by the coupling of a diazonium salt with a phenol in basic solution. The phenol in question, β-naphthol, is known to undergo electrophilic substitution reactions very easily at the C-1 position of the naphthalene ring. β-Naphthol is easily prepared from naphthalene by sulfonation of naphthalene to naphthalene-2-sulfonic acid (discussed in detail in Section 16.8), followed by the high-temperature alkali fusion of the sodium salt of the latter acid. The required diazonium component, benzenediazonium-4-sulfonate, is prepared by diazotization of sulfanilic acid, which in turn is formed by heating aniline bisulfate in the dry state. Aniline is, of course, readily prepared from benzene by way of nitrobenzene.

It is interesting to note that Orange II was first made commercially in 1876 by this series of reactions, and it is still made in this way today.

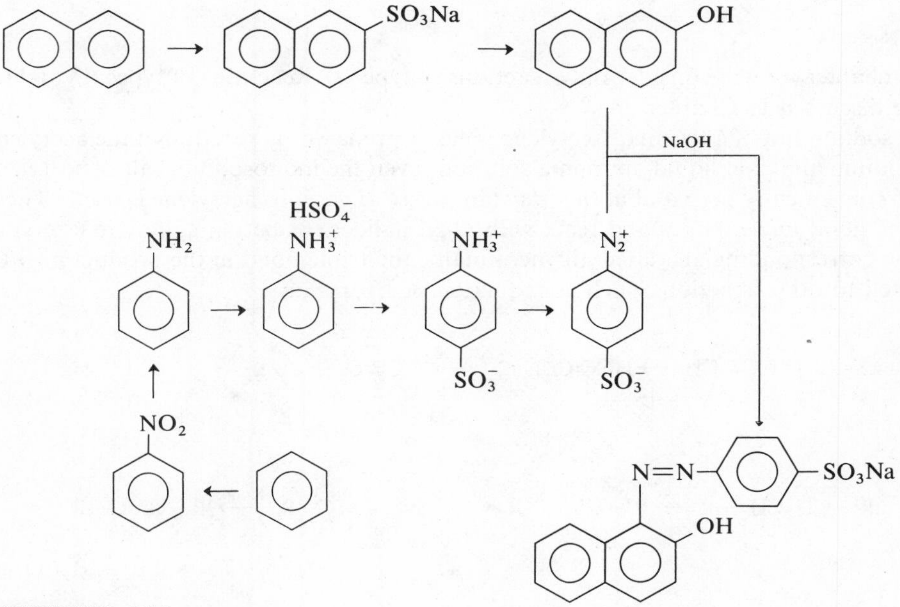

EXERCISE 24.6

Outline practical laboratory syntheses of the following compounds from benzene or toluene.

(a)

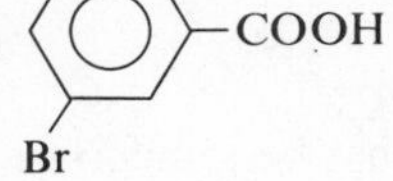

(b)

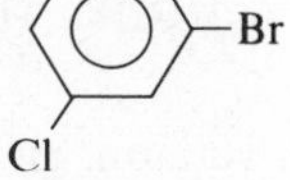

(c)

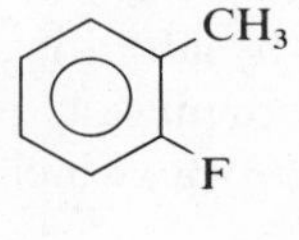

(d) Ph—OCH$_3$

(e) H_2N—⟨○⟩—⟨○⟩—NH_2 (f) Br—⟨○⟩—$\underset{\underset{CH_3}{|}}{C}HCH_2CH_2CH_3$

24.6   Elaboration of Carbon Chains Using Carbanion Intermediates. Alkylation of Carbanions

In the construction of larger organic molecules from smaller ones, the critical step usually involves the formation of a carbon–carbon bond. Although many reactions are known in which carbon–carbon bonds are produced by way of free-radical, carbene, or carbonium ion intermediates, there is no doubt that reactions involving carbanions or carbanion-like intermediates form the most useful group for this purpose. We will subdivide our discussion by considering reactions in which carbon–carbon bond formation involves (a) displacement of halogen (or other leaving group) from carbon by a carbanion, (b) addition of a carbanion to a carbonyl group, and (c) addition of a carbanion to an activated carbon–carbon double bond. The essential processes are

(a) $R^- + R'{-}X \rightarrow R{-}R' + X^-$

(b) $R^- + O{=}C\diagdown^{\diagup} \rightarrow R{-}\overset{|}{\underset{|}{C}}{-}O^-$

(c) $R^- + \overset{\diagdown}{\diagup}C{=}\overset{|}{C}{-}Y \rightarrow R{-}\overset{|}{C}{-}\underset{-}{\overset{|}{C}}{-}Y$

In this chapter we will consider only reactions of type (a). Reactions of types (b) and (c) will be discussed in Chapter 34.

The sodium salt of a terminal acetylene is easily prepared by reaction of the acetylene with sodium amide in liquid ammonia solution; even the monosodium salt of acetylene itself is conveniently prepared in this way (an excess of gaseous acetylene is used). These salts are good nucleophiles and react with alkyl halides (or better, sulfonate esters) to give the corresponding alkylated alkyne. Finally, the triple bond in the product may be subjected to other reactions, such as reduction or hydration.

$$HC{\equiv}CH \rightarrow HC{\equiv}C^-Na^+ \xrightarrow{R-X} HC{\equiv}C{-}R$$

$$\downarrow NaNH_2$$

$$R'{-}CH_2CH_2{-}R \leftarrow R'{-}C{\equiv}C{-}R \xleftarrow{R'-X} Na^+\underset{-}{C}{\equiv}C{-}R \xrightarrow{R-X} R{-}C{\equiv}C{-}R \rightarrow$$

$$R{-}CH_2CO{-}R$$

Example 1

Convert styrene into *n*-amylbenzene.

$$C_6H_5{-}CH{=}CH_2 \rightarrow C_6H_5{-}CH_2CH_2CH_2CH_2CH_3$$

In order to effect this conversion, an *n*-propyl group must be joined to the terminal carbon of styrene. This cannot be done directly, but it can be done easily if the styrene is first converted to phenylacetylene by addition of bromine and treatment with strong base. Reaction of the sodium salt of phenylacetylene with *n*-propyl bromide gives 1-phenyl-1-pentyne, which is readily converted to *n*-amylbenzene on catalytic reduction.

$$C_6H_5-CH=CH_2 \rightarrow C_6H_5-\underset{\underset{Br}{|}}{C}H-CH_2Br \rightarrow C_6H_5-C\equiv CH \rightarrow C_6H_5C\equiv C^-Na^+$$

$$\downarrow \text{\scriptsize } CH_3CH_2CH_2Br$$

$$C_6H_5-CH_2CH_2CH_2CH_2CH_3 \leftarrow C_6H_5-C\equiv C-CH_2CH_2CH_3$$

Example 2

Devise a synthesis of 2,7-dimethyl-4-octanone from starting materials containing no more than four carbon atoms.

$$\underset{\underset{CH_3CHCH_2COCH_2CH_2CHCH_3}{}}{\overset{\overset{CH_3}{|}}{} \qquad \overset{\overset{CH_3}{|}}{}}$$

Mental dissection of the desired molecule into its simplest units of four carbons or less shows that it may be viewed as a structure of the type $R-COCH_2-R$, where R equals isobutyl. Such a structure is the hydration product of a symmetrical alkyne, $R-C\equiv C-R$, which is readily prepared in several steps from acetylene itself and two equivalents of the alcohol $R-OH$ as the tosylate. It should be noted that the hydration of an unsymmetrical alkyne $R-C\equiv C-R'$ is usually not synthetically useful since a mixture of ketones $R-CH_2CO-R'$ and $R-COCH_2-R'$ will be formed; the exception to this rule is hydration of a terminal alkyne $R-C\equiv CH$ to a methyl ketone $R-COCH_3$.

$$(CH_3)_2CHCH_2OH \rightarrow (CH_3)_2CHCH_2OTs \xrightarrow{HC\equiv C^-Na^+} (CH_3)_2CHCH_2-C\equiv CH$$

$$\downarrow$$

$$(CH_3)_2CHCH_2-C\equiv C-CH_2CH(CH_3)_2 \xleftarrow{(CH_3)_2CHCH_2OTs} (CH_3)_2CHCH_2-C\equiv C^-Na^+$$

$$\downarrow$$

$$(CH_3)_2CHCH_2COCH_2CH_2CH(CH_3)_2$$

The well-known resonance stabilization of a carbanion by one or more adjacent carbonyl functions forms the theoretical basis of the two classical synthetic schemes known as the *malonic ester synthesis* (Section 20.13) and the *acetoacetic ester synthesis* (Section 20.15). The starting materials are diethyl malonate (malonic ester) and ethyl acetoacetate (acetoacetic ester), respectively. The usual syntheses of these starting materials were given in Chapter 20, although both are today cheap articles of commerce.

In the malonic ester synthesis, diethyl malonate is converted by sodium ethoxide into its sodium salt, which is then allowed to react with an alkyl halide (or alkyl sulfonate ester) capable of undergoing normal S_N2 displacement reactions. The resulting alkyl-malonic ester can be hydrolyzed by base to an alkylmalonic acid, which in turn is easily decarboxylated to an alkylacetic acid by heating above 150°C or by boiling with aqueous sulfuric acid. Since the initially produced alkylmalonic ester can form a sodium salt, it can be converted if desired into a dialkylmalonic ester and subsequently, into a dialkylacetic acid. The general scheme is shown. Note that the original malonic ester serves as the source of the acetic acid unit in the final product.

$$\text{EtOOC}\boxed{\text{CH}_2\text{COOEt}} \xrightarrow{\text{NaOC}_2\text{H}_5} \text{Na}^+ \ ^-\text{CH(COOC}_2\text{H}_5)_2$$

$$\downarrow \text{R—X}$$

$$\overset{\displaystyle R'}{\underset{\displaystyle |}{R-C(\text{COOC}_2\text{H}_5)_2}} \xleftarrow{R'-X} \text{Na}^+ \ R-\overset{-}{C}(\text{COOC}_2\text{H}_5)_2 \xleftarrow{\text{NaOC}_2\text{H}_5} R-\text{CH(COOC}_2\text{H}_5)_2$$

$$\overset{\displaystyle R'}{\underset{\displaystyle |}{R-C(\text{COOH})_2}} \qquad\qquad R-\text{CH(COOH)}_2$$

$$\downarrow \Delta \qquad\qquad\qquad\qquad\qquad \downarrow \Delta$$

$$\overset{\displaystyle R'}{\underset{\displaystyle |}{R\boxed{\text{CH—COOH}}}} \qquad\qquad R\boxed{\text{CH}_2\text{COOH}}$$

Example 3

Synthesize caproic acid by the malonic ester synthesis.

$$\text{CH}_2(\text{COOC}_2\text{H}_5)_2 \rightarrow n\text{-C}_5\text{H}_{11}\text{—COOH}$$

Mental isolation of the acetic acid unit of caproic acid results in rewriting its structure as n-C$_4$H$_9$—CH$_2$COOH, which immediately suggests its practical synthesis starting from malonic ester and n-butyl bromide. Thus, reaction of the sodium salt of malonic ester with n-butyl bromide gives diethyl n-butylmalonate, hydrolysis of which yields n-butylmalonic acid. Decarboxylation of the latter with hot aqueous sulfuric acid gives caproic acid.

$$\text{CH}_2(\text{COOC}_2\text{H}_5)_2 \rightarrow \text{Na}^+ \ ^-\text{CH(COOC}_2\text{H}_5)_2 \xrightarrow{\text{CH}_3\text{CH}_2\text{CH}_2\text{CH}_2\text{Br}}$$

$$\text{CH}_3\text{CH}_2\text{CH}_2\text{CH}_2\text{CH(COOC}_2\text{H}_5)_2$$

$$\downarrow$$

$$\text{CH}_3\text{CH}_2\text{CH}_2\text{CH}_2\text{CH}_2\text{COOH} \leftarrow \text{CH}_3\text{CH}_2\text{CH}_2\text{CH}_2\text{CH(COOH)}_2$$

Example 4

Synthesize 2-ethyl-1-butanol from malonic ester and other compounds containing four or less carbon atoms.

$$\text{CH}_2(\text{COOC}_2\text{H}_5)_2 \rightarrow \overset{\displaystyle \text{CH}_2\text{CH}_3}{\underset{\displaystyle |}{\text{CH}_3\text{CH}_2\text{CH—CH}_2\text{OH}}}$$

The key to this problem lies in the realization that the structural unit R$_2$CH—CH$_2$OH is synthetically equivalent to R$_2$CH—COOH, from which it is derivable by lithium aluminum hydride reduction. The latter is the decarboxylation product of the disubstituted malonic acid R$_2$C(COOH)$_2$, which may be obtained starting from the halide R—X. In the specific case under consideration, alkylation of the sodium salt of malonic ester by ethyl iodide affords diethyl ethylmalonate. This ester still contains an acidic hydrogen and is converted by sodium ethoxide to its sodium salt, which will react with a second equivalent of ethyl iodide to give diethyl diethylmalonate. Hydrolysis of the latter ester, followed by decarboxylation, gives diethylacetic acid. Lithium aluminum hydride reduction of this acid yields the desired alcohol.

$$CH_2(COOC_2H_5)_2 \rightarrow Na^+{}^-CH(COOC_2H_5)_2 \xrightarrow{C_2H_5I} C_2H_5-CH(COOC_2H_5)_2$$

$$(C_2H_5)_2C(COOH)_2 \leftarrow (C_2H_5)_2C(COOC_2H_5)_2 \xleftarrow{C_2H_5I} Na^+C_2H_5-\underset{\cdot}{C}(COOC_2H_5)_2$$

$$\downarrow \Delta$$

$$(C_2H_5)_2CH-COOH \rightarrow CH_3CH_2\overset{\displaystyle CH_2CH_3}{\underset{\displaystyle |}{CH}}-CH_2OH$$

In the acetoacetic ester synthesis, ethyl acetoacetate is converted by sodium ethoxide into its sodium salt. Reaction of the latter with an alkyl halide (capable of S_N2 reactivity) affords an ethyl alkylacetoacetate. Hydrolysis of the latter with cold dilute alkali gives a solution of the sodium salt of an alkylacetoacetic acid. Acidification of the sodium salt solution gives the free alkylacetoacetic acid, which decarboxylates very readily on mild heating to give a ketone. As in the malonic ester synthesis, the original mono-alkylated ester can be alkylated a second time. The entire general scheme is outlined. Note that the original acetoacetic ester serves as the source of an acetone unit in the final product.

$$\boxed{CH_3COCH_2}\!\!-\!\!COOC_2H_5 \xrightarrow{NaOC_2H_5} CH_3CO\bar{C}HCOOC_2H_5 \ Na^+$$

$$\downarrow R-X$$

$$CH_3CO\overset{\displaystyle R}{\underset{\displaystyle R'}{\underset{|}{\overset{|}{C}}}}-COOC_2H_5 \xleftarrow{R'X} Na \ salt \leftarrow CH_3CO\overset{\displaystyle R}{\underset{|}{-CH}}-COOC_2H_5 \rightarrow$$

$$CH_3CO\overset{\displaystyle R}{\underset{|}{-CH}}-COOH$$

$$\downarrow$$

$$CH_3CO\overset{\displaystyle R}{\underset{\displaystyle R'}{\underset{|}{\overset{|}{C}}}}-COOH \rightarrow \boxed{CH_3COCH}\overset{\displaystyle R}{\underset{\displaystyle R'}{}} \qquad CH_3COCH_2R$$

Example 5

Synthesize methyl *n*-amyl ketone from acetoacetic ester and any other compound containing no more than four carbon atoms.

$$CH_3COCH_2COOC_2H_5 \rightarrow CH_3COCH_2CH_2CH_2CH_2CH_3$$

Mental separation of the desired structure into the acetone unit derived from acetoacetic ester and an alkyl substituent shows that the latter must be an *n*-butyl group ($CH_3COCH_2-CH_2CH_2CH_3$). The synthesis can therefore be carried out by reaction of the sodium salt of acetoacetic ester with *n*-butyl bromide to give ethyl *n*-butylacetoacetate. Alkaline hydrolysis of the latter, followed by acid decarboxylation, yields methyl *n*-amyl ketone.

$$CH_3COCH_2-COOC_2H_5 \rightarrow CH_3CO\bar{C}H-COOC_2H_5 \ Na^+ \xrightarrow{n\text{-}C_4H_9-Br}$$

$$CH_3CO\overset{\displaystyle n\text{-}C_4H_9}{\underset{|}{-CH}}-COOC_2H_5$$

$$\downarrow$$

$$CH_3CO-CH-COONa$$
$$\underset{n\text{-}C_4H_9}{|}$$

$$\xleftarrow{H^+}$$

$$CH_3COCH_2-CH_2CH_2CH_2CH_3 \leftarrow CH_3CO\underset{\displaystyle CH_2CH_2CH_2CH_3}{\underset{|}{-CH}}-COOH$$

EXERCISE 24.7

Outline reasonable laboratory syntheses for the following compounds:

(a) $Ph-CH_2C\equiv C-CH_3$ from toluene, acetylene, and methanol

(b) $CH_3\underset{\underset{CH_3}{|}}{C}HCH_2\underset{\underset{CH_3}{|}}{C}HCOOH$ using malonic ester

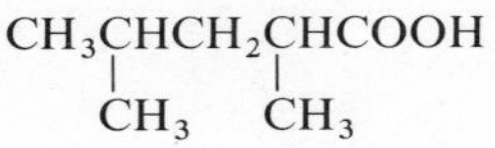

(c) $CH_3-\underset{\underset{CH_3}{|}}{C}HCH_2-\overset{\overset{O}{\|}}{C}-CH_3$ using acetoacetic ester

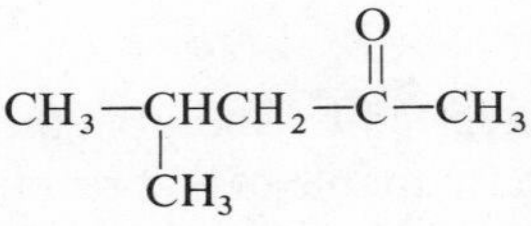

PROBLEMS

1. Outline syntheses of the following compounds. As starting materials you may use any compounds containing three carbons or less, plus malonic and acetoacetic esters, benzene, toluene, the xylenes, and naphthalene, plus anything especially indicated.

(a) $Ph-\underset{\underset{OH}{|}}{C}H-COOH$ (from benzaldehyde)

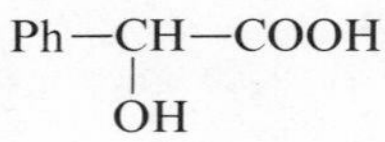

(b) $CH_3-\underset{\underset{CH_3}{|}}{C}H-CH_2-\overset{\overset{OH}{|}}{C}H-CH_2CH_3$

(c) $CH_3CH_2CH_2CH_2\underset{\underset{CH_3}{|}}{C}H-\overset{\overset{NH_2}{|}}{C}HCH_3$

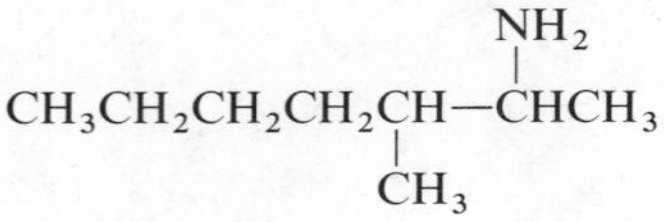

(d) $CH_2N\underset{CH_2CH_3}{\overset{CH_3}{<}}$

(e) $CH_3\underset{\underset{H_3C}{|}}{\overset{\overset{OH}{|}}{C}}-\underset{\underset{CH_3}{|}}{\overset{\overset{OH}{|}}{C}}-CH_3$

(f)

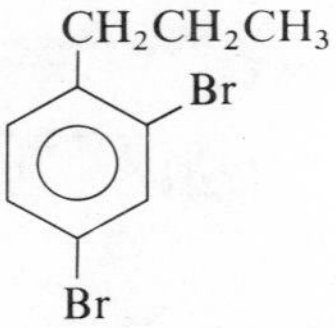

(g) $Ph\,CH_2CH_2\overset{\overset{O}{\|}}{C}-Ph$

(h)

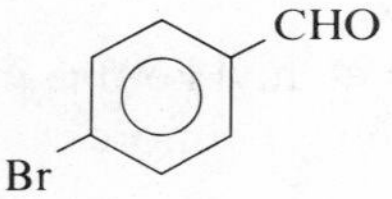

(i)

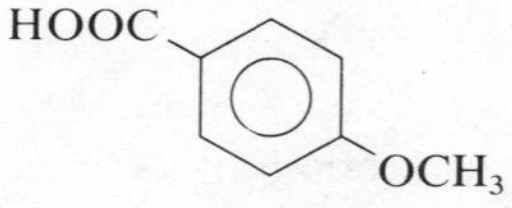

(j)

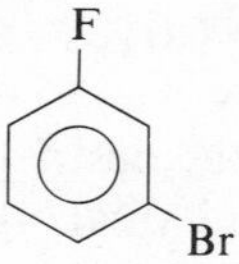

(k)

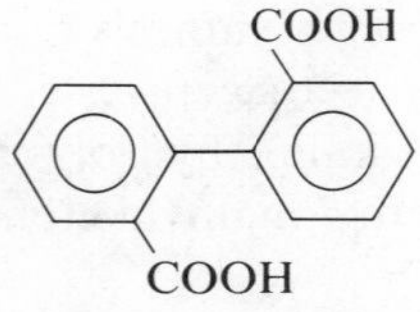

(l) $O_2N-$$-NO_2$

(m) $CH_3CH_2\underset{\underset{OH}{|}}{C}H-\underset{\underset{CH_3}{|}}{C}HCHO$

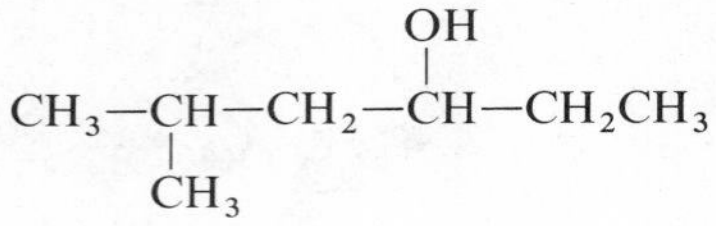

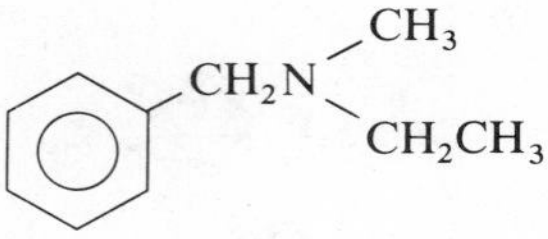

(n) COOH

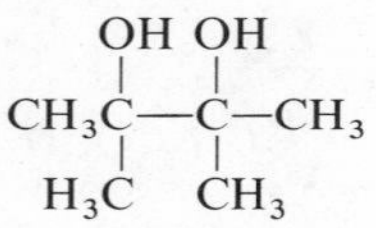

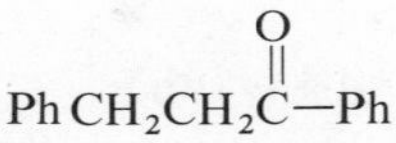

(o)
t-Bu

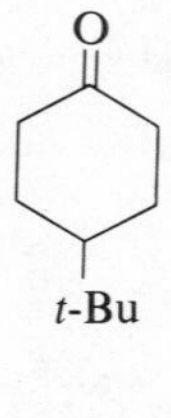

(p) $CH_2CH_2CH_2COOH$

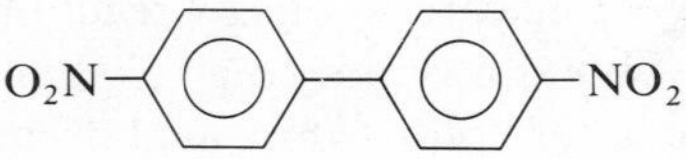

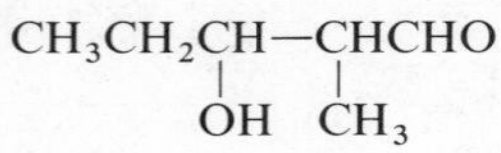

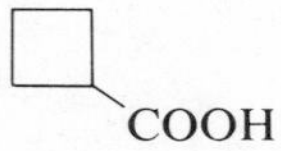

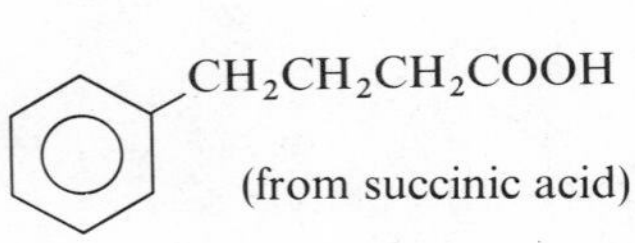

(from succinic acid)

(q) Ph—CH—C—Ph
      | ‖
     OH O

(r) $CH_3CH—CH—COOH$
         | |
        CH_3 CH_3

(s)   O
        ‖
  $CH_3CH_2C—CHCOOEt$
            |
           CH_3

2.   Outline simple direct methods for carrying out the indicated transformations.
   (a) $RCH_2OH \rightarrow RCH_2CH_2OH$
   (b) $RCH_2OH \rightarrow RCH_2CH_2CH_2OH$ (not by doing (a) twice)
   (c) $R—COOH \rightarrow RCH_2COOH$
   (d) $R—COOH \rightarrow RCH_2CH_2COOH$
   (e) $R—COOH \rightarrow RCH_2Ph$

    (f) $R—CH_2OH \rightarrow R—CH_2CH_2—\overset{\displaystyle O}{\overset{\|}{C}}—CH_3$

3.   How would you carry out the following syntheses?

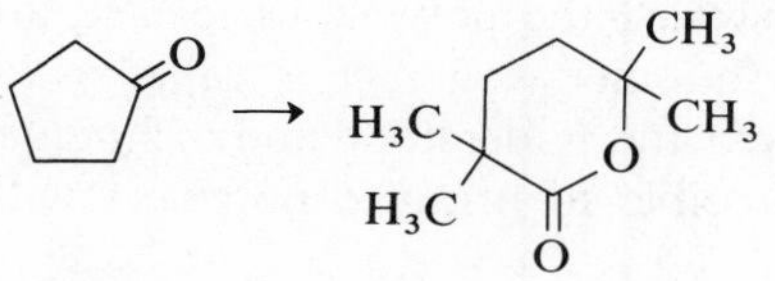

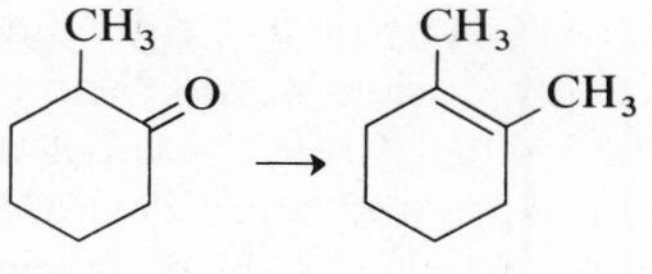

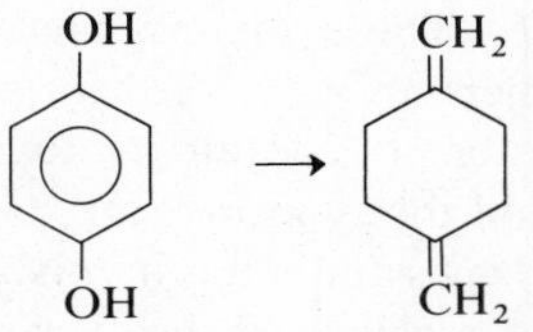

4.   Show all steps in a feasible synthesis of (a) *m*-bromophenol from benzene; (b) α-phenyl-alanine from benzene; (c) ethylene glycol dimethyl ether from ethylene and any one-carbon compounds.

5.   The drug "benzedrine" is 2-amino-1-phenylpropane. Show how it might be prepared starting with benzyl alcohol and any compound of four or fewer carbons.

6.   Show how to synthesize 3-methyl-3-pentanol from acetaldehyde as the only source of carbon.

7.   Show how to convert ethyl acetate into butyric acid.

CHAPTER 25

SYNTHETIC POLYMERS

25.1   Introduction

The term *polymer* is used to describe a very large molecule that is made up of many repeating molecular units. The starting units from which the polymer is formed are called *monomers*, and the reaction that joins the monomers together is called *polymerization*. As polymerization reactions have become better understood and techniques have become more sophisticated, it has proven possible to produce polymers with remarkable physical properties.

Initially the objectives of synthetic polymer chemists were to imitate commercially important natural polymers. A classic example was the discovery of nylon as a substitute for silk. Limitation of the supply of natural rubber, especially during World War II, led to a tremendous and successful effort to make synthetic rubber. From these beginnings, polymers were designed with characteristics different from and more desirable than the natural products they were intended to replace. A whole family of fabrics followed nylon, and synthetic leather followed synthetic rubber. These advances have had an enormous impact on our daily lives, as synthetic polymers are now used for so many things: fabrics for clothing and furniture, plastic eating utensils, containers, toys, toothbrushes, dishpans, synthetic rubber for tires, golf balls, and many more everyday items. Most of this development occurred during the 1950s and 1960s and it has involved large numbers of chemists. Karl Ziegler† and Giulio Natta†† received Nobel Prizes for the work of their respective research groups on the stereochemistry of polymerization.

Polymers are of great importance to our present-day economy. This aspect of the subject will be taken up in Section 35.16.

Polymers can be divided generally into two types: *condensation polymers*, formed by the elimination of small molecules such as water, and *addition polymers*, formed by successive addition of the repeating molecular units.

25.2   Condensation Polymers

Among polymers of this type the polyamides such as nylon are probably the best known. The driving force for polymerization is the elimination of water between an acid and an amine with the formation of an amide linkage. For the preparation of nylon 6,6, an equimolar mixture of adipic acid and hexamethylenediamine is first raised to a temperature of 270°C and a pressure of 150 pounds per square inch. After heating under reduced pressure to eliminate the last of the water, the polymer melt is extruded in a ribbon and then cut into pellets. The fiber is produced by spinning from the melt; it is

† Karl Ziegler. Born 1898, Kassel, Germany. University of Heidelberg, Max Planck Institute for Coal Research, Muelhelm/Ruhr. Nobel Prize, 1963.

†† Giulio Natta. Born 1903, Imperia, Italy. Rome University, Turin University, Polytechnic Institute of Milan. Nobel Prize, 1963.

also possible to mold the polymer.

$$\overset{O}{\underset{\|}{^-O-C}}-(CH_2)_4-\overset{O}{\underset{\|}{C}}-O^- \quad\text{(adipic acid)}$$
$$+$$
$$^+NH_3-(CH_2)_6-\overset{+}{N}H_3 \quad\text{(hexamethylenediamine)}$$

$$\rightarrow \left[\overset{H}{\underset{|}{N}}-\overset{O}{\underset{\|}{C}}-(CH_2)_4\overset{O}{\underset{\|}{C}}-NH-(CH_2)_6 \right]_n$$

Nylon 6,6

Polyesters can be formed similarly by the condensation of an acid with an ester, or by an ester interchange reaction. Terephthalic acid is an important starting material for the formation of this kind of polymer. It reacts best in the form of its ester with, for example, ethylene glycol, with the elimination of a low molecular weight alcohol. Calcium acetate catalyzes the alcohol interchange, and the reaction takes place at 200°C. The first product is a new monomer containing two ethylene glycol units. When heated to 280°C, this monomer loses ethylene glycol and polymerizes to the final ester. In addition to the reaction conditions of heat and pressure, the stoichiometry of the reactants is very important in condensation polymerization. For example, in the present case, 1:1 stoichiometry leads to a very high molecular weight polymer which is stable as a solid to 267°C. It can be spun into a fiber from a melt and is very widely used in the textile industry as *Dacron* or *Terylene*. Modification of the stoichiometry leads to a lower molecular weight polymer, which also has commercial utility, because it can be fabricated into a very tough fiber of high tear strength. The film *Mylar* is a polyester with this structure.

$$CH_3O-\overset{O}{\underset{\|}{C}}-\langle\bigcirc\rangle-\overset{O}{\underset{\|}{C}}-OCH_3 + 2\ HOCH_2CH_2OH \rightarrow$$

(Ester of Terephthalic acid)   (ethylene glycol)

$$HOCH_2CH_2O-\overset{O}{\underset{\|}{C}}-\langle\bigcirc\rangle-\overset{O}{\underset{\|}{C}}-OCH_2CH_2OH \rightarrow$$

$$\left[OCH_2CH_2O\overset{O}{\underset{\|}{C}}-\langle\bigcirc\rangle-\overset{O}{\underset{\|}{C}} \right]_n + n\ HOCH_2CH_2OH + 2\ CH_2OH$$

Dacron, also Terylene, also Mylar

In addition to molecules containing many amide groups or many ester groups, *polyurethans* are of increasing use, particularly in the manufacture of urethan foam cushions and padding. The urethan group is formed from an isocyanate by reaction with an alcohol. In the case of the polyurethan foams, a prepolymer is first formed containing hydroxyl end groups and having a molecular weight between 1000 and 2000. The diisocyanate is then added to this prepolymer to form the polyurethan linkage.

$$HOCH_2CH_2OH + HO\overset{O}{\underset{\|}{C}}-(CH_2)_4-\overset{O}{\underset{\|}{C}}-OH \rightarrow$$

(adipic acid)

$$HOCH_2CH_2O\left[\overset{O}{\underset{\|}{C}}-(CH_2)_4-\overset{O}{\underset{\|}{C}}-OCH_2CH_2-O\right]_nH \xrightarrow{\quad}$$

(CH_3 ... NCO ... NCO diisocyanate)

$$-N\left[\underset{CH_3}{\langle\bigcirc\rangle}\overset{H}{\underset{|}{N}}-\overset{O}{\underset{\|}{C}}-O-CH_2CH_2O\left[\overset{O}{\underset{\|}{C}}-(CH_2)_4-\overset{O}{\underset{\|}{C}}-O-CH_2CH_2-O\right]_n\overset{O}{\underset{\|}{C}}-\overset{H}{\underset{|}{N}}\right]_m$$

Polyurethan foam

For the formation of the foam, a built-in source of gas is necessary during the polymerization. This blowing, or foaming, agent is carbon dioxide.

It is produced by the deliberate addition of water to the reaction, which converts some of the isocyanate functions to amine groups with the liberation of the carbon dioxide. The amines react with more isocyanate with the formation of urea linkages.

Polyamides, polyesters, and polyurethans are long linear molecules without linkages interconnecting the individual strands. The other common type of polymer is referred to as *cross-linked*, and Bakelite, a phenol-formaldehyde resin, was one of the first commercially produced polymers of this type. The cross-linking provides a three-dimensional structure, so that such polymers form rigid, completely insoluble materials. The condensation of phenol with formaldehyde in the presence of an acid (a Friedel–Crafts reaction) can be controlled to give a low molecular weight product in which phenol moieties are connected by methylene groups. When the molecular weight is about 1000, this material is soluble and can be mixed with coloring agents, fillers, and a source of formaldehyde such as hexamethylenetetramine. This mixture can be melted upon application of heat and can be used to fill preformed molds. Upon further application of heat, the hexamethylenetetramine releases formaldehyde and ammonia. The formaldehyde causes further cross-linking and *thermosetting*, so that the final polymer is a three-dimensional network which is insoluble and rigid and, in certain instances, also brittle.

A thermoplastic material can be remelted many times without change, while a thermosetting material undergoes a permanent change (a chemical reaction) upon melting, and thereafter sets to a solid which cannot be remelted.

The handles of electrical appliances and electrical switches and plugs are generally made of a cross-linked thermosetting resin such as Bakelite.

Bakelite

25.3   Addition Polymers

The second major type of polymer is the *addition polymer*, which is usually prepared from monomers containing one or more double bonds. These polymerizations may occur by anionic, cationic, or free-radical mechanisms, as discussed in Section 15.14.

One kind of addition polymer prepared in large quantities is made from *vinyl chloride*. The polymerization is carried out in a water suspension which contains a soap as an emulsifier and a persulfate initiator. The molecular weight of the polymer can be as high as 1.5 million, and the result is a rigid polyvinyl chloride, which is used for pipes to replace cast iron pipes and also for panels and other molded parts. Polyvinyl chloride has good flame resistance and good electrical resistance. It can be made softer by mixing with a *plasticizer*, such as a low molecular weight aliphatic polyester; the polymer then has good properties for electrical wire coatings, for simulated leather (the so-called *vinyl leather*), and for transparent films used in such items as plastic raincoats.

$$CH_2=CHCl \xrightarrow[H_2O,\ CH_3(CH_2)_{16}\overset{O}{\underset{\|}{C}}-ONa]{K_2S_2O_8} X-CH_2\left(\underset{\underset{Cl}{|}}{CH}-CH_2\right)_n\underset{\underset{Cl}{|}}{CH}-Y$$

Polyvinyl chloride
Molecular weight to 1,500,000

The polymerization of vinyl chloride proceeds in three stages, which is characteristic of all vinyl addition polymerizations. As with other radical reactions, the first stage is called *initiation*, the second *propagation*, and the third *termination*. Initiation is brought about by organic or inorganic peroxides, azo compounds, or other materials that can generate free radicals.

Initiation

$$\underset{\underset{O}{\|}}{R}C-O-O-\underset{\underset{O}{\|}}{C}R \rightarrow 2\ R\overset{O}{\underset{\|}{C}}-O\cdot \rightarrow R\cdot + CO_2$$

or
$$K_2S_2O_8 \rightarrow\ \ 2\ KSO_4$$

or
$$\underset{CH_3}{\overset{CH_3}{\diagdown}}\underset{CN}{\overset{|}{C}}-N=N-\underset{CH_3}{\overset{CH_3}{C}}\underset{\overset{|}{CH_3}}{\overset{\diagup}{CN}} \rightarrow 2\ \underset{CH_3}{\overset{CH_3}{\diagdown}}\underset{CN}{\overset{|}{C}}\cdot + N_2 \quad \text{(See Section 22.6)}$$

In the propagation stage, the chain length grows by the successive additions of monomer molecules, each giving the more stable radical and, consequently, head-to-tail addition.

Propagation

$$R\cdot + CH_2=\underset{\underset{Cl}{|}}{CH} \rightarrow R-CH_2-\underset{\underset{Cl}{|}}{CH}\cdot \rightarrow RCH_2\underset{\underset{Cl}{|}}{CH}-CH_2-\underset{\underset{Cl}{|}}{CH}\cdot \xrightarrow{\text{etc.}}$$

Finally, termination takes place by coupling reactions, disproportionation, or chain-transfer reactions. Termination is sometimes controlled to regulate the molecular weight. However, many times an impurity in the monomer may act as a chain-transfer agent and limit the molecular weight to an undesirably low number. Obviously very small amounts of impurities can have very large effects upon the structure, and therefore upon the properties of the resulting polymer.

Termination: Coupling

$$2\ RCH_2\underset{\underset{Cl}{|}}{CH}\cdot \rightarrow R-CH_2\underset{\underset{Cl}{|}}{CH}-\underset{\underset{Cl}{|}}{CH}-CH_2R$$

Termination: Chain transfer

$$R\left(CH_2-\underset{\underset{Cl}{|}}{CH}\right)_n CH_2-\underset{\underset{Cl}{|}}{CH}\cdot + RSH \rightarrow R\left(CH_2-\underset{\underset{Cl}{|}}{CH}\right)_n CH_2-\underset{\underset{Cl}{|}}{CH_2} + RS\cdot$$

$$RS\cdot + CH_2=\underset{\underset{Cl}{|}}{CH} \rightarrow R-S-CH_2-\underset{\underset{Cl}{|}}{CH}\cdot \rightarrow \text{New chain}$$

MOLECULAR WEIGHT AND PHYSICAL PROPERTIES.   *It is usually necessary, as a rule of thumb, to have approximately 1000 repeating units before a polymer with "plastic" properties is obtained. At one extreme, polyethylene must have a molecular weight approaching 1,000,000 before it has the tough physical properties as we know them in items such as bottles, and dishpans. On the other hand, nylon, a polyamide, has the physical properties of a filament at a molecular weight of only about 50,000. Obviously the van der Waals attractions and the hydrogen bonding (second-order bonds) determine the nature of polymer strength and utility. One may envision the closely packed chains of a nonpolar polymer (polyethylene, polyvinyl chloride, etc.) sliding past one another with relative ease, giving the appearance of flexibility.*

These properties are a fortunate circumstance, since condensation polymers (poly-amide, ester, etc.) are polymerized to very high molecular weight only with great difficulty, because the reaction is an equilibrium process.

A second point of interest concerns the kinetics of the process involved. Condensation polymerization involves the random attack of any monomer on the nearest functional group that it collides with, whether this is another monomer or the terminal group on a growing polymer chain. Thus, if the reaction were stopped short of completion, thousands of oligomers of low molecular weight would be found, with essentially all of the monomers having been consumed. At this point the polymer would likely have the properties of a wax. In order to obtain polymers of the minimum molecular weight to give a good fiber, these relatively short chains must be further condensed to provide longer chains, and the process is repeated until the point of equilibrium is reached where depolymerization results via the reverse reaction.

On the other hand, a free-radical process is usually carried out by adding a low concentration of initiator. This starts the growing of relatively few polymer chains which grow to chains involving a molecular weight of a million while the bulk of the unreacted material is left as the monomer. However, the initiator is being thermally generated throughout the course of the reaction (e.g., by the decomposition of a peroxide), thus starting new chains until all of the monomer has been consumed. The reaction may reach a point where the rate is markedly accelerated due to the exothermicity of the polymerization involving the loss of a double bond. However, a point may also be reached when the viscosity of the reaction medium will slow the reaction, since the monomer will find it increasingly difficult to find a radical end on a growing chain with which to react. Thus in many cases the temperature is increased at the end of a radical process to drive the reaction to completion by decreasing the viscosity and generating new initiator molecules, R·. Viscosity problems are also prevalent in the condensation type of polymerization.

A *homopolymer* is the result of a polymerization of a single type of monomer. A *copolymer* results when two different types of monomers are polymerized together, generally containing a random sequence of no definite pattern which depends upon the amount of each of the monomers added and their reactivities toward the growing chain of the polymer. An excellent example is the copolymerization of vinylidene chloride with vinyl chloride. *Saran wrap* is the result of a suspension polymerization carried out in a manner very similar to the polymerization described for vinyl chloride alone, but in which vinylidene chloride is mixed with the vinyl chloride. The polymer has a good resistance to outdoor weathering and to all types of organic solvents, can be extruded for tubes and pipes, and can be spun into fiber. (The fiber is particularly useful for up-holstery of the type widely used in automobiles.) The polymer also has low moisture transmission and forms a very tough film, which is ideal for food packaging.

$$CH_2{=}CCl_2 + CH_2{=}\underset{\underset{\text{Cl}}{|}}{CH} \xrightarrow[\text{H}_2\text{O, soap}]{K_2S_2O_8} \underbrace{\Big(\!CH_2{-}CCl_2}_{17}{-}\underbrace{CH_2{-}\underset{\underset{\text{Cl}}{|}}{CH}\!\Big)}_{13}$$

(17 moles)   (13 moles)   17   13
                                                              (random)
                                                            Saran wrap

Methyl methacrylate will undergo free-radical polymerization to give a polymer with excellent optical properties which has a wide variety of uses, such as in contact lenses or clear sheets for windows. When these sheets, called *Plexiglas*, *Perspex*, or *Lucite*, are made, the polymerization is carried out to a syrup stage; the syrup is then poured into a mold or poured between vertical glass sheets, where the polymerization is allowed to finish.

$$CH_2=\underset{\underset{\text{methyl methacrylate}}{|}}{\overset{\overset{CH_3}{|}}{C}}\text{---}\overset{\overset{O}{\|}}{C}\text{---}OCH_3 \rightarrow \left(\text{---}CH_2\text{---}\underset{\underset{CH_3O_2C}{|}}{\overset{\overset{CH_3}{|}}{C}}\text{---}\right)_n$$

Plexiglass,
also Lucite,
also Perspex

Acrylonitrile is one of the few monomers that can be polymerized in water solution. The resulting homopolymer of acrylonitrile is also one of the few addition polymers that can be spun into a fiber. It is not possible to spin the polymer from a melt, because the polymer turns dark below its melting point. If the polymer is dissolved in dimethyl-formamide, it can be spun from this solvent. The resulting fiber is the well-known *Orlon*; it can be woven or knitted, and also can be blended with wool for these processes.

$$CH_2=\underset{\underset{\text{acrylonitrile}}{|}}{\overset{|}{\underset{CN}{CH}}} \rightarrow \left(\text{---}CH_2\text{---}\underset{\underset{CN}{|}}{CH}\text{---}\right)_n$$

Orlon

Styrene is a very versatile monomer, and it finds use in large quantities as a homo-polymer, as a crossed-linked polymer, and as a copolymer. Styrene is very reactive; it polymerizes to give a product with excellent clarity and good electrical properties, and one that can be foamed to give lightweight material with excellent structural properties suitable for synthetic furniture. One-room, igloo-type buildings can be constructed by conducting the final stages of the polymerization for their exterior walls in place at the construction site.

Styrene also can be effectively cross-linked to give an insoluble resin. This is accomplished by adding a small amount of divinylbenzene to styrene before the polymerization is carried out. If the cross-linked resin is then subjected to sulfonation using chloro-sulfonic acid or sulfuric acid, an ion-exchange resin results which is particularly useful in water softeners.

Styrene   divinyl benzene   Styrene resin

Styrene resin $\xrightarrow{\underset{\text{2. NaCl}}{\text{1. ClSO}_3\text{H}}}$ ... $\xrightarrow{\underset{\underset{Fe^{2+}}{\overset{Ca^{2+}}{Mg^{2+}}}}{\text{Hard water}}}$ ...

Cationic ion exchanger

One of the largest uses of styrene is in a copolymerization reaction with butadiene for the preparation of synthetic rubber. Butadiene is used in a larger amount; in the resulting polymer about 80% of it has been incorporated by 1,4 addition, and most of the double bonds remaining have the trans configuration. These double bonds are essential for the next step in the manufacture of synthetic rubber. The step is very complicated and little understood, but involves cross-linking of the polymer chains through the double bonds using elemental sulfur. The process is called *vulcanization* of rubber. The copolymer with a molecular weight range from 25,000 to 500,000 is consumed in large quantities in the manufacture of tire carcasses and tire treads.

$$CH_2=CH-CH=CH_2 + CH_2=CH \rightarrow$$

75%   25%

Synthetic rubber

ELASTICITY. *The special physical properties of rubber result from the structure of the polymer. Long flexible molecules tend to coil up in a random way. The molecules are uncoiled when the material is stretched. This uncoiled arrangement has a more specific geometry than the random coil, and hence a much lower entropy. Thus when the stretched material is released, the entropy increases and the rubber contracts. Single polymer chains can slip past one another, and this would lead to a permanent deformation of the sample upon the application of stress. Vulcanization supplies cross-linking of the chains so that such slippage cannot occur, and the product is elastic or "rubbery."*

Polymers with good cross-linking and thermosetting characteristics can be made by addition polymerization. For example, *epoxy resins* have developed an excellent reputation in the last few years as universal glue. In the formation of the epoxy resin, the polymerization is a distinctly two-stage reaction. First, a low molecular weight linear polymer is formed with very reactive epoxy groups at the end. This component is usually formed with a bisphenol and epichlorohydrin. The cross-linking agent is added in a second step; it is generally a polyfunctional amine such as diethylenetriamine, which, when mixed with the preformed epoxy polymer, cross-links the linear polyether. This reaction yields a resin with excellent adhesive strength and structural characteristics.

Cross-linked polymer

A variety of nylon called nylon 6 can be made by the condensation polymerization of caprolactam. The reaction is accomplished by an initiation which opens part of the caprolactam to the corresponding amino acid, which in turn reacts directly with additional lactam via a ring-opening chain reaction.

$$\text{(caprolactam)} + H_2O \rightarrow {}^{+}NH_3(CH_2)_5\overset{O}{\overset{\|}{C}}-O^-$$

$$\text{(caprolactam)} + {}^{+}\overset{+}{N}H_3(CH_2)_5\overset{O}{\overset{\|}{C}}-O^- \rightarrow \overset{+}{N}H_3-(CH_2)_5\overset{O}{\overset{\|}{C}}-NH(CH_2)_5-\overset{O}{\overset{\|}{C}}-O^-$$

$$\downarrow$$

$$\begin{bmatrix} -(CH_2)_5\overset{O}{\overset{\|}{C}}-\overset{H}{\overset{|}{N}}- \end{bmatrix}_n$$

Nylon 6

Ethylene oxide is a good example of a monomer than can be polymerized by either anionic or cationic catalysts. Lewis acid catalysts are generally used for the cationic catalysts, and the resulting polymer is one of the few that is soluble in water. This property leads to the use of polyethylene oxide as a surfactant (detergent), a thickener, or a sizing compound.

$$F_3B \cdot O\!\!\begin{array}{c}CH_2\\|\\CH_2\end{array} + O\!\!\begin{array}{c}CH_2\\|\\CH_2\end{array} + O\!\!\begin{array}{c}CH_2\\|\\CH_2\end{array} \rightarrow F_3\bar{B}O\!\!\begin{array}{c}CH_2\\|\\CH_2\end{array} O\!\!\begin{bmatrix}CH_2\\|\\CH_2\end{bmatrix} O\!\!\Big\}_n$$

$$B^- + n\,CH_2\!-\!\!\overset{O}{\frown}\!\!-CH_2 \rightarrow B(CH_2CH_2O)_n$$

25.4 Stereochemistry of Polymers

Since 1953, following the discoveries of Ziegler and Natta, the industrial use of ionic polymerization has expanded very rapidly. Ziegler and Natta developed catalysts which permit the stereochemical control of polymerizations of readily available and cheap starting material such as propylene. These so-called *Ziegler–Natta catalysts* are active initiators prepared from a transition metal halide and a reducing agent. The most commonly used is $Al(Et)_3 \cdot TiCl_4$, The growing chain reaction involves insertion of the monomer into the bond between the metal and the growing chain, as shown, for example, with propylene.

$$\underset{\underset{CH_2=CHCH_3}{|}}{M-CH_2}\overset{\overset{CH_3}{|}}{-CH}(CH_2\overset{\overset{CH_3}{|}}{-CH})_n \rightarrow M-CH_2\overset{\overset{CH_3}{|}}{-CH}-CH_2\overset{\overset{CH_3}{|}}{-CH}(CH_2\overset{\overset{CH_3}{|}}{-CH})_n$$

The resulting polymer differs from earlier polymers of propylene, which were branched and noncrystalline, and had weak mechanical properties. In contrast, with Ziegler–Natta catalysts, straight-chain polymers with high stereochemical regularity can be produced which have a high melting point and form very strong fibers. The early polymers of propylene had random stereochemistry. Such random polymers are called *atactic* (Figure 25.1) and are noncrystalline. Those with groups all on one side of an extended chain are called *isotactic*, and those polymers with groups alternating regularly from one side of the chain to another are called *syndiotactic* (Figure 25.1). These two types of polymers are in general crystalline. Isotactic polypropylene melts at 167°C.

Figure 25.1
The basic stereochemical polymer types.

Atactic (random)

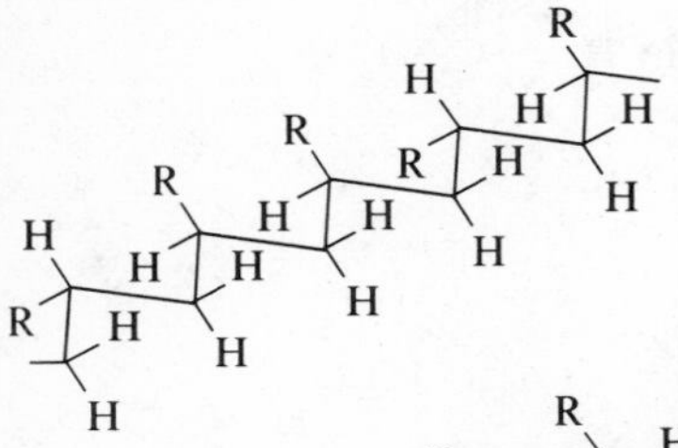

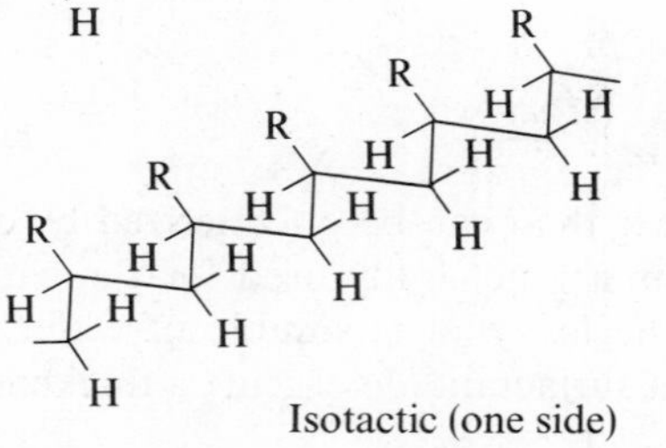

Isotactic (one side)

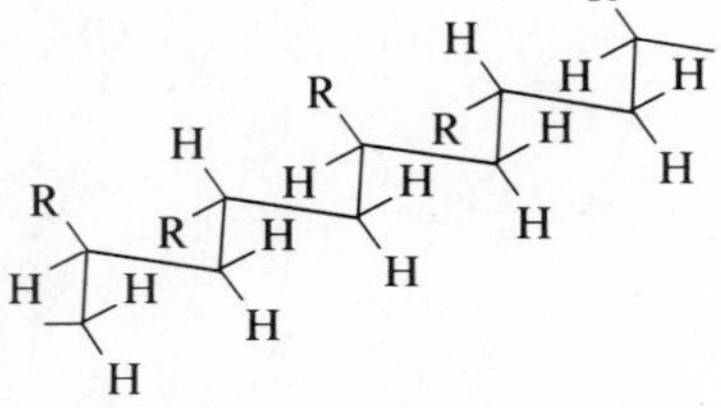

Syndiotactic (alternate)

The three-dimensional structures of the polymer chains help to explain their physical properties and uses. For example, an atactic polymer such as polypropylene can formally be considered in the stretched conformation (Figure 25.2). Actually, such a polymer is an equilibrium mixture of the possible conformations, and hence it tends to coil up like a ball of spaghetti in solution. Such an atactic material will not crystallize upon cooling, but rather forms a firm noncrystalline solid called a *glass*. Films resulting from slit extrusions of the atactic material can serve as, for example, the protective cover used by dry cleaners around suits and dresses. Since polypropylene has a very low electrical conductivity, it is also used as an electrical insulator and as a coating on electrical wires.

Figure 25.2

Atactic polypropylene, stretched. For clarity, the methyl groups are represented by the dark spheres.

Figure 25.3
Syndiotactic polypropylene, stretched.

Figure 25.4
Isotactic polypropylene, stretched.

Figure 25.3 shows the syndiotactic polymer. The methyl groups will exist primarily in the anti conformation in solution, and the polymer also crystallizes in this conformation.

As Figure 25.4 shows, the isotactic polymer would suffer unfavorable methyl–methyl repulsions if the backbone of the polymer were in the all-anti conformation. The backbone therefore adopts an all-gauche conformation, which means that the polymer has a helical structure. Crystalline polypropylene has a tight helical structure, with three monomer units per turn (Figure 25.5). The isotactic form of this polymer is used for a variety of molded objects.

Figure 25.5
Isotactic polypropylene, helical.

PROBLEMS

1. Suggest reasonable chemistry associated with the fact that the first drops of rain in a big industrial city sometimes cause nylons to weaken and run.

2. What commercial chemical reactions of terephthalic acid would be used to give a common polyester?

3. Discuss the several steps involved in the production of polyurethan foam.

4. Explain the difference between the main physical properties of Dacron and Bakelite in terms of their molecular structures.

5. How does a condensation polymer differ from an addition polymer? Give an example of each.

6. Name and give an example of each of the three separate stages of free-radical polymerization.

7. Write the structures for the following common polymeric materials:
    (a) Mylar   (b) Polyurethan
    (c) Bakelite   (d) Saran
    (e) Lucite   (f) Orlon

8. Write the industrial chemical reaction used to make water-softeners, and explain their operation in conversion of hard water to soft water.

9. Indicate the detailed mechanism for the condensation of epichlorohydrin with a bisphenol in the presence of a base.

10. The patent literature claims the light-catalyzed reaction of nitrosyl chloride with cyclohexane to form an intermediate useful in the formation of nylon 6. Suggest a reasonable structure for the intermediate and outline the further steps necessary for the nylon synthesis.

11. Explain why the structure of rubber leads to the well-known physical properties of the material.

12. Draw schematic formulas for atactic, isotactic, and syndiotactic polymers. Explain how and why their three-dimensional structures differ. Discuss their physical properties and commercial uses.

13. Give an example to illustrate ionic polymerization. For the products, give properties and uses which give them commercial value.

14. Methyl methacrylate is polymerized by treatment with free-radical initiators, such as di-*t*-butyl peroxide, to form one of the more important commercial plastics. Show: (a) how the initiator attacks methyl methacrylate; (b) the first step in the growth of the chain; (c) the structure of the repeating unit in the final polymer.

Optional Problem

1. A sample of styrene is polymerized with the help of a little azoisobutyronitrile as initiator. Hydrolysis of the resulting polymer releases 6 g of ammonia from 10 kg of polymer. If all the end groups are derived from the initiating radical (α-cyanoisopropyl), what is the average number of styrene units in the chain?

CHAPTER 26

ORGANOSULFUR CHEMISTRY

26.1 Introduction

Sulfur appears just below oxygen in Group VI of the periodic table. As are other second-row elements, sulfur is much more versatile as a reaction center than is its first-row counterpart. In oxygen compounds such as alcohols, ethers, and carbonyl compounds, the most apparent role of oxygen is often to alter the chemistry of the carbon atom to which the oxygen is attached. Similar effects are found in organosulfur compounds, but owing to the high reactivity of the sulfur atom itself towards electrophilic, nucleophilic, and even radical reagents, an overwhelming majority of reactions occur directly at sulfur. In contrast to oxygen, sulfur enters into p–p π bonding reluctantly. Silicon and phosphorus (Chapter 33) form p–p π bonds even less readily than sulfur.

Interest in the organic chemistry of sulfur, as in that of silicon and phosphorus, has greatly increased in recent years. Sulfur compounds are of prime importance in many industrial operations, in the pharmaceutical industry, and in the fundamental research laboratory as well. They are important participants in every metabolic process. The structural aspects of organosulfur chemistry in Sections 4.12, 4.13, 10.4, and 10.5 should be reviewed.

26.2 Thiols (Mercaptans)

The fundamental building blocks for the synthesis of other organosulfur compounds are the *thiols*, RSH. They are more acidic and more volatile than the corresponding alcohols and are well known for their disagreeable odors. *Butanethiol* is the defensive weapon of the skunk. *Propyl mercaptan* is evolved from freshly chopped onions; *allyl mercaptan* and *allyl disulfide* are partially responsible for the odor and flavor of garlic. Thiols are highly reactive substances, and in small quantities they play key roles in biological processes. Together with a number of other sulfur compounds, thiols occur as a small, though significant, fraction of crude petroleum.

Like hydrogen sulfide, thiols react with the ions of a number of heavy metals. The formation of insoluble mercury derivatives is a striking characteristic of thiols and is the origin of the common name, mercaptan (*mercurium captans*, capturing mercury). The dithiol $HSCH_2$—$CHSH$—CH_2OH, known as BAL (British anti-Lewisite), was developed as a protective agent against arsenical war gases (such as Lewisite) and is an effective antidote for poisoning by arsenic, mercury, and other heavy metals.

Thiols and their salts are considerably more nucleophilic than alcohols and alkoxides, respectively. Thiols are less basic than alcohols toward proton acids. Hydrogen sulfide is not as effective a leaving group as water and thiols do not react with reagents such as hydrogen bromide to yield alkyl bromides. Nevertheless, a large number of the reactions of thiols resemble those of alcohols.

EXERCISE 26.1

Suggest detailed mechanisms for the preceding three reactions.

Clearly, the most significant difference between the chemistry of alcohols and thiols is the ease with which thiols are oxidized. They yield disulfides with a variety of mild oxidizing agents such as I_2, HOCl, O_2 (in the presence of copper or iron catalyst), or H_2O_2. Vigorous oxidizing agents such as HNO_3 can oxidize the disulfide further, to a sulfonic acid. Oxidation of an alcohol increases the oxidation state of carbon, whereas oxidation of a thiol occurs at the sulfur atom.

$$RCH_2OH \rightarrow RCHO \rightarrow RCOOH$$

$$RCH_2SH \rightarrow RCH_2SSCH_2R \rightarrow RCH_2SO_3H$$

One-electron oxidation of an alcohol effects homolysis of a C—H bond (~ 85 kcal) rather than an O—H bond (~ 110 kcal), whereas one-electron oxidation of a thiol results in homolysis of an S—H bond (~ 80 kcal).

The formation of RS· from thiols is easy, and the free-radical addition of thiols to alkenes is a smooth and useful reaction. Thiols are very efficient chain-transfer agents, and little or no polymerization occurs in such reactions.

It might seem that the most straightforward way to prepare a thiol would be via the reaction of sodium hydrogen sulfide with an alkyl halide.

$$R—X + NaSH \rightarrow R—SH + NaX$$

However, unless one either employs a large excess of the hydrosulfide or passes hydrogen sulfide into the reaction mixture, significant quantities of sulfide may also be produced.

$$RSH + NaSH \rightleftharpoons RS^-Na^+ + H_2S$$

$$RS^-Na^+ + RX \rightleftharpoons RSR + NaX$$

Alkylation of the highly nucleophilic thiourea provides the basis for an excellent laboratory method for preparation of thiols which cleverly avoids this problem of sulfide formation.

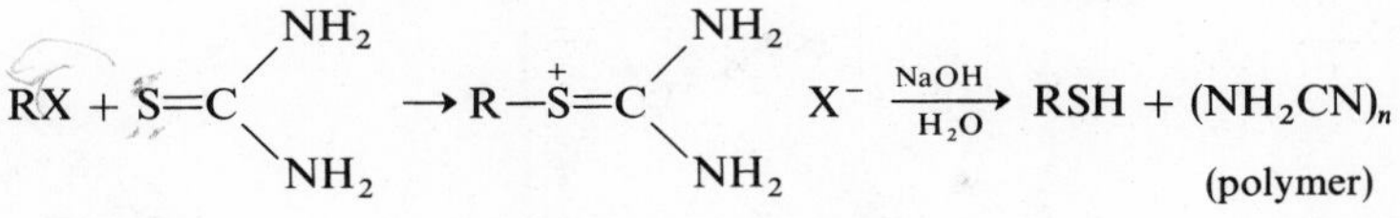

$$RX + S=C\overset{NH_2}{\underset{NH_2}{\big\langle}} \longrightarrow R\overset{+}{-}S=C\overset{NH_2}{\underset{NH_2}{\big\langle}} \;\; X^- \xrightarrow[H_2O]{NaOH} RSH + (NH_2CN)_n$$

S-Alkylisothiouronium salt   (polymer)

The *S*-alkylisothiouronium salts are stable, often crystalline compounds, which can be isolated and purified.

Thiols are also readily prepared by the action of sulfur on Grignard reagents, and by hydrolysis of thiol esters.

$$ArMgBr \xrightarrow[ether]{S} ArSMgBr \xrightarrow{H_3O^+} ArSH$$

$$R\overset{O}{\overset{\|}{S}}CCH_3 \xrightarrow[2.\; H_3O^+]{1.\; OH^-} RSH$$

26.3   Sulfides and Disulfides

For the most part, the reactivity of sulfides depends on the accessibility of the lone pairs on sulfur. Sulfides are weak Lewis bases, are highly nucleophilic, and are easily oxidized to sulfoxides and sulfones (Section 26.4). A characteristic reaction of a sulfide is the formation of an insoluble crystalline complex with mercuric chloride.

$$R_2S + HgCl_2 \longrightarrow R_2\overset{+}{S}-\overset{-}{H}gCl_2$$

The alkylation of a sulfide to a sulfonium salt appears to be a typical S_N2 reaction. With a dialkyl sulfide, the reaction proceeds rapidly under mild conditions.

$$R_2S + RX \longrightarrow R_3S^+ X^-$$

Both aryl and alkyl sulfides are readily accessible through nucleophilic or radical reactions.

$$RS^- + CH_3Br \longrightarrow RSCH_3$$

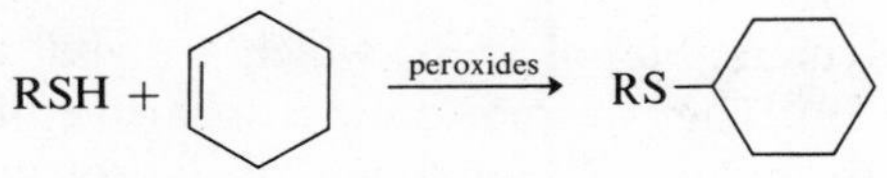

$$RSH + \text{(cyclohexene)} \xrightarrow{peroxides} RS-\text{(cyclohexyl)}$$

Although direct nucleophilic displacements do not usually occur on simple aryl halides (Section 17.8), the following reaction proceeds readily.

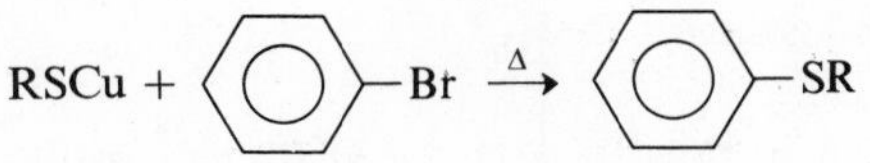

$$RSCu + \text{(aryl)}-Br \xrightarrow{\Delta} \text{(aryl)}-SR$$

Episulfides. Like epoxides, episulfides (thiiranes) readily undergo ring-opening reactions under a variety of conditions.

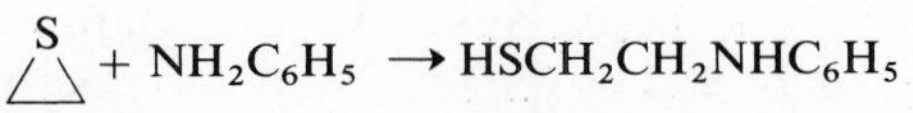

$$\overset{S}{\triangle} + NH_2C_6H_5 \longrightarrow HSCH_2CH_2NHC_6H_5$$

These substances, however, cannot be made by a direct "sulfidation" of alkenes. Although a number of methods are available for their synthesis, the most interesting and general method is the reaction of thiocyanate with an oxirane.

Disulfides are most readily prepared by mild oxidation of thiols (page 682), iodine being the best oxidizing agent.

$$2\,R{-}SH \xrightarrow{I_2} R{-}S{-}S{-}R$$

EXERCISE 26.2

Suggest a mechanism for the preceding oxidation.

Perhaps the most important reaction of disulfides is their reduction to thiols.

$$R{-}S{-}S{-}R \underset{[O]}{\overset{[H]}{\rightleftharpoons}} 2\,RSH$$

This reduction may be accomplished by a variety of reagents, including sodium hydrogen sulfite, sodium in ether, and lithium aluminum hydride. The formation and reduction of disulfide bonds is an extremely important biological process.

LIPOIC ACID. *Lipoic acid is an important co-factor in numerous biological oxidations and reductions, such as the conversion of pyruvate to acetate and carbon dioxide. This key biological material was first isolated in pure form in 1953; 30 mg of crystalline lipoic acid was obtained by hydrolysis and extraction of 10 tons of beef liver.*

Lipoic acid   Dihydrolipoic acid

Proteins are very complicated biological polymers (biopolymers) which are vital to the functions of every living system (Chapter 29). They are polyamides formed from α-amino acids, $RCH(NH_2)COOH$. *Cysteine* is an amino acid component of all proteins.

$$HSCH_2CHCOOH \qquad HOOCCH{-}CH_2{-}S{-}S{-}CH_2{-}CHCOOH$$
$$\underset{NH_2}{|} \qquad\qquad\qquad \underset{NH_2}{|} \qquad\qquad\qquad\qquad\quad \underset{NH_2}{|}$$

Cysteine   Cystine

The disulfide *cystine*, formed from cysteine, is an important structural unit of proteins which plays an important role in determining the gross shape of the molecule and serves as a cross-link between protein chains (Figure 26.1). The protein *insulin*, for example, consists of two long polyamide chains held together by cystine. The structural proteins of hair and skin have an especially high content of cystine as cross-links between protein chains. "Permanent" waves or curls in hair are achieved by the reduction and reformation of disulfide cross-links in the protein of hair.

Figure 26.1
Schematic illustrations of the utility of disulfide bonds of cystine (*a*) in determining the gross shape
of a protein molecule and (*b*) as cross-links between protein chains.

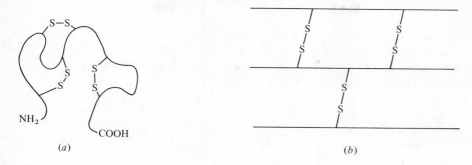

(*a*)   (*b*)

26.4   Sulfoxides and Sulfones

Dimethyl sulfoxide (DMSO) is an exceptionally powerful solvent for both polar and
nonpolar compounds. It is particularly useful as a reaction medium for bimolecular
nucleophilic reactions in which the attacking nucleophile bears a negative charge. Like
dimethylformamide, it is a very polar solvent but does not form hydrogen bonds with
unshared electron pairs; such solvents are known as *dipolar aprotic solvents*. DMSO has
the intriguing property of being rapidly absorbed into the skin—if a drop is placed on
the back of the hand, a mild garlic-like taste will be noticed almost immediately. Dimethyl
sulfoxide is of interest medicinally, for its ability not only to penetrate tissue, but also
to allay pain.

Some Reactions of Sulfoxides. Sulfoxides, with lone pairs on both oxygen and sulfur, act as *ambident
nucleophiles* (Section 19.15).

$$
\underset{\substack{\mathrm{O} \\ \parallel}}{CH_3-S-CH_3} + CH_3I \underset{\text{slow}}{\overset{\text{fast}}{\rightleftharpoons}} \underset{\substack{OCH_3 \\ |}}{CH_3-\overset{+}{S}-CH_3}\ I^-
$$

$$
\underset{\substack{\mathrm{O} \\ \parallel \\ | \\ CH_3}}{CH_2-\overset{+}{S}-CH_3}\ I^- \qquad\qquad \underset{\substack{OCH_3 \\ |}}{CH_3-\overset{+}{S}-CH_3}\ BF_4^-
$$

with AgBF$_4$ conversion.

O-Alkylation of sulfoxides occurs quite readily, but if the anion is nucleophilic, as in the case of
iodide, the reaction is reversible. With dimethyl sulfoxide, methyl iodide, and silver fluoroborate
(BF_4^- is a very poor nucleophile), dimethylmethoxysulfonium fluoroborate is rapidly formed.
After a prolonged reaction time, dimethyl sulfoxide and methyl iodide form trimethyloxosulfonium
iodide. Sulfoxides are easily oxidized to sulfones, but they are also reduced to sulfides by a variety
of reagents.

$$
{>}S{=}O + RSH \rightarrow {>}S + RSSR + H_2O
$$

$$
{>}S{=}O + HI \rightarrow {>}S + I_2 + H_2O
$$

$$
{>}S{=}O + R_3P \rightarrow {>}S + R_3P{=}O
$$

Sulfones are rather unreactive to attack occurring directly on sulfur or oxygen. Many sulfones may, however, be reduced to sulfides by lithium aluminum hydride.

$$R_2SO_2 \xrightarrow{\text{LiAlH}_4} R_2S$$

Other reactions of sulfones occur mainly on the α carbon (Section 26.6).

Sulfoxides and sulfones are prepared by oxidation of the corresponding sulfides. Sulfones are normally quite easy to prepare. Permanganate or excess hydrogen peroxide quantitatively converts a sulfide or a sulfoxide to a sulfone.

Sulfoxides are a little more difficult to obtain, since most reagents which will oxidize a sulfide will also oxidize a sulfoxide to a sulfone. Useful reagents for the laboratory include hydrogen peroxide (one equivalent in acetone) or sodium metaperiodate. When employed at low temperatures, the latter reagent will not produce any sulfone. Since sulfoxides are configurationally stable, geometrical isomers may be obtained upon oxidation of appropriate sulfides.

26.5   Sulfonium Salts

Sulfonium salts are configurationally stable, and they may be obtained in diastereomeric modifications.

Sulfonium salts, like ammonium and phosphonium salts, are subject to attack by nucleophilic reagents. In most cases attack occurs on the α carbon to regenerate a sulfide. An example is the pyrolysis of trimethylsulfonium bromide.

$$(CH_3)_3S^+ Br^- \rightarrow CH_3Br + CH_3SCH_3$$

However, when better leaving groups are present on the sulfur of a sulfonium salt, as in an alkoxy-sulfonium salt, attack occurs directly at the sulfur.

In this case, as well as in most other examples studied so far, nucleophilic substitution at trivalent sulfur occurs with inversion of configuration at sulfur. It is not known whether displacement reactions on sulfur occur directly or through the intervention of an intermediate.

26.6   Sulfur-Stabilized Carbanions

Carbanions adjacent to sulfur are stabilized by back-bonding to the sulfur atom. The bonding situation is similar to that discussed for sulfoxides in Section 10.5. As the sulfur becomes more electropositive in higher coordination states, both *d*-orbital participation and coulombic interaction contribute to the stability of the carbanion. The stability of a carbanion adjacent to a sulfur atom increases in the order

$$-S-CH_2^- \; < \; -SO-CH_2^- \; < \; -SO_2CH_2^- \; < \; \overset{+}{\underset{/}{\backslash}}S-CH_2^-$$

More about Sulfur-Stabilized Carbanions. Thioanisole reacts with *n*-butyllithium to form phenyl-thiomethyllithium, in contrast to anisole, which is converted to *o*-methoxyphenyllithium under the same conditions.

Such sulfur-stabilized lithio derivatives have much the same chemistry as ordinary organometallic reagents.

Methylsulfinyl carbanion, generated when dimethyl sulfoxide is warmed with sodium hydride or treated with *n*-butyllithium, is both a strong base and a powerful nucleophile.

$$CH_3SOCH_3 \xrightarrow{\text{NaH}} CH_3SOCH_2^- Na^+$$

It adds to nonenolizable ketones to give *hydroxy sulfoxides*; with readily enolizable ketones, enolate formation occurs exclusively. Intermediate cases are common.

$$(C_6H_5)_2CO + CH_3\overset{O}{\overset{\|}{S}}CH_2^- \; Na^+ \xrightarrow[\text{H}_2\text{O}]{\text{then}} (C_6H_5)_2\overset{OH}{\underset{}{C}}CH_2\overset{O}{\overset{\|}{S}}CH_3$$

$$C_6H_5CH_2COC_6H_5 + CH_3\overset{O}{\overset{\|}{S}}CH_2^- \; Na^+ \rightarrow C_6H_5CH=\overset{O^-Na^+}{\underset{}{C}}-C_6H_5$$

Esters which do not undergo facile proton removal react with two equivalents of methylsulfinyl carbanion to yield anions of keto sulfoxides. The methylsulfinyl group of such ketones is readily replaced by hydrogen using aluminum amalgam; the overall process provides a useful synthesis of ketones from esters.

$$R-\overset{O}{\overset{\|}{C}}-OCH_3 + 2\,CH_3\overset{O}{\overset{\|}{S}}CH_2^- \; Na^+ \rightarrow R-\overset{O}{\overset{\|}{C}}-\overset{-}{C}H-\overset{O}{\overset{\|}{S}}CH_3 \; Na^+$$

$$R-\overset{O}{\overset{\|}{C}}-CH_2R' \xleftarrow[\text{H}_2\text{O}]{\text{Al(Hg)}} R-\overset{O}{\overset{\|}{C}}-\underset{R'}{\overset{\|}{C}H}-\overset{O}{\overset{\|}{S}}CH_3 \qquad R-\overset{O}{\overset{\|}{C}}-CH_3$$

with branches labeled R'X and (1. H₂O; 2. Al(Hg)/H₂O)

Methylsulfinyl carbanion in dimethyl sulfoxide is an excellent reagent for the generation and reaction of Wittig reagents and other ylides.

The reactions of α-halo sulfones are novel. Unlike α-halo carbonyl compounds, these materials do not readily undergo nucleophilic substitution on carbon. In many cases, nucleophilic attack occurs on halogen with the sulfone-stabilized carbanion acting as the leaving group.

$$CH_3SO_2CH_2Br + RMgX \longrightarrow CH_3SO_2CH_2MgX + RBr$$

Dialkyl α-halo sulfones react with base to generate an intermediate episulfone, which usually gives up sulfur dioxide to yield an alkene.

$$RCH_2SO_2CHClR' \xrightleftharpoons{OH^-} RCHSO_2CHClR' \longrightarrow RCH \overset{SO_2}{\overset{\diagup\diagdown}{-}} CHR' \longrightarrow RCH{=}CHR' + SO_2$$

Sulfonium salts bearing α protons form ylides upon reaction with base.

$$-\underset{+}{\overset{|}{S}}-\underset{\underset{H}{|}}{C} \xrightleftharpoons[+H^+]{-H^+} \overset{+}{S}-\overset{-}{C} \leftrightarrow S{=}C$$

Trimethylsulfonium and trimethyloxosulfonium iodide show statistical deuterium exchange when warmed with deuterium oxide in the presence of a base; in contrast, tetramethylammonium salts do not incorporate deuterium under these conditions.

$$CH_3-\overset{\overset{O}{\|}}{\underset{\underset{CH_3}{|}}{S^+}}-CH_3I^- \xrightarrow[Na_2CO_3]{D_2O} CD_3-\overset{\overset{O}{\|}}{\underset{\underset{CD_3}{|}}{S^+}}-CD_3 \ I^- \xrightarrow{220°C} CD_3SOCD_3 + CD_3I$$

Pyrolysis of trimethyloxosulfonium-d_9 iodide provides a convenient synthesis of dimethyl sulfoxide-d_6 and methyl iodide-d_3.

Certain sulfur ylides of intermediate stability are excellent reagents for the transfer of methylene or substituted methylenes to carbonyl compounds or to electrophilic olefins or acetylenes. Several such reactions were discussed in Sections 19.10 and 19.17. Additional examples are illustrated.

$$CD_3-\overset{\overset{O}{\|}}{\underset{\underset{CD_3}{|}}{S^+}}-\overset{-}{CD_2} + \langle\bigcirc\rangle-CHO \longrightarrow \langle\bigcirc\rangle-\overset{\overset{O}{\diagup\diagdown}}{CH}-CD_2 + CD_3SOCD_3$$

$$CH_3OOC-C{\equiv}C-COOCH_3 + 2\,(C_6H_5)_2\overset{+}{S}-\overset{-}{C}(CH_3)_2 \longrightarrow CH_3OOC-\overset{H_3C\diagdown\quad\diagup CH_3}{\underset{H_3C\diagup\quad\diagdown CH_3}{\langle\rangle}}-COOCH_3$$

A number of sulfur ylides, especially those with a good leaving group on the sulfur atom, are quite unstable and decompose or rearrange upon generation. The ready collapse of the ylides derived from alkoxysulfonium salts is the basis of an interesting and useful method for oxidation.

$$CH_3-\underset{+}{\overset{\overset{O-CH_2R}{|}}{S}}-CH_3 \xrightarrow{B:} \left[H_3C-\overset{+}{\underset{CH_2}{S}}\overset{O\curvearrowleft CHR}{\diagup H} \right] \longrightarrow CH_3SCH_3 + RC\overset{\diagup\diagup O}{\underset{\diagdown H}{}}$$

Through the intervention of alkoxysulfonium salts, reactive halides and tosylates may be converted to carbonyl compounds.

$$RCH_2X \xrightarrow[\Delta]{CH_3SOCH_3} RCHO$$

$$X = Br^-,\ I^-,\ \text{or}\ p\text{-}CH_3C_6H_4SO_3^-$$

Alcohols, in a related reaction, may be oxidized to aldehydes or ketones by the use of dimethyl sulfoxide in the presence of any of a number of condensing agents, including phosphorus pentoxide, sulfur trioxide, acetic anhydride, and dicyclohexyl carbodiimide.

$$R_2CHOH + \langle\rangle\!-\!N{=}C{=}N\!-\!\langle\rangle + CH_3SOCH_3 \xrightarrow{H^+}$$

$$R_2C{=}O + \langle\rangle\!-\!NHCNH\!-\!\langle\rangle + CH_3SCH_3$$

26.7 Sulfur Acids and Derivatives

Sulfonic acids, RSO_3H, are very strong acids, comparable to sulfuric and perchloric acids, but they are much weaker oxidizing agents. Because of their weak oxidizing power, sulfonic acids, especially *p*-toluenesulfonic acid, are very useful acid catalysts. Aromatic sulfonic acids are almost always prepared by sulfonation of the corresponding hydrocarbon.

$$H_3C\!-\!\langle\bigcirc\rangle + H_2SO_4 \longrightarrow H_3C\!-\!\langle\bigcirc\rangle\!-\!SO_3H$$

Alkanesulfonic acids can be prepared from thiols, alkyl halides, or alkenes.

$$RSH \xrightarrow[\text{or } H_2O_2]{HNO_3} RSO_3H$$

$$RX + Na_2SO_3 \xrightarrow{S_N2} RSO_3Na$$

$$\overset{\text{O}}{\underset{\text{O}^-}{\overset{\|}{-}O\!-\!S:}} + RX \longrightarrow \overset{\text{O}}{\underset{\text{O}}{\overset{\|}{-}O\!-\!S\!-\!R}} + X^-$$

The sulfonation of aromatic hydrocarbons is reversible; hydrolysis is readily effected by boiling with strong mineral acids, such as hydrochloric acid (Sections 16.4 and 16.8).

$$ArSO_3H \xrightarrow[\Delta]{H_3O^+} ArH + H_2SO_4$$

Fusion of sulfonic acids with molten sodium hydroxide provides an important method for the production of phenols (Section 16.8).

$$ArSO_3H \xrightarrow[\sim 300°C]{NaOH} ArONa \xrightarrow{H_3O^+} ArOH$$

Amides and esters of sulfonic acids cannot be made directly from the acids, but are readily obtained from the sulfonyl chlorides.

$$RSO_3H \xrightarrow[\text{or } PCl_5]{SOCl_2} RSO_2Cl \xrightarrow{R'OH} RSO_2OR'$$
$$\xrightarrow{R'NH_2} RSO_2NHR'$$

R = alkyl or aryl

Alcohols and amines react with sulfonyl chlorides more rapidly than does water. Hence, esters and amides are often prepared in the presence of aqueous alkali, which removes the hydrogen chloride formed. For the formation of esters, pyridine is frequently used both as a solvent and as a basic catalyst (Section 20.5).

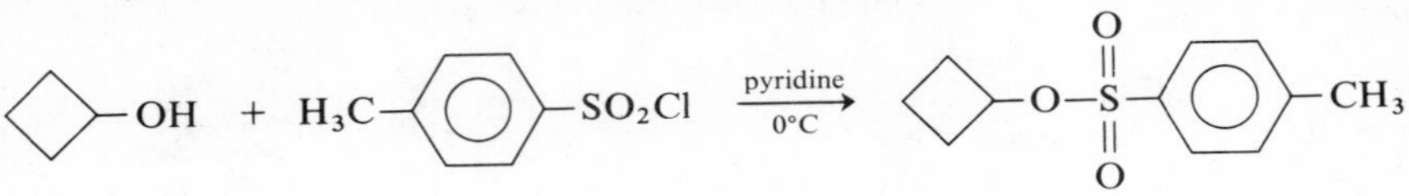

Sulfonates are exceptionally good leaving groups from carbon in nucleophilic substitution reactions, and conversion of an alcohol to a sulfonate is thus an important way of "activating" an alcohol for displacement by a variety of nucleophiles. The most commonly employed sulfonate esters are methanesulfonates, *p*-toluenesulfonates (*tosylates*), and *p*-bromobenzenesulfonates (known as *brosylates*).

EXERCISE 26.3

Suggest a useful synthetic scheme for the following transformation:

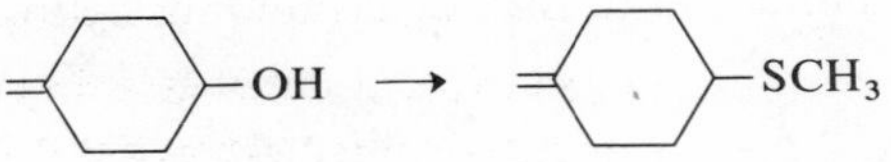

Sulfenes. Sulfonyl chlorides with α hydrogens react with base to produce highly reactive intermediates known as *sulfenes*. The reactivity of a sulfene is very much like that of a ketene. In the presence of compounds such as alcohols and amines addition occurs to produce sulfonates, sulfonamides, and so on.

$$CH_3SO_2Cl \xrightarrow{Et_3N} CH_2{=}SO_2 \xrightarrow{ROH} CH_3SO_3R$$

A sulfene

Sulfenes undergo cycloaddition reactions with electron-rich olefins.

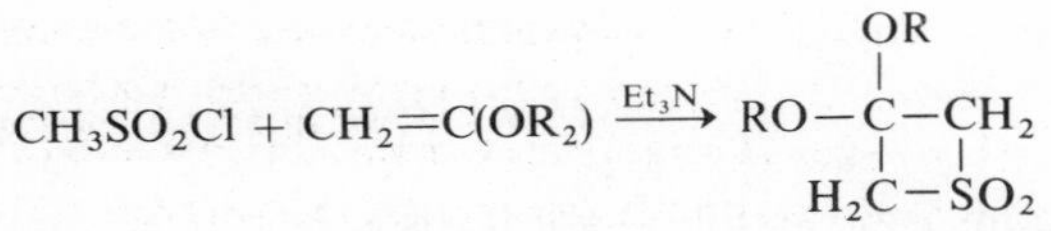

A number of sulfonamides are useful chemotherapeutic agents. The important antibacterial agents known as *sulfanilamides* or *sulfa drugs* are sulfonamide derivatives. The key structural unit in all sulfa drugs is the "sulfanilamido" grouping.

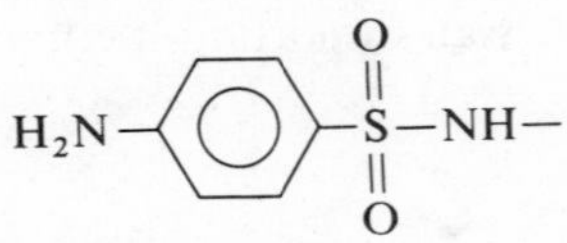

Sulfanilamido group 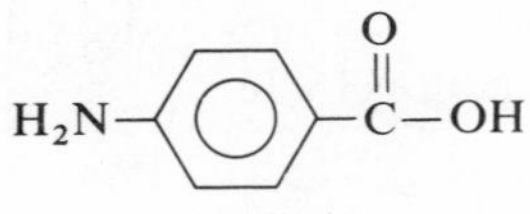   *p*-Aminobenzoic acid

These drugs are believed to compete with the normal microbiological utilization of *p*-aminobenzoic acid and thus act as bacteriostats against these organisms. Man and higher animals do not require *p*-aminobenzoic acid, and hence sulfa drugs do not act on the patient. More than 3000 sulfonamides have been synthesized and tested for their bacteriostatic activity. The two shown are representative of those currently in use.

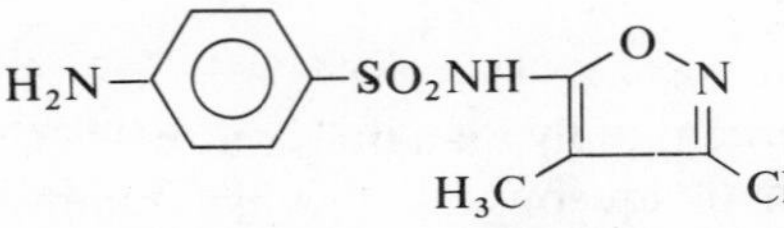

5-Sulfanilamido-3,4-dimethylisoxazole 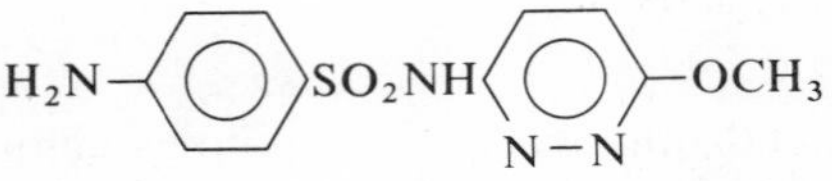   3-Sulfanilamido-6-methoxypyridazine

The methoxypyridazine is a fairly new product; it is long-acting and can be given in relatively small doses. Almost all of these compounds are synthesized by a common scheme.

DISCOVERY OF SULFA DRUGS. *Sulfanilamide was first synthesized in 1908. Shortly thereafter it was being used in the synthesis of azo dyes for wool. In 1932 it was found that mice infected with streptococci survived if treated with some of these dyes, but untreated mice died. The dyes were found to have no effect on the streptococci in a test tube, and hence it was reasoned that they were changed into an active form in the body. It was soon discovered that the active form was sulfanilamide itself.*

RELATED DRUGS. *Stemming mainly from the extensive studies on sulfa drugs, a number of other therapeutically useful materials have been discovered, for example,*

Tolbutamide,
an antidiabetic agent

Hydrochlorothiazide,
an antihypertensive agent

By far the largest use of sulfonic acids is in the form of their sodium salts as detergents. The principal advantage that detergents have over ordinary soaps is that they do not produce scums, even in hard water, because their calcium and magnesium salts are soluble. The general synthetic method used for the manufacture of most detergents is illustrated.

$R = C_8H_{17}-$ to $C_{12}H_{25}-$

At one time, the R groups of the olefins employed in the manufacture of detergents were highly branched. Such detergents were not destroyed by microorganisms in sewage treatment plants, which resulted in serious contamination of rivers and lakes. Unbranched alkyl chains are attacked by microorganisms. Today, all detergents manufactured in the United States are made from straight-chain alkenes and are said to be "biodegradable."

Other Sulfur Acids. Sulfinic acids, RSO_2H, may be prepared by the reaction of Grignard reagents with sulfur dioxide, or by the reduction of sulfonyl chlorides.

$$RMgX + SO_2 \xrightarrow[\text{2. H}_3\text{O}^+]{\text{1. Ether}} RSO_2H$$

$$RSO_2Cl + Zn \xrightarrow{H_2O} RSO_2H$$

Sulfinic acids themselves are not particularly stable, but their salts, esters, amides, and acid chlorides are quite stable. Amides and esters of sulfinic acids may be obtained in optically active forms.

Sulfenic acids, RSOH, are unstable and are not usually isolated. An exception is 1,1-dimethylethanesulfenic acid, which is produced by pyrolysis of di-*t*-butyl sulfoxide.

$$(CH_3)_3C-S \cdots CH_2 \xrightarrow{\Delta} (CH_3)_3CSOH + (CH_3)_2C{=}CH_2$$

Derivatives of sulfenic acids, such as esters (RSOR), amides ($RSNH_2$), and acid halides (RSCl) are relatively stable substances. Sulfenyl chlorides are prepared by the addition of 1 mole of chlorine to a disulfide.

$$RSSR + Cl_2 \rightarrow 2\,RSCl$$

26.8   Thiocarbonyl Compounds

In contrast to phosphorus and silicon, sulfur forms compounds in which the sulfur is involved in *p–p* π bonding. This type of bonding is found mainly in thiocarbonyl compounds. In general, such compounds do not have high stability, and their chemistry is of limited importance. Only a few illustrative examples will be presented here.

Thioacetic acid, which exists almost exclusively in the thiol form, is more reactive than acetic acid.

$$CH_3-C\overset{S}{\underset{OH}{\big<}} \rightleftharpoons CH_3-C\overset{O}{\underset{SH}{\big<}}$$

Like a thiol, it readily undergoes free-radical addition to unsaturates—usually the reaction takes place spontaneously and completely,

$$CH_3C\overset{O}{\underset{SH}{\big<}} + CH_2{=}CHC_6H_5 \rightarrow CH_3\overset{O}{\overset{\|}{C}}SCH_2CH_2C_6H_5$$

EXERCISE 26.4

Suggest a useful synthetic scheme to achieve the following transformation:

$$(CH_3)_3C-CH{=}CH_2 \rightarrow [(CH_3)_3C-CH_2CH_2-S]_2CH_2$$

Thioacetic acid rapidly acetylates aromatic amines, even in aqueous solution at room temperature.

$$CH_3C\overset{O}{\underset{SH}{\big<}} + NH_2C_6H_5 \rightarrow CH_3\overset{O}{\overset{\|}{C}}NHC_6H_5 + H_2S$$

Thioketones and thioaldehydes are generally unstable with respect to dimerization or polymerization. An exception is *thiobenzophenone*, a beautiful blue compound which can be made and handled with relative ease.

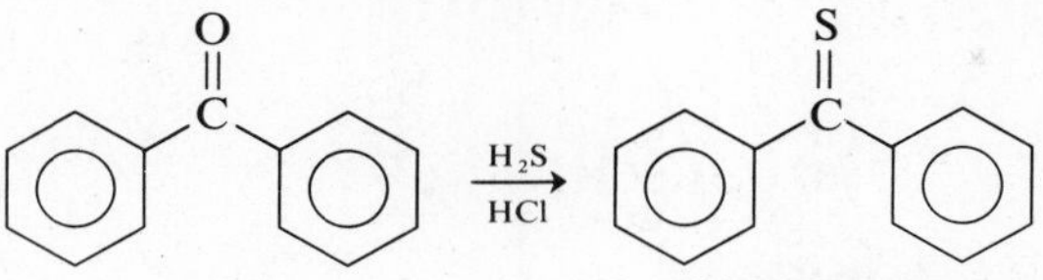

Thiobenzophenone

Few organic sulfur compounds are known for their pleasant odors; the odor of thio-acetone is said "to exceed all others."

Some Special Reactions of Sulfur Compounds. Thioamides can be prepared from amides by the action of phosphorus pentasulfide.

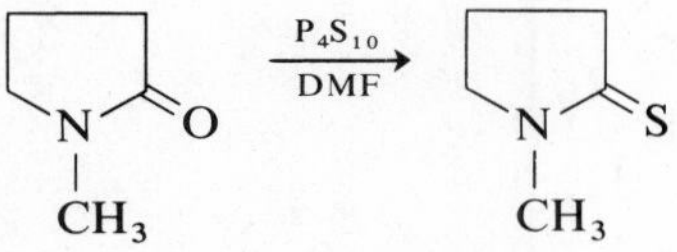

The acid-catalyzed hydrolysis of thioacetamide provides a convenient in situ source of hydrogen sulfide for inorganic qualitative analysis.

$$CH_3C\!\!\begin{array}{c}S\\ \diagup\hspace{-0.3em}\diagdown\\ NH_2\end{array} \xrightarrow[H_2O]{HCl} CH_3COOH + NH_4Cl + H_2S$$

Alkoxides add to carbon disulfide to produce xanthates (dithiocarbonates), which may be converted to the methyl xanthates by reaction with methyl iodide.

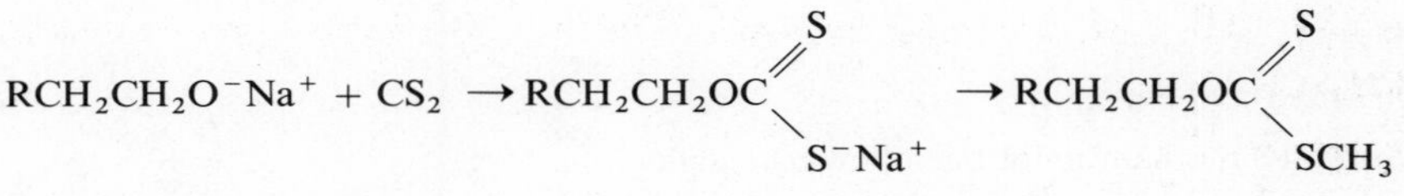

$$RCH_2CH_2O^-Na^+ + CS_2 \longrightarrow RCH_2CH_2OC\!\!\begin{array}{c}S\\ \diagup\hspace{-0.3em}\diagdown\\ S^-Na^+\end{array} \longrightarrow RCH_2CH_2OC\!\!\begin{array}{c}S\\ \diagup\hspace{-0.3em}\diagdown\\ SCH_3\end{array}$$

Pyrolysis of methyl xanthates (*Tschugaev elimination* reaction) produces alkenes. The overall process is often a convenient one for the conversion of an alcohol to an olefin without carbon-skeleton rearrangement (Section 20.16).

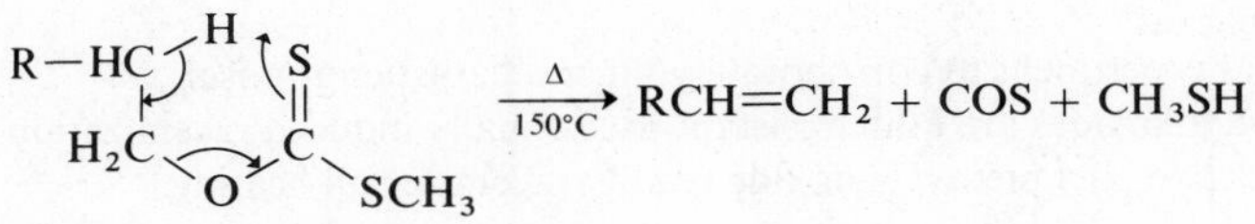

$$\xrightarrow[150°C]{\Delta} RCH{=}CH_2 + COS + CH_3SH$$

PROBLEMS

1. Thiols can be synthesized by a variety of methods. Suggest a suitable synthesis of each of the following thiols. Use a different method in each case.

(a) $CH_3CH_2CH_2SH$

(b)

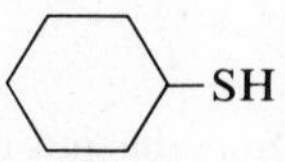

(c) $(CH_3)_3CSH$

(d)

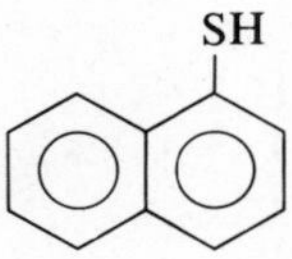

2. Outline suitable synthetic methods for the synthesis of the following compounds.

(a) $CH_3S{-}CH_2CH_2{-}C_6H_5$

(b) 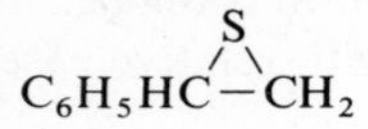

(c) $C_6H_5SSC_6H_5$

(d) 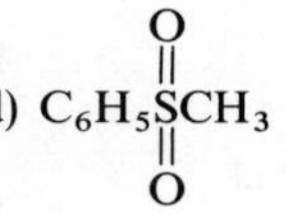

(e) 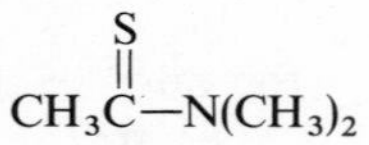

(f) $C_6H_5SO_3CH_3$

(g) $C_6H_5CH_2CH_2SO_3Na$

(h) 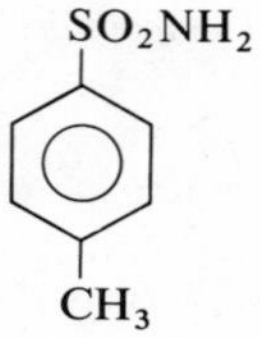

(i) 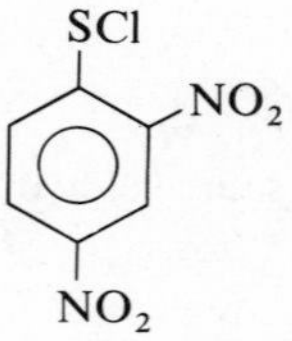

3. Write projection formulas for the possible stereoisomers of the following compounds.

(a) 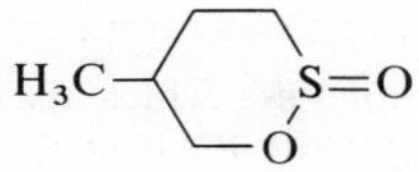

(b) 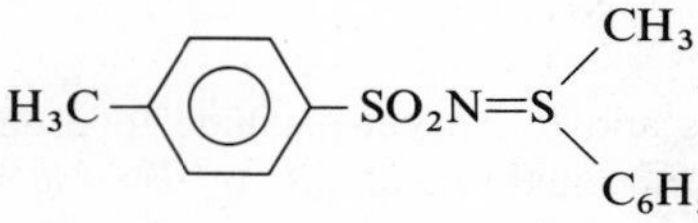

(c) 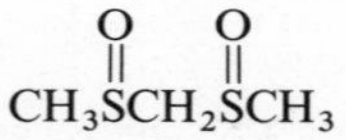

4. (a) Suggest a mechanism for the following reaction.

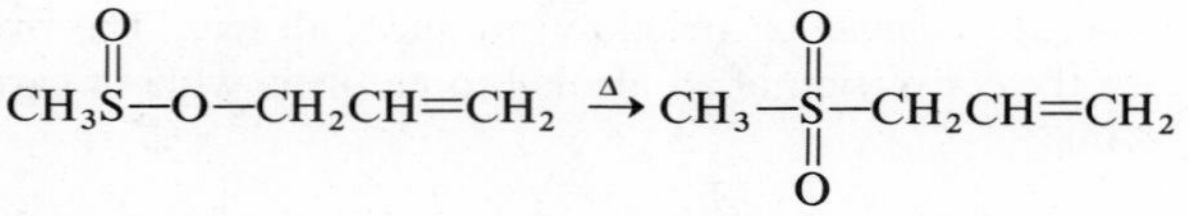

(b) Suggest an additional experiment to corroborate your mechanistic proposal.
(c) Most optically active sulfoxides are quite resistant to thermally induced racemization. However, optically active allyl methyl sulfoxide readily racemizes on heating. Explain.

5. Offer an explanation for the following observation.

6. Utilizing benzene and 2-aminodiazine, outline a synthetic route to "sulfadiazine."

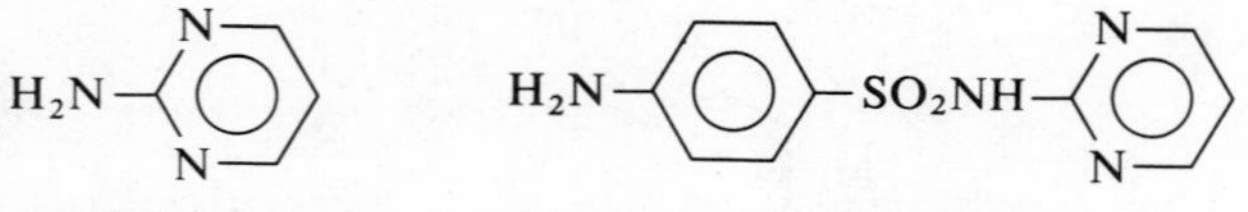

2-Aminodiazine   Sulfadiazine

7. (a) Would you expect the following exchange reaction to occur without racemization at sulfur? Explain.

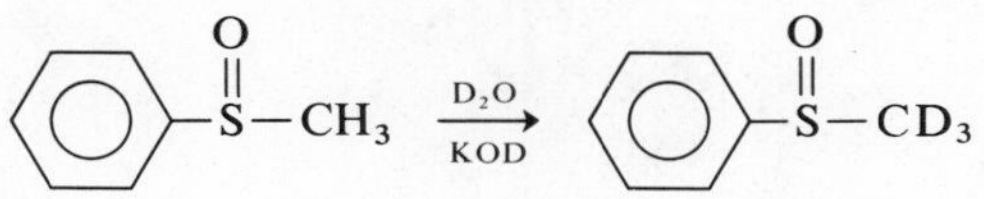

(b) Acetone and dimethyl sulfone have approximately the same acidity. What would be your estimate of the relative acidities of the following compounds?

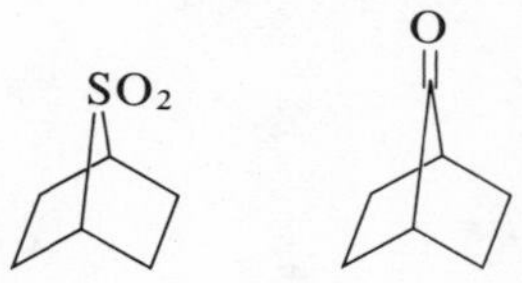

8. Considering the pharmacological role of sulfanilamide and other sulfa drugs, which of the following substances would you expect to have bacteriostatic activity?
   (a) Benzenesulfonamide
   (b) $p\text{-}H_2N\text{---}C_6H_4SO_2N(CH_3)_2$
   (c) *p*-Aminobenzenesulfonic acid
   (d) *p*-Toluenesulfonyl chloride
   (e) *p*-Nitrobenzoic acid
   (f) $p\text{-}H_2N\text{---}C_6H_4SO_2NHEt$

Optional Problems

1. The methylation of dimethyl sulfoxide can occur at either sulfur or oxygen. Suggest a physical method that would enable one to decide whether a particular reaction produced an *S*-methyl salt or an *O*-methyl salt of dimethyl sulfoxide.

2. (a) When methyl ethyl sulfide is treated with ethyl iodide at elevated temperatures, a mixture of salts is formed, including trimethyl- and triethylsulfonium iodide. Explain.
   (b) Suggest a method that would produce a diethylmethylsulfonium salt free from other contaminating salts.
   (c) The amino acid methionine acts as the methyl group donor in most biological methylation reactions. Transmethylation reactions involving methionine require adenosine triphosphate (see page 753). Consider your answer to part (a) and suggest a related mechanism by which the combination of ATP and methionine could achieve methylation of a nucleophilic substrate.

$$CH_3SCH_2CH_2\underset{\underset{\displaystyle NH_2}{|}}{CH}\text{---}COOH$$

Methionine

3. The *Kharasch reagent*, 2,4-dinitrobenzenesulfenyl chloride, is a valuable reagent for the preparation of crystalline derivatives of a large variety of functional classes of compounds, including amines, alkenes, and alkynes. Addition of 2,4-dinitrobenzenesulfenyl chloride to *cis*- and *trans*-2-butene gives rise to different products. Explain.

4. Suggest a mechanism for the following reaction:

5. Outline suitable synthetic methods using sulfur-containing reagents for the following transformations:

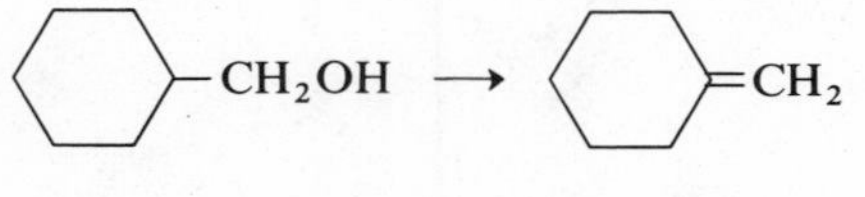

(b) $C_6H_5CH=CHCO_2CH_3 \rightarrow$

$$\underset{C_6H_5}{\overset{H}{\diagdown}}\triangle\underset{H}{\overset{CO_2CH_3}{\diagup}}$$

(c) $C_6H_5\overset{\overset{\textstyle O}{\|}}{C}OCH_3 \rightarrow C_6H_5\overset{\overset{\textstyle O}{\|}}{C}CH_3$

6. Outline the sequence of steps necessary to convert an alcohol to an olefin $(R-CH_2-CH_2-OH \rightarrow R-CH=CH_2)$ by means of a Tschugaev elimination reaction. What advantage does this method have over treating the alcohol with strong acid?

CHAPTER 27

CARBOHYDRATES

27.1   Introduction: Monosaccharide Chemistry

Carbohydrates received their name from the fact that the general empirical formula for many members of the class can be written as $C_n(H_2O)_n$, hydrated carbon. (Note, however, that not *all* carbohydrates are represented by this formula.) Sugars, starches, and cellulose, compounds which have important structural and energy functions in living materials, are all carbohydrates.

It would be difficult to overestimate the importance of carbohydrates to human beings. We eat them directly in such foods as bread, potatoes, corn, and peas, and indirectly, in meat, eggs, and fats from animals which feed on carbohydrates in the form of grains and grasses. Cotton and linen, the traditional clothing fabrics, are both almost pure carbohydrates. Only in very recent times have synthetic polymers (Chapter 25) begun to replace these natural fibers. Wood consists largely of cellulose, and hence a good portion of the houses in which we live, as well as much of our furniture, is constructed of carbohydrates. Finally, paper is mostly carbohydrate. The importance of paper in modern civilization is enormous. Try to imagine life without paper: no paper money, checks, income-tax forms; no books, newspapers, birth certificates, or milk cartons. College diplomas would have to be printed on sheepskin, and *Playboy* magazine would disappear from the corner drug store. Truly, this would be a different world!

The production of carbohydrates in nature occurs in green plants by a process called *photosynthesis* (Section 31.11). Plants contain the green pigment *chlorophyll* (Section 28.4), which catalyzes the conversion of carbon dioxide and water into sugar. The reaction is thermodynamically unfavorable, but proceeds because the necessary energy is supplied by the sun in the form of sunlight.

$$6\,CO_2 + 6\,H_2O \xrightleftharpoons[\substack{- \text{ energy, animal} \\ \text{metabolism}}]{+h\nu, \text{ chlorophyll}} C_6(H_2O)_6 + 6\,O_2$$

While plants build up carbohydrates from carbon dioxide and water, animals degrade carbohydrates to carbon dioxide and water. The animals obtain carbohydrates by eating plants and combine the carbohydrates with oxygen from the air to carry out the reverse of the photosynthesis reaction. The oxidation of carbohydrates supplies the animal with the energy (according to the above equation) necessary to sustain life, and it also regenerates carbon dioxide for use by plants in photosynthesis.

All carbohydrates are polyhydroxy aldehydes, polyhydroxy ketones, or molecules which yield polyhydroxy aldehydes or ketones on hydrolysis. *Monosaccharides* are the smallest carbohydrate molecules and include the four-, five-, and six-carbon sugars. *Sucrose*, table sugar, is one of the *disaccharides* (Section 27.8); they can be hydrolyzed to two monosaccharides. Polysaccharides (Section 27.9), which include starch and cellulose, yield many monosaccharide molecules upon hydrolysis.

The simplest monosaccharide is *glyceraldehyde*, which contains one asymmetric center and therefore exists as a pair of enantiomers. As discussed in Section 3.6, the

D configuration was assigned arbitrarily to the structure shown, and it turned out by chance to be correct.

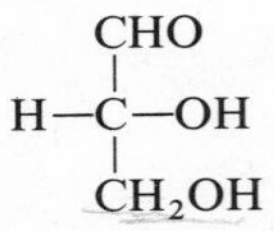

D-Glyceraldehyde 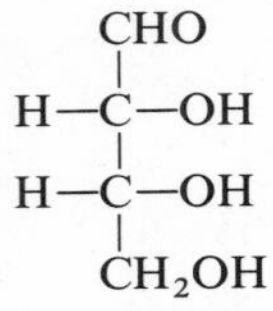   D-Erythrose 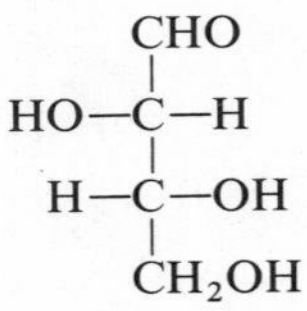   D-Threose

There are two asymmetric centers in the four-carbon sugars, and hence $2^2 = 4$ stereoisomers possible. By definition, the asymmetric carbon *farthest* from the aldehyde group determines the configuration, and this is D for the isomers shown, since it is the same as in D-glyceraldehyde (hydroxyl on the right in the Fischer projection) in each case. The carbon atoms of sugar are numbered starting with the aldehyde carbon as 1, so the configurations at C-2 in glyceraldehyde and at C-3 in erythrose and threose determine the overall configurations.

EXERCISE 27.1

Draw Fischer projections for L-threose and L-erythrose.

Monosaccharides with five carbon atoms are called *pentoses*, and six-carbon monosaccharides are called *hexoses*. Important examples of the pentoses are *ribose* and *deoxyribose*.

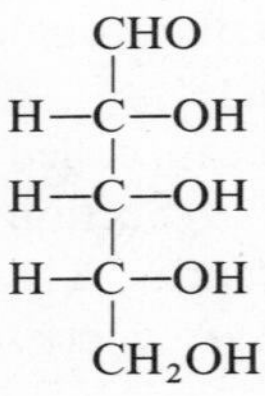

D-Ribose 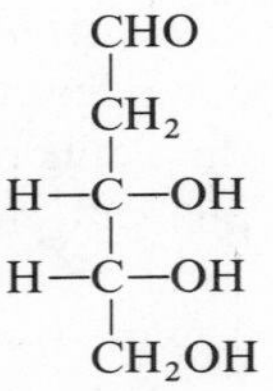   D-Deoxyribose

These compounds each contain an aldehyde group and are therefore known as *aldopentoses*. The most common six-carbon monosaccharide is *glucose*, an *aldohexose*, since it also contains an aldehyde group. *Fructose*, another common hexose, has a ketone group at C-2 and is called a *ketohexose*.

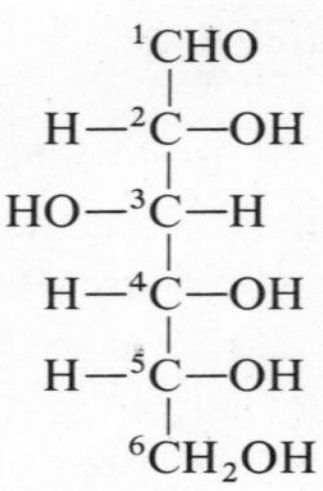

D-Glucose,
an aldohexose

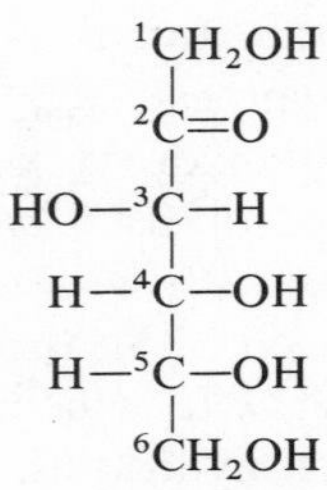

D-Fructose,
a ketohexose

For reference, the names and structures (Fischer projections) of all of the D-aldopentoses and D-aldohexoses are given here.

CHO	CHO	CHO	CHO
──OH	HO──	──OH	HO──
──OH	──OH	HO──	HO──
──OH	──OH	──OH	──OH
CH₂OH	CH₂OH	CH₂OH	CH₂OH
Ribose	Arabinose	Xylose	Lyxose

CHO	CHO	CHO	CHO
──OH	HO──	──OH	──OH
──OH	──OH	HO──	──OH
──OH	──OH	──OH	HO──
──OH	──OH	──OH	──OH
CH₂OH	CH₂OH	CH₂OH	CH₂OH
Allose	Altrose	Glucose	Gulose

CHO	CHO	CHO	CHO
HO──	HO──	──OH	HO──
HO──	──OH	HO──	HO──
──OH	HO──	HO──	HO──
──OH	──OH	──OH	──OH
CH₂OH	CH₂OH	CH₂OH	CH₂OH
Mannose	Idose	Galactose	Talose

Of all the sugars, glucose is by far the most common and the most important in nature. It is also thermodynamically the most stable of the aldohexoses, which is presumably one reason for its wide occurrence. The Fischer projection is often used to express the structure, but is misleading in some ways, and we want now to look more closely at the actual structure. As discussed in Sections 19.1 and 19.2, alcohols react reversibly with aldehydes to give hemiacetals (and acetals).

Hemiacetal formation is not very favorable with simple molecules, because although enthalpy favors the hemiacetal, entropy does not (Why?). When the alcohol and aldehyde are in the same molecule and arranged so that they can close a strainless six-membered ring upon hemiacetal formation, the ring closure becomes highly favorable. Glucose, therefore, closes a ring to form a hemiacetal, and only a tiny amount of the aldehyde form is in equilibrium with the hemiacetal in solution. Note that the ring closure converts the aldehyde carbon to an asymmetric hemiacetal carbon. There are consequently *two* hemiacetals in equilibrium with the aldehyde in solution; these are given the designations α and β as shown.

D-Glucose	D-Glucose	D-Glucose
(β-Hemiacetal, hydroxyl at C-1 on left in Fischer projection)	(Aldehyde form)	(α-Hemiacetal, hydroxyl at C-1 on right in Fischer projection)

Since the Fischer projection formula can lead to awkward drawings of bond lengths, as shown for the forms of glucose, another projection was introduced by Haworth. This formulation has been used extensively.

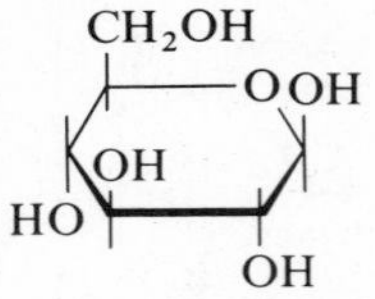

Haworth formulation
of β-D-Glucose

More recently, as more about the conformations of sugars has become known, ordinary conformational drawings of the type used for cyclohexane derivatives have come into common use. For β-D-glucose, although two different chair forms are in principle possible, the form with all of the groups equatorial is the important one.

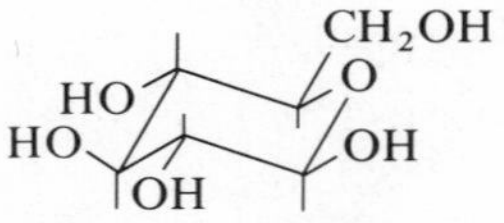

Conformation formulation
of β-D-Glucose

EXERCISE 27.2

Draw the two possible chair forms for α-D-glucose. Which one best represents the actual molecule?

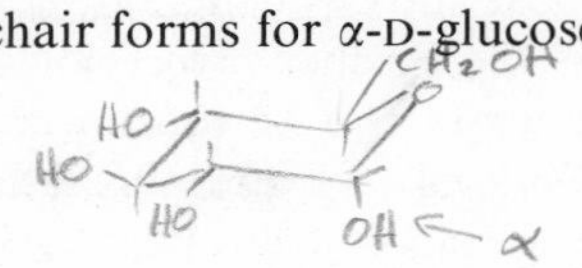

27.2   Mutarotation

Glucose exists in two crystalline forms. The fact that neither form contains a carbonyl group (as shown by the infrared spectra) suggests that these two forms are the α- and β-hemiacetals. X-Ray diffraction studies of one form of crystalline glucose, mp 150°C, showed the following structure, with all hydroxyl groups equatorial and all ring hydrogen atoms axial.

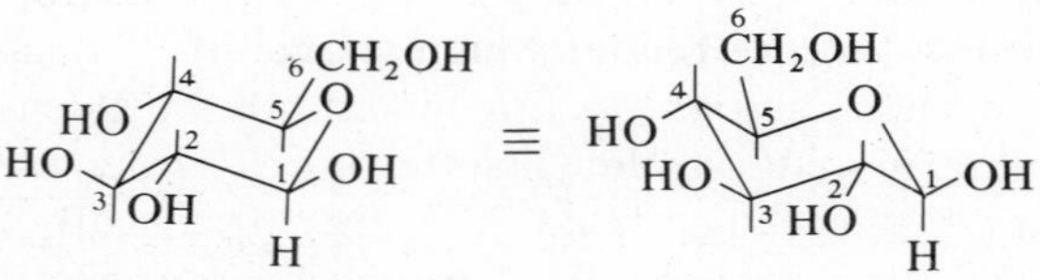

β-D-Glucose

Note that this crystalline material has the hydroxyl group on carbon atom 5 involved in the hemiacetal linkage. Although the aldehyde group is completely converted to the intramolecular hemiacetal in the crystalline, mp 150°C form, it has some existence in solution, since the optical rotation of a solution of glucose in water slowly changes. When determined on the freshly prepared solution, it has a value of +18.7°. This value slowly rises with time to +52.5°. From this solution, another crystalline form of glucose can be isolated, mp 146°C, which has a rotation, determined immediately upon dissolution, of +112°, but which also slowly changes to +52.5°. These new crystals again show no carbonyl stretching frequency in the infrared, and an X-ray structure determination indicates the same structure except that the hydroxyl group on the aldehyde carbon is axial.

| β Form | Aldehyde form | α Form |

The slow change of optical rotation in solution is called *mutarotation,* and it can be interpreted as involving the interconversion of hemiacetals through the aldehyde inter-mediate. The equilibrium mixture contains 64% of the β isomer, 36% of the α isomer, and only about 0.02% of free aldehyde. Although the equilibrium percentages will differ in different solutions, enough aldehyde is generally present in reaction mixtures to allow the occurrence of ordinary aldehyde reactions such as oxidation, reduction, and the formation of carbonyl derivatives. The fact that the aldehyde carbon atom is not asymmetric in the aldehyde form whereas in the hemiacetal it exists in the α and β forms made the original structural and stereochemical determinations difficult (Section 27.7).

It should be understood that the mirror image of D *is* L, *the mirror image of* (+) *is* (−), *but the mirror image of* α *is* α *and not* β, *as shown in the following example (i.e.,* α *implies an axial 1-hydroxyl group in both enantiomers).*

| α-D-(+)-Glucopyranose | mirror images | α-L-(−)-Glucopyranose |

Monosaccharides commonly mutarotate, exist as α- and β-hemiacetals, and give α- and β-methyl glycosides (Section 27.3). All of these reactions involve conversion of the symmetrical carbonyl carbon into an asymmetric carbon atom, with the concurrent production of two diastereomers. This isomerism is so common in carbohydrate chemistry that these particular diastereomers are given a special name. They are called *anomers,* and the carbon involved is called the *anomeric carbon.*

EXERCISE 27.3

Draw the conformation formula and name the compounds related to β-D-glucopyranose as follows: (a) the enantiomer; (b) the anomer; and (c) a diastereomer. Draw the enantiomer of (c) and name it also.

The complete name for the positive-rotating crystalline glucose is α-D-(+)-*gluco-pyranose.* The most fundamental property is signified by the D, which specifies the absolute stereochemistry of carbon 5, from which all other molecular stereochemistry can be related internally. The symbol α indicates the relation of the hemiacetal hydroxyl on carbon 1 to carbon 5, and the (+) indicates that the compound has a (+) rotation under the conditions of the experimental measurement. Lastly, the name *pyranose* indicates that the hydroxyl on carbon five is involved in hemiacetal formation, thus forming a six-membered oxygen containing ring, which can be viewed as a derivative of *pyran.*

Pyran

CONFIGURATIONS OF NATURAL SUGARS. *Most of the important naturally occurring monosaccharides are in the* D *series; the* L *configuration is in fact quite rare among natural sugars. Until a few years ago,* D-*glucose,* D-*mannose, and* D-*galactose were considered to be the most important, and certainly they are the most common, naturally occurring sugars. In recent years, the isolation and proof of the structures of various sugar-containing antibiotics have shown the existence in nature of most of the eight aldohexose configurations. For example, compounds derived from* L-*ido-,* D-*gulo-,* D-*talo, and* D-*allo-sugars have all been isolated from the cleavage of antibiotics.*

In the case of the aldopentoses, certain five-membered rings appear to be more stable than the corresponding six-membered rings. A five-membered ring would be a derivative of *furan* and not pyran and bears the name *furanose* instead of pyranose.

A sugar which contains a hydrogen atom in place of one of the hydroxyl groups is called a *deoxy sugar*, and they are common natural products. 6-Deoxy sugars, which contain a terminal methyl group instead of the hydroxymethyl group, are the most common of the deoxy sugars. *Rhamnose* is an interesting example of a commonly occurring 6-deoxy sugar because it exists in the L-*manno* configuration. *2-Deoxyribose* and *ribose* in their furanoside forms are very important components of nucleic acids (Section 28.9).

α-D-Ribofuranose   α-D-2-Deoxyribofuranose   β-L-Rhamnose

Fructose, an important ketohexose, also exists as a stable furanoside.

α-D-Fructofuranose   Keto form   Fischer projection of
                                             keto form

27.3   Glycosides, Acetals, and Ketals

The monosaccharides are unique in having many reactive functional groups on adjacent carbon atoms. For example, in the aldehyde form of glucose there are four secondary hydroxyl groups and one primary hydroxyl group, in addition to the aldehyde. The primary hydroxyl group has a reactivity which is only slightly different from those of the secondary hydroxyls, and the latter have even less difference in reactivity among themselves, although some differences can be noted and used. It is easy to understand that before the days of stereospecific reagents, knowledge of neighboring group participation, and the invention of high-resolution separation systems such as vapor-phase chromatography and thin-layer chromatography, almost all reaction products of carbohydrates were complex mixtures, which failed to crystallize. This situation led to a very bad reputation for the area of carbohydrate chemistry, an area thought by most chemists to be composed of gums and syrups which took weeks, months, or even years to crystallize. Since the only reliable method of purification available before about 1940 was recrystallization, progress was dependent upon the art of crystallization of a compound from a complex mixture of very similar compounds. A research group without a stockpile of seed crystals and without experience in the art was doomed to frustration. However, with the tools of modern-day reactions and high-resolution separations, carbohydrate derivatives can be purified to the point of crystallization, if necessary. Alternatively, they can be purified sufficiently without crystallization to be used in succeeding reactions.

Since an aldehyde or ketone is generally more sensitive to most reagents than is a primary or secondary alcohol, an important class of reactions in carbohydrate chemistry involves the protection of the aldehyde by conversion to an acetal. As an intermolecular reaction catalyzed by acid will occur between an aldehyde and an alcohol, so will an intramolecular hemiacetal of a monosaccharide form an acetal in the presence of an acid catalyst (Section 19.2). Since β-D-glucopyranose is itself in equilibrium with the α form and a small amount of the aldehyde form, it is understandable that a mixture of acetals forms. Acetals of this type are called *glycosides*; the specific name of the compound includes the radical of the alcohol (methyl in this case) as a separate word and the ending -*oside*. The glycosides of glucose with methanol are called *methyl* α-D-*glucopyranoside* and *methyl* β-D-*glucopyranoside*. Once the acid catalyst is quenched, the glycosides are stable and will not mutarotate. These compounds represent some of the most useful derivatives of monosaccharides, not only in the laboratory, but also in the chemistry of living organisms. Starches, celluloses, and nucleic acids all contain monosaccharides which are incorporated via glycoside linkages.

β-D-Glucopyranose   Methyl α-D-glucopyranoside   Methyl β-D-glucopyranoside

SUGAR DERIVATIVES IN NATURE. *Many natural products contain sugars attached to other types of chemical structures. In arbutin, the sugar is attached to a phenyl derivative. Arbutin is hydroquinone β-D-glucoside, and it occurs in many plants. In the autumn, leaves from certain pear trees turn black instead of yellow and red. This black color results from the fact that these leaves contain a high concentration of arbutin, which on enzymatic hydrolysis liberates hydroquinone, which is oxidized by air to a black dye.*

Arbutin

The moiety attached to the sugar is called the aglycone. *When the aglycone is a dye or pigment such as an anthocyanin or anthoxanthin (Section 30.8), the resulting compounds are the natural chemicals which provide the colors for flowers. When the aglycone is related to perhydrophenanthrene, the result is a class of therapeutically useful chemicals called* cardiac glycosides *(Section 30.7). A most powerful example is from the foxglove or* Digitalis *plant, in which the aglycone is* digitoxigenin

(*Section 30.7*). *The cardiac glycosides produce a slower and stronger heartbeat in humans. Some have been used by primitive tribes as poisons on the tips of arrows.*

An interesting natural aglycone is benzaldehyde cyanohydrin. *Many plants such as the apricot, bitter almond, plum, and peach contain large quantities of the gentiobiose glycoside in the kernels, leaves, and bark, and this compound is the precursor of oil of bitter almonds. Hydrolysis of the compound produces hydrogen cyanide along with benzaldehyde and the disaccharide gentiobiose (6-β-glucosylglucose).*

Amygdalin   Gentiobiose

$$+ \; PhC\overset{\displaystyle O}{\underset{\displaystyle H}{\big\|}} \; + \; HCN$$

Oil of bitter almonds

Protecting Groups. The use of an acetal as a protecting group has been discussed previously (Sections 19.2, 24.4). Acetals and ketals can be used effectively to protect certain of the hydroxyl groups during reactions of carbohydrates. For example, benzaldehyde will react with methyl glucoside to give the 4,6-benzylidene derivative, which has four of the six functional groups of glucose protected. The remaining two hydroxyl groups on carbons 2 and 3 can then be treated chemically as a diequatorial *trans-vic*-diol and converted to a 2,3-oxide or to 2,3 unsaturation, or to heteroatom derivatives. Important features of the benzylidene reaction are the generality and selectivity for ring formation at positions 4 and 6, and the selectivity in removal of the benzylidene group in the presence of the glycoside linkage. Acidified methanol or catalytic hydrogenolysis will remove the benzylidene group and leave the methyl glycoside intact.

Acetone also forms a ketal easily and has been used to protect hydroxyl groups and in some cases also the aldehyde group of sugars. Note that even though the most stable form of the hemiacetal of glucose itself is a pyranoside, the reaction leads to a furanose derivative.

1,2,5,6-Diisopropylidene-α-D-glucofuranose

In this one reaction, five of the six functional groups of glucose are protected. The one remaining hydroxyl group can then be subjected to secondary alcohol chemistry such as tosylation followed by displacement with inversion using a nitrogen nucleophile to give a 3-amino sugar derivative, or oxidation to a ketone followed by ketone reactions.

When acetone is used to make a ketal, the water which is generated may sometimes be harmful to the starting material or product in the presence of acid. A more elegant reagent to do the same transformation is 2,2-*diethoxypropane* (acetone diethyl ketal), which reacts by acetal–ketal interchange and generates alcohol instead of water.

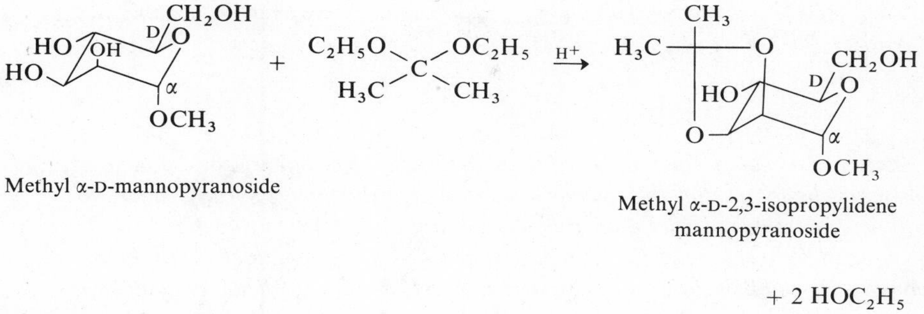

Methyl α-D-mannopyranoside

Methyl α-D-2,3-isopropylidene
mannopyranoside

$$+ \; 2 \; HOC_2H_5$$

EXERCISE 27.4

The ketal exchange proceeds very far to the right, as written in the preceding reaction. Why?

27.4 Osazones, Oximes, and Cyanohydrins

In addition to the formation of hemiacetals, acetals, and ketals, the carbonyl carbon of a monosaccharide reacts with other common carbonyl reagents such as phenylhydrazine, hydroxylamine, and hydrogen cyanide. With an excess of phenylhydrazine, monosaccharides react to give *osazones*. The reaction is unusual in that the hydroxyl adjacent to the carbonyl group is oxidized by the reagent to form a second carbonyl carbon, which then further reacts.

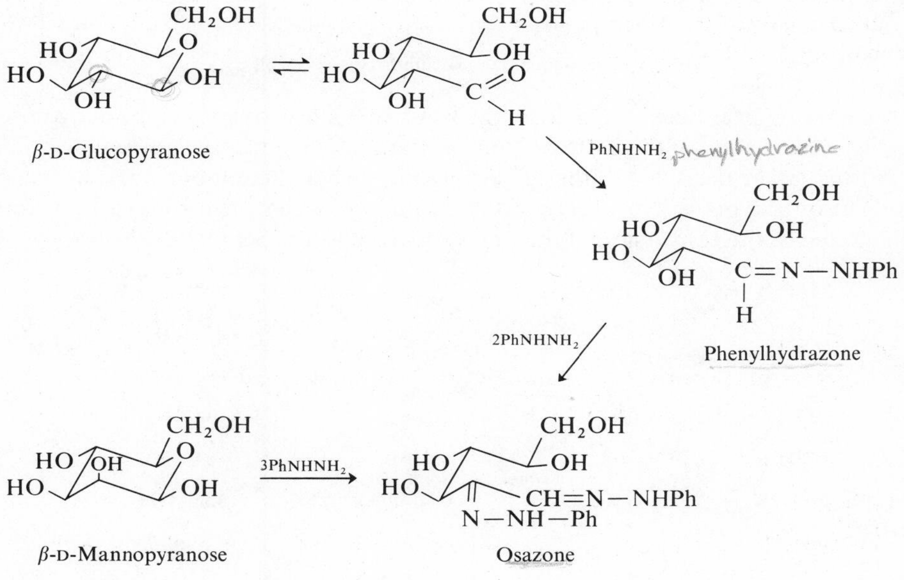

β-D-Glucopyranose

Phenylhydrazone

β-D-Mannopyranose

Osazone

It is possible to stop the reaction at the hydrazone stage, but commonly the osazone derivatives are made because they are high-melting solids which are easy to isolate and recrystallize. Although the principal use of osazones is for identification, they have the serious disadvantage that the asymmetric center at carbon-2 of the original monosaccharide has been lost. Thus, mannose and glucose, which differ only in the stereochemistry of carbon-2, give the same osazone. It is interesting that only one hydroxyl group is oxidized; excess reagent does not continue the oxidation progression down the chain. However, when a primary and a secondary hydroxyl group compete, the primary hydroxyl is the one that is oxidized, as shown by the oxidation of fructose to give the same osazone as that obtained from glucose and mannose.

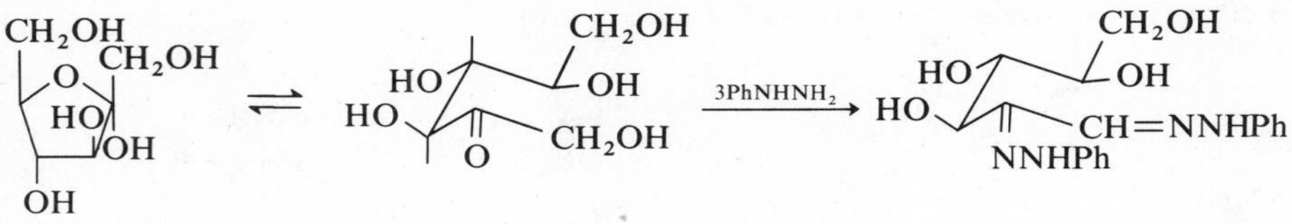

Fructose

Emil Fischer discovered phenylhydrazine in 1875, and after a few years of investigating its chemistry, he found that the reagent could be used to convert syrupy sugars to crystalline derivatives. At the time, this ability to prepare crystalline derivatives of sugars provided Fischer with the necessary means to work effectively with these compounds. He published his initial studies in 1884, and by 1891 had concluded his brilliant proof of the structure and stereochemistry of glucose (Section 27.7).

Hydroxylamine leads more readily to a simple derivative of the carbonyl group, an oxime. Oximes are intermediates in two important reaction sequences. The first involves reduction to the amine as illustrated in the preparation of 1-amino-1-deoxysorbitol. (The nomenclature of this class of compounds is discussed in Section 27.6.)

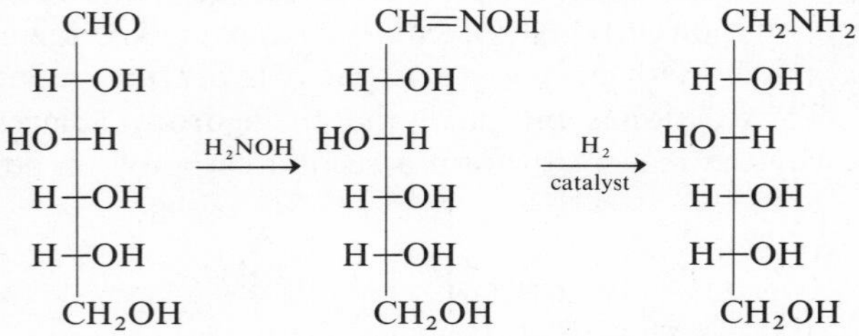

| Glucose | Glucose oxime | 1-Amino-1-deoxysorbitol |

The second important use results from the fact that a sugar oxime can be dehydrated to a nitrile, and because of the hydroxyl at C-2, the nitrile is in fact a cyanohydrin. The cyanohydrins can be degraded to the corresponding carbonyl compound and hydrogen cyanide. The overall process involves shortening a monosaccharide by one carbon atom, as is illustrated in the conversion of the hexose *glucose* to the pentose *arabinose*.

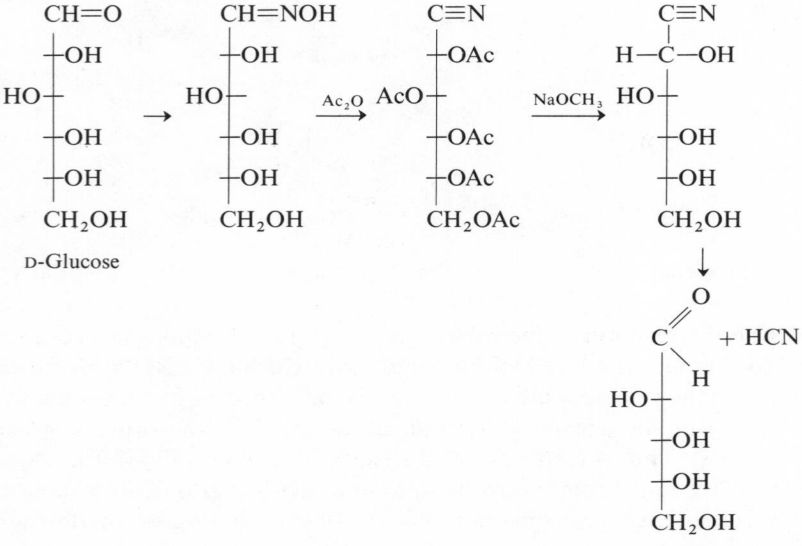

D-Glucose

D-Arabinose

Chain Lengthening and Chain Shortening. The reaction of hydrogen cyanide with a carbonyl compound to give a cyanohydrin is reversible and can be used in carbohydrate chemistry to decrease the length of the monosaccharide chain by one carbon or to increase the length by one carbon. Both shortening and lengthening the chain depend upon controlling the cyanohydrin equilibrium reaction.

$$\begin{array}{c} \diagdown \\ C=O + HCN \underset{}{\overset{CN^-}{\rightleftharpoons}} \quad \diagdown C \diagup \overset{OH}{\underset{CN}{|}} \\ \diagup \end{array}$$

← Chain shortening   Chain lengthening →

Generally, base is the catalyst and excess hydrogen cyanide is used to drive the reaction to the right. Conversely, hydrogen cyanide can be removed from the reaction mixture (or converted to cyanide ion) to drive the reaction to the left. One difference in the two synthetic sequences is that in chain shortening, a pure aldose gives a single aldose product, whereas in chain lengthening, a pure aldose gives two diastereomeric products because an additional asymmetric center is generated. For example, D-glucose gives only D-arabinose, but D-arabinose gives both D-glucose and D-mannose.

27.5   Oxidation

The fact that aldehydes and α-hydroxy ketones are easy to oxidize provides a qualitative test for the presence of these groups. Tollens' reagent $[Ag(NH_3)_2^+]$ and Fehling's solution $[Cu(NH_3)_4^{2+}]$ are useful test reagents to determine whether a sugar has a carbonyl carbon in the hemiacetal form. An important feature of the oxidation is that the aldehyde form can be readily detected even though it exists in very small amount in the equilibrium. If a sugar reduces the Tollens' reagent from $Ag(NH_3)_2^+$ to metallic silver, or if it reduces Fehling's solution from $Cu(NH_3)_4^{2+}$ to red cuprous oxide, it is said to be a *reducing sugar*. However, both of these reagents are alkaline, which limits the synthetic utility of the oxidation–reduction, since alkali causes the isomerization and decomposition of aldoses and ketoses.

Chemical isomerization of glucose to fructose, an internal oxidation–reduction reaction, can be accomplished by treatment with alkali, but a variety of other isomeric and decomposition products are also produced. For example, when D-glucose is treated with base, the unstable enediol is formed. In this transient intermediate the stereochemistry of carbon-2 is lost. The enediol can then revert back to any of the three more stable hydroxycarbonyl compounds.

Since D-fructose has a negative optical rotation and D-glucose has a positive optical rotation, the progress of the reaction can be followed in a polarimeter (described in Section 3.6).

Aldoses can be oxidized to the corresponding carboxylic acids using acidic reaction conditions. Bromine water has synthetic utility for the oxidation of aldoses but will not react with ketoses. The resulting acids as a class are called *glyconic acids*; the acid from glucose is called *gluconic acid*, that from mannose, *mannonic acid*, and so on.

The aldehyde is the group of an aldose which is most easily oxidized. Of the remaining hydroxyl groups, the primary hydroxyl group is oxidized before the secondary hydroxyl groups. *Nitric acid* is particularly useful as an oxidizing agent for producing dicarboxylic acids from aldoses.

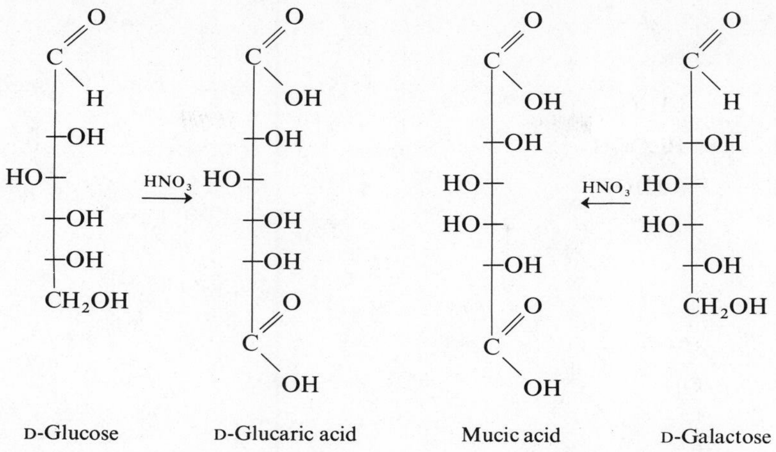

D-Glucose D-Glucaric acid Mucic acid D-Galactose

The name of the class of diacids is *glycaric acids* and the individual members include *glucaric acid* and *mannaric acid*. Galactose gives *mucic acid*, which is optically inactive because it has an internal plane of symmetry. The optical inactivity of this acid provided key evidence in the determination of the stereochemistry of galactose.

Ascorbic and Glucuronic Acids. Two other oxidation derivatives of monosaccharides are particularly important. Ascorbic acid is vitamin C, which is widely distributed in nature, especially in green plants. It functions as a biological oxidation–reduction reagent, acting as a hydrogen carrier.

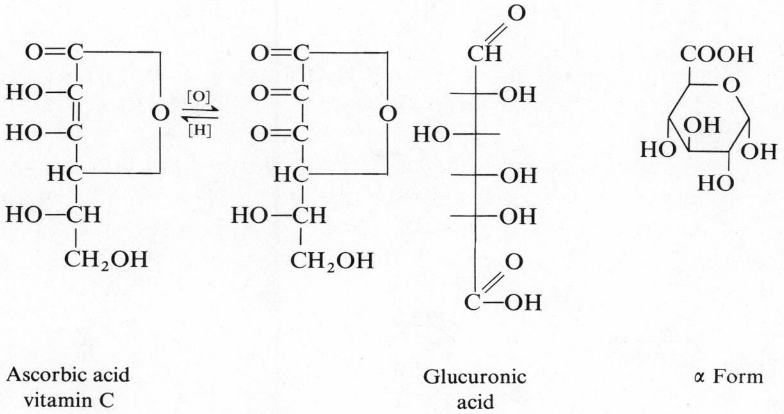

Ascorbic acid
vitamin C

Glucuronic
acid

α Form

Glucuronic acid, in which the primary hydroxyl group of glucose has been oxidized to a carboxylic acid while the aldehyde group remains intact, is a major building block in many naturally occurring polysaccharides (see Section 27.9).

The most important oxidation reaction involving the secondary alcohol groups of sugars is that with periodate. Periodic acid or sodium metaperiodate specifically oxidizes *vic*-diols, α-hydroxy carbonyl compounds, and α-dicarbonyl compounds, as shown.

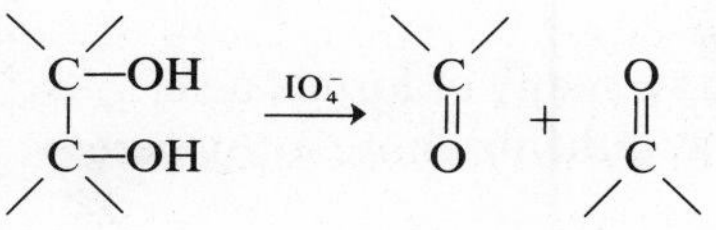

This reagent is tremendously important in structural determinations of carbohydrates. For example, an α-methyl glucopyranoside can be differentiated from an α-methyl glucofuranoside by this reagent as shown.

In the experiment, excess reagent is added and the amount of reagent used is determined, along with the identity and amounts of each product, such as formic acid or formaldehyde. Although the furanoside and the pyranoside each react with 2 moles of the reagent, the pyranoside gives 1 mole of formic acid while the furanoside gives 1 mole of formaldehyde. Note that if the first oxidation gives an α-hydroxycarbonyl compound, this is further oxidized until no *vic*-diols, α-hydroxycarbonyl compounds, or α-dicarbonyl compounds remain.

EXERCISE 27.5

Predict how many moles of formaldehyde and how many of formic acid would be obtained from methyl α-D-fructoside (a) if the furanose form were present; (b) if the pyranose form were present.

27.6 Reduction

The carbonyl group of an aldose or ketose can be reduced with sodium borohydride or by catalytic hydrogenation. The product is a polyhydric alcohol; such compounds are given the class name of *itols*. Mannose on reduction with sodium borohydride gives *mannitol*, but the reduction product of the most common monosaccharide, glucose, has the common name *sorbitol*.

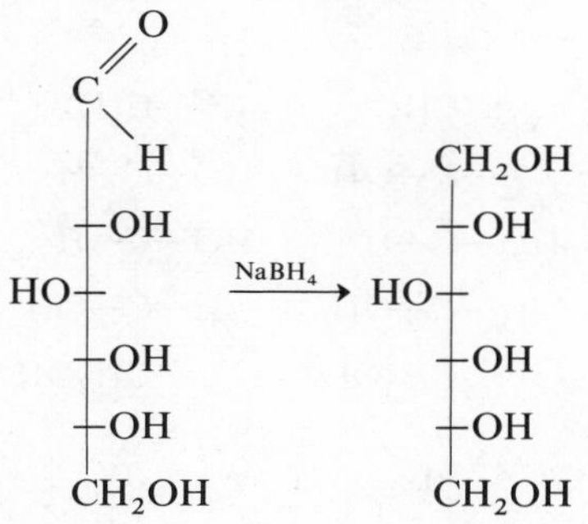

Many hexitols occur commonly in plants. For example, sorbitol occurs in red seaweed to the extent of 14%, and also to an appreciable extent in fruits such as pears, apples, cherries, and peaches. Mannitol is found in seaweed, grass, fruits, and fungi, but unlike sorbitol is also found in the exudates of plants. The name comes from the fact that the compound can be isolated as the edible, sweet-tasting, crystalline exudate of the flowering ash, *Fraxinus ornus*, thereby resembling the manna of the Bible (*Exodus* 16:14–36).

EXERCISE 27.6

Glucose is optically active, and upon reduction gives sorbitol, which is also optically active. Of the seven diastereomers of glucose, five give optically active glycitols upon reduction. The other two give optically inactive glycitols. Explain.

27.7 Fischer's Determination of the Structure of Glucose

Emil Fischer† and his students undertook to determine the total structure of glucose, and hence the configuration at each center, in the year 1888. This stereochemical determination, carried out with only the simple tools available at the time, was a true masterpiece of organic chemistry. Fischer had discovered phenylhydrazine a little earlier, and knew about osazone formation (Section 27.4). Two years earlier, the chain-lengthening reaction sequence discussed in Section 27.4 had become available. In addition, it was known that nitric acid oxidation of a hexose gave a glycaric acid (Section 27.5). Concepts of racemic forms, enantiomers, epimers, and meso compounds were well established, it being some 14 years after the proposal of van't Hoff and Le Bel concerning the tetrahedral carbon atom. Experimental techniques had been worked out for the separation of stereoisomers and for the measuring of the optical activity of such compounds. Only a few monosaccharides were known at this time, including glucose, fructose, arabinose, and mannose.

We will outline here in simplified form the procedure which Fischer used to determine the stereochemistry of glucose, neglecting the complications due to α and β forms. The structure, apart from stereochemistry, was known from the following reactions:

$$C_6H_{12}O_6 \xrightarrow[H_2O]{Br_2} C_6H_{12}O_7 \xrightarrow{HI, P} CH_3CH_2CH_2CH_2CH_2COOH$$

    Glucose   Gluconic acid   Hexanoic acid

† Emil Fischer. 1852–1919. Born Euskirchen, Germany. Universities of Erlangen, Würzburg, and Berlin. Nobel Prize, 1902.

The hexanoic acid shows that the six carbons are in a straight chain. Gluconic acid must, from the molecular formula, be a pentahydroxy acid. The hydroxyls must each be on different carbons (*gem*-diols are hydrates of carbonyls, and ordinarily are not stable; they lose water and give the carbonyl, Section 19.1). Bromine water is an oxidizing agent which specifically oxidizes aldehydes to acids. Thus glucose must be 2,3,4,5,6-pentahydroxypentanal.

Fischer arbitrarily decided that D-glyceraldehyde would be assigned the configuration now known to be correct (Section 3.6), and D-glucose then by convention would have the hydroxyl at C-5 on the right, but it was necessary to determine the configurations at C-2, 3 and 4.

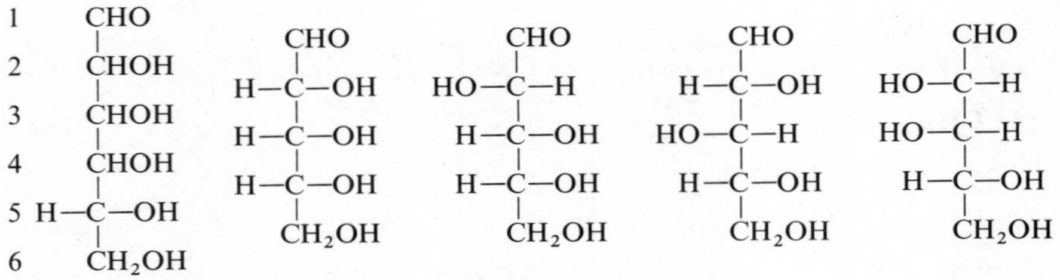

	CHO				
1	CHO				
2	CHOH	H—C—OH	HO—C—H	H—C—OH	HO—C—H
3	CHOH	H—C—OH	H—C—OH	HO—C—H	HO—C—H
4	CHOH	H—C—OH	H—C—OH	H—C—OH	H—C—OH
5	H—C—OH	CH₂OH	CH₂OH	CH₂OH	CH₂OH
6	CH₂OH				
	D-Glucose	I	II	III	IV

A key compound in this determination was D-*arabinose*, an aldopentose, which had to have one of the structures shown (I–IV). Nitric acid oxidation of arabinose gave an optically active dicarboxylic acid. Structures I and III would oxidize to give *meso*-dicarboxylic acids, and therefore they could not be correct.

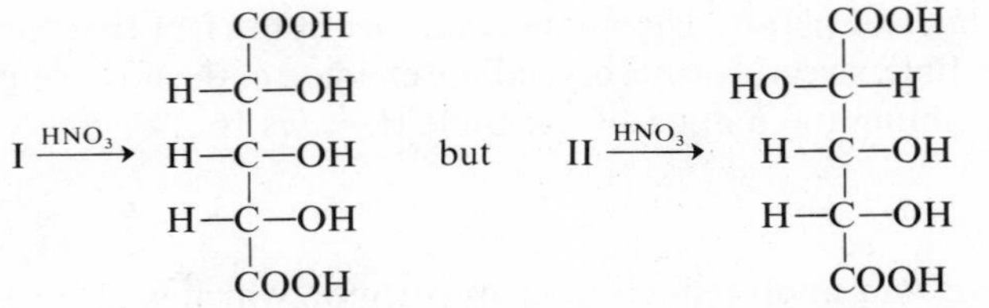

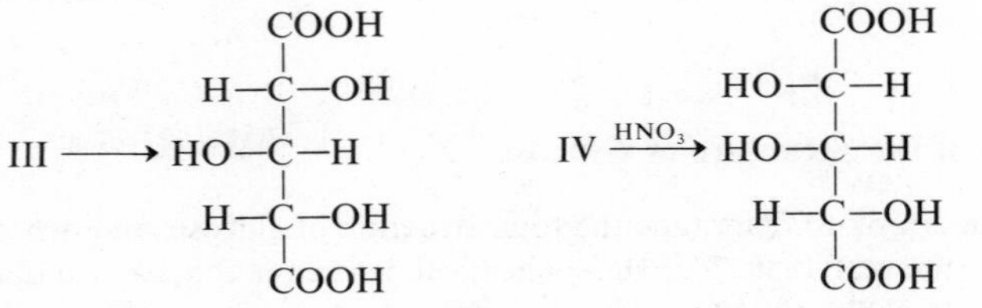

Arabinose is therefore either II or IV, and can be represented with the configuration in doubt at C-3 for the time being.

Chain extension (Section 27.4) of arabinose gave a mixture of compounds which could be separated, and which proved to be glucose and mannose. These two compounds gave the same osazone. Clearly, they differ in configuration only at C-2, which is the new asymmetric center created in the chain extension reaction. Structures V and VI must therefore represent glucose and mannose. We have to determine the configuration at C-4, and then decide which is glucose and which is mannose.

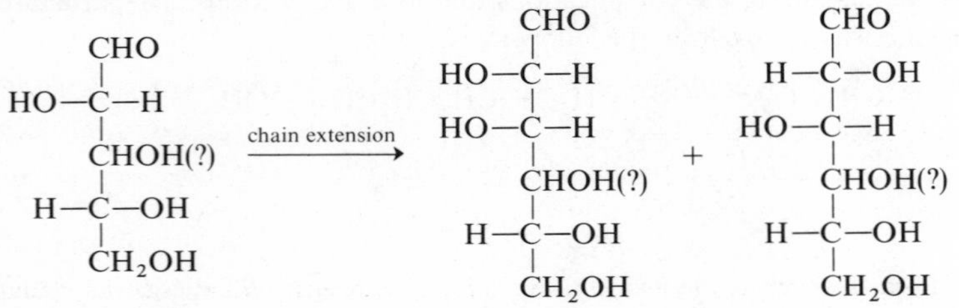

Both glucose and mannose upon nitric acid oxidation give glycaric acids which are optically active. This means that both of them must have the D configuration at C-4. If it were L, then structure VI would have oxidized to yield a meso diacid.

```
      CHO              CHO             COOH            COOH
      |                |               |               |
 H—C—OH          HO—C—H           H—C—OH          H—C—OH
      |                |               |               |
HO—C—H          HO—C—H          HO—C—H          HO—C—H
      |                |               |               |
 H—C—OH           H—C—OH          HO—C—H           H—C—OH
      |                |               |               |
 H—C—OH           H—C—OH           H—C—OH           H—C—OH
      |                |               |               |
    CH₂OH            CH₂OH           CH₂OH            COOH
     VII              VIII        Meso diacid    Optically active diacid
```

Structures VII and VIII, then, represent D-glucose and D-mannose. It only remains to decide whether VII is glucose and VIII mannose, or the other way around.

To decide this last point, Fischer and his colleagues made use of the fact that another aldohexose which they had recently synthesized and given the name gulose, and which had unknown stereochemistry, gave upon nitric acid oxidation the same glycaric acid (X) as that obtained from glucose. In order for this to be possible, glucose and gulose must have the same relative configurations at the asymmetric centers, but have their ends interchanged. Thus, if glucose were VII, gulose (actually L-gulose) would be IX. Upon oxidation, they would both yield the same glycaric acid (X).

```
      CHO             CH₂OH           COOH            CHO
      |                |               |               |
HO—C—H           H—C—OH          H—C—OH          H—C—OH
      |                |               |               |
HO—C—H          HO—C—H          HO—C—H          HO—C—H
      |        ≡       |      [O]      |       [O]      |
 H—C—OH           H—C—OH          H—C—OH          H—C—OH
      |                |       ⟶       |       ⟵        |
HO—C—H            H—C—OH          H—C—OH          H—C—OH
      |                |               |               |
    CH₂OH             CHO            COOH            CH₂OH
      IX     (rotated 180° in plane)    X             VII
```

Mannose, by difference, must be VIII. Upon oxidation it yields a glycaric acid which cannot be obtained from any other aldohexose. We can see why if we interchange the ends. We do not get another aldohexose, but only mannose again.

The sequence of experiments described above is conceptually simple, but ingenious. By showing only whether compounds are optically active, or if they are the same, it proved possible to determine all of the configurations involved. Similar methods have also been applied to the determination of the structures of all the aldopentoses and aldohexoses. The details are not much more complicated than those cited above.

27.8 Disaccharides

A *disaccharide* is a compound that can be hydrolyzed to two monosaccharides, or two molecules of the same monosaccharide. The important disaccharides will be discussed here.

Sucrose

Very few everyday items are pure chemicals. Water is one—hopefully it will remain relatively pure. Table sugar, sucrose, is another. Obtained from sugar cane or sugar beets, it is the organic chemical produced in pure form in the largest amount.

Sucrose is a disaccharide. Acid hydrolysis gives an equimolar mixture of the two monosaccharides of which it is composed: D-glucose and D-fructose. The facts that sucrose does not mutarotate, is not reducing, and does not give an osazone indicate that the carbonyl groups of the monosaccharides are present as a full acetal and a full ketal. The structure of sucrose, as determined by degradation and X-ray studies, is as follows:

Sucrose: α-D-Glucopyranosyl β-D-fructofuranoside

or

β-D-Fructofuranosyl α-D-glucopyranoside

The acid hydrolysis of sucrose can be followed with a polarimeter. The physical property of rotation is approximately additive. Since sucrose has a rotation of $+66°$ and the equilibrium mixture of glucose anomers has $+52°$, while fructose has a large negative rotation of $-92°$, at the end of the reaction the equimolar mixture of glucose and fructose will have a negative rotation. The reaction proceeds with inversion of rotation from a positive value to a negative value. Historically, this cleavage is called the *inversion* of sucrose and the product mixture is called *invert sugar*. The action of the enzyme *invertase* from yeast will accomplish the same cleavage. Commercially, glucose is called *dextrose*, and fructose is called *levulose*, after their respective signs of rotation.

The reaction is important commercially because the two mixed monosaccharides have a sweeter taste than sucrose, and are more useful for some purposes, such as the preparation of ice cream, soft drinks, and candy. Free glucose occurs in sweet fruit, and it is some-times called grape sugar *because it is the major sweet-tasting component of grapes. Fructose, on the other hand, occurs as a major sweet-tasting monosaccharide in honey. The partial conversion of glucose into fructose in order to imitate the sweet taste of the hydrolysis product of sucrose has been a commercial goal for many years. Recently a product derived solely from isomerization of glucose has been introduced into the market.*

Maltose

Maltose, or malt sugar, is the disaccharide resulting from the partial hydrolysis of starch by acids. The enzyme *diastase* from barley malt will convert starch from many sources such as corn, wheat, rye, or potatoes into maltose as an essential step in the fermentation of starch to alcohol.

Maltose is composed of two D-glucose units. It differs from sucrose in that it *is* reducing, it *does* mutarotate, and the hydroxyl group on the 4-carbon of one unit is involved in the glycoside linkage.

Maltose can be hydrolyzed by acid into D-glucose. Again an enzyme, called *maltase*, from yeast will accomplish the same cleavage and is used commercially in the fermenta-tion industry.

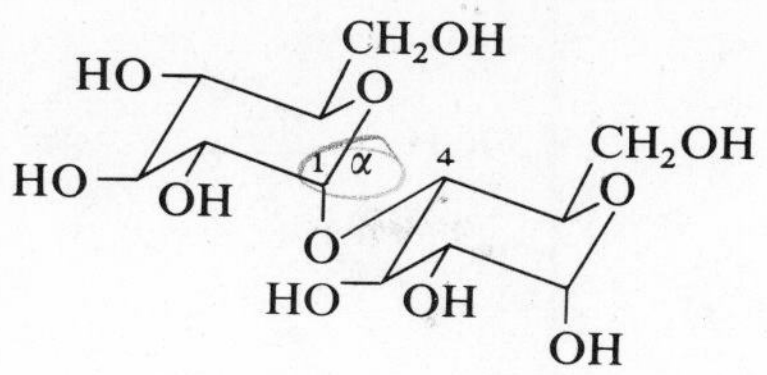

Maltose (α anomer)
4-*O*-α-D-Glucopyranosyl D-glucose

Cellobiose and Lactose

The partial acid hydrolysis of cellulose (cotton) gives the disaccharide *cellobiose*. This disaccharide is reducing, and it mutarotates; it is made up of two glucose units attached in a 1,4-disaccharide linkage in the same manner as maltose. Cellobiose, however, has a 1,4-β glycoside linkage while in maltose the 1,4 linkage is α.

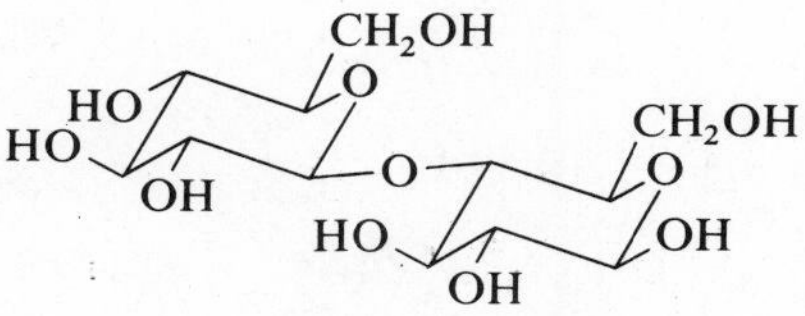

Cellobiose (β anomer)
4-*O*-β-D-Glucopyranosyl D-glucose

This difference is very important, because the enzymes that can hydrolyze the α linkage cannot hydrolyze the β linkage, and vice versa. The enzyme α-glucosidase (maltase) catalyzes the hydrolysis only of the α linkage of glucose, while β-glucosidase (called *emulsin* in the early literature) catalyzes the hydrolysis only of the β linkage of glucose.

Lactose, or milk sugar, is the disaccharide of galactose and glucose. It occurs in the milk of all animals to the extent of about 5%.

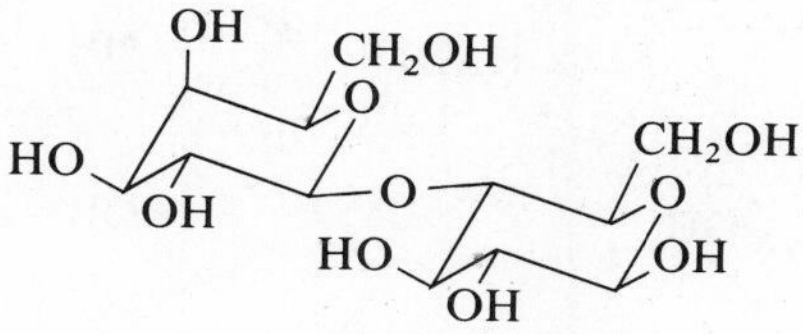

Lactose (β anomer)
4-*O*-β-D-Galactopyranosyl D-glucose

The Structure of Lactose. Assignment of the structure of lactose is based on the following reactions, which illustrate the type of chemistry used to prove the structure of more complex saccharides. Hydrolysis gives an equal amount of galactose and glucose. The α-methyl glycoside of lactose reacts with 3 moles of periodic acid and gives no formaldehyde, which indicates that the compound cannot have a furano- structure. Oxidation with bromine water, followed by hydrolysis gives D-gluconic acid and galactose, showing that glucose has the only free aldehyde carbon. Methylation followed by hydrolysis gives 2,3,4,6-tetra-*O*-methyl galactose and 2,3,6-tri-*O*-methyl glucose, indicating that the 1-hydroxyl group of galactose is attached to glucose through the 4 carbon of glucose. Finally, β-galactosidase and not α-galactosidase catalyzes the hydrolysis of lactose, showing that the disaccharide linkage is a β linkage.

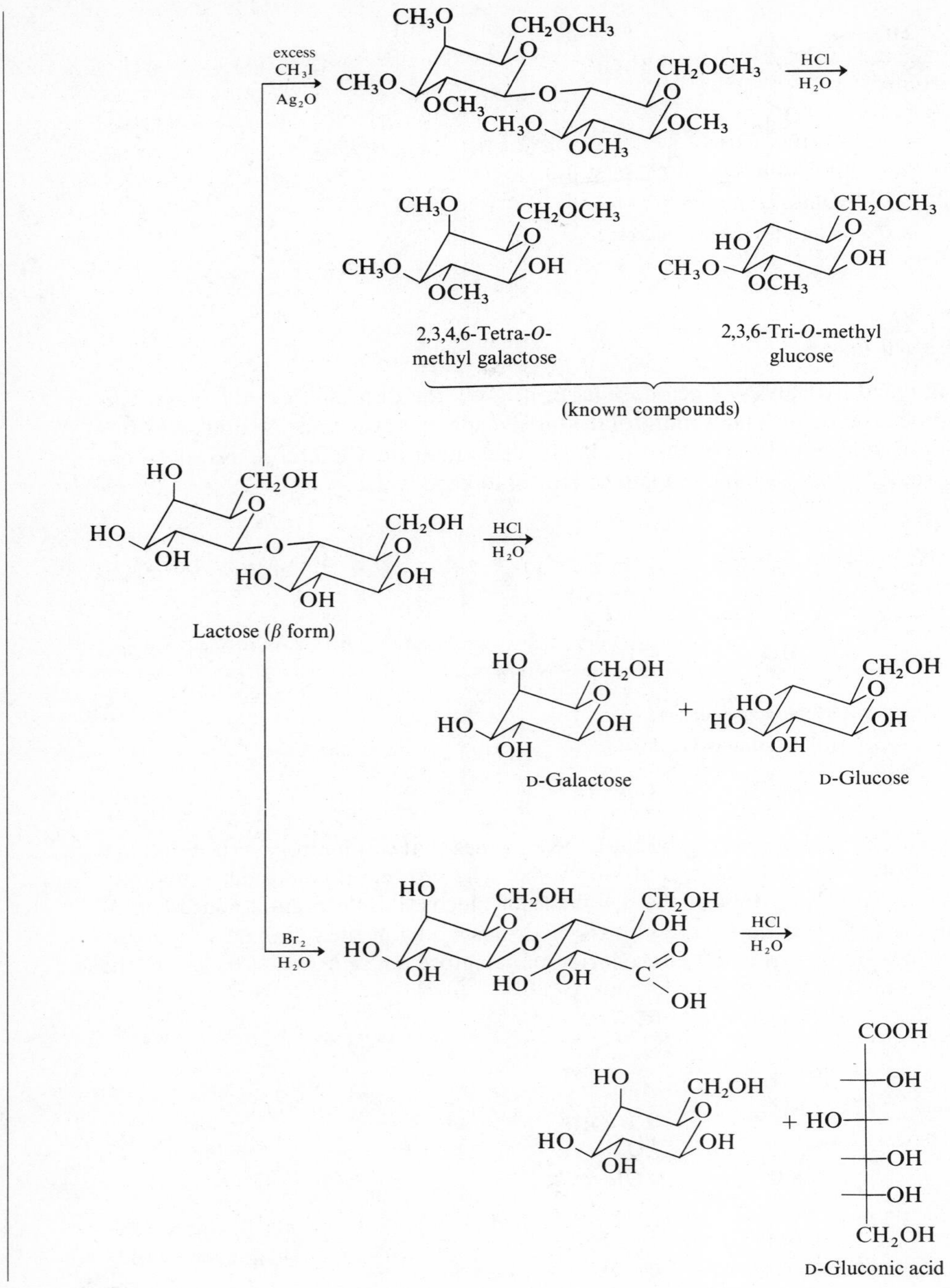
excess
CH_3I
Ag_2O
HCl
H_2O
2,3,4,6-Tetra-*O*-methyl galactose
2,3,6-Tri-*O*-methyl glucose
(known compounds)
Lactose (β form)
HCl
H_2O
D-Galactose
D-Glucose
Br_2
H_2O
HCl
H_2O
D-Gluconic acid

27.9 Polysaccharides

A *polysaccharide* is any molecule which can be hydrolyzed to a large number of monosaccharide molecules. If the monosaccharide molecules obtained upon hydrolysis are hexoses, the polymer may be referred to as a *hexosan*. There are two different important hexosans in nature: *starches*, which represent energy storage in living organisms, and *cellulose*, the basic structural material of many plants.

Natural polysaccharides containing polypentose units $(C_5H_8O_4)_n$ occur in large quantities in certain vegetable matter, such as oat hulls and corn cobs. They are given the name *pentosans*. The structures of these polysaccharides are not very well known, but they are a convenient source of furan derivatives (Section 28.2).

Starch

Starches are polymers composed of many repeating glucose units. Plants use starches as their principal food reserve, storing the carbohydrate in the form of granules in the seeds, fruits, tubers, or roots, depending on the plant. Starches from different plants differ in their chemical composition, and starches from one plant may have more than one chemical composition. One form of starch, amylose, is composed of about 250–300 glucose units attached via α-1,4-disaccharide linkages.

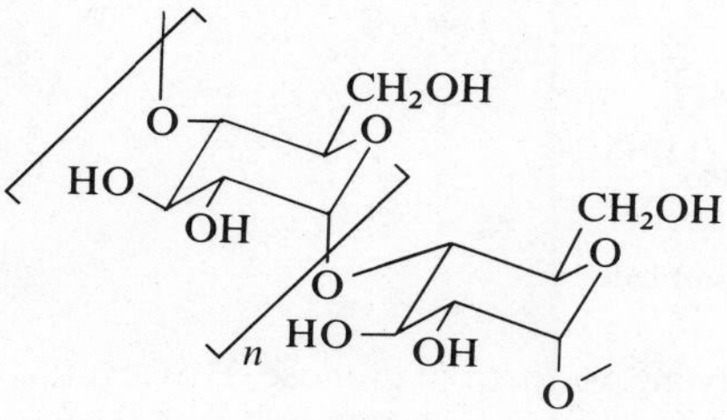

Amylose
$n = 250$–300

Amylopectin is a more complicated starch. It contains about 1000 glucose units in a structure which is branched.

Amylopectin. The amylopectin molecule has a branch about every 25 glucose units. The branches are attached through an α-1,6-disaccharide linkage.

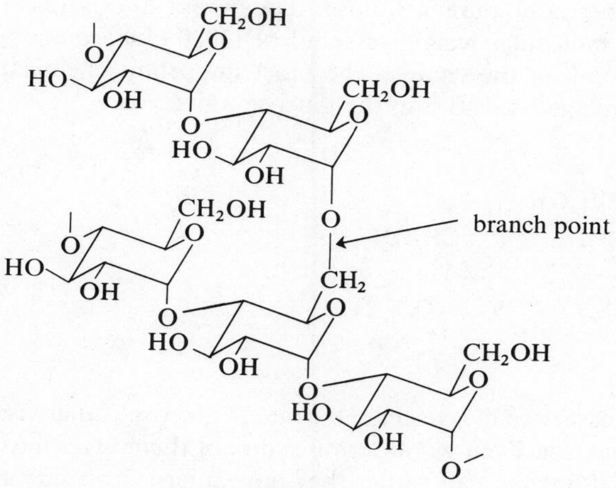

branch point

Amylopectin

All of the glucose units in amylopectin are α-glucosides, but at the branch point, glucose has the 4- and the 6-hydroxyls involved in glucoside linkage; these branches lead to a small amount of *isomaltose* on hydrolysis.

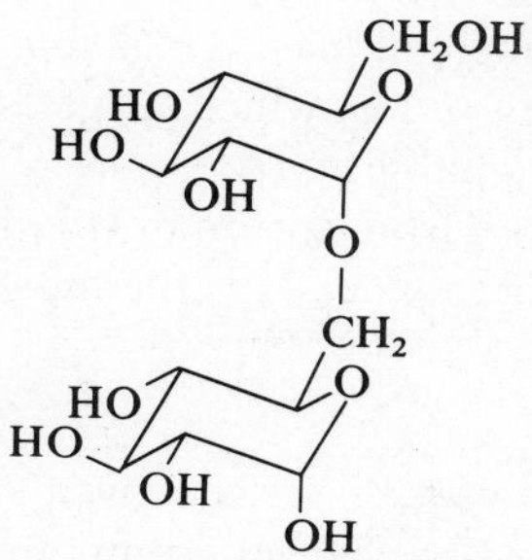

Isomaltose

Hot water will dissolve amylose, but not amylopectin, and thus provides a method of separating the two. The degree of branching in a given sample can be estimated by methylation followed by hydrolysis.

Glycogen is similar to amylopectin in chemical structure, but is much more branched and of higher molecular weight. It functions as the major carbohydrate reserve in animals, being stored in the liver and muscles. The 1- and 6-phosphate esters of glucose are important in the utilization of this stored glycogen.

β-D-Glucose-6-phosphate   β-D-Glucose-1-phosphate

Generally, the glucose-6-phosphate is the metabolically active form of glucose. However, glycogen is broken down by enzymatic action involving the cleavage of the polysaccharide by inorganic phosphate to give first glucose-1-phosphate and the polysaccharide with one less glucose unit. The 1-phosphate is then isomerized enzymatically to the 6-phosphate which is the starting compound for several metabolic pathways.

Cellulose

Cellulose is another glucose polymer found in most plants. This polymer is insoluble in water and has an important structural function in plants. Wood contains about 50% cellulose, and cotton fibers are essentially pure cellulose. The important physical properties result from the very high molecular weight of cellulose (3000 glucose units) and the fact that there is no branching in the chains. The most important chemical feature of cellulose is the 1,4-*beta* linkage used to join the glucose units.

Cellulose

Man does not have the enzymes necessary to cleave cellulose into D-glucose; otherwise we could eat wood and grass for breakfast. Even wood termites do not themselves have the enzymes necessary to cleave the β linkage, but rather they have microorganisms in their digestive tract which provide these enzymes. The same is true for ruminants, cud-chewing animals such as sheep, cows, camels, and giraffes which eat grass or leaves.

The hydroxyl groups of cellulose can be esterified by inorganic or organic acids to modify the properties of the polysaccharide. Partial nitration of cellulose with a mixture of concentrated nitric and sulfuric acids gives a product in which two of the three free hydroxyl groups per glucose unit are converted to the nitrate ester. When compounded with camphor, this material resulted in the first important commercial plastic, *celluloid*. The fully nitrated ester of cellulose is the commercial explosive *guncotton*, which suggests the fact that a major disadvantage of celluloid was its high flammability.

Cellulose acetate, produced by complete acetylation of cellulose from cotton or wood pulp, can be spun into yarn for cloth or extruded into film (cellophane). It is the most important industrial cellulose derivative.

Amino Sugars

Amino sugars, in which one or more of the hydroxyl groups of the carbohydrate are replaced by an amino group, are now known to be very common in nature. However, until several years ago only 2-amino-2-deoxy-D-glucose and 2-amino-2-deoxy-D-galactose had been isolated from natural sources. The most abundant amino sugar derivative is *chitin*, the polysaccharide made up of 2-acetamido-2-deoxyglucose units linked in a β-1,4 manner similar to that in cellulose. In fact, this polymer has many properties similar to those of cellulose, and it is used as a structural and defensive material in the invertebrate animal world. The exoskeletons of insects and crustaceans contain large amounts of this aminopolysaccharide. 2-Amino-2-deoxyglucose (glucosamine) can be prepared in 60–70% yield by the hydrolysis of crab shells with concentrated hydrochloric acid.

Chitin   2-Amino-2-deoxy-D-glucose
(Glucosamine, β form)

Hyaluronic acid is a polysaccharide of 2-amino-2-deoxyglucose and glucuronic acid; it is an important component of animal connective tissue and of the synovial fluid which is the natural lubricant of joints.

Hyaluronic acid

2-Amino-2-deoxygalactose is also an important naturally occurring amino sugar, known for many years as a component of the polysaccharide *chondroitin sulfate*. This polymer is among the principal polysaccharides of cartilage and is structurally similar to hyaluronic acid, except that the amino sugar is galactose instead of glucose, and a sulfate group is also present.

Chondroitin sulfate

Other Amino Sugars. The blood anticoagulant *heparin* is a polysaccharide similar to hyaluronic acid except that the 2-amino-2-deoxyglucose is a sulfamic acid derivative (the acetate group is replaced by $-SO_3H$), and some of the other hydroxyl groups are in the form of sulfates. The blood-group-specific polysaccharides of the red blood cells, which make up the A, B, O(H), and Rh groups, are more complicated polymers containing 2-amino sugar derivatives of glucose and galactose.

In recent years, 2-amino-2-deoxy monosaccharides in the D-gulo, D-talo, D-manno, and L-gluco configurations have been isolated. The tremendous effort recently made in the isolation and proof of structures of antibiotics has led to the recognition of several new classes of naturally occurring amino sugars. Soluble metabolic products of lower fungi and bacteria very often have the property of being extremely poisonous to certain other microorganisms. These are the antibiotics which, after isolation, purification, determination of structure, and manufacture, have been widely used in medicine to control infectious diseases.

An example of an antibiotic with two new classes of amino sugars is *Kanamycin*, which contains a 3-amino-3-deoxy-D-glucose as well as a 6-amino-6-deoxy-D-glucose derivative.

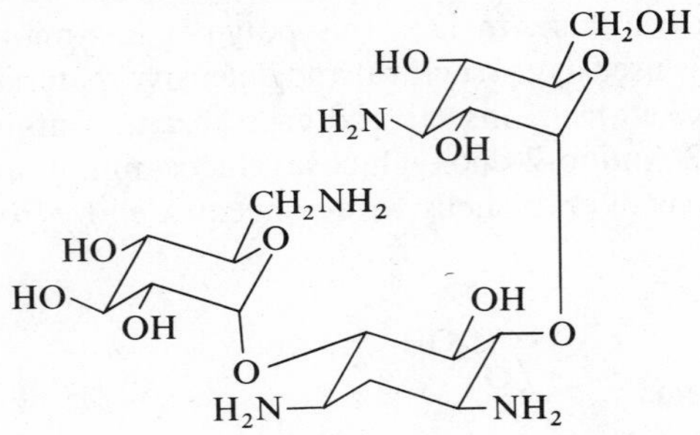

Kanamycin

The D-gluco derivative of another new class of amino sugars, a 4,6-dideoxy-4-amino mono-saccharide, was discovered in one antibiotic and the D-manno derivative in another. The mode of action of these antibiotics is complicated, but the recently discovered fact that the gluco and the galacto derivatives occur in the cell walls of certain bacteria suggests that these novel sugars may be involved.

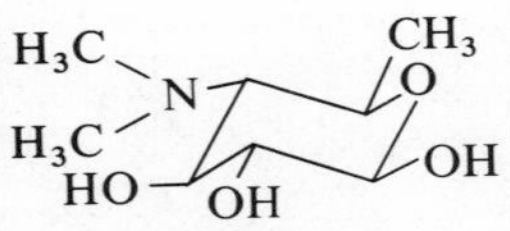

Amosamine
(D-gluco configuration)
from the antibiotic
amicetin

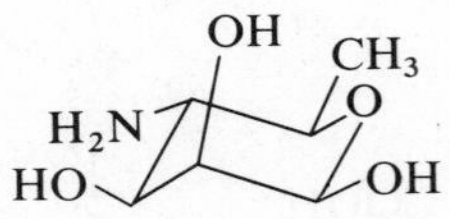

Persosamine from
the antibiotic
perimycin

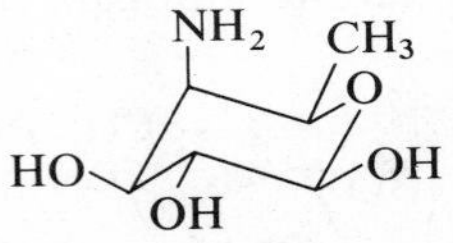

Thomosamine
from the cell wall

PROBLEMS

1. Why does the β isomer predominate in an equilibrium mixture of glucopyranoses?

2. How many isomeric D-aldohexoses are there, excluding α and β forms? Draw them in the Fisher and Haworth projections (use models if necessary).

3. Indicate the product(s) from the following reactions:
   (a) α-Methyl mannoside + periodic acid $\rightarrow$ (b) Maltose + Fehling's solution $\rightarrow$
   (c) Mannose + NaBH$_4$ $\rightarrow$ (d) Glucose + 3 phenylhydrazine $\rightarrow$
   (e) Arabinose + HCN $\rightarrow$ (f) Glucose + hydroxylamine $\rightarrow$

4. How would you differentiate between:
   (a) D-Mannose and D-fructose?   (b) D-Glucose and D-fructose?

5. What is the difference between mutarotation and racemization?

6. Convert D-glucose to:
   (a) Ethyl 2,3,4,6-tetra-O-acetyl-β-D-glucoside   (b) D-Fructose
   (c) D-Gluconic acid   (d) D-Glucaric acid

7. List five oxidizing agents used in carbohydrate chemistry and give an example of their use.

8. Define and give an example of the following:
   (a) Acetal   (b) Mutarotation   (c) Pyranose   (d) Invert sugar

9. Explain why sucrose is a nonreducing sugar whereas maltose is a reducing sugar.

10. Why is the formation of methyl glucoside not subject to base catalysis?

11. Carbohydrates have a variety of sweet tastes. Give the name and structural formula responsible for the sweet taste of (a) grape sugar, (b) malt sugar, (c) manna, (d) table sugar, (e) honey.

12. How is the configuration of D-fructose related to those of D-glucose and D-mannose?

13. Give the products of reaction of α-D-glucofuranose and α-D-galactopyranose with acetone and a catalytic amount of acid.

14. Write a mechanism for both the acid- and base-catalyzed mutarotation of α- and β-D-glucose.

15. Draw Haworth and conformation formulas for the following:
    (a) L-Maltose
    (b) Methyl 2,3,4,6-tetra-*O*-methyl-α-D-mannopyranoside
    (c) β-D-Arabinofuranosyl α-L-arabinofuranoside
    (d) L-Cellobiose

16. How many stereoisomers (diastereomers + enantiomers) are possible for each of the following:
    (a) Sucrose   (b) Diethyl tartrate
    (c) 2,3,4,5,6-Pentahydroxycaproic acid   (d) Methyl glycoside of an aldohexose

Optional Problems

1. When methyl 6-deoxy-β-D-gulopyranoside is treated with acetone and an acid catalyst, a product (I) is formed which must have either the structure A or B.

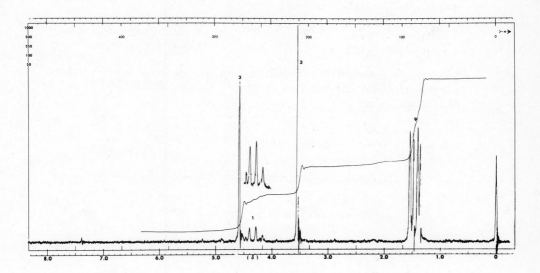

   Oxidation of the remaining free secondary hydroxyl group of I gave a ketone, II, which gave the nmr spectrum shown.

   NMR spectrum of ketone II, Optional Problem 1.

   Treatment of ketone II with D_2O and base gave a ketone, III, which gave the nmr spectrum also shown.

NMR spectrum of ketone III, Optional Problem 1.

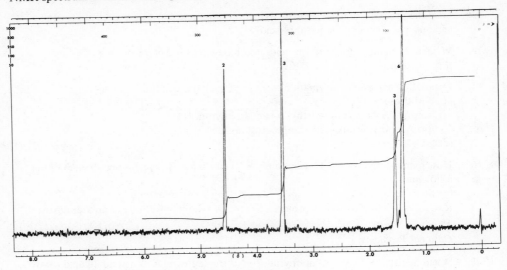

Give the structures of I and II, and interpret the nmr spectra.

2. When a chain-lengthening reaction sequence is carried out on D-glyceraldehyde, two aldotetroses can be obtained, D-erythrose and D-threose.

```
CHO              CHO
 |                |
 +-OH        HO-+
 |                |
 +-OH          +-OH
 |                |
CH₂OH          CH₂OH
```

When these are separated, and each undergoes the chain-lengthening sequence, a total of four aldopentoses is obtained, each of which has the D configuration.

```
CHO          CHO          CHO          CHO
 |            |            |            |
 +-OH     HO-+         +-OH     HO-+
 |            |            |            |
 +-OH      +-OH     HO-+      HO-+
 |            |            |            |
 +-OH      +-OH       +-OH       +-OH
 |            |            |            |
CH₂OH      CH₂OH      CH₂OH      CH₂OH
```

Using only the information from the chain-lengthening sequence, together with the results of nitric acid oxidations, how might you assign the structures of all the aldo-tetroses and aldopentoses?

CHAPTER 28

AROMATIC HETEROCYCLES AND NATURAL PRODUCTS CONTAINING THEM

28.1 Introduction

Heterocycles are cyclic compounds in which one or more of the ring carbons is replaced by another atom (a "hetero atom"). The literature of heterocyclic chemistry is enormous, and more than a quarter of the current chemical research papers are concerned with this vast field. In this chapter we shall consider some of the more important of the simpler aromatic heterocycles, including a few of their derivatives that occur in nature, some of which are essential components of living organisms. We will consider first those heterocycles containing only one hetero atom, and then proceed to heterocycles which contain more than one hetero atom.

The reader is referred to Section 11.8 for brief reviews of structure, nomenclature, and the theoretical basis of aromaticity in heterocyclic systems.

28.2 Furan

The numbering system and the principal resonance forms of furan are shown below.

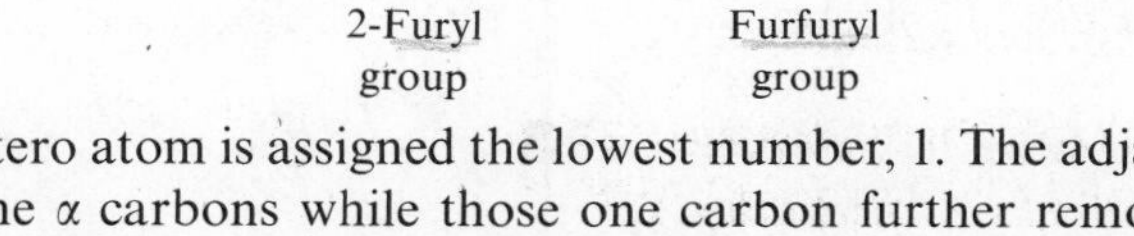

Ring carbons *activated* towards
electrophilic reagents

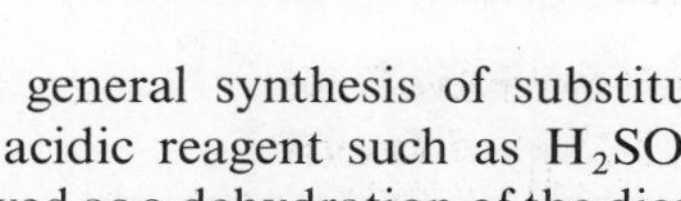

2-Furyl
group

Furfuryl
group

The hetero atom is assigned the lowest number, 1. The adjacent carbons may be referred to as the α carbons while those one carbon further removed are the corresponding β carbons. Other simple heterocycles follow a similar nomenclature scheme.

Synthesis. The most general synthesis of substituted furans is the dehydration of a 1,4-diketone by an acidic reagent such as H_2SO_4 or P_2O_5. Formally speaking, the reaction may be viewed as a dehydration of the dienol form of the diketone, although the mechanism of the reaction is actually more complex.

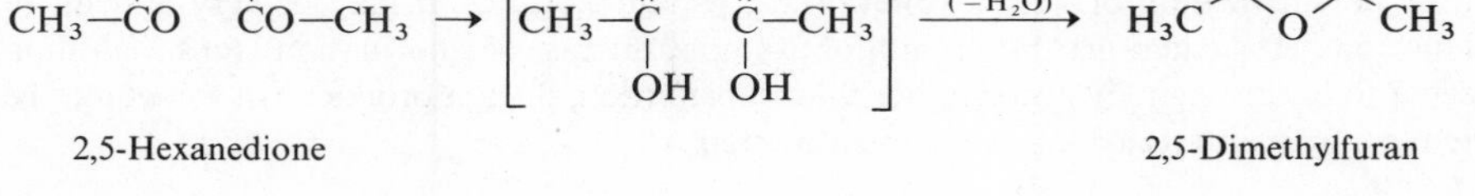

2,5-Hexanedione

2,5-Dimethylfuran

By far the cheapest and most readily available of all furan derivatives is furan-2-carboxaldehyde, commonly known as *furfural*. It is formed when vegetable products containing large quantities of pentose polysaccharides (pentosans, Section 27.9) are refluxed with aqueous sulfuric acid. It is manufactured on a large scale in this way from agricultural waste products such as oat hulls or corn cobs. Furfural is useful as a starting material for the preparation of other furans.

$$\text{Pentosans} \xrightarrow[\text{H}_2\text{O}]{\text{H}^+} \left[\begin{array}{c} \text{OH} \quad\quad \text{OH} \\ | \quad\quad\quad | \\ \text{CH——CH} \\ | \quad\quad\quad | \\ \text{CH}_2\text{OH} \quad \text{CH—CHO} \\ | \\ \text{OH} \end{array} \right] \xrightarrow{-3\text{H}_2\text{O}} \quad \text{Furfural}$$

A pentose
(open form)

Furan itself (bp 31°C) is prepared industrially by the catalytic decarbonylation of furfural in steam.

$$\text{(furan-CHO)} \xrightarrow{-\text{CO}} \text{Furan}$$

Chemistry. The conjugation energy of furan is estimated to be only about 16 kcal/mole, which is considerably less than that of benzene (36 kcal/mole). This is a result of the fact that furan has its sextet of π electrons only partially delocalized. Consequently, furan should, and does, have chemical properties intermediate between those of a highly delocalized aromatic system such as benzene, and those of a simple cyclic diene which is also an enol ether.

Many of the reactions of furfural parallel those of benzaldehyde. For example, it undergoes a reaction analogous to the benzoin condensation (Section 19.5) when treated with cyanide ion, and it undergoes the Cannizzaro reaction (Section 19.11) with strong aqueous base to give furfuryl alcohol and a salt of the corresponding acid, 2-furoic acid.

EXERCISE 28.1

What is the product formed when furfural is treated with a catalytic amount of cyanide ion? Write the mechanism of the reaction.

Furan can be reduced catalytically to give the stable saturated ether, *tetrahydrofuran* (often abbreviated as THF), which is a useful solvent.

$$\text{(furan)} \xrightarrow[100°C]{\text{Ni, 2H}_2} \text{Tetrahydrofuran}$$

Electrophilic Substitution. Furan undergoes electrophilic aromatic substitution reactions much more easily than does benzene. Most reactions of this type (for example, chlorination, nitration, sulfonation) are not of much practical importance, however, for the following reasons: (a) furan is very sensitive to strong acids (for instance, concentrated sulfuric acid causes a vigorously exothermic polymerization of furan); (b) even at low temperatures, it may be very difficult to control the number of entering substituents (for example, the case of chlorination); (c) 2,5 addition of a reagent to furan ring may occur rather than substitution. Such a product can sometimes be converted to a true substituted furan in a separate step.

(a) *Acid sensitivity*

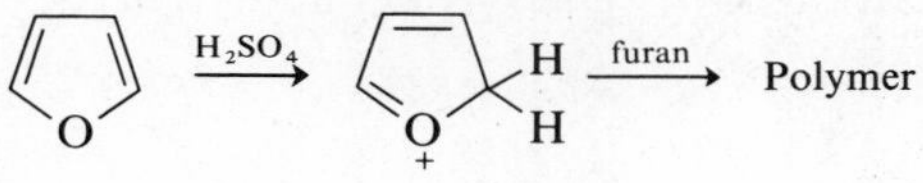

(b) *Great ease of substitution*

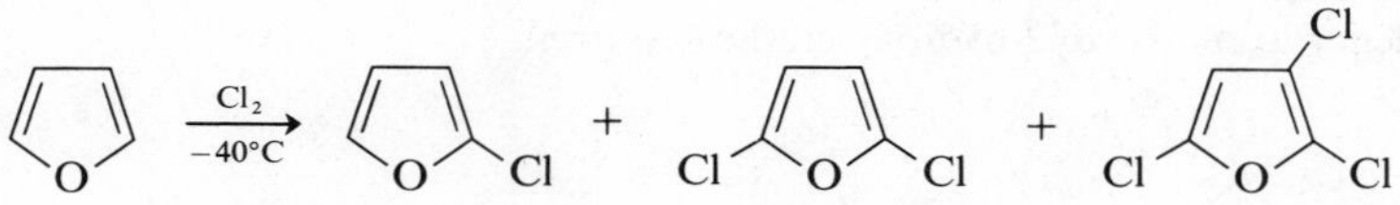

(c) *Formation of 2,5 addition product by initial attack of an electrophile*

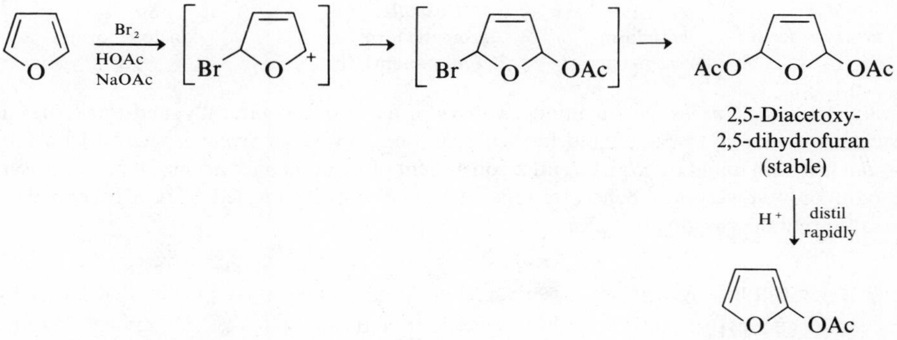

2,5-Diacetoxy-
2,5-dihydrofuran
(stable)

2-Acetoxyfuran

The best and most reliable electrophilic reaction of furan is Friedel–Crafts acylation, carried out under very mild reaction conditions, as illustrated below in the synthesis of 2-acetylfuran. Note that the α positions of furan are the most readily attacked by an electrophilic reagent.

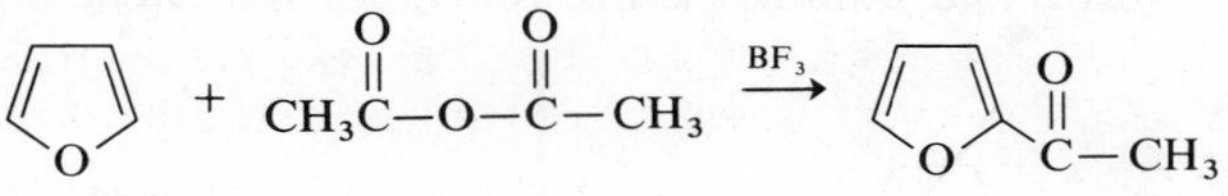

EXERCISE 28.2

Explain in terms of the Wheland intermediates why electrophilic substitution occurs preferentially at the α position.

One interesting consequence of the modest degree of aromaticity of furan is its ability to act as a diene component in the Diels–Alder reaction. This reaction is general for furans which do not bear electron-withdrawing groups (e.g., –CHO and –COOH). The Diels–Alder adducts of furans undergo dehydration to benzene derivatives on treatment with a mineral acid such as HBr; this reaction is sometimes quite useful synthetically, as illustrated below.

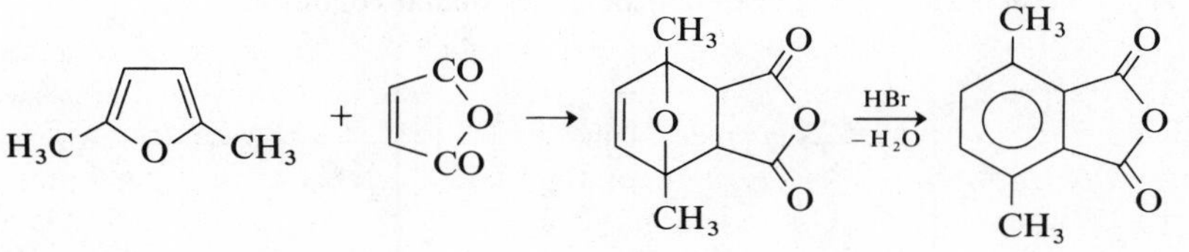

2,5-Dimethylfuran   Diels–Alder   3,6-Dimethylphthalic
adduct   anhydride

EXERCISE 28.3

Suggest a mechanism for the aromatization of the Diels–Alder adduct in the preceding reaction.

Hydroxyfurans. Another interesting result of the relatively low conjugation energy of furan is instability of the simple furan analogs of phenol and aniline. For example, whereas phenol shows no tendency to lose its benzenoid character by tautomerizing to a dienone, α,β-unsaturated γ-lactones show no tendency to enolize to 2-hydroxyfuran derivatives.

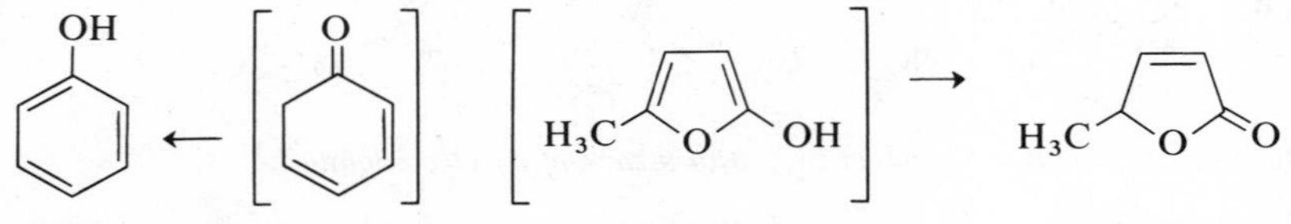

| Stable aromatic form | Unstable keto form | Unstable aromatic form (not present) | Stable lactone form |

Naturally Occurring Furans. Not many derivatives of furan occur naturally, and those that do are rarely known to play important biochemical roles (see, however, morphine, page 748). Furfuryl mercaptan has been found to be an essential constituent of natural coffee aroma; it has a pleasant coffee odor only at very low concentrations. It is undoubtedly formed from a carbohydrate precursor during the roasting of coffee.

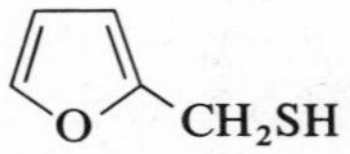

Furfuryl mercaptan

28.3   Thiophene

The important types of resonance forms and the numbering system for thiophene are shown below.

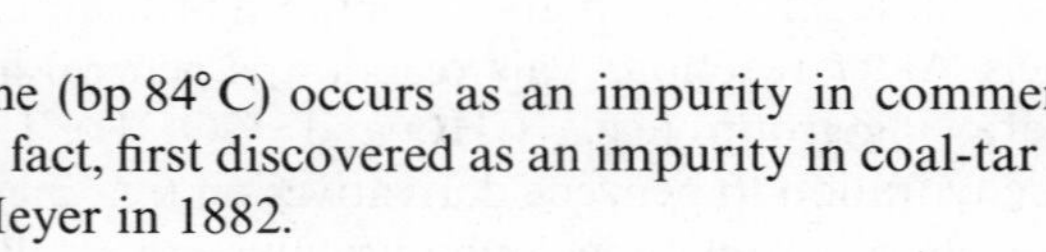

etc.   Ring carbons activated towards electrophilic reagents

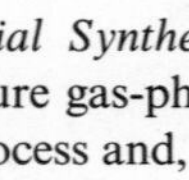

2-Thienyl group

Thiophene (bp 84°C) occurs as an impurity in commercial benzene of coal-tar origin. It was, in fact, first discovered as an impurity in coal-tar benzene by the German chemist Victor Meyer in 1882.

Commercial Synthesis of Thiophene. Thiophene is now manufactured cheaply by the high-temperature gas-phase reaction of butane and sulfur. Butadiene is undoubtedly an intermediate in this process and, indeed, is known to give thiophene under similar conditions.

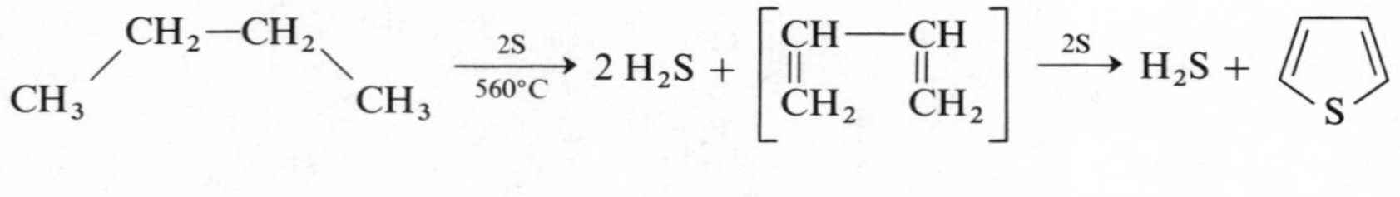

Synthesis. The most general synthesis of thiophenes from open-chain precursors consists of heating a 1,4-dicarbonyl compound with phosphorus pentasulfide. This is a more

widely applicable method than the corresponding synthesis of furans, since one or more of the reacting carbonyls may be in the form of a carboxylate ion, reduction of which must take place during the reaction. Thiophene itself was first synthesized in this way starting with sodium succinate.

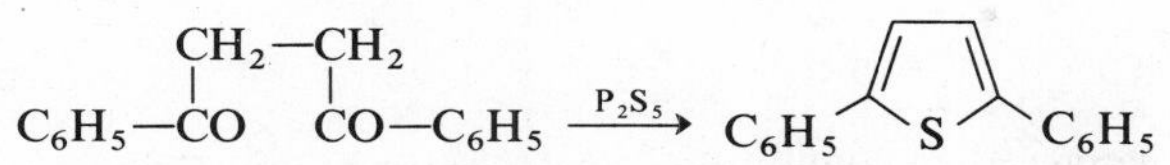

CH₂—CH₂ / C₆H₅—CO   CO—C₆H₅ $\xrightarrow{P_2S_5}$ 2,5-Diphenylthiophene

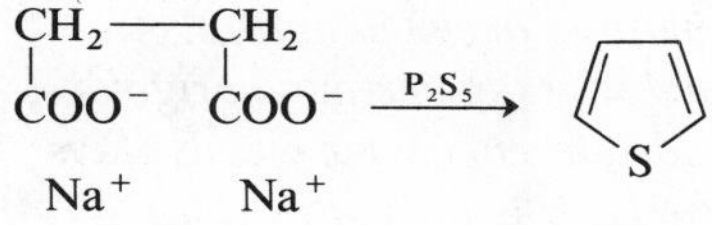

CH₂——CH₂ / COO⁻ Na⁺ COO⁻ Na⁺ $\xrightarrow{P_2S_5}$ Thiophene

Chemistry. The conjugation energy of thiophene has been estimated to be 29 kcal/mole, which is considerably higher than that of furan and close to that of benzene. It has been suggested that a factor contributing to the unusual stability of thiophene is participation to a small extent of the $3d$ orbitals of the sulfur atom in the bonding of the π-orbital system, but this is uncertain. Thiophene is much more stable to acids than is furan, but it gives polymers with such strong acids as 100% sulfuric acid, liquid hydrogen fluoride, and aluminum chloride.

The low nucleophilicity of thiophene is shown by the fact that it does not react with methyl iodide to give a sulfonium salt, whereas tetrahydrothiophene does react readily with methyl iodide as shown below.

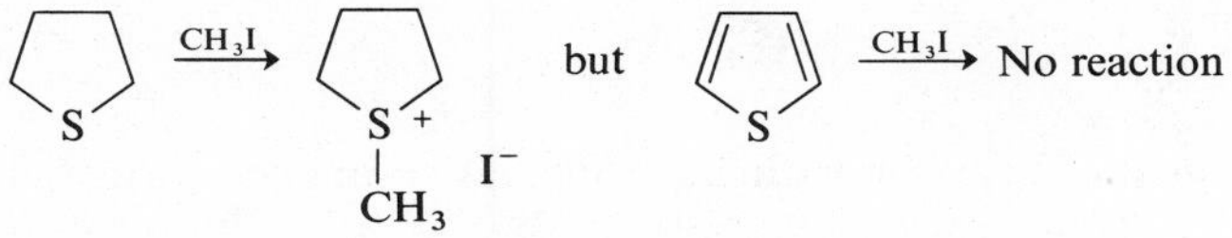

Thiophene undergoes electrophilic aromatic substitution much more rapidly than benzene; the α positions are attacked most readily. Mild reaction conditions are employed to avoid polymerization of the thiophene and to form monosubstituted products.

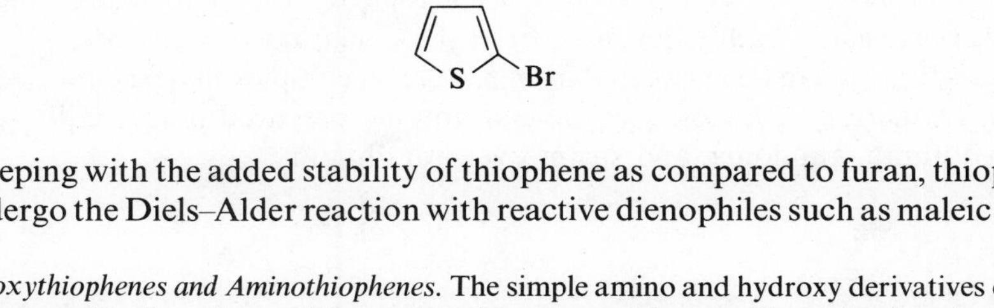

In keeping with the added stability of thiophene as compared to furan, thiophene does not undergo the Diels–Alder reaction with reactive dienophiles such as maleic anhydride.

Hydroxythiophenes and Aminothiophenes. The simple amino and hydroxy derivatives of thiophene are more stable than those of furan, though not as stable as aniline and phenol. For example, 2-aminothiophene undergoes the normal reactions of an aromatic amine (e.g., diazotization). On the other hand, although 2-hydroxythiophene exhibits some true phenolic properties (e.g., it gives a positive ferric chloride test), its spectroscopic properties show that it exists largely in the thiolactone form.

Minor component   Major component

EXERCISE 28.4

To determine the position of the preceding equilibrium, what spectra would be useful? What would you look for?

NATURALLY OCCURRING THIOPHENES. *Few thiophene derivatives occur in nature. An interesting exception is α,α-terthienyl, which occurs in the flowers of certain marigold species. The reduced thiophene derivative* biotin *is an important coenzyme which plays an essential role in some biochemical carboxylation reactions; it is involved in the biosynthesis of long-chain fatty acids from acetic acid (Section 30.2).*

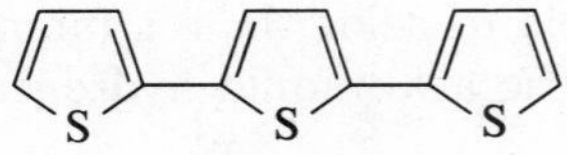

α,α-Terthienyl 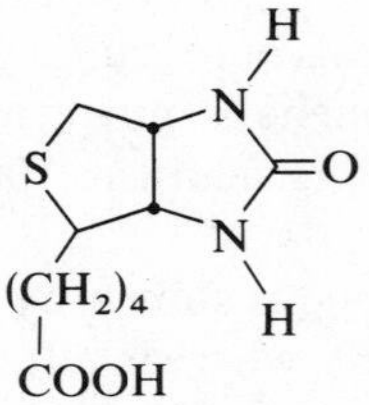   Biotin

28.4   Pyrrole

The numbering system for pyrrole, together with its principal resonance forms, are shown below.

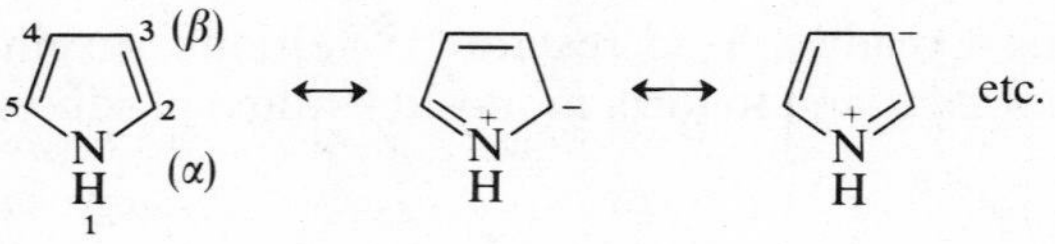

Ring carbons *activated* towards electrophilic reagents

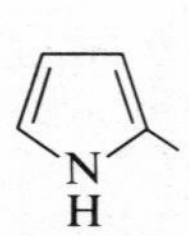

2-Pyrryl group

Synthesis. Pyrrole (bp 129°C) was first synthesized in 1860 by the pyrolysis of the ammonium salt of mucic acid (readily available from the oxidation of galactose, page 709). Even before this time, it had been isolated from *bone oil*, a complex material formed by the destructive distillation of bones. Pyrrole can now be prepared industrially by passing a mixture of furan, ammonia, and steam over hot alumina.

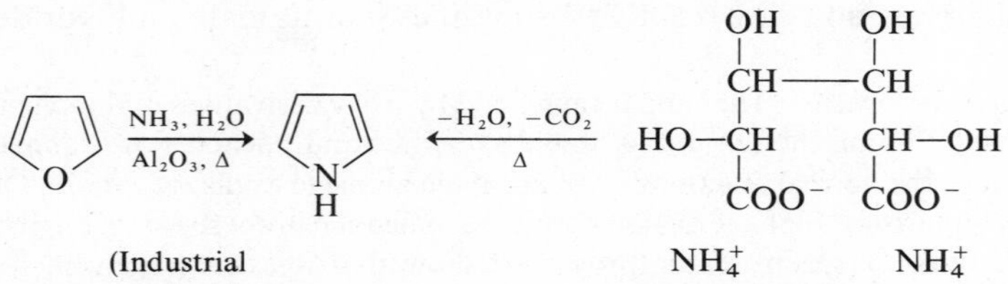

(Industrial synthesis)

Ammonium mucate

Substituted pyrroles have been prepared by a variety of methods. The simplest of these involves the reaction of a 1,4-diketone with ammonia or an amine.

1,4-Diketone synthesis

$$C_6H_5-CO \quad CO-CH_3 \xrightarrow{\ NH_3\ } C_6H_5 \underset{\overset{|}{H}}{\overset{N}{\diagup\!\!\diagdown}} CH_3$$

where the diketone is $\overset{CH_2-CH_2}{\underset{C_6H_5-CO \quad CO-CH_3}{}}$

Another much used synthesis, due to Knorr, employs the condensation of a β-dicarbonyl compound with an α-amino ketone. An advantage of Knorr's method is that it allows construction of the pyrrole ring from two smaller units. Since α-amino ketones are generally unstable and undergo self-condensation, they are usually generated right in the reaction mixture by the reduction of the corresponding α-oximino ketone (see Sections 22.2, 22.3).

Knorr synthesis

$$\underset{EtOOC}{\overset{CH_3-CO}{\diagdown\!\!\diagup CH_2}} \xrightarrow[HCl]{RONO} \underset{EtOOC}{\overset{CH_3-CO}{\diagdown C \diagup}} {\diagdown NOH} \xrightarrow[H^+]{Zn}$$

α-Oximino ketone

$$\underset{EtOOC}{\overset{CH_3-CO}{\diagdown CH \diagup}} {\diagdown NH_2} \xrightarrow{\quad \underset{O}{\overset{H_2C}{\diagdown}} \overset{COOEt}{\diagup C} \diagdown CH_3 \quad} H_3C \underset{EtOOC}{\diagup} \underset{\overset{|}{H}}{\overset{N}{}} \overset{COOEt}{} CH_3$$

α-Amino ketone

Chemistry. Pyrrole has a resonance energy of 21 kcal/mole, making it more like furan than thiophene in its reactivity. Like furan, pyrrole is protonated by aqueous mineral acid to give a reactive cation which is no longer aromatic and which can undergo polymerization easily. On the other hand, pyrrole is not protonated as easily as is an ordinary aliphatic or aromatic amine. It is almost neutral, because the lone pair of electrons of its nitrogen atom is very highly delocalized, since it makes up a portion of the aromatic sextet of the molecule. As a consequence, pyrrole does not react with alkyl halides to give quaternary salts.

$$\underset{\overset{|}{H}}{\overset{N}{\diagup\!\!\diagdown}} \xrightarrow{\ H^+\ } \underset{\overset{|}{H}}{\overset{N^+}{\diagup\!\!\diagdown}} \overset{H}{\diagdown H} \longrightarrow \text{Polymer, etc.}$$

Nonaromatic cation

Pyrrole has amphoteric properties; it is not only a weak base ($pK_a = 0.4$ for the cation) but also a very weak acid. Thus, pyrrole reacts with metallic potassium to give an ionic potassium compound. The pyrrole anion, which is greatly stabilized by resonance, is a reactive nucleophile. For example, it reacts rapidly with methyl iodide to give 1-methyl-pyrrole. Because of the low acidity of pyrrole ($pK_a = 16.5$), the anion is hydrolyzed to pyrrole by water.

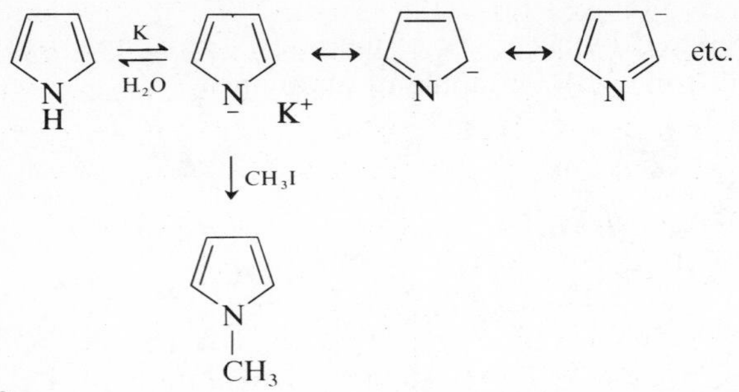

Pyrrole does not undergo the Diels–Alder reaction, nor, in general, do its substitution products, although a few isolated exceptions to this rule are known.

Electrophilic Substitution. Pyrrole is extremely reactive towards electrophilic substitution, its reactivity being comparable to that of phenol or aniline. For example, it reacts rapidly with iodine to give tetraiodopyrrole, it couples with benzenediazonium chloride, and it undergoes Friedel–Crafts acylation by acetic anhydride in the absence of a catalyst. A reaction of importance in pyrrole chemistry is the direct introduction of an aldehyde group by the Vilsmeier–Haack method (see page 592). As with furan and thiophene, the α positions of pyrrole are the most readily substituted.

Rapid halogenation

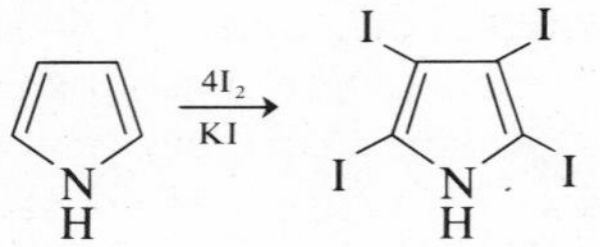

Diazonium coupling

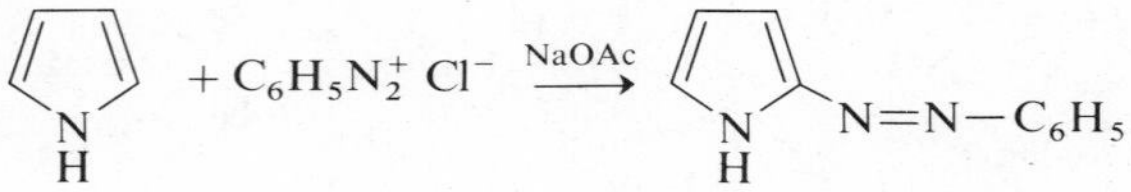

Acylation

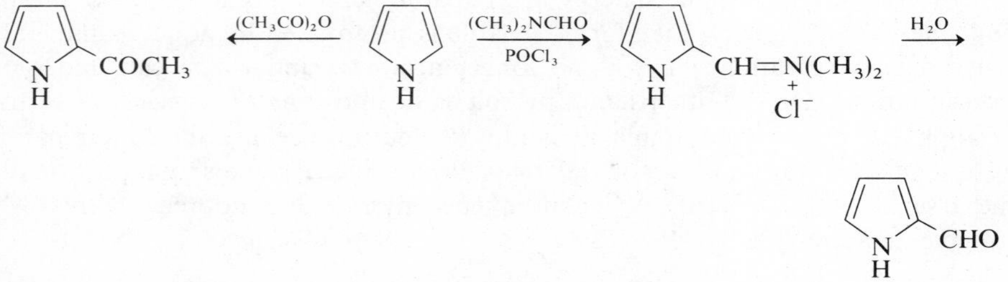

Naturally Occurring Pyrroles. Few genuine pyrroles occur in nature, but certain compounds formally derived from the pyrrole system are of very great biochemical importance. The simplest of these is the α-amino acid *proline*, which is a carboxy derivative of tetrahydropyrrole or *pyrrolidine*.

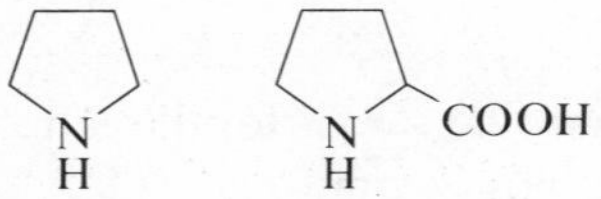

Pyrrolidine   Proline

The *porphyrins* are a remarkable class of compounds formally derived by joining four pyrrole units together through their alpha positions by way of CH (methine) bridges.

The porphyrins are not really pyrrole derivatives, but rather derivatives of a very stable new aromatic system of which the simplest member is known as *porphin*. The most striking characteristic of the porphyrins is the ease with which they form chelates with many metal ions, the metal being held tightly in the space between the four nitrogen atoms of the planar system. The porphyrins are highly colored. The basic system is

Porphin
(the simplest porphyrin)

The Fe^{2+} porphin complex

orange-red, but the color of an individual compound depends also upon the substituents it bears and the nature of the central metal atom, if any. Some partially reduced porphyrins are green.

The porphyrin system is of great importance because it forms the basic units of both the red blood pigment, *hemoglobin*, and the green leaf pigment, *chlorophyll*.

Hemoglobin consists of a protein portion called *globin* and an iron porphyrin complex called *heme*. The iron atom in heme is in the ferrous oxidation state. The function of hemoglobin in the blood is to transport oxygen to the tissues. This transport takes place by way of a hexacoordinate ferrous complex in which the iron atom of a heme unit is coordinated also to an imidazole nitrogen from the protein globin and to an oxygen molecule. The oxygen is easily released, probably in exchange for a water molecule. Carbon monoxide acts as a poison because the CO forms a much more stable complex with hemoglobin than does oxygen. Even rather low concentrations of CO in

Heme

Oxygen transport by hemoglobin

the air can cause death by suffocation by binding with most of the hemoglobin in the bloodstream. Hemin $[(RN)_4Fe^+]$ is the oxidized form of heme and is derived from ferric ion; it is the prosthetic group (attached nonprotein portion) of a number of important enzymes such as *catalase*, a protein capable of decomposing hydrogen peroxide to oxygen and water with great efficiency.

Biosynthesis of Heme. In recent years, biochemists have succeeded in elucidating the major steps in the biogenesis of heme. Glycine condenses with succinic acid (as the active form, succinyl coenzyme A, page 754) to give α-amino-β-ketoadipic acid, which decarboxylates to δ-amino-levulinic acid. Two molecules of the latter acid condense together in a reaction similar to the Knorr pyrrole synthesis to give a substituted pyrrole known as *porphobilinogen*. Four molecules of porphobilinogen then condense together with the loss of ammonia to give a compound known as *uroporphyrin III*, which, as the name implies, has been isolated from urine. It should be noted that the condensation which forms uroporphyrin III is unusual in that one of the four pyrrole units becomes turned around to give an unsymmetrically substituted porphyrin. Finally, conversion of uroporphyrin III to heme is fairly straightforward and involves decarboxylation of all the acetic acid units to methyls, and degradation of two propionic acid chains to vinyls, followed by insertion of the iron atom.

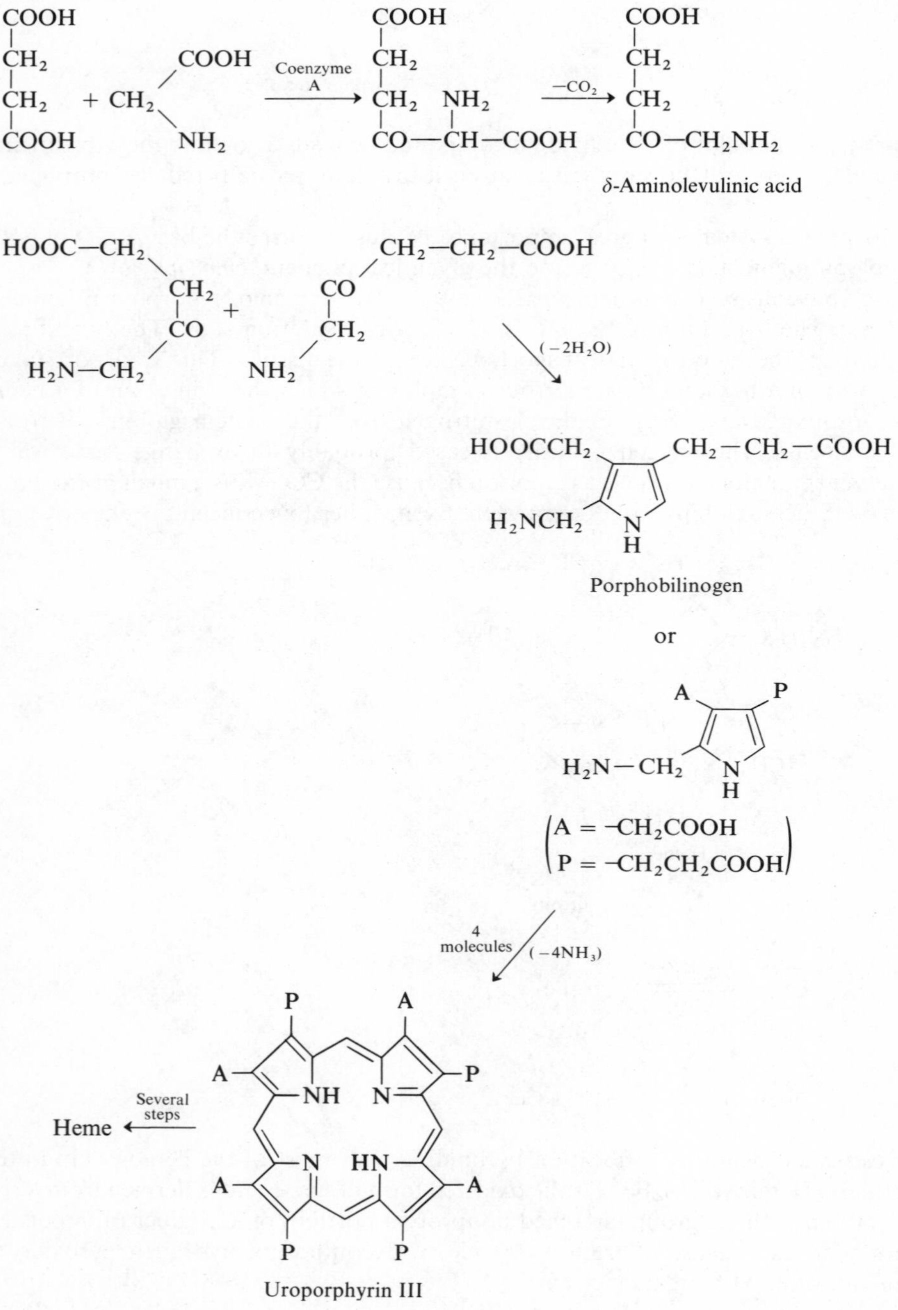

δ-Aminolevulinic acid

Porphobilinogen

or

$$\begin{pmatrix} A = -CH_2COOH \\ P = -CH_2CH_2COOH \end{pmatrix}$$

Heme

Uroporphyrin III

Chlorophyll is the green pigment of plants and plays an essential role in the process of photosynthesis; it is actually a mixture of closely related compounds. The structure of chlorophyll *a*, the major pigment, is given below.

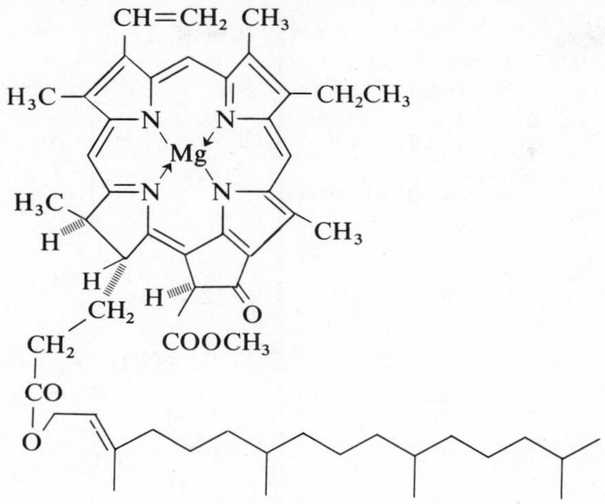

Chlorophyll *a*

Several interesting features of the structure should be noted. It is a magnesium complex of a *dihydroporphyrin*. It contains a modified propionic acid chain in the form of a cyclic β-keto ester. It also contains a propionic acid chain esterified with the diterpene alcohol *phytol*, a feature which imparts fat solubility to the molecule. The most striking fact about the chlorophyll molecule, however, is its very close structural similarity to heme. This suggests that the importance of porphyrins of this general structure goes back before the evolutionary separation of the plant and animal kingdoms.

A group of porphyrin-containing enzymes called cytochromes *are part of the electron-transport or respiratory chain in all cells capable of aerobic metabolism. This includes bacteria, which are possibly the most primitive living things known.*

The total synthesis of chlorophyll *a* was achieved in 1960 by R. B. Woodward† and his co-workers at Harvard, an accomplishment which should suggest to the reader the present refined state of the art of organic synthesis.

28.5 Indole

When a benzene ring is fused to the α,β positions of pyrrole, the resulting compound is called *indole*. The numbering system and some important resonance forms for this compound are shown below.

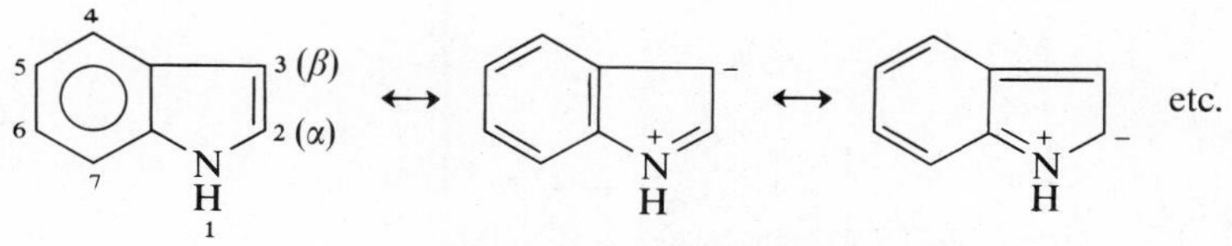

Activated towards electrophilic reagents, particularly at C-2 and C-3

Synthesis. The most general method of forming the indole system is the *Fischer indole synthesis.* In this reaction, the phenylhydrazone of an aldehyde or ketone is heated with a strong acid under nonhydrolytic conditions. Fused zinc chloride, and more recently, polyphosphoric acid ($H_3PO_4 + P_2O_5$) have been most used as reagents. Although it is a very general reaction, it fails in the simplest instance—the conversion of acetaldehyde phenylhydrazone into indole itself. The mechanism of the reaction is believed to be

† Robert B. Woodward. Born 1917, Boston. Harvard University. Nobel Prize 1965.

related to that of the benzidine rearrangement; some of the proposed intermediates are shown below.

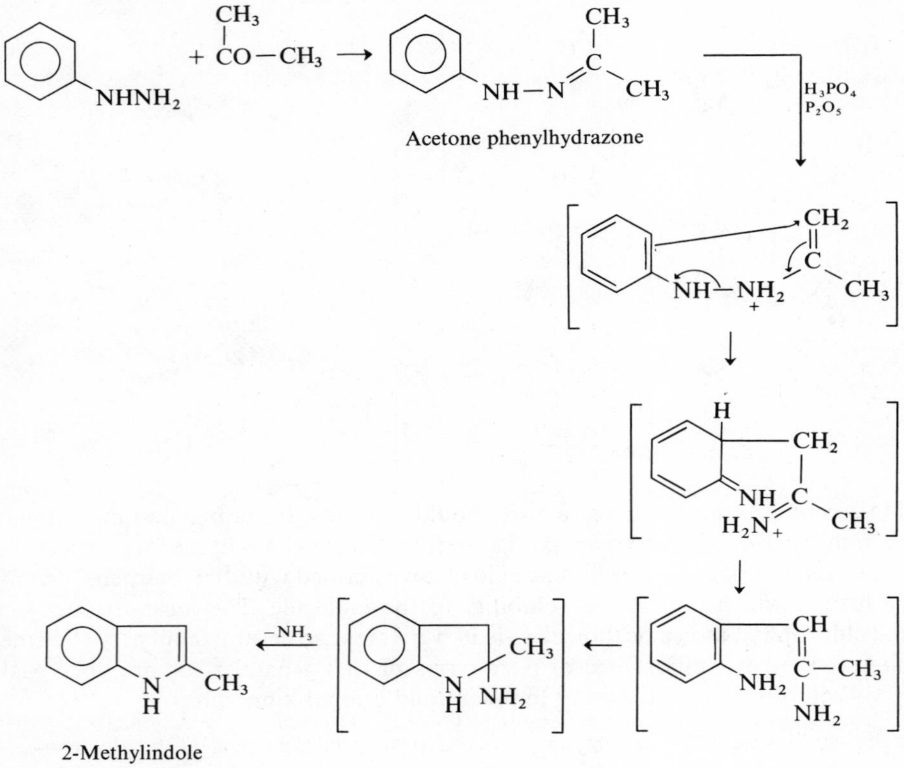

Acetone phenylhydrazone

2-Methylindole

Other Indole Syntheses. Some indoles can be prepared by the reduction of an aromatic nitro compound having an appropriately situated carbonyl group in an ortho side chain. For example, mild reduction of *o*-nitrophenylpyruvic acid (page 601) yields indole-2-carboxylic acid.

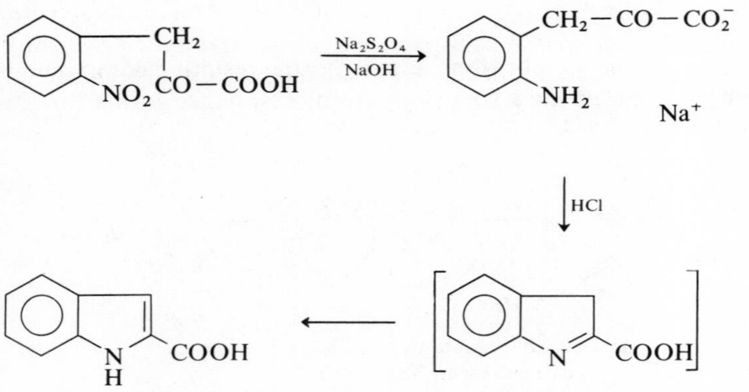

Indole itself is best prepared by an unusual dehydration reaction in which *N*-formyl-*o*-toluidine is heated with potassium *t*-butoxide in the absence of a solvent. Indole is available commercially at the present time.

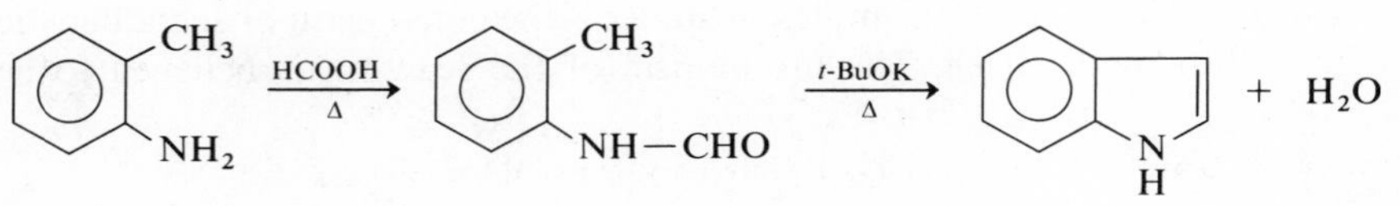

EXERCISE 28.5

Suggest a mechanism for the preceding reaction.

Chemistry. Indole (mp 52°C) forms colorless crystals having a powerful odor which is pleasant and flowery in low concentrations; it is, in fact, used commercially in perfume formulations. Nevertheless, indole and its β-methyl derivative (skatole) are responsible for the foul odor of feces! As in pyrrole, the lone pair of electrons of the indole nitrogen forms part of the aromatic π-electron system; indole has a resonance energy of about 47 kcal/mole. Like pyrrole, indole is practically neutral, but it may be converted to a potassium salt by reaction with metallic potassium.

Indole reacts readily with electrophilic reagents, but the usual substitution reactions (halogenation, nitration, etc.) are of little importance in indole chemistry. As with pyrrole, the Vilsmeier–Haack reaction (Section 21.5) cleanly introduces an aldehyde function; the more reactive β position of indole is attacked preferentially in electrophilic substitutions.

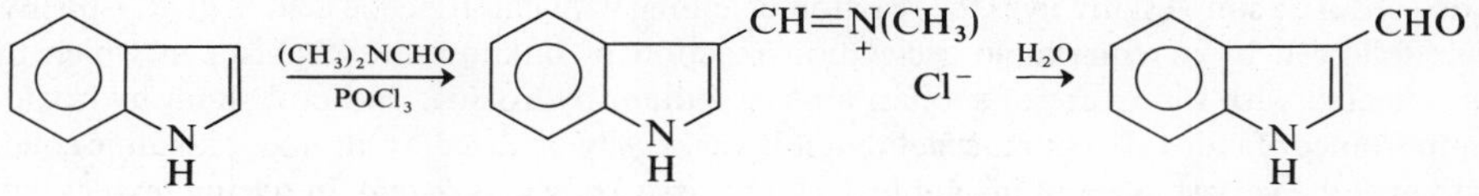

Indole-3-carboxaldehyde

The β position of indole is sufficiently nucleophilic to enter into the Mannich reaction (Section 21.3) with great ease. Thus, indole reacts at room temperature with formaldehyde and dimethylamine in acetic acid solution to give 3-(dimethylaminomethyl)indole, commonly known as *gramine*. Gramine was first characterized as a natural constituent of barley.

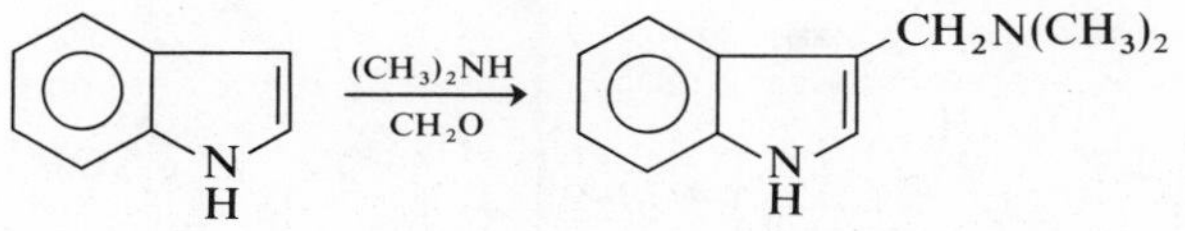

Gramine

The quaternary salts of gramine behave as if they were reactive halides, and they appear to undergo displacement of trimethylamine by a variety of anions. In reality, the reactions involve an elimination step followed by a Michael-type addition reaction (Section 19.17), as illustrated below in the synthesis of indole-3-acetonitrile.

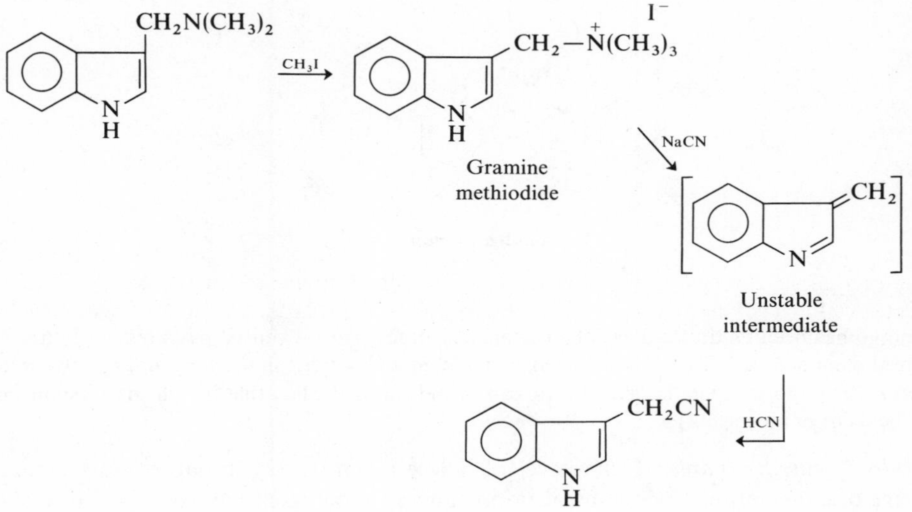

Gramine
methiodide

Unstable
intermediate

Hydroxyindoles. 2-Hydroxyindole is not stable as the enol but is well known as its lactam tautomer, *oxindole*. Oxindole forms by the spontaneous dehydration of *o*-aminophenylacetic acid, which is produced by the reduction of *o*-nitrophenylacetic acid.

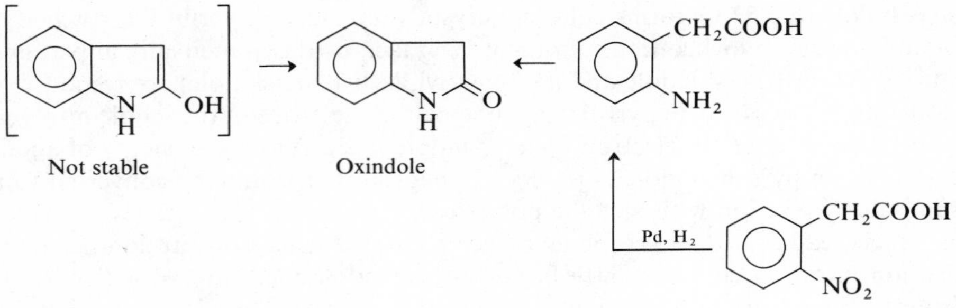

Not stable   Oxindole

3-Hydroxyindole is known as *indoxyl*, and it shows chemical properties attributable to both the enol and keto forms; it probably exists mainly as the enol. Many syntheses of indoxyl have been devised. The simplest involves the reaction of aniline with chloroacetic acid to give *N*-phenylglycine, followed by a remarkable cyclization reaction of unknown mechanism in which the latter is heated with a mixture of sodium amide, sodium hydroxide, and potassium hydroxide. The importance of indoxyl lies in the fact that it is very easily oxidized by air under alkaline conditions to give the very stable and insoluble dark blue dye known as *indigo*. In dyeing textiles with indigo, the indigo is first reduced by sodium dithionite in the presence of base to a soluble salt of leucoindigo. The textile is moistened with an aqueous solution of this soluble salt, and then exposed to air, which causes oxidation and precipitation of indigo in the fibers.

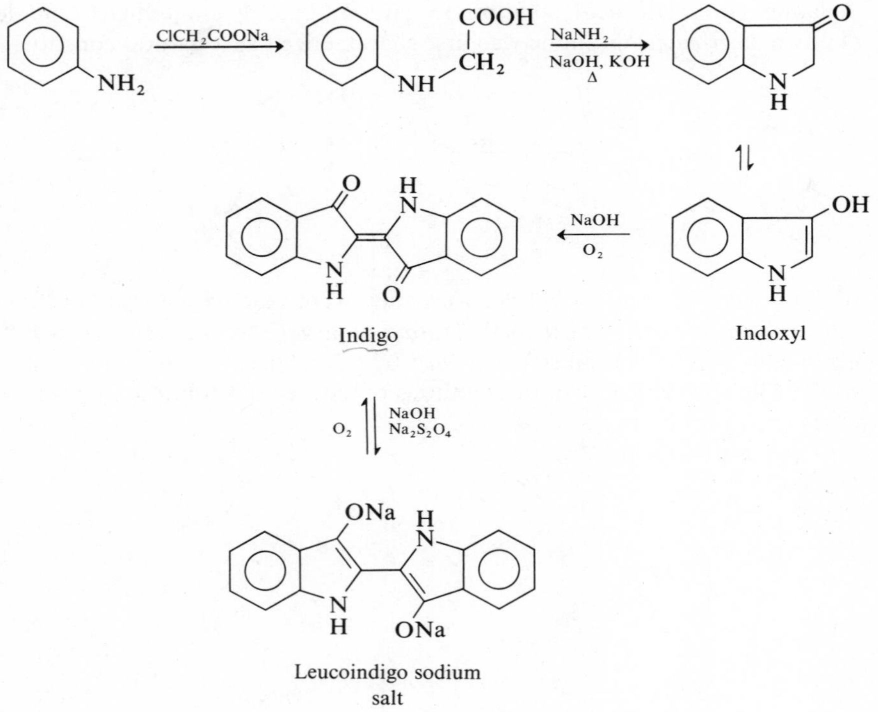

Indigo   Indoxyl

Leucoindigo sodium
salt

Indigo has been used as a dyestuff since ancient times, since it can be prepared easily from a natural plant source (*Indigofera tinctoria*), which contains indoxyl in the form of its β-glycoside, *indican*. (Its importance in modern culture can be judged by the fact that it is the dye responsible for the color of blue jeans.)

Naturally Occurring Indoles. Derivatives of indole occur widely in nature, and some of them are of considerable biochemical importance. Indole itself has been isolated from certain flower oils, including oil of jasmine. The most important single derivative of indole is the amino acid *tryptophan*. The biogenesis of tryptophan has not been completely elucidated, but it is believed to involve a condensation of serine with indole; the indole, in turn, appears to be formed from anthranilic acid and two carbons from the sugar *ribose*.

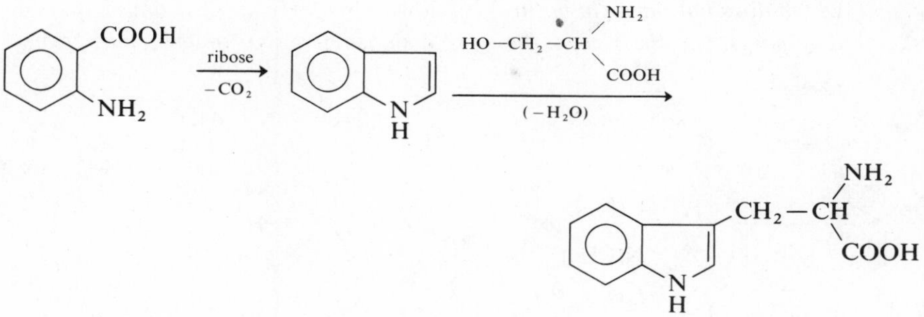

Tryptophan

Microorganisms, including intestinal bacteria, can cause degradation of the tryptophan side chain. Oxidative deamination of tryptophan gives indole-3-pyruvic acid, which is then oxidized to indole-3-acetic acid. Decarboxylation of the latter acid yields skatole (3-methylindole). Indole-3-acetic acid, known as *auxin*, occurs in plants, in which it functions as a growth hormone.

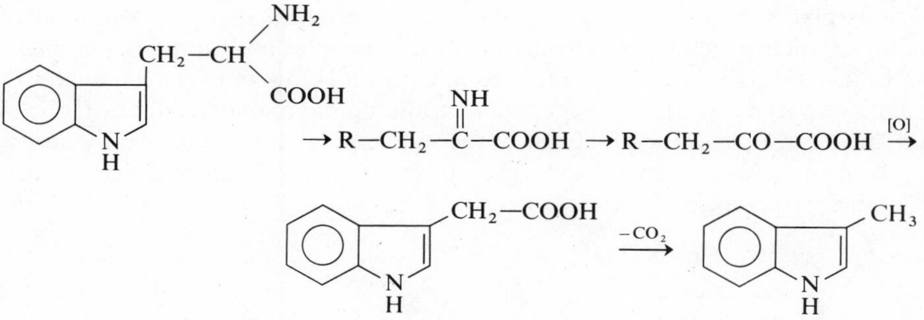

Indole-3-acetic acid
(Auxin)

Skatole

IMPORTANT COMPOUNDS RELATED TO TRYPTOPHAN. *Biological oxidation of tryptophan at the 5 position, followed by decarboxylation, yields an important hormone called serotonin. Serotonin affects blood pressure, promotes intestinal peristalsis, and even appears to be involved in mechanisms of psychic phenomena in the brain.*

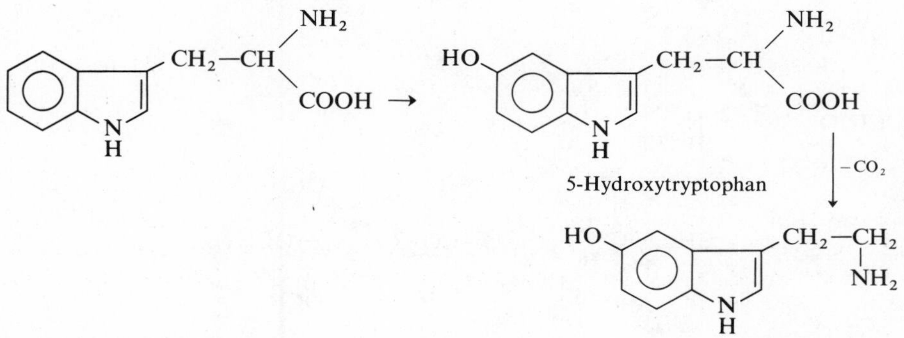

5-Hydroxytryptophan

Serotonin
(5-Hydroxytryptamine)

*Other derivatives of the decarboxylated form of tryptophan (tryptamine) produce
powerful psychic effects and are classified in the group of drugs known as* hallucinogens.
One of these is psilocin, *which occurs (mostly as a phosphate ester) in some species of
Mexican mushrooms. A much more complex structure of this type is* lysergic acid, *which
is produced by the ergot fungus in the form of peptide derivatives. The diethylamide of
lysergic acid (which does not occur in nature) is known popularly as* LSD *and is the
most active hallucinogen yet discovered, the effective dose being far under a milligram.*

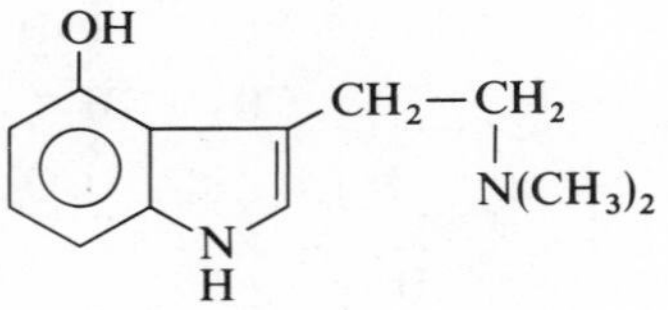

Psilocin
(4-Hydroxy-*N*,*N*-dimethyltryptamine)

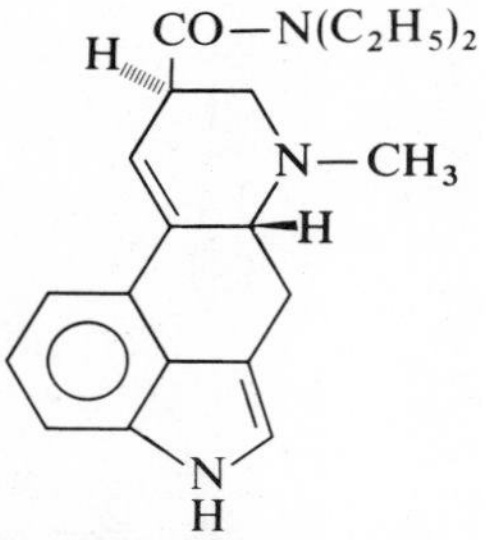

Lysergic acid diethylamide (LSD)

The *alkaloids* constitute the very broad group of complex heterocyclic bases, exclusive
of the nucleic acids (Section 28.9) and proteins (Section 29.1), which are widely distributed
in the plant kingdom. Of the several thousand or so alkaloids which have been isolated
from various plants, about 500 may be classified as *indole alkaloids*. It is beyond the
scope of this chapter to go into the chemistry of these complex and, at times, pharmacologically potent substances. A few structures are shown below in order to suggest the
variety and complexity of structure encountered among the indole alkaloids. It should
be noted, however, that in the plants all of the indole alkaloids are originally derived
from tryptophan by way of tryptamine; the "tryptamine unit" can be detected easily
in most of their structures.

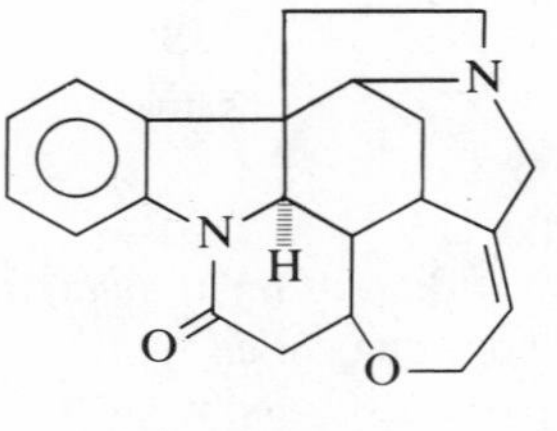

Strychnine
(a powerful poison)

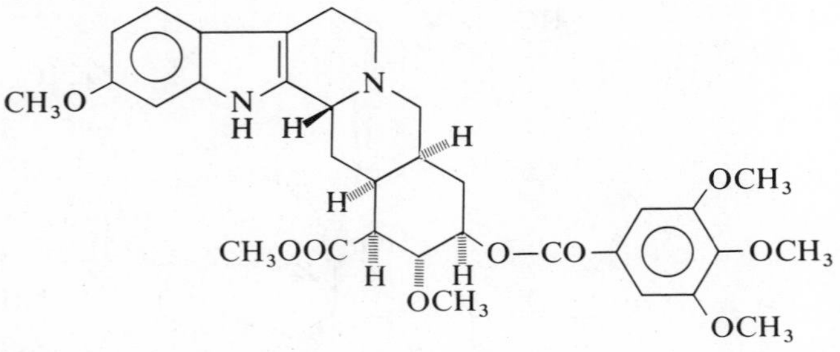

Reserpine
(a tranquilizer)

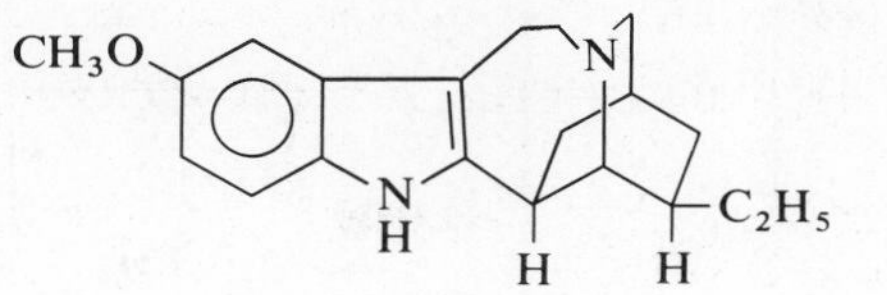

Ibogaine
(a stimulant)

28.6 Pyridine

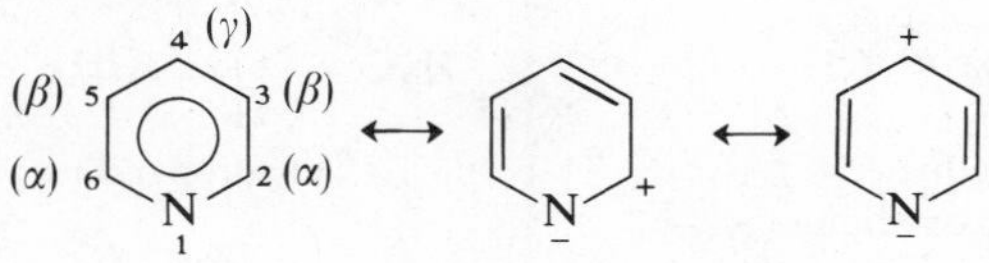

Ring atoms *deactivated* towards
electrophilic attack

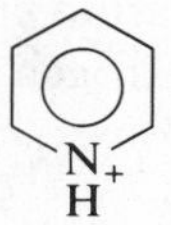

Pyridinium ion

The nomenclature of the simple pyridines requires special attention, since trivial names are generally used for the methylpyridines and for the carboxylic acids. Thus, the mono-methylpyridines are *picolines*, the dimethylpyridines are *lutidines*, and the trimethyl-pyridines are *collidines*. Note that three isomeric monosubstituted pyridines are possible, compared to only one analogous benzene derivative.

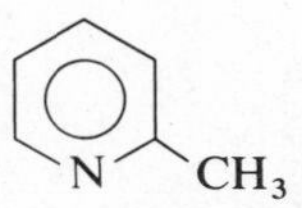

α-Picoline 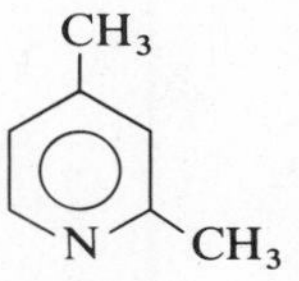   2,4-Lutidine 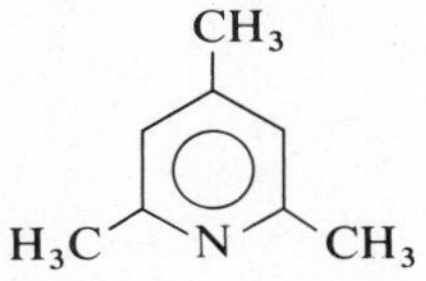   2,4,6-Collidine 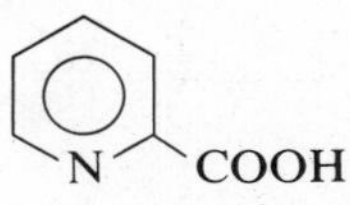   Picolinic acid

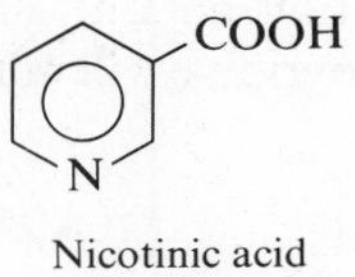

Nicotinic acid 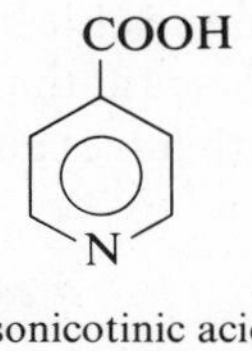   Isonicotinic acid

Pyridine and the simpler methylated pyridines occur in coal tar and are readily available commercially. Most other simple pyridine derivatives can be prepared from these compounds by interconversion reactions, just as benzene derivatives are almost always made from other benzene derivatives or from benzene itself.

Hantzsch Synthesis of Pyridines. A number of syntheses have been devised, however, in which the pyridine nucleus is created from open-chain precursors. The *Hantzsch synthesis* is illustrated below.

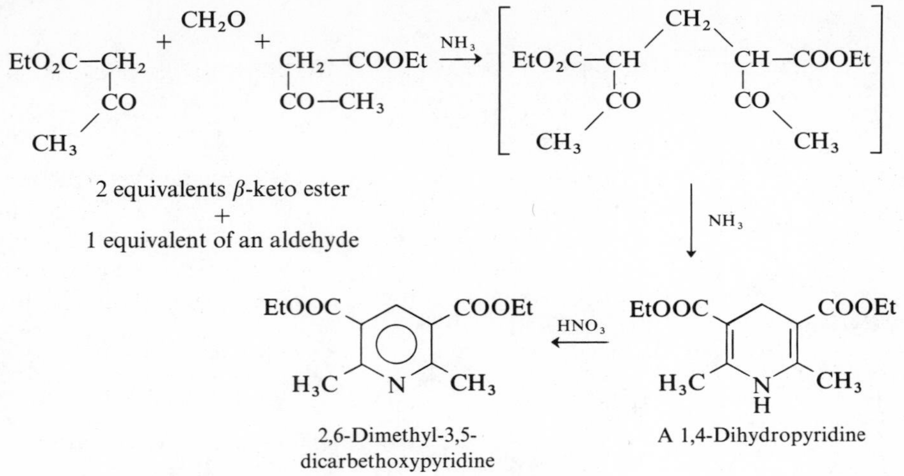

2 equivalents β-keto ester
+
1 equivalent of an aldehyde

2,6-Dimethyl-3,5-
dicarbethoxypyridine

A 1,4-Dihydropyridine

Chemistry. Pyridine itself (bp 115°C) is a water-miscible liquid with a very characteristic and disgusting odor quite different from the usual fishy odor of simple aliphatic tertiary amines. The pyridine system is greatly stabilized by resonance, its conjugation energy being 23 kcal/mole. In contrast to pyrrole, the lone pair of electrons on the nitrogen atom of pyridine does not form a part of the aromatic sextet of the molecule. Consequently, pyridine has basic properties ($pK_a = 8.6$ for the pyridinium ion) and forms stable pyridinium salts with mineral acids. In fact, since pyridine is a powerful solvent for most organic compounds, as well as a very stable base, it is commonly used as a scavenger for mineral acids in the synthesis of esters and amides from acid chlorides (Section 20.5).

Because of the greater electronegativity of nitrogen as compared to carbon, the significant dipolar resonance contributors to the pyridine molecule are those having a partial positive charge at the *alpha* and *gamma* positions of the ring. The pyridinium ion also has a partial positive charge at these positions, no charge separation being necessary in this case.

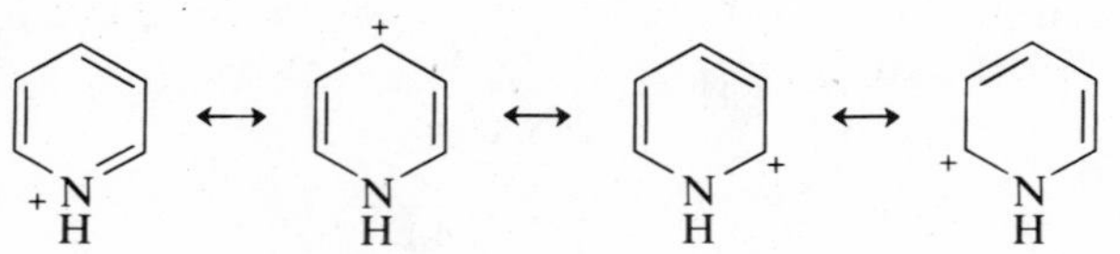

In both pyridine and the pyridinium ion, the entire ring is *deactivated* towards electrophilic reagents, but the *beta* positions (C-3 and C-5) are less deactivated than positions 2, 4, and 6, which bear a partial positive charge. The overall resonance picture is somewhat analogous to that in nitrobenzene. Electrophilic substitution into the pyridine (or pyridinium) ring, therefore, takes place at the β position, but only under very vigorous conditions, as illustrated below. As with nitrobenzene, pyridine will not undergo Friedel–Crafts substitutions at all.

Electrophilic substitution in pyridine

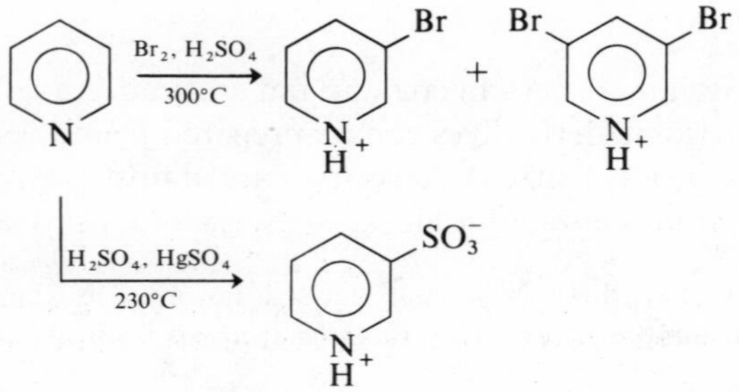

EXERCISE 28.6

Explain in terms of the Wheland intermediates why electrophilic substitution in pyridine occurs preferentially at the β position.

In contrast to both benzene and pyrrole, pyridine undergoes some unusual reactions with strong *nucleophilic* reagents. The most useful reaction of this type, discovered by the Russian chemist Chichibabin, involves the direct introduction of an amino group into pyridine by sodium amide to give 2-aminopyridine. Another example of nucleophilic substitution of pyridine is the reaction of pyridine with phenyllithium to give 2-phenylpyridine.

Nucleophilic substitution in pyridine

$+ H_2$

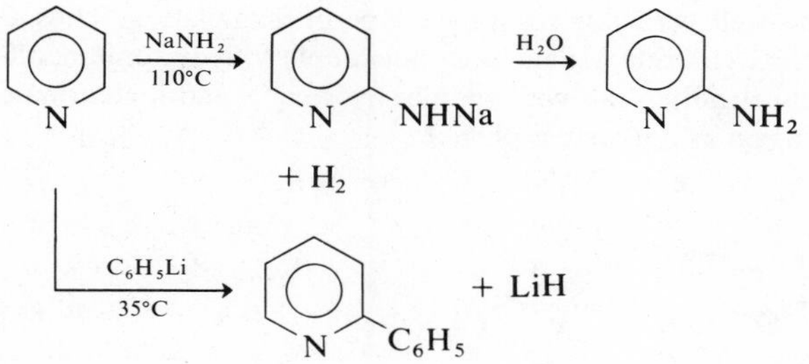

EXERCISE 28.7

Suggest mechanisms for the preceding reactions. Explain why these reactions occur, while analogous reactions do not occur with benzene.

The stability of a pyridine ring to oxidation is at least as great as that of a benzene ring which bears similar substituents. Thus, the pyridine carboxylic acids are easily prepared by the side-chain oxidation of alkyl pyridines. For example, oxidation of β-picoline or of nicotine (page 743) gives nicotinic acid.

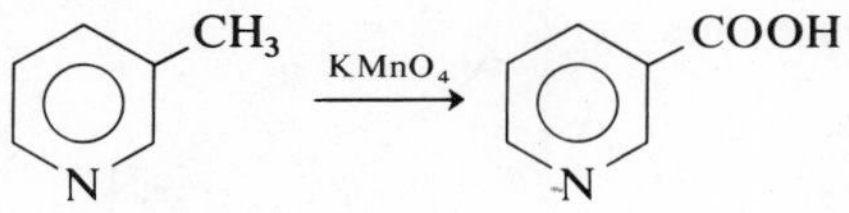

Nicotinic acid

In general, the catalytic reduction of pyridines to piperidine derivatives takes place more readily than the corresponding reduction of benzene derivatives.

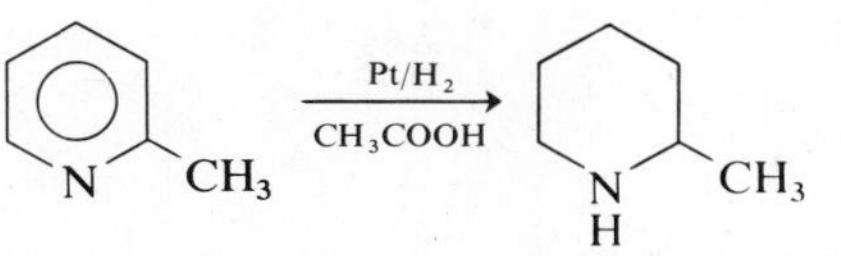

α-Picoline α-Methylpiperidine

Hydroxypyridines and Aminopyridines. 3-Hydroxypyridine has properties typical of those of a normal phenol; for example, it gives a colored complex with ferric chloride. 2-Hydroxypyridine and 4-hydroxypyridine are usually called α-*pyridone* and γ-*pyridone*, respectively, and are usually written as keto tautomers. They may best be viewed as resonance hybrids of the keto forms and dipolar pyridinium structures.

3-Hydroxypyridine   2-Pyridone   (pyridine contributor)
(a true phenol)

4-Pyridone   (pyridine contributor)

Their chemical properties correlate well with this resonance type of formulation. Thus, 2-pyridone is not phenolic: It gives no ferric chloride test and does not couple with diazonium salts. On the other hand, it forms a crystalline sodium salt with sodium hydroxide, and it chlorinates readily para to the oxygen-bearing carbon as if it were a phenol.

Similarly, of the three isomeric aminopyridines, 3-aminopyridine is most like aniline in its reactions. For example, diazotization of 3-aminopyridine gives a fairly stable diazonium salt which can be coupled with phenols to give azo compounds. In contrast, the diazonium salt formed by diazotization of 2-aminopyridine decomposes instantly to give 2-pyridone. All three of the aminopyridines are, however, true amines and not imino tautomers.

In addition to salt formation, the electron pair of the pyridine nitrogen can take part in reactions which result in the formation of stable transformation products. Thus, oxidation of pyridine with hydrogen peroxide in acetic acid gives pyridine N-oxide. Pyridine also reacts as a nucleophile with reactive halides to give N-alkylpyridinium salts.

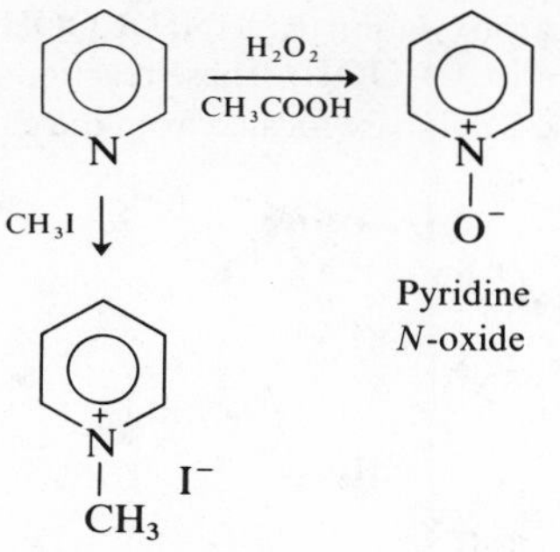

Pyridine
N-oxide

N-Methylpyridinium
iodide

Naturally Occurring Pyridines. A number of pyridine derivatives occur in nature and some of them play very important biochemical roles.

Nicotinic acid, in the form of nicotinamide, is a member of the vitamin B family. The complex quaternary salts of nicotinamide, known to biochemists as NAD (nicotinamide adenine dinucleotide) and NADP (nicotinamide adenine dinucleotide phosphate), play an essential role in fundamental oxidation–reduction processes of many types; among these are cell respiration reactions, fatty acid synthesis, photosynthesis, and the process of vision. The basic reaction involved, shown schematically below, is a reversible reduction of the pyridinium ion of the quaternized nicotinamide to a 1,4-dihydropyridine.

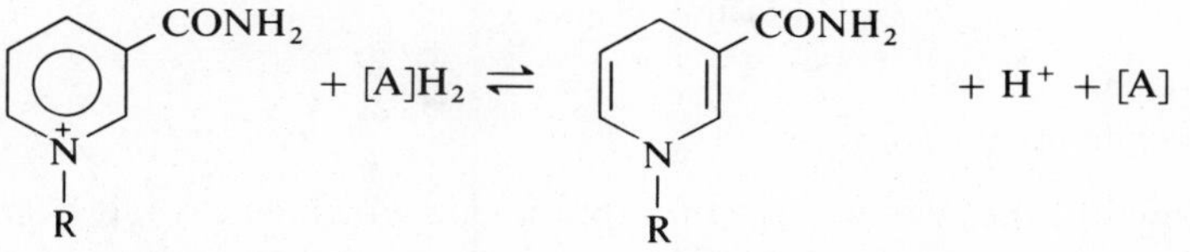

| A quaternized nicotinamide (NAD or NADP) | A reduced substrate | A 1,4-dihydropyridine (reduced NAD or NADP) | An oxidized substrate |

Nicotinic acid is produced in the animal organism by a remarkable degradation starting from tryptophan. As its name implies, it was first prepared in the laboratory by the oxidation of nicotine, the major alkaloid of tobacco. Nicotine, which is very poisonous, is a simple pyridine which bears a reduced pyrrole (pyrrolidine) unit as a substituent in the β position.

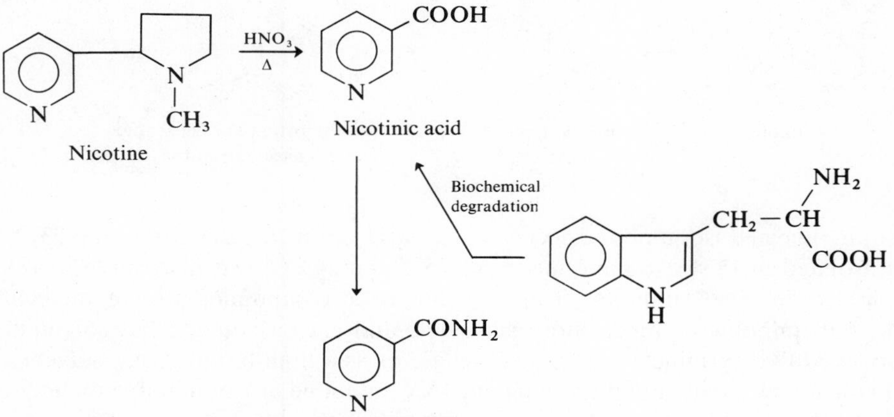

Nicotine

Nicotinic acid

Biochemical degradation

Nicotinamide

Pyridoxine. Vitamin B_6, or *pyridoxine*, is a derivative of 3-hydroxypyridine. Its oxidized phosphate ester, known as *pyridoxal-5-phosphate*, plays an essential role in a number of biochemical transformations of amino acids. Among these reactions are decarboxylation ($RCHNH_2COOH \rightarrow RCH_2NH_2$) and oxidative deamination ($RCHNH_2COOH \rightarrow RCOCOOH$). These reactions are believed to take place by way of a trivalent metal chelate of the Schiff base formed from the amino acid and pyridoxal-5-phosphate.

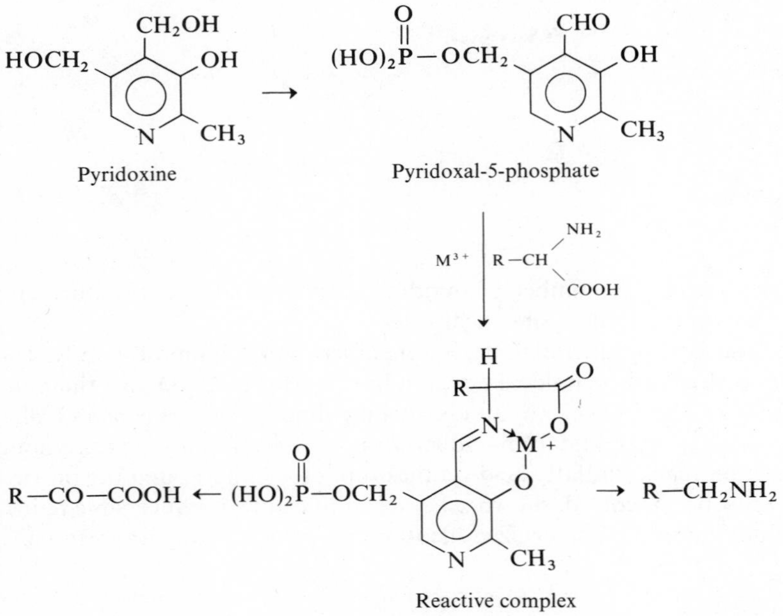
CH₂OH
HOCH₂
OH
N
CH₃
Pyridoxine
O
(HO)₂P—OCH₂
CHO
OH
N
CH₃
Pyridoxal-5-phosphate
M³⁺
NH₂
R—CH
COOH
H
R
O
N
M
+
O
O
R—CO—COOH
(HO)₂P—OCH₂
N
CH₃
R—CH₂NH₂
Reactive complex

28.7 Quinoline and Isoquinoline

Quinoline and isoquinoline are the two analogs of naphthalene which can result from the fusion of a benzene ring to a pyridine ring. The numbering systems and some of the principal resonance forms are shown below.

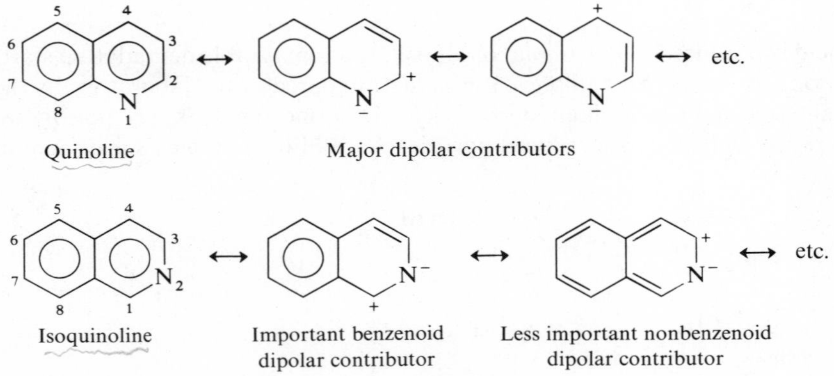
5
4
3
2
6
7
8
N
1
etc.
+
N
Quinoline
Major dipolar contributors
5
4
3
6
7
N
2
8
1
N⁻
etc.
Isoquinoline
Important benzenoid dipolar contributor
Less important nonbenzenoid dipolar contributor

Both quinoline and isoquinoline occur in coal tar, from which the former (bp 237° C) was first isolated in 1834. Isoquinoline (mp 26.5° C, bp 243° C) was discovered in 1885 as an impurity in crude quinoline from coal tar. Both compounds are commercially available, but quinoline is much more accessible and cheaper, and it has sometimes been employed like pyridine as an acid scavenger or as a high-boiling basic solvent.

In general, the nitrogen-containing ring of either quinoline or isoquinoline undergoes chemical reactions similar to those of pyridine, whereas the carbocyclic ring undergoes reactions similar to those of benzene.

Synthesis. Quinoline itself is easily synthesized by the unusual reaction known as the *Skraup synthesis.* In this reaction, a mixture of aniline, glycerol, and sulfuric acid is heated in the presence of a mild oxidizing agent, usually either nitrobenzene or arsenic pentoxide. The reaction proceeds by way of the dehydration of glycerol to acrolein, followed by a Michael addition of aniline to the acrolein, ring closure of the Michael product, dehydration, and finally oxidation of the resulting dihydroquinoline to quinoline. Although none of the intermediates is isolated, the overall yield of quinoline is quite good. The entire reaction scheme is outlined below.

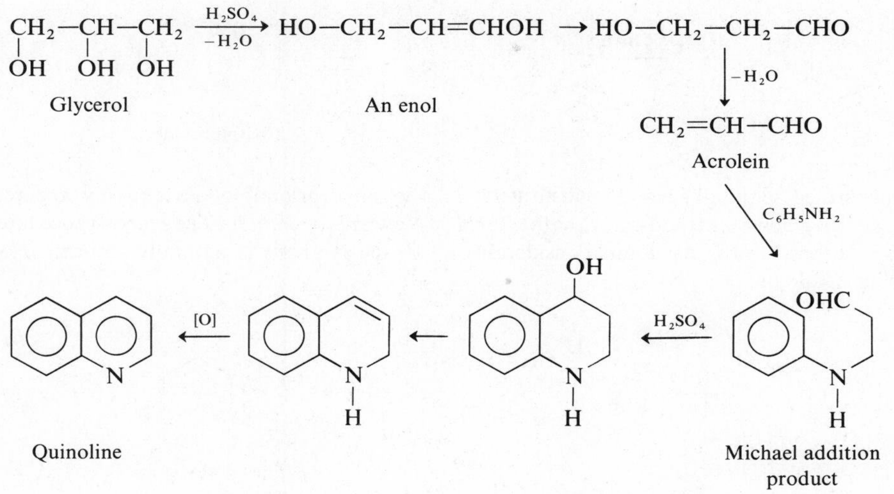

The Skraup synthesis is applicable to a great variety of substituted anilines; arsenic pentoxide is the usual oxidant in these cases, since nitrobenzene would be converted by way of aniline to quinoline itself, which would contaminate the desired product. Simple 2- or 4-substituted anilines give only one product, but 3-substituted anilines give a mixture of 5- and 7-substituted quinolines. *o*-Phenylenediamine can undergo a double Skraup condensation to give a tricyclic heterocycle, *o-phenanthroline*, which has found considerable use in analytical chemistry as a special indicator for redox titrations.

Substituted quinolines from the Skraup synthesis

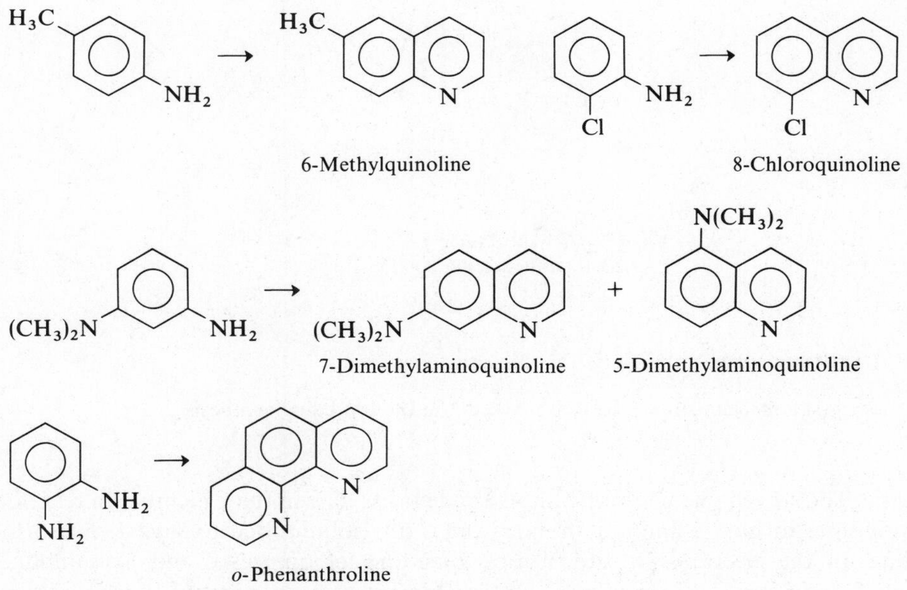

6-Methylquinoline

8-Chloroquinoline

7-Dimethylaminoquinoline

5-Dimethylaminoquinoline

o-Phenanthroline

EXERCISE 28.8

Write the structure of the product that will be obtained from each of the anilines listed, via a Skraup synthesis: (a) *o*-toluidine, (b) 3,5-dimethylaniline, (c) 1,4-phenylenediamine.

Isoquinoline may be synthesized from benzaldehyde by a cyclization reaction known as the *Pomeranz–Fritsch synthesis*. Benzaldehyde is converted to its Schiff base with aminoacetal (free aminoacetaldehyde is not used since it is unstable and condenses with itself); cyclization of this Schiff base by sulfuric acid gives isoquinoline.

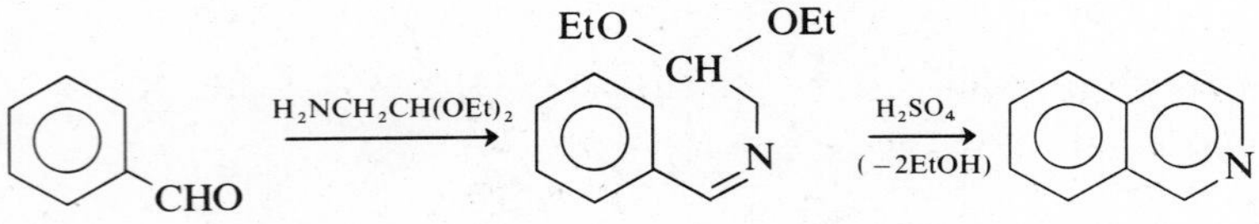

Isoquinoline

1-Substituted isoquinolines and 1-substituted 1,2,3,4-tetrahydroisoquinolines are easily prepared by use of a ring-closure method known as the *Bischler–Napieralski synthesis*. The general procedure, which is outlined below, has found considerable use in the synthesis of naturally occurring isoquinoline alkaloids.

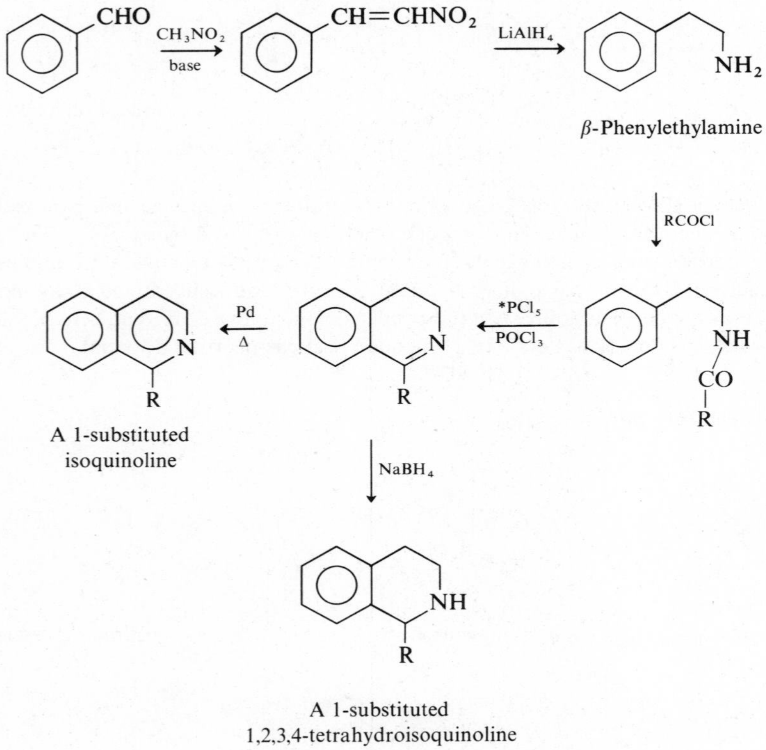

β-Phenylethylamine

A 1-substituted
isoquinoline

A 1-substituted
1,2,3,4-tetrahydroisoquinoline

EXERCISE 28.9

Suggest a mechanism for the step marked * in the preceding synthesis.

Chemistry. The strong nucleophile sodium amide takes part in the Chichibabin reaction with quinoline to give 2-aminoquinoline, and with isoquinoline to give 1-aminoisoquinoline. In the electrophilic substitution reactions of quinoline and isoquinoline, positions 5 and 8 are most reactive, C-5 being somewhat more reactive in isoquinoline and C-8 being somewhat more reactive in quinoline. For example, sulfonation of quinoline at 220°C gives quinoline-8-sulfonic acid. Alkali fusion of the latter gives 8-hydroxyquinoline (*oxine*), a compound which forms insoluble chelates with many metals and which has been much used in inorganic quantitative analysis.

Some transformation products of quinoline

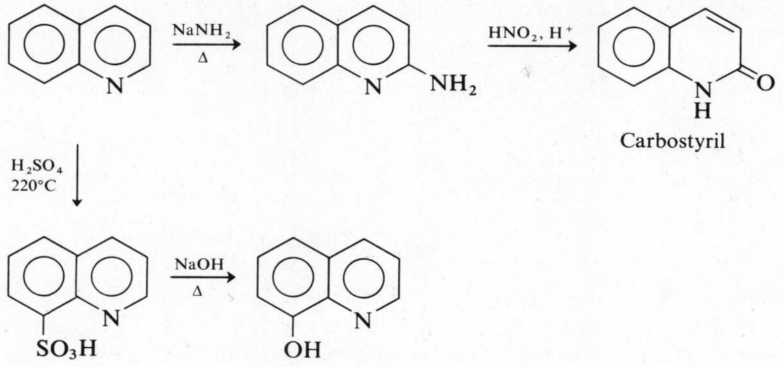

Carbostyril

8-Hydroxyquinoline
(oxine)

Some transformation products of isoquinoline

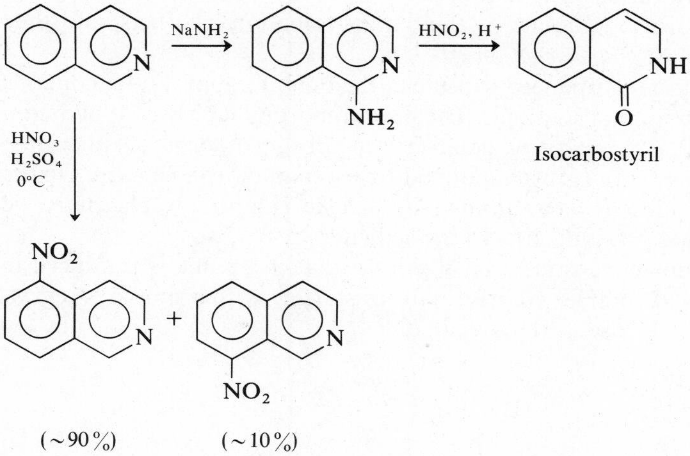

Isocarbostyril

$(\sim 90\%)$ $(\sim 10\%)$

Naturally Occurring Quinolines and Isoquinolines. A relatively small number of quinoline derivatives occur in plants as alkaloids. By far the most important quinoline alkaloid is *quinine,* a constituent of cinchona bark. Quinine is the longest known of the antimalarial drugs, and is still today the most effective agent against some of the most virulent strains of malaria. The quinoline ring system in quinine is believed to arise in nature by way of a complex degradation of the indole unit of an indole alkaloid precursor. Quinine has been synthesized [R. B. Woodward and W. von E. Doering, 1944], but it is still most cheaply prepared from cinchona bark.

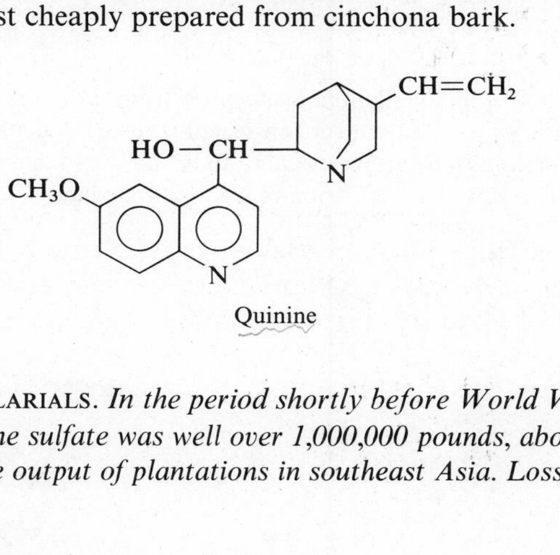

Quinine

ANTIMALARIALS. *In the period shortly before World War II, the annual world production of quinine sulfate was well over 1,000,000 pounds, about 90% of which originated from the output of plantations in southeast Asia. Loss of this area in 1942 to the*

Japanese armies led to very extensive government-sponsored programs in search of synthetic antimalarials. A number of useful antimalarial drugs have been developed. Some of these, such as chloroquine *and* primaquine, *are quinoline derivatives.*

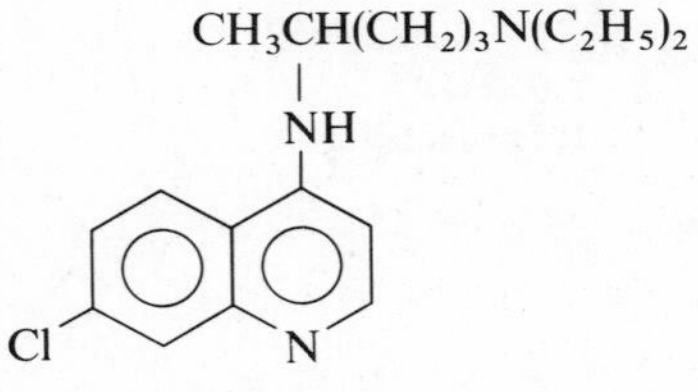

Chloroquine

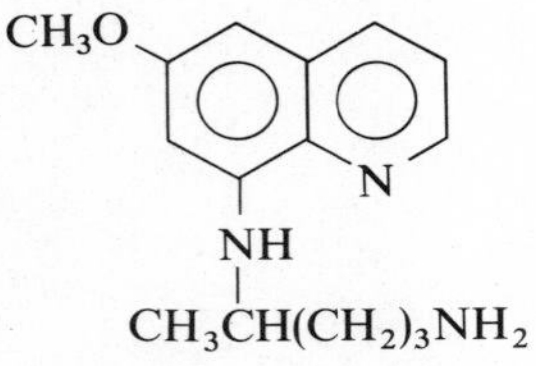

Primaquine

Unfortunately, it seems that new strains of malaria have recently appeared which are more or less resistant to some or all of the synthetic antimalarials. There seems to be a continuing need for new synthetic antimalarials to combat the new strains of the protozoan as they develop.

The isoquinoline ring system constitutes the common structural feature of several hundred alkaloids of highly varied structure. Most of these compounds are derivatives of 1-benzyl-1,2,3,4-tetrahydroisoquinoline or their transformation products, and they arise in the plant by way of *Mannich reactions*.

Opium is the dried sap of the unripe seed capsule of the opium poppy, and it contains about 30% of a complex mixture of alkaloids. The most important constituent of opium (and about 10% by weight) is the narcotic, habit-forming drug *morphine*. The diacetate ester of morphine, known as *heroin*, is even more addictive than morphine itself. On the other hand, morphine monomethyl ether, known as *codeine*, is both a weaker narcotic and less addictive, and it has been much used in medicine.

Recent studies using radioactive tracers have proven that morphine is produced in the poppy plant by a series of complex transformations starting with a simple 1-benzyl-1,2,3,4-tetrahydroisoquinoline base as the precursor.

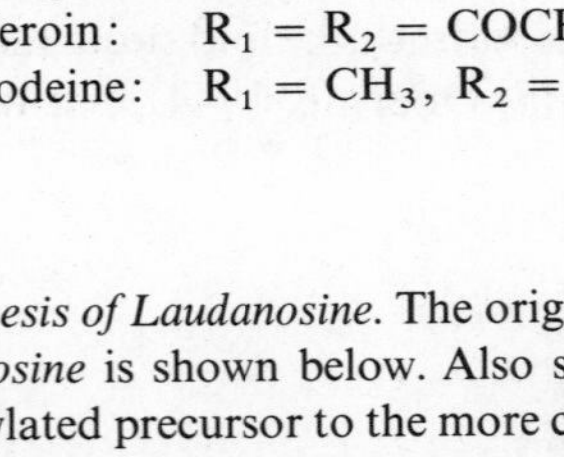

Morphine: $R_1 = R_2 = H$
Heroin: $R_1 = R_2 = COCH_3$
Codeine: $R_1 = CH_3, R_2 = H$

Biosynthesis of Laudanosine. The origin of the simple opium alkaloid *laudanosine* from the amino acid *tyrosine* is shown below. Also shown is the postulated conversion of laudanosine and its unmethylated precursor to the more complex alkaloids *tetrahydropalmatine* and *glaucine*. In these two compounds a new ring has been formed as a result of an oxidation reaction in the plant.

Tyrosine

3,4-Dihydroxyphenylalanine
(DOPA)

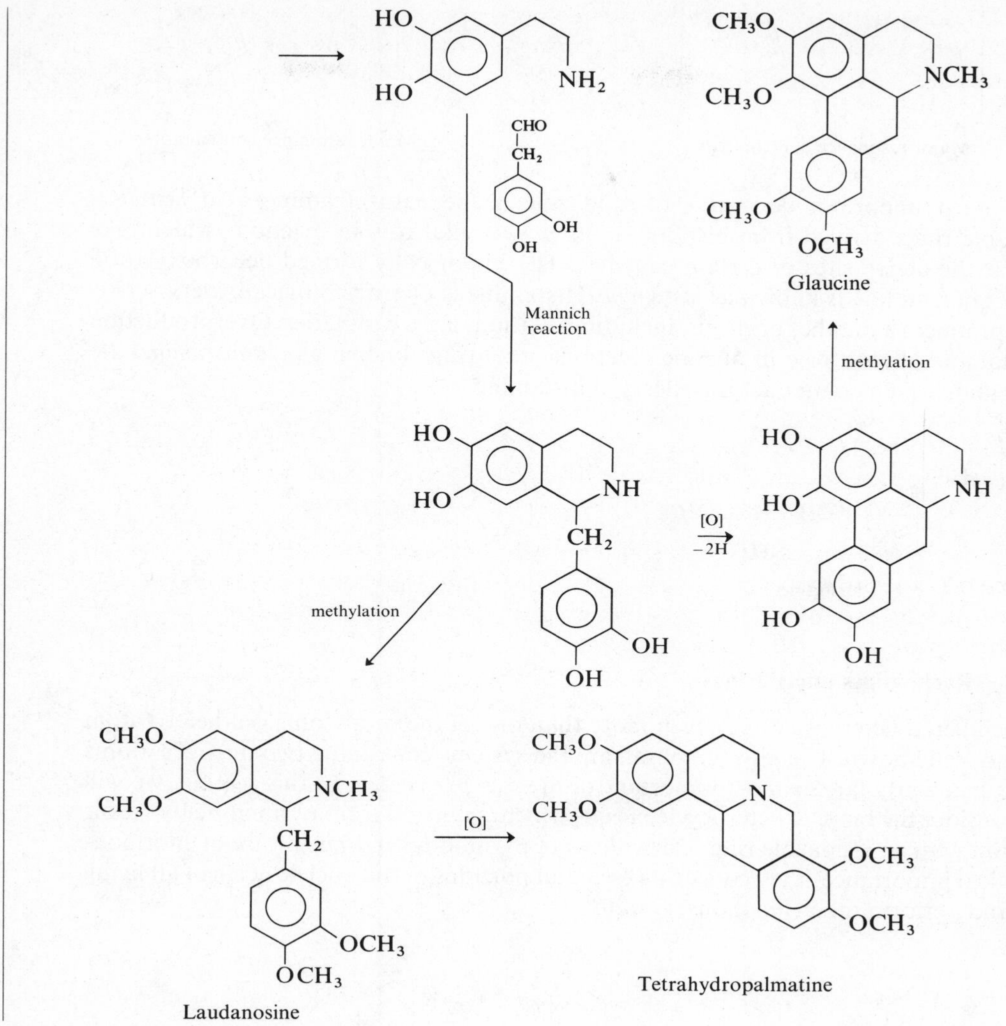

Glaucine

Laudanosine

Tetrahydropalmatine

28.8   Imidazole and Related Heterocycles

Many five-membered heterocyclic systems are known in which more than one of the ring atoms is a hetero atom (Section 11.8). A few of the more common of these are shown below.

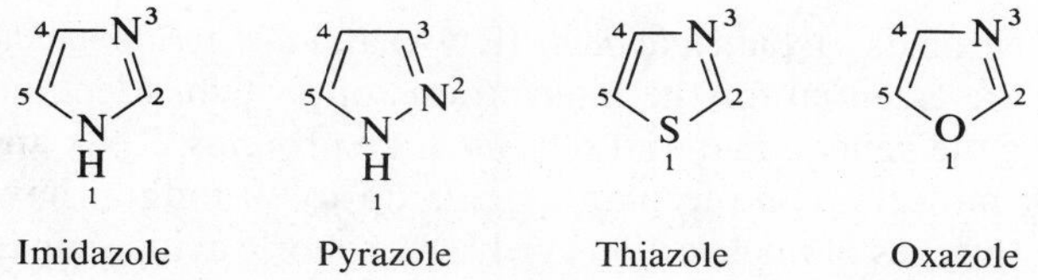

Imidazole   Pyrazole   Thiazole   Oxazole

The most important of these systems is *imidazole.* Imidazole (mp 90°C) is formally related to pyrrole, but it is much more stable than pyrrole to oxidation, reduction, and acids. Imidazole is not only more basic than pyrrole; it is even more basic than pyridine. The reason for this is that protonation of one of the two nitrogens (N-3) of imidazole does not destroy the aromatic sextet of the ring system. The protonated form, in fact, is particularly stable since two equivalent resonance structures can be written for it. Similar reasoning explains why imidazole is also somewhat more acidic than pyrrole.

Major resonance contributors   Major resonance contributors

The most important derivative of imidazole is the natural amino acid *histidine*. Imidazole rings derived from histidine units play a vital role in reactions which take place at the active sites of certain enzymes. The biologically formed decarboxylation product of histidine is known as *histamine*. Histamine is pharmacologically very active, and it produces a number of effects, including dilation of the capillaries. Overproduction of histamine plays a role in allergic reactions; the drugs known as *antihistamines* are compounds which counteract the effects of histamine.

Histidine   Histamine

28.9   Pyrimidines and Purines

Six-membered heterocycles in which more than one of the ring atoms is a hetero atom are also well known. The most common are the systems containing two nitrogen atoms shown below. By far the most important of these is *pyrimidine*. In this section, we will also consider the bicyclic heterocycle *purine*, which is derived from pyrimidine by means of fusion with an imidazole ring. Derivatives of pyrimidine and purine are of enormous biological importance; they constitute essential portions of the nucleic acids of all living cells and perform other functions as well.

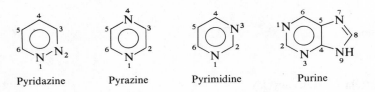

Pyridazine   Pyrazine   Pyrimidine   Purine

In the brief discussion that follows, we will consider neither the fundamental chemistry of purine and pyrimidine nor the methods of synthesis of purine and pyrimidine derivatives; instead we will concentrate our attention on the constitution of the vitally important *nucleic acids*.

Cells contain two types of nucleic acids, *ribonucleic acids* (RNA) and *deoxyribonucleic acids* (DNA). These compounds are essential for the biosynthesis of proteins (Sections 29.1, 29.10). DNA also constitutes the genetic material of cells. Like proteins, RNA and DNA are high molecular weight molecules; molecular weights up to 10 million have been observed. On hydrolysis, both types of nucleic acids yield phosphoric acid, a sugar, and a mixture of purine and pyrimidine bases. The sugar from RNA is *ribose*, while that from DNA is *deoxyribose*. The major bases from DNA are the purines *adenine* and *guanine* and the pyrimidines *cytosine* and *thymine*. RNA yields mainly adenine, guanine, cytosine, and another pyrimidine base, *uracil*. Note the biochemical abbreviations for these bases, given in parentheses.

Mild degradation of a nucleic acid yields a mixture of acids known as *nucleotides*. Each nucleotide contains the elements of one purine or pyrimidine base, one phosphate unit, and one pentose unit. The phosphate unit may be selectively removed by further careful hydrolysis to convert a nucleotide into a *nucleoside*, a molecule built up of a

DNA $\xrightarrow{\text{hydrolysis}}$ H_3PO_4 + β-D-Deoxyribose + Adenine (A)

Guanine (G) + Cytosine (C) + Thymine (T)

RNA $\xrightarrow{\text{hydrolysis}}$ H_3PO_4 + β-D-Ribose + Adenine + Guanine + Cytosine + Uracil (U)

pentose joined to a purine or pyrimidine base. In a nucleotide, C-1 of the sugar is joined to N-1 of a pyrimidine or N-9 of a purine; the phosphoric acid unit is present as an ester at C-5 of the sugar.

Adenosine (a nucleoside)

Deoxycytidylic acid (a nucleotide)

In a nucleic acid chain, the phosphoric acid is esterified to form a bridge between C-5 of the sugar of one nucleoside and C-3 of the sugar of another nucleoside. In this way, the sugar-phosphate units can form a long backbone or framework, which bears purine and pyrimidine base substituents at regular intervals. A typical segment of a DNA chain is shown.

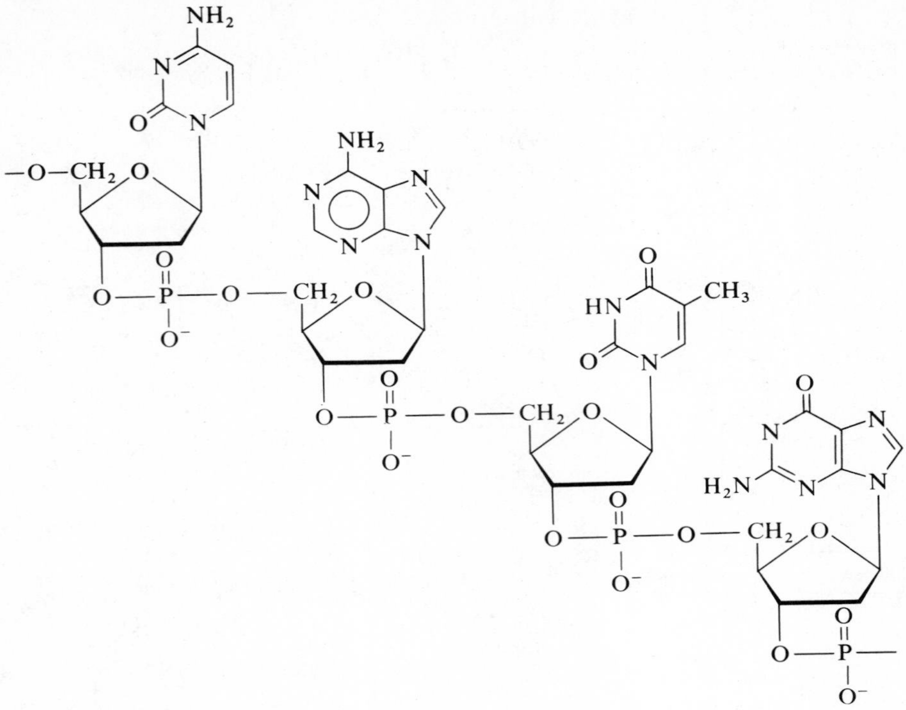

Watson[†] and Crick[††] in 1953 proposed the now-accepted double helical structure of DNA. According to their analysis, the DNA molecule actually consists of two complementary strands which are twisted about a common axis as helices having the same chirality (handedness). Each adenine unit of one chain is specifically hydrogen-bonded to a thymine of the opposite chain, and each guanine of one chain is similarly bonded to a complementary cytosine unit.

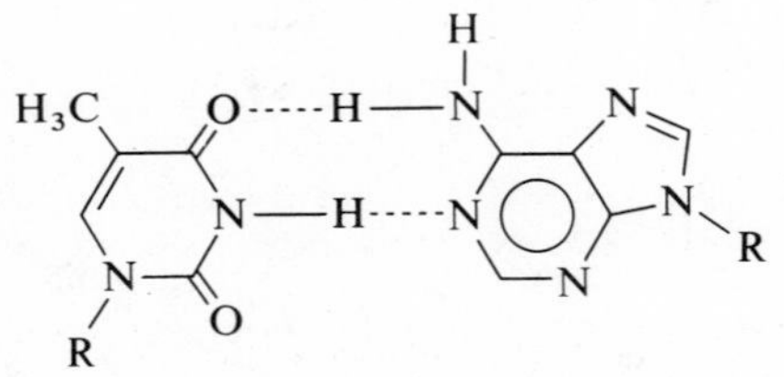

Thymine–adenine
(T to A)
hydrogen bonding

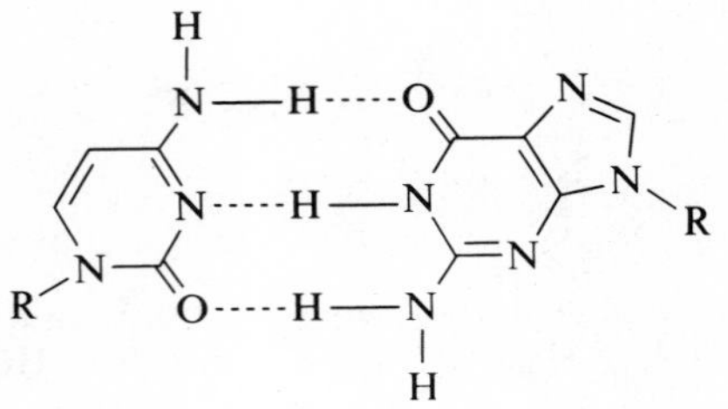

Cytosine–guanine
(C to G)
hydrogen bonding

The double helical structure of DNA is shown schematically in the drawing. The helical strands represent the sugar-phosphate backbones, which are held nicely in place by hydrogen bonding between the complementary base units. The order of the bases on the chain of the DNA molecule is extremely significant biologically: It is the fundamental source of the hereditary information of the genes.

[†] James D. Watson. Born 1928. Harvard University. Nobel Prize 1962.
[††] F. H. C. Crick. Born 1916, England. Cambridge University. Nobel Prize 1962.

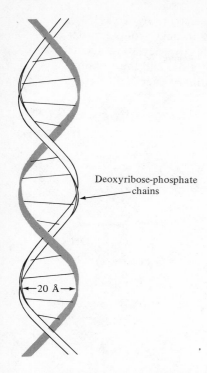

Deoxyribose-phosphate
chains

←20 Å→

A molecule of DNA reproduces itself by a remarkably simple mechanism. The two strands of the DNA molecule dissociate, and then free nucleotides hydrogen bond with the nucleotides of the dissociated strands. An enzyme catalyzes the polymerization of these free nucleotides in an order complementary to that of the original strands, producing two new double-stranded DNA molecules identical to the original one. It has been said that this simple process is the "secret of life." If not the secret of life, it is at least the secret of why children look much more like their relatives than like elephants or oak trees.

Nucleosides and nucleotides serve other very important biochemical roles as portions of essential biological catalysts (coenzymes). Adenine units are most frequently encountered in these compounds.

Numerous enzymes require the presence of a small nonprotein moiety more or less tightly bound to the protein for efficient performance of catalytic function. Since their nonprotein moieties are intimately involved with the overall reaction, they are termed coenzymes.

Examples of such nucleotides are the previously mentioned (page 743) redox catalyst NAD, and adenosine triphosphate (ATP), which functions as a pool for chemical energy in cells because of its energy-rich triphosphate unit.

Adenosine triphosphate (ATP)

Nicotinamide adenine dinucleotide
(NAD)

A third very important adenine nucleotide derivative is coenzyme A (CoA—SH), which plays a very significant role in biosynthesis, especially in acyl group transfer reactions (Section 30.2). Acyl derivatives of CoA—SH are effective acylating agents because of diminished resonance interaction between the sulfur atom and the carbonyl group, as compared with oxygen-carbonyl delocalization in ordinary esters.

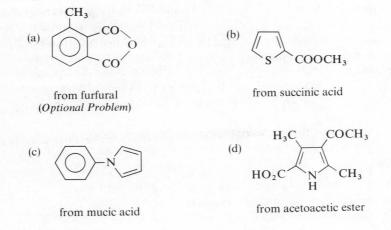

R = H; Coenzyme A (CoA—SH)

R = CH₃CO; Acetyl coenzyme A

PROBLEMS

1.   Outline syntheses for the following:

(a)

from furfural
(*Optional Problem*)

(b)

from succinic acid

(c)

from mucic acid

(d)

from acetoacetic ester

2.   Compare the acidities and basicities of pyrrole and pyrrolidine.
   (a) Which of the two is more basic and why?
   (b) Which of the two is more acidic and why?

3.   The blood of lobsters contains a blue copper porphyrin complex.
   (a) As a model for the lobster blood pigment, draw the structure of the Cu^{2+} pigment of octamethylporphin.
   (b) What charge, if any, does the complex of (a) have?

4.   Nicotinic acid plays an essential role in a number of biochemical reactions.
   (a) What type of nicotinic acid derivative is involved in these reactions?
   (b) What is the mechanism of action of these derivatives as biochemical reagents?

5.   Attempts to synthesize the isomers 4-methylimidazole and 5-methylimidazole have always given one and the same substance. Why?

6.   The nitration of pyridine with a mixture of HNO_3 and H_2SO_4 proceeds very slowly even at 200°C.
   (a) Give the theoretical basis of this observation.
   (b) What is the structure of the nitropyridine formed in this reaction?

7. Outline syntheses of the following:

(a)

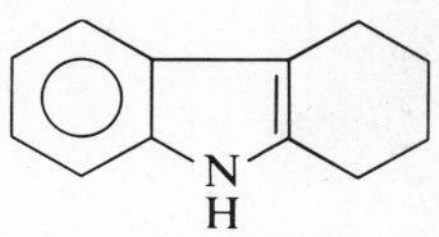

from cyclohexanol
(*Optional Problem*)

(b) 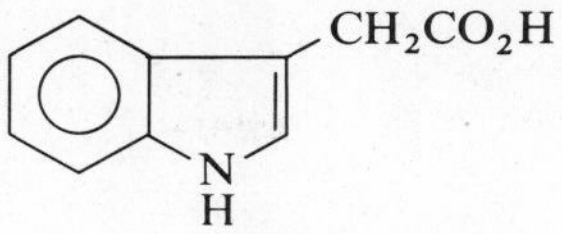 CH_2CO_2H

from indole
(*Optional Problem*)

(c)

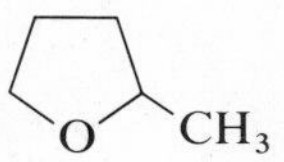

from arabinose

(d) 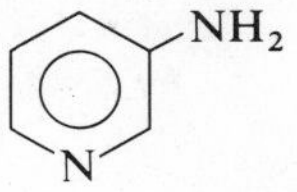 NH_2

from β-picoline

(e) 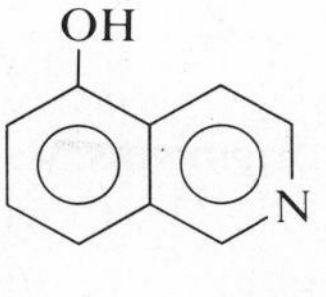 OH

from isoquinoline

8. Cells contain two types of nucleic acids, commonly referred to as RNA and DNA.
   (a) What do the abbreviations RNA and DNA stand for?
   (b) What are the similarities between RNA and DNA?
   (c) What are the differences between RNA and DNA?
   (d) In nucleic acid chemistry, the abbreviations A, C, G, T, and U are commonly employed. Give the structures and names for the compounds represented by these letters.
   (e) What is the chemical basis of the Watson and Crick double helix structure for DNA?

9. The nmr spectrum of a neutral compound C_6H_9N shows only unsplit signals at δ 2.07, 2.20, 5.73, 6.37, and 7.50 in the ratio 3:3:1:1:1. After brief shaking with D_2O, the broad signal at δ 7.50 vanished. What is the structure of the compound?

Optional Problems

1. 3-Hydroxypyridine is the only one of the three isomeric monohydroxypyridines which behaves as a normal phenol. Why?

2. Outline syntheses of the following:

(a) 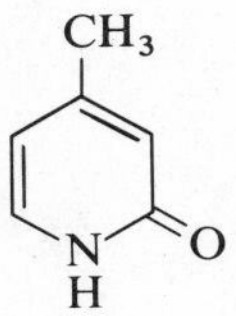 CH_3

from γ-picoline

(b)

CH_3

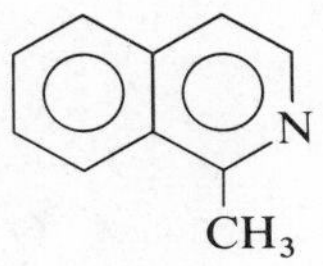

from benzaldehyde

CHAPTER 29

AMINO ACIDS, PEPTIDES, AND PROTEINS

29.1   Introduction

Of the three important types of organic polymers produced by living organisms, we have discussed two, polysaccharides and nucleic acids, in Chapters 27 and 28. The third class of biopolymers is the *proteins*, polymers of amino acids. These ubiquitous macro-molecules constitute nearly three-fourths of the dry material of most living systems, and, indeed, they are involved in the structure and function of every living organism.

Proteins are composed of α-*amino acids* joined together through amide linkages which are called *peptide bonds*:

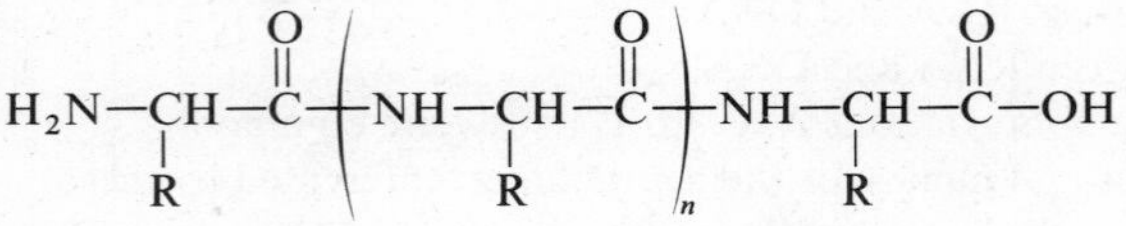

$$H_2N-\underset{R}{CH}-\overset{O}{\underset{}{C}}\left(NH-\underset{R}{CH}-\overset{O}{\underset{}{C}}\right)_n NH-\underset{R}{CH}-\overset{O}{\underset{}{C}}-OH$$

Partial hydrolysis of proteins by acids, bases, or enzymes yields smaller polyamides. Complete hydrolysis can be accomplished to give the individual amino acid components.

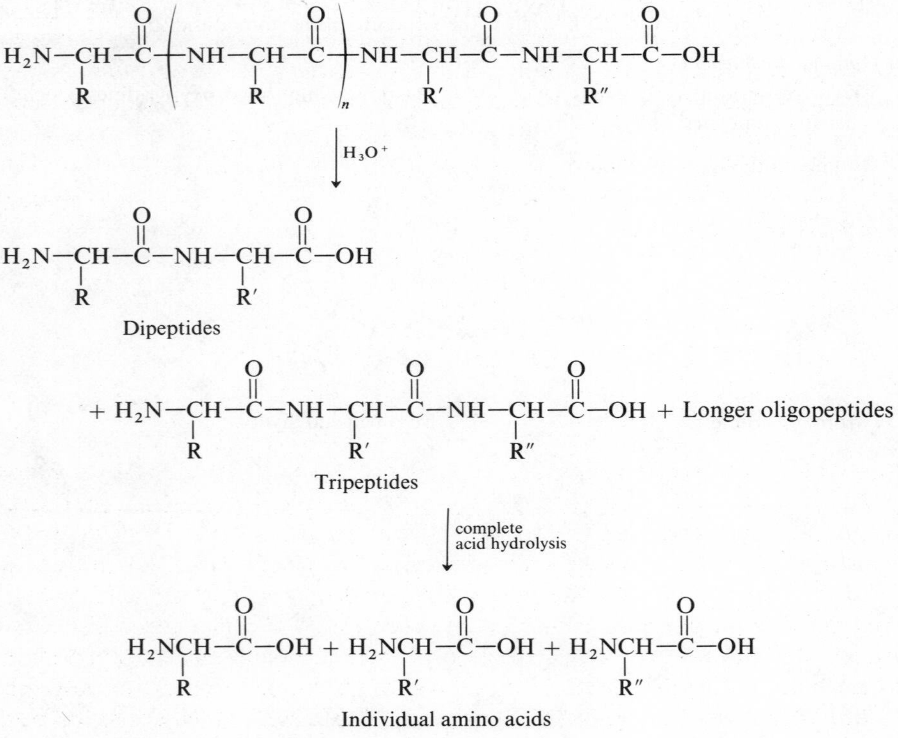

$$H_2N-\underset{R}{CH}-\overset{O}{\underset{}{C}}\left(NH-\underset{R}{CH}-\overset{O}{\underset{}{C}}\right)_n NH-\underset{R'}{CH}-\overset{O}{\underset{}{C}}-NH-\underset{R''}{CH}-\overset{O}{\underset{}{C}}-OH$$

$$\downarrow H_3O^+$$

$$H_2N-\underset{R}{CH}-\overset{O}{\underset{}{C}}-NH-\underset{R'}{CH}-\overset{O}{\underset{}{C}}-OH$$

Dipeptides

$$+ H_2N-\underset{R}{CH}-\overset{O}{\underset{}{C}}-NH-\underset{R'}{CH}-\overset{O}{\underset{}{C}}-NH-\underset{R''}{CH}-\overset{O}{\underset{}{C}}-OH + \text{Longer oligopeptides}$$

Tripeptides

$$\downarrow \text{complete acid hydrolysis}$$

$$H_2N\underset{R}{CH}-\overset{O}{\underset{}{C}}-OH + H_2N\underset{R'}{CH}-\overset{O}{\underset{}{C}}-OH + H_2N\underset{R''}{CH}-\overset{O}{\underset{}{C}}-OH$$

Individual amino acids

The molecular weights of proteins range from 6000 for insulin to 41,000,000 for the protein portion of tobacco mosaic virus. Polyamides of molecular weight less than 5000 are usually termed *polypeptides*. The large proteins are highly organized complexes of smaller subunits. In the case of tobacco mosaic virus protein, many identical subunits, each with a molecular weight of 17,500, are associated by noncovalent interactions. It seems likely that very few proteins of molecular weight greater than 100,000 will be found to consist of only one continuous polypeptide backbone.

The total book of instructions of any living system is contained in the *chromosomes* of every cell of that system. The genetic material is the nucleic acid DNA, described in Section 28.9. DNA has not only the critical function of reproducing itself, but also the important function of transferring information by causing the synthesis of a second type of nucleic acid called RNA (Section 28.9). This transfer of information from one place to another place using the same language (polynucleic acid) is called *transcription*. The major function of RNA is to transfer this information from nucleic acids to proteins. The transfer from one language (nucleic acid) to another language (polyamide) is called *translation*.

Some proteins are purely structural (skin, hair, and muscle fiber), many more have catalytic functions (enzymes), others have an overall regulatory function (hormones), and some participate in immunological defense mechanisms (antibodies).

Natural polypeptides achieve their ability to carry out biological functions by virtue of their specific sequences of amino acids and their exact three-dimensional arrangement of these amino acids. The first step in the study of a protein is determination of the amino acid sequence, called the *primary structure*. With the advent of more sophisticated techniques, increasingly detailed aspects of protein structure are being investigated. These include the nature of the spatial relationship of near neighbors, sometimes called the *secondary structure*; the gross folding of one chain, *tertiary structure*; and the spatial relationship of one polypeptide chain to another, *quaternary structure*.

29.2 Naturally Occurring Amino Acids

From all natural sources, over 100 amino acids have been isolated and identified to date. The great majority of these naturally occurring amino acids have the amino group attached to the carbon α to the carboxylic acid. With very few exceptions, the α carbon also bears a hydrogen atom. The fourth bond of the α carbon is joined to the group which has over 100 variations. Thus, most of the naturally occurring amino acids differ only in the structure of the organic residue attached to the α carbon. An interesting and important fact of protein chemistry is that all amino acids isolated from human proteins have the L configuration at the α carbon, although some amino acids isolated from microbiological sources are the mirror images (that is, in the D configuration) of amino acids isolated from human proteins.

L Configuration

Of the amino acids isolated from living material, only about 20 are naturally occurring components of proteins. The remainder are found as intermediates or end products of metabolism. All living species are able to synthesize amino acids. Many species, however, are deficient in their ability to synthesize within their own metabolic system *all* of the amino acids that are necessary for the life of their species. The eight amino acids with this special significance for the human species are called *essential amino acids* (Table 29.1). They are essential not because they are the only amino acids required for human functioning, but because they are essential in the *diet* of the human species since our cells cannot synthesize them. The other 12 amino acids (Table 29.2) which are found in the

Table 29.1   Essential Amino Acids

Structure	Name	Abbreviation
CH₃CH—CH(NH₂)COOH CH₃	L-(+)-Valine	Val
(CH₃)₂CHCH₂—CH(NH₂)COOH	L-(−)-Leucine	Leu
CH₃CH₂CH—CH(NH₂)COOH CH₃	L-(+)-Isoleucine	Ile
CH₃CH—CH(NH₂)COOH OH	L-(−)-Threonine	Thr
CH₃S(CH₂)₂—CH(NH₂)COOH	L-(−)-Methionine	Met
C₆H₅—CH₂—CH(NH₂)COOH	L-(−)-Phenylalanine	Phe
indole—CH₂—CH(NH₂)COOH	L-(−)-Tryptophan	Trp
H₂N(CH₂)₄—CH(NH₂)COOH	L-(+)-Lysine	Lys

Table 29.2   Other Common Amino Acids

Structure	Name	Abbreviation
CH₃—CH(NH₂)COOH	Alanine	Ala
HN=CNH(CH₂)₃—CH(NH₂)COOH NH₂	Arginine	Arg
HOOCCH₂—CH(NH₂)COOH	Aspartic acid	Asp
HOOCCHCH₂SSCH₂—CH(NH₂)COOH NH₂	Cystine	CyS-SCy
HSCH₂—CH(NH₂)COOH	Cysteine	CySH
HOOC(CH₂)₂—CH(NH₂)COOH	Glutamic acid	Glu
H₂NCH₂COOH	Glycine	Gly
imidazole—CH₂—CH(NH₂)COOH	Histidine	His
proline—COOH	Proline	Pro
HOCH₂—CH(NH₂)COOH	Serine	Ser
HO—C₆H₄—CH₂—CH(NH₂)COOH	Tyrosine	Tyr
H₂NCOCH₂—CH(NH₂)COOH	Asparagine	Asn
H₂NCO(CH₂)₂—CH(NH₂)COOH	Glutamine	Gln

biochemicals derived from human beings can be synthesized in individual cells from simpler starting materials containing carbon, hydrogen, oxygen, and nitrogen.

The various coexisting species have different sets of amino acids which they require but are unable to synthesize. However, all creatures contain within themselves all amino acids, so that any species may normally acquire its needed amino acids from others. Man may acquire his daily minimum of essential amino acids by eating such dishes as filet mignon from the cow, Dover sole from the fish, and eggs Benedict from the chicken. Vegetarians can survive because there are sources of plant protein that contain all of the essential amino acids. Rice has a high protein content, as do legumes (peas, beans). Corn, wheat, and rye are other grains that have a significant quantity of plant protein which includes the essential amino acids. Proteins eaten by humans (and other animals) are completely hydrolyzed to amino acids, and these are then used as building blocks to construct the proteins of the individual.

29.3   Chemical and Physical Properties of Amino Acids

Amino acids are high-melting solids which, because of their two polar groups, would be expected to be insoluble in organic solvents but soluble in water. Since the carboxylic acid function is acidic and the amino group basic, the amino acids actually exist as *dipolar ions* (*zwitterions*), rather than in the un-ionized forms shown in the previous section.

$$R-\underset{:NH_2}{\overset{|}{CH}}-CO_2H \;\rightleftharpoons\; R-\underset{^+NH_3}{\overset{|}{CH}}-CO_2^-$$

Amino acids with no ionizable side chains have two ionization constants, with pK_a's of about 2 and 9.

$$R-\underset{^+NH_3}{\overset{|}{CH}}-CO_2H + H_2O \rightleftharpoons R-\underset{^+NH_3}{\overset{|}{CH}}-CO_2^- + H_3O^+ \qquad K_a \sim 10^{-2}$$

$$R-\underset{^+NH_3}{\overset{|}{CH}}-CO_2^- + H_2O \rightleftharpoons R-\underset{NH_2}{\overset{|}{CH}}-CO_2^- + H_3O^+ \qquad K_a \sim 10^{-9}$$

If an electrical potential is placed across two electrodes in a solution of an amino acid, the amino acid will migrate to the anode or the cathode, depending upon the pH. At one pH, called the *isoelectric point*, there is no *net* migration of the amino acid because the concentration of the anion is the same as the concentration of the cation:

$$\left[R-\underset{NH_2}{\overset{|}{CH}}-CO_2^- \right] = \left[R-\underset{^+NH_3}{\overset{|}{CH}}-CO_2H \right]$$

The isoelectric point is an individual characteristic of an amino acid; for example, it is pH 6.0 for glycine, pH 5.5 for phenylalanine, pH 11.2 for arginine, and pH 3.2 for glutamic acid.

The amino acids with functional groups that are ionizable have ionization constants characteristic of those functional groups. For example, the side chain of glutamic acid has a pK_a of 4.3 and that of arginine has a pK_a of 13.2.

$$^-O_2C-\underset{^+NH_3}{\overset{|}{CH}}-CH_2CH_2-CO_2H + H_2O \rightleftharpoons {}^-O_2C-\underset{^+NH_3}{\overset{|}{CH}}-CH_2CH_2-CO_2^- + H_3O^+$$

$$^-O_2C-\underset{\underset{NH_2}{|}}{CH}-CH_2CH_2CH_2-NH-\overset{\overset{+NH_2}{||}}{C}-NH_2 + H_2O \rightleftharpoons$$

$$^-O_2C-\underset{\underset{NH_2}{|}}{CH}-CH_2CH_2CH_2-NH-\overset{\overset{NH}{||}}{C}-NH_2 + H_3O^+$$

Saturated carboxylic acids absorb in the infrared at 1725–1700 cm^{-1}. Amino acids, however, absorb at 1400 and 1600 cm^{-1}, absorption frequencies characteristic of the carboxylate ion. When a neutral amino acid solution is made acidic, the 1720 cm^{-1} carbonyl stretching frequency of the carboxylic acid appears. This is consistent with the proposed dipolar structures.

Amino acids undergo most of the reactions characteristic of carboxylic acids and aliphatic amines. Amino acid esters are relatively unstable, and they are usually obtained as hydrochloride salts. The amino group reacts with nitrous acid as do other aliphatic amino groups (Section 21.1). The accompanying evolution of nitrogen is, in fact, often used to analyze for free amino groups in amino acids and their derivatives.

29.4   Primary Structure and Biological Activity of Polyamides

The number of possible random combinations of the 20 or so amino acids found in hormones, enzymes, and all other proteins is almost infinite. However, biological activity is not achieved by randomness, but by a very precise ordering of the combined amino acids. Many scientists are now studying the primary structure—the amino acid sequence—of the polypeptides of biological importance for human beings. In this section we will give some examples of the relationship between sequence and activity for polypeptides of varying chain length.

Even a single amino acid may exhibit potent biological activity: for example, *thyroxine* is a hormone which is an active principle for animals which have a thyroid gland.

Thyroxine

This relatively simple molecule exerts a profound effect upon the metabolism of almost every cell in the body.

Oxytocin and bradykinin are both polypeptides composed of nine amino acids, but different acids and in different sequences. Their resulting biological functions are strikingly different.

Oxytocin is one of the most physiologically active compounds known.

Cy · Tyr · Ile · Gln · Asn · Cy · Pro · Leu · Gly(NH$_2$)

Oxytocin

Oxytocin is responsible for uterine contractions during childbirth and acts upon lactating mammary glands to stimulate the ejection of milk. It is interesting that only the female of the species produces this relatively simple polypeptide. It is even more interesting that this specific chemical is equally effective in causing a chicken to lay an egg or a cow to give down her milk to a farmer on a cold morning, or in causing a pregnant female human to give birth to a child. Chemically the oxytocin from chickens, cows, and hogs is identical. Oxytocin obtained from chickens is used clinically for the induction of labor.

Bradykinin is also a very active substance. It is released by blood plasma globulins in response to a wasp sting, and is a potent pain-causing agent.

Arg · Pro · Pro · Gly · Phe · Ser · Pro · Phe · Arg

Bradykinin

Obviously any change in the amino acid sequence of bradykinin or oxytocin, whether it was substitution, deletion, or addition, would result in a profound modification of the biological activity.

Larger natural polypeptides may perform the same function in different species without being *identical* in primary structure. For example, insulin, a hormone which controls carbohydrate metabolism, differs in the arrangement of 4 of its 51 amino acids in each of many different species. However, bovine insulin may be used to compensate for the insulin deficiency of human beings suffering from diabetes.

Proteins of more than 100 amino acids are transferred between species with difficulty because of immunological problems (discussed in Section 29.5). For example, enzymes which perform identical functions in different species cannot simply be transferred between these species. There are differences in the amino acid sequences which result in a recognizably changed three-dimensional structure (Section 29.5). Very large proteins such as those in hair, muscle, and skin are present in such a complex arrangement that, except for identical twins, no individual of a species can recognize and use the hair, muscle, or skin of another.

A more dramatic example of the importance of the amino acid sequence is provided by the polypeptide *globin*, the protein moiety of hemoglobin (see Section 28.4 for a discussion of the structure and function of hemoglobin). Globin has 146 amino acid residues in a very specific order, and for the human being, a substitution, a deletion, or an addition of even one amino acid to the number or the sequence may result in serious disease, or possibly death. The disease called *sickle cell anemia* is a molecular disease suffered by people whose globin differs from normal only in that the sixth amino acid in the series of 146 is valine, rather than glutamic acid. Victims of this disease, which is hereditary, are unable to utilize oxygen at the normal rate and therefore must avoid high, oxygen-rare altitudes and any exercise that is physically taxing on their red blood cells. The formula below shows the substitution that distinguishes the globin of a normal human from one who has sickle cell anemia.

Normal Globin
Val · His · Leu · Thr · Pro · *Glu* · Glu · Lys · · · ·

Sickle-cell Globin
Val · His · Leu · Thr · Pro · *Val* · Glu · Lys · · · ·

Under conditions of oxygen deficiency or abnormal physical activity requiring rapid oxygen metabolism, the red blood cells of people with this disease take the shape of a "sickle" or quarter moon, and they completely cease to function unless oxygen is administered effectively and immediately.

Enzymes are even more complex polypeptide material. Every living cell contains thousands of enzymes, each of which is responsible for catalyzing a single specific chemical reaction. The complete chemical structure has been elucidated for several enzymes. Recently, one enzyme, *ribonuclease*, containing 124 amino acids in a specific sequence, has been synthesized (Section 29.9). *Chymotrypsin* has been purified to the point where it has crystallized and the precise number of amino acid residues (246) and their precise sequence have been determined. X-Ray structure determination has established its three-dimensional structure at a resolution of better than 3 Å. At this resolution individual atoms cannot be discerned, but the overall shape, and the twists and turns of various segments can be seen (Section 29.7).

29.5   Immunochemistry

The human body reacts immediately whenever it is subjected to the introduction of any foreign substance, including larger polypeptides. It examines alien material very carefully for unfamiliar chemical structural characteristics and, should it recognize any, it causes the production of the specific polypeptide which is able to specifically bind to the foreign matter, so precipitating it from the surrounding medium.

In immunological terms, any such foreign substance is an *antigen*. The main encasing protein is gamma globulin of the blood of the host and is called an *antibody*. By a mechanism not completely understood, this initial antigen–antibody reaction elicits the production of greater amounts of the specific antibody required. Excess antibodies remain in the bloodstream, where they afford the body a specific type of immunity for as long as they remain in excess. Should the offending antigen return while they are present, it will immediately be precipitated and the body will suffer no harmful effects. Unfortunately, immunity is not necessarily a permanent condition; its duration may range from several hours to a lifetime, depending on the nature of the antigen. Thus, immunity from smallpox is normally long-term, while that from the common cold lasts only a matter of days or weeks.

It is important to note that immunity is highly specific for a given antigen. Each new foreign cell that invades the body elicits a new supply of specific antibodies, which are stored in the blood as gamma globulins. Quite obviously, the gamma globulin blood fractions of individuals will vary to the extent to which they have been exposed to different foreign cells.

In this antigen–antibody phenomenon, we have a more precise explanation for the failure of skin and kidney and heart transplants among individual members of the same species. The body of the receptor looks upon the skin or kidney cells of the donor as foreign matter and immediately sets up an antibody-type rejection mechanism. Only between identical siblings, whose bodies are made up of protein materials that have identical structures and are therefore not "foreign," can such transplants be successful. One approach used today is to attempt to suppress production of gamma globulins. Drugs are known which accomplish this purpose. The patient is then able to receive a foreign substance, for example, a heart, but has lost immunity and is therefore susceptible to all diseases from which he had previously been cured. Further, globulin synthesized in the body after the heart transplant still does not accept the heart as nonforeign material and finally rejects it by the antibody–antigen reaction.

29.6   Determination of the Structures of Peptides

In naming peptides, *amino* or *N-terminal end* refers to the end with the free amino group and *carboxy* or *C-terminal end* refers to the end with the free carboxyl group. By convention, the *N*-terminal end is written to the left and the *C*-terminal end to the right. The amino acids are then named left to right, replacing *ine* with *yl*, except for the *C*-terminal amino acid, as in the example shown.

$$\underset{\substack{(CH_3)_2CH-CH_2}}{H_2N-CH}-\overset{\overset{\displaystyle O}{\|}}{C}-NH-\underset{\substack{CH_3}}{CH}-\overset{\overset{\displaystyle O}{\|}}{C}-NH-\underset{\substack{CH_2CH_2-S-CH_3}}{CH}-\overset{\overset{\displaystyle O}{\|}}{C}-OH \qquad (Leu \cdot Ala \cdot Met)$$

Leucylalanylmethionine

The first step in determining the primary structure of a peptide is to hydrolyze it to its individual amino acids and to assess which ones are present and how many of each.

Analysis of Amino Acids. Peptides are hydrolyzed in $6N$ HCl at $105°C$; base cannot be used because it racemizes the α carbons. Tryptophan is sensitive to acid and is partially destroyed in the hydrolysis, which can be corrected for in quantitative studies. Instead of glutamine and asparagine, ammonia, glutamic, and aspartic acids are isolated.

The mixture of amino acids obtained upon hydrolysis can be separated and analyzed by use of an "amino acid analyzer." In this automatic equipment, aliquots of the mixture of amino acids are placed on separate columns of a sulfonic acid ion exchange resin. One column is held at pH 5.3 and used for basic amino acids, ammonia, and tryptophan. A second is held at pH 3.25 for the other amino acids while 0 to 250 ml of elutant pass through the column; the pH is then increased to 4.25 while 250–500 ml of elutant pass through. Sodium citrate buffer solutions elute the acids, and the eluted solutions are mixed with ninhydrin and heated.

The reagent *ninhydrin* produces a blue color with primary α-amino acids by the following series of reactions:

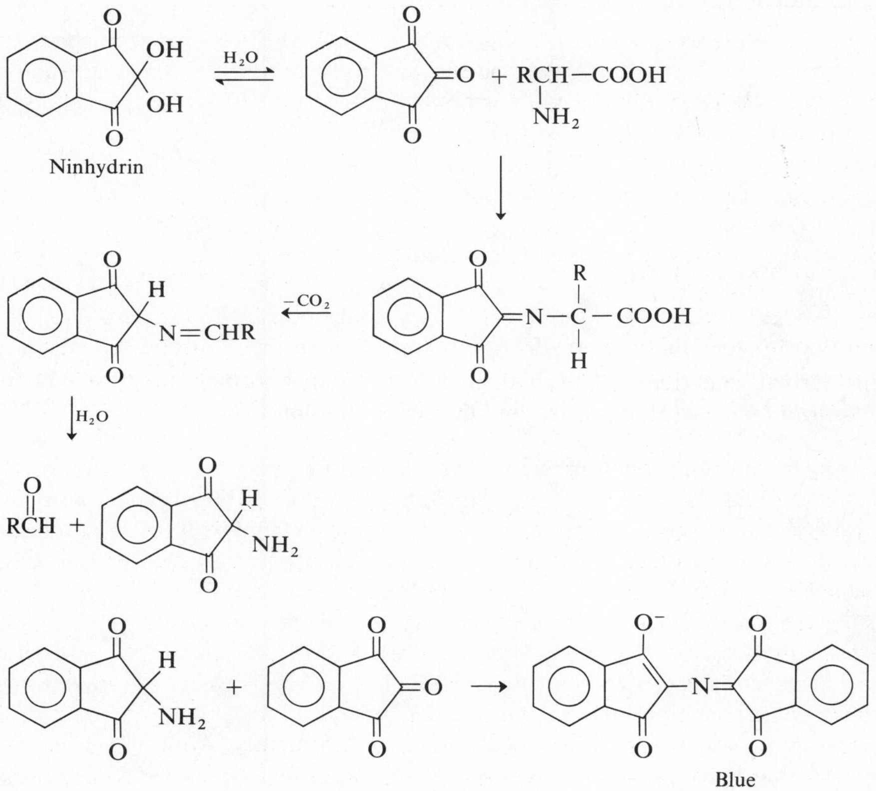

A spectrophotometer measures the optical absorption of the products of the ninhydrin reaction, and the recorder continuously plots the milliliters of eluate versus intensity of the ninhydrin color. The position of the absorption peak (in ml), which depends on the volume of buffer needed to elute a particular amino acid, is characteristic for each amino acid; the quantity of the acids is obtained from the areas under their peaks.

Gas chromatography is also useful for analyzing mixtures of small amounts of amino acids. Amino acids are too nonvolatile to be studied directly; their esters, for example, trimethylsilyl esters, have sufficient volatility, however.

After determining the identities of the amino acids present, and their ratios, the next big problem is to determine the sequence of the amino acids in a peptide.

One common technique used to determine the N-terminal amino acid is to allow the amino group to react with 1-fluoro-2,4-dinitrobenzene (nucleophilic aromatic substitution, Section 17.8) and then to hydrolyze the peptide:

The N-(2,4-dinitrophenyl) derivative is isolated and identified.

An alternate procedure for determination of the N-terminal amino acid, which does not hydrolyze the peptide, is called *Edman degradation*. An N-phenylthiocarbamyl derivative is prepared with phenyl isothiocyanate.

When this derivative is treated with hydrogen chloride in nitromethane or acetic acid, a thiohydantoin forms without destroying the remaining linkages.

The thiohydantoin is identified and the nature of its R group characterizes the N-terminal amino acid. This procedure can be continued on the remaining chain; there is now available commerically an automated procedure which the manufacturer claims will perform 30 successive Edman degradations on a purified protein.

To determine the *C*-terminal end, the peptide can be heated with anhydrous hydrazine to convert the amide linkages in the chain into hydrazides:

$$H_2N-\underset{R^1}{CH}-\overset{O}{\overset{\|}{C}}-NH-\underset{R^2}{CH}-\overset{O}{\overset{\|}{C}}-(\underset{R^x}{NHCH}-\overset{O}{\overset{\|}{C}})_n-NH-\underset{R^3}{CH}-\overset{O}{\overset{\|}{C}}OH$$

C-Terminal amino acid

$$\downarrow \text{NH}_2\text{NH}_2$$

$$H_2N-\underset{R^1}{CH}\overset{O}{\overset{\|}{C}}NHNH_2, \quad H_2N\underset{R^2}{CH}\overset{O}{\overset{\|}{C}}NHNH_2, \text{ etc.,} \quad + \quad H_2N\underset{R^3}{CH}\overset{O}{\overset{\|}{C}}OH$$

Free *C*-terminal
amino acid

The *C*-terminal amino acid is identified as the free acid, whereas the others in the chain are obtained as hydrazides.

Certain carboxypeptidases, which are enzymes obtained from the pancreas, attack *C*-terminal peptide bonds and free the *C*-terminal amino acid. However, they continue acting on the remaining peptide and systematically liberate the newly formed *C*-terminal acids; for example,

$$\text{Phe} \cdot \text{Ala} \cdot \text{Gly} \cdot \text{Met} \cdot \text{Glu} \xrightarrow{\text{carboxypeptidase}} \text{Phe} \cdot \text{Ala} \cdot \text{Gly} \cdot \text{Met} + \text{Glu}$$
$$\downarrow$$
$$\text{Phe} \cdot \text{Ala} \cdot \text{Gly} + \text{Met}$$
$$\downarrow$$
$$\text{etc.}$$

The action of the enzyme cannot be stopped after it has released Glu. The enzyme proceeds to attack the tetrapeptide and release Met, and then to attack the tripeptide, and so on. Thus, the sequence of only a limited number of units can be obtained before the situation gets too mixed up to sort out. The identities of the amino acids which are freed are determined as a function of incubation time, and as much sequencing is done as is possible from the data. If the *C*-terminal end is in the form of the amide, carboxypeptidase does not act to free it.

To illustrate some of the techniques employed in amino acid sequence determination, we will follow an example of such a determination. Using an amino acid analyzer and a crude molecular weight determination, α-MSH, a melanocyte-stimulating hormone from pituitary glands, was found to have the molecular formula: (Arg,Glu,Gly,His,Lys, Met,Phe,Pro,Ser$_2$,Trp,Tyr,Val,NH$_3$). The commas between the abbreviations indicate that the sequence is unknown or unspecified. The acids were present in equimolar quantities, except for serine.

No *N*-terminal amino acid was found in the Edman degradation or dinitrophenylation reaction and no *C*-terminal amino acid was liberated by carboxypeptidase. As we will see later, this is due to tie-up of the the *N*-terminal end as the *N*-acetyl derivative and the *C*-terminal as the amide:

$$\text{CH}_3\overset{O}{\overset{\|}{C}}\text{NH}-(\alpha\text{-MSH})-\overset{O}{\overset{\|}{C}}\text{NH}_2$$

It could also have meant that the peptide chain was cyclic. Thus, the amino group and the carboxyl group must be free if these procedures are to work.

Chymotrypsin, another pancreatic enzyme, preferentially attacks peptide bonds whose carbonyl function is furnished by one of the aromatic amino acids tyrosine, tryptophan, and phenylalanine, although it will also catalyze the hydrolysis of bonds with leucine, methionine, asparagine, and glutamine. After chymotryptic hydrolysis of α-MSH, three peptide fragments were isolated:

$$(\text{Arg,Glu,Gly,His,Lys,Met,Phe,Pro,Ser}_2,\text{Trp,Tyr,Val,NH}_3) \xrightarrow{\text{chymotrypsin}}$$

$$(\text{Ser,Tyr}) + (\text{Glu,His,Met,Phe,Ser}) + (\text{Arg,Gly,Lys,Pro,Trp,Val})$$

Analysis of the serine in the dipeptide (Ser,Tyr) showed it to be in the form of the *N*-acetyl derivative. Thus, Ser · Tyr is the *N*-terminal end of α-MSH, and a partial structure of α-MSH is

$$\underset{\text{CH}_3\overset{\displaystyle\text{O}}{\overset{\|}{\text{C}}}\text{-Ser}\cdot\text{Tyr}}{}\cdots\left\{\begin{matrix}(\text{Glu,His,Met,Phe,Ser})\\(\text{Arg,Gly,Lys,Pro,Trp,Val})\end{matrix}\right\}\text{-NH}_2$$

The pentapeptide fragment gave phenylalanine as the *C*-terminal amino acid upon carboxypeptidase action, leading to the partial structure (Glu,His,Met,Ser) · Phe. From an Edman degradation, it was found that serine is *N*-terminal: Ser · (Glu,His,Met) · Phe. Two more Edman degradations gave, first, methionine, and second, glutamic acid:

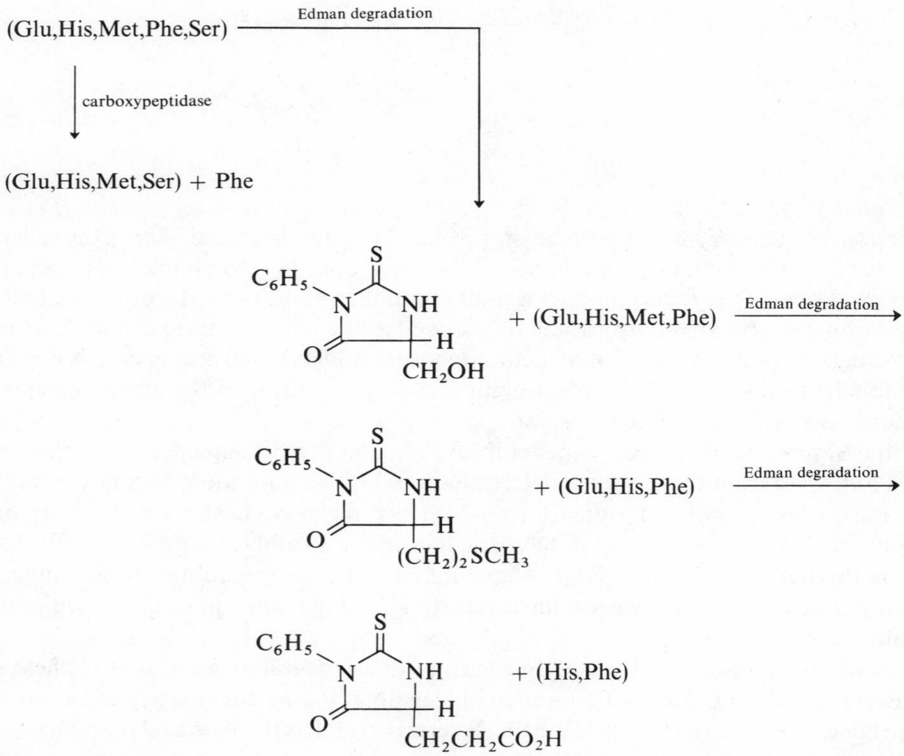

Thus, the pentapeptide is Ser · Met · Glu · His · Phe. Histidine is placed fourth in line because that is the only slot left.

The hexapeptide (Arg,Gly,Lys,Pro,Trp,Val) was inert to carboxypeptidase, and, therefore, represents the *C*-terminal end of α-MSH. Further chymotryptic hydrolysis of this hexapeptide gave (Arg,Trp) and (Gly,Lys,Pro,Val). The dipeptide must be Arg · Trp because chymotrypsin attacks the carbonyl function of tryptophan and not of arginine:

$$(\text{Arg,Gly,Lys,Pro,Trp,Val}) \xrightarrow{\text{chymotrypsin}} \text{Arg} \cdot \text{Trp} + (\text{Gly,Lys,Pro,Val})$$

12*N* HCl

(Gly,Lys,Pro) + NH$_3$ + (Gly,Lys)
+ (Pro,Val) + (Lys,Pro)

Edman degradation

carboxypeptidase

No reaction

+ (Lys,Pro,Val)

The tetrapeptide (Gly,Lys,Pro,Val) was subjected to the Edman degradation, and glycine was found to be the *N*-terminal amino acid. It was partially hydrolyzed in 12*N*HCl at 37°C for 120 hours. The following peptides were obtained, along with ammonia: (Gly,Lys,Pro) + (Gly,Lys) + (Pro,Val) + (Lys,Pro) + NH$_3$. The ammonia is formed because the *C*-terminal end is in the amide form. Since the Edman reaction established Gly as the amino terminal residue of this peptide, the isolation of the dipeptides (Gly,Lys), (Lys,Pro), and (Pro,Val) establishes the obligatory sequence Gly · Lys · Pro · Val(NH$_2$). The presence of tripeptide containing Gly,Lys, and Pro adds strength to the sequence assignment. The complete hexapeptide must, therefore, be Arg · Trp · Gly · Lys · Pro · Val(NH$_2$).

At this point, the information known about α-MSH is

$$\underset{\displaystyle CH_3\overset{\textstyle O}{\overset{\|}{C}}}{}\!-\!\text{Ser} \cdot \text{Tyr} + \text{Ser} \cdot \text{Met} \cdot \text{Glu} \cdot \text{His} \cdot \text{Phe} + \text{Arg} \cdot \text{Trp} \cdot \text{Gly} \cdot \text{Lys} \cdot \text{Pro} \cdot \text{Val(NH}_2)$$

If Tyr and Ser, and Phe and Arg, which were cleaved by chymotrypsin, are joined, there is only one way to put the sequence together:

Ac-Ser · Tyr · Ser · Met · Glu · His · Phe · Arg · Trp · Gly · Lys · Pro · Val(NH$_2$)

This sequence is consistent with all data concerning the primary structure of α-MSH.

A method for determination of the primary structures of proteins which is currently under investigation involves the use of a mass spectrometer to fragment the molecule and a computer to sort out and interpret the results.

29.7 Proteins

In spite of the fact that their molecular weights range up to millions, many proteins have been crystallized or at least purified until they behave as homogeneous substances. Care must be taken in the investigation of proteins, because they can be altered quite easily by changes in pH, by uv radiation, by heat, and by organic solvents. Such alteration is generally referred to as *denaturation. Simple* proteins, for example the enzyme lysozyme, are hydrolyzed only to amino acids. Others contain non-amino acid portions, called *prosthetic groups*, and were originally referred to as *conjugated proteins*. In *nucleoproteins* (from cell nuclei), the prosthetic groups are nucleic acids; *mucoproteins* contain complex polysaccharides. Some prosthetic groups are much simpler, as exemplified by the oxidation–reduction enzymes known as flavoproteins, which contain bound derivatives of the vitamin riboflavin.

Proteins are amphoteric dipolar ions which migrate in an electric field and have characteristic isoelectric points. Even though the chain composing the backbone of the proteins is comprised of relatively stable amide linkages, proteins are reactive and exhibit highly specific behavior. This reactivity is associated with the free active groups on the side chains, for example, amino groups from lysine, guanido groups from arginine, or sulfhydryl groups from cysteine. Many proteins contain several peptide chains held together by cross linkages. Disulfide bonds between cysteines can link two chains, or even remote parts of the same chain; for example, beef insulin contains an A chain of 21 amino acids connected via two disulfide linkages to a B chain of 30 amino acids, forming a cyclic protein:

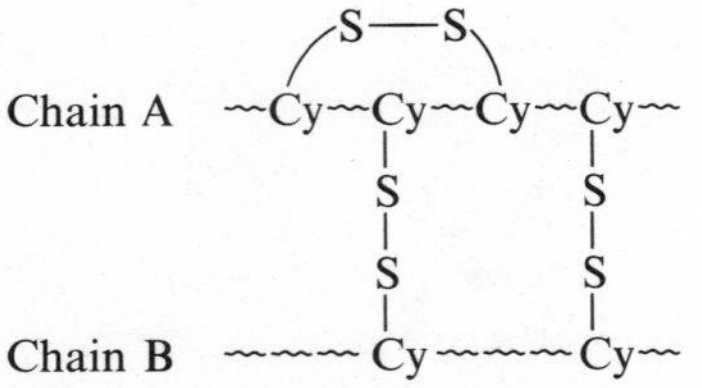

The discussion thus far has been involved with the characterization of polypeptides as a linear array of amino acids, that is, primary structure. One must not neglect, however, the manner in which these chains are arranged three-dimensionally. For instance, the finding that a particular amino acid side chain of an enzyme is involved in the catalysis of some reaction tells nothing about the details of its involvement; that is, we don't know whether it actually participates in the reaction, or is involved in the binding of the reactant (substrate) to the enzyme, or is merely necessary for maintaining the overall three-dimensional structural integrity of the enzyme molecule by interactions among the side chains of the constituent amino acids. All of these roles, however, stipulate that the amino acid must be located very exactly. This spatial organization of proteins, as mentioned in the introduction to this chapter, is currently a topic of intense investigation in many laboratories.

An invaluable technique for studying three-dimensional protein structure is X-ray crystallography. An X-ray diffraction pattern is obtained from a crystal, and a structure is proposed, if possible, which would be expected to give such a pattern. From X-ray determinations of amino acid and peptide structures, the amide portion of the chain has been found to be planar and anti. The following representation shows bond lengths and angles of a unit in the peptide chain:

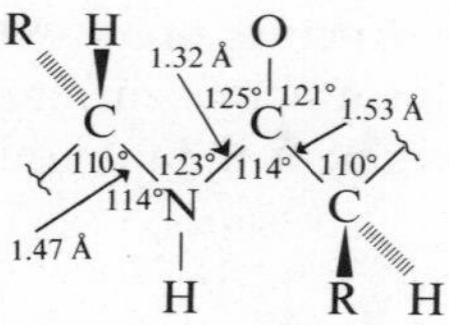

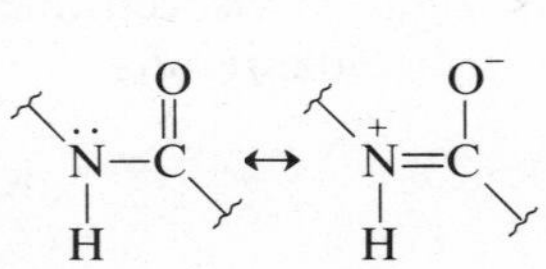

Anti coplanar

The carbon–nitrogen bond of the amide linkage has approximately 40% double-bond character, due to resonance. This resonance interaction strongly hinders rotation about that bond. Very importantly, however, rotations are free for bonds between the amide groups and the α carbons as well as for the α and the carbonyl carbons, thus permitting many conformations for the protein.

X-Ray techniques were also instrumental in elucidating the two major ways in which the peptide backbone can interact with itself. This level of organization is referred to as *secondary structure*. The first of these two types of interaction is shown in Figure 29.1, and is known as the α helix. Note that each amide group is hydrogen-bonded to the amide group which is the third one from it in either direction along the chain. There are 3.6 amino acid units per turn of the helix. The side chains extend away from the axis of the

Figure 29.1
The α helix.

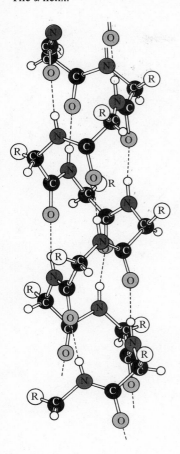

helix. All natural amino acids are of the L configuration and to date, all protein helices have been found to be right-handed. This is a very common structural component of proteins; an extreme example is the oxygen-carrying protein *hemoglobin*, which is about 75% α helix. The helical regions are interrupted in several places by a proline residue, which you will realize from recalling its structure, cannot participate in α-helix formation.

Quantitatively of less importance is the so-called β or pleated sheet structure, commonly seen in the fibrous proteins such as those found in silk, hair, and feathers. This is depicted in Figure 29.2. Notice that the chains are antiparallel. You can easily appreciate that steric crowding between R groups would make the straight-chain representation unfavorable. Thus, while silk, with a high percentage of Gly and Ala, could assume this configuration, bulky side chains would prohibit its formation. It is, of course, not obligatory that all parts of a protein molecule have either of these configurations.

The interaction of various parts of the protein with each other via the amino acid side chains determines the *tertiary* structure of the protein. The bonds involved might be salt linkages such as between an —NH$_2$ of Lys and a carboxyl of Asp, hydrogen bonds such as between Ser and His, or van der Waals forces such as between Tyr and Phe. Disulfide bonds between cysteine residues on adjacent chains often help to stabilize the tertiary structure. X-Ray crystallography has been used to determine the actual three-dimensional configurations of a number of proteins. *Myoglobin*, a protein similar to hemoglobin, has the shape shown in Figure 29.3, as determined by Perutz† and Kendrew.†† The resolution of this X-ray study (and several other similar studies) is not

† Max F. Perutz. Born 1914, Vienna, Austria. Cambridge University. Nobel Prize 1962.
†† John C. Kendrew. Born 1917, Oxford, England. Cambridge University. Nobel Prize 1962.

Figure 29.2
The β-pleated-sheet structure of proteins.

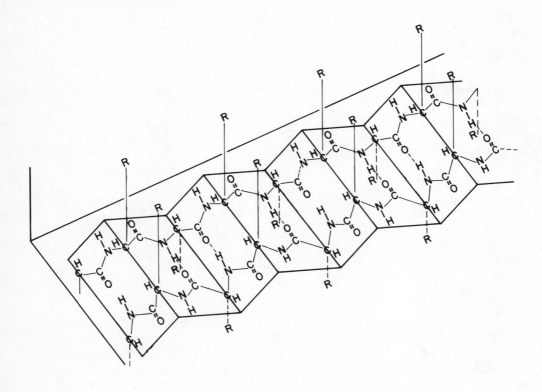

Figure 29.3
The X-ray structure of myoglobin. (From R. E. Dickerson in H. Neurath (ed.), *The Proteins* **II**, Academic Press, New York, 1964, p. 634.)

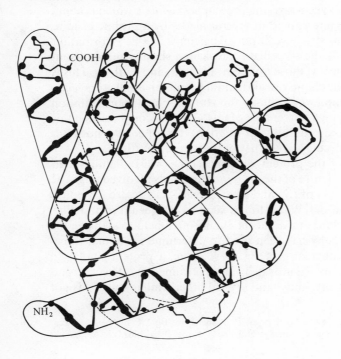

good enough to be able to see individual atoms; only gross shapes are discernible. The orientation of the peptide chain within this gross structure can be deduced since the primary structure of the protein is completely known. One of the consistent features of all protein structures studied so far is the presence of large numbers of polar amino acid residues on the surface of the molecule, with large clusters of nonpolar residues in the interior in contact with each other.

There is one further level of organization in proteins, the *quaternary structure*, which describes the way multiple subunits (not always identical) can aggregate to form large complexes. As mentioned before, tobacco mosaic virus protein is actually a multiple of small subunits. As is usually the case with viruses, the protein complex forms a protective sheath around the nucleic acid core of the virus, which, of course, contains the genetic information required for the production of more virus particles.

Many sequential reactions in metabolism are efficiently catalyzed by well-organized complexes of enzymes which obviate the necessity of having the product of one enzymatic reaction float free in the cell waiting until it randomly collides with the enzyme required for its next transformation. Several of these complexes have been broken down into their individual enzyme components. The separated components can subsequently be reassociated *in vitro*, and they will exhibit the original overall metabolic transformations. This experimental result shows that after synthesis of the individual enzymes, spontaneous assembly can produce the efficient complex observed in the cell.

29.8   The Structural Basis of Enzyme Catalysis

Having now looked at various factors which influence the overall structures of proteins, we are in a position to establish in a more meaningful way the correlation of structure with function which imparts to enzymes their extraordinary specificity and catalytic power. These characteristics (at least in enzymes that require no prosthetic groups for activity) must be determined solely by the specific spatial relationships among individual amino acid side chains of the polypeptide. No types of enzyme catalysis have yet been found which are mechanistically different from reactions carried out in test tubes, and likewise, no enzyme-catalyzed reactions have ever been documented which would not occur (eventually) without catalysis. It is noteworthy, however, that some enzymes have the capacity to speed up reactions by a factor of 10^{10} beyond their rates without catalysis.

As an example to illustrate a structure–function relationship, we will use the enzyme *chymotrypsin*, which was mentioned in Section 29.6. As was described there, this proteolytic (peptide-hydrolyzing) enzyme preferentially attacks peptide bonds whose carbonyl function is furnished by an aromatic amino acid.

Some time before the three-dimensional structure of chymotrypsin had been established, a number of amino acids had been suspected of being components of the so-called "active site" of the enzyme. A short description of several experiments which led to these suspicions will illustrate the type of approach used to investigate the mechanism of action of an enzyme.

1. Reaction of the enzyme with low concentrations of diisopropylfluorophosphate led to rapid inactivation of the enzyme. Upon hydrolysis, the diisopropylphosphate group was found to be covalently linked to a serine residue.

2. The pseudo-substrate 3-(*p*-toluenesulfonamido)-1-chloro-4-phenyl-2-butanone

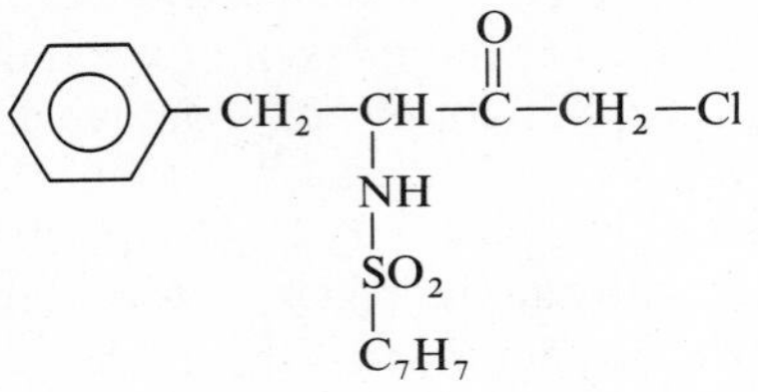

was found to react covalently with the enzyme in 1:1 stoichiometry, leading to complete loss of activity. Notice the designed similarity of the compound to a phenylalanine-containing peptide, suggestive that this compound is brought specifically into the region of the active site by the specificity-determining portions of the enzyme. Upon hydrolysis of the enzyme, the reagent was found to have reacted with a histidine residue.

3. Further evidence implicating histidine as a component of the active site involved the drastic change in the enzyme's activity as the pH of the reaction was varied near the pK of an imidazole nitrogen.

4. When the enzyme reaction was carried out in D_2O rather than in water, the rate of hydrolysis decreased by over half, thus implicating a proton transfer (general acid–base catalysis) in at least the rate-determining step.

Subsequent X-ray analysis of the crystalline enzyme revealed that what would appear to be the active site is rather close to the surface of the molecule, as if designed to approach a rather large substrate. The high specificity of the enzyme would seem to be determined by two relatively short peptides within the enzyme which consist entirely of small non-polar amino acids forming a kind of pocket into which the aromatic substrate would be held by van der Waals forces. Nearby were histidine and serine residues, and also in the same area was found an aspartic acid which could facilitate protonation of the histidine ring. Very importantly, these amino acids are not consecutive as one might at first think, but are actually separated from each other linearly by many other amino acids. Histidine is number 57, aspartic acid 102, and serine 195. The remainder of the protein is presumably involved in holding these catalytic and specific segments in the proper neighboring relationship.

The overall mechanism of action of chymotrypsin, shown in the following figures, was postulated before X-ray data were available (with the exception of the initial proton donation by aspartic acid). The confirmation by X-ray analysis of the feasibility of the proposed chemical mechanism is a striking example of the mutual benefit which can be derived from different but complementary lines of investigation of a single problem. The proposed mechanism of action of chymotrypsin is illustrated as follows:

(a) *Initial approach of the substrate* (after proton transfer from Ser to Asp via His)

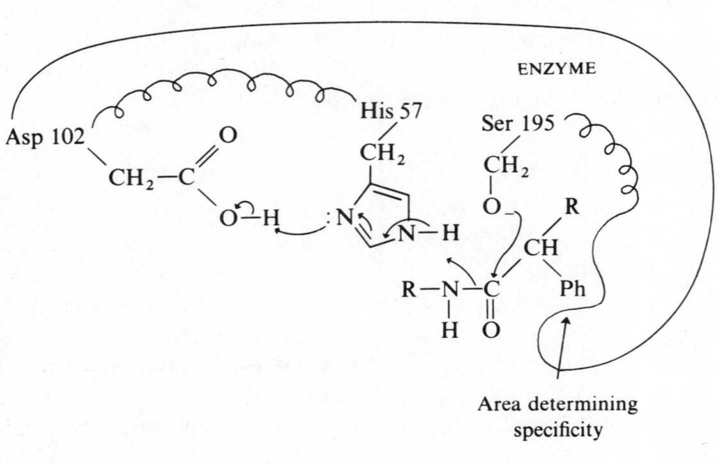

Area determining
specificity

(b) *Formation of an acyl enzyme intermediate*

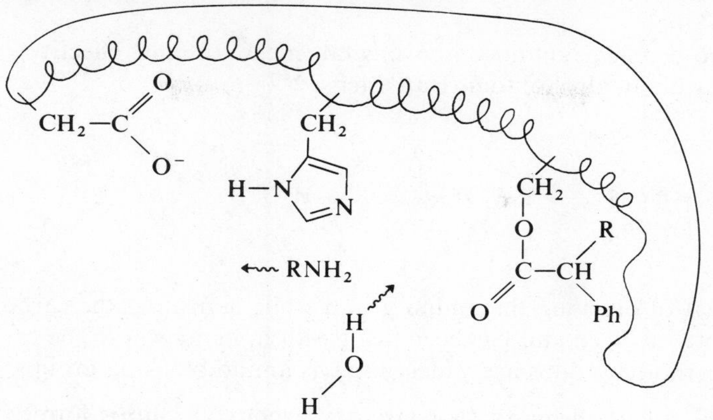

(c) *Deacylation*

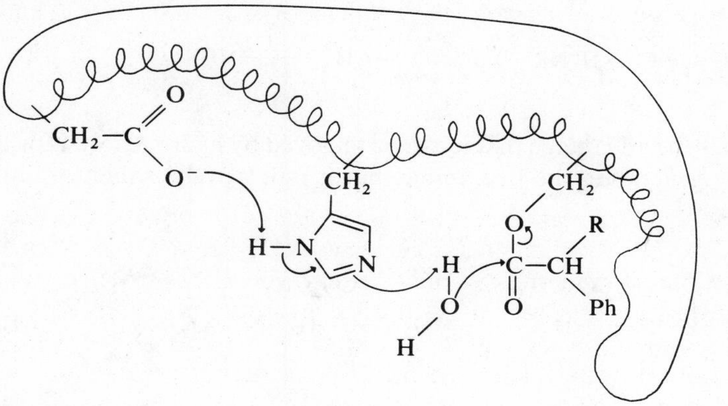

(d) *Product release*

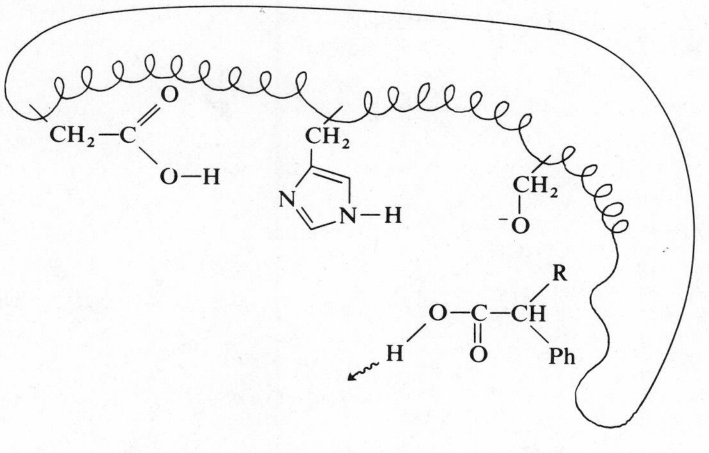

29.9 Peptide Synthesis

Peptide synthesis has long been an intriguing area of organic chemistry. The ability to duplicate in the laboratory one of the most complex processes of nature holds a fascination for the organic chemist. In any synthetic sequence directed toward the preparation of a particular polypeptide, there are difficulties to be encountered characteristic of the side-chain functional groups of the individual amino acids. These problems are too numerous and varied to go into here. However, there are some problems which are common to all peptide syntheses. The two main difficulties seem to be (1) blocking the amino group of an amino acid while activating the acid group of the same molecule;

and, (2) blocking the acid group of an amino acid while leaving the primary amino group free to react.

The second of the two problems outlined above is taken care of quite effectively by treating the amino acid with an alcohol to give an ester.

$$R-\overset{+NH_3}{\underset{}{CH}}-\overset{O}{\underset{}{C}}-O^- + R'OH \xrightarrow{H^+} R-\overset{NH_2}{\underset{}{CH}}-\overset{O}{\underset{}{C}}-OR' + H_2O$$

The first problem, that of blocking the amino group while activating the carboxyl group, is somewhat more involved and has been dealt with in many ways. The carbobenzoxy and *t*-butoxycarbonyl groups are widely used as amino blocking groups.

1. *Carbobenzoxy.* The N-carbobenzoxy (N-benzyloxycarbonyl) group is formed by treating an amino acid with benzyl chloroformate.

$$\bigcirc-CH_2O-\overset{O}{\underset{}{C}}-Cl + H_2NR \rightarrow \bigcirc-CH_2O-\overset{O}{\underset{}{C}}-NHR$$

This protecting group has the advantage that it can be removed by hydrogenolysis or by acid hydrolysis, thereby generating the free amine, but it is relatively stable to dilute alkali.

$$\bigcirc-CH_2O-\overset{O}{\underset{}{C}}-\overset{H}{\underset{}{N}}-\overset{CO_2CH_3}{\underset{R}{C}}-H \xrightarrow[Pd/C]{H_2} H_2N-\overset{CO_2CH_3}{\underset{R}{C}}-H + CO_2 + \bigcirc-CH_3$$

$$\bigcirc-CH_2O-\overset{O}{\underset{}{C}}-\overset{H}{\underset{}{N}}-\overset{CO_2CH_3}{\underset{R}{C}}-H \xrightarrow{(HBr/HOAc)}$$

$$\bigcirc-CH_2Br + CO_2 + H_2N-\overset{CO_2CH_3}{\underset{R}{C}}-H$$

$$\bigcirc-CH_2-O-\overset{O}{\underset{}{C}}-\overset{H}{\underset{}{N}}-\overset{CO_2CH_3}{\underset{R}{C}}-H \xrightarrow[OH^-]{dilute}$$

$$\bigcirc-CH_2-O-\overset{O}{\underset{}{C}}-\overset{H}{\underset{}{N}}-\overset{CO_2H}{\underset{R}{C}}-H + CH_3OH$$

2. *t-Butoxycarbonyl.* The N-*t*-butoxycarbonyl group is formed by treatment of the amino acid with *t*-butoxycarbonyl chloride (*t*-butyl chlorocarbonate) at 0°C or by treatment of the amino acid with the more stable *t*-butoxycarbonyl azide at slightly higher temperatures.

$$(CH_3)_3C-O-\overset{O}{\underset{}{C}}-X + H_2NR \rightarrow (CH_3)_3C-O-\overset{O}{\underset{}{C}}-\overset{}{\underset{H}{N}}-R$$

$$X = -Cl, -N_3$$

The *N-t*-butoxycarbonyl group can be removed by dilute acid, leaving the free amine, but it is unaffected by hydrogenolysis or dilute base.

As far as activating the acid function is concerned, it is necessary to convert the $-OH$ of the acid to a better leaving group.

$$\underset{\underset{\displaystyle O}{\|}}{R-C}-OH \rightarrow \underset{\underset{\displaystyle O}{\|}}{R-C}-X \xrightarrow{H_2NR'} R-\underset{\underset{\displaystyle H}{|}}{\underset{\underset{\displaystyle N}{|}}{\overset{\overset{\displaystyle O}{\|}}{C}}}-R'$$

Many such groups have been used and include the following:

1. *Acid chlorides*

$$R-\overset{\overset{\displaystyle O}{\|}}{C}-Cl + H_2N-\underset{\underset{\displaystyle R'}{|}}{\overset{\overset{\displaystyle CO_2CH_3}{|}}{C}}-H \rightarrow R-\overset{\overset{\displaystyle O}{\|}}{C}-\underset{\underset{\displaystyle H}{|}}{N}-\underset{\underset{\displaystyle R'}{|}}{\overset{\overset{\displaystyle CO_2CH_3}{|}}{C}}-H + HCl$$

2. *Esters*

$$R-\overset{\overset{\displaystyle O}{\|}}{C}-OCH_3 + H_2N-\underset{\underset{\displaystyle R'}{|}}{\overset{\overset{\displaystyle CO_2CH_3}{|}}{C}}-H \rightarrow R-\overset{\overset{\displaystyle O}{\|}}{C}-\underset{\underset{\displaystyle H}{|}}{N}-\underset{\underset{\displaystyle R'}{|}}{\overset{\overset{\displaystyle CO_2CH_3}{|}}{C}}-H + CH_3OH$$

3. *Mixed anhydrides of alkyl carbonic acid*

$$R-\overset{\overset{\displaystyle O}{\|}}{C}-O-\overset{\overset{\displaystyle O}{\|}}{C}-OR'' + H_2N-\underset{\underset{\displaystyle R'}{|}}{\overset{\overset{\displaystyle CO_2CH_3}{|}}{C}}-H \rightarrow R-\overset{\overset{\displaystyle O}{\|}}{C}-\underset{\underset{\displaystyle H}{|}}{N}-\underset{\underset{\displaystyle R'}{|}}{\overset{\overset{\displaystyle CO_2CH_3}{|}}{C}}-H + CO_2 + R''OH$$

4. *Acyl azides*

$$R-\overset{\overset{\displaystyle O}{\|}}{C}-N_3 + H_2N-\underset{\underset{\displaystyle R'}{|}}{\overset{\overset{\displaystyle CO_2CH_3}{|}}{C}}-H \rightarrow R-\overset{\overset{\displaystyle O}{\|}}{C}-\underset{\underset{\displaystyle H}{|}}{N}-\underset{\underset{\displaystyle R'}{|}}{\overset{\overset{\displaystyle CO_2CH_3}{|}}{C}}-H + HN_3$$

Of the four activating groups shown above, the acyl azide is most widely used. This method was developed in 1902 and to date is the only method which does not result in some racemization of the carboxyl component in the coupling sequence.

Carbodiimide Coupling. A reagent which, in one step, activates the carboxyl group and effects the coupling between an amino group and an acid with the removal of water is *N,N'*-dicyclo-hexylcarbodiimide (Section 21.3).

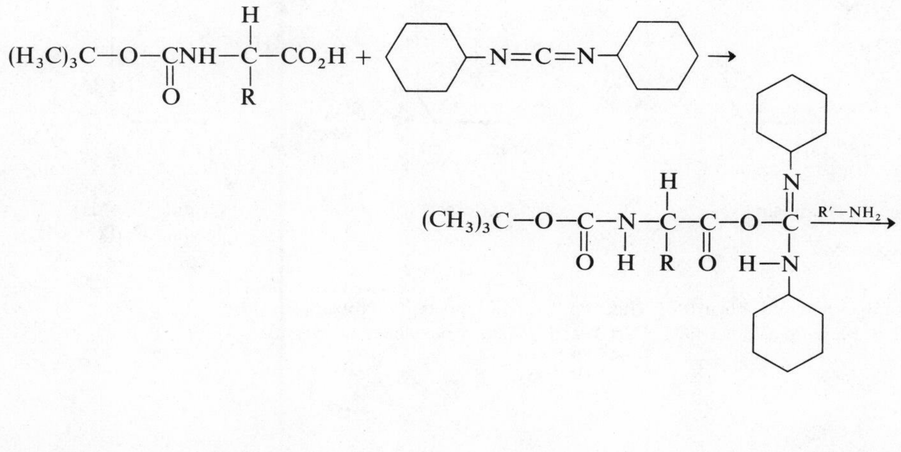

$$(CH_3)_3C-O-\underset{\underset{O}{\parallel}}{C}-\underset{\underset{H}{\mid}}{N}-\underset{\underset{R}{\mid}}{\overset{\overset{H}{\mid}}{C}}-\overset{\overset{O}{\parallel}}{C}-NHR' + \text{ (cyclohexyl)}-NH-\overset{\overset{}{}}{\underset{\underset{O}{\parallel}}{C}}-NH-\text{(cyclohexyl)}$$

One can well imagine how it would be possible to build up any length chain with amino acids in any desired sequence by adding on one at a time. In the laboratory, however, this is not the usual method. Normally small (two, three, or four unit) polypeptides are constructed and then these units are coupled as if they were themselves amino acids. V. du Vigneaud,[†] in fact, employed this method in his landmark synthesis of oxytocin in 1954.

The main disadvantage of this synthetic approach is the racemization which is nearly always a problem in each step; the purification of intermediates of two, three, or four polypeptide units to optical purity is consequently very difficult.

A recent and rather novel approach to polypeptide synthesis is that of Merrifield.[††] The method, essentially, is to bind an amino acid through the carboxyl group to a highly porous polymeric resin. The *t*-butoxycarbonyl protection can then be removed from the amino group by merely washing the resin with acid. By then washing the resin with an activated acyl compound, the polypeptide chain is built up. In this method, the purification of smaller intermediates is eliminated, but, depending upon the accumulated amount of racemization, the problem of purification of the final polypeptide product still remains. By this method biologically active *ribonuclease* was synthesized by assembling the 124 amino acids using 369 chemical reactions and 11,931 steps of the "peptide synthesis machine," which carries out the operations with a minimum of human intervention.

The purity of the final protein presents a difficult synthetic problem, which can be understood using the ribonuclease synthesis as an example. Suppose that a 90% yield of pure product is obtained when each amino acid is added, the other 10% of the product being racemic or other impurity. As most of us know from our laboratory work, a 90% yield is usually pretty good. After 124 steps, each with a 90% yield, the overall yield is $(90\%)^{124} = 0.0002\%$. A 95% yield on each step will give an overall yield of 0.2%, while if the yield can be raised to 99% on each step, the overall yield can be raised to 30%. Clearly, yield and purity are extremely critical problems in protein synthesis.

29.10   Protein Biosynthesis

Ribonucleic acids have the general formula shown in Section 28.9. Note that the nitrogen bases cytosine, uracil, guanine, and adenine occur in a precise and characteristic sequence in any given ribonucleic acid chain.

Guanosine   Cytidine   Uridine (R = H)
                                                         Thymidine (R = CH₃)

[†] Vincent du Vigneaud. Born 1901, Chicago. Cornell University. Nobel Prize 1955.
[††] Robert B. Merrifield. Born 1921, Fort Worth, Texas. Rockefeller University.

A more wieldy general formula results from the following abbreviations. The letters U, G, A, C, and T represent the nucleosides (ribose–nitrogen base conjugates) uridine, guanosine, adenosine (Section 28.9), cytidine and thymidine, respectively.

The letter p represents the phosphate unit. Notice (Section 28.9) that the phosphate esters link at 5′, 3′, which gives a directionality to the polymer. Thus by convention, the 5′ end of the chain is written to the left in our abbreviation and the 3′ end to the right. So, the segment of DNA chain shown on Page 752 can be abbreviated:

—CpApTpGp—

There are three major classifications of RNA; they are designated according to their functional properties. *Messenger RNAs* (mRNA) carry the genetic information from DNA for subsequent translation into specific protein sequences. *Transfer RNAs* (tRNA), previously called soluble RNAs, have molecular weights of 25,000–30,000 corresponding to 75–90 nucleotides. *Ribosomal RNAs* (rRNA) are much larger, having molecular weights of 0.5–1 million. The two latter types of RNA will be discussed below.

The mechanisms by which the ribonucleic acids perform their varied and complicated functions are the subject of intensive study among biochemists today. One key fact has emerged (mentioned in Section 28.9), which has defied attempts at disproof. It is the very specific hydrogen bonding which exists between AU base pairs and between GC base pairs. The diagram presented on page 752 actually depicts an AT pair but inspection of the structures of T and U will show that a direct substitution does not alter the binding properties. No such analogous forces exist between AC, AG, UG, or UC pairs. Thus, a trinucleotide such as GpUpC will be strongly attracted to its complementary tri-nucleotide CpApG, less strongly to one such as CpApC, and not at all to one such as ApCpU. This binding specificity is believed to contribute importantly to the process of protein synthesis in the living cell.

How does this synthesis take place? First, the free amino acids which either have been synthesized by the body or derived from ingested nutrients become esterified to the 3′-OH end of a specific tRNA. This molecule is currently the subject of much attention and a short look at its structure as it is understood today will be profitable. The exact nucleotide sequence of a number of tRNAs has now been established and preliminary structural characteristics have been described on the basis of X-ray data. As stated above, all tRNA molecules are approximately the same size and in addition they share other common features. Invariably, they terminate on the 3′ end with the sequence ~pCpCpA—OH. Also, they all undergo a certain amount of chemical modification after their initial synthesis, leading to a number of modified bases such as

Dihydrouridine
(diHU)

Pseudouridine
(ψ)

These unusual bases are present in every tRNA in the form of (a) a looped out region with a sequence locally rich in diHU and (b) another loop sequence which is invariably —pGpTpψpCpGp—. With all these similarities, where then are tRNAs different, and how does each amino acid invariably become attached to only one species of tRNA? The one answer with which all can agree involves a region very near the center of the chain and consists of a triplet of nucleotides whose sequence is different for each of the amino acid–specific tRNAs studied thus far. This trinucleotide sequence is called the *anticodon* region for reasons soon to become apparent. There are also localized heterogeneities in the diHU loop from one species of tRNA to another.

Although exact three-dimensional models are not yet available, we can represent all these facts schematically in Figure 29.4, where XXX represents the anticodon, hydrogen bonding is indicated by dotted lines, and p's have been omitted for the sake of brevity.

Figure 29.4
A schematic diagram of transfer ribonucleic acid (tRNA).

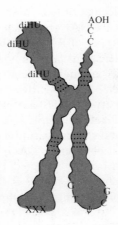

The enzyme which joins the amino acid to the tRNA catalyzes first the "activation" of the amino acid with the high-energy biochemical adenosine triphosphate (ATP) (Section 28.9).

$$\text{ATP} + \text{HO}-\overset{\overset{\text{O}}{\|}}{\text{C}}-\underset{\underset{\text{NH}_2}{|}}{\text{CH}}-\text{R}^1 \xrightarrow[\substack{\text{specific}\\\text{for R}^1}]{\text{enzyme}} \text{Adenine-ribose}-\text{O}-\overset{\overset{\text{O}}{\|}}{\underset{\underset{\text{OH}}{|}}{\text{P}}}-\text{O}-\overset{\overset{\text{O}}{\|}}{\text{C}}-\underset{\underset{\text{NH}_2}{|}}{\text{CH}}-\text{R}^1 + \text{H}_2\text{P}_2\text{O}_7^{2-}$$

Aminoacyl adenylate

The second step involves the actual esterification:

$$\text{Adenine-ribose}-\text{O}-\overset{\overset{\text{O}}{\|}}{\underset{\underset{\text{OH}}{|}}{\text{P}}}-\text{O}-\overset{\overset{\text{O}}{\|}}{\text{C}}-\underset{\underset{\text{NH}_2}{|}}{\text{CH}}-\text{R}^1 + {\sim}\text{CpCpA}-\text{OH} \xrightarrow{\text{same enzyme}}$$

tRNA specific
for R¹

$$\sim\text{CpCpA}-\text{O}-\overset{\overset{\text{O}}{\|}}{\text{C}}-\underset{\underset{\text{NH}_2}{|}}{\text{CH}}-\text{R}^1 + \text{Adenine-ribose}-\text{O}-\overset{\overset{\text{O}}{\|}}{\underset{\underset{\text{OH}}{|}}{\text{P}}}-\text{O}^-$$

Aminoacyl tRNA (aatRNA)   Adenosine monophosphate (AMP)

This reaction is carried out with each amino acid, each time utilizing an amino acid–specific enzyme and tRNA, until all amino acyl tRNA esters have been produced, each with a specific anticodon. It is in this form that the amino acids are ready to be polymerized into polypeptide linkages.

The actual formation of the peptide bond occurs on a nucleoprotein particle called the *ribosome*. Every living cell capable of synthesizing protein contains many ribosomes, and even though there are minor differences depending on the source, they are always composed of two large strands of RNA (rRNA) with which are associated some 60 or 80 smaller proteins. The functional nucleoprotein particle is roughly pear-shaped with a diameter of about 200 Å. It is with the ribosome that the mRNA interacts prior to protein synthesis. After formation of the mRNA–ribosome complex, different amino acyl tRNA molecules in the surrounding medium come into contact with it. If the exposed anticodon loop is exactly complementary to the specific triplet (the codon) on the ribosome-stabilized mRNA, it will form a hydrogen-bonded triplet of base pairs. Although the exact sequence of events which follows is not known with certainty, strong evidence indicates that the ψ-containing loop of the tRNA becomes attached to the ribosome and further stabilizes the ternary aatRNA–mRNA–ribosome complex. If only two or three nucleotides are capable of pairing, the association will not be strong enough for the ψ loop to "lock" the complex and the "wrong" aatRNA will diffuse away and be replaced by another until a correct match is made. After this happens, the following codon on the mRNA (the next three nucleotides) is in a position to react with its complementary anticodon on another tRNA. When two such alignments have been made, the carboxyl group of the first amino acid participates in amide bond formation with the free amino group of the recently incoming amino acyl tRNA. This enzyme-catalyzed reaction, of course, frees the first amino acid from its tRNA, which by unknown means senses this change and diffuses away from the complex, leaving behind a dipeptidyl–tRNA–mRNA– ribosome complex. The ribosome then moves "down" the mRNA just enough to bring the next (third) codon into such a position that it can now react with its own anticodon on yet another amino acyl tRNA. This sequence of reactions is repeated until some chain-termination signal on the mRNA causes synthesis to stop and the finished protein to be released for use as a hormone, enzyme, or structural protein. An intermediate stage in the process is depicted schematically in Figure 29.5.

Figure 29.5
A schematic diagram of polypeptide biosynthesis.

RIBOSOME

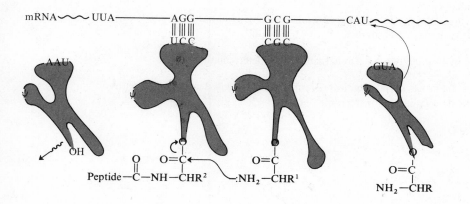

Using known values of hydrogen bond energies, theorists have calculated that if the genetic code were a doublet or quadruplet one, life as we know it would not be possible. The attractive force between two hydrogen-bonded base pairs is inadequate to keep the large tRNA molecule in place on the ribosome sufficiently long for peptide bond formation to occur. Conversely, four base pairs would be so strongly bonded that proteins might require months or more to be synthesized. The actual measured rate of protein synthesis in the living cell is about two amino acids per second.

The next several years should see a tremendous increase in the knowledge not only of the details of this complex process but also of such intriguing topics as the transcriptional and translational control of protein synthesis, the design of specific drugs to control the growth of harmful bacteria and viruses, and control of the rejection problem in tissue and organ transplants.

PROBLEMS

1. In living systems the transfer of information is of prime importance. Describe the processes called *translation* and *transcription*.

2. Give a definition and example of:
   (a) An essential amino acid
   (b) The peptide bond
   (c) Polypeptide
   (d) Oligopeptide
   (e) Tripeptide
   (f) Enzyme
   (g) Structural protein

3. What is meant by the primary, secondary, tertiary, and quaternary structure of polypeptides?

4. Define the isoelectric point of an amino acid and explain why arginine has an isoelectric point 5 pH units higher than does glycine, and glutamic acid has one about 3 pH units lower than that of glycine.

5. Describe the molecular disease of sickle-cell anemia. Explain why a human being cannot use a blood transfusion from a monkey, but can use insulin from a cow.

6. Explain the difference in the chances of the success of a heart transplant between identical twins and a heart transplant between nonidentical twins.

7. Describe the molecular basis of immunity.

8. Glutathione is a tripeptide which is an important regulator of the oxidation–reduction reactions of cells in animals. From the following experimental results, suggest a structure for glutathione:
   (a) Enzymatic or acid hydrolysis give glycine, cysteine, and glutamic acid in equimolar amounts.
   (b) Mild hydrolysis gives two dipeptides: one on further hydrolysis gives cysteine and glutamic acid, and the other gives cysteine and glycine.
   (c) Carboxypeptidase liberates glycine.
   (d) 2,4-Dinitrophenylation gives N-(2,4-dinitrophenyl)glutamine.
   Devise a synthesis of glutathione.

9. Describe by formula two N-terminal amino acid determinations.

10. Compare the merits of the chemical C-terminal amino acid determination with the enzymatic determination for the same purpose.

11. Complete:

   (a) $CH_3-\underset{\underset{OH}{|}}{CH}-\underset{\underset{NH_2}{|}}{CH}-CO_2H \xrightarrow{HIO_4}$

   (b) $CH_3CO_2H \xrightarrow[\text{2. 2NH}_3]{\text{1. Br}_2, \text{P}}$

   (c) $CH_3CHO \xrightarrow[\text{2. 2H}_2O]{\text{1. NH}_3, \text{HCN}}$

   (d) $(CH_3)_2CH-\underset{\underset{NH_2}{|}}{CH}-CO_2H \xrightarrow{HNO_2}$

(e) $\xrightarrow{\text{HCl}}$

(f) *Optional Problem.* $-CH_2-\underset{\underset{NH_2}{|}}{CH}-CO_2H + 2$ $\rightarrow$

(g) $-\overset{O}{\overset{||}{C}}Cl + CH_3-S-CH_2CH_2-\underset{\underset{NH_2}{|}}{CH}-CO_2H \xrightarrow{\text{NaOH}}$

(h) $-N=C=S$ + $-CH_2\underset{\underset{NH_2}{|}}{CH}\overset{O}{\overset{||}{C}}NH\underset{\underset{CH_3}{|}}{CH}-CO_2H \xrightarrow[\text{medium}]{\text{alkaline}} A \xrightarrow[\text{H}_2\text{O}]{\text{HCl}} B$

(i) $N^-K^+ + ClCH_2CO_2C_2H_5 \rightarrow A \xrightarrow[\text{H}_2\text{O}]{\text{HCl}} B$

(j) $-CH_2O\overset{O}{\overset{||}{C}}Cl +$ $-CH_2\underset{\overset{+}{N}H_3}{\overset{|}{C}}HCO_2^- \rightarrow A$

$A \xrightarrow{\text{SOCl}_2} B \xrightarrow[\overset{+}{N}H_3]{\overset{(CH_3)_2CHCH_2\overset{|}{C}HCO_2^-}{}} C \xrightarrow{\text{H}_2/\text{Pd}} D$

12. Suggest a synthesis for:
    (a) Ala · Pro · Val   (b) Asp · Ile · Gly   (c) Thr · Arg · Lys

13. Synthesize lysine from the oxime of cylohexanone.

14. Discuss the stereochemical implications of obtaining L-Val· L-Ile · L-Lys by resolution of DL-Val· DL-Ile · DL-Lys.

15. Vasopressin is a posterior pituitary hormone which acts on the kidney to reduce excretion of water and brings about a rise in blood pressure:

$$\overset{\displaystyle \lceil \rule{1em}{0.4pt}S\rule{1.5em}{0.4pt}S\rule{1em}{0.4pt}\rceil}{Cy \cdot Tyr \cdot Phe \cdot Gln \cdot Asn \cdot Cy \cdot Pro \cdot Lys \cdot Gly(NH_2)}$$

Lysine vasopressin

(a) Devise a scheme for determining the peptide sequences.
(b) Devise a synthesis of the following part of the chain: CySH · Pro · Lys · Gly(NH$_2$).

16. Describe the major structural difference between DNA and RNA.

17. Describe the role of tRNA in protein biosynthesis.

18. Describe the function of the anticodon or nodoc.

19. What is the maximum number of different amino acids possible in human protein?

20. A certain tetrapeptide is found to yield on hydrolysis 2 moles of alanine, one of glycine, and one of valine. Write the formula for each possible structurally isomeric tetrapeptide that could give this result.

CHAPTER 30

TERPENES AND RELATED
NATURAL PRODUCTS

30.1 Introduction

Acetic acid is one of the most fundamental organic compounds. It has long been a familiar and cheap industrial chemical, and is well known as the flavoring constituent of vinegar. Only in recent years, however, have we discovered that this simple substance is also the most important single building block used by all living organisms in the elaboration of countless thousands of more complex molecules, including structures of the most diverse sort, many of which play essential biochemical roles. In this chapter we shall examine some of the more important types of natural products derived from acetic acid and also some intermediate steps in the biosynthesis of these compounds. We will consider particularly the *fatty acids*, the *terpenes*, the *carotenoids*, and the *steroids*.

ABOUT BIOSYNTHESIS. *The unravelling of biosynthetic pathways is one of the most exciting and active areas of current chemical research and is an example of a field in which organic chemistry and biochemistry merge. Much knowledge of biosynthesis has been obtained by studying the incorporation by an organism of a radioactive precursor (such as $^{14}CH_3CO_2H$) into a natural product, which can then be systematically degraded chemically to show exactly which carbon atoms of the molecule are radioactive.*

30.2 The Origin of Fats

As discussed earlier (Section 8.11) naturally occurring fats are esters of glycerol with the higher fatty acids; the most abundant of these acids are the straight-chain saturated C_{16} and C_{18} acids, palmitic and stearic acids. These and other natural fatty acids are biosynthesized from a number of molecules of acetic acid; since each acetic acid unit contains two carbon atoms, it is not surprising that all of the common natural fatty acids contain an *even* number of carbon atoms. All of the reactions involved are enzyme-catalyzed. The steps, however, are all straightforward reactions which are analogous to well-known laboratory reactions.

The first step in fatty acid biosynthesis involves the "activation" of the ordinarily unreactive acetic acid molecule. This occurs by esterification with the thiol group of a large molecule called *coenzyme A* and abbreviated here as HS—CoA (see page 754). The methyl of the resulting acetyl—CoA is quite reactive and is easily carbonated by carbon dioxide to give an even more reactive molecule, malonyl—CoA. Biotin (page 728) plays an essential role in this carbonation reaction.

$$CH_3CO_2H \xrightarrow{HS-CoA} CH_3-CO-S-CoA \xrightarrow{CO_2} \overset{\displaystyle CO_2H}{\underset{\displaystyle }{CH_2}}-CO-S-CoA$$

Acetyl-CoA　　　　　　Malonyl-CoA

Details of the Biosynthesis of Fatty Acids. Acetyl-CoA and malonyl-CoA are transferred selectively to two different but very close thiol groups (shown as −SH and −*SH) on a special enzyme (Figure 30.1). The two close functions then undergo a condensation (with loss of carbon dioxide) which is very similar to the acetoacetic ester synthesis (Section 20.15). The resulting acetoacetyl enzyme next undergoes the simple transformations of reduction of a ketone to an alcohol, dehydration of the alcohol, and reduction of the alkene to give the *butyryl* enzyme. The butyryl group then moves over to the thiol originally occupied by the acetyl group, another malonyl group becomes attached, and the process begins a second cycle of steps resulting in the formation of a *hexanoyl* enzyme. Further cycles take place until a C_{16} or C_{18} acyl group is formed when, for reasons not yet clear, liberation of the fatty acid takes place. The enzyme (*fatty acid synthetase*) thus functions as an incredibly efficient assembly-line factory, which the originally attached acetyl group never leaves until it has become the hydrocarbon end of a palmitic or stearic acid molecule. The efficiency of this enzyme (molecular weight about 2.3 million) is such that one molecule of enzyme at 25°C and pH 6.8 incorporates about 3200 molecules of malonyl-CoA into fatty acids every minute.

Figure 30.1
Fatty acid synthesis.

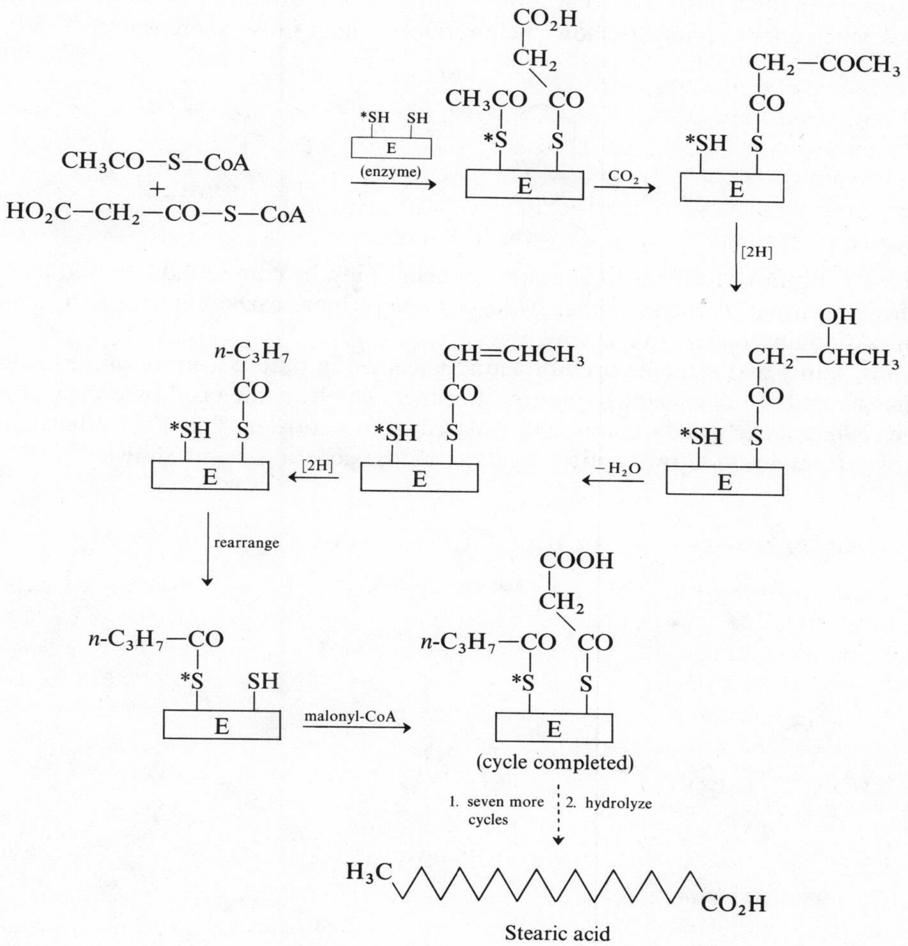

30.3   Terpenes: Classification and Origin

It has been known since antiquity that the odoriferous constituents of a plant could be greatly concentrated in the form of an "essential oil" by gentle heating of the plant material. Later, steam distillation was recognized as a superior method of preparing such oils, some 60 of which were already known to pharmacists by 1592. Investigations of the chemical constituents of essential oils during the nineteenth century led to the discovery of a number of isomeric hydrocarbons of the composition $C_{10}H_{16}$, which came to be known as *terpenes*. Further investigations uncovered a number of oxygenated terpenes, mostly alcohols or ketones, as well as other less volatile plant constituents containing skeletons of 15, 20, or 30 carbon atoms. Considering the "terpene" unit to be one of 10 carbon atoms, the following nomenclature evolved:

Class	Number of Carbons
Monoterpenes	10
Sesquiterpenes	15
Diterpenes	20
Triterpenes	30

As the structures of an increasing number of terpenes were determined, it became clear that practically all of them could be dissected in theory into units of the same five-carbon building block, the skeleton found in the hydrocarbon isoprene, C_5H_8. This realization lead to the formulation of the *isoprene rule*, which stated that all terpenes should be formally divisible into isoprene units. A few examples of simple acyclic terpenes which obey the rule are shown below. (Dotted lines show isoprene units.)

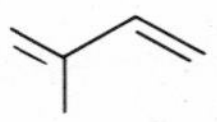

Isoprene
(C_5H_8)

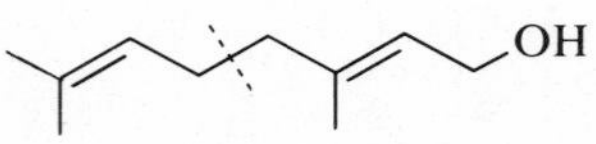

Geraniol
($C_{10}H_{18}O$)

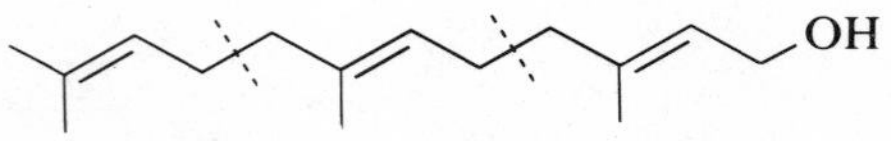

Farnesol
($C_{15}H_{26}O$)

The few exceptions to the isoprene rule are believed to be compounds derived in the plant from "normal" terpenes, either by loss of one or more carbon atoms, or by some type of carbonium ion rearrangement.

We now know that terpenes are not actually formed in nature from isoprene, which itself has never been detected as a natural product. The true universal precursor of all terpenes is *mevalonic acid*, a compound isolated from nature only in 1956. Mevalonic acid arises from acetyl-CoA ("active" acetate) by the general scheme shown:

$$2\,CH_3CO-S-CoA \rightarrow CH_3COCH_2CO-S-CoA$$

Acetyl-CoA   Acetoacetyl-CoA

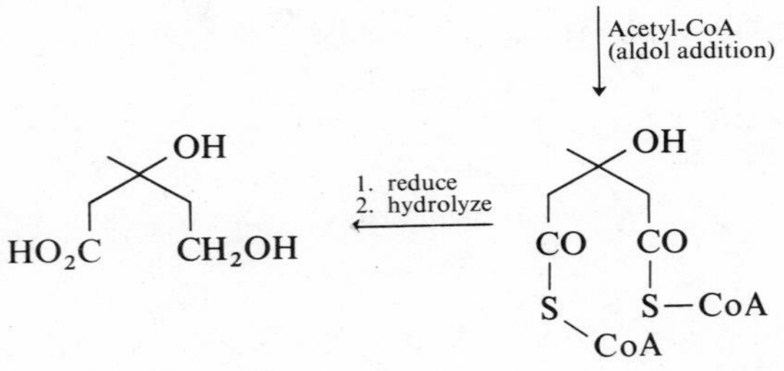

Mevalonic acid

In the reactions which are shown below, for example, in Figure 30.2, it will be noted that nature employs phosphate and, especially, pyrophosphate as good leaving groups in the same way that the synthetic organic chemist employs halides or sulfonate esters.

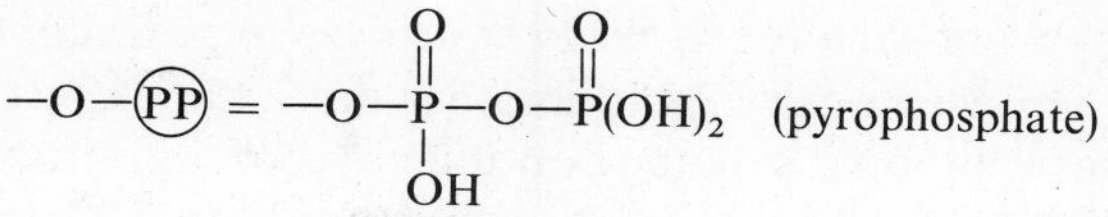

$$-O-\text{(PP)} = -O-\overset{\overset{\displaystyle O}{\|}}{\underset{\underset{\displaystyle OH}{|}}{P}}-O-\overset{\overset{\displaystyle O}{\|}}{P}(OH)_2 \quad \text{(pyrophosphate)}$$

In the biosynthesis of polyisoprenes (Figure 30.2), mevalonic acid is activated by phosphorylation, followed by decarboxylative elimination (Section 20.11) to give

Figure 30.2
Biosynthesis of the polyisoprenes.

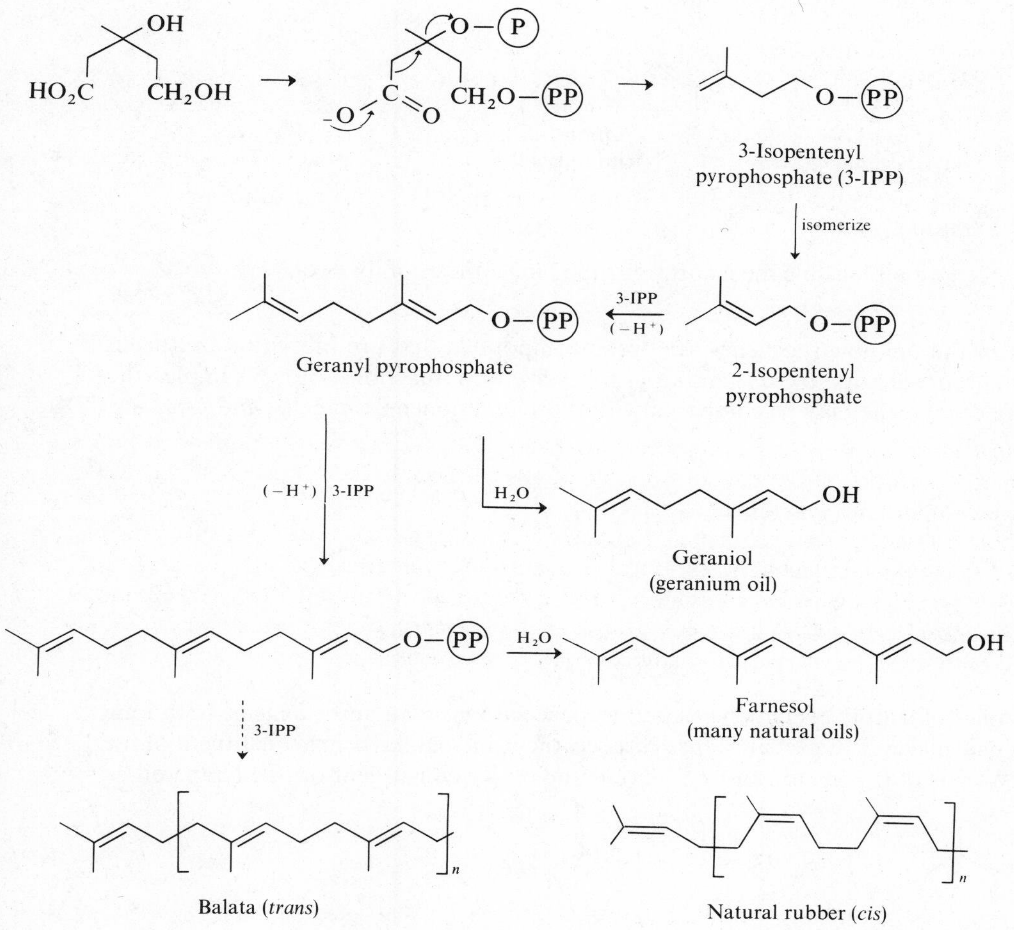

3-isopentenyl pyrophosphate. Isomerization of the latter to 2-isopentenyl pyrophosphate yields a molecule which can easily ionize and add to a molecule of 3-isopentenyl pyrophosphate in a reaction mechanistically reminiscent of the formation of diisobutylene from isobutylene (Section 15.6).

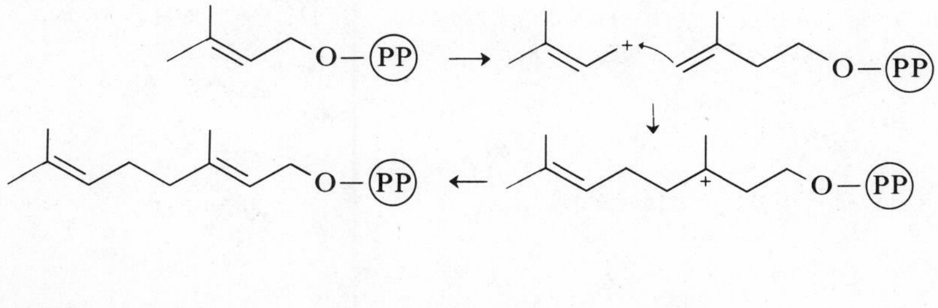

The initial reaction product, geranyl pyrophosphate, can easily hydrolyze to geraniol. It can also, however, give a carbonium ion which can add to another molecule of 3-iso-pentenyl pyrophosphate to give farnesyl pyrophosphate. Continued repetition of the process leads to an all-*trans* isoprene polymer known as *balata*, which occurs in the latex of certain tropical trees. The more common *natural rubber* is formed in a similar manner in the latex of a tree which contains enzymes giving rise to an all-*cis* polyisoprene.

30.4   More Complex Terpenes

In addition to the terpenes formed directly from isopentenyl pyrophosphate, various allylic alcohol isomers and assorted oxidation and reduction products of these occur naturally. A few are indicated below.

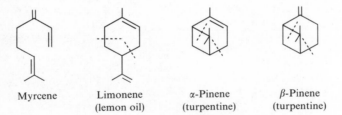

Linalool
(lavender oil)

Citronellal
(citronella oil)

Myrcene
(oil of bay leaves)

EXERCISE   30.1

Suggest a plausible mechanism for the biosynthesis of linalool.

Most of the unknown terpenes are cyclic compounds that are biosynthesized from open-chain precursors by carbonium ion cyclization reactions. For example, the structure of myrcene may be compared with those of limonene, α-pinene, and β-pinene.

Myrcene

Limonene
(lemon oil)

α-Pinene
(turpentine)

β-Pinene
(turpentine)

Examples of simply cyclic oxygenated terpenes are *menthol* and *camphor*, both long used in pharmaceutical preparations; *carvone*, the principal flavoring constituent of the caraway seeds of rye bread; and *1,8-cineole*, the major constituent of eucalyptus oil.

Menthol
(mint oil)

Carvone
(caraway oil)

Camphor
(camphor oil)

1,8-Cineole
(eucalyptus oil)

Structure and Stereochemistry of Some More Complex Terpenes. The absolute configurations of many terpenes are known, and a few are shown below with the aid of perspective formulas.

Menthol

Camphor

1,8-Cineole

Some unusual structures among the *sesquiterpenes* are the hydrocarbon *caryophyllene* and the tricyclic alcohol *cedrol*, which imparts its characteristic odor to cedar wood. The best known of the *diterpenes* is *abietic acid*, the major constituent of pine rosin, a by-product of turpentine manufacture. Because it is one of the cheapest of all organic substances, rosin is used in the manufacture of such products as varnishes and laundry soaps. *Phytol* is the most widespread of the open-chain diterpenes, and it occurs in esterified form in the chlorophyll molecule (Section 28.4).

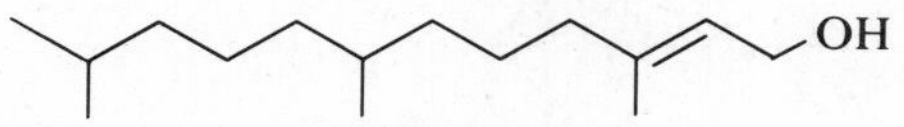

Phytol

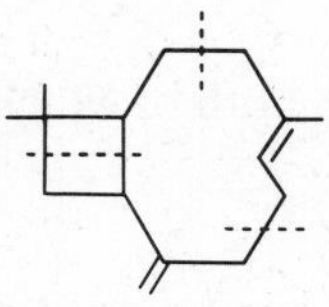

Caryophyllene
(clove oil)

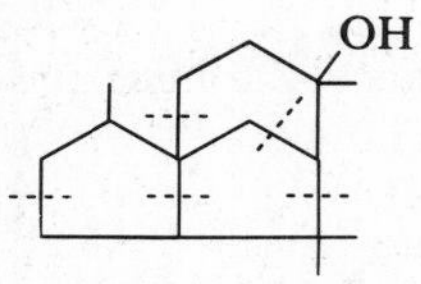

Cedrol
(cedar wood)

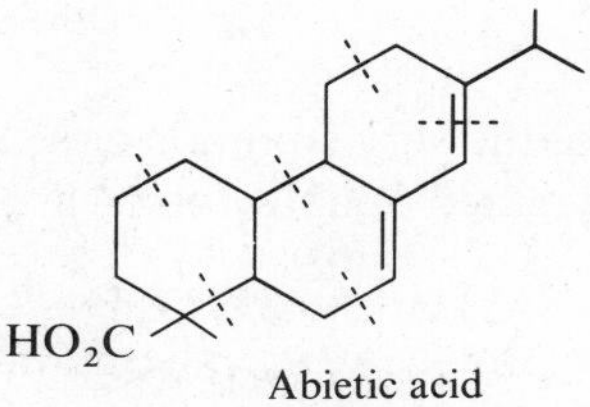

Abietic acid
(rosin)

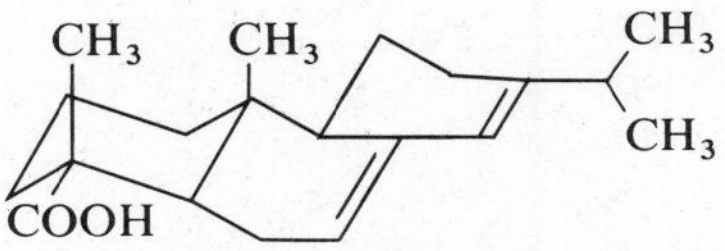

Stereochemistry of abietic acid

EXERCISE 30.2

Vigorous dehydrogenation of abietic acid yields the hydrocarbon retene, $C_{18}H_{18}$. Suggest a structure for retene.

Farnesyl pyrophosphate undergoes an enzymatically catalyzed reductive coupling reaction to join two farnesyl groups in a "tail-to-tail" manner, forming *squalene*, the most important of all the *triterpenes*. Originally an obscure curiosity obtained from shark liver oil, squalene is now recognized as the biosynthetic precursor of the steroids.

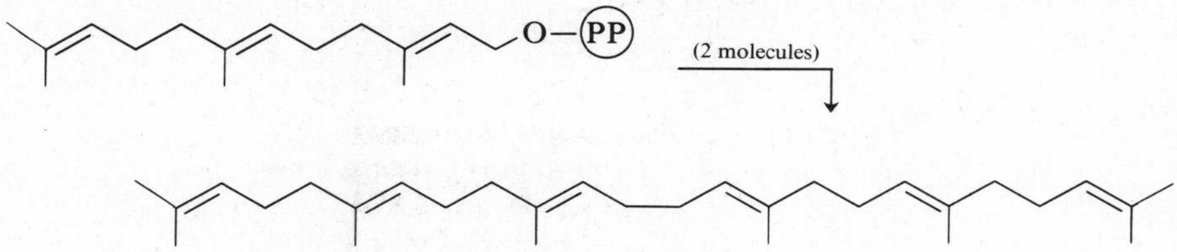

(2 molecules)

Squalene
$(C_{30}H_{50})$

30.5   The Carotenoids

The *carotenoids* are a special group of terpenes which are widely distributed in both the plant and animal kingdoms. They are yellow, orange, or red pigments whose color is due to a large number of conjugated double bonds.

The carotenoids arise by a "tail-to-tail" coupling reaction of the C_{20} analog of farnesyl pyrophosphate. The first detectable reaction product, the C_{40} hydrocarbon *phytoene*, is further modified by the enzymes of the organism by dehydrogenation and sometimes also cyclization and oxidation to give a variety of C_{40} carotenoids.

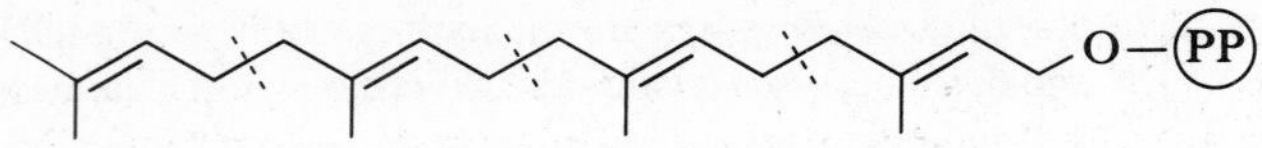

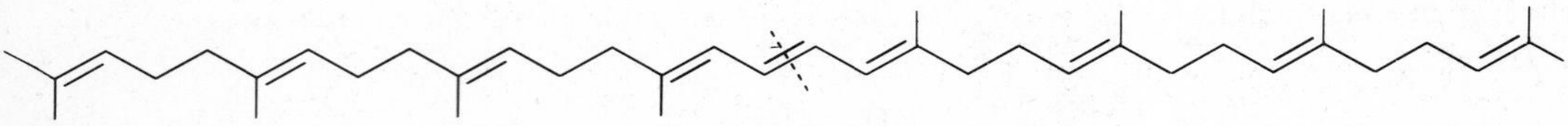

Phytoene

↓

Other carotenoids

The structures of the very common carotenoids, *β-carotene* and *lycopene*, both of which contain 11 conjugated double bonds, are as follows:

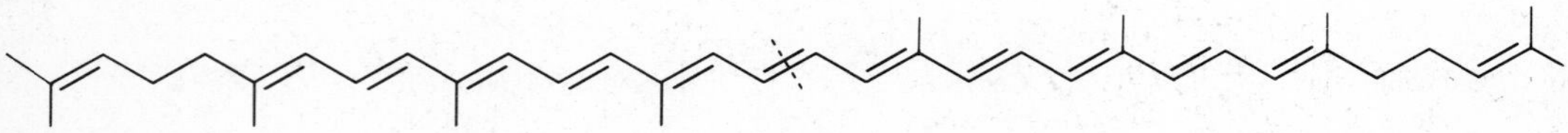

Lycopene (tomatoes, paprika)

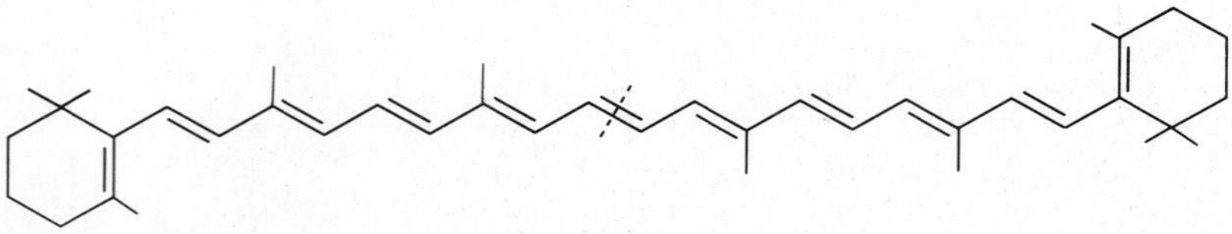

β-Carotene (carrots)

EXERCISE 30.3

Predict all of the products which would result from the ozonolysis of lycopene, followed by a reductive work-up. In what ratios would these products be obtained, assuming excellent yields?

In mammalian organisms, including man, *β*-carotene readily undergoes oxidative cleavage at the central double bond to give two equivalents of an aldehyde known as *retinal*. Biochemical reduction of the aldehyde carbonyl yields the important growth factor, *vitamin A$_1$*.

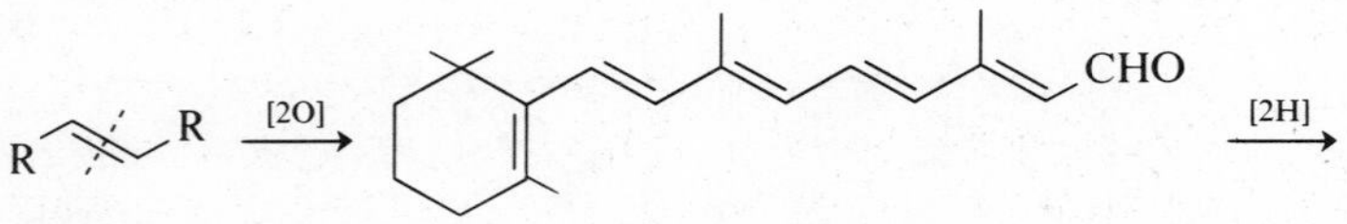

β-Carotene   Retinal

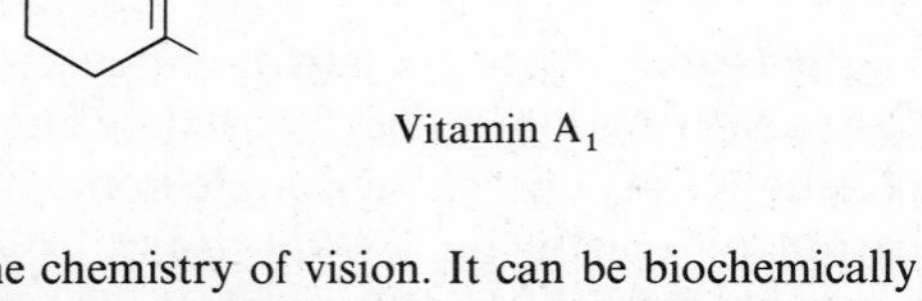

Vitamin A$_1$

Chemistry of Vision. Retinal plays a key role in the chemistry of vision. It can be biochemically converted to its 11-cis isomer, *neoretinal b*, which in turn reacts with a protein called *opsin* to give the Schiff base *rhodopsin*, the principal photosensitive pigment (visual purple) of the retina. When light strikes the retina, the cis double bond of rhodopsin isomerizes back to the more stable trans configuration. The Schiff base linkage in rhodopsin is, however, stable only when the 11-cis double bond is present, and hydrolysis now takes place to liberate opsin and ordinary all-*trans*-retinal. These products can now enter the same reaction cycle once more. We do not yet understand how the photochemical isomerization triggers off the resulting impulse from the optic nerve to the brain.

Retinal
(all-*trans*)

Neoretinal b
(11-*cis*)

H_2O

H_2N — opsin

trans-Rhodopsin
(unstable)

Rhodopsin (stable)

light

30.6 Cholesterol, the Fundamental Steroid

Steroids constitute a large and very important class of compounds which have in common the tetracyclic ring system (perhydrocyclopentanophenanthrene) indicated:

The steroid ring system

Although steroids occur in all plant and animal organisms, the most important ones are those of animal origin, some of which play essential biological roles. The most abundant animal steroid is the crystalline alcohol *cholesterol*, $C_{27}H_{46}O$. It was first isolated from human gall stones in the early nineteenth century. It forms about one-sixth of the dry weight of nerve and brain tissue, and is obtained commercially by the extraction of cattle spinal cords. The human body not only can synthesize cholesterol, but can also absorb it from food through the intestines into the bloodstream. Too high a concentration of cholesterol in the blood can lead to its precipitation in the circulatory vessels, resulting in high blood pressure and arteriosclerosis.

Intensive research in recent years has proven that cholesterol biosynthesis takes place by way of squalene; the sequence is outlined in Figure 30.3. Oxidation of squalene first gives squalene 2,3-epoxide. Acid-catalyzed ring opening of the epoxide while the molecule is held in the proper conformation on an enzyme surface leads to a truly remarkable concerted ring closure in which the entire tetracyclic steroid nucleus is constructed stereospecifically. Subsequent immediate rearrangement of several methyls and hydrogens leads to the first isolable cyclization product, *lanosterol*. Lanosterol has, in fact, long been known to chemists as a principal constituent of lanolin (wool fat). Final conversion of lanosterol to cholesterol involves the loss of three methyl groups, the shift of one double bond and the reduction of another double bond. The process is not as simple as it may at first appear, since about 20 separate enzymatically controlled steps seem to be involved.

Figure 30.3
The biosynthesis of cholesterol.

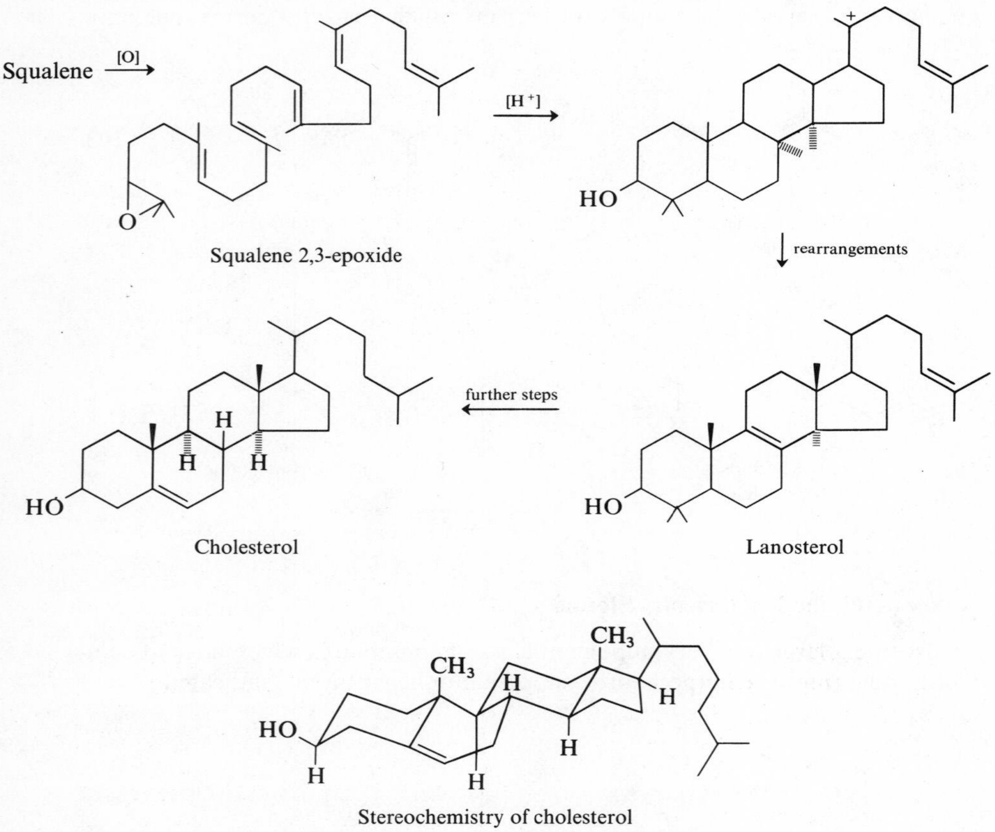
Squalene
[O]
Squalene 2,3-epoxide
[H⁺]
HO
rearrangements
Lanosterol
further steps
Cholesterol
Stereochemistry of cholesterol

The saturated hydrocarbon corresponding to cholesterol is called *cholestane*. The numbering system shown for cholestane is that universally used for steroids.

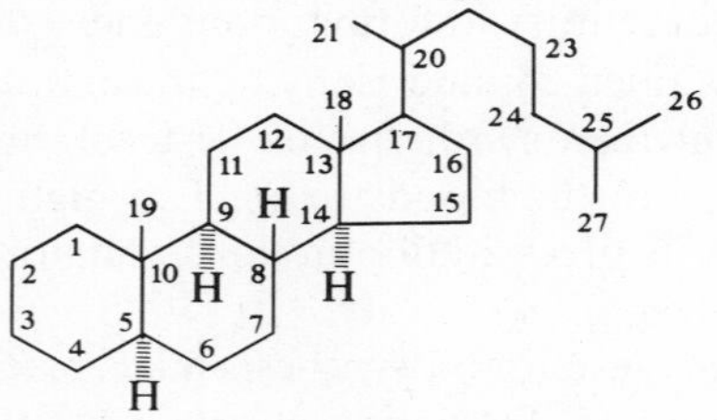

Cholestane

It will be noted that all three ring junctions in cholestane are trans fusions. The molecule is rather flat, with all three cyclohexane rings in the chair form. The side chain at C-17 is equatorial, whereas the so-called *angular methyl groups* (C-18 and C-19) are axial. The rigidity of the steroid nucleus is such that specific substituted steroids will have substituents of fixed conformation; for example, the halide shown has two axial bromines and an equatorial acetoxy group. Indeed, the study of steroid derivatives was a major stimulus to the development of conformational analysis.

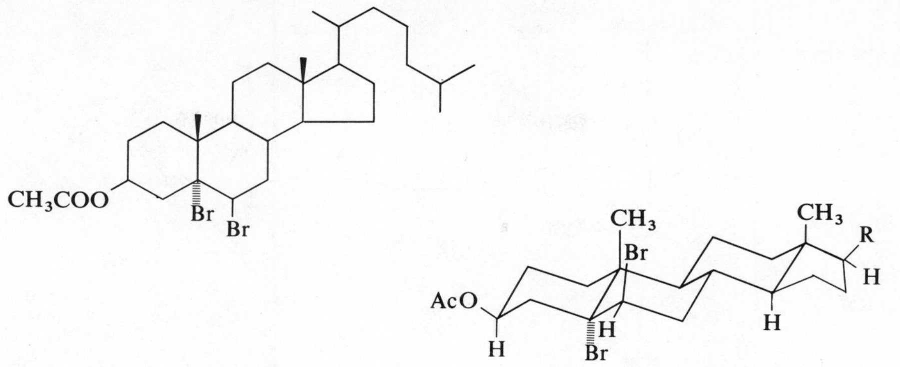

3β-Acetoxy-5α,6β-dibromocholestane

(Notice the use of α and β, respectively, to indicate
substituents below and above the average plane of
the ring system.)

EXERCISE 30.4

Predict the structure and stereochemistry of the principal product obtained
by allowing cholesteryl methyl ether to react with diborane and treating the
resulting intermediate with alkaline hydrogen peroxide.

30.7   Other Important Steroids

The biochemical degradation of cholesterol in the body leads to a host of physiologically important compounds, a few of which will be mentioned here.

7-Dehydrocholesterol, which is present in fairly high concentration in skin, undergoes
a complex series of photochemical reactions upon exposure to sunlight. One of the
products is the ring-cleaved steroid calciferol, or *vitamin D₃*, which prevents the disease
rickets by regulating calcium metabolism. Over a million dollars worth of calciferol per
year is manufactured in the United States, using cholesterol as the starting material for
the required 7-dehydro derivative.

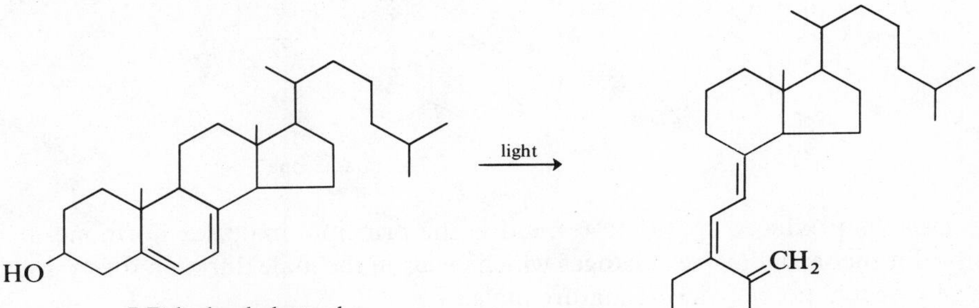

7-Dehydrocholesterol

light →

Calciferol
(Vitamin D₃)

Bile Acids. Cholesterol undergoes a series of reactions in the liver involving double-bond reduction,
ring oxygenation, and partial side-chain destruction to give several closely related acids, known
as the *bile acids* because they are secreted in the bile. *Cholic acid* is the most important of them.
In the form of certain simple peptides, exemplified by glycocholic acid, the bile acids act as natural
detergents, emulsifying fats in the intestine and aiding in their digestion. Note the unusual cis
fusion of the A, B rings of cholic acid.

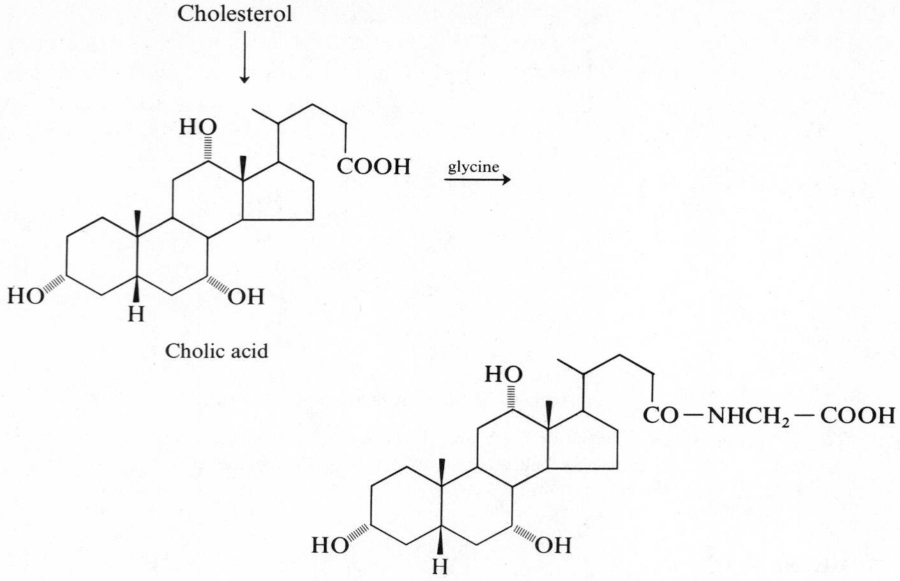

Cholesterol

Cholic acid

glycine →

Glycocholic acid

Extensive biochemical degradation of the cholesterol side chain in man as well as other mammals leads to a group of C_{21}, C_{19}, and C_{18} steroids which are the universal mammalian hormones of the adrenal cortex and of the gonads.

The adrenal hormones govern a wide variety of metabolic processes and are necessary for life. The best known member of the group is *cortisone*, shown below. Cortisone has attracted much interest as a drug for the treatment of arthritis and various other inflammatory conditions. Chemical modification of the cortisone molecule has yielded a number of nonnatural analogs, such as *dexamethasone*, which are superior for special medical uses.

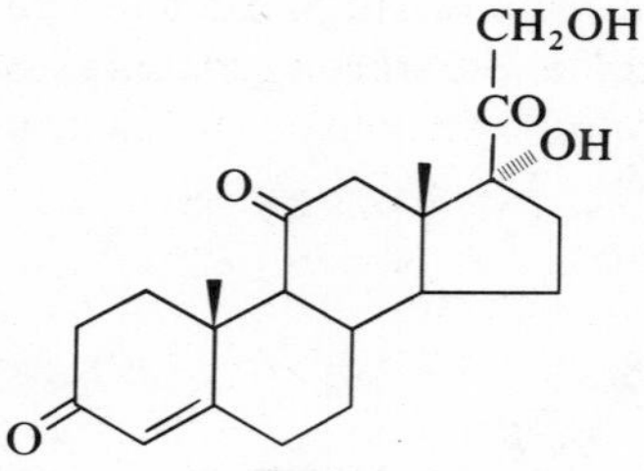

Cortisone

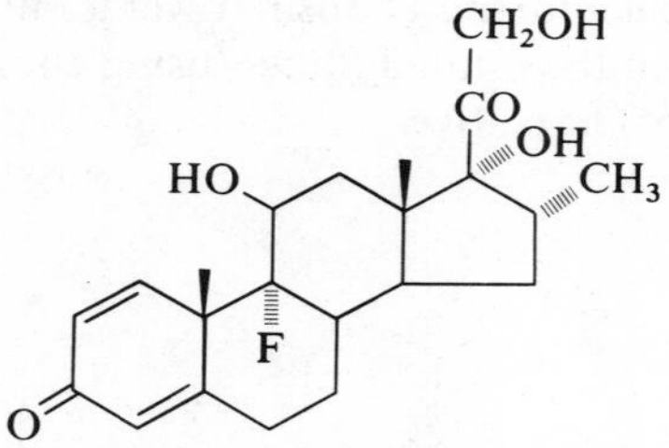

Dexamethasone

Testosterone is produced by the testes and is the principal male sex hormone. It is responsible for the secondary sex changes which occur in the male during puberty and is necessary for sexual potency in the mature male.

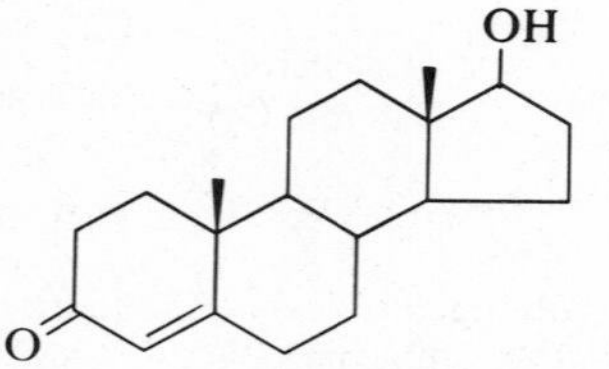

Testosterone

There are two distinct types of female sex hormones. One is exemplified by *progesterone*, the major corpus luteum hormone, the most important function of which is the maintenance of pregnancy. Remarkably enough, progesterone also functions as the biosynthetic precursor of the male hormone testosterone. The other major female hormones are the estrogens *estradiol* and *estrone*, which effect the estrus and menstrual cycles. These compounds are C_{18} steroids in which the C-19 methyl has been lost and ring A has become aromatic. The male hormone testosterone is the biosynthetic precursor of estradiol.

Progesterone

Estrone

Estradiol

Estrogens are useful clinically in the treatment of menopausal hormone deficiency. In this regard, 17α-ethynylestradiol (from estrone and sodium acetylide), has been found to be a much more active estrogen than either estrone or estradiol. In the course of a search for similar modified steroid hormones, the related ketone compounded with the 3-methyl ether of 17-α-ethynylestradiol was found to be a remarkably effective oral contraceptive which is marketed under the name *Enovid*. This and related products must be ranked among both the most profitable and the most socially significant products of the pharmaceutical industry.

17α-Ethynylestradiol

Enovid ketone

The present large demand for both cortisone-related drugs and oral contraceptives requires a cheap, large-scale source of suitable steroidal starting materials. Unfortunately, efficient laboratory methods for the selective degradation of the side chain of cholesterol have never been discovered. The best starting material at present is *diosgenin*, a steroid which occurs as a glycoside in the tubers of a readily cultivated Mexican yam of the genus *Dioscorea*. Diosgenin can be degraded in a few simple steps in over 60% yield to 16-dehydroprogesterone, which is readily converted in a reasonable number of chemical operations into the sex hormones, the oral contraceptives, and the cortisone-type drugs. The latter always contain an oxygenated function at C-11 which cannot be easily introduced chemically. However, the direct conversion of progesterone to 11α-hydroxyprogesterone can be carried out enzymatically in about 90% yield by the mold *Rhizopus nigricans*; this reaction has become extremely important in the large-scale manufacture of cortisone and related drugs. This process illustrates that, whereas ordinary chemical reactions at alkane-type sites in a molecule are generally quite unselective, biochemical reactions which are enzyme-catalyzed can show remarkable selectivity.

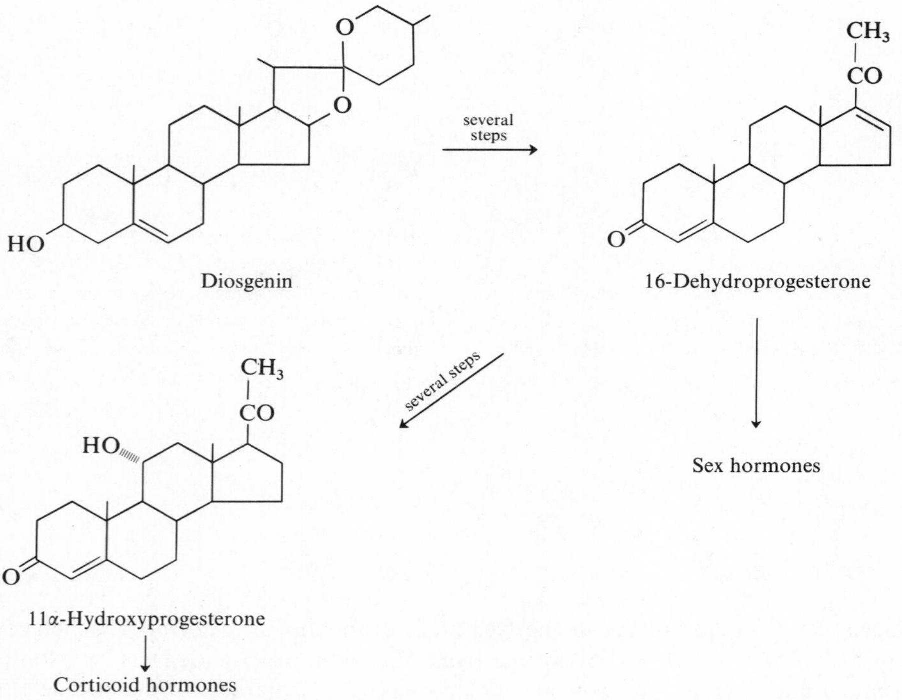

Diosgenin

several steps

16-Dehydroprogesterone

several steps

Sex hormones

11α-Hydroxyprogesterone

Corticoid hormones

Cardiac Glycosides. The cardiac glycosides constitute a group of steroids, mainly of plant origin, which have a powerful action on the heart. Hydrolysis yields one or more sugars (some of them very rare and unusual) and a *steroidal aglycone* containing a lactone ring attached to C-17. *Digitalis* is an extremely valuable drug which is used in the treatment of heart disease. It is prepared by extraction of the purple foxglove (*Digitalis purpurea*) and contains a complex mixture of glycosides, a principal aglycone of which is *digitoxigenin*.

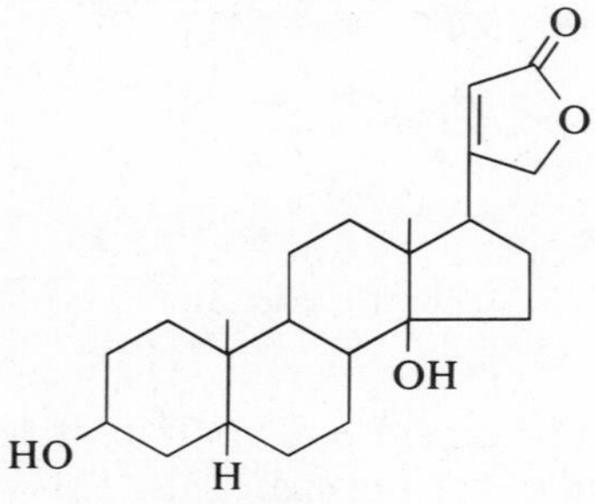

(Note the cis A/B and C/D ring fusions)

Digitoxigenin

The Molting Hormone of Insects. The compound which effects the transformation of a larval into a pupal form has been found to be a highly oxygenated cholesterol derivative. Approximately 25 mg of this hormone, known as *ecdysone*, was isolated in 1954 from 500 kg of silkworm pupae. In 1965, the complete structure was determined by X-ray analysis and in 1966 two syntheses were reported from readily available plant steroids. Since ecdysone can kill insects by causing premature molting and yet has no apparent effect on higher animals, some hopes have been raised that it may prove to be a very effective and elegant insecticide.

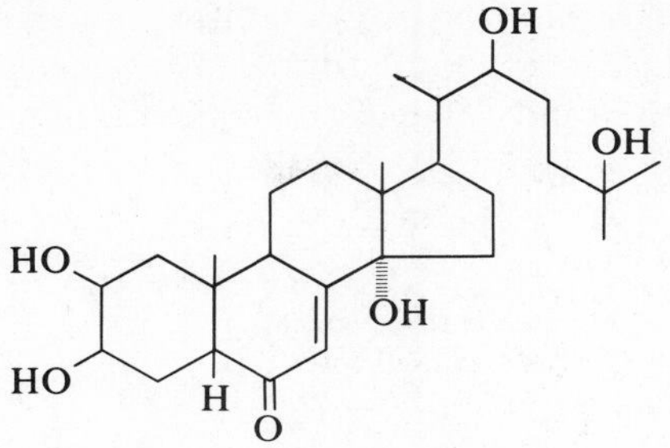

Ecdysone

30.8   Other Natural Products Derived from Acetic Acid

We have already seen that acetic acid, in the form of acetyl-CoA, can be built up by condensation with malonyl-CoA to a unit of the type CH_3COCH_2COSR during the course of fatty acid synthesis. If this process continues, long linear β-diketone chains build up which can serve as starting materials, by way of cyclic aldol reactions, for the formation of a wide variety of natural products, mostly aromatic phenols. Compounds derived from acetic acid in this general manner have been called *acetogenins*. The biosynthetic formation of two representative acetogenins is outlined below.

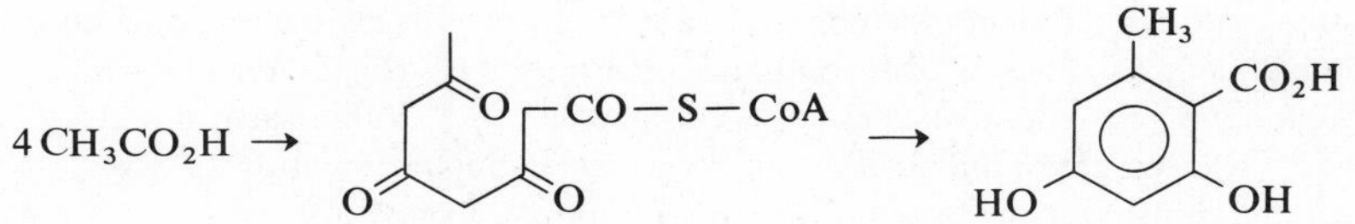

Orsellinic acid
(a lichen acid)

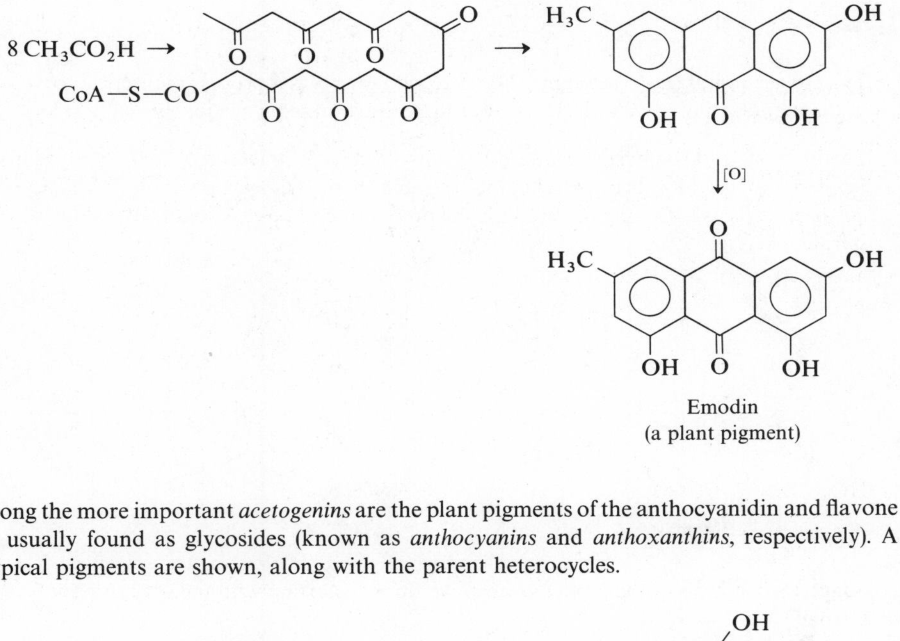

Emodin
(a plant pigment)

Among the more important *acetogenins* are the plant pigments of the anthocyanidin and flavone types, usually found as glycosides (known as *anthocyanins* and *anthoxanthins*, respectively). A few typical pigments are shown, along with the parent heterocycles.

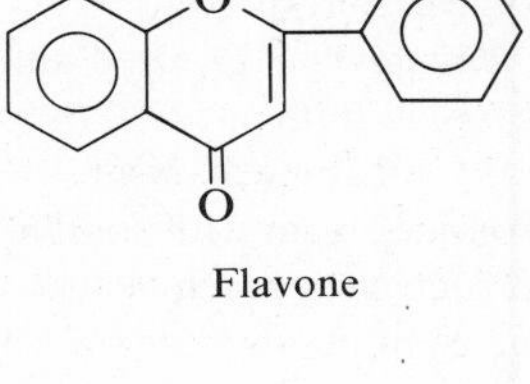

Flavone

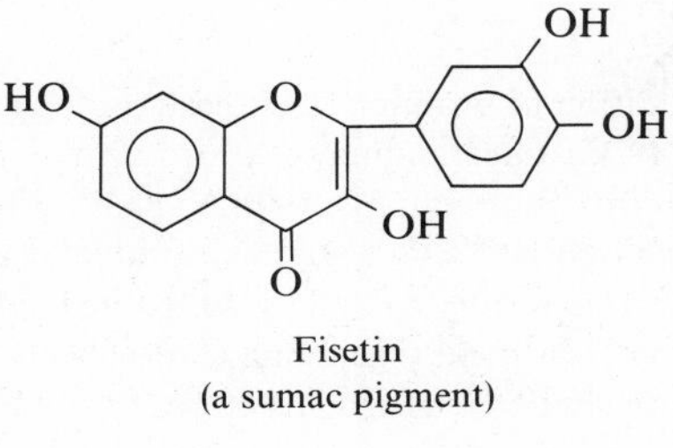

Fisetin
(a sumac pigment)

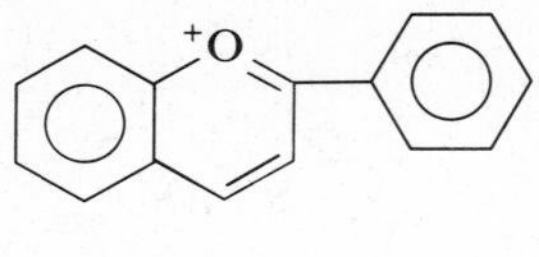

Anthocyanidin cation

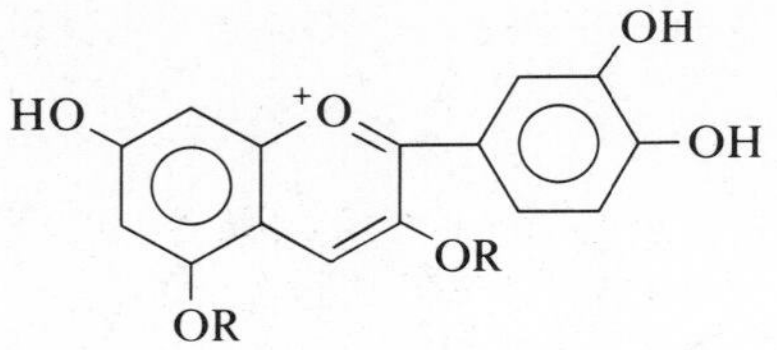

Cyanin (a rose pigment)
(R = β-D-glucose)

PROBLEMS

1. Suggest a detailed stepwise mechanism for the formation of geranyl pyrophosphate from 3-isopentenyl pyrophosphate.

2. Natural rubber is attacked readily by ozone. If the resulting material is treated with H_2O_2 in acetic acid, the major product isolated is levulinic acid, $C_5H_8O_3$.
    (a) What is the structure of levulinic acid?
    (b) If a rubber plant is fed radioactive sodium acetate labeled *only* at the acetate methyl ($*CH_3CO_2Na$), radioactive rubber can be obtained from the latex of the plant after a short time. Degradation of this rubber by ozone yields radioactive levulinic acid. Which specific carbon atoms of the levulinic acid would you expect to be radioactive?

3. Citral is the major constituent of lemon grass oil. When citral is heated for some hours with dilute aqueous alkali, it is converted into a neutral oil ($C_8H_{14}O$). Ozonolysis of this oil, followed by oxidative work-up, yields acetone and levulinic acid.
    (a) What is the structure of the alkali transformation product from citral?
    (b) Give a mechanism for the formation of this compound from citral.

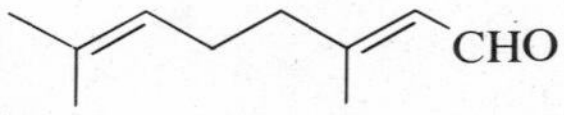

Citral

4. The conversion of cholesterol into 7-dehydrocholesterol is a process of importance in the manufacture of vitamin D_3. Suggest one reaction sequence for this conversion.

5. The plant steroid stigmasterol is readily available on a commercial scale from soybeans. Suggest a method for its conversion into the acid shown below, a compound which has been used as a starting material for the production of pharmaceutically valuable steroids.

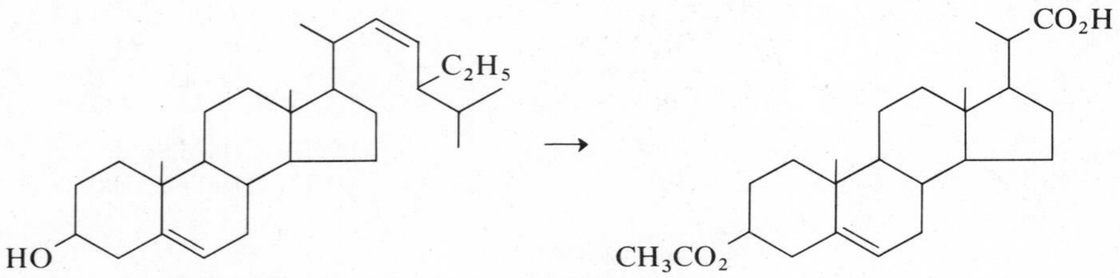

Stigmasterol

6. Suggest a synthesis of the oral contraceptive Enovid starting with the sex hormone estrone.

7. The addition of bromine to cholesterol takes place rapidly to give dibromide A (m.p. 114°C). On standing in chloroform at 40°C, dibromide A is slowly converted into an equilibrium mixture containing 85.5% of an isomeric dibromide B (m.p. 143°C). This reaction has been suggested to involve an internal rearrangement mechanism, since its rate is not affected by added bromide ion. Both dibromides react with sodium iodide in acetone to regenerate cholesterol, but dibromide A reacts very much faster than dibromide B. Assign structures to A and B, and name the compounds systematically.

8. Predict the structure of the neutral crystalline compound formed when cortisone reacts with excess periodic acid.

9. (a) The nmr spectrum of dihydrotestosterone acetate is shown. Interpret as many features as you can.

   (b) Predict the infrared spectrum of dihydrotestosterone acetate in the 1600–1800 cm^{-1} region.

NMR spectrum of dihydrotestosterone acetate, Problem 9.

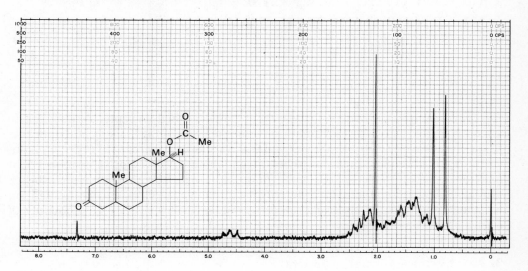

10. The antibiotic *aureomycin*, which has the structure shown, is produced by a fungus. If the fungus is allowed to grow in the presence of $CH_3-^{14}CO_2H$, which carbon atoms of the resulting antibiotic would you expect to contain radioactivity?

Aureomycin

CHAPTER 31

ULTRAVIOLET SPECTRA
AND PHOTOCHEMISTRY

Electronic spectroscopy and *photochemistry* are discussed in this chapter. Although these are often treated as two distinct topics, an understanding of the fundamental principles of the former is necessary to the development of modern concepts of organic photochemistry. If a chemical change is to be brought about by the action of light, that light must be absorbed by the species undergoing the change. The absorption of visible or ultraviolet light by a molecule is ordinarily the result of an electronic transition and can be studied by means of electronic spectroscopy. We will first examine the nature of electronic absorption spectra.

31.1   Electronic Absorption Spectra

When a molecule is irradiated with visible or ultraviolet light, it may undergo an *electronic transition* during which the molecule absorbs a quantum of energy, and an electron is excited from the orbital it occupies in the ground state to another orbital of higher energy (Section 9.1). It is essential, of course, that the frequency of the radiation correspond to the energy separation between the two orbitals involved ($\Delta E = h\nu$).

As an example of a common type of electronic excitation, we may consider ethylene, which absorbs ultraviolet radiation at 170 nm. The ground state of ethylene ($H_2C{=}CH_2$) may be described by 12 molecular orbitals: 6 bonding molecular orbitals corresponding to the four C—H σ bonds, the one C—C σ bond, and the C—C π bond; and 6 antibonding orbitals (5 σ^* and 1 π^*). The electronic configuration of ground-state ethylene will have all 12 valence electrons occupying the six bonding orbitals (Figure 31.1). The absorption of 170 nm light by ethylene results in the promotion of an electron from a bonding π orbital to a π^* orbital. The first excited state of ethylene (Figure 31.1) has the same molecular orbitals as does ground-state ethylene, but the *electronic configuration* is different. Excited ethylene would have 10 electrons in the five σ-bonding orbitals, and 1 electron each in the π and π^* orbitals. This kind of electronic excitation is termed a $\pi \rightarrow \pi^*$ *transition*.

Figure 31.1
Ethylene orbitals involving primarily the C=C bond.

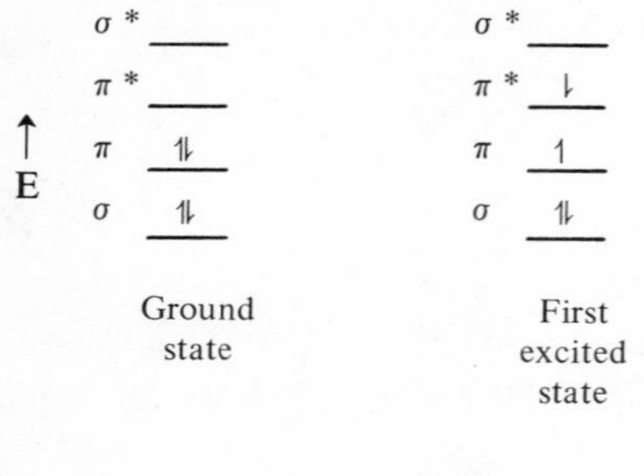

The ultraviolet and visible spectra recorded for molecules are *absorption spectra.* They are measured by placing the substance in a spectrometer which analyzes the transmitted energy relative to the incident energy for a given wavelength. Most excited states are short-lived, and one can reasonably ask, What happens to the absorbed energy? The major fate of the absorbed energy in the ultraviolet region is reemission of light as *phosphorescence* or *fluorescence,* or its conversion into thermal energy. However, as will be taken up in Section 31.7, in some cases the absorbed energy induces *photochemical reactions.*

For a given excitation process, a molecule will absorb a discrete amount of energy which is related to the frequency of the light that causes the transition by the equation

$$E = h\nu = hc/\lambda$$

where h is Planck's constant, ν is the frequency, λ is the wavelength, and c is the velocity of light. The amount of energy involved in the excitation is inversely proportional to the wavelength of light needed to cause the transition. Light of short wavelength is more energetic than light of long wavelength. In ultraviolet and visible spectroscopy, we are concerned with wavelengths of about 50 to 900 nm, corresponding to electronic excitation energies of 1000 to 35 kcal/mole (for example, the excitation of an electron of ethylene to the π^* orbital, λ_{max} 170 nm, requires 135 kcal/mole). These are quite high energies and are exceeded only by radiation in the cosmic ray, gamma ray, and X-ray regions. Since air is opaque to radiation of very short wavelength, measurements below 190 nm must be carried out in vacuum, and the region of the electromagnetic spectrum of wavelength 50 to 190 nm is often called the *vacuum ultraviolet.* This region is not accessible with the usual spectrometers, and measurements at these wavelengths are not often made.

If all molecules of a substance were to absorb ultraviolet radiation of a given wavelength, we would expect to observe a series of *absorption lines,* corresponding to each discrete transition. However, the molecules in any group exist in a number of different vibrational states, each state differing from the next by a relatively small amount of energy. When this group of molecules undergoes the same electronic transition, there are simultaneous changes in the vibrational and rotational states by varying amounts. The sum of these absorptions gives rise to an *absorption band,* rather than an absorption line. Electronic absorption bands are therefore usually quite broad as compared to infrared or nmr (nuclear magnetic resonance) bands.

The wavelength of light corresponding to maximum absorption (the peak of an absorption band) is designated as λ_{max}. The intensity of a particular absorption band is usually given by the *molar extinction coefficient,* ε (or $\log \varepsilon$), derived from the Beer-Lambert Law as

$$\varepsilon = \frac{\log I_0/I}{cl}$$

where I_0 is the intensity of the incident light, I is the intensity of the transmitted light ($\log I/I_0 = A$ = optical density as recorded on most spectrometers), c is the molar concentration, and l is the path length of the solution in centimeters. The magnitude of ε for a particular absorption is associated with the *probability* of the particular electronic transition. Not all transitions have the same probability; those with a high probability will have extinction coefficients which are large ($\varepsilon = 10^4 - 10^5$), while those with low probability will show small extinction coefficients ($\varepsilon = 10^0 - 10^3$). Unfortunately, there is no *simple* way to predict these probabilities. There are, however, some rules that can be used as a guide and these are given in the next section.

31.2   Types of Electronic Transitions

Up to this point, we have mentioned only the electronic transition that involves excitation of an electron from one molecular π orbital to a higher-energy one, the $\pi \longrightarrow \pi^*$ transition. Other important transitions may be designated as $\sigma \longrightarrow \sigma^*$, $n \longrightarrow \sigma^*$, and $n \longrightarrow \pi^*$.

Since σ bonds are in general very strong, the separation between σ and σ^* orbitals is very large, and the energy required to cause a $\sigma \rightarrow \sigma^*$ *transition* is very high; therefore, organic compounds in which *all* of the valence electrons are utilized in σ-bond formation do not show absorption in the normal ultraviolet region. Saturated hydrocarbons, for example, methane, propane, and cyclohexane, are of this type, and the λ_{max} for each of these compounds is below 140 nm.

The excitation of an electron of an unshared pair (nonbonding electrons) on nitrogen, oxygen, sulfur, or halogens to an antibonding σ-molecular orbital is called an $n \rightarrow \sigma^*$ *transition*. Since the energy of an n orbital is higher than that of a σ orbital (Figure 31.2), these transitions are of lower energy than $\sigma \rightarrow \sigma^*$ transitions. Examples of molecules showing absorption because of $n \rightarrow \sigma^*$ transitions are methanol, λ_{max} 183 nm ($\varepsilon = 500$); 1-iodobutane, $\lambda_{max} = 257$ nm ($\varepsilon = 486$); trimethylamine, $\lambda_{max} = 227$ nm ($\varepsilon = 900$).

Figure 31.2

Relative energies and extinction coefficients of electronic spectra (H, high extinction; L, low extinction).

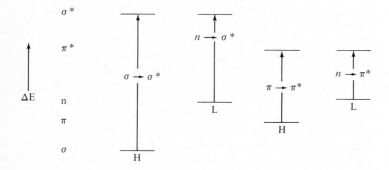

If an unshared pair of electrons is associated with an atom that is attached to or is part of an unsaturated center in a molecule, a still lower energy transition is possible. This involves the excitation of an n electron to an antibonding π orbital: the $n \rightarrow \pi^*$ *transition*. This type of transition is an important feature in the spectra of aldehydes and ketones. For example, the $n \rightarrow \pi^*$ transition for acetone occurs at 279 nm ($\varepsilon = 15$).

It would be profitable to consider in more detail the absorption characteristics of a compound containing a carbonyl group $>C{=}O$, as compounds containing this group are very common, and the spectral features of these compounds are of practical use. Two bands can be seen in the spectrum of a ketone or aldehyde, corresponding to a high-intensity $\pi \rightarrow \pi^*$ transition at short wavelength (about 180–200 nm) and a low-intensity (less probable) $n \rightarrow \pi^*$ transition at about 280 nm. In simple cases it is easy to tell whether a transition is $n \rightarrow \pi^*$ or $\pi \rightarrow \pi^*$ by inspection, since the former have low transition probabilities ($\varepsilon < 200$) while the latter are quite high ($\varepsilon > 1000$). In complex molecules intermediate values are sometimes found.

Figure 31.3 depicts an orbital-electron representation of these two carbonyl group transitions. The orbitals involved in the excitation are shown; however, the average electron distribution is not adequately pictured. It is quite apparent that for the "allowed" (high-intensity) $\pi \rightarrow \pi^*$ transition, both orbitals have their axis in the same plane (paper); whereas for the "forbidden" (low-intensity) $n \rightarrow \pi^*$ excitation perpendicular planes are involved. In Figure 31.4, the ultraviolet spectrum of cyclopentanone is given as a typical example.

Because saturated hydrocarbons, and alcohols and ethers containing only saturated alkyl groups, do not absorb (are transparent) in the 200–1000 nm range, they are the

Orbital–electron representation of $\pi \rightarrow \pi^*$ and $n \rightarrow \pi^*$ transitions for a carbonyl group (π and *n* orbitals are shown as solid loops, the π^* orbital is grey, σ bonds are shown as solid lines; only one *n* orbital is shown.)

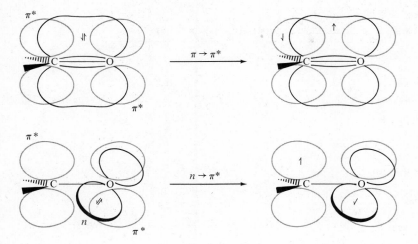

most useful solvents for spectral determinations in this region. Solvents used in ultraviolet spectroscopy are isooctane (2,2,4-trimethylpentane), water, methanol, ethanol, tetrahydrofuran, and dioxane.

31.3 Chromophoric Groups

An isolated, covalently unsaturated group that shows a characteristic absorption in the ultraviolet (or visible) region is called a *chromophore*. If a series of compounds all have the most useful solvents for spectral determinations in this region. Solvents used in ultraviolet spectroscopy are isooctane (2,2,4-trimethylpentane), water, methanol,

Figure 31.4
Ultraviolet spectrum of cyclopentanone in ethanol at a concentration of 3.8×10^{-2} moles per liter (1 cm quartz cell).

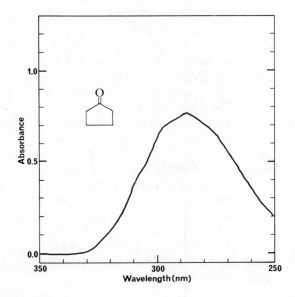

same chromophore, and if perturbing structural features, such as attached heteroatoms or additional conjugated unsaturated groups (see next section), are absent, all of the compounds will absorb at nearly the same wavelength. A list of the absorptions of some typical, isolated chromophoric groups is given in Table 31.1.

Table 31.1   Characteristic Absorption for Selected Unsaturated Chromophoric Groups

Chromophore	Compound	λ_{max}(nm)	ε_{max}	Solvent
$C{=}C$	Ethylene	170	15,800	(Vapor)
	trans-2-Hexene	184	10,000	(Vapor)
	Cyclohexene	182	7,600	Hexane
$-C{\equiv}C-$	1-Octyne	185	2,000	Heptane
		222	126	
$C{=}O$	Acetaldehyde	277 $(n \rightarrow \pi^*)$	8	Water
		290 $(n \rightarrow \pi^*)$	16	Heptane
	Acetone	279 $(n \rightarrow \pi^*)$	15	Heptane
$C{=}O$ / HO	Acetic acid	204	60	Water
$C{=}O$ / Cl	Acetyl chloride	235	53	Hexane
$C{=}N{-}OH$	Acetone oxime	190	5,000	Water
$C{=}N_2$	Diazomethane	410	1,200	(Vapor)
$-C{\equiv}N$	Acetonitrile	160	Weak	(Vapor)
$-N{=}N-$	Azomethane	340	5	Ethanol
$-N^+(O)(O^-)$	Nitromethane	271	19	Ethanol
$S{=}O$	Cyclohexyl methyl sulfoxide	210	1,500	Ethanol

In general, alkyl substituents attached to a double bond cause a shift of the absorption maximum to longer wavelengths (a *red shift*); consider, for example, ethylene, λ_{max} 170 nm, in comparison with 1-butene, λ_{max} 175 nm, and isobutylene, λ_{max} 188 nm. This shift to longer wavelength can be qualitatively explained as resulting from changes in the π and π^* energy levels as a result of the inductive effect of the alkyl group. Since the red shift corresponds to a decrease in energy, the π-energy level was raised, or the π^* level lowered, or some of each. Cyclic alkenes show absorption characteristics that closely resemble those of acyclic compounds, indicating that the presence or absence of a ring, or its size, have little influence on the ultraviolet absorption.

When a heteroatom (O, N, S, Cl, etc.) containing a nonbonding electron pair is attached to a double bond, the compound absorbs at a longer wavelength than if the heteroatom were absent. The groups bearing these atoms are said to be *auxochromic* (color-enhancing), because, while they do not in themselves show absorption above 200 nm, yet, when attached to a given chromophore, they alter both the wavelength and the intensity of an absorption maximum. Common auxochromic groups are *hydroxyl*, *alkoxyl*, *amino*, *sulfhydryl*, and *halogen*. For example, benzene shows λ_{max} 255 nm ($\varepsilon = 230$); whereas aniline, $C_6H_5\overset{..}{N}H_2$, has λ_{max} 280 nm ($\varepsilon = 1430$).

When auxochromic groups are attached directly to a carbonyl group, the $\pi \rightarrow \pi^*$ transition exhibits the expected red shift; however, the $n \rightarrow \pi^*$ transition is significantly displaced to shorter wavelength (*blue shift*). Often these two transitions are very close in energy, and either may be at longer wavelength depending on the heteroatom. It is difficult to disentangle these absorptions in such compounds as carboxylic acids, esters, or amides.

EXERCISE 31.1

Draw the structure of diazomethane (CH_2N_2) showing all of the valence shell atomic orbitals. Draw the molecular orbitals, indicate which are occupied by electrons, and indicate their relative energies. Predict what kinds of features will be found in the ultraviolet spectrum, and discuss the fact that the compound has a bright yellow color.

EXERCISE 31.2

Suggest an explanation in terms of orbitals for the fact that azobenzene is a deep red-orange color, while hydrazobenzene is colorless.

31.4   Conjugated Systems

If two (or more) chromophoric groups in a molecule are separated by two or more single bonds, the ultraviolet spectrum of the molecule will usually be a simple addition of the spectra for the two isolated chromophores. If the two chromophoric groups are conjugated, however, they essentially form a new chromophore, and a marked effect is seen in the spectrum. For example, in the conjugated molecule butadiene, λ_{max} 217 nm ($\varepsilon = 21,000$), the π and π^* orbitals have energies which are much closer together than are those in ethylene (see Figure 7.15), resulting in a lower excitation energy. All conjugated, acyclic dienes show intense $\pi \rightarrow \pi^*$ absorption in the 215–230 nm region, corresponding to a red shift of some 40 nm with respect to the unconjugated alkene chromophore. Further conjugation with another chromophore results in an additional red shift with an accompanying increase in intensity. Extreme examples are the carotenoids (Section 30.5), which contain many conjugated double bonds and are highly colored.

Monocyclic 1,3-dienes show a much more marked red shift; however, the absorption intensity is quite reduced. Typically, 1,3-cyclopentadiene shows λ_{max} 239 nm ($\varepsilon = 3400$), and for 1,3-cyclohexadiene λ_{max} is 256 nm ($\varepsilon = 8000$). Table 31.2 summarizes the absorption characteristics of some conjugated dienes.

Table 31.2   Absorption Data for Conjugated Alkenes

Compound	λ_{max}(nm)	ε_{max}
1,3-Butadiene	217	21,000
cis-1,3-Pentadiene	223	22,600
trans-1,3-Pentadiene	223.5	23,000
2,3-Dimethyl-1,3-butadiene	226	21,400
1,3-Cyclopentadiene	239	3,400
1,3-Cyclohexadiene	256	8,000
cis-$C_6H_5CH{=}CHC_6H_5$	280	10,500
trans-$C_6H_5CH{=}CHC_6H_5$	295	29,000
1,3,5-Hexatriene	253	50,000
	263	52,500
	274	50,000

Compounds that contain a series of conjugated chromophoric groups will appear colored if they absorb radiation above 400 nm. Because ultraviolet bands are usually broad, a peak at λ_{max} 350 nm with a reasonably high extinction coefficient will usually extend into the visible region. As a general rule, a compound will appear colored if it contains four or five conjugated chromophoric and auxochromic groups. There are some important exceptions to this generalization: α-diketones, azo and diazo compounds, thiocarbonyl compounds and monomeric nitroso compounds are all colored.

Prediction of Ultraviolet Spectra. Several empirical rules (referred to as the *Woodward–Fieser Rules*) have been developed which enable one to predict the λ_{max} of conjugated dienes having alkyl substituents located on the unsaturated linkages. The rules work reasonably well because of the approximately additive nature of the effects of substituents. A diene base value of 217 nm (butadiene) is used, and for each alkyl group attached to the doubly-bonded carbons, 5 nm is added to the base value. In addition, 5 nm is also added for each double bond of the conjugated system that is exocyclic to a ring. The calculated values are usually within 2 or 3 nm of the experimental values. Two examples of the calculation of λ_{max} are given below.

For 2,4-hexadiene

$$CH_3CH=CH-CH=CHCH_3$$

$$[\lambda_{max}^{obs}\ 227\ nm]$$

	217 nm	(base)
	10 nm	(2 methyl groups)
λ_{max}^{calcd}	227 nm	

For 3-cyclohexylidenepropene

$$[\lambda_{max}^{obs}\ 236.5\ nm]$$

	217 nm	(base)
	10 nm	(2 alkyl groups, a, b)
	5 nm	(exocyclic double bond)
λ_{max}^{calcd}	232 nm	

EXERCISE 31.3

Calculate λ_{max} for

When dealing with conjugated dienes contained in alicyclic systems, the calculations are modified somewhat. If the double bonds are in two rings (heteroannular dienes), the base used is 214 nm; with homoannular dienes (both double bonds in the same ring) the base value is 253 nm. Again, a 5 nm correction is added for each alkyl substituent and exocyclic double bond.

For

$$[\lambda_{max}^{obs}\ 235\ nm]$$

214 nm (base)
15 nm (3 alkyl groups, a, b, c)
5 nm (exocyclic double bond)
λ_{max}^{calcd} 234 nm

And for

Ergosterol
$$[\lambda_{max}^{obs}\ 282\ nm]$$

253 nm (base)
20 nm (4 alkyl groups, a–d)
10 nm (2 exocyclic double bonds)
λ_{max}^{calcd} 283 nm

Conjugated Carbonyl Groups. Compounds having a carbonyl group in conjugation with a carbon–carbon double bond show an intense absorption in the 215–250 nm range ($\pi \rightarrow \pi^*$, red shift because of conjugation), and a weaker $n \rightarrow \pi^*$ transition around 310–330 nm (also shifted to longer wavelength by conjugation). Sometimes the $n \rightarrow \pi^*$ band cannot be observed because it is obscured by the very intense ($\varepsilon \sim 10,000$–$20,000$) $\pi \rightarrow \pi^*$ band. Table 31.3 gives some absorption data for typical conjugated aldehydes and ketones, and the spectrum of mesityl oxide is given in Figure 31.5.

Table 31.3 Absorption Data for Conjugated Aldehydes and Ketones in Alcohol Solution

Compound	λ_{max}(nm)	ε_{max}
CH₃CCH=CH₂ (O)	213	7,100
	320	27
CH₃C—C=CH₂ (O, CH₃)	218	7,800
	315	25
CH₃C—CH=C (CH₃, CH₃) (O)	236	11,700
	315	57
CH₃CH=CHCHO	218	18,000
	320	30
(cyclohexenone)=O	227	10,300

Figure 31.5
Ultraviolet spectrum of mesityl oxide in ethanol. Curve (A): 2.2×10^{-2} moles per liter, 1 cm cell. Curve (B): 7.3×10^{-5} moles per liter, 1 cm cell.

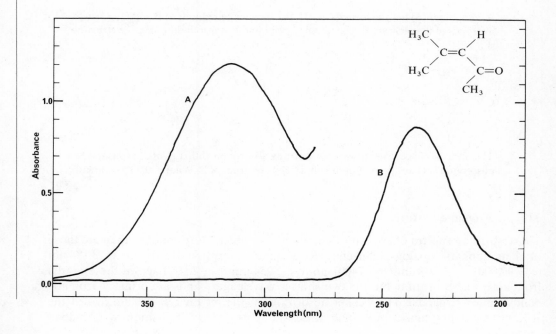

The Woodward–Fieser rules for predicting the absorption maxima ($\pi \rightarrow \pi^*$) of α,β-unsaturated ketones have found wide utility, especially for characterization of unknown structures. The parent system is considered to be

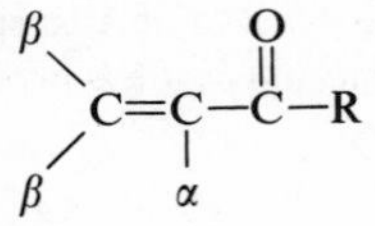

to which a base value of 215 nm is assigned if the enone system is acyclic or in a six-membered ring (for a five-membered ring enone the base is 202 nm). For an α-alkyl subsituent, 10 nm are added; for each β-alkyl group, 12 nm are added. An additional 5 nm is added if the carbon–carbon double bond is exocyclic. By application of this technique, the predicted λ_{max} of mesityl oxide would be

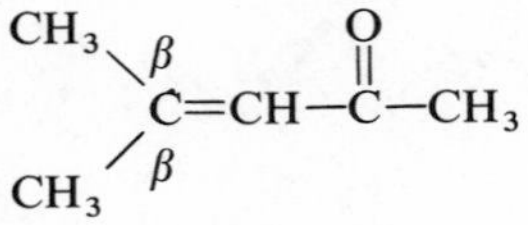

215 nm (base)
24 nm (2 β-alkyl groups)
λ_{max}^{calcd} 239 nm

Mesityl oxide
[$\lambda_{max}^{obs} = 237$ nm]

Another example is

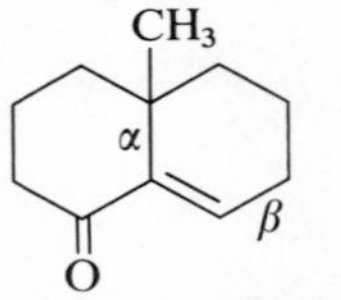

215 nm (base)
10 nm (α-alkyl group)
12 nm (β-alkyl group)
5 nm (exocyclic double bond)
λ_{max}^{calcd} 242 nm

[$\lambda_{max}^{obs} = 244$ nm]

These empirical correlations have found extensive application. Increments have been assigned for α and β auxochromic groups, and for additional conjugated double bonds. Further, similar empirical correlations have been made for α,β-unsaturated aldehydes and α,β-unsaturated acids.

EXERCISE 31.4

A compound (A) has the formula $C_{11}H_{16}O$ and can be reduced to B, $C_{11}H_{18}O$, with hydrogen in the presence of palladium. Compound B was found to have the structure shown.

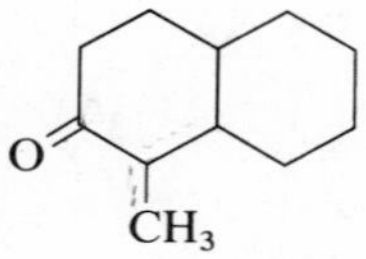

(B)

The ultraviolet spectrum of A showed strong absorption with λ_{max} at 225 nm, and this absorption was not present in the ultraviolet spectrum of B. What is the structure of A?

31.5   Aromatic Systems

The absorption spectra of aromatic compounds are much more complex than are those of their aliphatic analogs. Benzene shows three absorption bands, at λ_{max} 184 nm ($\varepsilon = 47{,}000$), λ_{max} 204 nm ($\varepsilon = 7400$), and λ_{max} 254 nm ($\varepsilon = 204$). Each of these results from a $\pi \rightarrow \pi^*$ transition, but the two shorter wavelength bands are primary aromatic bands (called E bands). The weaker absorption in the region 230–270 nm (called the B band) contains considerable fine structure. This $\pi \rightarrow \pi^*$ transition is forbidden (would not occur in the symmetrical rigid molecule) but becomes weakly allowed by coupling with vibrational motions of the molecule which destroys the symmetry. The uv spectrum of benzene is delineated in Figure 31.6.

Figure 31.6
Ultraviolet spectrum of benzene in hexane solution.

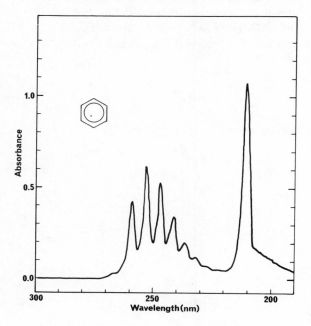

The attachment of almost any substituent to the benzene ring results in a red shift of both the E and the B bands. If the attached group is a chromophore (an unsaturated group), the B band undergoes a red shift of about 30 nm together with an increase in intensity. Also, a new, very intense $\pi \rightarrow \pi^*$ band appears in the 240–290 nm region, and this often obscures the B band.

Substitution on the benzene ring by auxochromic groups ($-OH$, $-NH_2$, $-OR$, $-Cl$, etc.) also shift the E and B bands to longer wavelength. Usually the B band is altered in such a way that the intensity is increased and the fine structure is diminished.

31.6   Excited States

The photochemistry of molecules in solution is really the chemistry of excited states. By carefully controlling the frequency of light employed, it becomes possible to excite selectively the electrons associated with specific groups of atoms in a molecule without significantly altering the energy levels of other electrons. It is this potential selectivity which makes photochemistry such a valuable tool—reactions can be run under mild conditions and at low temperatures, and specific products can be obtained that would be inaccessible under thermal conditions because of unfavorable equilibria or side reactions.

Electronic excitation causes a reorganization of the valence electrons in a molecule. The electron distributions in excited states are different from those of the ground state. Chemical changes are controlled mainly by valence-shell electron distributions, and the chemistry of molecules in electronically excited states will be considerably different from that of ground-state molecules.

Before considering specific photochemical processes, we should examine the factors involved in the generation, lifetimes, and destruction of photoexcited states. This approach is facilitated by inspection of Figure 31.7 (*a Jablonski diagram*), which represents the energy transformations that result from absorption of ultraviolet radiation by a molecule. The molecule is excited to one of the excited *singlet* electronic states (here called S_1 and S_2) in which one electron is in an orbital of higher energy than it was in the ground state. (There are a great many such states possible, as any electron may be promoted to any empty orbital, an antibonding orbital such as π^* or σ^* or a higher atomic orbital such as $3d$, $4p$, $5f$, etc.) A singlet (all electron spins paired, i.e., $\downarrow\ \uparrow$) excited state is generated on direct irradiation because molecules in the ground state are singlets (with rare exceptions) and excitation follows the law of conservation of spin (i.e., transitions between states of different multiplicity are forbidden). The conversion from ground-state singlet (S_0) to the first excited triplet (T_1) is thus of exceedingly low probability (forbidden transition).

Figure 31.7
Energy transformations from absorption of ultraviolet radiation.

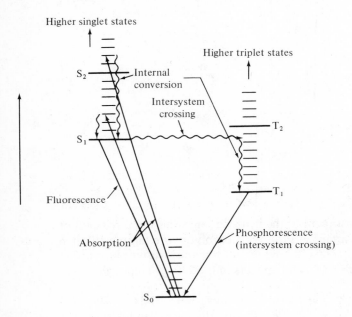

If the excited molecule is in state S_2 (or any higher S state) it drops back to the singlet excited state of lowest energy (S_1) by a series of radiationless transitions (indicated by wavy lines), called *internal conversion*. This whole process takes place in about 10^{-10} to 10^{-12} seconds. The excess vibrational and rotational energy which molecules attain via the radiationless process is rapidly dissipated as heat by collisions with adjacent molecules (including solvent).

From S_1, the molecule may decay by several major pathways: (1) it may give up energy and go back to S_0 by emitting radiation of the appropriate wavelength, a process which is termed *fluorescence* (fluorescence lifetimes are on the order of 10^{-7} to 10^{-9} seconds); (2) it may give up energy as heat (thermal deactivation) and drop back to S_0; (3) it may react chemically (photochemistry of S_1); or (4) it may undergo radiationless crossover, requiring spin-flipping, to T_1 (the first excited *triplet*). The latter process is called *intersystem crossing*, and the lifetimes are of the order of 10^{-11} to 10^{-7} seconds—often fast enough to compete with fluorescence for deactivation of S_1.

Triplet states have electrons that are not spin-paired; they are diradicals. The first excited triplet (T_1) is of lower energy than S_1 because electronic repulsions are less. [Hund's rule applies to molecules as it does to atoms; when two orbitals each contain one electron, the configuration with parallel spins ↑ ↑ (the triplet) is of lower energy than the configuration of electrons with antiparallel spins ↓ ↑ (the singlet).] Therefore, intersystem crossing followed by internal conversion is an exothermic process. The T_1 state is much longer lived than the S_1 state. The emission of radiation associated with a $T_1 \rightarrow S_0$ conversion is called *phosphorescence*; such triplet–singlet conversions (just like singlet–triplet excitations) have a low probability, however. Consequently T_1 lifetimes are usually of the order of 10^{-4} second. T_1 persists for a longer time than S_1, and the majority of *photochemical reactions* occur from this (T_1) excited state.

For many molecules, intersystem crossing $(S_1 \rightarrow T_1)$ is not very efficient. If this were the only way to produce excited triplets, photochemistry via T_1 would be rather limited. Fortunately, it is possible to selectively excite a molecule that produces triplets in high yield (by intersystem crossing), and then allow this molecule (if its triplet energy, E_T, is higher than the triplet energy of the acceptor) to transfer its excitation energy to a second molecule. Since the transfer of energy requires overall spin conservation, the second molecule is converted to its first excited triplet, while the donor molecule goes from a triplet to a ground-state singlet. This intermolecular method for generating triplets is called *sensitization*. Sensitization may be depicted in stepwise fashion as follows, where D is the *sensitizer* (donor) molecule and A is the suitable *acceptor* whose triplet we wish to generate.

$$D_0 \xrightarrow{h\nu} D^1 \qquad \text{(excitation)}$$

$$D^1 \rightarrow D^3 \qquad \text{(intersystem crossing)}$$

$$D^3 + A_0 \rightarrow D_0 + A^3 \qquad \text{(energy transfer with conservation of spin)}$$

$$A^3 \rightarrow \text{Products} \qquad \text{(photochemistry)}$$

A few common sensitizers are benzene ($E_T = 85$ kcal/mole), benzophenone ($E_T = 70$ kcal/mole), biacetyl ($E_T = 55$ kcal/mole), and chrysene ($E_T = 57$ kcal/mole).

What happens during a photochemical reaction to the total energy of the system between the point at which a photon (quantum of light) is absorbed by a molecule and the time ground-state products are formed? The system has absorbed a large amount of light energy and we would like to know where it ends up. A general scheme is as follows:

$$S_0 \xrightarrow{h\nu} S^* \begin{array}{l} \nearrow \text{Radiant energy (emission)} + S_0 \\ \rightarrow \text{Thermal energy (nonradiative)} + S_0 \\ \searrow \text{Chemical energy } (\Delta G, \text{nonradiative}) \end{array}$$

The first two represent *photophysical processes*, and all three pathways can be in competition. The chemical energy is utilized by fragmentation of the molecule giving radical or ionic intermediates, or it causes concerted rearrangements to occur. The products ultimately end up in their ground states. Since the reaction $S^* \rightarrow$ products is exothermic, some of the energy will show as ΔG for this reaction. Furthermore, if the overall reaction $S_0 \rightarrow$ products is endothermic, a portion of the chemical energy is retained as internal energy in these products.

31.7   The Photochemistry of Ketones

We will begin our study of photochemical reactions by looking at ketones. These compounds undergo a variety of reactions which are well understood. There appear to be four primary photochemical processes which are important for ketones in solution: (1) cleavage of the bond α to the carbonyl group; (2) cleavage of a bond β to the carbonyl accompanied by intramolecular hydrogen abstraction; (3) intermolecular hydrogen abstraction by the carbonyl oxygen atom; and (4) addition of the carbonyl oxygen atom to a carbon–carbon double bond. Each of the primary reactions occurs from the n, π^*

triplet state (T_1 in Figure 31.7). The reaction products that are finally isolated arise by way of secondary reactions which occur *after* the primary stage. In many cases the four processes are competitive, and the *major* pathway followed is sensitive to structural variations in the ketone and to the choice of solvent.

α-Bond cleavage is exemplified by the photolysis of cyclohexanone. This reaction results in the formation of mixture of 5-hexenal, cyclopentane, and carbon monoxide.

Note that while an arrow with a two-pronged head (⤳) is used to represent the motion of an electron pair, the motion of a single electron is represented by an arrowhead with a single prong (⇀).

The accepted mechanism detailed above involves initial fragmentation to give a diradical. This is often called *Type I cleavage*. Loss of carbon monoxide (photodecarbonylation) gives the pentamethylene diradical, which will collapse to cyclopentane. Alternatively, the initial diradical can undergo intramolecular hydrogen abstraction via a favored, six-membered cyclic transition state leading to the unsaturated aldehyde. In solution the latter secondary process is usually favored. Photodecarbonylation becomes important if ring strain is relieved or if relatively stable radicals are produced by α cleavage.

The β-cleavage reaction (*Type II cleavage*) occurs whenever hydrogen atoms are suitably positioned five atoms from the carbonyl oxygen. This photodecomposition also involves intramolecular hydrogen transfer utilizing a cyclic transition state of six member atoms, as shown for methyl neopentyl ketone.

If, however, a relatively stable radical can be generated by the *intramolecular* hydrogen abstraction, then cyclobutanol formation can compete with β elimination. For example,

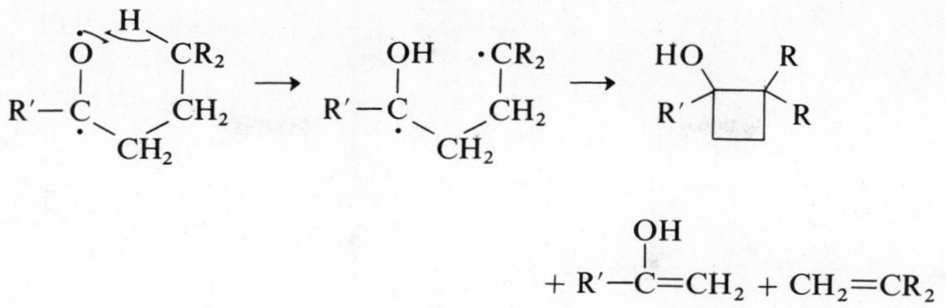

$$+ \ R'-\overset{OH}{\underset{|}{C}}=CH_2 + CH_2=CR_2$$

When ketones and aldehydes are irradiated in solvents that can donate hydrogen atoms, bimolecular reduction to a pinacol will occur. The most useful solvents for this purpose are alcohols (especially secondary alcohols) and alkylbenzenes such as cumene or toluene. If the alcohol chosen is derived from the ketone to be reduced, only one product results. The proposed mechanism involves *intermolecular hydrogen abstraction* by the carbonyl oxygen atom of the photoexcited ketone, as shown below for the photoreduction of benzophenone by an alcohol. A benzhydrol radical and an alcohol radical are produced. The alcohol radical transfers another hydrogen atom to benzophenone to give a ketone ($R_2C=O$) and a second benzhydrol radical. Coupling of two benzhydrol radicals affords the pinacol.

$$Ph_2C=O \xrightarrow{hv} S_1 \rightarrow Ph_2\dot{C}-\dot{O} \quad (T_1, n, \pi^*)$$

$$Ph_2\dot{C}-\dot{O} + R_2CHOH \rightarrow Ph_2\dot{C}-OH + R_2\dot{C}-OH$$

$$R_2\dot{C}-OH + Ph_2C=O \rightarrow Ph_2\dot{C}-OH + \underline{R_2C=O}$$

$$2Ph_2\dot{C}-OH \rightarrow \underset{\underset{OH \ \ OH}{|\qquad|}}{Ph_2C-CPh_2}$$

Benzopinacol

Finally, the fourth primary process can occur if a ketone (or aldehyde) is photolyzed in the presence of an alkene. Addition of the n, π^* triplet of the ketone to the alkene (*anti*-Markovnikov orientation, see Section 15.8) gives a biradical. Spin inversion and secondary cyclization lead to a trimethylene oxide (an oxetane).

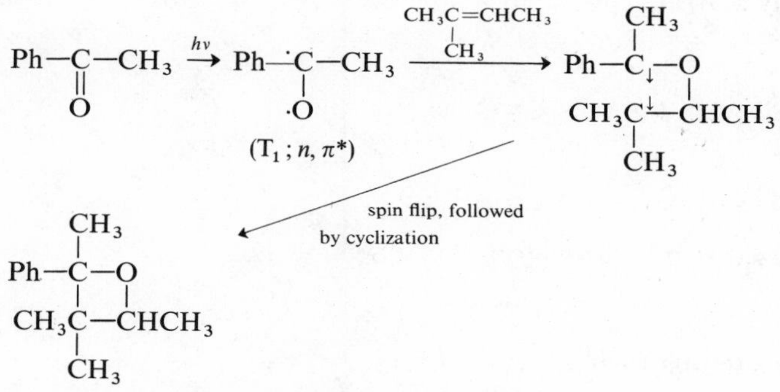

2-Phenyl-2,3,3,4-tetramethyloxetane

EXERCISE 31.5

Predict the products of the following photochemical reactions of ketones:

(a)

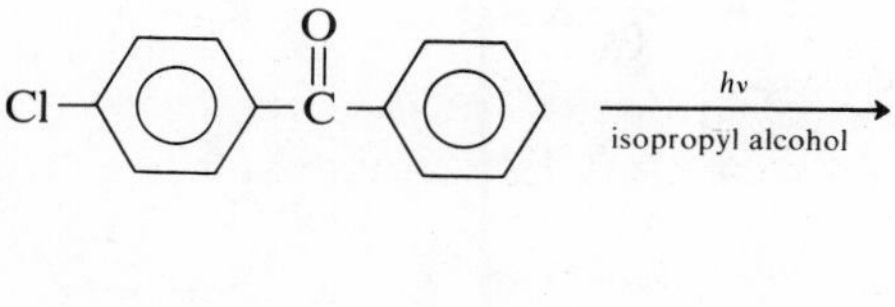

(b)

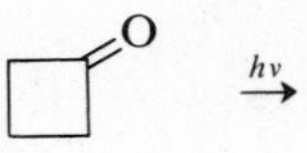

(c)

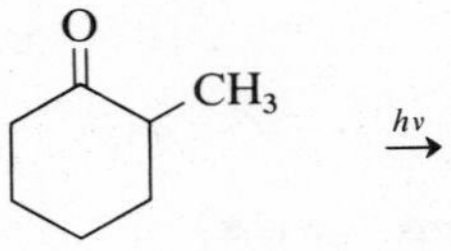

(d)

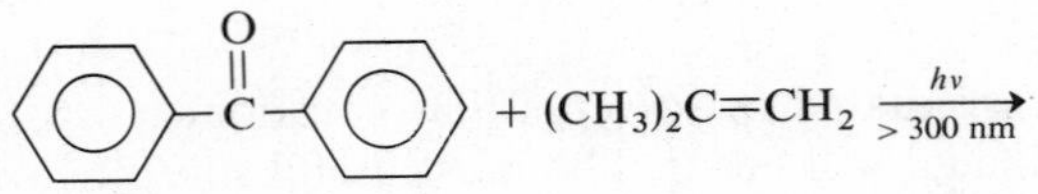

EXERCISE 31.6

Explain the fact that acetophenone ($E_T = 74$ kcal/mole) will not add to a conjugated diene ($E_T = 60$ kcal/mole) to give an oxetane. Rather the diene undergoes dimerization instead.

31.8   The Photodecomposition of Diazoalkanes

One of the most important methods for the generation of carbenes is the photodecomposition of diazoalkanes. Methylene ($:CH_2$) is produced photochemically from diazomethane (Section 22.8). It may be "trapped" by addition to an alkene or by insertion

$$CH_2N_2 \xrightarrow{hv} :CH_2 + N_2$$

into carbon–hydrogen bonds. An especially useful carbene, *carboethoxymethylene*, may be generated by the photodecomposition of ethyl diazoacetate. If this reaction is carried out in the presence of an alkene, a carboethoxycyclopropane results.

$$N_2CHCOOC_2H_5 \xrightarrow{hv} \quad \text{—COOC}_2H_5 + N_2$$

α-Diazoketones also lose nitrogen smoothly upon ultraviolet irradiation to give α-ketocarbenes, which usually rearrange to ketenes:

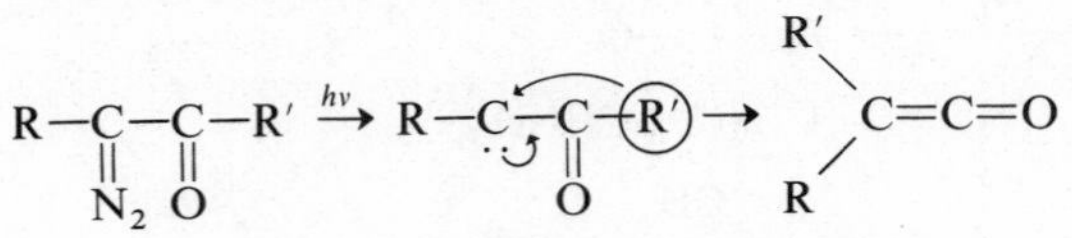

$$R-\underset{\underset{N_2}{\|}}{C}-\underset{\underset{O}{\|}}{C}-R' \xrightarrow{hv} R-\overset{..}{C}-\underset{\underset{O}{\|}}{C}-R' \rightarrow \underset{R}{\overset{R'}{\diagdown}}C=C=O$$

α-Ketocarbene   A ketene

This reaction is a light-catalyzed *Wolff rearrangement* (see Section 22.8).

31.9   Photochemical Cycloaddition Reactions of Alkenes

The addition reaction between two substituted alkenes has become a very important synthetic route to substituted four-membered ring compounds (cyclobutanes). These are [2 + 2] cycloadditions; some of the reactions proceed smoothly under thermal conditions, but the light-catalyzed additions are more general.

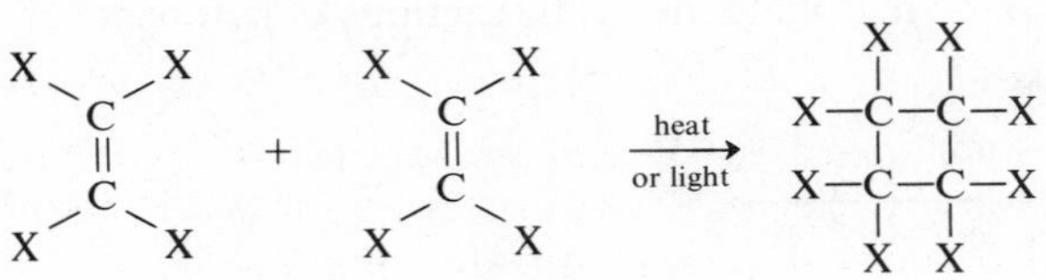

The intermolecular cycloadditions between two identical alkenes are *photodimerizations*, and, if the two alkene groups are in the same molecule, intramolecular photoaddition can occur. These photocycloaddition reactions can be made to occur by direct irradiation, and under these circumstances an excited singlet state of one alkene reacts with the ground state of the other alkene. One of the alkenes is usually conjugated; thus direct excitation can occur at reasonably long wavelengths. Photochemical addition reactions can also be sensitized, and this reaction proceeds by way of triplet states. In several cases, the sensitized and unsensitized reactions lead to different products.

Some useful photodimerization reactions are summarized here.

Intramolecular photocycloadditions give rise to products containing unusual carbon skeletons, as shown in the following cases.

It is not required that intramolecular photoadditions occur at both ends of one double bond. These reactions may involve a conjugated diene or triene with the resulting product containing a ring of more than four atoms. Such rearrangements are termed *electro-cyclic reactions* (see also Section 31.10), and they are often highly stereospecific.

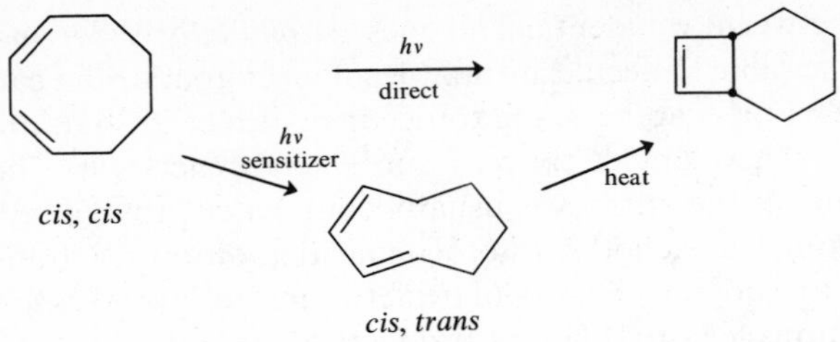

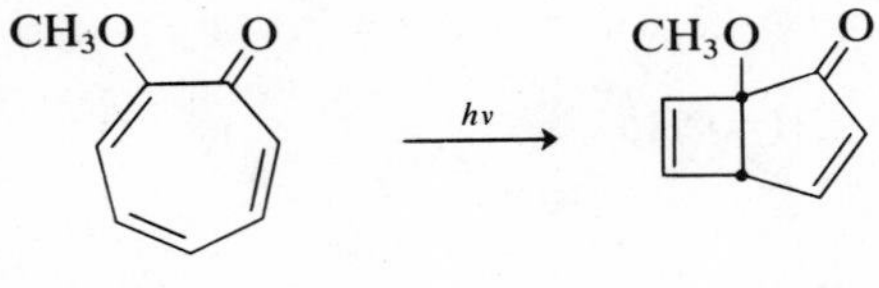

Photocycloaddition reactions of alkenes to other alkenes often take place quite readily. Several important reactions in which cyclohexenones and cyclopentenones are added to other alkenes have recently been studied. Although the detailed mechanisms of these reactions have not been completely worked out, the unusual orientation and stereochemistry encountered offer striking synthetic promise.

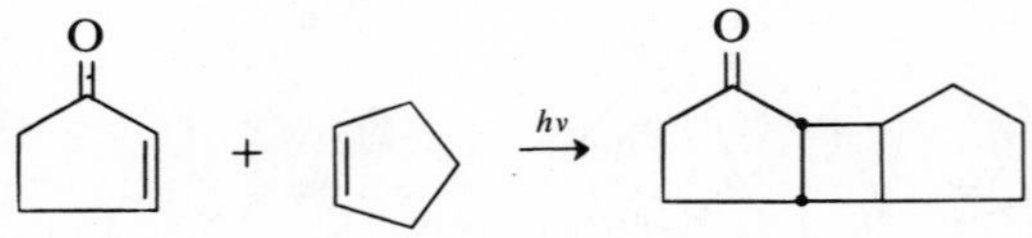

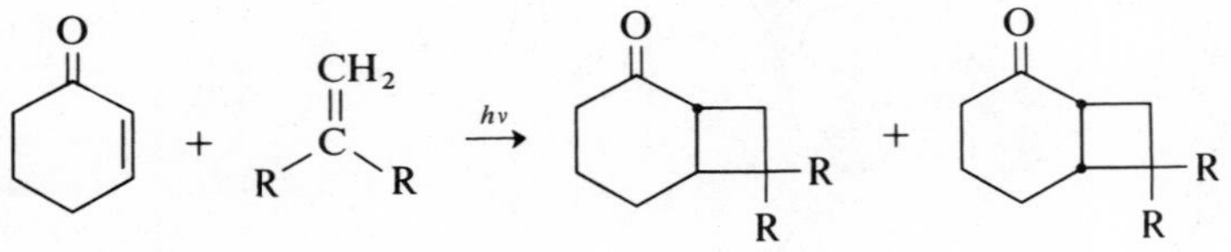

$R = CH_3$ or OCH_3

Thermal $[2 + 2]$ cycloaddition reactions are most successful with (1) fluoroalkenes of the type $R_2C=CF_2$; (2) activated alkenes such as $CH_2=CH—X$, where X is, for example, $—COR$, $—COOR$, $—C\equiv N$, $—C=C$; and (3) allenes (1,2-dienes). Some representative examples are shown.

(more stable diradicals)

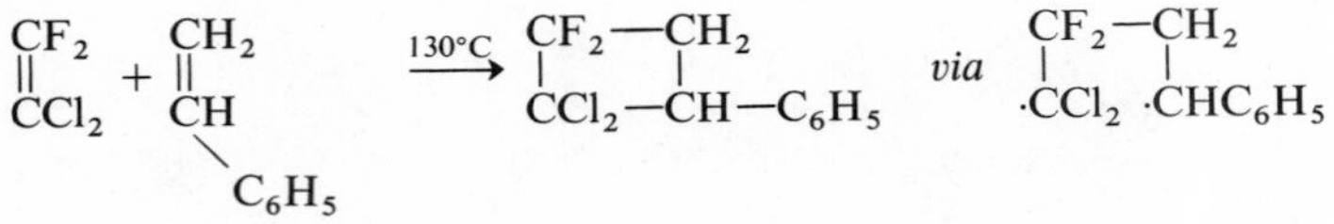

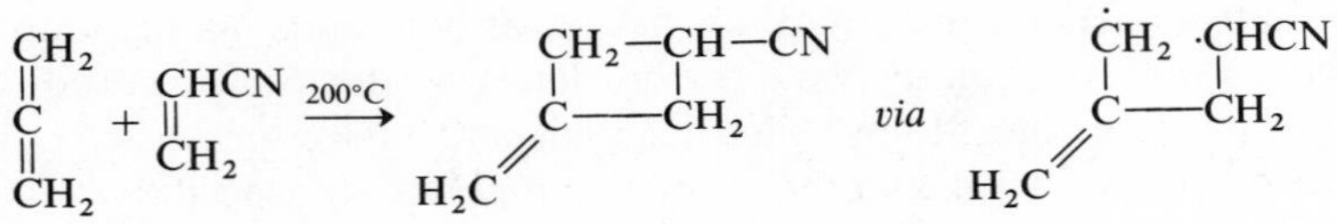

Unlike Diels–Alder reactions (Section 15.12), the thermal [2 + 2] cycloadditions are not concerted, but most probably occur in two distinct steps. In the first stage the two π bonds are broken and *one* new σ bond is formed, generating a diradical intermediate. Subsequently, the diradical collapses to the cyclobutane product. This diradical mechanism is very useful for predicting the products from the cycloadditions of unsymmetrical ethylenes. One merely has to choose which of the possible diradicals would be the most stable. In the three examples shown above, at least two diradical intermediates are theoretically possible for each reaction. The predictably more stable of each set, that which leads to the observed product, is shown at the right side of each equation.

It is of interest to note that octafluorocyclobutane, which can be prepared by the thermal cyclodimerization of tetrafluoroethylene, is nontoxic and widely used as the aerosol for spray-on whipped cream.

EXERCISE 31.7

Give the products of the following photocycloaddition reactions:

(a) $PhCHO + (CH_3)_2C{=}CHCH_3 \overset{hv}{\rightarrow}$

(b) $\overset{hv}{\rightarrow}$

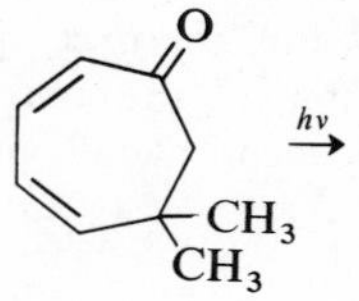

(c) $+ CH_2{=}CHOCH_2Ph \overset{hv}{\rightarrow}$

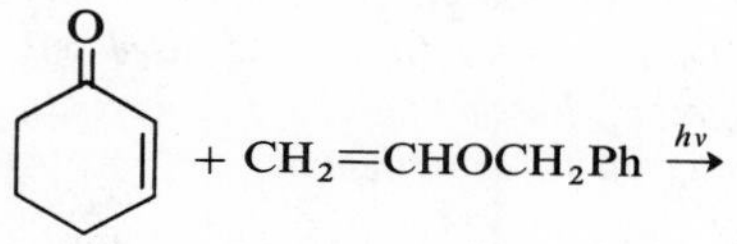

(d) $+ \underset{CHCN}{\overset{CHCN}{||}} \overset{hv}{\rightarrow}$

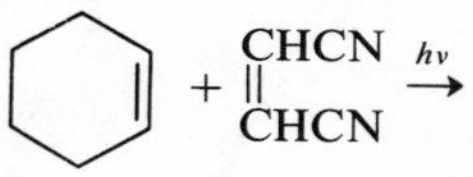

EXERCISE 31.8

Explain the orientation observed in the following thermal cycloaddition:

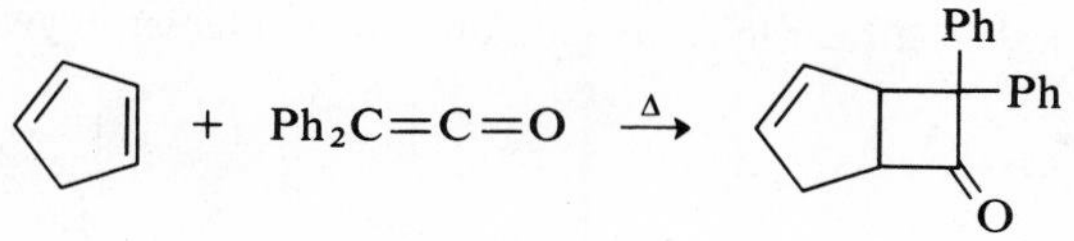

$+ \quad Ph_2C{=}C{=}O \quad \overset{\Delta}{\rightarrow}$

31.10 Orbital Correlations in Intra- and Intermolecular Cycloadditions

A cycloaddition reaction between two unsaturated species A and B to give a cyclic product C can proceed by two extreme mechanisms: a stepwise (nonconcerted) pathway by way of a diradical intermediate (Equation 1); and a concerted process (Equation 2).†

$$A + B \rightarrow [\cdot A{-}B\cdot] \rightarrow C \quad nonconcerted \tag{1}$$

$$A + B \rightarrow C \qquad\qquad concerted \tag{2}$$

If we assume that the reactants A and B are ground-state singlets (all electrons spin-paired), then for a thermally induced nonconcerted reaction the intermediate diradical $\cdot A{-}B\cdot$ when compared

---

† A third mechanism, stepwise involving a dipolar intermediate is also possible (e.g., $A + B \rightarrow \underset{+}{A}{-}\underset{-}{B:} \rightarrow C$).

to the reactants has one less bonding orbital, one less antibonding orbital and two nonbonding orbitals. The two unpaired electrons are contained in these nonbonding orbitals, with the overall result being that bonding electrons in the starting materials have been converted to nonbonding electrons in the intermediate. In most cases this will be an endothermic process associated with a relatively high energy of activation, and the amount of endothermicity will depend on the relative stability of the bonding orbital involved.

On the other hand, the concerted process (Equation 2) in its most favorable sense is characterized by a smooth transition of the bonding molecular orbitals in the starting materials (A + B) to those in the product (C) in such a way as to preserve bonding character at all stages of the reaction. If a pathway such as this is available, it should be associated with a relatively low activation energy.

Having delineated two pathways for cycloaddition reactions, we would now like to know whether both are possible. If both can occur, the concerted pathway should prevail because it will usually be associated with a lower activation energy. In order to analyze a cycloaddition reaction in terms of whether a concerted process is to be favored, it is necessary to examine the participating orbitals of the reactants, allow them to interact as the reaction proceeds, and follow them through the transition state to the product. In other words, we must determine which orbitals of the product arise from each participating orbital of the reactants. For concerted reactions, all bonding orbitals in the reactants must correlate† with all bonding orbitals in the product. On the other hand, if in going to the transition state a bonding orbital in the reactants becomes no longer bonding, a high energy barrier is imposed and the reaction will not be concerted. We are able to conclude that a concerted reaction will either be "allowed" or "forbidden." Importantly, if the concerted reaction is "allowed" it will be associated with a clean and predictable stereochemical outcome.

The terms "allowed" and "forbidden" are not to be construed as absolute. They derive from the spectroscopic terms which relate transition probabilities and intensities. In the sense used here "allowed" means concertedness is permitted, but not obligatory. Furthermore, if a concerted reaction is "forbidden," the probable pathway will be one involving more than one step.

How are orbitals correlated? The method can be illustrated by considering a common transformation; namely, a butadiene ⇌ cyclobutene interconversion. The essential bonds to be

considered are the four π-molecular orbitals of butadiene, the π and π^* orbitals of the cyclobutene double bond (C-2—C-3) and the σ and σ^* orbitals of the cyclobutene single bond formed or broken (C-1—C-4). The π-molecular orbitals of butadiene, π_1, π_2, π_1^*, π_2^* (see Section 7.14) are shown below in terms of the atomic p orbitals and their lobe designations which interact to give the actual molecular orbitals.

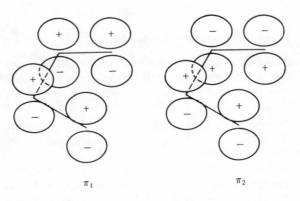

π_1 π_2

---

† The "following-through" or transformation of an orbital of starting material into an orbital of product is known as a *correlation* of these orbitals.

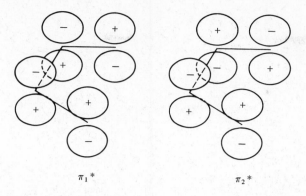

$$\pi_1^* \qquad\qquad \pi_2^*$$

Since there are only four π electrons, these are aligned in pairs in the two bonding π orbitals. For simplification purposes, examine the *highest occupied molecular orbital* (HOMO) π_2 (opposite-sign lobes at C-1 and C-4). In the conversion to cyclobutene, rotation of the atomic orbitals on C-1 and C-4 with rehybridization from p to sp^3 is the manner in which the cyclobutene σ bond can be formed. Rotation in a *conrotatory* fashion (both clockwise or both counterclockwise) pushes a plus lobe at C-1 into a plus lobe at C-4 (or minus lobe into minus lobe), a bonding inter-action which allows smooth transition directly to the σ orbital (signs of overlapping lobes must be identical for bonding) of the cyclobutene.

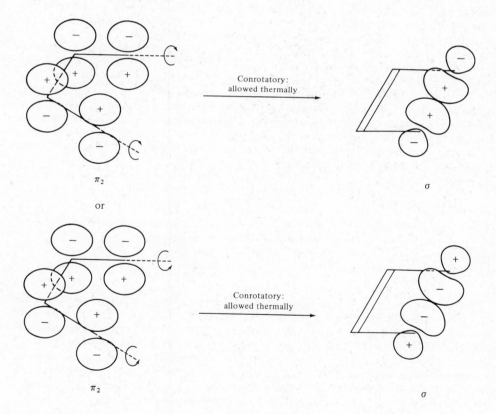

On the other hand, *disrotatory* rotation (one clockwise and one counterclockwise, two possi-bilities) would force a plus lobe to interact with a minus lobe, and this necessarily would show repulsion leading to an antibonding orbital of the cyclobutene.

Thus a concerted ring closure of butadiene to cyclobutene is thermally "allowed" in a con-rotatory manner (bonding HOMO passes to a bonding MO).

Consider, however, a photochemically induced reaction. The first excited state of butadiene involves an electronic configuration which has two electrons in π_1 and one electron each in π_2 and π_2^*. The highest occupied molecular orbital is π_1^* (like-sign lobes at C-1 and C-4), and dis-rotatory closure will allow correlation with the cyclobutene σ orbital.

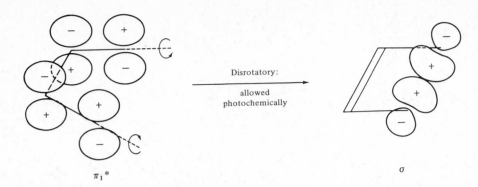

$\pi_1{}^*$ Disrotatory: allowed   photochemically σ

Reactions such as this are intramolecular cycloadditions, called *electrocyclic reactions* (see also Section 31.9), in which a single bond is formed between the terminal atoms of a conjugated π-electron system (or vice versa). As the correlations work out, thermally allowed electrocyclic reactions (ground state) will be conrotatory if the number of π electrons in the polyene is equal to $4q$ (where q is any integer, 0, 1, 2, ... ; therefore $4q$ can be 0, 4, 8, 12, ... total π electrons) and disrotatory if the number of π electrons is equal to $4q + 2$ (therefore $4q + 2$ can be 2, 6, 10, 14, ... total π electrons). For butadiene $\rightleftharpoons$ cyclobutene the total number of π electrons is 4, and conrotatory transformation is concerted. In the case of a 1,3,5-hexatriene $\rightleftharpoons$ 1,3-cyclohexadiene reaction, 6 π electrons are involved and the thermal reaction will be disrotatory. The photochemically allowed electrocyclic reactions (excited state) are opposite: disrotatory if the total number of π electrons in the polyene is $4q$, and conrotatory if this π-electron total is $4q + 2$.

A more accurate treatment involves examining *all* pertinent orbitals, and this is shown in Figure 31.8 for the conrotatory interconversion of butadiene and cyclobutene. Conrotatory motion for π_1 will convert it into either the π-bonding orbital or the σ^* orbital of cyclobutene. The first is anticipated because it represents a bonding orbital of reactant passing into a bonding orbital of product.† Similarly, π_2 can correlate directly with either σ or π^* of cyclobutene; and again bonding character can be preserved if σ results. Thus *both* bonding orbitals of butadiene can pass directly to both bonding orbitals of cyclobutene if conrotatory closure occurs. Also, note that the antibonding orbitals are directly related (as they must be): π_1^* goes to σ^* (rather than π) and π_2^* goes to π^* (rather than σ). *All orbitals correlate.*

EXERCISE 31.9

These orbital correlations can be done in either direction. Show that conrotatory ring-opening of cyclobutene to butadiene would lead to the following $\sigma \rightarrow \pi_2$ (not π_2^*); $\pi \rightarrow \pi_1$ (not π_1^*); $\pi^* \rightarrow \pi_2^*$ (not π_2); and $\sigma^* \rightarrow \pi_1^*$ (not π_1).

Orbital energy diagrams that show correlation of reactant orbitals with product orbitals are called *correlation diagrams*. Figure 31.8 is a correlation diagram for the "thermally allowed" conrotatory butadiene $\rightleftharpoons$ cyclobutene interconversion. It is shown in more simplified fashion as Figure 31.9a. Figure 31.9b is the correlation diagram for a disrotatory process. This process is not allowed for the ground-state reaction (thermal) because π_2 in butadiene containing two electrons would pass to the antibonding (π^*) orbital of cyclobutene. An energy barrier would have to be overcome. However, in the first excited state of butadiene π_1^* contains an electron and it is transformed into a bonding orbital (π) in cyclobutene if disrotatory motion occurs.

The key to the analysis of concerted reactions is correlation of orbitals, and such correlations can be carried out by theoretical calculations. However, because of their phase properties, orbitals can also be analyzed qualitatively in terms of their symmetry characteristics. As a concerted reaction proceeds it must do so with conservation of orbital symmetry. From such analyses have

† At first glance the correlations may seem strange because in proceeding from π_1 to π of cyclobutene extra interactions and nodes are seen to fade away. The difficulty is in the fact that we are representing molecular orbitals in terms of their atomic orbital components and examining only the end result. A more detailed and universal molecular orbital treatment is mixing of π_1 and π_1^* as the reaction proceeds leading to π and σ^*.

Figure 31.8
Molecular orbitals of butadiene and cyclobutene correlated for conrotatory interconversion.

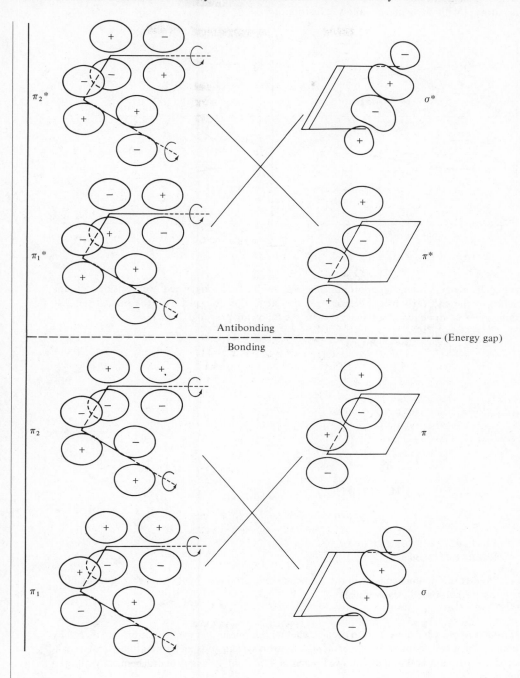

come the common terms (*used in the same sense as we have above*) "symmetry-allowed" *and*
"symmetry-forbidden" *concerted reactions. The principle of conservation of orbital symmetry,*
therefore, assists us in making qualitative correlations of orbitals. The chief proponents of this
principle are R. B. Woodward and R. Hoffmann,† and the selection rules for concerted reactions
are called the Woodward–Hoffmann Rules.

† Roald Hoffmann. Born 1937, Zloczow, Poland. Harvard and Cornell Universities.

Figure 31.9

Correlation diagrams for butadiene ⇌ cyclobutene interconversion: (*a*) thermally allowed conrotatory; (*b*) photochemically allowed disrotatory.

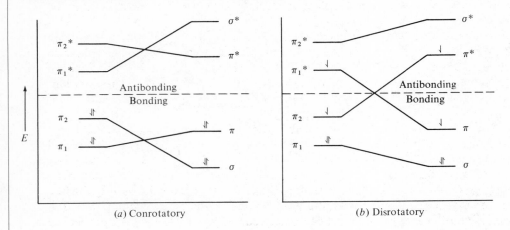

Stereochemistry becomes important in electrocyclic reactions when we consider groups attached to the end carbons of the conjugated system. For example, with the *trans, trans*-2,4-hexadiene → 3,4-dimethylcyclobutene system, the following prevails:

EXERCISE 31.10

Predict the stereochemistry of the 2,4-heptadiene produced by thermal ring opening of *cis*-3-ethyl-4-methylcyclobutene.

A similar approach can be used to predict whether intermolecular cycloadditions are thermally and photochemically concerted. When an m π-electron system adds its termini to an n π-electron system, the reaction is thermally allowed when $m + n = 4q + 2$, and photochemically allowed when $m + n = 4q$.

In a practical sense, this means that thermal cycloadditions of two ethylenes ($m = n = 2$, $m + n = 4$) to give cyclobutanes are stepwise, diradical processes; but the photochemical reactions may be concerted (Section 31.9). Diels–Alder reactions ($m = 4, n = 2; m + n = 6$) are predicted to be thermally concerted processes (Section 15.12).

31.11 Photochemistry in Nature

Some of the most complex photochemical processes occur in nature. The naturally occurring processes of photosynthesis, vision, skin pigmentation, photochemical growth acceleration, and chemiluminescence represent intricate combinations of photochemical reactions, energy transfer steps, and chemical interconversions that are remarkably efficient. Through the joint efforts of biochemists, photochemists, and synthetic organic chemists, progress in unraveling the details of these processes has been accelerated. We may expect many important scientific discoveries in the near future to come out of this area of investigation.

Photosynthesis in the higher green plants is associated with the formation of glucose from carbon dioxide and water. In the overall process, the carbon dioxide is *reduced* to glucose and the water is *oxidized* to oxygen. However, this reaction requires much energy, which is supplied by radiant solar energy, for example, light, as shown in the equation:

$$6\,CO_2 + 6\,H_2O + h\nu \longrightarrow C_6H_{12}O_6 + 6\,O_2$$

On the molecular level, photosynthesis is exceedingly complex. Although the overall process of conversion of CO_2 to sugar is termed *photosynthesis*, light is involved in only the first few stages. The electronic energy so acquired then triggers a complicated series of energy transfers and dark reactions leading ultimately to glucose. Obviously the first step in photosynthesis must involve the absorption of light by a chromophore. The electronic excitation energy then must be transferred between molecules to a proper site where, finally, it can be utilized as chemical energy.

The light acceptor in green plants is the pigment *chlorophyll* (Section 28.4). Actually there are several types of chlorophylls, all having the basic chromophoric system of four pyrrole rings joined in a flat, cyclic arrangement around a central Mg^{2+} ion. They differ in the structures of the side chains attached to the pyrroles. The structure of chlorophyll *a* is shown.

Chlorophyll *a*

The long hydrocarbon chain shown at the bottom is the alcohol *phytol*, which is attached to the chlorophyllin by an ester linkage, and which is lipid, or fat, soluble. The chlorophyll molecules are contained in *chloroplasts*, the "power packs" of photosynthetic cells. In the chloroplast are many closely packed, disklike structures containing the chlorophyll, proteins, and lipids in a double membrane arrangement as illustrated in Figure 31.10. This closely packed, highly ordered arrangement is absolutely necessary for the photosynthetic function, undoubtedly because energy transfer requires molecules to be held close together in space. If chlorophyll were the only light-absorbing species present, photosynthesis would be efficient only in the region where chlorophyll *a* absorbs strongly (about 650–700 nm). Highly colored, fat-soluble carotenoids (Section 30.5) are also present, however. These accessory light acceptors also absorb radiant energy and transfer it to the chlorophyll molecules.

Figure 31.10
Arrangement of chlorophyll in chloroplast.

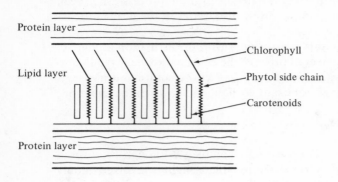

In photosynthesis, radiant energy absorbed at any place in an aggregate of chlorophyll molecules is transferred between such molecules to a reaction site. The details of this energy transfer process are still not completely understood. It does seem that excitation of two types of chlorophyll acceptors simultaneously is essential. A donor molecule (similar to the *cytochromes* of the respiratory chain) acquires excitation energy, gives up electrons, and is converted to an oxidized form. This molecule then triggers a series of electron-transferring reactions which leads ultimately to the acquisition of electrons from ^-OH of water. The ^-OH is oxidized to oxygen and the donor molecule is reduced. Coupled with this oxidation–reduction cycle is the reaction between ADP and inorganic phosphate to give the energy-rich compound ATP. The formation of ATP in this fashion is called *photophosphorylation*. Nearby the released electrons are involved with excited chlorophyll in another oxidation–reduction sequence, leading to the reduction of nicotinamide–adenine dinucleotide phosphate ($NADP^+$) to its reduced form NADPH. Carbon dioxide enzymatically reacts with a five-carbon sugar diphosphate, producing 2 moles of 3-phosphoglyceric acid. These are then reduced to 2 moles of 3-phospho-glyceraldehyde (one of which contains the CO_2) by the action of enzyme, 2ATPs and 2NADPHs. The phosphoglyceraldehydes enter the glycolysis cycle to produce glucose; ATP is converted back to ADP and phosphate, and NADPH is oxidized back to $NADP^+$. The sequence is illustrated in equation form, and has been confirmed by studies with $^{14}CO_2$. (See Section 28.9 for a discussion of ATP and ADP.)

$$CO_2 + \text{C-5-Sugar diphosphate} \xrightarrow{\text{enz.}} 2\ \overset{\displaystyle COOH}{\underset{\displaystyle CH_2OPO_3H}{\overset{\displaystyle |}{\underset{\displaystyle |}{CHOH}}}}$$

3-Phosphoglyceric Acid

$$\downarrow \begin{array}{l} +2ATP \\ +2NADPH \end{array}$$

$$\text{Glucose} \xleftarrow{\text{glycolysis}} 2\ \overset{\displaystyle CHO}{\underset{\displaystyle CH_2OPO_3H}{\overset{\displaystyle |}{\underset{\displaystyle |}{CHOH}}}} + 2\,ADP + 2\,P + 2\,NADP^+$$

Repetition of the sequence is net photosynthesis.

Much of the chemical work in identifying the many carbon compounds produced from the CO_2 via the photosynthetic pathway to glucose has been carried out by M. Calvin[†]

† Melvin Calvin. Born 1911, St. Paul, Minnesota. University of California (Berkeley). Nobel Prize 1961.

and his group at Berkeley. While their work is beyond the scope of this text, we can mention the basic idea used. A plant was fed $^{14}CO_2$ and then was subjected to irradiation for varying periods. After a few seconds of photosynthetic activity, it was found that the ^{14}C had been incorporated into one or two simple compounds. When the period of photosynthetic activity was gradually increased, the ^{14}C was found to be carried progressively through a whole series of compounds, thus establishing the overall synthetic pathway.

The chemistry of *vision*, a photochemical topic, was discussed in Section 30.5, since carotenoids were centrally involved.

Chemiluminescence, either chemical or biological, is the situation whereby the products of oxidation reactions are generated in electronically excited states. Deactivation of these states to ground states is accompanied by the emission of light. A familiar biological example is the firefly.

PROBLEMS

1. Calculate the optical density (A) of a $0.001M$ solution of acetone in heptane contained in a quartz cell of 0.5 cm path length at 279 nm.

2. A compound shows λ_{max} 235 nm in ethanol, and a $0.0001M$ solution in a 1.0 cm quartz cell shows optical density (A) equal to 1.03. Calculate ε_{max} for the compound.

3. List in order of increasing energy the types of electronic transitions that would be expected for the following compounds:

   (a) Formaldehyde, $CH_2{=}\ddot{O}$:
   (b) Methyl vinyl ketone, $CH_2{=}CHCCH_3$

   $\qquad\qquad\qquad\qquad\qquad\qquad \overset{\|}{\underset{\ddot{O}:}{}}$

   (c) 1-Octene, $CH_3(CH_2)_5CH{=}CH_2$

4. The absorption spectrum of *trans*-azobenzene, $Ph{-}\ddot{N}{=}\ddot{N}{-}Ph$, shows a λ_{max} at 430 nm $(\varepsilon_{max} \sim 500)$ and a second λ_{max} at 320 nm $(\varepsilon_{max} \sim 25{,}000)$. To what types of transitions do the absorption bands correspond?

5. For which of the following pairs of isomeric compounds will ultraviolet spectroscopy be a useful tool for distinguishing the members? Explain.

   (a) $CH_2{=}CHCH_2CH{=}CHCH_3$ and $CH_3CH{=}CHCH{=}CHCH_3$

   (b) $CH_3COOCH_2CH_3$ and $CH_3CH_2COOCH_3$

   (c)

   (d)

   (e) $(CH_3)_2CHCH_2CCH_3$ and $CH_3CH_2CH_2CH_2CCH_3$

   $\qquad\qquad\qquad\quad \overset{\|}{O} \qquad\qquad\qquad\qquad\qquad\quad \overset{\|}{O}$

   (f)

   (g)

(h) 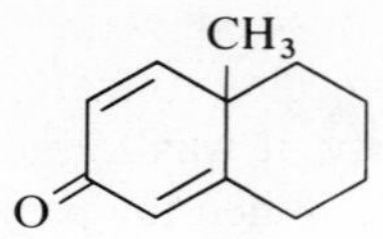 [bicyclic structure with CH₃ and O]   and   [bicyclic structure with CH₃ and O]

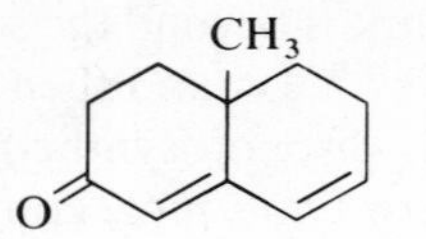

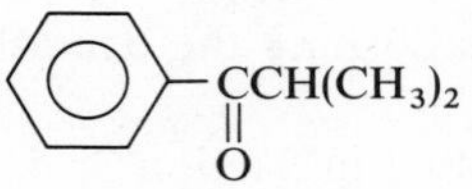

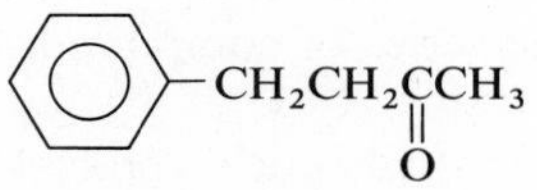

(i) [benzene ring]—$\overset{\text{O}}{\underset{\|}{C}}$CH(CH$_3$)$_2$ and   [benzene ring]—CH$_2$CH$_2\overset{\text{O}}{\underset{\|}{C}}CH_3$

(j) BrCH$_2$CH$_2$CH$_2\overset{\text{O}}{\underset{\|}{C}}$CH=CH$_2$ and   CH$_3\underset{\text{Br}}{\underset{|}{C}}HCH_2\overset{\text{O}}{\underset{\|}{C}}$CH=CH$_2$

6. Predict the products of the following reactions.

(a) 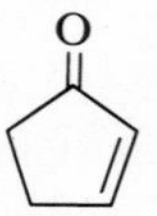 [cyclopentenone, O] + (CH$_3$)$_2$CH=CH$_2$ $\xrightarrow{h\nu}$

(b) 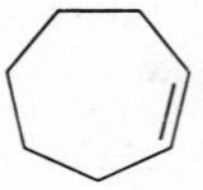 [cyclooctene ring] + CH$_3\overset{\text{O}}{\underset{\|}{C}}CHN_2$ $\xrightarrow{h\nu}$

(c) (CH$_3$)$_3$CCH$_2\overset{\text{O}}{\underset{\|}{C}}CH_3$ $\xrightarrow{h\nu}$

(d) CH$_2$=$\underset{\overset{|}{\text{CH}_3}}{C}$CH=CH$_2$ $\xrightarrow[\text{sensitizer}]{h\nu}$

(e) 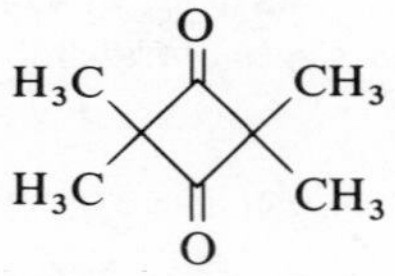 [cyclobutane-1,3-dione with H₃C, CH₃, H₃C, CH₃ and two C=O] $\xrightarrow[\text{benzene}]{h\nu}$ 2 CO + ?

(f) 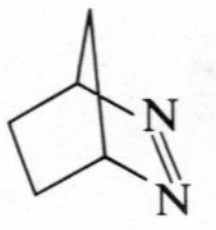 [bicyclic azo compound with N=N] $\xrightarrow{h\nu}$ N$_2$ + ?

(g) 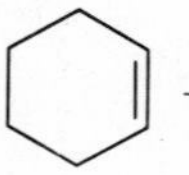 [cyclohexene ring] + :N≡N$^+$—N$^-$—$\overset{\text{O}}{\underset{\|}{C}}$—OCH$_3$ $\xrightarrow{h\nu}$

excess

7. Suggest mechanisms for the following photoreactions:

(a) C$_6$H$_5\overset{\text{O}}{\underset{\|}{C}}CH_2CH_2CH_3$ $\xrightarrow{h\nu}$ C$_6$H$_5\overset{\text{O}}{\underset{\|}{C}}CH_3$ + CH$_2$=CH$_2$

(b) CH$_3\overset{\text{O}}{\underset{\|}{C}}CH_2CH_2CH_2$CH=CH$_2$ $\xrightarrow{h\nu}$ CH$_3\overset{\text{O}}{\underset{\|}{C}}CH_3$ + CH$_2$=CHCH=CH$_2$ +

CH$_2$=CH—[cyclobutane with OH and CH$_3$]   +   [cyclohexene with OH and CH$_3$]

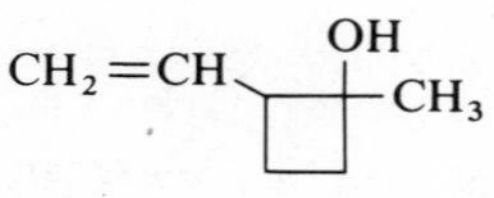

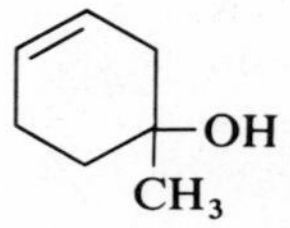

(c)

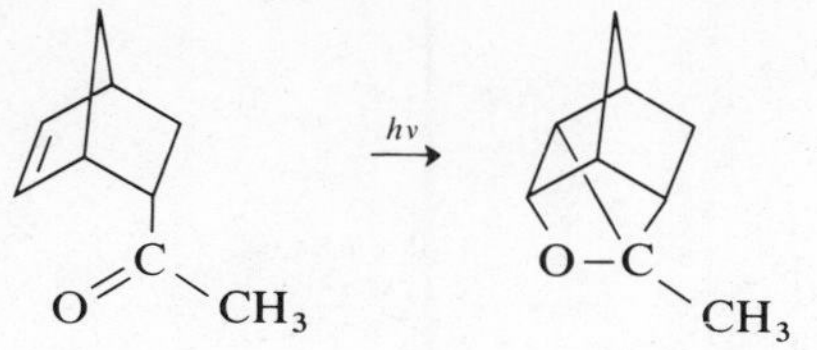

(d)

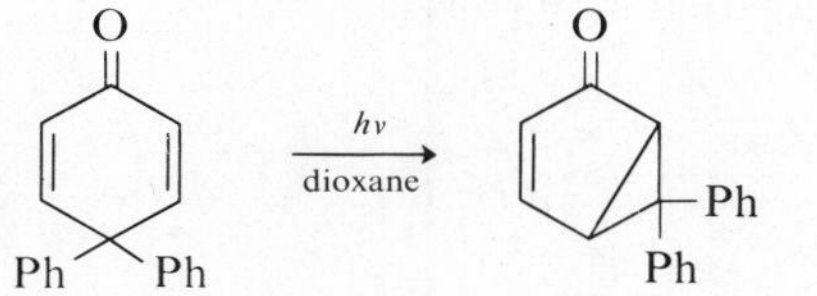

(e)

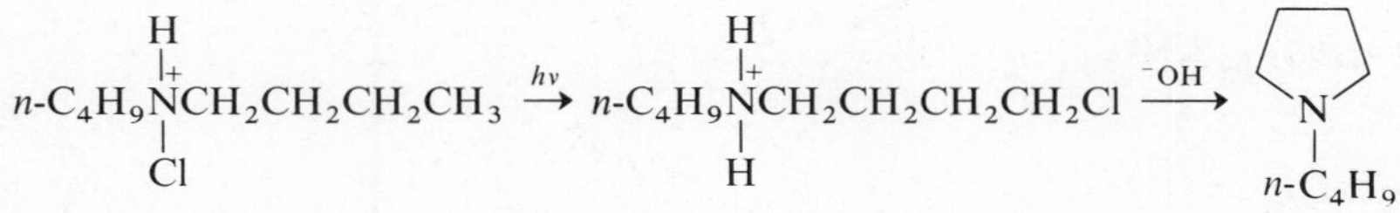

(f)

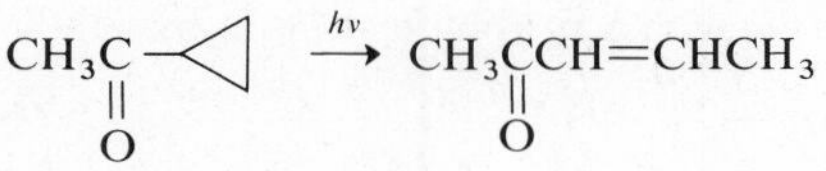

(g)

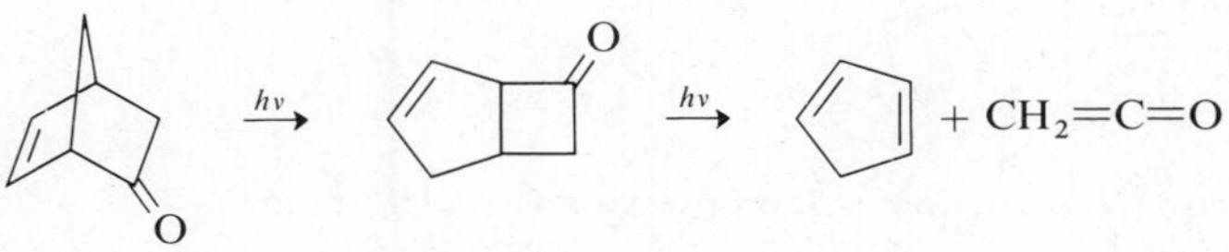

(h)

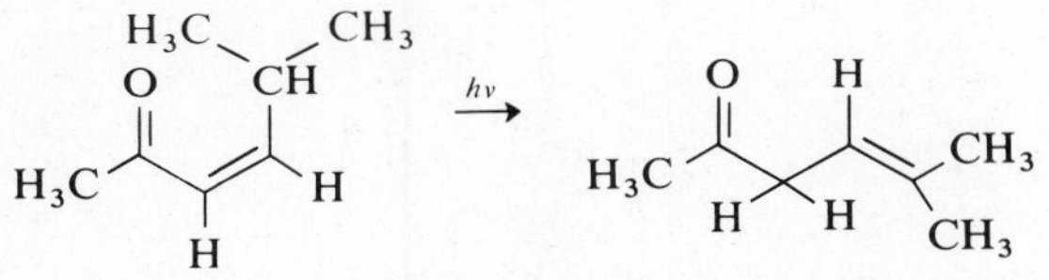

Optional Problems

1. The following dienes in ethanol have λ_{max}'s at 231 nm (ε 21,000), 236 nm (ε 12,000), 245 nm (ε 18,000), 265 nm (ε 6,400), and 282 nm (ε 11,900). Which diene corresponds to which spectrum?

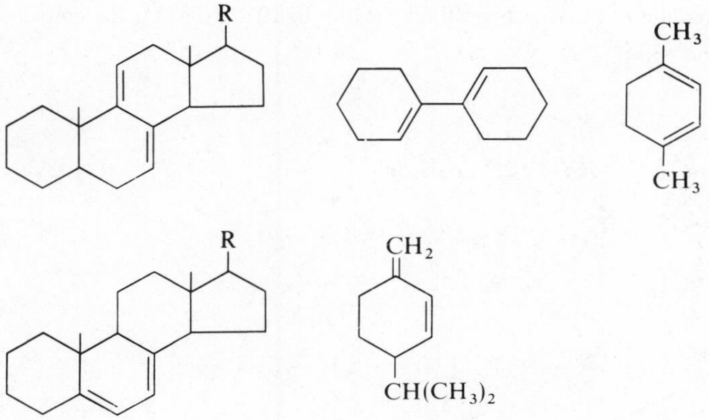

2. Suggest a reason for the fact that *o*-benzylbenzophenone (A) does not photoreduce in isopropanol or in methanol solution, but when A is irradiated in MeOD, deuterium is introduced onto the benzylic carbon atom (*Hint*: Compare the Type II cleavage, Section 31.7).

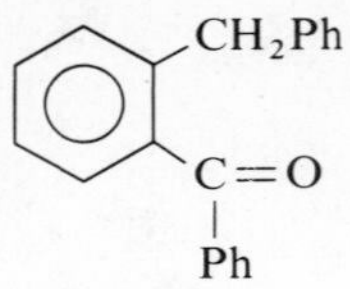

CH$_2$Ph

C=O   (A)

Ph

3. Predict the products (including stereochemistry) of the following:

(a)   CH$_3$ $\xrightarrow{\Delta}$

CH$_3$

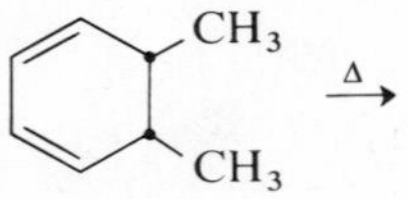

(b)   CH$_3$ $\xrightarrow{h\nu}$

CH$_3$

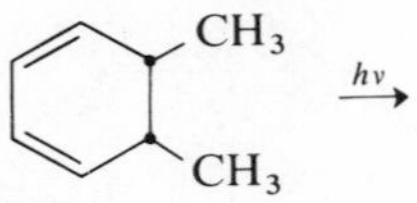

4. Will the following reaction go more smoothly with activation by heat or by light?

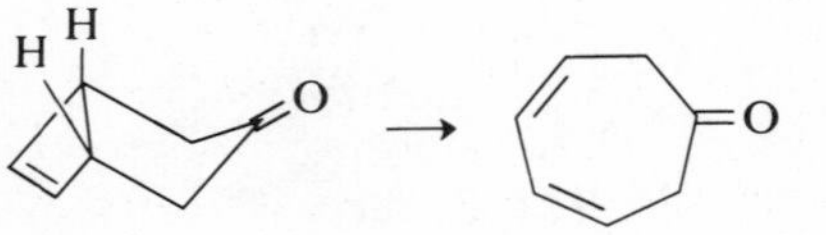

H H

O → O

5. Consider the electrocyclic reaction cyclopropyl cation → allyl cation:

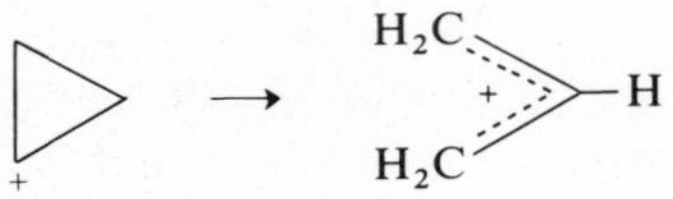

H$_2$C

+ → + —H

H$_2$C

Will this be concerted in a conrotatory or a disrotatory manner?

6. Explain the formation and respectable thermal stability of the product in the following reaction:

O $\xrightarrow{h\nu}$ O

O O

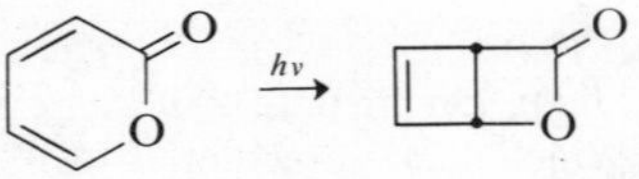

7. The sequence below represents a two-step electrocyclic transformation. What is the structure of the intermediate A? What conditions (heat or light) are best for the conversion of A to the final product?

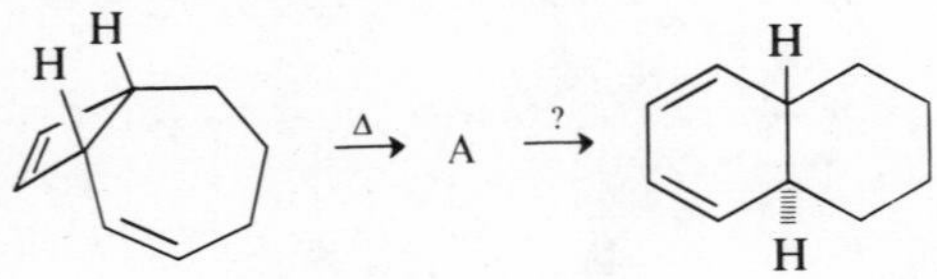

H H

$\xrightarrow{\Delta}$ A $\xrightarrow{?}$

H

H

CHAPTER 32

NMR, MASS SPECTROMETRY, AND IDENTIFICATION OF ORGANIC COMPOUNDS

32.1   Introduction

Instrumentation is having a tremendous impact on modern chemistry. Many current specializations within the field of chemistry involve the use of complex electronic equipment which was unknown or in a very rudimentary state before World War II. Weights, titration endpoints, pH, melting points, and concentrations are examples of types of data which now can be automatically determined by relatively inexpensive equipment. In addition, such techniques as ultraviolet spectroscopy, X-ray crystallography, mass spectrometry, infrared spectroscopy, nuclear magnetic resonance spectroscopy, and gas chromatography, which were undiscovered or in their infant stages in the 1930s, are now indispensable tools of organic and analytical chemists, and both these tools and the data they gather are the subjects of current intensive study by physical and theoretical chemists.

Every practicing organic chemist at some time or other is faced with the problem of identifying an unknown compound. The compound may be a simple, but unexpected reaction product, or it may be a complex naturally occurring substance whose structure has never before been determined. In either case, today's organic chemist will most likely turn first to instrumental methods of studying his unknown compound. After deriving as much information as possible with the available instrumentation, he may then apply chemical methods to fill in the gaps and to confirm or disprove his postulated structure.

The identification of unknowns was described in general terms in Section 5.1, and the student should reread that section now. Among the many tools that can help in structure determination, nmr spectroscopy, introduced in Chapter 5, is the most useful. Infrared spectroscopy (Chapter 9) and ultraviolet spectroscopy (Chapter 31) are commonly available and are also very useful.

In this chapter we will discuss in further detail nmr spectroscopy, and see how still more information can be extracted from nmr spectra. Mass spectrometry will then be introduced, and some of the usefulness of this technique will be explored. We will then study in a general way how to attack an unknown structure using spectroscopic methods, and, finally we will take up the simultaneous use of all kinds of chemical and physical data for determining molecular structures. Such structural problems are often referred to as *roadmaps*, because one has to follow through on all the information available along different paths, in order to arrive at the final destination: the structure of the compound in question.

It may be mentioned at this point that the exact structures of many complicated molecules have been determined with precision by a method of structural analysis using X-rays. In essence, the method allows the chemist to take a picture of a molecule, using X-rays to locate atoms just as we use light rays to locate objects in ordinary photography. A requirement for the successful determination of structure by this method is that the substance exist in crystalline form. In order to develop a three dimensional picture, many individual photographs must be taken from different angles, followed by laborious calculations to correlate the individual photographs. As the X-ray method was being developed in the 1930s, the new amino sugar isolated from crab shells was proved to be 2-aminoglucose by taking about 3,000 individual X-ray pictures, each by hand, followed by three years of tedious and intricate calculations. By contrast, recently the structure of α-methyl 4,6-bisdeoxy-4-dimethylaminotalose methiodide was determined using a diffractometer which can automatically take 300 X-ray pictures a day, and using 35 minutes (or 65 dollars worth) of CDC 1604 computer time.

Even with modern techniques, it may take several weeks to determine the structure of an average molecule by X-ray crystallography. Many structural problems are more easily solved by other methods, but X-ray crystallography is often successful where other methods fail. The method is ordinarily used by specialists, and not usually by organic chemists, so we will not discuss it further in this text.

32.2   Nuclear Magnetic Resonance Spectroscopy

You will recall that when two chemically different adjacent protons align themselves with respect to an external magnetic field, the effect of one nucleus is transferred to the other. The size of this coupling interaction is called the *coupling constant*, J, and is expressed in Hz (Hertz) (1 Hz $\equiv$ 1 cycle per second). The magnetic moments of nuclei are independent of the applied field strength; therefore, J is independent of the field strength.

The magnitude of the coupling constant is a function of the dihedral (torsional) angle ω between the two vicinal C—H bonds:

This relationship can be described theoretically by the Karplus equation:

$$J_{\text{vicinal}} = 4.22 - 0.5 \cos \omega + 4.2 \cos^2 \omega$$

In Figure 32.1, this dependence of J on ω is presented graphically. Some generalizations concerning the magnitude of the coupling constants for protons attached to aliphatic carbon atoms are given in Table 32.1. Coupling constants in olefinic systems were discussed in Section 7.5.

For an example of coupling in a cyclohexyl system, we can use the diastereomeric 4-t-butylcyclohexyl bromides discussed in Section 6.8. In isomer I, the proton alpha to the bromine (bound to the same carbon) is axial; its nmr signal is split by two equivalent adjacent axial protons with $J_{aa} \approx 10$ Hz and is further split by two equatorial protons with $J_{ea} \cong 5.5$ Hz. Thus, the signal appears as a triplet of triplets. For isomer II, the proton alpha to bromine is equatorial; its signal is split nearly equally by the four

Figure 32.1
The dependence of the magnitude of J_{vicinal} on the dihedral angle, ω.

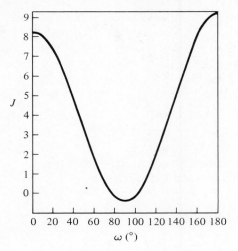

Table 32.1   Spin–Spin Coupling Constants for Protons Attached
             to Aliphatic Carbon Atoms

Structure	$J_{A,B}$ range
$H_A-\overset{\vert}{\underset{\vert}{C}}-H_B$	$J_{A,B}$ = 9–15 Hz[a]
$H_A-\overset{\vert}{\underset{\vert}{C}}-\overset{\vert}{\underset{\vert}{C}}-H_B$	$J_{A,B}$ = 0–9 Hz[b]
$H_A-\overset{\vert}{\underset{\vert}{C}}-\overset{\vert}{\underset{H_B}{C}}-X$	$J_{A,B}$ = 0–8.5 Hz (X is a heteroatom)[b]
	$J_{a,a}$ = 6–14 Hz $\quad$ $J_{a,e}$ = 0–6 Hz $\quad$ $J_{e,e}$ = 0–6 Hz

[a] The magnitude of J depends upon the H_A-C-H_B angle, that
is, the hybridization of the carbon atom.
[b] The magnitude of J depends on the dihedral angle.

adjacent protons, that is, $J_{ee} \sim J_{ea} \sim 3.5$ Hz. Therefore, the signal appears as a multiplet approaching a quintet in this case.

I   II

Other examples can be found in nmr data from the carbohydrates III–V. For the anomers III and IV, the proton at C-1 is seen quite far downfield from the rest of the protons in the molecule, so it is easy to tell which peak corresponds to that particular proton. The magnitude of the coupling constants J_{aa} and J_{ae}, respectively, can be used to differentiate the β form (III) from the α form (IV).

EXERCISE 32.1

Estimate the δ values for the protons on C-1 and C-2 in isomer III.

III
$J_{aa} = 8$ Hz

IV
$J_{ae} = 3.2$ Hz

Similarly, the configuration at C-4 in structure V can be deduced as axial from the nmr spectrum because the observed coupling constant $J = 8$ Hz is characteristic of J_{aa}.

V
$J_{ae} = 3.2$ Hz
$J_{aa} = 8$ Hz

EXERCISE 32.2

(a) What would you expect the magnitude of the coupling constants for the protons on C-4 and C-5 to be in the nmr spectrum of the C-4 epimer of V?

(b) The two protons H_β and $H_{\beta'}$ on the carbon atom beta to the ring in 1,2-dibromo-1-phenylethane are diastereotopic:

Draw the other Newman projections resulting from rotation about the C-1—C-2 bond and convince yourself that H_β and H'_β are never in equivalent environments. Predict the nmr spectrum of this compound.

As noted in Section 5.5, the multiplets in real nmr spectra are less symmetrical than those in idealized examples. Turn back to Figure 5.11 and note that the pattern produced by the ethyl group looks more like:

than the predicted symmetrical multiplets:

The inner peaks, that is, the peaks nearer to the other coupled multiplet, are larger than the outer peaks. Symmetrical multiplets are found only when the chemical shift difference between two sets of coupled nuclei is very large compared to their coupling constant.

In order to understand the origin of this effect, we will consider a simple two-spin system:

$$\begin{array}{c} \overset{|}{-C}-\overset{|}{C}- \\ \underset{H_A}{|}\ \underset{H_B}{|} \end{array}$$

Let us suppose that $J_{AB} = 10$ Hz and that H_A has a chemical shift of δ 5.0 and H_B has a chemical shift of δ 5.1 (corresponding to a chemical shift difference of δ 0.1 or 6 Hz in a 60 MHz spectrum). We would then predict the following pattern:

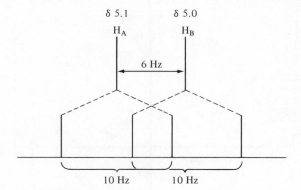

However, theoretical calculations indicate that due to spin–spin coupling with the second nucleus it is forbidden for the energy states (hence absorption lines) of one nucleus to cross the energy states of a second nucleus as they do in this predicted pattern. So, in order to avoid the crossing of energy states, the inner lines become more intense than the outer lines, and the chemical shifts of H_A and H_B are located at the "center of gravity" of the individual doublets, rather than as predicted above.

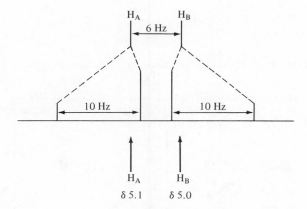

This kind of four-line pattern is frequently observed and is given the special name, *AB quartet*. On the other hand, if the chemical shift difference between coupled hydrogens is very large, a simple, symmetrical AX pattern is observed:

The AX quartet in the spectrum of uracil in D_2O, for example, approaches this extreme (Figure 32.2). The transition between these two types of patterns is a gradual one; and,

Figure 32.2
NMR spectrum of uracil in deuterium oxide solution. Note AX quartet produced by hydrogens H_A and H_X.

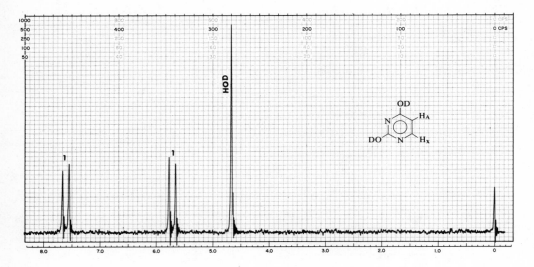

as chemical shift differences become smaller and smaller, the inner lines become more intense at the expense of the outer lines (Figure 32.3). In the limiting case when the two chemical shifts become identical, the outer lines disappear, no matter what the value of the coupling constant. This is why equivalent protons do not show splitting from coupling with one another. Similar arguments can be applied to coupled spin systems containing more than two nuclei.

Figure 32.3
NMR spectrum of p-trifluoromethyltoluene. Note AB quartet produced by aromatic hydrogens.

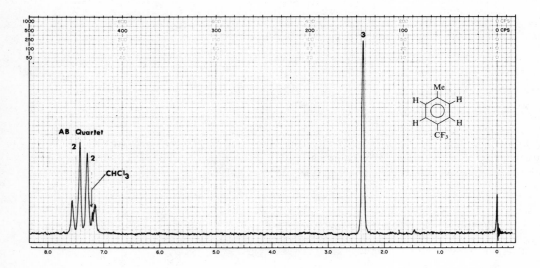

The distortion of symmetry of the lines within a multiplet can be useful in interpreting spectra; the peaks of coupled multiplets "grow" toward each other. Thus if we find a triplet that appears as:

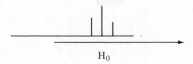

we know that we must look *downfield* for the chemical shift of the two nuclei responsible for coupling leading to the triplet.

Spin-coupled systems involving more than two protons all of which have similar chemical shifts lead to very complicated spectra, which often cannot be completely analyzed without the aid of computer calculations. An example of such a spectrum is illustrated in Figure 32.4. In the case of most complex molecules, only certain portions of the molecule will give rise to recognizable coupling patterns, for example, Figure 32.5.

Figure 32.4

NMR spectrum of allyl vinyl ether. The multiplet near $\delta\,4.2$ consists of 8 lines for H(d) and 4 lines each for H(f) and H(g). The multiplet near $\delta\,5.3$ is produced by H(a) and H(b). The 12-line multiplet at $\delta\,5.90$ is produced by H(c). The quartet at $\delta\,6.45$ is assigned to H(e).

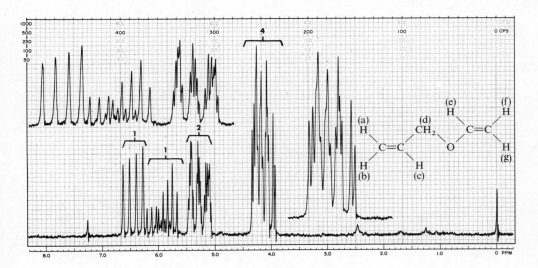

Earlier we had assumed that coupling does not occur over more than three bonds. The most important exception to this is the case of allylic coupling, that is, J_{AX} and J_{BX} in the following system:

$$J_{AB} = 0\text{–}3.5\ \text{Hz} \qquad J_{BC} = 11\text{–}18\ \text{Hz}$$
$$J_{AC} = 6\text{–}14\ \text{Hz} \qquad J_{BX} = 0\text{–}3\ \text{Hz}$$
$$J_{AX} = 0\text{–}3\ \text{Hz} \qquad J_{CX} = 0\text{–}9\ \text{Hz}$$

Figure 32.5
NMR spectrum of cholesterol.

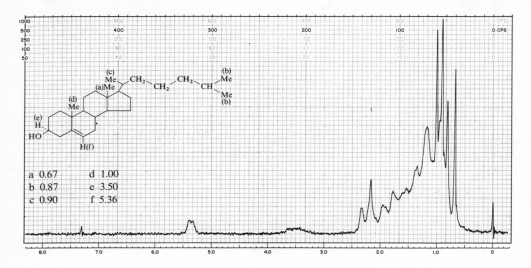

Two examples of this are the complex spectra produced by allyl vinyl ether (Figure 32.4) and allyl iodide (Figure 32.6). Note that the coupling over four bonds is generally weak compared to coupling over three.

Figure 32.6
NMR spectrum of allyl iodide.

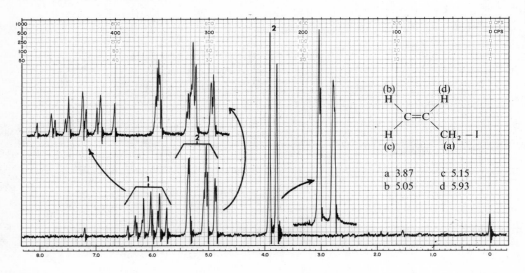

EXERCISE 32.3

Estimate all of the coupling constants you can from Figure 32.6. Compare these with the ranges of typical values given above for allylic coupling.

As a summary of spin–spin coupling, consider the following points:
1. Equivalent nuclei (e.g., the three protons of a methyl group) do not interact to cause observable splitting.

2. When a nucleus interacts with *n* equivalent nuclei it will give rise to a signal (multiplet) of *n* + 1 lines. This interaction is limited, in the usual case, to distances of not more than three bonds.

3. The spacing within each multiplet due to a particular coupling is a constant (*J*).

4. The value of the coupling constant is significantly influenced by the relative spatial orientation of the interacting nuclei, i.e. the dihedral angle, ω.

5. In the idealized case, the relative intensities within a multiplet are given by the coefficients in the binomial expansion of $(r + 1)^n$ (where *n* is the number of equivalent interacting nuclei), as discussed in Section 5.5.

6. In actual spectra, where the ratios of chemical shift differences to coupling constants are not infinitely large, the inner lines of each multiplet (i.e., those closer to the other multiplet) become more intense than the outer lines. In multiple spin systems with chemical shifts of the same order of magnitude as coupling constants, nmr spectra are often not interpretable by simple inspection.

32.3 Mass Spectrometry

A *mass spectrum* is a record of the "damage" done to molecules when they are bombarded in the gas phase by an electron beam, in an instrument called a *mass spectrometer*. The starting molecules are destroyed and broken into pieces. Usually it is possible to decide from the data what these pieces are, and then to deduce the structure of the original molecule. Mass spectra may also be used to determine the extent and location of isotopic incorporation.

During the interaction between a molecule and an energetic electron, energy is transferred to the molecule. One way the excited molecule dissipates the energy it has picked up is by ejecting an electron and becoming positively charged:

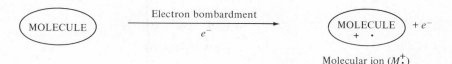

Molecular ion ($M^{\ddagger}$)

If it still has sufficient energy, this *molecular ion* ($M^{\cdot+}$) can fragment at one or more bonds, forming a fragment ion and a neutral molecule or radical.

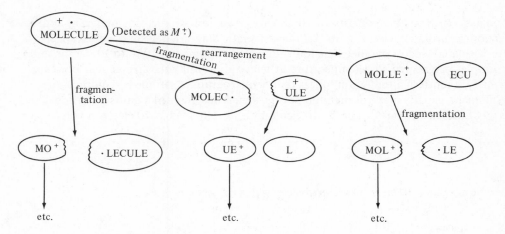

Generally the sample pressure in the mass spectrometer is not allowed to rise above 10^{-5} mm. Thus, intramolecular fragmentations and rearrangements of the ions occur, but the probability of intermolecular reactions between ions and/or neutral molecules is low. The relative concentrations of the ions are dependent upon the relative rates of formation and subsequent fragmentation and rearrangement of all the ions. Thus, ions are formed the masses of which correspond to the molecular weight of the sample and to fragments of the sample molecules.

Since many types of ions can form from large molecules, one might predict that random fragmentation would occur upon interaction with energetic electrons. This is not the case, however. Certain ions are formed in preference to others. It is usually possible to rationalize these preferred fragmentations and rearrangements in terms of the concepts presented earlier in this text. For example, tertiary ions are formed in preference to secondary, which are formed in preference to primary. Also, ions with the charge delocalized over more than one atom are preferentially formed. For example, the fragmentations of ethylamine can be rationalized in the following way. It is usually easier for the energetic molecule to lose a nonbonding rather than a bonding electron (why?), so we can predict the molecular ion easily enough. Two different fragmentations are then expected, and are observed:

$$CH_3CH_2\ddot{N}H_2 \xrightarrow{e^-} CH_3{-}CH_2\overset{+}{N}H_2 + e^-$$
$$\text{Molecular ion, M}^{\cdot+}$$

$$CH_3CH{=}\overset{+}{N}H_2 + H\cdot \qquad CH_2{=}\overset{+}{N}H_2 + CH_3\cdot$$

Thus, a mass spectrum should be interpreted with consideration of the relative stabilities of the cations and the relative stabilities of the neutral radicals and molecules formed in the fragmentations and rearrangements.

EXERCISE 32.4

Predict the preferred fragmentations of:

(a) $CH_3CH_2CH_2NH_2$ (b) $CH_3CH_2NHCH_3$

(c) CH_3CH_2OH (d) $(CH_3O)_2CH_2$

(e)

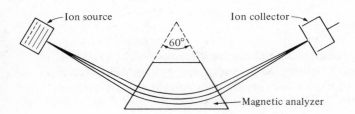

A mass spectrometer consists of three units—an ion source, an analyzer, and a detection-recording device. Figure 32.7 is a schematic diagram of a simple mass spectrometer with a 60° sector magnet. The ion source is maintained at 10^{-7} to 10^{-9} mm, and the samples are heated to a temperature at which they will volatilize at that pressure. Routinely, a tenth of a milligram to less than a microgram of sample is required.

A filament, usually made of rhenium or tungsten, is heated until it emits electrons. The energy of these electrons can be controlled and is usually held at 70 electron volts (eV).

Figure 32.7
Schematic diagram of a simple mass spectrometer with a 60° sector magnet.

Note that this energy is very high, about 20 times the energy of an average bond in a molecule.

The ions are accelerated out of the ion source by an electric field as soon as they are formed. Since the part of the sample which was not ionized, and the radicals and neutral molecules formed in the fragmentation and rearrangement of ions (for example, $\widehat{MOLEC\cdot}$ and $\widehat{ECU}$), are not charged, they are not accelerated out of the ion source, but are pumped away. The analyzer region into which the ions are led separates them into groups according to their ratio of mass (m) to charge (e), m/e. Since most of the ions from organic molecules are singly charged, that is, $e = +1$, the separation is essentially according to mass, m. Electric, magnetic, or a combination of electric and magnetic fields can be used for the separation.

Electric or photographic *detection* is used to observe the presence of the ions. A *mass spectrum*, for example, Figure 32.8, is a record of which m/e groups are present and what their relative abundances are. Instruments vary in their ability to resolve the ions into m/e groups. An instrument of relatively high resolving power can, for example, separate molecular ions of formula $C_3H_6O_2$ and $C_4H_{10}O$, which have the exact masses 74.0604 and 74.0968, respectively. On the other hand, instruments of lower resolving power

Figure 32.8

An actual mass spectrum photographically recorded from m/e 32 to m/e 56 by a five-element galvanometer system at sensitivity levels decreasing in the ratios of $1:3:10:30:100$.

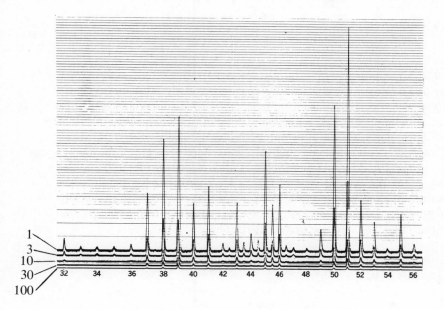

separate ions only to the unit mass, and $C_3H_6O_2$ and $C_4H_{10}O$ could not be separated but would be found as a single peak at m/e 74, which would be resolved from m/e 73 and 75. The mass-spectral data discussed in this chapter have been obtained from instruments which resolve ions to the unit m/e. Data from instruments of this lower resolving ability are more commonly available to organic chemists than data from high-resolution mass spectrometers.

Organic chemists can use data obtained from mass spectra in many ways. The ones that we will discuss in this chapter are (1) for obtaining the exact molecular weight of the molecule; and (2), for obtaining structural information from interpretation of the fragmentation patterns.

In Figure 32.8 is a part of a mass spectrum in the form it is obtained from the instrument. This spectrum was measured and redrawn in bar graph form. Each response on the recorder (and subsequently on the bar graph) is called a *peak*. The *relative heights* of the peaks are reflections of the relative concentrations of the m/e groups. For example, the mass spectrum of phthalic anhydride is shown in Figure 32.9. The peaks at highest m/e are

Figure 32.9
Computer-drawn bar graph of mass spectral data from phthalic anhydride. The molecular formula is $C_8H_4O_3$ corresponding to a molecular weight of 148.

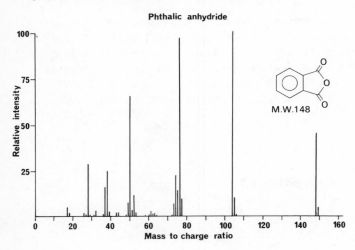

found at m/e 148, 149, and 150, and arise from molecular species. Exact molecular weight and, often, molecular formulas can be obtained from the molecular ion region in a mass spectrum. Since individual molecules are ionized, separated, detected, and recorded, the molecular ion region contains peaks due to species containing the lightest isotopes of the elements present and species containing one or more naturally occurring heavy isotopes. In Table 32.2 are the natural abundances of the isotopes of elements frequently found in organic compounds. In Table 32.3 are relative intensities of peaks in the molecular ion regions of a few molecules; M refers to the molecular ion species containing only the lightest isotope of each element; its intensity is taken as 100 by definition. M + 1 and M + 2 refer to species containing one or two heavier isotopes. (Very comprehensive tables of this type exist and are useful for reference.)

Table 32.2   Natural Abundances of Isotopes

		Heavy isotopes		
Light isotopes	Natural abundance, %	Natural abundance, %		Natural abundance, %
^1H	99.985	^2H	0.015	
^{12}C	98.893	^{13}C	1.107	
^{14}N	99.64	^{15}N	0.36	
^{16}O	99.759	^{17}O	0.037	^{18}O 0.204
^{32}S	95.0	^{33}S	0.76	^{34}S 4.2
^{19}F	100			
^{35}Cl	75.8			^{37}Cl 24.2
^{79}Br	50.537			^{81}Br 49.463
^{127}I	100			

Table 32.3   Relative Intensities of Typical Molecular Ion Species

Formula	Light isotopes	Heavy isotopes		
	M	*M* + 1	*M* + 2	*M* + 3
$C_6H_{12}O_4$	100 (*m/e* 148)	6.83 (*m/e* 149)	1.00 (*m/e* 150)	
$C_8H_4O_3$	100 (*m/e* 148)	8.83 (*m/e* 149)	0.94 (*m/e* 150)	
$C_9H_{12}N_2$	100 (*m/e* 148)	10.68 (*m/e* 149)	0.52 (*m/e* 150)	
$C_{11}H_{16}$	100 (*m/e* 148)	12.14 (*m/e* 149)	0.67 (*m/e* 150)	
C_9H_8S	100 (*m/e* 148)	10.63 (*m/e* 149)	4.83 (*m/e* 150)	
$C_5H_{11}Br$	100 (*m/e* 150)	5.58 (*m/e* 151)	97.8 (*m/e* 152)	5.46 (*m/e* 153)
$C_5H_{11}Cl$	100 (*m/e* 106)	5.58 (*m/e* 107)	32.7 (*m/e* 108)	1.83 (*m/e* 109)

In the mass spectrum of phthalic anhydride ($C_8H_4O_3$), peaks at *m/e* 148–150 are molecular ion species, with *m/e* 148 corresponding to 8 ^{12}C, 4 ^1H, 3 ^{16}O, and *m/e* 149 and 150 corresponding to molecular ions with one or more naturally occurring heavy isotopes, such as 7 ^{12}C, 1 ^{13}C, 4 ^1H, 3 ^{16}O for *m/e* 149 and 8 ^{12}C, 4 ^1H, 2 ^{16}O, 1 ^{18}O for *m/e* 150.

EXERCISE 32.5

Careful measurement of the peaks in the molecular ion region of the mass spectrum of an unknown gave *m/e* 148, 100%; *m/e* 149, 10.6%; *m/e* 150, 4.8%. What are the molecular weight and elemental composition of the unknown? (*Hint*: See Table 32.3.)

Expulsions of neutral molecules from ions are also observed in the mass spectrum of phthalic anhydride (Figure 32.9). The molecular ion expels CO_2, followed by CO, followed by C_2H_2:

$$C_8H_4O_3^{+\cdot} \rightarrow C_7H_4O^{+\cdot} + CO_2$$
m/e 148   *m/e* 104

$$\hookrightarrow C_6H_4^{+\cdot} + CO$$
m/e 76

$$\hookrightarrow C_4H_2^{+\cdot} + C_2H_2$$
m/e 50

In this case, the fragmentation is governed by the stabilities of the neutral species expelled: carbon dioxide, carbon monoxide, and ethylene. The remaining ions, $C_4H_2^{+\cdot}$ and $C_6H_4^{+\cdot}$, are highly unsaturated.

The presence of bromine in the mass spectrum of ethyl bromide, which is given in Figure 32.10, can be recognized by the peaks of nearly equal intensities at *m/e* 108 and 110, due to the ^{79}Br and ^{81}Br isotopes (refer to Table 32.2).

EXERCISE 32.6

In the mass spectrum of ethyl chloride, the ions $C_2H_5^{35}Cl^{+\cdot}$ and $C_2H_5^{37}Cl^{+\cdot}$ are formed at *m/e* 64 and 66. Predict their relative intensities. (*Hint*: See Table 32.2.) What would the intensities of the peaks in the molecular ion region in the mass spectrum of ethyl iodide look like?

Figure 32.10
Mass spectrum of ethyl bromide.

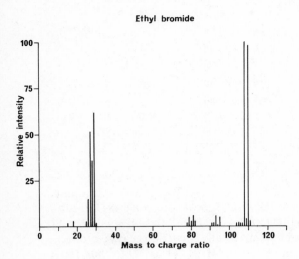

The major fragmentation pathway for the molecular ion of ethyl bromide is elimination of Br·.

$$C_2H_5 \overset{\frown}{-} Br^{·+} \rightarrow C_2H_5^+ + Br·$$
$$\quad m/e\ 108,\ 110 \qquad m/e\ 29$$
$$\hookrightarrow C_2H_3^+ + H_2$$
$$m/e\ 27$$

These reactions in the mass spectrometer appear strange at first sight, and different from others encountered in previous chapters. However, one should keep in mind that:

1. All the reactions involve ions.
2. The energy required for the reactions is acquired via the interactions of the original molecules with highly energetic electrons.
3. The reactions occur in the gas phase and are unimolecular, that is, there is no interaction with other ions and molecules, or with a solvent.

Often it is possible to recognize structural features of a molecule from the peaks found in its mass spectrum. Thousands of mass spectra have been interpreted, and the fragmentations of most types of organic compounds are now categorized, even though they may not be well understood. Although the actual structures of the ions are not known, it is possible to suggest structures and to use them as visual "crutches" in the interpretation of a mass spectrum, as we did for ethylamine (page 836).

For the purpose of illustration, we will look at the most intense peaks in the mass spectra of two compounds having unit molecular weights of 74: 1-butanol and diethyl ether. The peaks are given in Table 32.4. Although the molecular ion of 1-butanol is not

Table 32.4   Mass-Spectral Data for 1-Butanol and Diethyl Ether

Compound	M·+	Most intense peaks in the mass spectra
$CH_3CH_2CH_2CH_2OH$	m/e 74	m/e 56, 43, 41, 31, 29, and 27
$CH_3CH_2OCH_2CH_3$	m/e 74	m/e 74, 59, 45, 31, 29, and 27

among the most intense in its mass spectrum, it is present in the complete spectrum, at m/e 74. The formation of m/e 56 by loss of 18 mass units from m/e 74 corresponds to the loss of H_2O:

$$C_3H_7-{}^1CH_2-\overset{+}{\overset{\cdot}{O}}-H \rightarrow C_4H_8^{+\cdot} + H_2O$$
$$\underset{m/e\ 74}{} \qquad \underset{m/e\ 56}{}$$

$$C_3H_7\cdot + {}^1CH_2\overset{+}{=}\overset{\cdot}{O}-H \qquad C_3H_7^+ + {}^{\cdot 1}CH_2OH$$
$$\underset{m/e\ 31}{} \qquad\qquad \underset{m/e\ 43}{}$$

$$\hookrightarrow C_3H_5^+ + H_2$$
$$\underset{m/e\ 41}{}$$

The peak at m/e 31, formed by cleavage of C-1—C-2 with the charge retained on C-1, is the most intense peak in the mass spectrum of 1-butanol, and along with $M^{\cdot+}$ minus H_2O is characteristic of a primary alcohol. The peak at m/e 43 results if the C-1—C-2 bond cleaves with the charge retained on C-2. The peaks at m/e 43 ($C_3H_7^+$) and m/e 29 ($C_2H_5^+$) result from cleavages of carbon–carbon bonds and are commonly present in the mass spectra of compounds with an aliphatic chain. The peaks at m/e 41 ($C_3H_5^+$) and m/e 27 ($C_2H_3^+$) are formed by a subsequent elimination of molecular hydrogen from m/e 43 and 29.

In comparison, the molecular ion of diethyl ether eliminates $CH_3\cdot$, followed by C_2H_4 via a rearrangement process[†]:

$$CH_3\overset{\frown}{-CH_2}-\overset{+\cdot}{O}-\overset{\alpha}{C}H_2\overset{\beta}{C}H_3 \rightarrow CH_3\dot{} + CH_2=\overset{+}{O}-\overset{\alpha}{C}H_2\overset{\beta}{C}H_3$$
$$\underset{m/e\ 74}{} \qquad\qquad\qquad\qquad \underset{m/e\ 59}{}$$

$$CH_2=\overset{+}{O}-H + \overset{\alpha}{C}H_2=\overset{\beta}{C}H_2 \longleftarrow$$
$$\underset{m/e\ 31}{}$$

The peak at m/e 45 is formed via m/e 73 (not one of the six most intense peaks):

$$\overset{\beta}{C}H_3\overset{\alpha}{C}H_2-\overset{+\cdot}{O}-CH_2CH_3 \qquad m/e\ 74$$

$$\overset{\beta}{C}H_3\overset{\alpha}{C}H_2-\overset{+}{O}=CHCH_3 + H\cdot$$
$$\underset{m/e\ 73}{}$$

$$H-\overset{+}{O}=CH-CH_3 + \overset{\beta}{C}H_2=\overset{\alpha}{C}H_2$$
$$\underset{m/e\ 45}{}$$

The peaks at m/e 29 and 27 are again $C_2H_5^+$ and $C_2H_3^+$, respectively.

Cleavage of bonds next to the carbonyl function is a characteristic fragmentation of aldehydes and ketones.

$$R-\overset{\overset{+\cdot}{\underset{\|}{O}}}{C}-R' \longrightarrow R-C\equiv O^+ + \cdot R'$$
$$\longrightarrow R^+ + CO$$
$$\longrightarrow {}^+O\equiv C-R' + \cdot R$$
$$\longrightarrow R'^+ + CO \cdot$$

[†] For the convention regarding the meaning of the single-pronged arrow, see page 810.

From these peaks, information on the identities of R and R′ can be obtained. Ketones and other compounds containing carbonyl groups with γ hydrogen also undergo a characteristic γ-hydrogen rearrangement process.

An alkene, comprised of the β and γ carbon atoms, is eliminated from the molecular ion.

Fragmentation pathways such as those suggested above for ketones can be supported by labeling with stable isotopes. For example, the formation of m/e 58 by the migration of a γ hydrogen and elimination of ethylene from the molecular ion of 2-pentanone is confirmed by deuterium labeling.

Peaks at m/e 43 and 71 in the mass spectrum of 2-pentanone are characteristic of the methyl and the propyl groups on the carbonyl.

In the mass spectrum of 2-pentanone-5-d_3, the peak at m/e 71 is shifted to m/e 74, whereas the peak at m/e 43 is unshifted: $\overset{+}{O}\equiv C-CH_2CH_2CD_3$, m/e 74

EXERCISE 32.7

The molecular ion of an isomer of 2-pentanone is also found at m/e 86. Intense peaks are found at m/e 71 and 43, but not at m/e 58. What is the compound? Another isomer has intense peaks at m/e 86 and m/e 57. What is it?

EXERCISE 32.8

Pentanal has major peaks in its mass spectrum at m/e 86, 71, and 44. Suggest fragmentation pathways for their formation.

Absorption peaks in nmr and ir spectra are characteristic of functional groups and their immediate environment and are generally independent of the rest of the molecule.

Thus, it is possible to tabulate absorption positions. In the mass spectrometer, however, a molecular ion fragments, and these fragmentations are dependent upon the structure of the entire molecule. Fragmentations due to the presence of one functional group may completely dominate the spectrum. For this reason it is impossible to construct a table of *m/e*'s characteristic of particular functional groups. One must be familiar with fragmentations which each type of functional group can produce, and interpret the mass spectrum in terms of the competing paths by which the molecular ion fragments.

Mass Spectrometry in Determining the Intramolecular Nature of a Reaction. The Hofmann degradation of carboxamides has been shown to be intramolecular by the labeling experiment described here. Upon treatment of a mixture of *m*-deuteriobenzamide and ^{15}N-labeled benzamide with sodium hypobromite, aniline that gave only molecular ions of *m/e* 94 in the mass spectrometer was obtained.

$$m\text{-deuteriobenzamide (}^{14}NH_2\text{, D) and benzamide (}^{15}NH_2\text{) } \xrightarrow{\text{NaOBr}} \text{ Aniline (M}^{\cdot+}, m/e\ 94)$$

If the reaction had been intermolecular with the nitrogen becoming separated from the aromatic ring prior to aniline formation, species with molecular ions *m/e* 93, 94, and 95 would have been formed:

$^{14}NH_2$ (H)	$^{14}NH_2$ (D)	$^{15}NH_2$ (H)	$^{15}NH_2$ (D)
M$^{\cdot+}$, *m/e* 93	M$^{\cdot+}$, *m/e* 94	M$^{\cdot+}$, *m/e* 94	M$^{\cdot+}$, *m/e* 95

The fact that only the species with molecular ions *m/e* 94 were formed is evidence that the reaction is intramolecular:

$$m\text{-D-benzamide-}^{14}NH_2 \xrightarrow{\text{NaOBr}} m\text{-D-aniline-}^{14}NH_2 \quad \text{Molecular weight 94}$$

$$\text{benzamide-}^{15}NH_2 \xrightarrow{\text{NaOBr}} \text{aniline-}^{15}NH_2 \quad 94$$

Since neither the total deuterium content nor the total ^{15}N content changes during the reaction, the two possible reaction routes cannot be distinguished by a procedure that gives average abundances of deuterium and ^{15}N-label in the aniline. Thus, a combustion analysis would be useless. However, the mass spectrometer records the presence of individual molecular species as ions, rather than an average.

32.4   Spectrometric Identification

It is often possible to identify a compound totally or partially from spectroscopic data alone. In this section, we will look at ir, nmr, and mass spectra of three compounds in order to illustrate how these data can be used for such characterization.

Example 1

Table 32.5 presents the complete nmr spectrum of *N*-ethylaniline, seven of the most abundant ions in its mass spectrum, and selected absorption bands from its ir spectrum. The peak at m/e 121 in the mass spectrum represents the molecular ion and gives the molecular weight. (The *Nitrogen rule*—that any molecule with an odd molecular weight contains an odd number of nitrogen atoms—is applicable here, and suggests the presence of 1 nitrogen atom.) The isotope peaks at m/e 122 and 123 have 9.2% and 0.4% intensity relative to m/e 121; these are the isotopic abundance ratios expected for $C_8H_{11}N$.

Table 32.5   Spectral Data for *N*-Ethylaniline, ⟨O⟩— $NHCH_2CH_3$

Ir (partial spectrum)	Nmr (complete spectrum)	Mass spectrum (partial spectrum), m/e
$3430\ cm^{-1}$ (medium)	δ 1.11 (triplet, $J = 7.0$ Hz;	121 ($M^{\cdot+}$)
$1315\ cm^{-1}$ (strong)	relative integration: 3H)	106
$750\ cm^{-1}$ (strong)	δ 3.31 (quartet, $J = 7.0$ Hz;	79
$690\ cm^{-1}$ (strong)	2H)	77
	δ 6.65 (singlet; 1H)	65
	δ 6.4–7.3 (complex; 5H)	53
		51

The ir spectrum is characteristic of an aromatic amine. The single band at $3430\ cm^{-1}$ represents the NH stretching absorption: the C—N vibration absorbs at $1315\ cm^{-1}$. The two bands at 750 and $690\ cm^{-1}$ identify the presence of a monosubstituted benzene ring.

The absorption at δ 6.65 (singlet, 1 H) in the nmr spectrum is concentration-dependent, and therefore due to one proton on nitrogen, N—H. The ethyl group is recognized from the triplet and quartet, integrating for 3H and 2H, at δ 1.11 and δ 3.31, respectively. The coupling constant, 7.0 Hz, is in the range found for H_A—$\overset{|}{\underset{|}{C}}$—$\overset{|}{\underset{|}{C}}$—$H_B$. The five H's of the aromatic ring account for the complex absorption at δ 6.4–δ 7.3.

The most intense peak in the mass spectrum is m/e 106, 15 mass units lower than the molecular ion peak, due to elimination of a methyl radical. The stable molecules HCN and C_2H_2 are lost from fragments via complex rearrangements and fragmentation processes:

⟨O⟩—$\overset{+\cdot}{N}H$—CH_2CH_3 → ⟨O⟩—$\overset{+}{N}H$=CH_2 + $CH_3\cdot$

m/e 121 m/e 106

↓   ↓

$C_6H_5^+$ + $\cdot NHCH_2CH_3$ $C_6H_7^+$ + HCN

m/e 77 m/e 79

↓   ↓

$C_4H_3^+$ + C_2H_2 $C_4H_5^+$ + C_2H_2

m/e 51 m/e 53

Example 2

Spectral data from our second example, *trans*-4-phenyl-3-buten-2-one, are given in Table 32.6. A molecular weight of 146 is obtained from the mass spectrum.

Table 32.6   Spectral Data for *trans*-4-Phenyl-3-buten-2-one.

$$\bigcirc\!\!-\!\!\overset{H}{\underset{H}{C}}\!\!=\!\!C\!-\!\overset{O}{\overset{\|}{C}}\!-\!CH_3$$

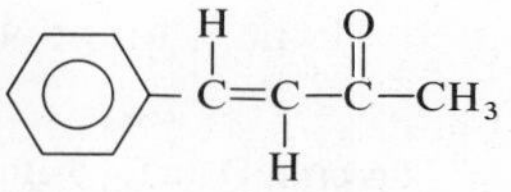

Ir *(partial spectrum)*	Nmr *(complete spectrum)*	Mass spectrum *(partial spectrum)*, m/e
1665 cm^{-1} (strong)	δ 2.35 (singlet; relative integration, 3H)	146 (M$\cdot^{+}$)
1610 cm^{-1} (strong)		131
1585 cm^{-1} (medium)	δ 6.70 (doublet, $J = 16.2$ Hz; 1H)	103
1490 cm^{-1} (medium)		77
1455 cm^{-1} (strong)	δ 7.4 (complex; 5H)	51
1075 cm^{-1} (medium)	δ 7.48 (doublet, $J = 16.2$ Hz; 1H)	43
980 cm^{-1} (strong, broad)		
752 cm^{-1} (strong)		
690 cm^{-1} (medium)		

The monosubstituted benzene ring is easily recognized from the ir absorptions bands at 752 and 690 cm^{-1}. The bands at 1610, 1585, 1490, and 1455 cm^{-1} are due to the aromatic ring. The complex nmr absorption at δ 7.4, which integrates for 5H, and the peak at m/e 77 (C$_6$H$_5^{+}$), are also consistent with the presence of the phenyl group. The strong ir absorption at 1665 cm^{-1} is the C=O stretching of a conjugated ketone. The broad absorption band at 980 cm^{-1} and the medium absorption band at 1075 cm^{-1} result from C—H bending of the trans-disubstituted C=C. The fact that the double bond is trans-disubstituted can also be seen from the nmr doublets (1H each) at δ 6.70 and δ 7.48 with $J = 16.2$ Hz (Section 7.5).

The fragmentations of the bonds between the carbonyl and the α carbons are seen in the mass spectrum:

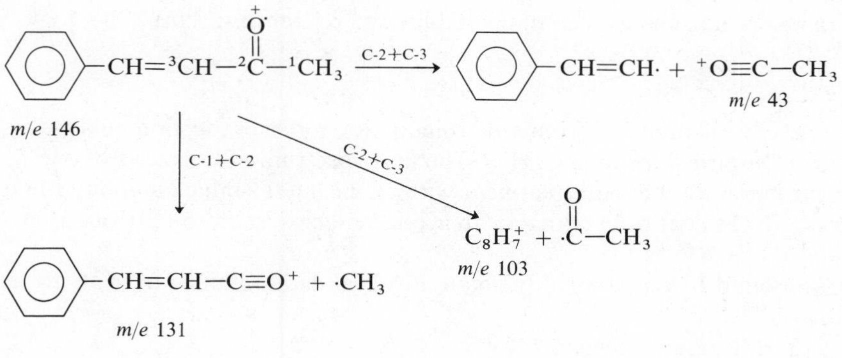

The peak at m/e 43 and the singlet (3H) at δ 2.35 in the nmr spectrum are consistent with the methyl ketone structure.

Example 3

The nmr spectrum (Table 32.7) of 3-butyn-2-ol is nearly sufficient to establish the structure. The mass spectrum contributes the molecular weight, 70. The ir spectrum establishes the presence of the alcohol (3350 cm^{-1}), but the $C \equiv C$ stretching vibration can be difficult to see from the ir spectrum because the 2080 cm^{-1} band is so weak. The $C-H$ stretching vibration of the mono-substituted alkyne is found at 3280 cm^{-1}.

Table 32.7   Spectral Data for 3-Butyn-2-ol, $^1CH_3 - {}^2CH - {}^3C \equiv {}^4CH$
$\qquad\qquad\qquad\qquad\qquad\qquad\qquad\qquad\qquad | $
$\qquad\qquad\qquad\qquad\qquad\qquad\qquad\qquad\quad OH$

Ir (*partial spectrum*)	Nmr (*complete spectrum*)	Partial mass spectrum, m/e
3350 cm^{-1} (broad, strong)	δ 1.42 (doublet, $J = 7.1 \text{ Hz}$; 3H)	70 (M^{+})
3280 cm^{-1} (strong, sharp)	δ 2.40 (doublet, $J = 2.3 \text{ Hz}$; 1H)	
2080 cm^{-1} (very weak)	δ 4.08 (broad singlet; 1H)	
	δ 5.50 (octet, $J = 7.1$ and 2.3 Hz; 1H)	

The hydroxyl proton is seen in the nmr spectrum as a broad singlet at δ 4.08, which is concentration-dependent. The doublet at δ 2.40 is due to the acetylenic proton with $J_{2,4} = 2.3 \text{ Hz}$. The methyl group is seen as a doublet at δ 1.42 with $J_{1,2} = 7.1 \text{ Hz}$. The C-2 proton has a multiplicity of 8 at δ 5.50.

From these three examples, we can see the large amount of data revealed by instrumental techniques without any chemical reactions being performed (except for ion formation, fragmentation, and rearrangement in the mass spectrometer). Except for the mass spectrometer, which requires microgram quantities of sample, no sample has been consumed. With simple molecules, instrumental data are usually sufficient to establish the structure. With more complex molecules, chemical, physical, and spectral data must be expertly and artfully woven together in order to arrive at a reasonable and consistent picture of molecular structure.

32.5   Roadmaps

When *roadmap* problems are worked, the physical, chemical, and spectroscopic data available for the compounds in question must be scrutinized carefully. The data should be listed and each item examined to see what it indicates about structure, after which a total or partial structure should be postulated. As much as possible should be deduced from the data before one consults compiled tables and reference spectra.

Example 1

Compound I is obtained from a petroleum fraction. Combustion analysis gives an empirical formula C_6H_{12}. The nmr spectrum of I consists of one sharp peak at δ 1.9. Upon treatment with ozone, an unstable compound Ia is formed. Treatment of Ia with zinc in acetic acid cleaves Ia to only one compound, Ib.

Compound Ib was studied in detail. Physical data obtained from Ib are as follows:
(a) Colorless liquid; density, 0.7908
(b) Bp, 56°C
(c) Infinitely soluble in water, ethanol, ether, benzene, chloroform
(d) Water solution is neutral

The ir spectrum of Ib has absorption bands at 3000, 1712, 1425, and 1360 cm^{-1}, among others. The nmr spectrum consists of a single sharp peak at $\delta\,2.07$. A molecular ion peak is present in the mass spectrum at m/e 58 and the most intense peak is m/e 43.

Now we are ready to examine these data and draw initial conclusions on Ib. The ir band at 1712 cm^{-1} is characteristic of a saturated ketone. To test this deduction we can attempt carbonyl reactions on Ib. Indeed, an oxime (mp 59°C) and a *p*-nitrophenylhydrazone (mp 152°C) can be prepared. From the molecular weight of 58 and the single peak in the nmr spectrum, it is likely that Ib is acetone:

$$CH_3-\overset{\overset{O}{\|}}{C}-CH_3 \qquad CH_3-\overset{\overset{+}{\overset{\cdot}{O}}}{\underset{}{C}}-CH_3 \rightarrow CH_3C\equiv\overset{+}{O} + CH_3\cdot$$

O←1712 cm^{-1} δ 2.07 m/e 58 m/e 43

By checking the above data against data in reference books and handbooks, it can be seen that all the information about Ib is consistent with acetone. For example, Table 32.8 shows comparisons of acetone and a few other ketones and their derivatives.

Table 32.8   Some Data on Ketones

Ketone	Bp, °C	MW	Oxime mp, °C	p-Nitrophenylhydrazone, °C
Acetone	56°	58	59°	152°
2-Butanone	80°	72	—	129°
2-Pentanone	102°	86	58°	117°
3-Pentanone	102°	86	69°	141°
Ib	56°	m/e 58	59°	152°

Following the reaction map from acetone back to Ia and I, we can see that I is 2,3-dimethyl-2-butene.

This roadmap is an example of the degradation of a molecule to a simpler molecule which can be easily identified, in this case a C_6 to a C_3 molecule. After identifying the smaller molecule, one can use his familiarity with the degradation reactions to travel back to the structure of the original molecule.

Example 2

Compound II is water-insoluble, but is soluble in dilute sodium hydroxide. This is behavior characteristic of an acid. When II is heated to determine its melting point, it melts at 103–104°C with decomposition. At 180°C, it readily gives off a gas and the residue is a new compound, IIa. The mass spectrum of II cannot be obtained due to decomposition at the temperature required to volatilize it into the ion source. Combustion analysis gives the empirical formula $C_9H_8O_3$.

Major peaks in the mass spectrum of IIa are at m/e 120, 105, and 77.

The difference between $C_9H_8O_3$, which has a molecular weight of 164, and IIa, which has a molecular ion at m/e 120, is 44 mass units. Thus decomposition of II to IIa could be a decarboxylation reaction.

$$C_9H_8O_3 \rightarrow C_8H_8O + CO_2$$

II	IIa	
164	120	44

Infrared absorptions at 1690, 1612, 1600, 1460, and 1440 cm^{-1} indicate that IIa is an aryl ketone. The nmr spectrum consists of aromatic peaks in the δ 7–8 region (5H) and a singlet (3H) at δ 2.59. From these spectra, it appears that IIa is acetophenone.

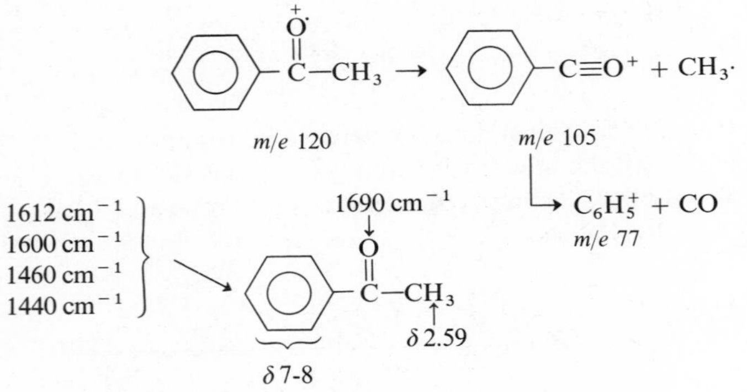

The reaction of IIa with NaOCl in water converts it to the acid IIb, which can be identified as benzoic acid on the basis of a melting point and a mixture melting point with an authentic sample.

Thus, the roadmap sequence can be followed to 3-oxo-3-phenylpropanoic acid:

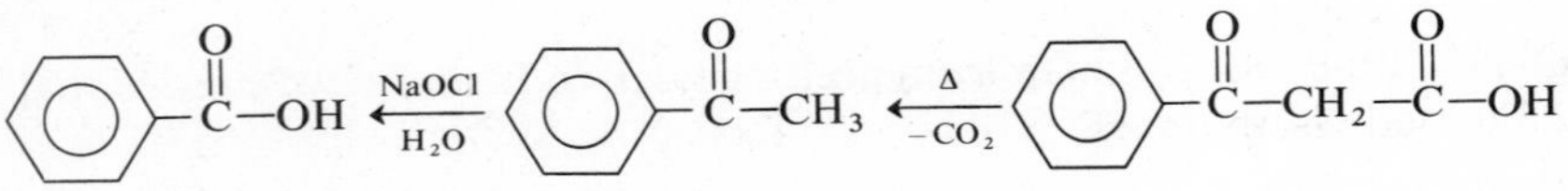

The reported melting point of 3-oxo-3-phenylpropanoic acid is the same as the melting point determined for II, 103–104°C.

Example 3

In this example, we will attempt to deduce the structure of III from reactions, without use of spectroscopy. In order to test the structure arrived at for III, we will synthesize it.

From a combustion analysis, III was found to have an empirical formula $C_6H_{15}N$. Since III is insoluble in water but soluble in aqueous hydrochloric acid, the nitrogen is present in the form of an amine. When III is treated with benzenesulfonyl chloride and excess sodium hydroxide (Hinsberg test), an insoluble compound is formed which is unaffected by acid. Thus, III is a secondary amine.

A quaternary ammonium hydroxide is formed by reaction of III with excess methyl iodide followed by silver oxide. Hofmann elimination by heating gives ethylene and compound IIIa, which is $C_6H_{15}N$, an isomer of III. Treatment of IIIa with excess methyl iodide, followed by silver oxide, gives a second quaternary ammonium hydroxide. Upon heat, it pyrolyzes to

C_4H_8, an olefin (IIIb) which can be hydrated by concentrated sulfuric acid to the alcohol IIIc. Oxidation of the alcohol IIIc gives a C_4H_8O ketone IIId.

We can summarize these reactions as follows:

$$C_6H_{15}N + HCl \rightleftharpoons C_6H_{15}\overset{+}{N}H + Cl^-$$
III

$$C_6H_{15}N + \langle\bigcirc\rangle-SO_2Cl \xrightarrow{NaOH} C_6H_{14}NSO_2-\langle\bigcirc\rangle + HCl$$
III

$$\downarrow {\scriptstyle H^+}$$

No reaction

Deduction: $C_6H_{14}\Big\{ \searrow N-H$

$$C_6H_{14}\Big\{-\overset{|}{\underset{\cdot\cdot}{N}}-H + CH_3-I \rightarrow C_6H_{14}\Big\{-\overset{CH_3}{\underset{|}{\overset{|+}{N}}}-CH_3 \quad I^-$$

$$\downarrow {\scriptstyle Ag_2O}$$

$$C_4H_9-N\overset{CH_3}{\underset{CH_3}{\diagdown}} + CH_2=CH_2 \xleftarrow{\Delta} C_6H_{14}\Big\{\overset{+}{N}\overset{CH_3}{\underset{CH_3}{\diagup}} \quad OH^-$$
$$+ HOH$$

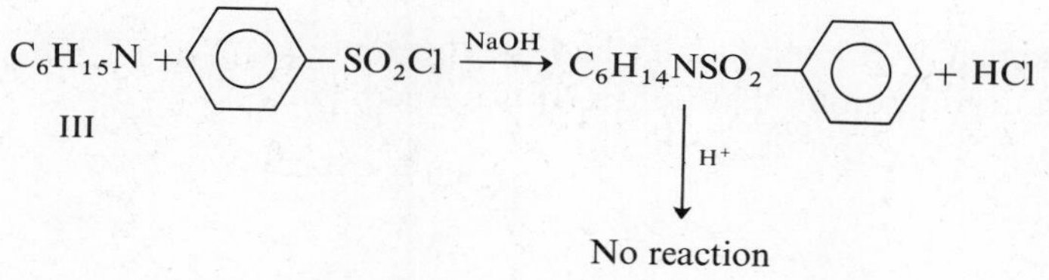

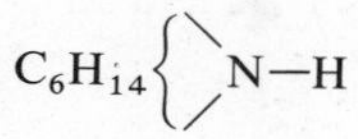

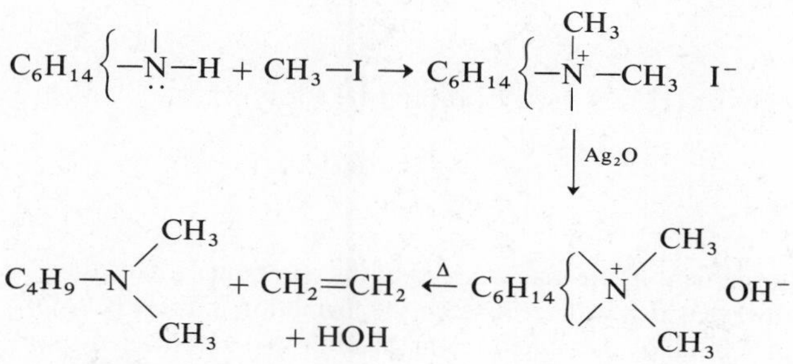

IIIa
$(C_6H_{15}N)$

Deduction: $CH_3CH_2-\overset{H}{\underset{|}{N}}-C_4H_9$

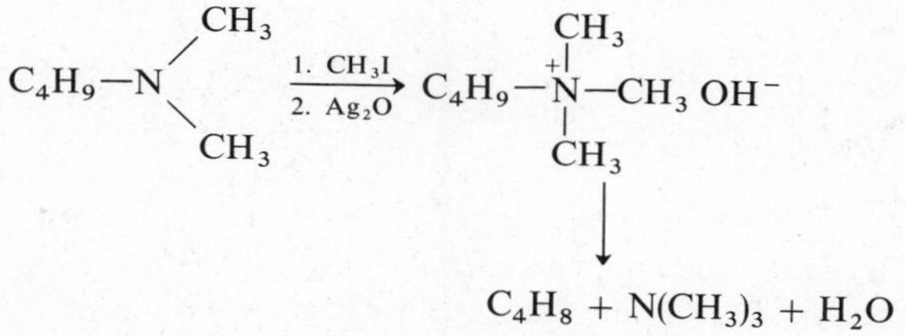

$$C_4H_9-N\overset{CH_3}{\underset{CH_3}{\diagdown}} \xrightarrow[\text{2. } Ag_2O]{\text{1. } CH_3I} C_4H_9-\overset{CH_3}{\underset{CH_3}{\overset{|}{\underset{|}{\overset{+}{N}}}}}-CH_3 \quad OH^-$$

$$\downarrow$$

$$C_4H_8 + N(CH_3)_3 + H_2O$$
IIIb

$$C_4H_8 \xrightarrow{H_2SO_4} C_4H_{10}O \xrightarrow{Cr_2O_7^{2-}} C_4H_8O$$
IIIb $\qquad$ IIIc $\qquad$ IIId

Deduction: IIIc is a secondary alcohol; a primary alcohol would be oxidized to a carboxylic acid and a tertiary alcohol would not be oxidized to a compound with the same number of carbon atoms.

Compound IIIb must be 1-butene or 2-butene. It cannot be isobutylene because isobutylene is hydrated to a tertiary alcohol:

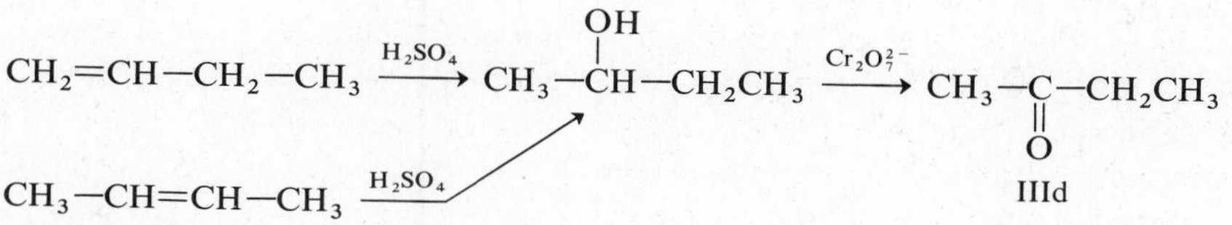

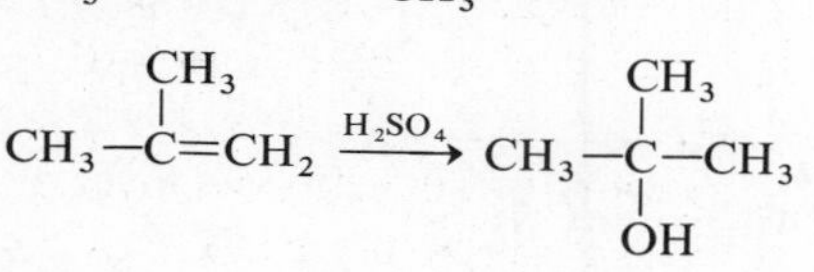

$$CH_2=CH-CH_2-CH_3 \xrightarrow{H_2SO_4} CH_3-\overset{OH}{\underset{|}{CH}}-CH_2CH_3 \xrightarrow{Cr_2O_7^{2-}} CH_3-\overset{}{\underset{\overset{||}{O}}{C}}-CH_2CH_3$$

$$CH_3-CH=CH-CH_3 \xrightarrow{H_2SO_4} \qquad\qquad\qquad\qquad\qquad\qquad \text{IIId}$$

$$CH_3-\overset{CH_3}{\underset{}{\overset{|}{C}}}=CH_2 \xrightarrow{H_2SO_4} CH_3-\overset{CH_3}{\underset{OH}{\overset{|}{\underset{|}{C}}}}-CH_3$$

Two structures are now possible for III, namely *N*-ethyl-*sec*-butylamine and *N*-ethyl-*n*-butylamine:

$$CH_3CH_2{-}NH{-}\underset{\underset{CH_3}{|}}{CH}CH_2CH_3 \qquad CH_3CH_2{-}NH{-}CH_2CH_2CH_2CH_3$$

When 2-butanone reacts with ethylamine and hydrogen in the presence of a platinum catalyst, a compound identical to III is formed. Only *N*-ethyl-*sec*-butylamine is consistent with this synthesis.

$$\underset{CH_3CH_2}{\overset{CH_3}{>}}C{=}O + H_2NCH_2CH_3 + H_2 \xrightarrow{Pt} \underset{CH_3CH_2}{\overset{CH_3}{>}}CH{-}NH{-}CH_2CH_3$$

III

Thus, the correct structure of III has been obtained by its synthesis by a well-known reaction.

PROBLEMS

1. In (a)–(d) peaks are listed prominent in the mass spectra of the compounds named. Suggest fragmentation pathways which will account for the formation of these peaks, as was done in this chapter for 1-butanol, diethyl ether, methyl *n*-propyl ketone, and so on.
   (a) In the mass spectrum of benzamide, intense peaks are found at m/e 121, 105, 77, and 51. Write a fragmentation scheme.
   (b) In the mass spectrum of *n*-butane, prominent peaks are found at m/e 58, 57, 43, 29, and 15. Suggest a scheme.
   (c) Major peaks in the mass spectrum of coumarin are as follows:

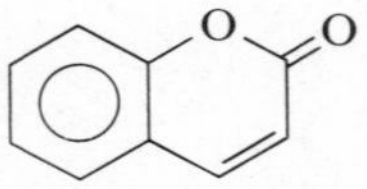

m/e 148	0.9%
147	9.9%
146	100.0%
118	79.0%
90	31.0%

   Interpret these peaks in terms of the structure of coumarin.
   (d) Some of the major peaks in the mass spectrum of *n*-propylbenzene are as follows:

m/e 120	(62%)
105	(4%)
91	(100%)
77	(3%)
51	(4%)

2. Identify the following compounds from the data given:

   (a) 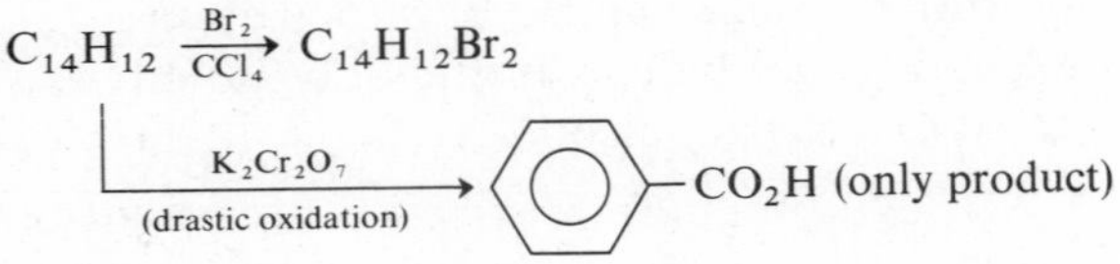 $C_{14}H_{12} \xrightarrow[CCl_4]{Br_2} C_{14}H_{12}Br_2$

   $\xrightarrow[\text{(drastic oxidation)}]{K_2Cr_2O_7}$ ⬡$-CO_2H$ (only product)

   (b)

   $\xrightarrow{(CH_3CO)_2O} A \xrightarrow[CH_3CO_2H]{Br_2} B \xrightarrow{H_3O^+} C$

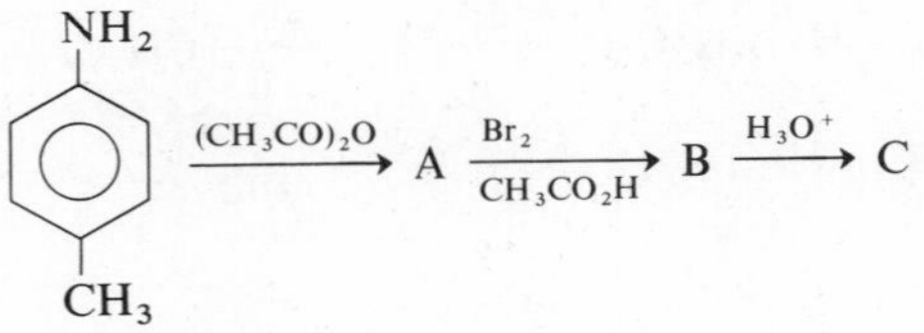

   (c) $CH_2{=}CH_2 \xrightarrow[H_2O]{Cl_2} C_2H_5OCl \xrightarrow{H_2SO_4} C_4H_8OCl_2 \xrightarrow{KOH} C_4H_6O$

(d) $CH_3(CH_2)_3OH \xrightarrow[250°C]{Cu} C_4H_8O \xrightarrow{OH^-} C_8H_{16}O_2 \xrightarrow[\text{warm}]{\text{dil. HCl}} C_8H_{14}O$

$$\downarrow \begin{matrix} H_2, \\ Ni \end{matrix}$$

$$C_8H_{18}O$$

(e) $C_5H_{11}Br \xrightarrow[H_2O]{NaOH} C_5H_{12}O$

$$\downarrow KCN$$

$C_6H_{11}N \xrightarrow{H_3O^+} C_6H_{12}O_2 \xrightarrow[H^+]{CH_3CH_2OH} C_8H_{16}O_2$

$$\downarrow \begin{matrix} 1.\ C_2H_5O^- \\ 2.\ H^+ \end{matrix}$$

$$C_{14}H_{26}O_3$$

(f) $C_{13}H_{11}ON$ (a neutral compound) $\xrightarrow{20\% \text{ NaOH}} C_6H_7N$ + solution

$$\downarrow H_3O^+$$

$$C_7H_6O_2$$

3. The product of the condensation of pulegone I with ethyl acetoacetate in alcoholic sodium ethoxide is called "pulegone acetone." Structures II–V have been proposed for pulegone acetone at various times.

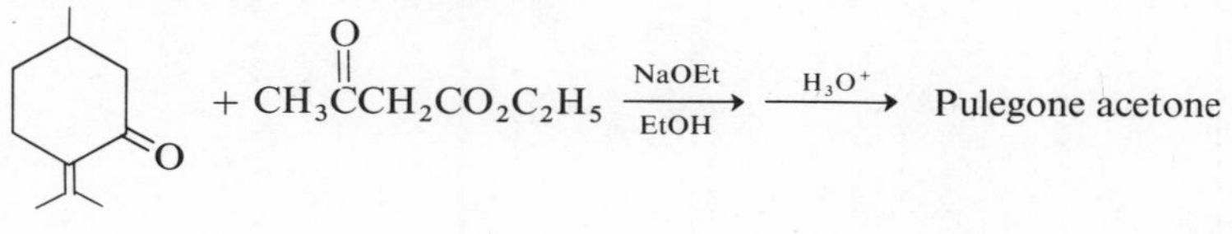

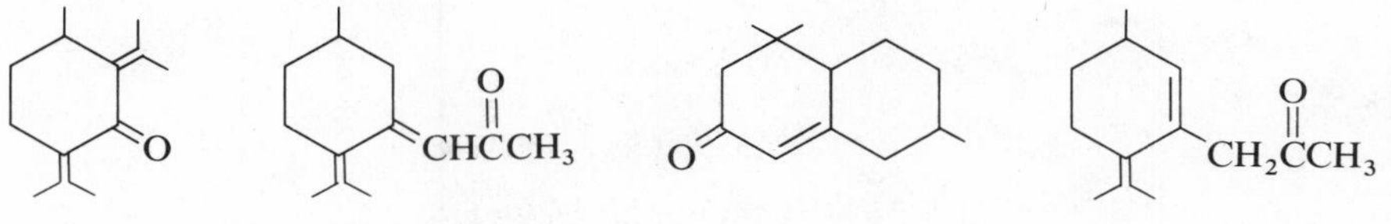

The following data are now available from pulegone acetone:
Ir (selected bands): 1675 and 1640 cm^{-1}

Nmr:

δ	Splitting	Integration
0.97	doublet	3
1.11	singlet	6
1.2–2.0	multiplet	8
2.3	singlet	2
6.1	singlet	1

(a) What is the correct structure of pulegone acetone? Interpret the ir and nmr data in terms of your answer.

(b) Ozonation of pulegone acetone yields an acid, $C_{13}H_{20}O_4$, which on heating forms a $C_{12}H_{18}O_2$ compound. The latter compound has no olefinic hydrogens in its nmr spectrum, but its ir spectrum has a strong band at 1775 cm^{-1} and a medium band at 1686 cm^{-1}. What are the structures of the two products from pulegone acetone?

4. Identify the major product (I) of the following reaction and interpret the data on page 852 in support of your answer.

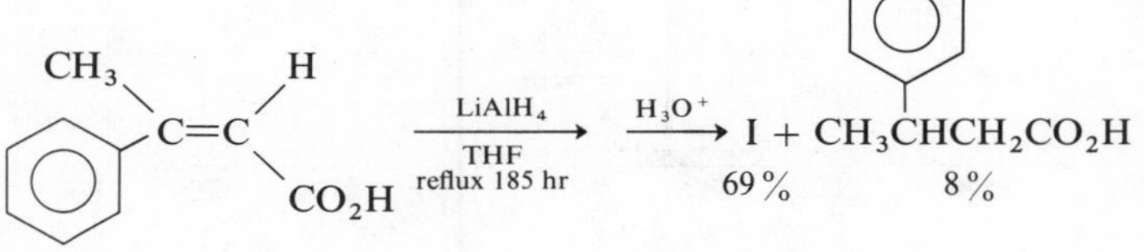

For I :   Combustion analysis : C, 90.88 % ; H, 9.21 %
          Ir (selected bands) :   3030, 1613, 1449, 1020, 847, 758 cm^{-1}

Nmr :	δ	Integration
	0.68	4 (multiplet)
	1.22	3 (singlet)
	7.11	5 (multiplet)

5.   The nmr and ir spectra of an unknown compound are given. The relative intensities of peaks in the molecular ion region of its mass spectrum are

m/e 201	2.0 %
200	20.0 %
199	2.0 %
198	20.0 %

What is the compound?

NMR spectrum of unknown compound, Problem 5.

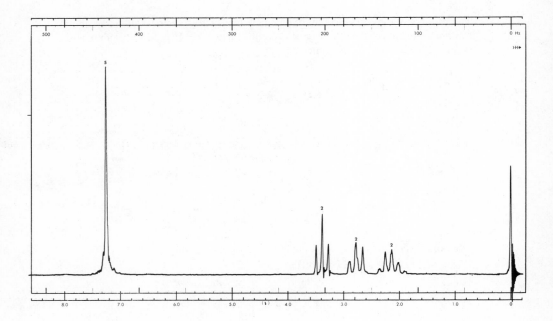

Infrared spectrum of unknown compound, Problem 5.

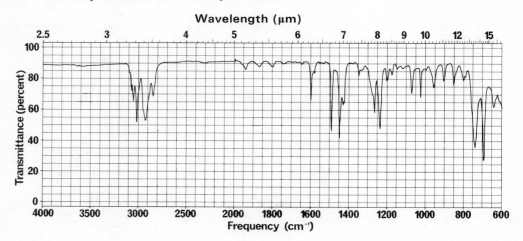

6. Identify compounds I, II, and III from the following scheme. The ir, nmr, and uv spectra of compound I are given.

$$I \atop C_6H_{10}O \quad \xrightarrow{H_2/catalyst} \quad {II \atop C_6H_{12}O}$$

ir (selected bands): 2950, 2820, 2710, 1722 (strong), 1470, 1370 cm^{-1}

$$\xrightarrow{NaBH_4} \quad {III \atop C_6H_{12}O}$$

ir (selected bands): 3620, 3015, 2950, 1665 (weak), 1470, 1370, 830 (medium) cm^{-1}

Infrared spectrum of compound I, Problem 6.

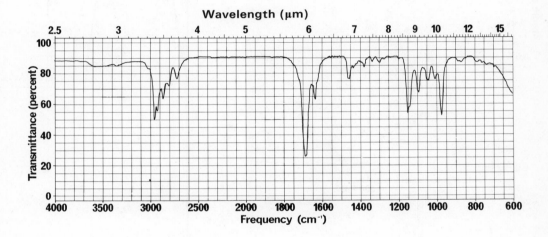

NMR spectrum of compound I, Problem 6.

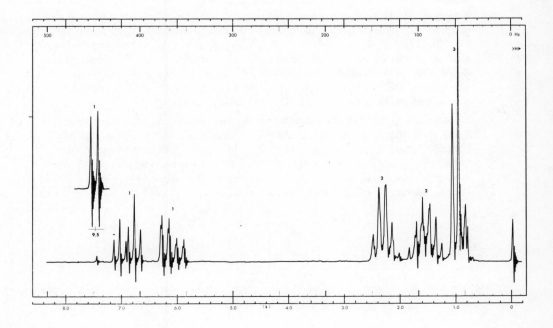

Ultraviolet spectrum of compound I, Problem 6 in ethanol at a concentration of 1×10^{-4} moles per liter employing a one cm quartz cell.

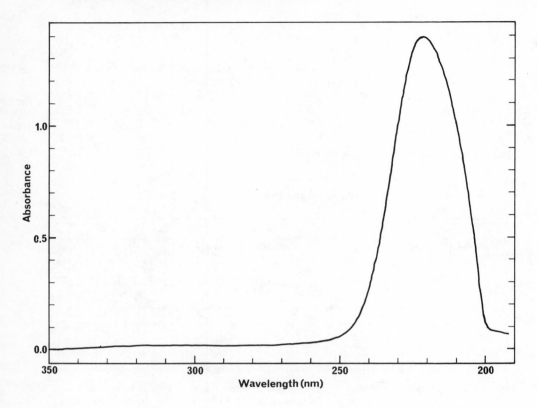

7. The infrared spectrum of a compound $C_{10}H_{17}N$ (I) shows no bands in the 2.8–3.0 μm and 5.8–6.0 μm regions. Compound I reacts with methyl iodide to give a solid $C_{11}H_{20}NI$ (II), which on boiling with dilute HCl gives a neutral liquid $C_6H_{10}O$ (III), the infrared spectrum of which shows a strong band at 5.73 μm. Basification of the aqueous mother liquor from this reaction liberates a base identified as piperidine. Compound III exchanges three hydrogens for deuterium in acidified D_2O. Assign structures to I-III.

8. A liquid $C_7H_{16}O$, insoluble in water, is found to react with 57% HI at 100° to give two products: C_2H_5I and $C_5H_{11}I$. The latter substance is converted to $C_5H_{12}O$ by warming with dilute NaOH. The compound $C_5H_{12}O$ does *not* give a yellow precipitate when warmed with iodine and aqueous base, but it is converted to $C_5H_{11}Cl$ by conc. HCl slowly when heated, and by conc. HCl containing zinc chloride quickly at room temperature. Heating $C_5H_{11}Cl$ with alcoholic KOH gives C_5H_{10}. Outline these transformations, and identify $C_7H_{16}O$ as precisely as you can.

9. A colorless liquid, $C_{10}H_{14}O$, gave the following test results: Ac_2O, a sweet-smelling liquid produced; I_2/aq. NaOH, bright yellow solid slowly formed; Na metal, gas bubbles evolved slowly; CrO_3/H_2SO_4, a dark blue-green color immediately formed; hot alkaline $KMnO_4$, compound slowly dissolved and benzoic acid precipitated after subsequent acidification; Br_2/CCl_4, not decolorized. The liquid exists as one *dl* pair. Write a structure consistent with these observations.

CHAPTER 33

ORGANOSILICON AND
ORGANOPHOSPHORUS CHEMISTRY

33.1   Organosilicon Chemistry

Silicon occupies a position in the periodic table which is intermediate between carbon and the metals of Group IV. Reactions occur with much greater facility at the silicon atom than at carbon atoms. In fact, reactions at a silicon atom occur so fast that it has not been practical to carry out kinetic studies on them by conventional techniques. We will find a number of similarities in the chemistry of carbon and silicon. However, four important differences in the chemistry of these two elements should be kept in mind.

1. Silicon, like carbon, is normally tetracovalent; but unlike carbon, silicon, with its low-lying d orbitals, can readily expand its octet to a coordination number of 5 or 6.

2. The atomic radius and the electron polarizability of silicon are much greater than those of carbon.

3. Silicon is electropositive compared to carbon and hydrogen; thus for either hydrogen or carbon bonded to silicon, the latter is the positive end of the dipole. Recall that a hydrogen attached to carbon is *positive* relative to the carbon.

$$\overset{\delta^+}{\geqslant}\!Si \rightarrow \overset{\delta^-}{C}\!\leqslant \quad \overset{\delta^+}{\geqslant}\!Si \rightarrow \overset{\delta^-}{H} \quad \text{but} \quad \overset{\delta^-}{\geqslant}\!C \leftarrow \overset{\delta^+}{H}$$

4. Silicon, like other second-row elements, is reluctant to participate in p–p π bonds.

The student may find it advantageous at this time to briefly review Sections 4.17 and 10.6 on the structure and nomenclature of silicon compounds.

EXERCISE 33.1

The proton magnetic resonance spectrum of tetramethylsilane appears as a singlet at $\delta\,0.00$. Offer an explanation which accounts for the high field strength necessary to observe this resonance.

33.2   Nucleophilic Substitutions and Siliconium Ions

Silicon compounds are much more susceptible to bimolecular nucleophilic substitution than are the corresponding carbon compounds.

$$\geqslant\!Si\!-\!X + Z^- \rightarrow Z\!-\!Si\!\leqslant + X^-$$

The reaction profile (Figure 33.1) resembles that for an S_N2 reaction at carbon, with the important difference that $3d$-orbital participation (Figure 33.2) may be involved in the stabilization of transition states and/or unstable intermediates whose structures and free energy closely approximate the transition state. Note that such participation would make the silicon atom electron-rich in the transition state. Although very few kinetic

Figure 33.1
Reaction profile for bimolecular displacement on silicon.

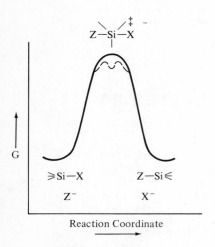

studies of reactions of silicon have been carried out, it does appear from the effects of electron-donating and electron-withdrawing substituents, that a significant amount of negative charge is accumulated at silicon in the transition state of a bimolecular substitution reaction.

Figure 33.2
(a) The transition state for an S_N2 mechanism at carbon. (b) Trigonal bipyramid transition state or unstable intermediate for an S_N2 mechanism at silicon involving 3d-orbital participation.

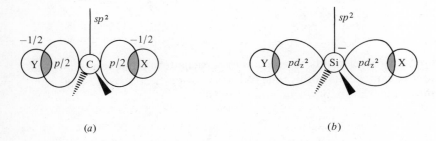

(a)   (b)

One might anticipate by analogy to carbon chemistry that such bimolecular substitution reactions would lead to inversion of configuration at the silicon atom. It has been found, mainly from the work of Sommer† and co-workers, that with a good leaving group (especially in polar solvents which stabilize the departing anion by solvation), inversion of configuration does almost always occur. However, inversion is not the only pathway by which bimolecular substitution can occur at silicon. Bimolecular substitu-

† Leo H. Sommer. Born 1917. Pennsylvania State University and University of California (Davis).

tion reactions are very rapid in bridgehead silicon compounds, in contrast to the highly inert carbon analogs (Sections 17.2, 17.3). Here again, the difference can be accounted for by mechanisms not available in carbon chemistry. Participation by $3d$ orbitals in two different mechanisms leading to retention of configuration at the central silicon atom gives intermediates with the following geometries:

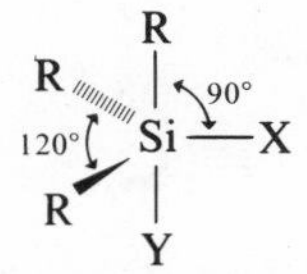

Trigonal bipyramid 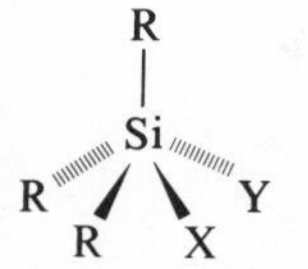   Tetragonal pyramid

Interchange of Apical and Equatorial Substituents. As a reaction of a given molecule proceeds along the reaction coordinate, the nuclei (and electrons) assume positions corresponding to the minimum possible free energy. These positions must be the same in the forward and reverse reactions; that is, both the forward and reverse reactions must occur by the same mechanism. This is called the *principle of microscopic reversibility.* Note that in the trigonal bipyramid shown above, the leaving and entering groups (X and Y) do not occupy like positions; X is in an equatorial position and Y is in an apical position. If this were the transition state it would imply that in the forward reaction a group Y would enter from the apical direction and in the reverse reaction a similar group X would enter from the equatorial direction. Such a situation is unlikely to obtain. We can get out of this dilemma by suggesting that a process which is termed *pseudo-rotation* occurs. By pseudo-rotation, a trigonal-bipyramid molecule is transformed by deforming bond angles in such a way that the molecule appears to have been rotated by 90°. In the illustration below the group that is towards the observer remains fixed while the apical (vertical) groups are pushed backwards (transforming a 180° bond angle to a 120° bond angle) and the remaining two equatorial groups are pulled forward and apart slightly (transforming a 120° bond angle to a 180° bond angle).

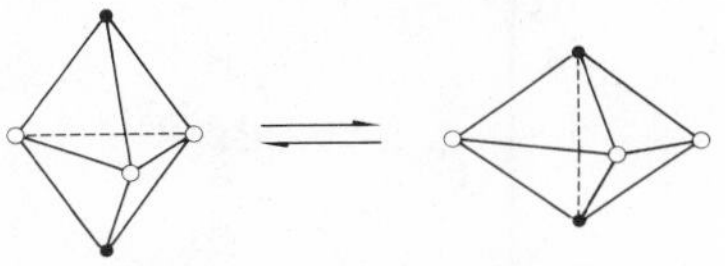

Note that this process of pseudo-rotation results in an interchange of apical and equatorial substituents. Because of the principle of microscopic reversibility, a trigonal bipyramid with an entering and leaving group occupying unlike positions is not likely to represent a transition state, but more probably represents a metastable intermediate of sufficient lifetime to undergo pseudo-rotation.

Bimolecular substitution reactions which occur with retention of configuration at the silicon atom are not limited to bridgehead compounds. Retention of configuration at silicon is often observed with acyclic compounds with poor leaving groups, especially in nonpolar solvents. In a large number of such reactions, the attacking reagent (E–Y) may give an electrophilic assist to the leaving group (X).

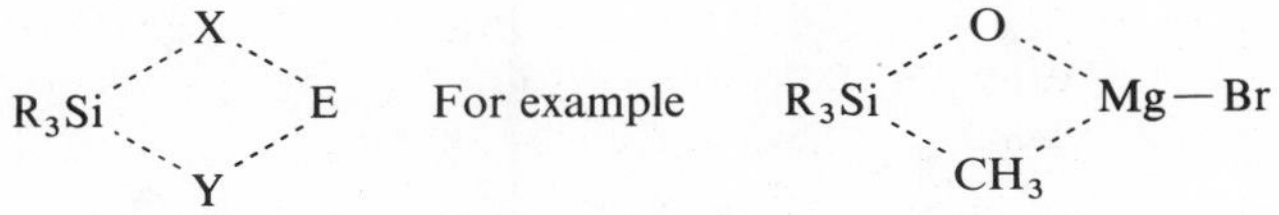

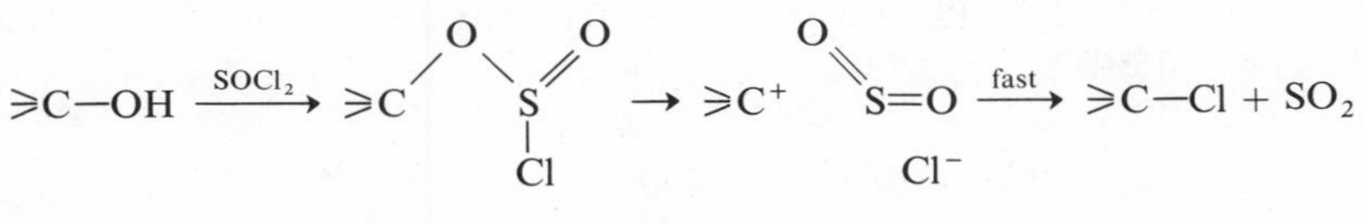

Nucleophilic substitution reactions with retention of configuration at carbon sometimes occur via ion-pair formation (Section 18.3), but such reactions occur at silicon atoms without the involvement of siliconium ion pairs. *A priori*, it might be predicted that siliconium ions would intervene in nucleophilic substitution reactions as readily as would carbonium ions, especially since silicon is more electropositive than carbon.

$$R_3\overset{*}{C}-X \xrightarrow[\text{slow}]{S_N1} R_3C^+ \xrightarrow[\text{fast}]{Y^-} R_3C-Y$$
$$\qquad\qquad\qquad X^- \qquad\qquad \text{racemic}$$

$$R_3\overset{*}{Si}-X \xrightarrow[\text{slow}]{S_N1\text{-Si}} R_3Si^+ \xrightarrow[\text{fast}]{Y^-} R_3Si-Y$$
$$\qquad\qquad\qquad\quad X^- \qquad\qquad \text{racemic}$$

Such reactions are very uncommon if they occur at all. No unequivocal example of a reaction by this path is as yet known. When even poor nucleophiles are present, it appears that the S_N1 Si pathway is simply unable to compete with S_N2 Si reactions. This may be because siliconium ions are generally less stable than carbonium ions, but more likely the reason is that bimolecular substitution occurs so readily at the silicon atom that mechanisms involving siliconium ions have no chance to compete.

The Unimportance of Siliconium Ions. The triphenylsilyl halides show no tendency to dissociate. Triphenyl carbonium ions are highly stable because of delocalization involving p–p π bonds between the central atom and the rings. Such resonance forms involving doubly bonded silicon apparently make little contribution to the stability of triphenylsiliconium ions.

$$(C_6H_5)_3C-X \longrightarrow (C_6H_5)_3C^+ \ X^-$$
$$(C_6H_5)_3Si-X \overset{}{\nrightarrow} (C_6H_5)_3Si^+ \ X^-$$

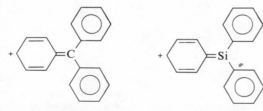

Important contributions   Unimportant contributions

33.3   Silanions

Organosilylmetallic compounds, such as triphenylsilyllithium, are well known. In principle, such compounds can be considered as containing stable *silanions*. The silyl anions are not formed as readily as are the analogous carbanions. However, once formed, their reactions are largely predictable by analogy with organometallic compounds. Compounds of the type $R_3Si^-M^+$ are readily accessible from disilanes when one, two, or all three R groups are aryl.

$$R_3SiSiR_3 + 2\,M \rightarrow 2\,R_3Si^-\ M^+$$

It is possible to prepare such compounds when all three R groups are alkyl, but they are generally known only as transient reaction intermediates.

Recall that the direction of polarization of the Si—H bond is opposite to that of a C—H bond. Treatment of compounds such as triphenylsilane with strong bases such as methyllithium does not result in the formation of triphenylsilyllithium, but rather methyltriphenylsilane and lithium hydride.

$$(C_6H_5)_3SiH + CH_3Li \xrightarrow{\text{ether}} (C_6H_5)_3SiCH_3 + LiH$$

33.4 Organosilicon Free Radicals

Organosilyl radicals are involved in a number of reactions which are of synthetic importance. Simple silyl radicals are formed more readily from silanes than are the analogous free radicals from hydrocarbons.

$$R_3Si-H \rightarrow R_3Si\cdot + \cdot H \qquad \Delta H^\circ = +76 \text{ kcal}$$

$$R_3C-H \rightarrow R_3C\cdot + \cdot H \qquad \Delta H^\circ = +98 \text{ kcal}$$

Triphenylsilyl radicals do not appear to have the high stability associated with the carbon analogs such as triphenylmethyl. (Recall that a similar situation obtains for the siliconium ions.) Compounds such as $(C_6H_5)_3C-Si(C_6H_5)_3$ or $(C_6H_5)_3Si-Si(C_6H_5)_3$ show no tendency to dissociate into radicals, in marked contrast to $(C_6H_5)_3C-C(C_6H_5)_3$, which cannot even be formed (Section 12.4). Once formed, radicals such as $(C_6H_5)_3Si\cdot$ are highly reactive; they even abstract chlorine from chlorobenzene.

33.5 Silenes

Divalent silicon species, *silenes*, analogous to carbenes or methylenes, can be generated by α-elimination reactions. General approaches to the generation of silenes include the reaction of dihalosilanes with metals, or the thermolysis of di- or polysilanes.

Dimethylsilene

Two characteristic reactions of carbenes are insertion into single bonds (Section 23.9) and addition across multiple bonds (Sections 15.13, 22.8, 31.8).

$$CH_2: + R-H \rightarrow R-CH_2-H$$

Although silenes have not been studied in great detail, both insertion and addition reactions have been observed.

Although silacyclopropanes per se have not been isolated from reactions of silenes such as dimethylsilene, they are presumedly formed as intermediates.

33.6 Preparation and Reactions of Organosilicon Compounds

The ultimate raw material from which all organosilicon compounds are made is silica, SiO_2, which is by far the most abundant constituent of the earth's crust. Compared to most carbon compounds, silicon compounds are relatively expensive. The high cost can be attributed to the large expenditure of energy which is required for the conversion of the abundant silica to silicon, or to silicon tetrahalides, from which silicon compounds are made.

$$SiO_2 + C \xrightarrow[\text{furnace}]{\text{Electric}} Si + 2CO$$

$$SiO_2 + C + 2Cl_2 \xrightarrow{1000°C} SiCl_4 + CO_2$$

Organosilicon chlorides, which are by far the most important intermediates in organosilicon chemistry, are prepared either from elemental silicon or from silicon tetrachloride. Reaction of silicon with alkyl or aryl chlorides at high temperatures in the presence of copper catalysts produces mixtures of organosilicon chlorides. This direct synthesis is an important commercial process. The method is effectively limited to the preparation of lower alkyl and simpler arylsilicon chlorides.

$$CH_3Cl + Si \xrightarrow{Cu}{400°C} SiCl_4 + CH_3SiHCl_2 + CH_3SiCl_3 + (CH_3)_2SiCl_2$$

Transformations of the products of the "direct synthesis" (mainly by nucleophilic substitution reactions) provide virtually all of the important organosilicon compounds. A number of representative nucleophilic substitution reactions of silicon halides are illustrated by the following equations.

$$SiCl_4 + 4CH_3MgBr \longrightarrow (CH_3)_4Si$$

$$(CH_3)_3SiCl \xrightarrow{NH_3} (CH_3)_3SiNHSi(CH_3)_3$$

$$(CH_3)_3SiCl \xrightarrow{ROH} (CH_3)_3SiOR$$

The conversion of alcohols to trimethylsilyl ethers by reaction with trimethylsilyl chloride has utility in that the ethers are unusually volatile—much more so than the starting alcohols. This increased volatility is often useful and even necessary for the study of alcohols by mass spectroscopy and vapor-phase chromatography.

The silyl halides are important sources of disilanes and higher silanes, as well as organosilylmetallic compounds. The synthesis of Si—Si bonds can be achieved by the interaction of a silyl halide and an active metal.

$$R_3SiX + 2M \rightarrow R_3SiM + MX$$

$$R_3SiM + R_3SiX \rightarrow R_3Si-SiR_3 + MX$$

The reactivities of these silylmetallic compounds are much like those of typical organometallic compounds.

$$Ar_3SiLi + CH_3-\overset{\overset{\displaystyle O}{\|}}{C}-CH_3 \rightarrow Ar_3Si-\overset{\overset{\displaystyle OH}{|}}{\underset{\underset{\displaystyle CH_3}{|}}{C}}-CH_3$$

The silicon–oxygen single bond is an extraordinarily strong bond (Si—O ~ 105 kcal vs. C—O, 85 kcal), which undoubtedly accounts for the high thermal stability of silicon–oxygen compounds. It is highly probable that the sigma bond between silicon and oxygen is augmented by some p–d π overlap.

$$\geqslant Si-\overset{..}{\underset{..}{O}}-R \leftrightarrow \geqslant \overset{-}{Si}=\overset{+}{\underset{..}{O}}-R$$

$$\geqslant Si-OH \xrightarrow{\text{OH}^-} \geqslant Si-O^- \leftrightarrow \geqslant \overset{-}{Si}=O$$

The fact that silanols are somewhat more acidic than the corresponding alcohols may be a reflection of back-bonding to silicon. In general, silanols and their salts behave much like alcohols and alkoxides.

EXERCISE 33.2

Since silicon is more electropositive than carbon, silylamines reasonably might be expected to be more basic than the corresponding organic amines. They are, in fact, much weaker bases. Offer an explanation.

Silanols are formed by the hydrolysis of a number of silicon compounds; water alone is usually sufficient to bring about the hydrolysis.

$$R_3SiX \xrightarrow{\text{H}_2\text{O}} R_3SiOH$$

X = halogen, OR, OCOR, H, etc.

The outstanding characteristic of silanols is the ease with which they condense to form siloxanes.

$$2R_3SiOH \rightarrow R_3SiOSiR_3 + H_2O$$

Polymeric materials obtained by the condensation of diols and/or triols are known as *silicones*, since these materials may be formally considered as polymers of the silicon analogs of ketones, $>Si=O$. Monomeric "silicones" are unknown, even as transient reaction intermediates. This is a further example of the reluctance of silicon to form p–p π bonds.

EXERCISE 33.3

Di-*t*-butylsilanediol is stable to heat and acid. It will not lose water, even with dehydrating agents above 400°C. Offer an explanation.

Silanes containing Si—H bonds may be prepared from silyl halides by the preferential displacement of halogen with organometallic reagents, or by reduction with lithium aluminum hydride.

$$HSiCl_3 + RMgCl \longrightarrow RSiHCl_2$$

$$R_3SiCl + LiAlH_4 \longrightarrow R_3SiH$$

As noted earlier, the silicon–hydrogen bond is polarized in such a way that the hydrogen is negative. In such compounds, nucleophilic substitution may result in the displacement of hydride. As might be expected (page 858) such a reaction involving a poor leaving group usually proceeds with retention of configuration at the silicon atom.

$$R_3Si-H + LiAlD_4 \longrightarrow R_3Si-D$$

$$R_3Si-H + OH^- \xrightarrow{H_2O} R_3Si-OH + H_2$$

The formation of Si—C bonds by the addition of silicon hydrides to alkenes and alkynes is an important process in the laboratory as well as in industry. Such a reaction can be achieved under free-radical conditions and is usually initiated by light or peroxide catalysts. The overall process is a chain reaction, but it can easily be controlled to give simple addition products, since the silicon hydrides are efficient chain-transfer agents.

$$R_3SiH + CH_2=CH_2 \xrightarrow[\text{or } h\nu]{\text{cat.}} R_3SiCH_2-CH_3$$

The addition of silane hydrides can also be catalyzed by certain heavy metals. At room temperature, chloroplatinic acid, H_2PtCl_6, is effective in mole ratios as low as 10^{-9}. Intermediates of the type R_3SiPtH may possibly intervene in such reactions.

$$CH_3SiHCl_2 + CH_2=CHC_6H_5 \xrightarrow{H_2PtCl_6} CH_3SiCl_2CH_2CH_2C_6H_5$$
$$83\%$$

Bond Strengths of C—Si and Si—Si Bonds. The chemistry of compounds of the type R_4Si is strongly influenced by the relatively high stability of the Si—C bond. Compounds such as tetramethylsilane are chemically quite inert. Nevertheless, the high susceptibility of the silicon atom to nucleophilic attack is manifested even in compounds in which a central silicon atom is surrounded by four carbon atoms.

$$(CH_3CH_2)_4Si + Br_2 \xrightarrow{AlBr_3} \left[\overset{\delta+}{(CH_3CH_2)_3Si} - \overset{\delta-}{CH_2CH_3} \atop \underset{\delta-}{Br_3AlBr} - \underset{\delta+}{Br} \right] \longrightarrow (CH_3CH_2)_3SiBr + CH_3CH_2Br$$

The low energy of the Si—Si bond (53 kcal) compared to the C—C bond (83 kcal) suggests that silicon chains will be less stable than the corresponding hydrocarbons. Compounds of the series Si_nH_{2n+2} analogous to the hydrocarbons are known only to $n = 6$. The principal method of synthesis of the silicon–silicon bond is provided by the reaction of active metals with silyl halides as discussed previously. Characteristic reactions of these compounds are illustrated.

$$\geqslant Si-Si\leqslant + 2H_2O \xrightarrow{OH^-} 2\geqslant SiOH + H_2 \text{ (quantitative evolution of hydrogen)}$$

$$(CH_3CH_2)_3Si-Si(CH_2CH_3)_3 + I_2 \longrightarrow 2(CH_3CH_2)_3SiI$$

33.7   Commercial Aspects of Silicon Chemistry

Almost all of the organosilicon materials of commerce are polymeric siloxanes or silicones. The silicone oils are mainly linear polymers of the type

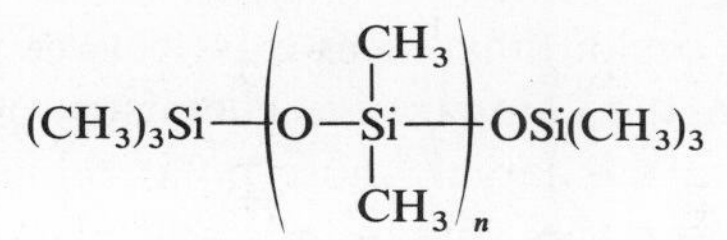

$$(CH_3)_3Si-\left(O-\underset{\underset{\displaystyle CH_3}{|}}{\overset{\overset{\displaystyle CH_3}{|}}{Si}}\right)_n OSi(CH_3)_3$$

Such compound, up to $n = 2000$, are fluids at room temperature. The silicone resins and silicone rubbers are cross-linked polymers. Such cross-linking is achieved in a number of ways. One of the most common methods is the addition of controlled amounts of methyltrichlorosilane to dimethyldichlorosilane before hydrolysis.

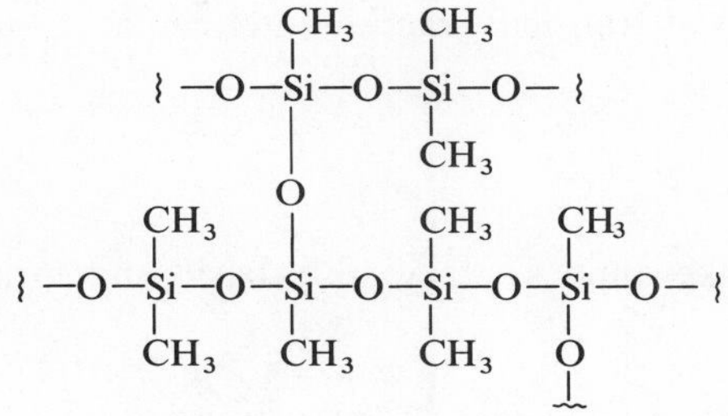

$$\}-O-\underset{\underset{\displaystyle O}{|}}{\overset{\overset{\displaystyle CH_3}{|}}{Si}}-O-\underset{\underset{\displaystyle CH_3}{|}}{\overset{\overset{\displaystyle CH_3}{|}}{Si}}-O-\}$$

$$\}-O-\underset{\underset{\displaystyle CH_3}{|}}{\overset{\overset{\displaystyle CH_3}{|}}{Si}}-O-\underset{\underset{\displaystyle CH_3}{|}}{\overset{\overset{\displaystyle }{|}}{Si}}-O-\underset{\underset{\displaystyle CH_3}{|}}{\overset{\overset{\displaystyle CH_3}{|}}{Si}}-O-\underset{\underset{\displaystyle O}{|}}{\overset{\overset{\displaystyle CH_3}{|}}{Si}}-O-\}$$

Other types of cross linking can be achieved by the use of vinylsilanes in the polymerization process, or by curing linear polymers in the presence of free-radical catalysts such as benzoyl peroxide.

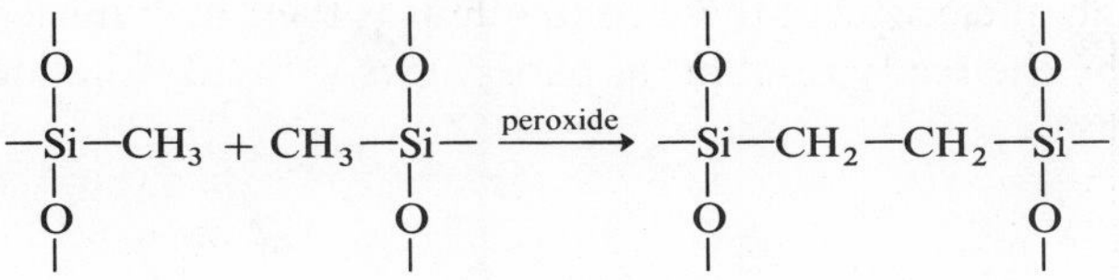

$$-\underset{\underset{\displaystyle O}{|}}{\overset{\overset{\displaystyle O}{|}}{Si}}-CH_3 + CH_3-\underset{\underset{\displaystyle O}{|}}{\overset{\overset{\displaystyle O}{|}}{Si}}-\xrightarrow{\text{peroxide}} -\underset{\underset{\displaystyle O}{|}}{\overset{\overset{\displaystyle O}{|}}{Si}}-CH_2-CH_2-\underset{\underset{\displaystyle O}{|}}{\overset{\overset{\displaystyle O}{|}}{Si}}-$$

The utility of the silicones is based primarily on what they do *not* do; these materials are highly inert—they are water-repellent, stable at extremes of temperatures, good electrical insulators, fairly inert to chemical attack, and they are nontoxic. Some of the more important uses of the silicones are listed here:

Silicone Oils: Treatment of fabrics to make them water-repellent and stain-resistant, antistick finishes on paper, polishes, antifoam agents, dielectric fluids, water-barrier pharmaceutical creams, and lubricants for use under extreme conditions of heat or cold.

Silicone Resins: Electrical insulators and water-repellent paints and finishes which have outstanding resistance to weather, sunlight, oxidation, and high-energy radiation.

Silicone Rubbers: Seals, gaskets, and so on, especially under conditions of high temperatures or wide variation in temperature.

Reactive silicon compounds are included in a number of formulations designed to alter surface properties.

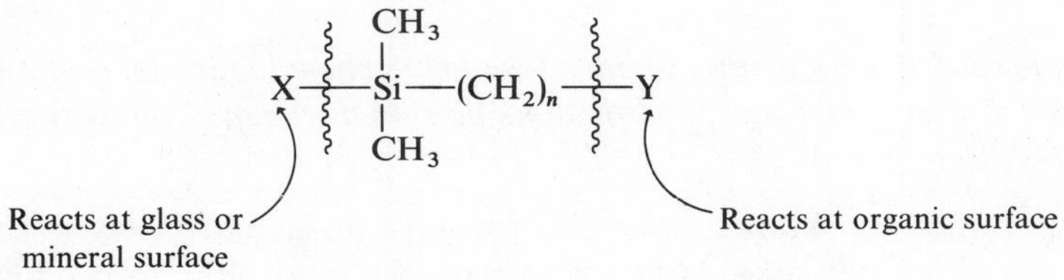

$$X\{-\underset{\underset{\displaystyle CH_3}{|}}{\overset{\overset{\displaystyle CH_3}{|}}{Si}}-(CH_2)_n-\}-Y$$

Reacts at glass or mineral surface   Reacts at organic surface

Compounds of the general type illustrated above are used to bind the finish to fiberglass automobile bodies.

33.8   Organophosphorus Chemistry

The versatility of organic phosphorus compounds in both structure and reactivity follows from the electronic structure of the atom. Phosphorus falls just below nitrogen in the periodic chart, and there are a number of similarities in the chemistry of the organic derivatives of these two elements. The same general types of differences exist between the chemistry of nitrogen and phosphorus as exist in the comparative chemistry of carbon and silicon. Phosphorus has accessible d orbitals, is larger, more polarizable, and more electropositive than nitrogen. Trivalent phosphorus compounds and phosphorus anions are better nucleophiles than analogous nitrogen derivatives. Furthermore, phosphorus centers are much more electrophilic, that is, much more subject to nucleophilic attack, than are similar nitrogen centers. The coordination of nitrogen is limited to 4, whereas phosphorus can increase its coordination number to 5 or 6 by expansion of its octet. As has already been noted in Section 10.6, phosphorus compounds with coordination numbers of 5 and 6 exist not only as transient reaction intermediates, but also as stable compounds.

33.9   Phosphorus Compounds as Nucleophiles

Tervalent organic phosphorus compounds, like amines, are weakly basic and form adducts with acids.

$$(CH_3)_3P: + HX \rightarrow (CH_3)_3\overset{+}{P}-H \ X^- \qquad pK_a \ 8.65 \ [cf. \ (CH_3)_3\overset{+}{N}-H, \ pK_a \ 9.76]$$

$$R_3P: + BF_3 \rightarrow R_3\overset{+}{P}-\overset{-}{B}F_3$$

However, the most pronounced characteristic of these compounds is their high nucleophilic reactivity, as exemplified by the ready reaction of phosphines with alkyl halides to produce phosphonium salts.

$$R-X + R_3P: \rightarrow R_4P^+ \ X^-$$

A COMPARISON OF PHOSPHINES WITH AMINES AS NUCLEOPHILES. *The rate of such a reaction increases with alkyl substitution on the phosphine, because of the electron-donating properties of the alkyl groups.*

$$\leftarrow \text{More reactive} \qquad \text{Less reactive} \rightarrow$$
$$R_3P > R_2PH > RPH_2 > PH_3$$

The reverse rate order is usually found in the reaction of amines with alkylating agents because of steric factors which are much more important with the small nitrogen atom than with the larger phosphorus atom.

$$\leftarrow \text{Less reactive} \qquad \text{More reactive} \rightarrow$$
$$R_3N < R_2NH < RNH_2 < NH_3$$

Triphenylphosphine reacts readily with methyl iodide, whereas triphenylamine is inert; in the amine there is greater steric hindrance, and the lone pair on nitrogen is significantly delocalized into the aromatic rings.

One of the most useful and best known reactions in phosphorus chemistry is the Arbusov reaction—the reaction of an alkyl halide with a trialkyl phosphite to produce a phosphonate ester.

$$RX + (R'O)_3P \rightarrow (R'O)_3\overset{+}{P}-R \ X^- \rightarrow R'X + (R'O)_2\overset{O}{\overset{\|}{P}}-R$$

$$CH_3I + (CH_3CH_2O)_3P \rightarrow [(CH_3CH_2O)_3\overset{+}{P}-CH_3 \ I^-]$$

$$\rightarrow (CH_3CH_2O)_2\overset{O}{\overset{\|}{P}}-CH_3 + CH_3CH_2I$$

Note that the by-product in this reaction is an alkyl halide (R'X); if this halide is more reactive than the initial RX, mixtures may be formed. Phosphites, with the electron-withdrawing alkoxy groups on the phosphorus, are much less nucleophilic than phosphines. Hence such alkylation reactions often require long reflux times. With triaryl phosphites, the reaction stops at the first stage to give triaryloxyphosphonium salts, $(ArO)_3\overset{+}{P}{-}R\ X^-$.

EXERCISE 33.4

What principal products would you expect from the following reaction?

$$(CH_3CH_2O)_3P + CH_3CH_2Br \xrightarrow{150°C}$$
$$\text{(trace amount)}$$

EXERCISE 33.5

Suggest a reasonable mechanism to account for the following observation:

$$2(CH_3CH_2O)_3P + BrCH_2CH_2Br \rightarrow$$

$$(CH_3CH_2O)_2\overset{\overset{O}{\|}}{P}{-}CH{=}CH_2 + (CH_3CH_2O)_2\overset{\overset{O}{\|}}{P}H + 2CH_3CH_2Br$$

Phosphorus Anions. Phosphorus anions in which negative charge is borne principally by the phosphorus are extraordinary nucleophiles. Characteristic reactions are illustrated.

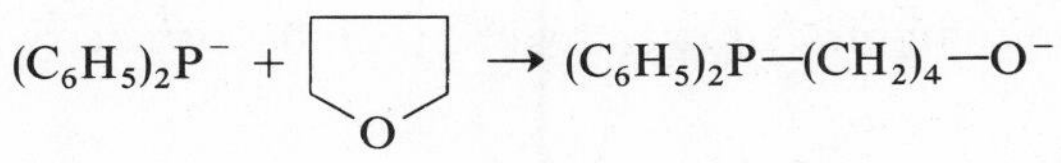

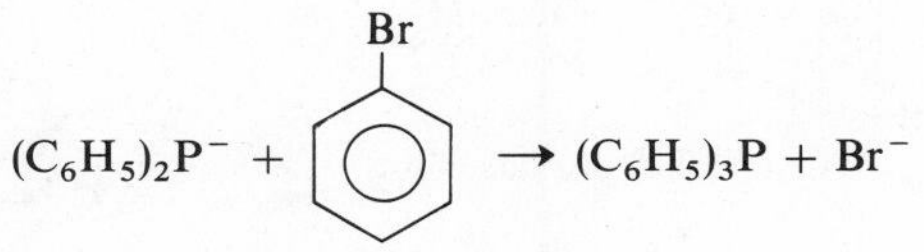

$$(C_6H_5)_2P^- + \text{[cyclic ether]} \rightarrow (C_6H_5)_2P{-}(CH_2)_4{-}O^-$$

$$(C_6H_5)_2P^- + \text{[bromobenzene]} \rightarrow (C_6H_5)_3P + Br^-$$

The high nucleophilicity of phosphorus is also exemplified by its reactions at centers other than carbon. A number of intriguing and useful reactions are known in which nucleophilic phosphorus attacks halogen, oxygen, sulfur, or nitrogen. Best known are the reactions of tervalent phosphorus compounds at oxygen centers. The overall result is commonly the removal of an oxygen atom from the molecule.

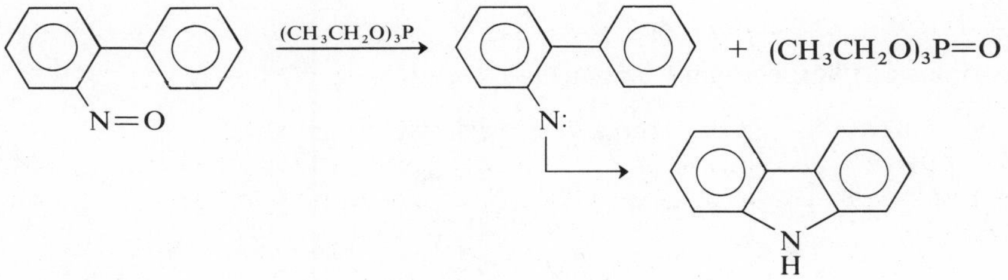

Attack by tervalent phosphorus which results in the removal of a sulfur atom from a compound is the basis for an interesting method developed by Corey† for the interconversion of *cis-* and *trans-*alkenes.

† Elias J. Corey. Born 1928, Methuen, Massachusetts. University of Illinois and Harvard.

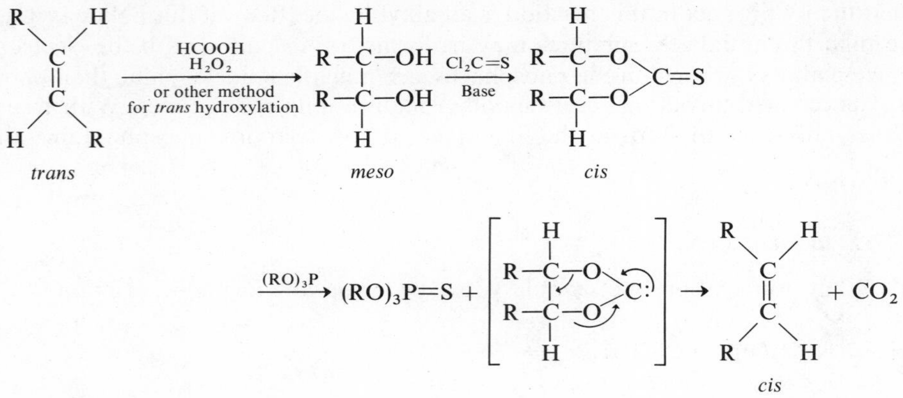

33.10   Nucleophilic Attack on Phosphorus Centers

Halides, except fluoride, are readily displaced from tervalent phosphorus by a wide variety of nucleophiles.

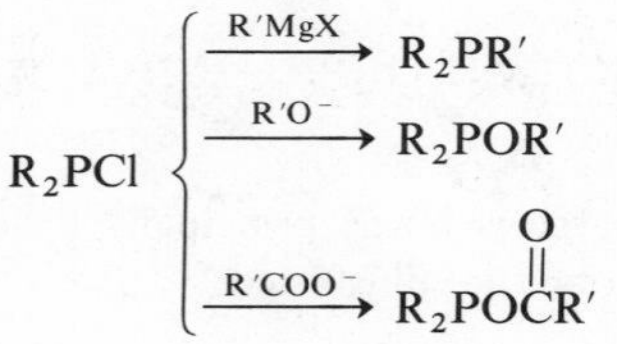

Under appropriate conditions, alcohols, amines, or even hydride can be displaced.

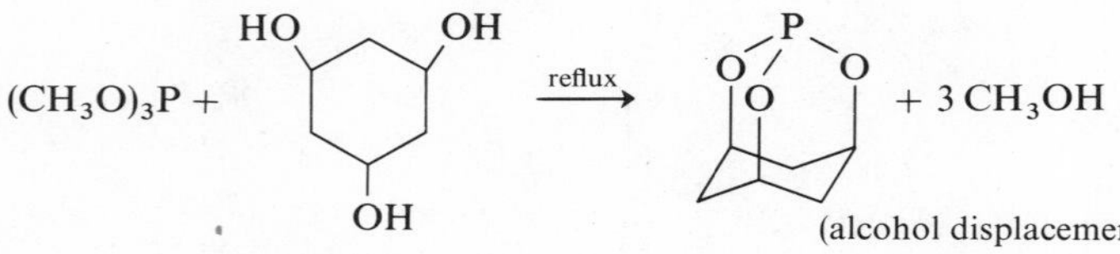

(alcohol displacement)

$$(CH_3CH_2O)_2P-N(CH_3)_2 + ArOH \xrightarrow{H^+} (CH_3CH_2O)_2POAr + HN(CH_3)_2$$

(amine displacement)

$$(CH_3)_2PH + NaNH_2 \rightarrow (CH_3)_2PNH_2 + NaH$$

(hydride displacement)

33.11   Reactions of Phosphonium Compounds

Phosphonium compounds can undergo a wide variety of reactions.

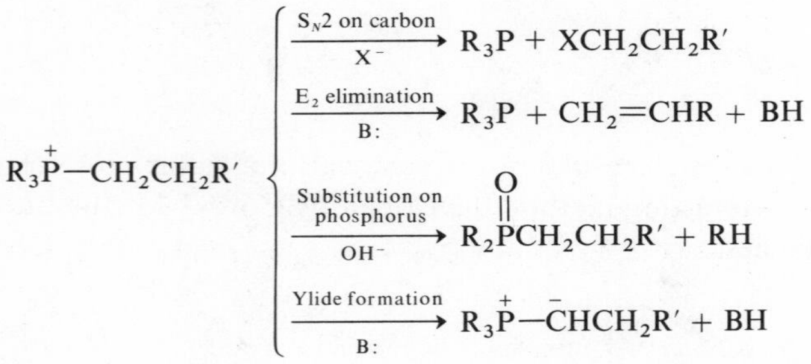

Displacement at carbon and bimolecular elimination reactions are not as common in the chemistry of phosphonium salts as they are in the chemistry of quaternary ammonium salts. Whenever possible, the latter react with bases and undergo β elimination, whereas phosphonium salts give eliminations only in cases when the intermediate carbanion has special stabilization, for example,

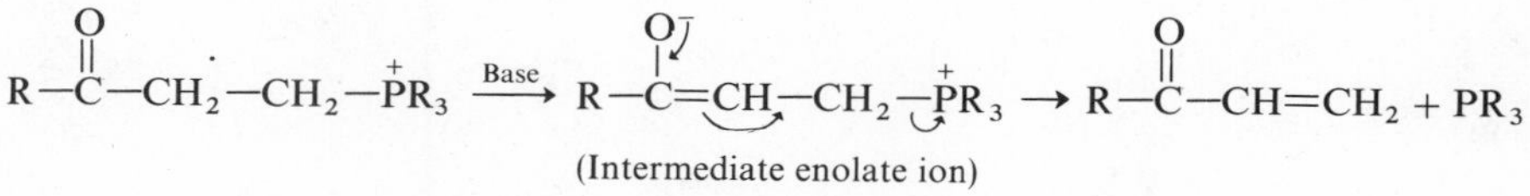

$$R-\overset{\overset{\displaystyle O}{\|}}{C}-CH_2-CH_2-\overset{+}{P}R_3 \xrightarrow{\text{Base}} R-\overset{\overset{\displaystyle O}{|}}{C}=CH_2-CH_2-\overset{+}{P}R_3 \rightarrow R-\overset{\overset{\displaystyle O}{\|}}{C}-CH=CH_2 + PR_3$$

(Intermediate enolate ion)

Thermal Decomposition of Phosphonium Hydroxides. From the point of view of chemistry at the phosphorus center, the most thoroughly studied example of nucleophilic attack on phosphonium salts is the thermal decomposition of phosphonium hydroxides.

$$R_4P^+\ {}^-OH \xrightarrow{\Delta} R_3P{=}O + RH$$

From kinetic studies, this reaction has been found to be third order—first order in phosphonium ion and second order in hydroxide—implying that in the rate-controlling step, two hydroxides are involved. Furthermore, the configuration at the phosphorus atom is inverted during the reaction, as demonstrated by the following sequence beginning with optically active ethylmethylphenylphosphine. It can safely be assumed that the configuration at the phosphorus is unchanged during the oxidation and alkylation reactions.

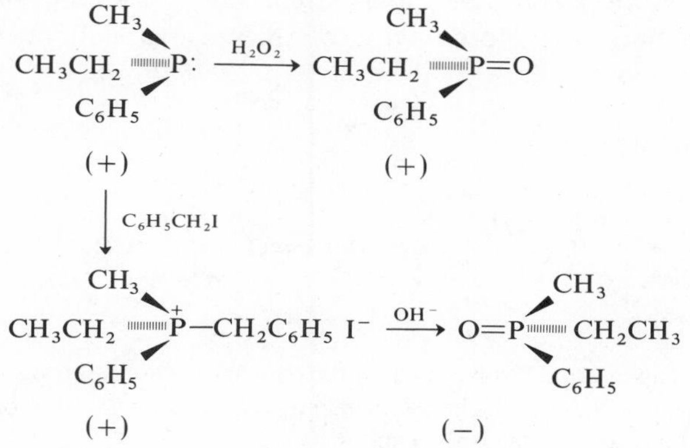

The above factors suggest the following mechanism:

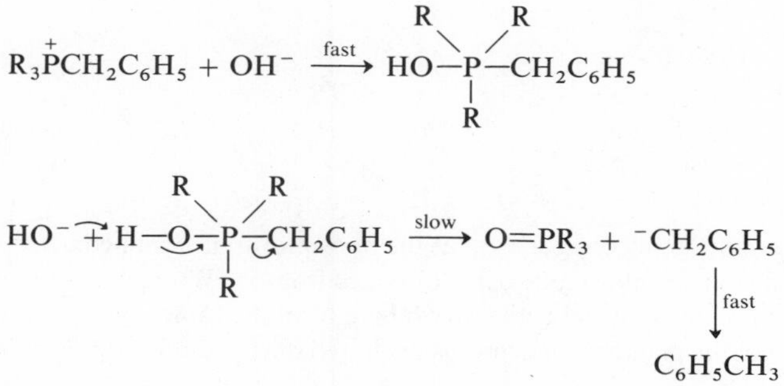

Tervalent phosphorus compounds react readily with halogens and related compounds to give adducts which may exist in the solid state in the pentacovalent form.

$$R_3P + X_2 \rightarrow R_3\overset{+}{P}{-}X\ X^- \rightleftharpoons R_3PX_2$$

In solution such compounds are largely in ionized form, and they effectively behave as phosphonium salts containing an extremely labile leaving group. The reaction of alcohols with PCl_5 to give alkyl chlorides is well known (Section 18.3).

$$ROH + \overset{+}{P}Cl_4 \, Cl^- \rightarrow RO\overset{+}{P}Cl_3 \, Cl^- \rightarrow RCl + POCl_3$$
$$+$$
$$HCl$$

Similarly

$$ROH + (C_6H_5)_3\overset{+}{P}X \ X^- \rightarrow (C_6H_5)_3\overset{+}{P}-O-R + HX \rightarrow (C_6H_5)_3P{=}O + RX$$
$$X^-$$

$$R = \text{alkyl or aryl} \qquad X = I, Br, Cl$$

The latter reaction is particularly interesting in that it provides one of the few effective methods for the conversion of a phenol to an aryl halide.

EXERCISE 33.6

Predict the product of the reaction of (R)-2-butanol with triphenylphosphorus dibromide.

Strong bases react with phosphonium salts to give ylides stabilized by p–d π conjugation. The utility of the Wittig reaction for the production of alkenes was elaborated upon earlier (Section 19.10).

Mechanism of the Wittig Reaction

$$(C_6H_5)_3\overset{+}{P}-\overset{-}{C}H_2 + \ \overset{\backslash}{\underset{/}{}}C{=}O \rightarrow \left[\begin{array}{c} {\geq}P-CH_2 \\ | \qquad | \\ O-C{\leq} \end{array} \right] \rightarrow (C_6H_5)_3P{=}O + \ \overset{\backslash}{\underset{/}{}}C{=}CH_2$$

The Wittig reaction formally involves an internal displacement at the phosphorus atom through a four-membered transition state or intermediate. Such a four-membered ring could be most comfortably accommodated by the following pentacovalent states,

Tetragonal pyramid   Trigonal bipyramid

either of which would result in retention of configuration at the phosphorus atom. In contrast to direct attack by hydroxide (see above), the phosphine oxide obtained from the Wittig reaction and that obtained by direct oxidation of an optically active phosphine have the same configuration, indicating that the configuration of the phosphorus center is unaltered during the Wittig reaction.

Highly stabilized ylides such as $(C_6H_5)_3\overset{+}{P}-\overset{-}{C}HCOOCH_3$ are often ineffective in Wittig reactions. An alternative method for obtaining the same types of products involves the condensation of α carbanions of phosphonate esters with carbonyl compounds. Although these reagents are not formally derived from phosphonium salts, nor are they ylides, the mechanism of the reaction follows the same lines as the Wittig reaction.

$$(CH_3CH_2O)_2\overset{\overset{\displaystyle O}{\|}}{P}CH_2CN \xrightarrow{base} (CH_3CH_2O)_2\overset{\overset{\displaystyle O}{\|}}{P}-\overset{-}{C}HCN \xrightarrow{>C=O}$$

$$\diagdown C=CHCN + (CH_3CH_2O)_2\overset{\overset{\displaystyle O}{\|}}{P}-O^-$$

33.12 The Biological Role of Phosphorus

Phosphate derivatives are ubiquitous and play important roles in biological systems, ranging from mobile energy sources such as pyrophosphates to purely structural functions in the hereditary material deoxyribonucleic acid (DNA).

Compounds whose reactions with substrates commonly present in physiological environments are accompanied by large negative free energy changes ($\Delta G°$) are known as "high-energy" or "energy-rich" compounds. Adenosine triphosphate (ATP, see page 753), an end product of the major metabolic pathways, is the most important mobile carrier of metabolically available energy in living cells.

$$ATP + 2H_2O \xrightarrow{pH\ 7} ADP + HPO_4^{2-} + H_3O^+$$
$$(\Delta G° = -7400\ cal)$$

By the judicious coupling of reaction sequences, the energy available from the hydrolysis of such pyrophosphate bonds provides the driving force for a large number of endergonic reactions in biosynthesis and metabolism. A somewhat simplified example of such a coupled reaction sequence is illustrated in the equations below for the formation of an ester.

$$CH_3CO_2H + ATP \xrightarrow{enzyme} CH_3\overset{\overset{\displaystyle O}{\|}}{C}-O-\overset{\overset{\displaystyle O^-}{|}}{\underset{\underset{\displaystyle O}{\|}}{P}}-O\text{-5'-adenosine} + HO-\overset{\overset{\displaystyle O^-}{|}}{\underset{\underset{\displaystyle O}{\|}}{P}}-O-\overset{\overset{\displaystyle O^-}{|}}{\underset{\underset{\displaystyle O}{\|}}{P}}-OH$$

$$CH_3\overset{\overset{\displaystyle O}{\|}}{C}-O-\overset{\overset{\displaystyle O^-}{|}}{\underset{\underset{\displaystyle O}{\|}}{P}}-O\text{-5'-adenosine} + CoASH \rightarrow$$

$$CH_3\overset{\overset{\displaystyle O}{\|}}{C}-S-CoA + \text{adenosine-5'-O}-\overset{\overset{\displaystyle O^-}{|}}{\underset{\underset{\displaystyle O}{\|}}{P}}-OH$$
$$(AMP)$$

$$CH_3\overset{\overset{\displaystyle O}{\|}}{C}-S-CoA + ROH \rightarrow CH_3\overset{\overset{\displaystyle O}{\|}}{C}-OR + CoASH$$

Summing these reactions gives

$$CH_3CO_2H + ROH + ATP \rightarrow CH_3COOR + AMP + HO-\overset{\overset{\displaystyle O^-}{|}}{\underset{\underset{\displaystyle O}{\|}}{P}}-O-\overset{\overset{\displaystyle O^-}{|}}{\underset{\underset{\displaystyle O}{\|}}{P}}-OH$$

Note that the overall sequence is not unlike that which is utilized in the laboratory.

$$CH_3COOH + PCl_5 \longrightarrow CH_3\overset{\overset{O}{\|}}{C}-O-PCl_4 + HCl$$

$$CH_3COOPCl_4 + Cl^- \longrightarrow CH_3C\overset{\nearrow O}{\underset{\searrow Cl}{}} + {}^-O-PCl_4$$

$$CH_3C\overset{\nearrow O}{\underset{\searrow Cl}{}} + ROH \longrightarrow CH_3COOR + HCl$$

Apparently a very important role of phosphate is that it can serve as a binding site by which the so-called *coenzymes* (frequently vitamin derivatives, see page 753) attach to the enzymes. Several examples of coenzymes are given below.

Pyridoxal phosphate
(Vitamin B$_6$ phosphate)

Thiamine pyrophosphate

In the polymeric phosphates RNA and DNA (Section 28.9), perhaps the principal role of the phosphate is in the determination of molecular shape.

While many phosphorus compounds play a central role in sustaining living systems, other phosphorus derivatives can lead to certain and rapid death. *Sarin* is one of the deadliest of the so-called nerve gases.

$$(CH_3)_2CHO-\overset{\overset{O}{\|}}{\underset{\underset{CH_3}{|}}{P}}-F$$

Isopropyl methylphosphonofluoridate
[Sarin, GB (German Agent B)]

The lethal dose of this material for man may be less than 1 mg. Such nerve agents are cholinesterase inhibitors; they chemically inhibit the transmission of nerve impulses. A number of such fluorophosphate derivatives were found stockpiled in large quantities in Germany by the allied forces at the end of World War II. It is an interesting historical consideration to note that at that time, no other country had effective chemical warfare agents of such potency.

PROBLEMS

1. Predict the product and stereochemistry (retention, inversion or racemization at silicon) in each of the following reactions:

    (a) $R_3SiCl + CH_3MgBr \rightarrow$

    (b) $R_3SiOCH_3 + LiAlH_4 \rightarrow$

    (c) $R_3SiH + Br_2 \rightarrow$

    (d) $R_3SiH + NaNH_2 \rightarrow$

    (e)

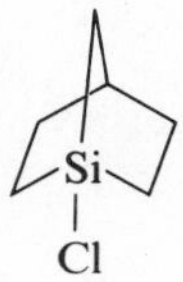

    $+ H_2O \rightarrow$

2. Propose reasonable mechanisms for the following reactions:

    (a) $2R_3SiOH \xrightarrow{H^+} R_3SiOSiR_3 + H_2O$

    (b)

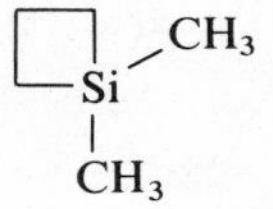

    (c) $R_3SiH + CH_2{=}CH_2 \xrightarrow{h\nu} R_3SiCH_2CH_3$

3. Because they are much more volatile than the alcohols from which they are made, trimethylsilyl ethers are often used in mass spectroscopic studies. Upon electron bombardment of these ethers in the gas phase, ions such as $(CH_3)_3Si^+$ are readily formed.

    $(CH_3)_3SiOR \xrightarrow[\text{electron}]{\text{high energy}} (CH_3)_3Si^+ + \text{Other products}$

    No such ions have ever been observed in solution chemistry. Offer an explanation.

4. The following compounds are readily available in large quantities:

    $SiCl_4, HSiCl_3, H_2SiCl_2, (CH_3)_2SiCl_2, (CH_3)_3SiCl$

    Using one or more of the above as a starting material devise syntheses of the following compounds:

    (a) $(CH_3)_2Si(CH{=}CH_2)_2$

    (b) $(CH_3CH_2)_3SiSi(CH_2CH_3)_3$

    (c) $Cl_3SiCH_2CH_2CH{=}CH_2$

    (d)

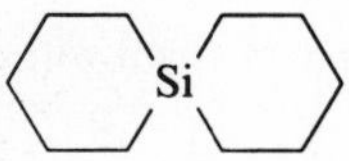

    (e) $(C_6H_5)_3SiOCH_2CH_3$

    (f) $(CH_3CH_2)_3SiH$

5. Suggest methods of synthesis of the following compounds from materials which you anticipate would be readily available:

    (a) $_3P$

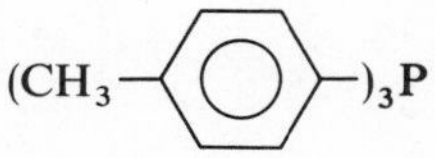

    (b) $(CH_3O)_2\overset{\displaystyle O}{\overset{\displaystyle \|}{P}}CH_2C_6H_5$

    (c) $(CH_3)_2\overset{\displaystyle O}{\overset{\displaystyle \|}{P}}OCC_6H_5$

    (d) $(CH_3)_4P^+ I^-$

    (e) $(C_6H_5)_2\overset{\displaystyle O}{\overset{\displaystyle \|}{P}}$$-CH_3$

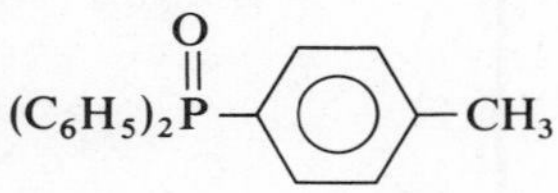

    (f) $(C_6H_5)_2P{-}O{-}CH_2CH_2OH$

6. Suggest methods for the following transformations using phosphorus-containing reagents:

(a)

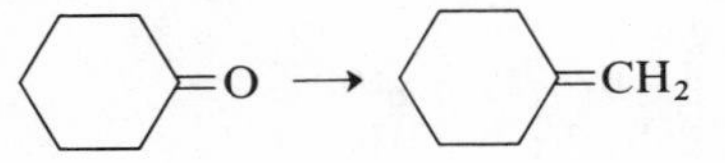

(b) 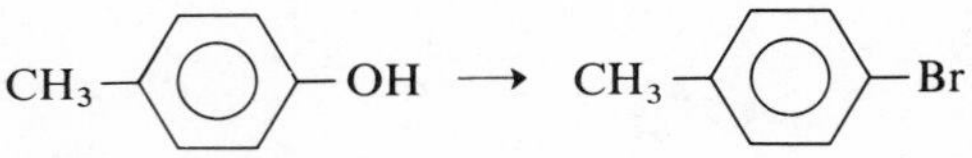 CH_3—⬡—OH → CH_3—⬡—Br

(c) $CH_3^{131}I \rightarrow CH_3CH_2^{131}I$

(d)

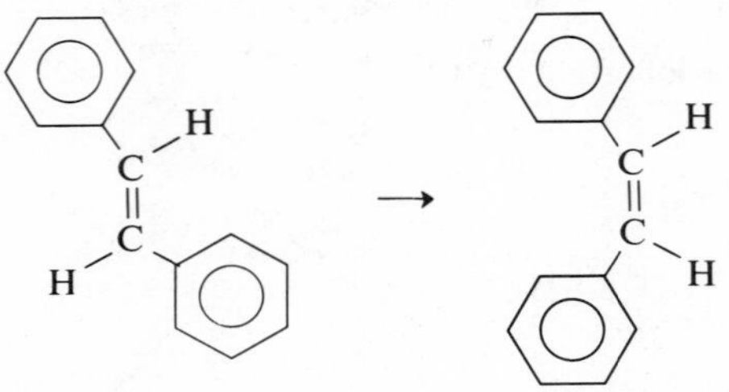

(e)

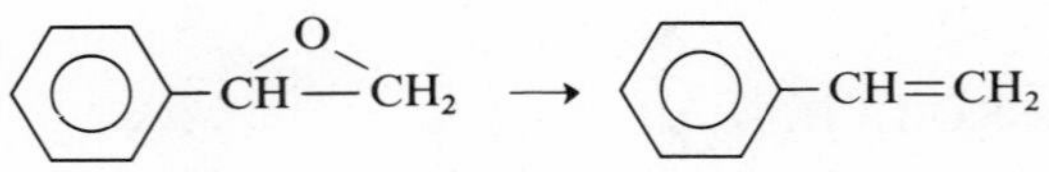

(f) $CH_3CH_2OH \rightarrow CH_3CH_2Br$

7. A large variety of useful and interesting radical reactions occur at phosphorus. Two series of phosphorus radicals are known—the seven-electron phosphino radicals $R_2P\cdot$, and the nine-electron phosphoranyl radicals $R_4P\cdot$. Suggest how such radicals might be generated.

8. Suggest a synthesis of $(CH_3CH_2)PCH_2CH_2CH_2CH_3$, employing $(CH_3CH_2)_2PH$ as a starting material.

9. What are the special properties of triphenylphosphine that make it useful as a starting point in the Wittig reaction sequence? Why could not triphenylamine be used?

10. Tricresyl phosphate (TCP), a mixture of isomeric tritolyl phosphates, excluding the highly toxic ortho isomer as much as possible, is used as an additive to high-pressure lubricants, as a nonflammable hydraulic fluid, and as a lead scavenger in gasoline. Suggest a suitable method for the commercial production of TCP.

Optional Problems.

1. Propose a mechanism consistent with the following observations:

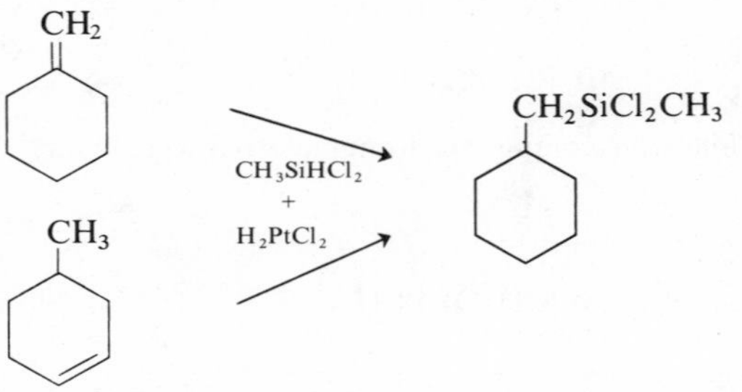

2. Propose mechanisms consistent with the following observations:

$$CH_3CH_2CH_2—C\equiv CH + HSiCl_3 \xrightarrow[\text{(cat. amt.)}]{Et_3N} $$

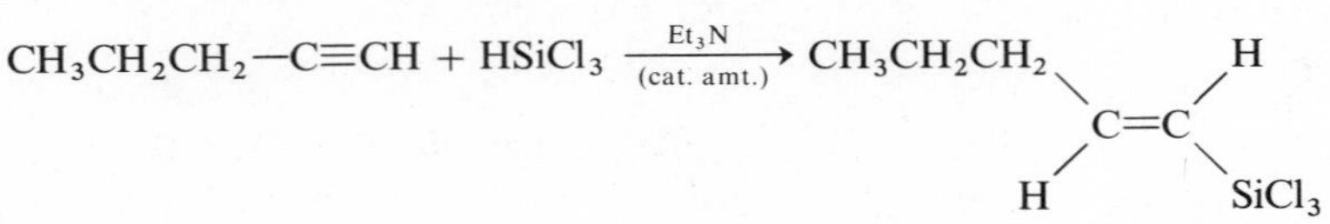

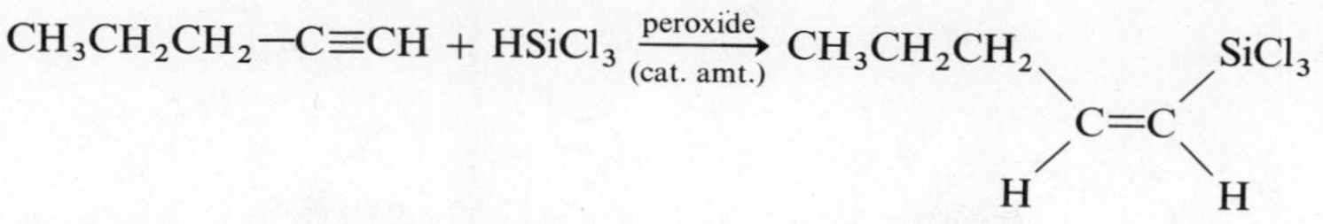

$$CH_3CH_2CH_2\text{—}C\equiv CH + HSiCl_3 \xrightarrow[\text{(cat. amt.)}]{\text{peroxide}} \underset{\substack{\\ }}{CH_3CH_2CH_2} \diagdown \begin{array}{c} \\ C=C \\ H \end{array} \diagup \begin{array}{c} SiCl_3 \\ \\ H \end{array}$$

3. Suggest a reasonable mechanism for the following reaction:

$$CCl_4 + HSiCl_3 \xrightarrow[\text{(catalyst)}]{(n\text{-Bu})_3N} HCCl_3 + SiCl_4$$

4. Pentacovalent phosphorus compounds normally have trigonal-bipyramidal structures. In such structures the more electronegative substituents show a strong preference for the apical positions. With these facts in mind, suggest an explanation for the following data obtained by nuclear magnetic resonance studies. (*Hint*: See page 857.)

CH_3PF_4 One kind of methyl
            One kind of fluorine

$(CH_3)_2PF_3$ One kind of methyl
            Two kinds of fluorines in the ratio $2:1$

$(CH_3)_3PF_2$ One kind of methyl
            One kind of fluorine

CHAPTER 34

THE PHILOSOPHY AND PRACTICE OF ORGANIC SYNTHESIS. PART II

In Chapter 24 we examined briefly the question of how the organic chemist can accomplish the synthesis of one organic compound from another by designing a series of consecutive reactions, that is, a multi-step synthesis. In this chapter we shall explore this subject in somewhat more detail and discuss the use of a number of additional and more complicated synthetic schemes.

34.1   The Synthetic Use of Carbanion Addition Reactions

The Addition of "Carbanions" to Carbonyl Groups

Many useful synthetic schemes involve as the essential step the addition of a Grignard reagent (or an organolithium compound) to the carbonyl group of an aldehyde, ketone, or ester. Esters and ketones give tertiary alcohols; aldehydes give secondary alcohols, with the exception of formaldehyde, which gives primary alcohols. The resulting alcohols can, of course, be subjected to further reactions to yield ultimately many other types of compounds. The formation of various types of alcohols by Grignard additions is summarized in Table 34.1. Also included in this list is the Grignard reaction with the noncarbonyl reagent, ethylene oxide, which results in the formation of a primary alcohol containing two new carbon atoms.

Table 34.1 Alcohols Formed from RMgX

Reactant	Product
H—CHO	R—CH$_2$OH
(ethylene oxide)	R—CH$_2$CH$_2$OH

R'—CHO	R—CH—R'
	    |
	   OH

R'—CO—R'	OH
	    |
	R—C—R'
	    |
	   R'

R'—CO—R''	OH
	    |
	R—C—R'
	    |
	   R''

R'—COOR''	OH
	    |
	R—C—R (The group R'' in the ester
	    | component is lost as R''OH.)
	   R'

A Wittig reagent, also called a phosphonium ylide or phosphorane (Sections 19.10, 33.11), is easily prepared from the commercially available triphenylphosphine and almost any primary or secondary halide. The initially formed alkyltriphenylphosphonium salt is treated with a base (usually *n*-butyllithium) to give the corresponding phosphonium ylide. The latter is not usually isolated but is allowed to react with an aldehyde or ketone to give an alkene. Since no acid is used in this method of alkene formation, the location of the double bond is assured. Thus thermodynamically unstable alkenes unavailable by the acid-catalyzed dehydration of alcohols may be prepared. All types of Wittig reagents will add preferentially to the aldehyde or ketone carbonyl function, even in the presence of an ester group.

$$R-CH_2X + (C_6H_5)_3P \rightarrow R-CH_2-P(C_6H_5)_3^+ X^- \rightarrow R-\overset{-}{C}H-\overset{+}{P}(C_6H_5)_3$$

$$\updownarrow$$

$$(C_6H_5)_3PO + R'_2C=CH-R \xleftarrow{R'_2C=O} R-CH=P(C_6H_5)_3$$

Example 1

Outline a synthesis of 1,1-diphenylethane from benzene.

$$C_6H_6 \rightarrow (C_6H_5)_2CHCH_3$$

The desired hydrocarbon has the general structure R_2-CH-R' and is clearly derivable by dehydration of the corresponding tertiary alcohol $R'R_2COH$ to an alkene (1,1-diphenylethylene, in this case) followed by catalytic hydrogenation of the alkene. A tertiary alcohol in which at least two of the substituents at the carbinol carbon are the same is best prepared by the reaction of a Grignard reagent with an ester. In our example, the necessary alcohol is easily obtained from phenylmagnesium bromide and an ester of acetic acid, such as ethyl acetate. Note that the two similar substituents of the carbinol arise from the Grignard reagent, whereas the third substituent and the carbinol carbon atom arise from the acyl group of the ester; the alkoxyl of the ester is not incorporated into the product.

$$C_6H_6 \rightarrow C_6H_5Br \rightarrow C_6H_5MgBr$$

$$2 C_6H_5MgBr + CH_3COOC_2H_5 \rightarrow (C_6H_5)_2C\overset{OH}{\underset{CH_3}{\diagup\diagdown}}$$

$$(C_6H_5)_2CHCH_3 \xleftarrow{H_2/Pd} \quad \downarrow \quad (C_6H_5)_2C=CH_2$$

Since the tertiary carbinol that was prepared is a *benzyl*-type alcohol, the hydroxyl group can be removed by hydrogenolysis without necessitating dehydration, thereby saving one step.

Example 2

Convert isobutyl alcohol into 2,2-dideuterio-3-methyl-1-butanol.

$$(CH_3)_2CHCH_2OH \rightarrow (CH_3)_2CHCD_2CH_2OH$$

The problem is essentially one of the conversion of a primary alcohol, $R-CH_2OH$, into its next higher homolog, $R-CH_2CH_2OH$, ignoring for the moment the added complication of the specific incorporation of two deuteriums. The general change $R-CH_2OH \rightarrow R-CH_2CH_2OH$ is most easily carried out by way of the reaction of $R-CH_2-MgX$ and formaldehyde. In the special case under consideration, we must first convert $R-CH_2OH$ into its deuterated analog $R-CD_2OH$. This is done conveniently by oxidation of the alcohol to the acid, $R-COOH$, followed by reduction of the acid with the commercially available $LiAlD_4$ (lithium aluminum deuteride). The complete reaction sequence is shown.

$$(CH_3)_2CH-CH_2OH \rightarrow (CH_3)_2CH-COOH \rightarrow (CH_3)_2CH-CD_2OH$$
$$\downarrow PBr_3$$
$$(CH_3)_2CH-CD_2CH_2OH \leftarrow (CH_3)_2CH-CD_2MgBr \leftarrow (CH_3)_2CH-CD_2Br$$

Example 3

Convert *n*-butyl alcohol into 3-methyl-3-hexanol.

$$CH_3CH_2CH_2CH_2OH \rightarrow CH_3CH_2CH_2\overset{\overset{\displaystyle CH_3}{|}}{\underset{\underset{\displaystyle OH}{|}}{C}}CH_2CH_3$$

In general terms, this problem requires the replacement of the two alpha hydrogens of a primary alcohol by two *different* alkyl groups as follows:

$$R-CH_2OH \rightarrow R\overset{\overset{\displaystyle R'}{|}}{\underset{\underset{\displaystyle R''}{|}}{C}}OH$$

Direct alkylation of the primary alcohol is, of course, out of the question. The grouping $-CH_2OH$ must first be oxidized to some kind of carbonyl function which can then react with a Grignard reagent. Conversion of our alcohol $R-CH_2OH$ to an ester such as $R-COOCH_3$ via the acid $R-COOH$ will not solve our problem, since $R-COOCH_3$ will react with a Grignard reagent to give a carbinol having only *two* different kinds of substituents [that is, $R(R')_2COH$]. We must, therefore, introduce our two new alkyl groups R' and R'' in a stepwise manner. The carbinol $RR'R''COH$ can be made by the addition of $R''MgX$ to the ketone $R-CO-R'$. On the other hand, controlled oxidation of $R-CH_2OH$ to the aldehyde $R-CHO$ can be carried out using chromic acid in pyridine; and reaction of $R-CHO$ with a Grignard $R'MgX$ yields the secondary alcohol $R'R-CHOH$. The two ends of the puzzle are tied together by the oxidation of the latter secondary alcohol to the necessary ketone intermediate $R-CO-R'$. Proceeding from the general to the specific problem at hand, the following synthesis may be proposed:

$$n\text{-}C_3H_7-CH_2OH \rightarrow n\text{-}C_3H_7-CHO \xrightarrow{CH_3MgBr} n\text{-}C_3H_7-\overset{\overset{\displaystyle OH}{|}}{CH}-CH_3 \rightarrow$$

$$n\text{-}C_3H_7-CO-CH_3$$
$$\downarrow \begin{array}{c} C_2H_5MgI \\ \text{then} \\ NH_4Cl/H_2O \end{array}$$
$$n\text{-}C_3H_7-\overset{\overset{\displaystyle CH_3}{|}}{\underset{\underset{\displaystyle C_2H_5}{|}}{C}}-OH$$

Example 4

Synthesize 2-*n*-butyl-1-methylenecyclohexane starting from cyclohexanone.

A satisfactory solution to this problem involves the solution of three smaller but interrelated problems: (a) replacement of the carbonyl oxygen atom by an alkyl group; (b) introduction of a second, different alkyl group; and (c) introduction of an olefinic bond in a thermodynamically unstable position. In the case under consideration, it is best to introduce the *n*-butyl substituent while the carbonyl group is still present to provide activation. Direct alkylation of ketones by way of the anions is usually unsatisfactory, however, since the reaction cannot be stopped at the monoalkylation stage (Section 19.15). The best procedure is to further activate the ring toward monosubstitution by formylation. The alkylation will then proceed cleanly, and the formyl group can be removed via a reverse Claisen reaction.

The 2-*n*-butylcyclohexanone prepared in this way will react with methylmagnesium bromide to give 1-methyl-2-*n*-butylcyclohexanol. Dehydration of the latter tertiary alcohol will not give the desired alkene, however, but rather the more substituted and thermodynamically more stable 1-methyl-2-*n*-butylcyclohexene.

The desired alkene can be prepared, however, by substituting a Wittig reaction, a procedure in which no acid is used, for the Grignard addition and acid-dehydration steps. Thus, reaction of methyl bromide with triphenylphosphine, followed by reaction of the resulting phosphonium salt with *n*-butyllithium, gives methylenetriphenylphosphorane. Direct condensation of the latter ylide with 2-*n*-butylcyclohexanone yields the desired olefin. The sequence of operations is outlined below.

The formation of an α,β-unsaturated carbonyl compound by the base-catalyzed condensation of the carbonyl group of an aldehyde or ketone with the "active methylene" group of another aldehyde or ketone is a reaction of enormous synthetic utility. Bases of only moderate strength, such as sodium hydroxide or sodium ethoxide, suffice as catalysts, and the reactions are often simple and convenient to carry out. Aldehyde carbonyl groups condense more rapidly than ketonic carbonyl groups; aromatic aldehydes are particularly good carbonyl components since they lack α-hydrogen atoms and therefore cannot function as enolate components in self-condensations.

Acid-catalyzed aldol condensations, which proceed through enols rather than enolate anions as intermediates, are also sometimes useful synthetically.

Condensations using aromatic aldehydes generally give α,β-unsaturated carbonyl compounds directly in the presence of a basic catalyst. In the case of aliphatic carbonyl components, mild base conditions are usually used to prepare the intermediate "aldol," or β-hydroxycarbonyl compound; the latter is subsequently dehydrated by heating with a little acid or a small amount of iodine.

$$Ar-CHO + R-CH_2-CO-R \xrightarrow{OH^-} Ar-CH=\overset{\overset{\displaystyle R}{|}}{C}-COR$$

$$R-CH_2-CHO + R-CH_2-CHO \xrightarrow[\text{(mild)}]{OH^-} R-CH_2-\overset{\overset{\displaystyle OH}{|}}{CH}-\overset{\overset{\displaystyle R}{|}}{CH}-CHO$$

$$\downarrow{\scriptstyle I_2 \text{ or } H^+}$$

$$R-CH_2CH=\overset{\overset{\displaystyle R}{|}}{C}-CHO$$

The *Perkin condensation* of an aromatic aldehyde with acetic anhydride and sodium acetate is an unusual case of an aldol-type reaction.

$$ArCHO + (CH_3CO)_2O \xrightarrow[\text{heat}]{AcO^-} ArCH=CHCOOH$$

Acetate ion functions as the base to generate the enolate anion of the anhydride, which is the other reactant.

$$CH_3CO-O-COCH_3 \underset{}{\overset{AcO^-}{\rightleftharpoons}} \overset{-}{C}H_2CO-O-COCH_3 \xrightarrow{ArCHO}$$

$$Ar\overset{}{C}HCH_2CO-O\overset{O}{\overset{\|}{-C}}-CH_3$$
$$\underset{O^-}{\overset{}{\rule{1cm}{0.4pt}}}$$

$$\downarrow$$

$$ArCH=CHCOOH \leftarrow ArCH=CHCOO^- + HOAc \leftarrow Ar\overset{\overset{\displaystyle \overset{}{C}OAc}{|}}{C}HCHCO_2^-$$
$$\underset{\overset{\displaystyle |}{H}}{} \quad {}^-OAc$$

α,β-Unsaturated carbonyl compounds are useful intermediates for the synthesis of many other compounds. The olefinic double bonds can be selectively reduced, usually by palladium and hydrogen; on the other hand, the carbonyl groups can usually be selectively reduced by NaBH₄ or LiAlH₄. Also, as discussed later in this chapter, these compounds are useful reactants in Michael additions.

$$R_2C=\overset{\overset{\displaystyle R}{|}}{C}-CH-R \xleftarrow{NaBH_4} R_2C=\overset{\overset{\displaystyle R}{|}}{C}-CO-R \xrightarrow{Pd, H_2} R_2CH-\overset{\overset{\displaystyle R}{|}}{CH}-CO-R$$
$$\underset{\overset{\displaystyle |}{OH}}{}$$

The formation of a β-keto ester by the reaction of the enolate anion of an ester with the carbonyl group of another ester molecule is another very general reaction of great synthetic importance. One of the simplest examples is the previously discussed condensation of two ethyl acetate molecules to give ethyl acetoacetate (Claisen condensation, Section 20.14). Two different ester components can be used if one of them has no hydrogen atoms alpha to the carbonyl group of the ester. A particularly useful component in the latter category is *diethyl oxalate*, since the compounds formed decarboxylate on hydrolysis to give α-keto acids.

Bimolecular condensation of an ester having an active methylene group

$$R{-}CH_2COOC_2H_5 + R{-}CH_2COOC_2H_5 \rightarrow R{-}CH_2{-}CO{-}\overset{\overset{\textstyle R}{\textstyle |}}{C}H{-}COOC_2H_5$$

Condensation of an ester having no active methylene groups with an ester having an active methylene group

$$Ar{-}COOC_2H_5 + R{-}CH_2COOC_2H_5 \rightarrow Ar{-}CO{-}\overset{\overset{\textstyle R}{\textstyle |}}{C}H{-}COOC_2H_5$$

Synthesis of α-keto acids from diethyl oxalate

$$R{-}CH_2COOC_2H_5 + \overset{\textstyle COOC_2H_5}{\underset{\textstyle COOC_2H_5}{|}} \rightarrow R{-}\overset{\overset{}{\underset{\textstyle COOC_2H_5}{|}}}{C}H{-}CO{-}COOC_2H_5$$

↓ hydrolysis

$$R{-}CH_2{-}CO{-}COOH \xleftarrow{\text{heat}} R{-}\overset{\overset{}{\underset{\textstyle COOH}{|}}}{C}H{-}CO{-}COOH$$

Like ethyl acetoacetate, other β-keto esters are useful synthetic intermediates which can be alkylated by way of their sodium salts. Hydrolysis followed by decarboxylation affords a wide variety of ketones.

Example 5

Convert acetone into 3-methyl-2-buten-1-ol.

$$CH_3COCH_3 \rightarrow (CH_3)_2C{=}CHCH_2OH$$

The simplest solution to this problem involves the realization that the product, although it contains only five carbon atoms, resembles the C-6 system which is obtained by the self-condensation of two acetone molecules. Thus, condensation of one acetone molecule with another acetone molecule in the presence of mild base gives the β-hydroxyketone known as *diacetone alcohol;* this compound is readily dehydrated by iodine to give the unsaturated ketone known commonly as *mesityl oxide*. At this point, we just about have the compound we are trying to prepare, but we must first convert the group $-COCH_3$ to the group $-CH_2OH$, a process which must first involve oxidation of the ketone to an acid RCOOH. Since this acid contains an alkene linkage, we cannot use a vigorous oxidizing agent. On the other hand, the haloform reaction is ideal for our purpose, since it simply involves mild halogenation of the ketone followed by alkaline cleavage. The C-5 unsaturated acid thus obtained (β,β-dimethylacrylic acid) is finally reduced to the desired alcohol by lithium aluminum hydride. The entire sequence is outlined below.

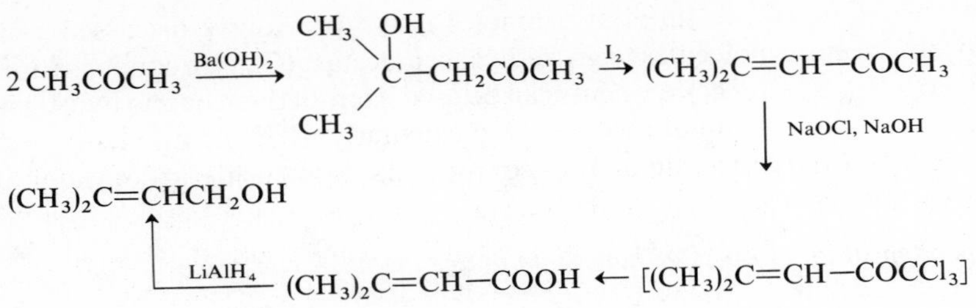

$$2\,CH_3COCH_3 \xrightarrow{Ba(OH)_2} \underset{CH_3}{\overset{CH_3\quad OH}{C-CH_2COCH_3}} \xrightarrow{I_2} (CH_3)_2C=CH-COCH_3$$

$$\Big\downarrow \text{NaOCl, NaOH}$$

$$(CH_3)_2C=CHCH_2OH$$

$$\xuparrow{} $$

$$\underset{LiAlH_4}{\big\vert\longleftarrow} (CH_3)_2C=CH-COOH \leftarrow [(CH_3)_2C=CH-COCCl_3]$$

Example 6

Convert benzaldehyde into 1,5-diphenyl-3-aminopentane.

$$C_6H_5CHO \rightarrow C_6H_5CH_2CH_2\underset{NH_2}{CHCH_2CH_2C_6H_5}$$

Once we realize that the carbon bearing the amino group could have originated from a carbonyl carbon atom, we can then proceed to recognize that the resulting skeleton is derivable from the condensation of two benzaldehyde molecules with one molecule of acetone. This skeletal relationship is as follows:

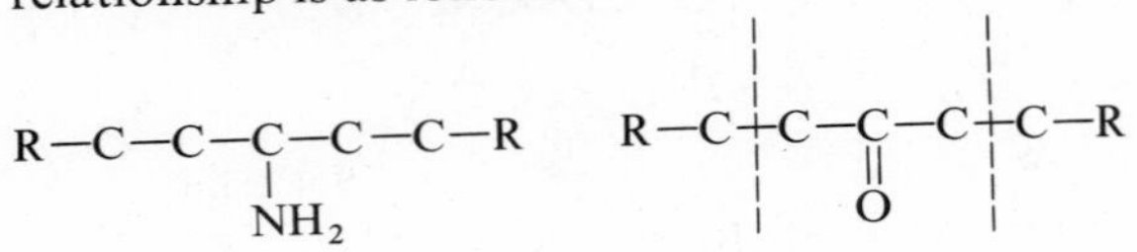

$$R-C-C-\underset{NH_2}{C}-C-C-R \qquad R-C\!\!+\!\!C-\underset{O}{\overset{\Vert}{C}}-C\!\!+\!\!C-R$$

Filling in the details, two benzaldehyde molecules and one of acetone are condensed to give the doubly unsaturated *dibenzalacetone*. Mild catalytic reduction of the latter gives the saturated ketone *1,5-diphenyl-3-pentanone*. Conversion of the latter to its oxime, followed by reduction of this oxime by zinc in acetic acid, yields the desired amine.

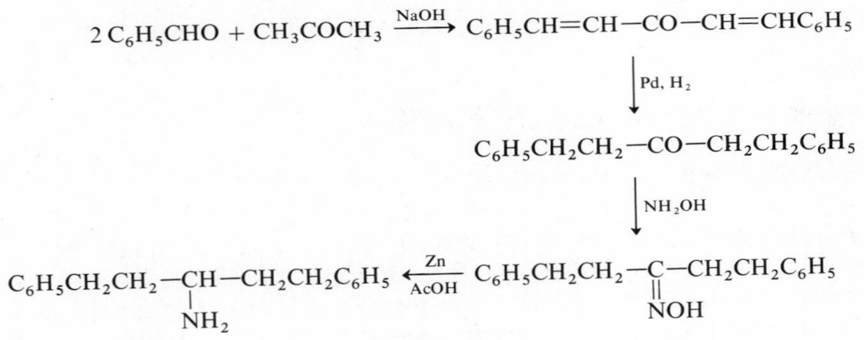

$$2\,C_6H_5CHO + CH_3COCH_3 \xrightarrow{NaOH} C_6H_5CH=CH-CO-CH=CHC_6H_5$$

$$\Big\downarrow Pd,\,H_2$$

$$C_6H_5CH_2CH_2-CO-CH_2CH_2C_6H_5$$

$$\Big\downarrow NH_2OH$$

$$C_6H_5CH_2CH_2-\underset{NH_2}{CH}-CH_2CH_2C_6H_5 \xleftarrow[AcOH]{Zn} C_6H_5CH_2CH_2-\underset{NOH}{\overset{\Vert}{C}}-CH_2CH_2C_6H_5$$

Example 7

Synthesize 4-methyl-1-hepten-5-one from starting materials each of which has no more than three carbon atoms.

$$CH_2=CH-CH_2-\underset{}{\overset{CH_3}{CH}}-CO-CH_2-CH_3$$

Inspection of the structure of the desired ketone shows that it may be viewed as a diethyl ketone in which an allyl group has replaced a hydrogen alpha to the carbonyl group.

Allyl group → $\overbrace{C=C-C}\overbrace{C-C-C-C}$ ← Diethyl ketone moiety

with the diethyl ketone moiety carbon bearing $\underset{\overset{|}{C}}{\overset{C\ O}{\overset{\|}{}}}$

Direct introduction of an allyl group into this position is best carried out if a β-keto ester corresponding to diethyl ketone is used, rather than diethyl ketone itself. Such a β-keto ester can be prepared by the condensation of two molecules of ethyl propionate catalyzed by sodium ethoxide. The solution of this synthetic problem therefore involves only a slightly more complex analog of the acetoacetic ester synthesis.

$$CH_3CH_2COOH + C_2H_5OH \xrightarrow{H^+}$$

$$2\,CH_3CH_2COOC_2H_5 \xrightarrow{NaOEt} \xrightarrow{H^+} \underset{\overset{|}{COOC_2H_5}}{CH_3CH-CO-CH_2CH_3}$$

$$\downarrow NaOEt$$

$$\downarrow CH_2=CH-CH_2Cl$$

$$\underset{\overset{|}{COOC_2H_5}}{CH_2=CHCH_2-\overset{\overset{\overset{\displaystyle CH_3}{|}}{}}{C}-CO-CH_2CH_3}$$

$$H_2O \downarrow \overset{NaOH}{_{dilute}}$$

$$H^+ \downarrow (-CO_2)$$

$$CH_2=CHCH_2-\underset{}{\overset{\overset{\displaystyle CH_3}{|}}{CH}}-CO-CH_2CH_3$$

Example 8

Prepare α-ketoglutaric acid from maleic anhydride.

$$\text{maleic anhydride} \rightarrow \underset{\overset{|}{CH_2-COOH}}{\overset{CO-COOH}{\underset{}{\overset{|}{CH_2}}}}$$

Catalytic reduction of maleic anhydride, followed by hydrolysis, readily yields succinic acid. The conversion R—COOH → R—CO—COOH will then yield the desired α-keto acid. This type of conversion can generally be carried out if the acid has a methylene group alpha to the carboxyl group. In the case under consideration, the succinic acid is first converted to a simple ester such as the diethyl ester. The latter is then condensed with one equivalent of diethyl oxalate. Mild acid hydrolysis yields a β-keto acid intermediate, which readily loses carbon dioxide to give α-ketoglutaric acid. An excess of diethyl oxalate should be avoided in the condensation step, since diethyl succinate has two reactive methylene groups and reaction can occur at both sites under these conditions.

$$
\text{(maleic anhydride)} \xrightarrow[\text{Pd}]{H_2} \text{(succinic anhydride)} \xrightarrow{H_2O} \begin{array}{l} CH_2-COOH \\ | \\ CH_2-COOH \end{array} \xrightarrow[H^+]{EtOH} \begin{array}{l} CH_2-COOEt \\ | \\ CH_2-COOEt \end{array}
$$

$$
\downarrow \begin{array}{l} COOEt \\ | \\ COOEt, \end{array} NaOEt
$$

$$
\downarrow H^+
$$

$$
\begin{array}{l} CO-COOH \\ | \\ CH_2 \\ | \\ CH_2-COOH \end{array} \xleftarrow{-CO_2} \left[\begin{array}{l} CO-COOH \\ | \\ CH-COOH \\ | \\ CH_2-COOH \end{array} \right] \xleftarrow{H_2O, H^+} \begin{array}{l} CO-COOEt \\ | \\ CH-COOEt \\ | \\ CH_2-COOEt \end{array}
$$

$$
\text{undesirable} \downarrow \begin{array}{l} COOEt \\ | \\ COOEt, \end{array} NaOEt
$$

$$
\begin{array}{l} CO-COOEt \\ | \\ CH-COOEt \\ | \\ CH-COOEt \\ | \\ CO-COOEt \end{array}
$$

Addition of a Carbanion to an Activated Double Bond: Michael Additions

The 1,4 addition of a stabilized carbanion to an α,β-unsaturated carbonyl compound, α,β-unsaturated nitrile, or α,β-unsaturated nitro compound is known as the *Michael reaction* (Section 19.17). This reaction provides one of the most useful methods known for the creation of new carbon–carbon bonds.

$$
R_3CH \xrightarrow{OR^-} R_3C^- \xrightarrow[\substack{O \\ \| \\ (Z = -CR, -CN, -NO_2)}]{R_2C=C-Z} R_3C-\underset{\underset{R}{|}}{\overset{\overset{R}{|}}{C}}-\overset{\overset{R}{|}}{C}-Z \xrightarrow{H^+} R_3C-\underset{\underset{R}{|}}{\overset{\overset{R}{|}}{C}}-\underset{\underset{H}{|}}{\overset{\overset{R}{|}}{C}}-Z
$$

The active hydrogen component (which furnishes the carbanion) is sometimes referred to as the *donor*; the unsaturated compound is the *acceptor*.

The Michael additions most useful in synthesis are those in which a donor of fairly high acidity (e.g., a β-dicarbonyl compound) adds to an appropriate acceptor in the presence of a catalytic amount of an alkoxide ion or hydroxide ion, or even a base as weak as a secondary amine. Some of the more commonly employed donors and acceptors used in Michael reactions are listed below. In the usual practical synthetic application, either the donor or the acceptor is a simple reactive reagent, while the other component is a more complex molecule whose structure is being elaborated.

Donor	Acceptor
$CH_2(COOEt)_2$	$CH_2=CH-COOEt$
CH_3CO-CH_2COOEt	$CH_2=CH-CN$
$NC-CH_2COOEt$	$CH_2=CH-COCH_3$
CH_3-NO_2	$CH_2=CH-CHO$

In considering a projected synthesis, the student will recognize that the use of the Michael reaction is immediately suggested when the desired product contains *electron-*

$$
Y-\overset{|}{\underset{|}{C}}\!\!\mid\!\overset{|}{\underset{|}{C}}-\overset{|}{\underset{|}{C}}-Z \leftarrow Y-\overset{|}{\underset{|}{C}}H + \overset{\diagdown}{\diagup}C=\overset{|}{C}-Z
$$

$$
Y-\overset{|}{\underset{|}{C}}-\overset{|}{\underset{|}{C}}\!\!\mid\!\overset{|}{\underset{|}{C}}-Z \leftarrow Y-\overset{|}{C}=C\overset{\diagup}{\diagdown} + H\overset{|}{\underset{|}{C}}-Z
$$

withdrawing groups (e.g., anion-stabilizing groups) *separated by a chain of three carbon atoms.* In the very common case in which both the donor and acceptor are carbonyl compounds, the Michael adduct is a 1,5-dicarbonyl compound of some sort.

$$\underset{1}{-C}-\underset{2}{C}-\underset{3}{C}-\underset{4}{C}-\underset{5}{C}-$$

with O double bonds on carbons 1 and 5.

Example 9

Devise a simple synthesis of propane-1,2,3-tricarboxylic acid from fumaric acid.

$$\begin{matrix} H \diagdown \;\diagup COOH \\ C \\ \| \\ C \\ \diagup \;\diagdown \\ HOOC \quad H \end{matrix} \rightarrow \begin{matrix} CH_2{-}COOH \\ | \\ CH{-}COOH \\ | \\ CH_2{-}COOH \end{matrix}$$

   Inspection of the product reveals the presence of a 1,5-dicarbonyl system. Division of the molecule into donor and acceptor portions shows that it is formally derived from the acceptor fumaric (or maleic acid) acid and the donor acetic acid.

$$\begin{matrix} CHCOOH \\ \| \\ CHCOOH \end{matrix} + CH_3COOH \rightarrow \begin{matrix} CH_2COOH \\ | \\ CH{-}COOH \\ {-}\!\!+\!\!{-} \\ CH_2COOH \end{matrix}$$

Direct reaction of a mixture of these acids with base merely converts them to carboxylate salts, which are too unreactive to participate in a Michael reaction. The fumaric acid is readily activated as a Michael acceptor by converting it into diethyl fumarate. Acetic acid is somewhat activated as a donor by conversion into ethyl acetate. The latter is still a very weak acid and a poor Michael donor, however, and we can obtain much better results by substituting for it the more acidic diethyl malonate. In the last step of the synthesis, the extra carbonyl group of the malonic acid unit is removed as carbon dioxide by heating.

$$HOOC{-}CH{=}CH{-}COOH \rightarrow EtOOC{-}CH{=}CH{-}COOEt$$

$$\downarrow CH_2(COOEt)_2, \ NaOEt$$

$$\begin{matrix} CH_2COOH \\ | \\ CHCOOH \\ | \\ CH(COOH)_2 \end{matrix} \leftarrow \begin{matrix} EtOOC{-}CH_2{-}CH{-}COOEt \\ | \\ CH(COOEt)_2 \end{matrix}$$

$$\downarrow$$

$$\begin{matrix} CH_2COOH \\ | \\ CHCOOH \\ | \\ CH_2COOH \end{matrix}$$

Example 10

Synthesize β,δ-diphenylvaleric acid from simple and cheap starting materials.

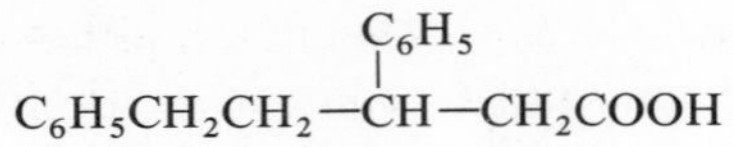

$$\overset{\displaystyle C_6H_5}{\underset{|}{C_6H_5CH_2CH_2-CH-CH_2COOH}}$$

Inspection of the structure of the desired compound reveals the absence of a 1,5-dicarbonyl system. The structure is such, however, that this acid could be readily prepared by reduction (e.g., Wolff–Kishner reduction) of the δ-keto acid shown below, which *does* contain this system. This keto acid is, in fact, the formal adduct of the donor acetic acid to the acceptor benzalacetophenone, as shown.

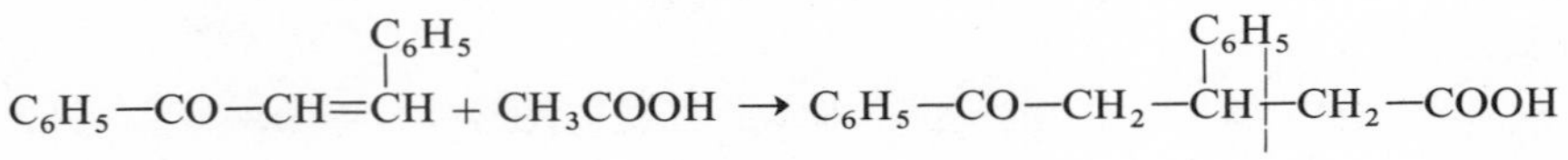

$$C_6H_5-CO-CH{=}CH + CH_3COOH \rightarrow \overset{\displaystyle C_6H_5}{\underset{|}{C_6H_5-CO-CH_2-CH\!-\!CH_2-COOH}}$$

In actually putting the molecule together in the laboratory, we would use the excellent Michael donor *diethyl malonate* as the source of our acetic acid unit. *Benzalacetophenone*, as its name implies, is simply the condensation product of benzaldehyde with acetophenone. The final synthesis of our diphenylvaleric acid is outlined below:

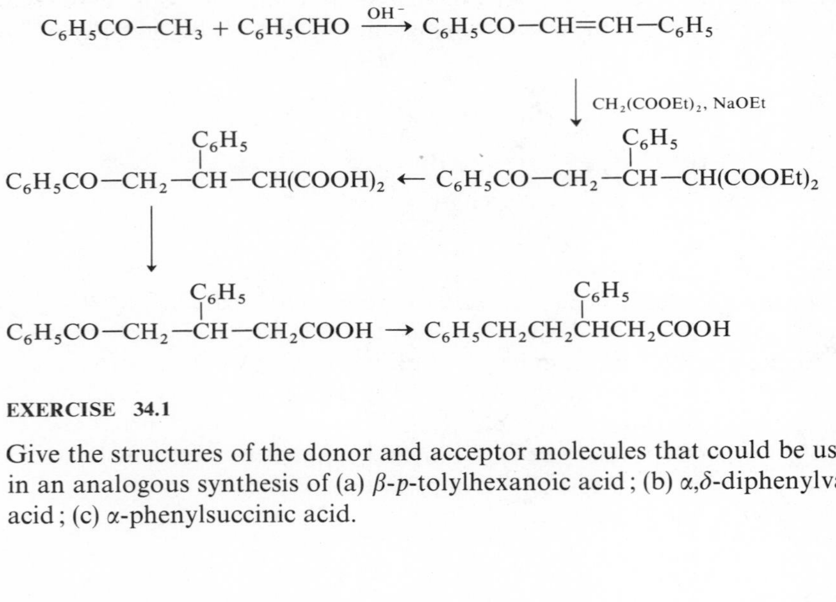

$$C_6H_5CO-CH_3 + C_6H_5CHO \xrightarrow{\ OH^-\ } C_6H_5CO-CH{=}CH-C_6H_5$$

$$\downarrow \text{CH}_2(\text{COOEt})_2,\ \text{NaOEt}$$

$$\overset{\displaystyle C_6H_5}{\underset{|}{C_6H_5CO-CH_2-CH-CH(COOH)_2}} \leftarrow \overset{\displaystyle C_6H_5}{\underset{|}{C_6H_5CO-CH_2-CH-CH(COOEt)_2}}$$

$$\downarrow$$

$$\overset{\displaystyle C_6H_5}{\underset{|}{C_6H_5CO-CH_2-CH-CH_2COOH}} \rightarrow \overset{\displaystyle C_6H_5}{\underset{|}{C_6H_5CH_2CH_2CHCH_2COOH}}$$

EXERCISE 34.1

Give the structures of the donor and acceptor molecules that could be used in an analogous synthesis of (a) β-p-tolylhexanoic acid; (b) α,δ-diphenylvaleric acid; (c) α-phenylsuccinic acid.

34.2   The Making and Breaking of Carbocyclic Rings

When a carbon–carbon bond is broken, a molecule proceeds from a ground state in which the bond length is normal to a transition state in which it is stretched. It usually makes very little difference whether the bond is part of a ring or not; the change from ground state to transition state, and hence the rate of reaction, is similar in either case. Thus the oxidative cleavage of the double bond in cyclohexene does not show a rate that is especially different from that of 2-hexene. This parallelism between open-chain and unstrained cyclic compounds which exists for bond-breaking or ring-opening reactions does *not*, however, apply to ring-closure reactions. If two acyclic compounds react to form an acyclic product, that product usually will be relatively strainless, and it will form at a certain rate. If, on the other hand, two similar starting compounds are already joined together, then the reaction leads to a ring. The transition state through which the reaction proceeds has the ring completely formed, except for the one bond which is only partially formed. If the ring is strained (as in cyclopropane, say), then the energy of the transition state is higher than that of the analogous open-chain reaction by the amount of ring strain present. Such a ring closure is thus difficult and proceeds slowly.

As an example, consider a comparison of the following reactions:

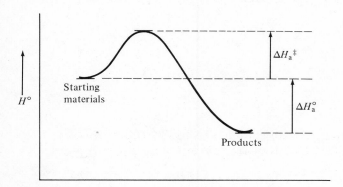

(a) $CH_3CH_2Br + {}^-CH\begin{smallmatrix}COOEt\\COOEt\end{smallmatrix} \rightarrow CH_3CH_2{-}CH\begin{smallmatrix}COOEt\\COOEt\end{smallmatrix}$

(b) ${}^-C(COOEt)(COOEt){-}(CH_2)_4{-}CH_2Br \rightarrow$

(c) ${}^-C(COOEt)(COOEt){-}CH_2{-}CH_2Br \rightarrow$

Reaction (a), which involves only open-chain materials, can be considered as our standard of reference. The reaction coordinate diagram is as shown in Figure 34.1,

Figure 34.1
Reaction coordinate diagram for reaction (a).

where we are looking now at the activation energy (enthalpy) of the reaction, not its free energy. The reaction is exothermic (ΔH_a° is negative), but proceeds at a moderate rate since $\Delta H_a^\ddagger$ is sizable.

The corresponding diagram for reaction (b) will be essentially identical with that for reaction (a), since starting materials and products are all strainless. Reaction (c), however, while having strainless starting materials, has a strained product, and hence a strained transition state. If we plot reactions (a) and (c) on the same reaction coordinate diagram, the results are as shown in Figure 34.2. Most of the ring strain in product (c) is already present in (c)‡, and hence the ring closure of the cyclopropane ring is rendered more difficult.

The argument which we have just gone through to show why the ring closure of a cyclopropane is rather difficult can be applied in a general way to all ring-closure reactions. The small rings (3- and 4-membered) are strained (angle strain) and more difficult to close than the common (5- to 7-membered) rings. The medium-sized rings (8- to 11-membered) are difficult to close because they are also strained, as was discussed

Figure 34.2
Reaction coordinate diagram for reactions (a) and (c).

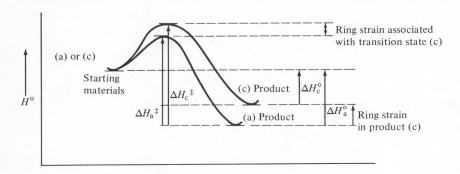

in detail in Section 3.5. Thus we can look at the total ring strain of a ring as a function of its size (Table 3.4), and then attempt to predict the relative rates of ring closure on that basis. The results of such a prediction would be fairly good, but certainly not perfect. For example, large rings (12 or more ring atoms) are essentially strainless and should form easily if only ring strain were considered; but the reaction does not take place under ordinary circumstances.

$$Br-(CH_2)_{11}C\overset{COOEt}{\underset{COOEt}{}} \longrightarrow (CH_2)_{11}\quad C\overset{COOEt}{\underset{COOEt}{}}$$
$$\text{No yield}$$

Instead, a polymer is formed.

$$Br-(CH_2)_{11}C\overset{COOEt}{\underset{COOEt}{}} \longrightarrow$$

$$Br-(CH_2)_{11}-\overset{COOEt}{\underset{COOEt}{C}}\overset{}{\underset{}{\left[-(CH_2)_{11}-\overset{COOEt}{\underset{COOEt}{C}}-\right]_n}}(CH_2)_{11}-\overset{COOEt}{\underset{COOEt}{CH}}$$

The rate of the cyclization reaction is slow compared to the rate of polymerization. These relative rates do not result from an unfavorable enthalpy of the cyclization reaction, as in the case of the formation of the cyclopropane previously discussed, but rather ring closure is slow because of an unfavorable *entropy*. The difficulty is that the two reactive ends of the molecule are so far apart that it is improbable that they will find one another. Rather, they will find other molecules; hence bimolecular reactions, leading ultimately to polymer, become predominant. The entropy of ring closure ($\Delta S^{\ddagger}$) becomes less and less favorable as the chain length becomes longer. It is very favorable for the closure of a cyclopropane, because the two ends are very close together, and it becomes increasingly unfavorable the larger the ring that is being formed.

In order to summarize the effects of enthalpy and entropy on ring-closure reactions in a general way, we might look at the yields obtained under standard conditions from the same type of reaction. The effect of enthalpy on yield is toward poor yields for the small and medium-sized rings, good yields for the common and large rings (Figure 34.3). The entropy of ring closure becomes increasingly unfavorable with increasing ring size. The free energy of ring closure is a combination of these two quantities as usual ($\Delta G^{\ddagger} = \Delta H^{\ddagger} - T\Delta S^{\ddagger}$), and the resulting points are indicated by X's.

Figure 34.3
The yield of ring-closure reactions as a function of ring size. The experimental points are indicated by X's.

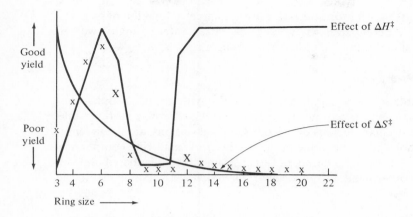

Syntheses of Large Rings. Naturally, ingenious people have found ways to get around the limitations which appear to be imposed by the effects diagrammed in Figure 34.3. The large rings, for example, are formed in poor yield under normal circumstances because polymerization (a sequence of bimolecular reactions) is faster. Suppose that the reaction is carried out in very dilute solution. One molecule then is essentially unable to find another one, and ring closure, which proceeds slowly, does so in high yield. In more precise terms, the rates of ring closure ($Rate_C$) and dimerization (polymerization) ($Rate_D$) are given by

$$Rate_C = k_C \, [monomer]$$

$$Rate_D = k_D \, [monomer]^2$$

since the first is a monomolecular process, and the second is bimolecular. We know that k_C is much smaller than k_D because of an unfavorable $\Delta S^{\ddagger}$, as already discussed. The actual rate $Rate_C$ is also smaller than the rate $Rate_D$ when the monomer concentration is 1 molar. Suppose we dilute the solution by a factor of 10. Then $Rate_C$ is only 0.1 of k, but $Rate_D$ has gone down by a factor of $(0.1)^2$, so it is now only 0.01 of k_D. If the solution becomes sufficiently dilute, $Rate_C$ must eventually surpass $Rate_D$, even though k_C is smaller than k_D.

If we now return to reactions (a)–(c) on page 885, we can also compare them with respect to $\Delta S^{\ddagger}$. As mentioned earlier, (c) has a more favorable $\Delta S^{\ddagger}$ than does (b), but (b) has a more favorable $\Delta G^{\ddagger}$ than does (c). When we compare (a) and (b), we find that they have similarly favorable $\Delta H^{\ddagger}$'s, but (b) has the more favorable $\Delta S^{\ddagger}$. With (b), the ring closure involves some loss of rotational freedom, and $\Delta S^{\ddagger}$ is mildly unfavorable. In the case of (a), two molecules are being joined to give one. The large translation entropy of the two molecules is greatly reduced in forming a single product molecule. Bimolecular reactions therefore have strongly unfavorable values for $\Delta S^{\ddagger}$. Because of the unfavorable $\Delta S^{\ddagger}$ for (a), the $\Delta G^{\ddagger}$ of (b) is more favorable than that for (a).

These facts lead to some important generalizations regarding ring-closure reactions:

1. Ring closure of a five- or six-membered ring is easier and faster than an analogous reaction in an open-chain system.

2. Ring closure other than five- or six-membered rings is slower and more difficult than an analogous reaction in open-chain systems, and may be slower than polymerization.

3. As the reaction medium is made more dilute, the ratio of ring closure to polymerization increases, since the chances of one molecule being able to find another go down as the solution is diluted.

The synthetic organic chemist is frequently confronted with the problem of constructing a new ring of carbon atoms. A very large number of reactions have been used to close carbocyclic rings; most of these reactions, *but not all of them*, may be viewed as special applications of reactions which are also used in connecting carbon chains. Since the best synthetic methods for forming a ring are very much a function of ring size, the formation of rings of different sizes will be considered separately. Finally, we will consider briefly the occasional synthetic utility of *breaking* a ring.

Small Rings (Three and Four Carbon Atoms)

Because of the considerable strain present in small rings, the synthesis of cyclopropanes and cyclobutanes can never be carried out using reactions which are at all reversible. Such reactions as intramolecular versions of Friedel–Crafts acylations, aldol condensations, or ester condensations are of no value in the synthesis of small-ring compounds, although they are very useful in the building of the unstrained five-membered and six-membered rings. On the other hand, intramolecular *alkylation* is a valuable method in small-ring synthesis.

Alkylations, in which a strongly basic carbanion reacts to yield a weakly basic anion such as halide or tosylate, are thermodynamically very strongly favored in the forward direction. In practice, they are found in general to be quite irreversible.

The necessary starting material is a halide (or sulfonate) bearing at least one "active hydrogen" on the carbon atom γ or δ to the carbon bearing the halogen. Activation is achieved by any adjacent anion-stabilizing group, such as –COR, –COOR, or –CN.

X = halide, or sulfonate   A cyclopropane
Y = –CN, –COR, etc.

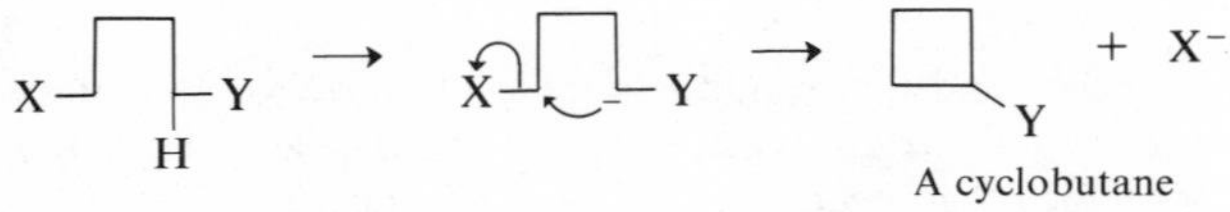

A cyclobutane

Since the required starting materials (γ- or δ-halo esters, ketones, or nitriles) are often not very easy to prepare, a useful variation of this synthesis involves a double alkylation of a 1,2-dihalide or a 1,3-dihalide with an active hydrogen component, usually malonic ester. The reaction is illustrated below. Note the formation of by-products derived from two molar equivalents of malonic ester.

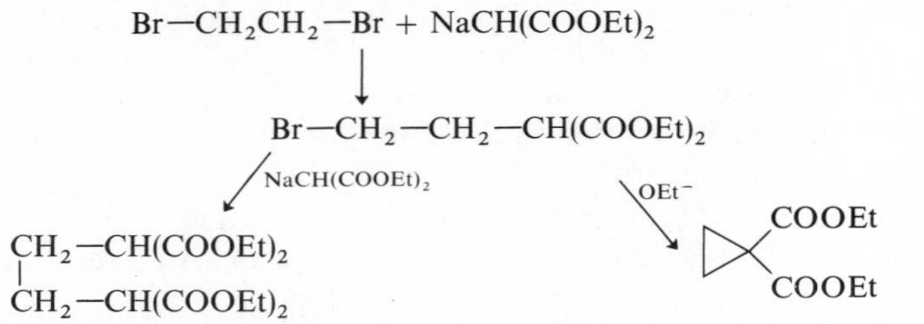

$$Br—CH_2CH_2—Br + NaCH(COOEt)_2$$

$$\downarrow$$

$$Br—CH_2—CH_2—CH(COOEt)_2$$

NaCH(COOEt)$_2$ ↙   ↘ OEt$^-$

CH$_2$—CH(COOEt)$_2$
|
CH$_2$—CH(COOEt)$_2$

By-product derived from
*inter*molecular alkylation

COOEt

COOEt

A cyclopropane derived from
*intra*molecular alkylation

The most generally useful method for the synthesis of cyclopropanes, however, involves the addition of methylene to the double bond of an alkene (see Section 15.13). Four-membered rings can often be conveniently prepared by [2 + 2] cycloaddition reactions (see Section 31.9).

Example 1

Synthesize 1-methylbicyclo[4.1.0]heptane from readily available starting
materials.

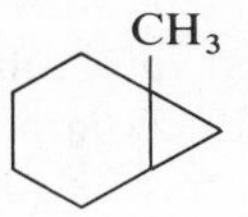

The desired product is simply the product of the addition of a methylene
group (Section 15.13) to 1-methylcyclohexene, which can be prepared very
easily from cyclohexanone by reaction with methylmagnesium bromide,
followed by dehydration with acid or an iodine catalyst.

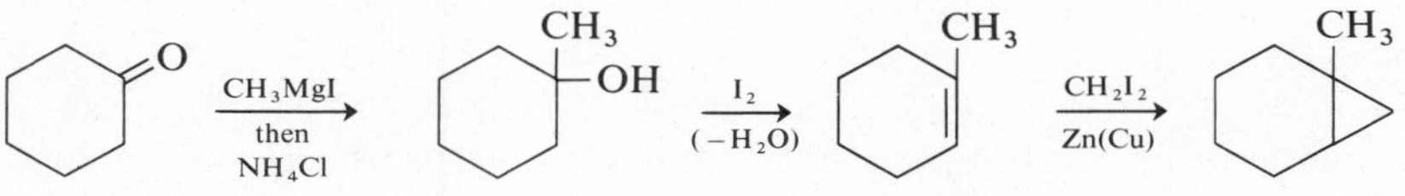

Example 2

Synthesize the spiroheptanecarboxylic acid shown, starting with readily
available organic reagents.

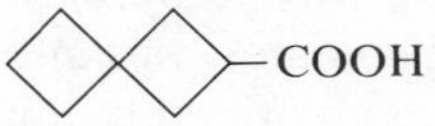

The key to the solution of the problem is the realization that the carboxyl
group and the carbon atom to which it is attached are derivable from a
molecule of malonic ester, while the rest of the molecule is derivable from
a 1,3-dihalide:

The necessary 1,3-dihalide is itself easily obtained from the 1,3-diol which
is the lithium aluminum hydride reduction product of cyclobutane-1,1-
dicarboxylic acid or one of its esters.

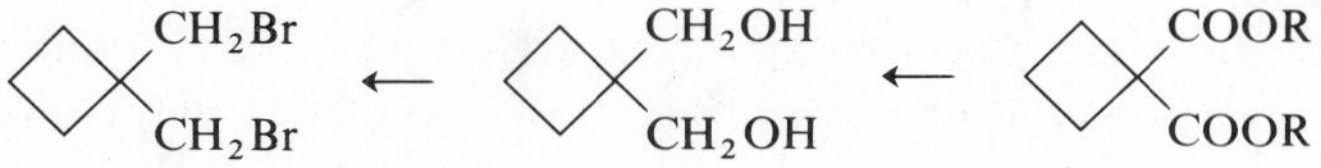

The diethyl ester of cyclobutane-1,1-dicarboxylic acid is easily prepared
directly from 1,3-dibromopropane and malonic ester in the presence of
sodium ethoxide. The entire synthesis from 1,3-propanediol and malonic
ester is as follows:

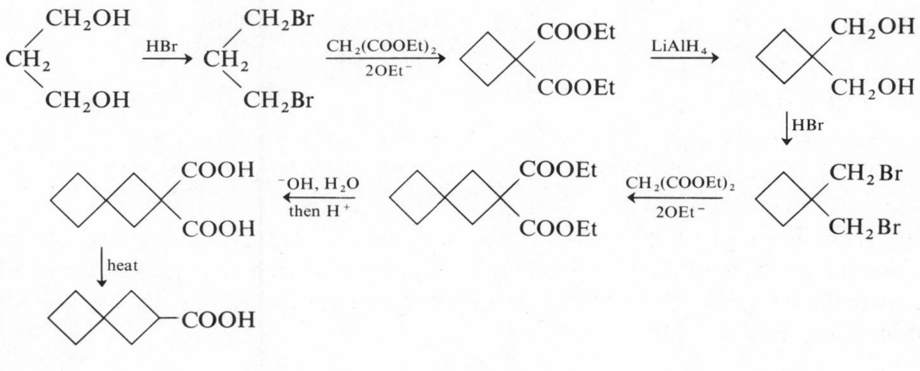

Common Rings (Five, Six, and Seven Carbon Atoms)

Since five-membered and six-membered rings are practically strainless, and since the atoms which must be joined together to form such rings are never very far apart, the formation of cyclopentane and cyclohexane rings can be accomplished by a wide variety of intramolecular reactions. In general, cycloheptane rings can be formed in similar ways, but the yields are usually not as good. As in the case of small rings, the common rings can be prepared from dihalides (1,4-, 1,5-, and 1,6-) and a suitable one-carbon ring source such as malonic ester:

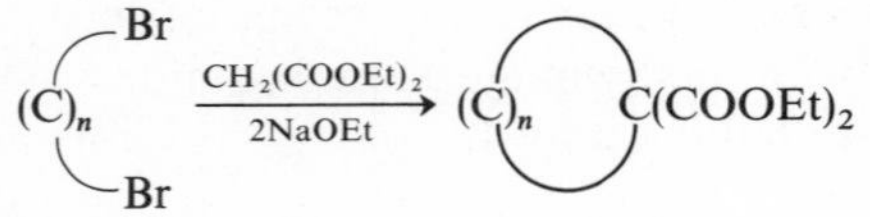

$n = 4, 5, or 6$

Of greater general utility in the synthesis of common rings are a series of potentially reversible reactions which are useless in the synthesis of small rings. These are (a) the intramolecular Friedel–Crafts synthesis, (b) the intramolecular ester condensation or *Dieckmann synthesis*, and (c) intramolecular aldol-type condensations. Let us examine these briefly one by one.

The Intramolecular Friedel–Crafts Acylation. The fusion of a new five- or six-membered ring to an already existing benzene ring is usually most easily accomplished by an intramolecular Friedel–Crafts acylation reaction. The most common variants of this reaction involve treatment of an acid chloride with aluminum chloride or simply heating the free acid with polyphosphoric acid (PPA, a solution of P_2O_5 in H_3PO_4). The ring closure of *o*-benzoylbenzoic acid to anthraquinone in warm sulfuric acid is remarkable in that the reaction takes place despite the presence of a deactivating carbonyl group ortho to the position of ring closure. Note the origin of the starting materials in the following simple cases:

A synthesis of 1-indanone

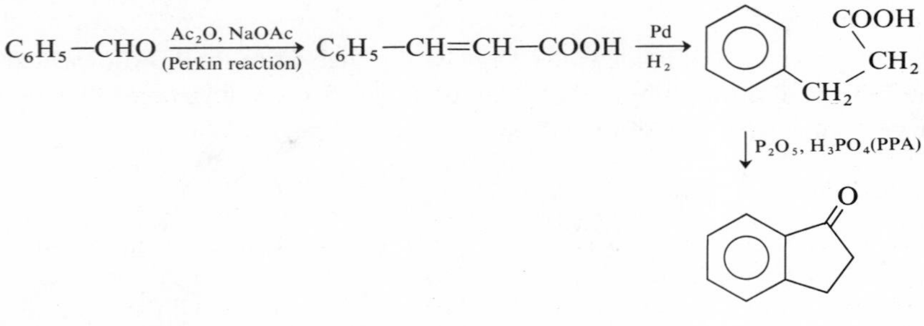

A synthesis of 1-tetralone

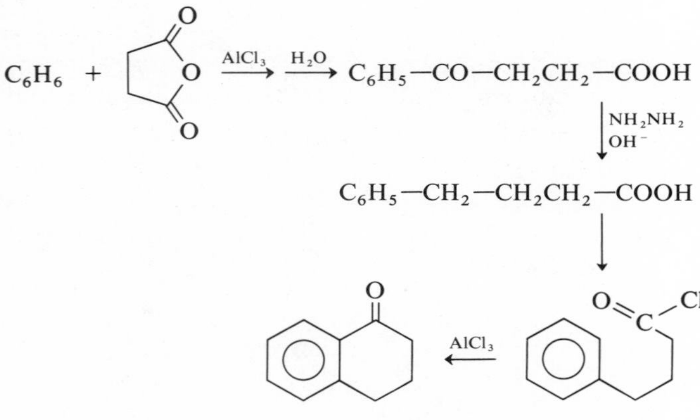

A synthesis of 9,10-anthraquinone

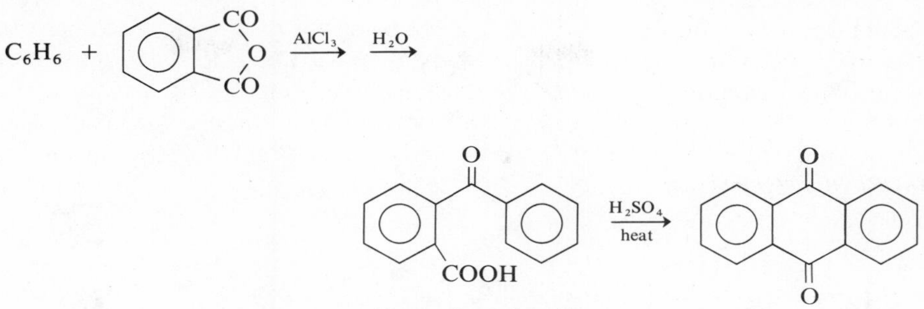

o-Benzoylbenzoic acid

It should be noted that tetralones and anthraquinones are useful starting materials for the synthesis of a wide variety of naphthalene and anthracene derivatives.

The Dieckmann Synthesis. The Dieckmann reaction consists of the intramolecular cyclization of an ester of a dicarboxylic acid in the presence of a strong base. It is merely a special application of the synthesis of β-keto esters in which a ring is formed. The reaction is most frequently used for the formation of five-membered rings. The best known and most useful example is the synthesis of 2-carbethoxycyclopentanone from the diethyl ester of adipic acid. Adipic acid is a cheap article of commerce, since it is employed in the manufacture of nylon (Sections 25.2, 35.13).

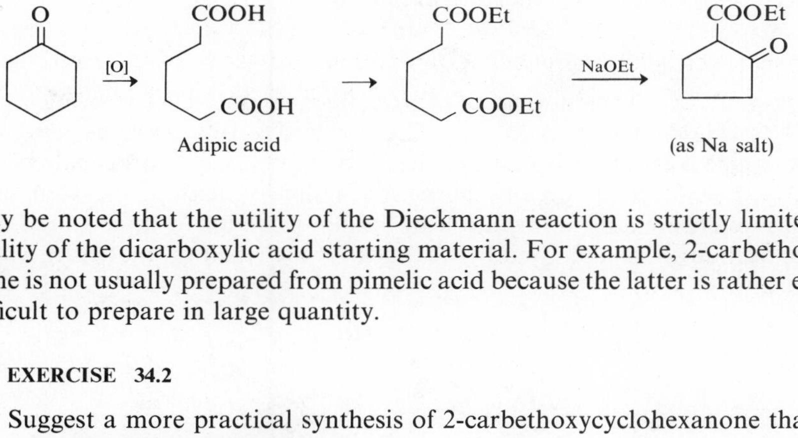

Adipic acid   (as Na salt)

It may be noted that the utility of the Dieckmann reaction is strictly limited by the availability of the dicarboxylic acid starting material. For example, 2-carbethoxycyclohexanone is not usually prepared from pimelic acid because the latter is rather expensive and difficult to prepare in large quantity.

EXERCISE 34.2

Suggest a more practical synthesis of 2-carbethoxycyclohexanone than that using the Dieckmann reaction.

Intramolecular Aldol-Type Reactions. Many 1,4-, 1,5-, or 1,6-dicarbonyl compounds that contain various combinations of aldehyde, ketone, or ester functions are capable of undergoing base-catalyzed (and sometimes acid-catalyzed) intramolecular aldol-type reactions. Depending upon the nature of the starting material, the product contains a new cyclopentene or cyclohexene ring in which the double bond is conjugated with a carbonyl group. In the case of certain keto esters, a cyclic β-diketone may result. Following are examples of a few of the many possibilities:

1,4-Dicarbonyl compounds

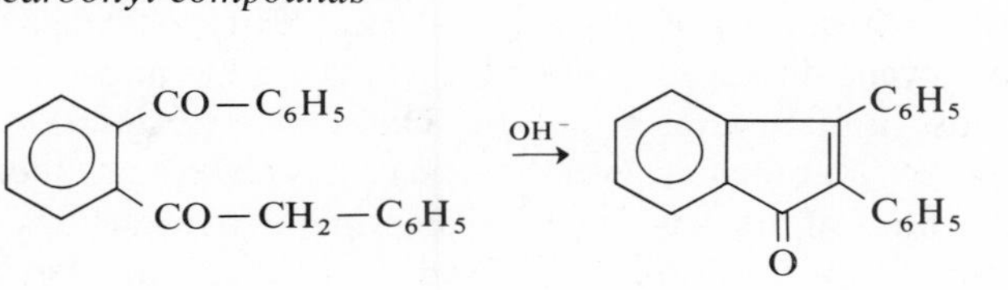

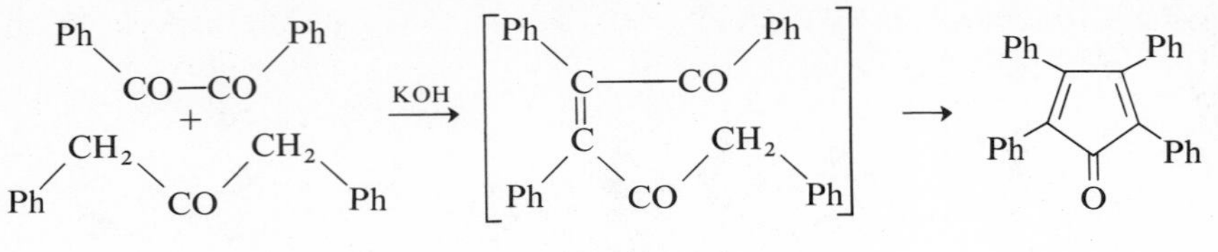

Not isolated

1,5-Dicarbonyl compounds

$$CH_3CO-CH_2CH_2-CH(COOEt)_2 \xrightarrow{OEt^-}$$

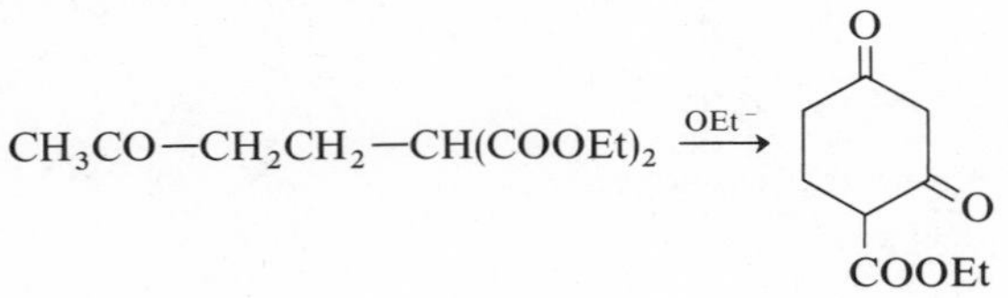

1,6-Dicarbonyl compounds

$$C_6H_5CO-CH_2CH_2CH_2CH_2-COOCH_3 \xrightarrow{OMe^-} C_6H_5-CO$$

The most useful cyclizations are those of 1,5-dicarbonyl compounds, since these are usually easily prepared from α,β-unsaturated carbonyl compounds by the *Michael reaction*. This important type of synthetic sequence is discussed in more detail in several of the examples (Examples 5 and 6) in the next section.

Special Syntheses of Compounds Containing a Six-Membered Ring

The simplest synthesis of a cyclohexane derivative often is not one involving ring closure, but rather one involving the reduction of a cheap and readily available benzene derivative. Thus, cyclohexane itself is best prepared by the catalytic hydrogenation of benzene. Similarly, phenol yields cyclohexanol, and aniline yields cyclohexylamine. 2-Cyclohexenone is easily prepared from anisole by lithium reduction in liquid ammonia (Birch reduction, Section 16.10), followed by treatment of the resulting enol ether with acid, as shown below.

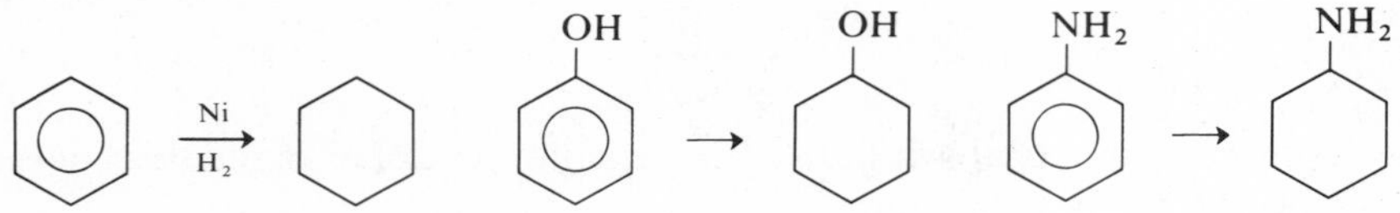

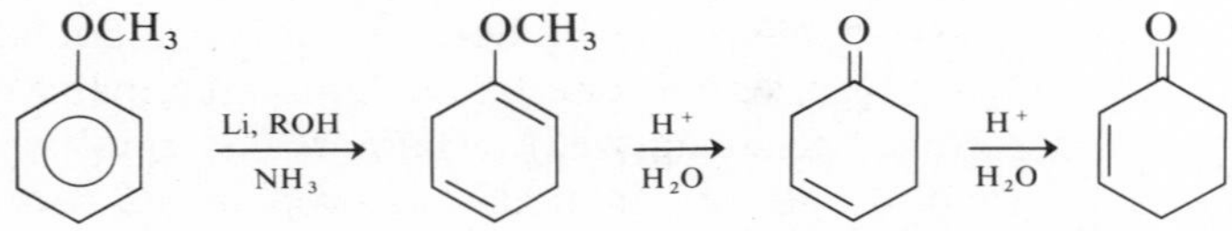

(stable conjugated isomer)

The Diels–Alder reaction (Section 15.12) provides the most versatile single method for the synthesis of six-membered rings. Structures of considerable complexity, particularly bridged compounds derived from cyclic dienes, may often be synthesized in a few steps from readily available compounds. In attempting to use the Diels–Alder reaction in a synthesis, the student must remember that the new cyclohexane ring is always produced by cis addition of a diene (four carbons of the new ring) to a dienophile (two carbons of the new ring). The specific position of the new double bond in the product can also be advantageous for further transformations. Finally, the stereospecific aspects of the Diels–Alder reaction (see Section 15.12) greatly enhance its synthetic utility.

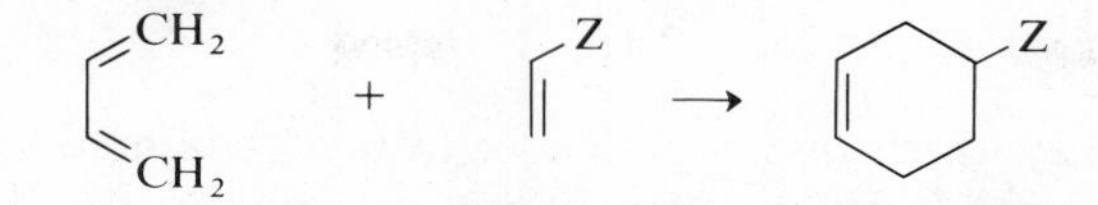

| A simple open-chain diene | A dienophile | A 4-substituted cyclohexene |

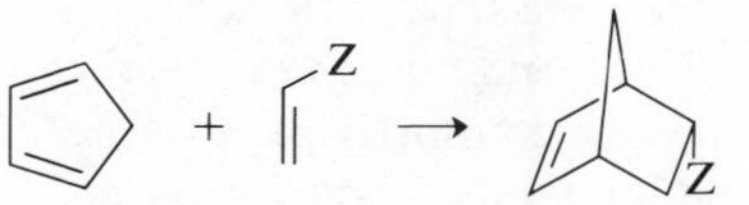

A bicyclo[2.2.1]heptene
(substituent Z *endo*)

Some miscellaneous examples of syntheses involving the construction of normal-sized rings are given in the examples.

Example 3

Synthesize 2-indanone from *o*-xylene.

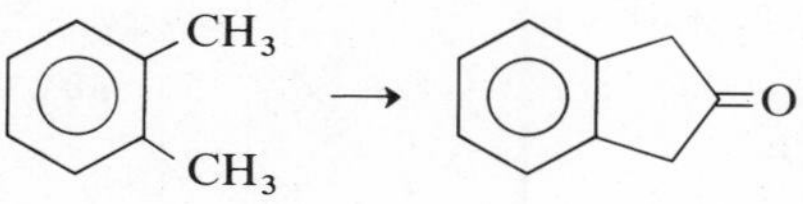

Synthetically speaking, 2-indanone is equivalent to the β-keto ester, 1-carbethoxy-2-indanone, from which it can be obtained by mild hydrolysis followed by decarboxylation. The β-keto ester is the Dieckmann cyclization product of α,α'-dicarbethoxy-*o*-xylene. The latter diester can be prepared from *o*-xylene by the straightforward process of side-chain halogenation, reaction with sodium cyanide, and conversion of the resulting dinitrile to the diethyl ester by direct reaction with ethanol and sulfuric acid.

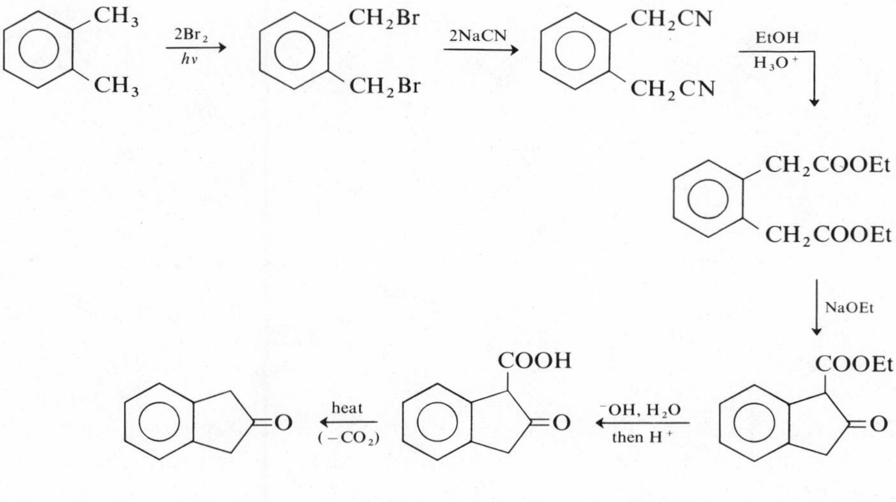

Example 4

Synthesize 1-methyl-7-isopropylnaphthalene from an inexpensive derivative of benzene.

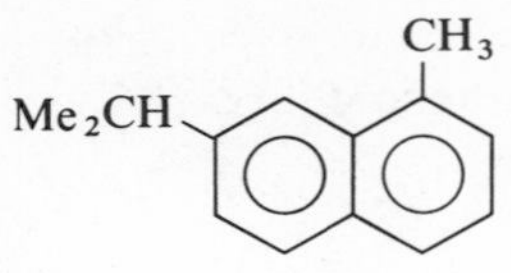

CH$_3$

Me$_2$CH

In a problem involving the synthesis of a naphthalene from a benzene derivative, we will usually attempt to build up one of the two rings by use of an intramolecular Friedel–Crafts acylation if the desired substituents allow us to use this method.

In the case under consideration this is possible if we start with isopropyl-benzene (cumene), but not if we try to start with toluene. The reason is that the Friedel–Crafts reaction of isopropylbenzene will go mostly para to the original alkyl group. The ring-closure step then puts the carbonyl group of the cyclic ketone meta to this group, which will eventually become a β substituent of the new naphthalene ring. The ketonic carbonyl, on the other hand, becomes an obvious point of eventual attachment of the α substituent. The key intermediates which must be visualized in working out this synthesis backwards are shown below in generalized form.

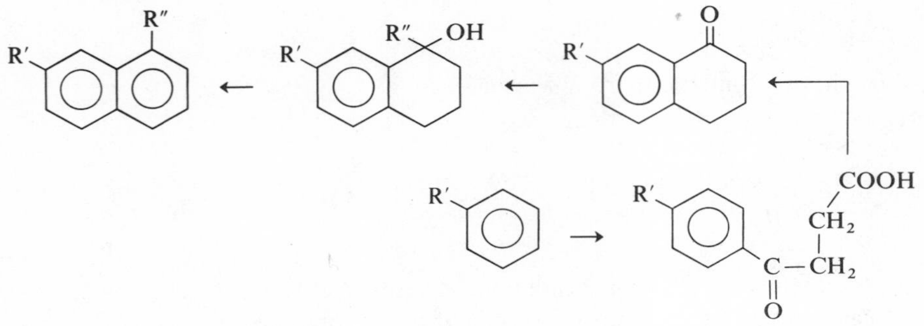

R″   R″   OH   O

R′ ← R′ ← R′ ←

R′ → R′   COOH
CH$_2$
C—CH$_2$
O

The specific intermediates needed are given in the following scheme. The last step is an aromatization of a dihydronaphthalene to a naphthalene by loss of two hydrogens. This type of reaction is easily accomplished by heating the partially reduced naphthalene with palladium on carbon, sulfur, or tetrachloro-p-benzoquinone (chloranil) (Sections 16.9, 23.6).

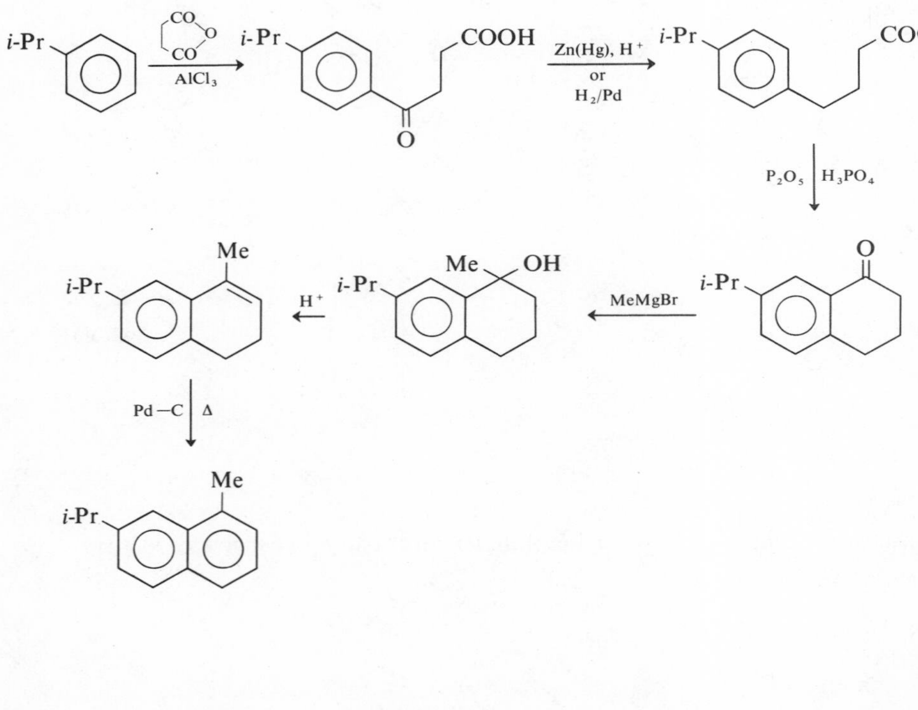

i-Pr $\xrightarrow[\text{AlCl}_3]{\begin{smallmatrix}CO\\CO\end{smallmatrix}O}$ i-Pr   COOH $\xrightarrow[\substack{\text{or}\\ \text{H}_2/\text{Pd}}]{\text{Zn(Hg), H}^+}$ i-Pr   COOH
O

$\downarrow$ P$_2$O$_5$ | H$_3$PO$_4$

Me   Me   OH   O

i-Pr $\xleftarrow{\text{H}^+}$ i-Pr $\xleftarrow{\text{MeMgBr}}$ i-Pr

Pd—C | Δ $\downarrow$

Me

i-Pr

Example 5

Convert 2-methylcyclohexanone into the decalone derivative shown.

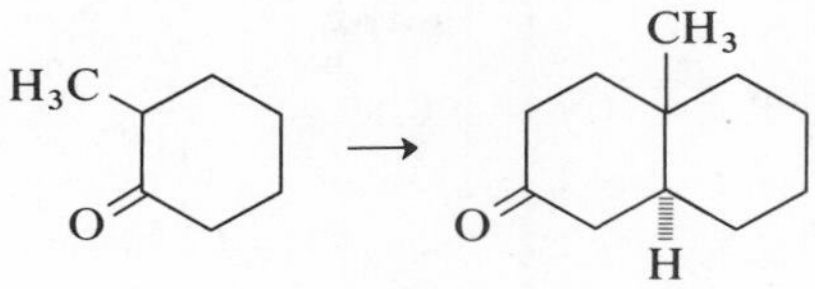

This conversion is a simple example of a very general method of building rings which was first introduced by the British chemist, Sir Robert Robinson, in 1937. Robinson's method has since seen much use in the synthesis of complex, naturally occurring steroids and terpenes.

In the problem stated above, the saturated bicyclic ketone is obtained by mild catalytic reduction of the corresponding α,β-unsaturated ketone having a double bond at the position of ring juncture. This cyclohexenone is the cyclic aldol condensation product of an open 1,5-diketone; the latter is in turn simply the Michael addition product of methyl vinyl ketone and 2-methylcyclohexanone. Despite the fact that 2-methylcyclohexanone is a rather poor Michael donor, the unsaturated bicyclic ketone can actually be prepared in the laboratory in one operation by refluxing a solution containing both methyl vinyl ketone and 2-methylcyclohexanone with a strong base: The success of this reaction undoubtedly is due to the stability of the α,β-unsaturated ketone as the final product of a series of reversible reactions. (In other Robinson-type ring syntheses, the best conditions must be found by trial and error for each case, and sometimes it is best to isolate the intermediate Michael addition product.)

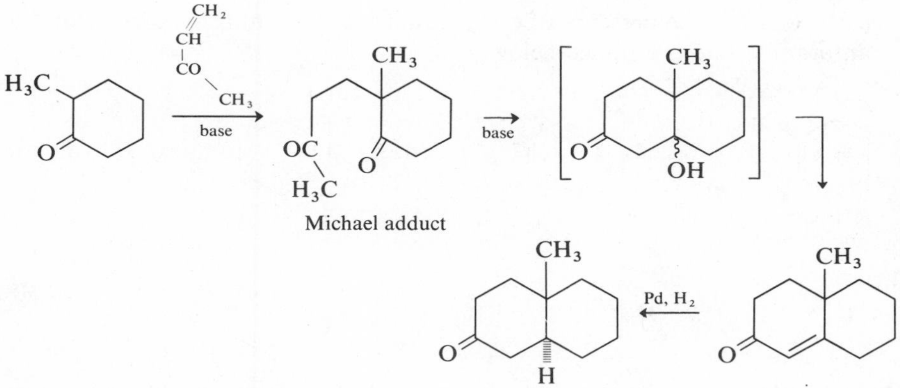

Example 7

Prepare the α,β-unsaturated nitro compound shown starting with cheap, simple, commercial chemicals.

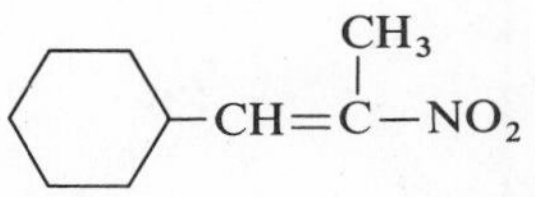

The desired compound is the product of the aldol condensation between nitroethane and cyclohexanecarboxaldehyde. By far the simplest way of preparing the latter is by mild, catalytic reduction of 3-cyclohexene-carboxaldehyde, the Diels–Alder adduct of the very cheap diene and dienophile, butadiene and acrolein.

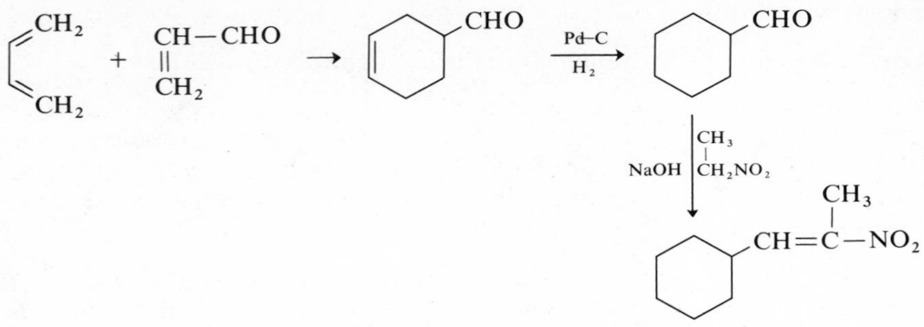

Example 7

Synthesize the hydrocarbon shown from readily available starting materials.

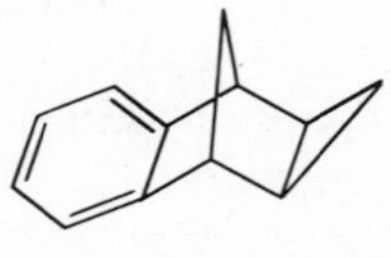

The presence of a cyclopropane ring in this molecule immediately suggests
the addition of a methylene group (Section 15.13). Indeed, addition of
methylene to the alkene part of the rest of the molecule would give the
required *exo*-cyclopropane preferentially over its endo isomer, since the
addition will tend to take place from the less hindered side of the alkene.
The tricyclic alkene looks at first like a complex structure, but careful
inspection shows that it is simply the Diels–Alder adduct of cyclopentadiene
and benzyne. Benzyne, of course, is too unstable to be isolated, but it is
easily generated as needed by the slow decomposition of *o*-benzenediazonium-
carboxylate in the presence of cyclopentadiene. The entire synthesis from
anthranilic acid is outlined below.

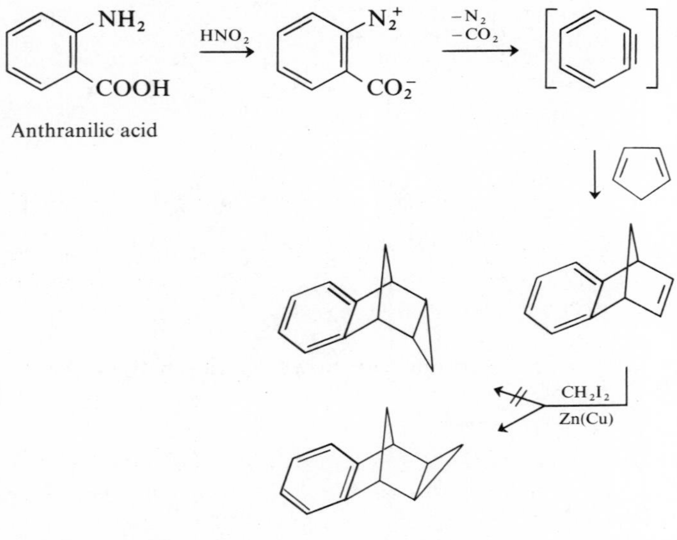

Anthranilic acid

Medium-Sized Rings and Large Rings (Eight or More Atoms)

The formation of rings containing eight or more carbon atoms by most methods (e.g., Dieckmann
synthesis, aldol condensation, intramolecular alkylation, and acylation) is very difficult. Unless
the ring closures are carried out under conditions of very high dilution, the formation of linear
polymers takes place much more rapidly than does the ring closure involving the two distant
ends of the long chain. The worst yields in such reactions (sometimes no yield at all) are encountered

in the C-9 to C-11 series, because cycloalkanes of this ring size are very strained internally. The synthetic reaction which provides the principal and very useful exception to this rule is the *acyloin condensation* of a diester, a reaction which gives very satisfactory yields of both medium-sized ring and large-ring compounds (Sections 20.8, 20.17). It has been postulated that the reason for the success of this reaction for the closure of large rings is that the two ends become attached to nearby sites on the surface of the sodium. The acyloins (α-hydroxy ketones) which are obtained in this way may be converted into a variety of other compounds; a few of the more common acyloin transformations are indicated below.

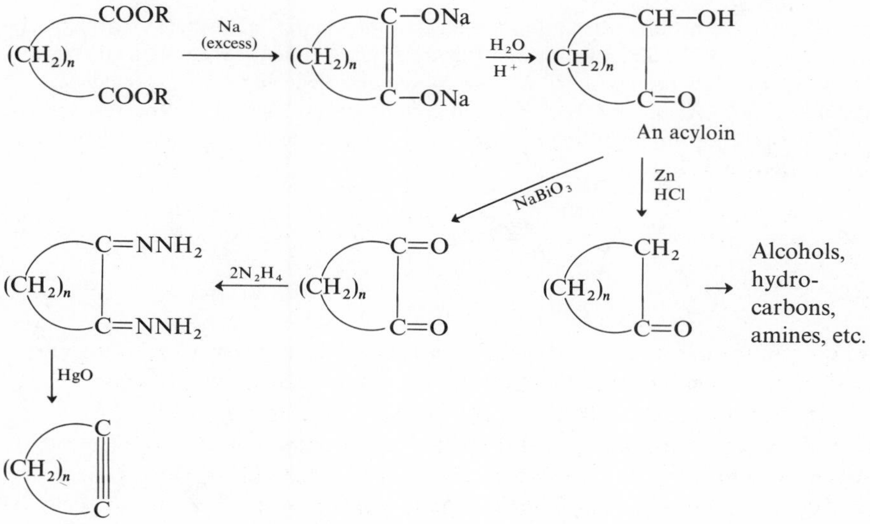

An acyloin

A new synthesis of large-ring (macrocyclic) compounds has recently (1968) been discovered by Story.† It involves the controlled thermolysis of unstable, dimeric ketone peroxides, which can usually be made from ketones and hydrogen peroxide. An example is the preparation of cyclodecane from cyclohexanone diperoxide:

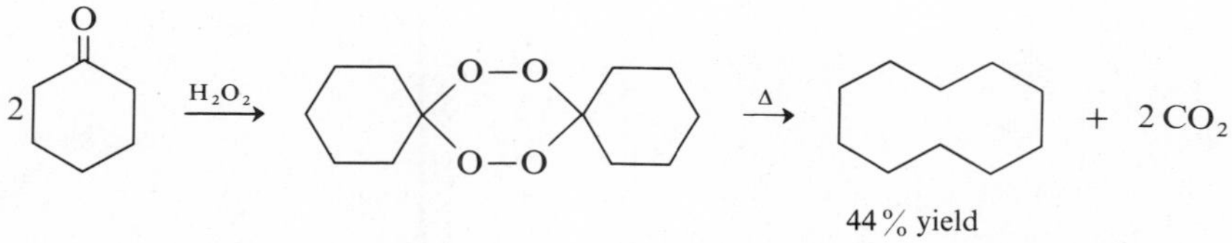

44% yield

This reaction promises to be one of broad utility for the formation of a variety of substituted macrocyclic structures.

Advantage also has been taken of the oxidative dimerization reaction of 1-alkynes for the production of unsaturated macrocyclic compounds (Sondheimer). Terminal alkynes can be oxidatively coupled to give diynes, according to the following reaction:

$$2\,R-C\equiv C-H \xrightarrow[\text{air, 20°C}]{\text{CuCl, NH}_4\text{Cl}} R-C\equiv C-C\equiv C-R + H_2O$$

Apparently, the reaction involves ionization of the 1-alkyne to the alkynide ion ($R-C\equiv C^-$), followed by a one-electron oxidation to the alkyne radical, $R-C\equiv C\cdot$. Coupling of two of the radicals generates the dimeric product. Two different 1-alkynes have been cross-dimerized in this manner; however, mixtures of the two self-dimers and the desired product are obtained. Bis-1-alkynes can also be cyclized under modified conditions. In addition to linear dimers, linear tetramers, and higher polymers, the very interesting cyclic dimers have been separated. A large number of annulenes (Section 11.9) have been prepared by starting with diacetylenes containing double bonds as well, and then reducing the triple bonds in the products to double bonds (Section 15.15).

† P. R. Story. Born 1933, Cape Girardeau, Missouri. Bell Telephone Laboratories, University of Georgia.

$$H-C\equiv C-(CH_2)_3-C\equiv C-H \xrightarrow[\substack{H_2O, \text{ ethanol} \\ 55°C}]{CuCl, \text{ air}} HC\equiv C(CH_2)_3C\equiv C-C\equiv C(CH_2)_3C\equiv CH$$

$$+$$

$$[HC\equiv C(CH_2)_3C\equiv C-C\equiv C(CH_2)_3C\equiv C]_2$$

$$+$$

$$\begin{array}{c} CH_2-C\equiv C-C\equiv C-CH_2 \\ | \qquad\qquad\qquad\qquad | \\ CH_2 \qquad\qquad\qquad\quad CH_2 \\ | \qquad\qquad\qquad\qquad | \\ CH_2-C\equiv C-C\equiv C-CH_2 \end{array}$$

Until very recently, no medium-sized or large-ring compounds were available as cheap articles of commerce. Methods for the dimerization and trimerization of butadiene (using certain organo-metallic catalysts) have now been developed, and 1,5-cyclooctadiene and 1,5,9-cyclododecatriene are prepared industrially. Partial hydrogenations to cyclooctene and cyclododecene, respectively, are quite practical, and the latter can then be transformed into other compounds such as cyclo-octanone and cyclododecanone.

$$2\ CH_2{=}CH{-}CH{=}CH_2 \xrightarrow{\text{catalyst}} \text{(ring)} \xrightarrow[\text{Pd}]{H_2} \text{(ring)}$$

$$3\ CH_2{=}CH{-}CH{=}CH_2 \longrightarrow \text{(ring)}$$

Example 8

Synthesize cyclononanol from available starting materials.

The most practical synthesis of this compound is one involving straightforward transformations of the nine-membered acyloin, *azeloin*. As its common name implies, azeloin is the cyclic acyloin derived from azelaic acid, the C-9, α,ω-dicarboxylic acid. Many schemes can be devised for the synthesis of azelaic acid, but the most practical method of preparing it, and one which is commercially feasible, is the oxidation of oleic acid. Oleic acid is an inexpensive natural product since it is available by the alkaline hydrolysis of many unsaturated natural oils, such as olive oil.

$$CH_3(CH_2)_7CH{=}CH(CH_2)_7COOH \xrightarrow{O_3} \xrightarrow{CH_3CO_3H}$$

Oleic acid

$$HOOC(CH_2)_7COOH + CH_3(CH_2)_7COOH$$

Azelaic acid   Nonanoic acid

$$\Big\downarrow EtOH_2^+ \quad EtOOC(CH_2)_7COOEt \xrightarrow[\text{xylene}]{4Na} \begin{array}{c} \\ \downarrow \substack{H_2O \\ H^+} \end{array}$$

Azeloin

An alternative synthesis from cyclooctene would be:

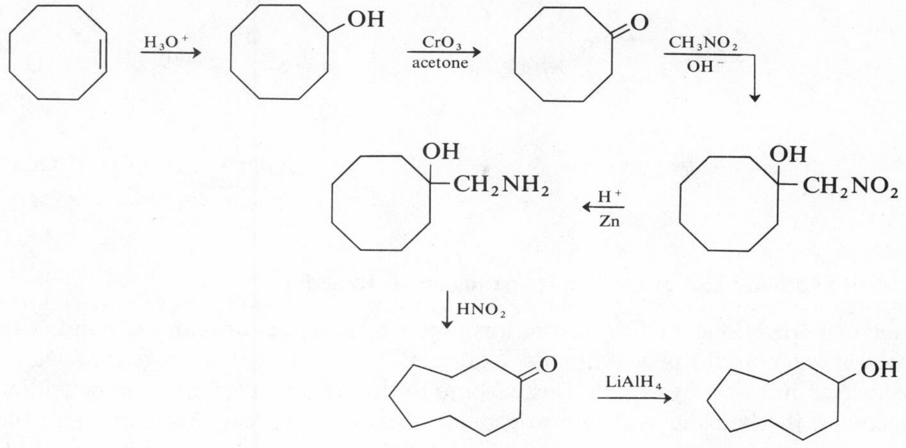

Syntheses Employing Ring-Cleavage Reactions

There are numerous examples in the literature of synthetic organic chemistry which illustrate the clever use of *ring-cleavage* reactions in the preparation of compounds which would otherwise be quite difficult or tedious to obtain. Advantage is often taken of the ready availability of many unsaturated six-membered-ring compounds as starting materials, which are themselves derived from Diels–Alder additions or cheap aromatic precursors. Most often, the ring-cleavage step is an oxidation. One specific example will best illustrate this kind of synthesis.

Example 9

Consider the practicality of synthesizing *meso*-1,2,3,4-tetracarboxybutane by a ring-cleavage method.

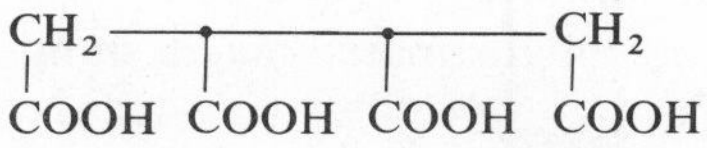

$$
\begin{array}{c}
CH_2 \text{----} \text{----} CH_2 \\
|\quad\ |\quad\ |\quad\ | \\
COOH\ COOH\ COOH\ COOH
\end{array}
$$

This tetracarboxylic acid could be obtained by the oxidation (e.g., oxidative ozonolysis) of a number of cyclic dienes or monounsaturated cyclic diacids. The possibilities (*a*)–(*g*) can be considered.

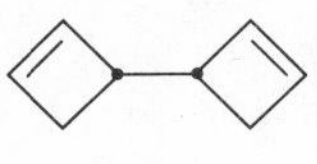

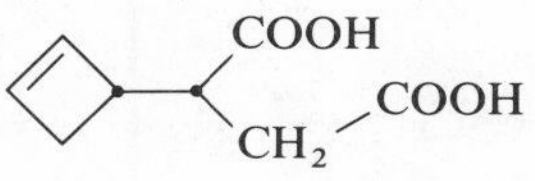

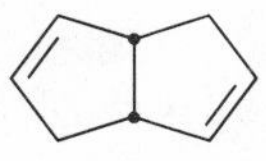

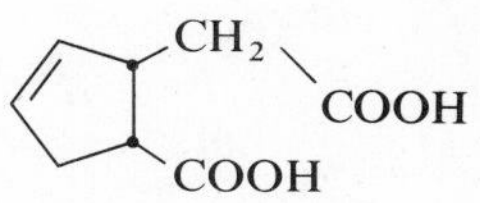

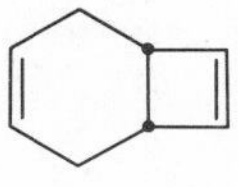

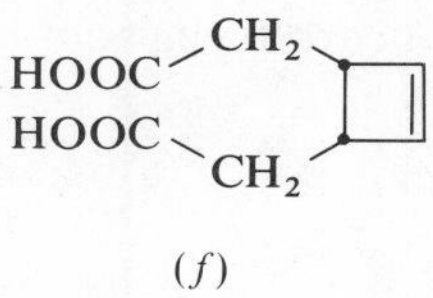

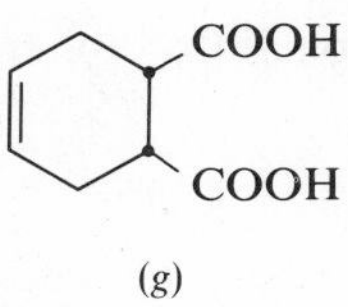

Of the above compounds, the only one which would be a readily available starting material is (g), which is the acid from hydrolysis of the Diels–Alder adduct of butadiene and maleic anhydride. The following synthesis could, therefore, be used:

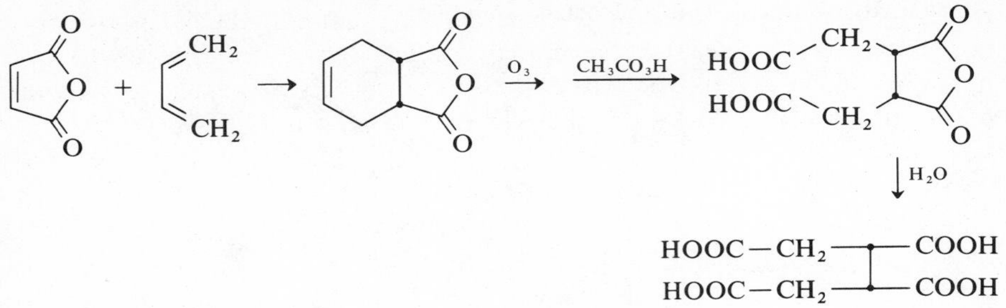

34.3   The Synthetic Use of Carbon Rearrangement Reactions

Rearrangement reactions leading to the formation of new carbon–carbon bonds can sometimes be very useful in a synthetic sequence. Among the many reactions which have been used in this way are various carbonium ion rearrangements, the benzidine rearrangement, the benzilic acid rearrangement, the Favorski rearrangement, and the Wolff rearrangement. A few examples of the use of such rearrangements are given.

Example 1

Synthesize 2-amino-3,3-dimethylbutane from a readily available and cheap starting material.

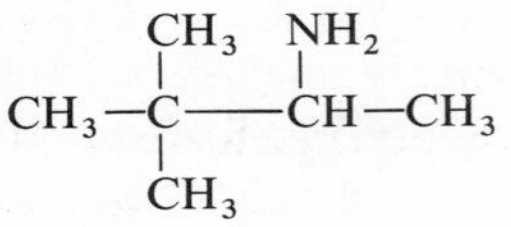

A primary amine of this type is easily made by reduction of the oxime of the related ketone. In the specific case given above, the ketone is methyl *t*-butyl ketone, better known as pinacolone. Pinacolone is most readily obtained by the acid-catalyzed rearrangement of the diol *pinacol* (2,3-di-methylbutane-2,3-diol), which is prepared by the bimolecular reduction of acetone ("pinacol reduction," Section 19.11) using amalgamated magnesium as the reducing agent.

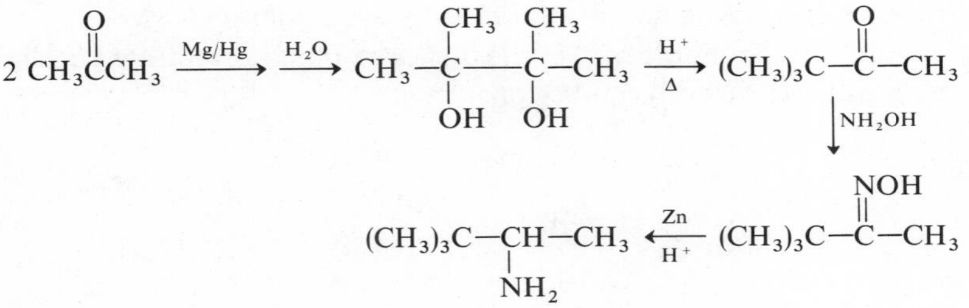

Example 2

Convert *o*-nitrotoluene into biphenyl-3,3′-dicarboxylic acid.

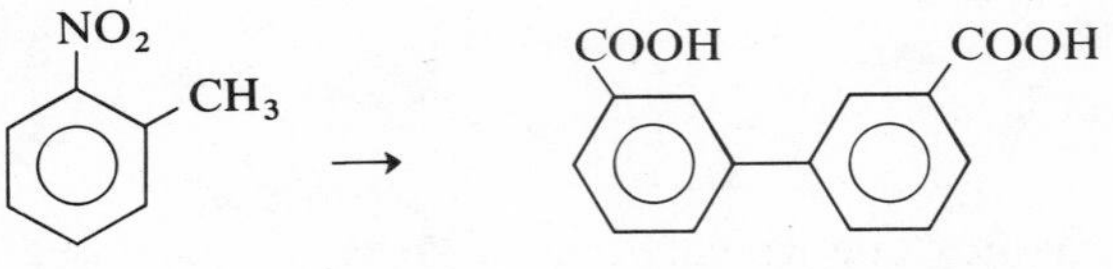

This problem illustrates the use of the benzidine rearrangement in the synthesis of biphenyl derivatives. In the case above, *o*-nitrotoluene is reduced by zinc and alkali to *o*-hydrazotoluene. Aqueous mineral acid causes facile rearrangement of the latter to 3,3'-dimethyl-4,4'-diaminobiphenyl. Diazotization of both amino groups of this diamine, followed by deamination with hypophosphorous acid, gives 3,3'-dimethylbiphenyl. Permanganate oxidation of the latter hydrocarbon yields the desired acid.

Example 3

Convert cyclohexanone into cycloheptanone.

This problem illustrates the use of a ring expansion for synthetic purposes. (See page 619 for a discussion of the principles involved.) The specific case mentioned is of practical importance, since cycloheptanone is actually best made in this way. Three different procedures have been used.

The first involves direct ring expansion of cyclohexanone by diazomethane (Section 19.10). The second involves reduction of cyclohexanone cyanohydrin and reaction of the resulting amino alcohol with nitrous acid (the Demyanov method, Section 21.1). The third (and perhaps best) differs from the second only in that the required amino alcohol is prepared by the aldol addition of nitromethane to cyclohexanone, followed by reduction.

Example 4

Convert *m*-nitrobenzoic acid into *m*-nitrophenylacetic acid.

This problem illustrates the use of the *Arndt–Eistert synthesis* (Section 22.8), a general method for converting an acid R—COOH into the homologous acid R—CH$_2$COOH, under very mild conditions. The acid is transformed into the corresponding acid chloride, which is then added to an excess (at least 2 molar equivalents) of ethereal diazomethane. The resulting α-diazo ketone is rearranged to the homologous acid with the loss of nitrogen by treatment with silver or silver oxide catalyst. (See also Section 22.8 for the photochemical ring contraction of a cyclic α-diazo ketone.)

34.4   Stereospecific and Stereoselective Reactions

Reactions in which a starting material gives one diastereomer at a higher rate (preferentially) than another diastereoisomer are said to be *stereoselective*. Reactions may be completely stereoselective, highly stereoselective, or show low stereoselectivity. A reaction is said to be *stereospecific* when two stereoisomeric starting materials give different diastereomeric products. For example, osmium tetroxide is said to be a stereospecific reagent for *cis*-hydroxylation, because *trans*-2-butene gives the *dl*-diastereoisomer while *cis*-2-butene gives the meso diastereoisomer.

Stereospecific *trans*-hydroxylation can be accomplished by stereospecific *cis*-epoxidation followed by stereospecific epoxide opening in a trans manner.

The terms *stereoselective* and *stereospecific* differ in the following way. When we speak of stereoselectivity we are referring to the fact that there is produced a predominance of one of several possible diastereomers in a reaction, regardless of the stereochemistry of the starting material or of the reaction pathway. On the other hand, stereospecificity means that a reaction of a single stereoisomeric starting material will lead to a specific diastereomeric product, such that all atoms which undergo configurational changes do so in a characteristic way (often predictable) dependent upon the reaction mechanism. Obviously an isomeric starting material which is subject to this same stereospecific reaction must produce a different diastereomer than the first isomer did.

Some chemists consider that stereoselective and stereospecific differ only in degree. In this usage a stereospecific reaction is one that produces a specific diastereoisomer to the extent of 95% or more over any others; and stereoselective reactions are reactions that produce one diastereomer in larger amounts than others, but not to the extent of 95%. We do not believe these definitions are as useful.

34.5 Syntheses of Stereoisomers

During the 100 years prior to 1940, excellent synthetic methods were developed for the interconversion of functional groups, the modification of chains, the formation of rings, and the utilization of protecting and directing groups. However, most of the major achievements in multistep synthesis have been accomplished since 1945, and they have depended to a crucial extent upon synthetic methods which were developed after 1940. These newer methods generally involve some elements of stereochemistry, and their discovery was in part motivated by the increasing importance of medicinal chemicals, most of which are active in only a single stereochemical form.

The synthesis of a compound containing an asymmetric carbon atom generally results from the reaction of a starting material containing a trigonal carbon atom, and in the simplest case gives a pair of enantiomers in equal amounts. When two asymmetric centers are generated in the same reaction, or when a second asymmetric center is introduced in the presence of the first, the resulting products are diastereomers, and they are usually formed in unequal amounts. In recent years, many synthetic reactions have been developed which allow the chemist to predict and to control the relative amounts of the diastereomers formed. The important factors involved in the determination of the stereochemical result of such reactions are (1) the energy differences between the ground state and the possible transition states, which can often be deduced from a consideration of the reacting conformation of the molecule and the direction of approach of the reagent (kinetic control); (2) the energy differences between the products themselves, which is largely a conformational matter (thermodynamic control).

Relative Energies of the Transition States

When a reagent can react with a molecule in two stereochemically different ways, the most favored path will be that which has the smallest increase in free energy between the ground state and the transition state. Although a prediction of the free energy of the transition state is very difficult, it is possible to estimate qualitative free energy differences between different possible transition states in certain cases, and a few such examples will be discussed.

The addition of bromine to a double bond is a stereospecific trans addition, as discussed in Section 15.4. Thus bromine adds to cyclohexene to give *trans*-1,2-dibromocyclohexane. Actually, there is more to the stereochemistry of the reaction than just trans addition. The additional stereochemical feature can be detected experimentally only by using a more complicated molecule than cyclohexene. Consider the addition of bromine to *trans*-2-octalin as an example.

There are two diastereomers possible which contain the bromines trans to one another, but only one of these is formed. This product contains both bromines in axial, rather than equatorial positions. This diaxial product is a kinetic product, which upon heating can be converted into the thermodynamic product, which is a mixture of the two diastereomers shown.

The above example actually represents a very commonly observed stereochemical outcome for addition to a cyclohexene. If the addition is trans, then the diaxial product is ordinarily formed in a kinetically controlled process. The reverse is also true—a trans elimination from a cyclohexane ring which yields a cyclohexene proceeds most readily if the departing groups are axial. The reason for the general preference of diaxial addition–elimination, when a trans process is taking place, can be seen in terms of the structure of the alkene. The groups entering or leaving ought to be anti-coplanar to permit the formation of or attack upon the p orbitals from which the π bond is formed. Diaxial groups are anti-coplanar, the diequatorial ones are not.

Actually, the addition of bromine is a special case, which differs from the above somewhat in that a bromonium ion intermediate is initially formed; and the ring opening of this ion determines the outcome of the reaction. Consider the addition of bromine to cyclohexene. The bromonium ion is first formed, and it can open in the following possible ways:

The ring opening is a displacement as in the S_N2 reaction, and the bromine atoms ought to be 180° apart as one enters and one leaves. This is possible in case 2, but not in case 1 (use models). Attack at C-1 can occur and yield diaxial opening only if the ring goes into a twist-boat form:

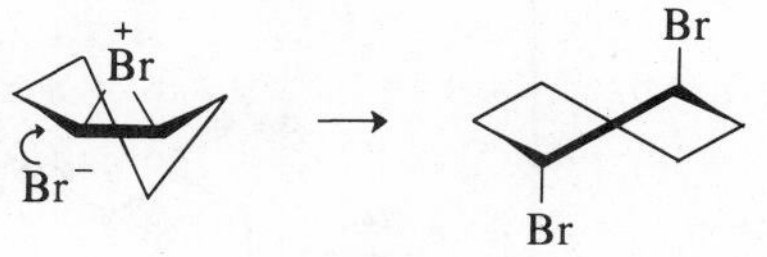

While this is not an impossible process, the product (and hence the transition state) contains a boat rather than a chair form, and hence this reaction is quite slow.

The general rules, then, are that trans addition to a cyclohexane tends to give a diaxial product. So does the opening of a three-membered ring fused to a cyclohexane (bromonium ion, or as we will see, an epoxide). The reverse of each of these reactions also proceeds best from a diaxial starting material.

The following two epoxides react with hydrogen bromide to give bromohydrins which are structural isomers. (The *t*-butyl group is in position 3 relative to the hydroxyl in one case, and position 4 in the other.)

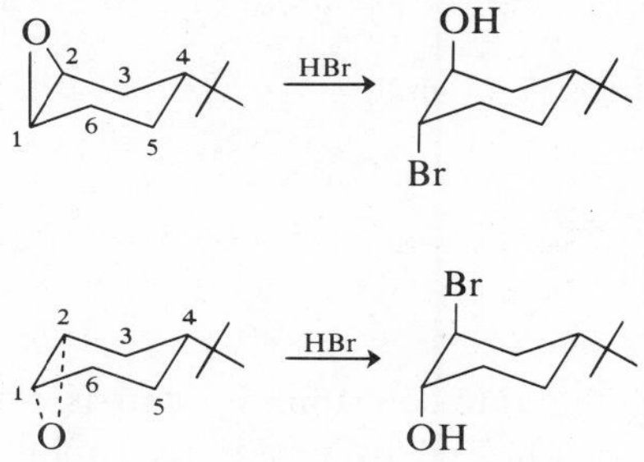

In the first example, attack of the bromide with inversion at C-2 of the "protonated" epoxide would require a transition state that would resemble a twist conformation because the product must be formed initially in the twist conformation. On the other hand, attack by bromide at C-1 leads directly to a chair conformation of the product. Attack at C-1 would be expected to be the preferred route because the energy of the transition state would be lower than in attack at C-2. In the second example, the epoxide is opened in the opposite direction (attack by bromide at C-2) because the product is the one resulting from the transition state having a chair conformation rather than that from the more unstable twist conformation.

Example 1

Outline a synthesis of *trans*-2-deuteriocyclohexanol, uncontaminated by its cis isomer, from phenol.

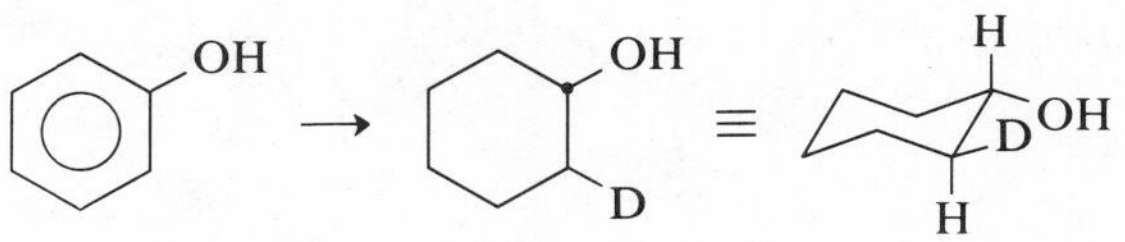

The key observation to be made is that the hydroxyl group and the deuterium atom are trans, and this suggests that both of these asymmetric centers must be introduced simultaneously. The best way to ensure that a hydroxyl group is formed trans to an adjacent group (or atom) is to cleave an epoxide—the new nucleophile will always end up trans to the liberated hydroxyl group. An epoxide can be converted to an alcohol with lithium aluminum hydride, a reaction that involves nucleophilic attack of the epoxide by hydride (Section 18.9). Since we desire to introduce deuterium instead of hydrogen, we would use lithium aluminum deuteride. The desired cyclohexene oxide can be prepared from cyclohexene, which in turn comes from dehydration of cyclohexanol. Cyclohexanol may be obtained by catalytic hydrogenation of phenol. The overall sequence is as follows:

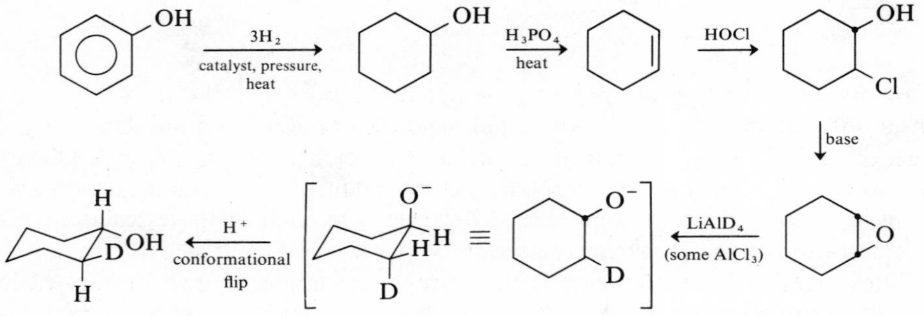

Bromination of a substituted cyclohexanone gives the 2-axial bromo ketone in a kinetically controlled reaction. The axial bromo ketone can be isolated, or it may be allowed to equilibrate with the equatorial isomer.

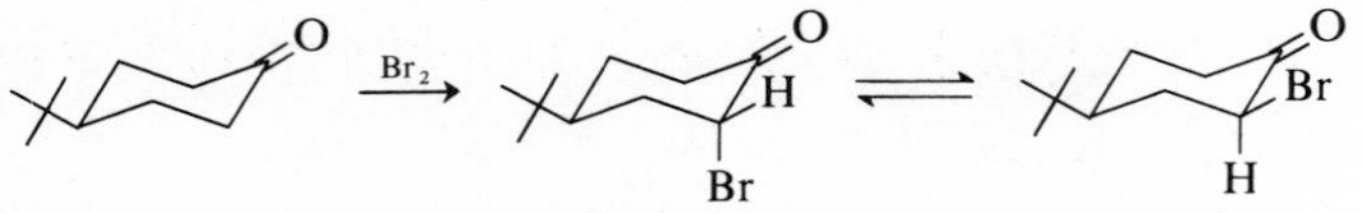

In the acid-catalyzed bromination of a ketone, the rate-determining step is the enolization of the ketone (Section 19.13), and this is followed by rapid electrophilic addition of bromine to the enol double bond. In the absence of steric effects, bromination of an enol (or an enol acetate) will produce the *axial* product by attack of the bromine from the side of the double bond that results directly in the chair conformation of the product. This attack involves a lower transition-state energy than attack which results in a twist conformation of the product, and it is the usual mode of addition. The student should recognize that this is a specific case of the general rule of diaxial addition to a

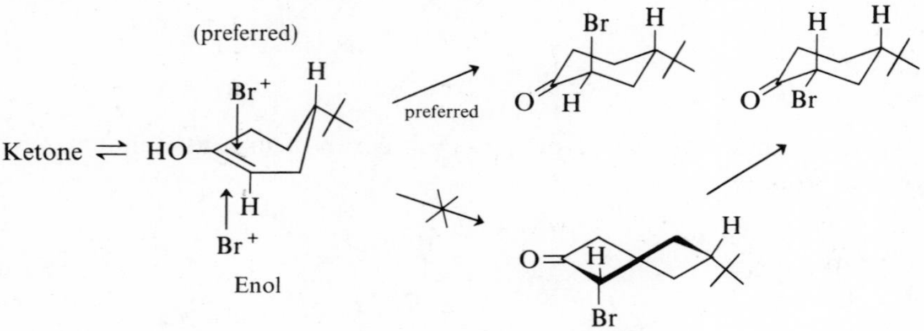

cyclohexene double bond. In the presence of hydrogen bromide (a by-product of the reaction), the initially formed axial bromo ketone (*trans*) will enolize and equilibrium is set up with the equatorial bromo ketone (*cis*). If the latter is more stable, it can be isolated after equilibrium is established.

Neighboring Group Reactions. Functional groups near one another in a molecule can determine the stereochemistry of reactions in which they can become involved (Section 18.4). For example, silver acetate and iodine in dry acetic acid will react with cyclohexene to give *trans*-1,2-cyclohexanediol diacetate, but the same reagents in the presence of one equivalent of water will give the *cis*-diol monoacetate.

The explanation of the change in stereochemistry involves the predicted *trans*-iodo acetate intermediate in which the iodine is readily displaced with inversion by the oxygen of the neighboring *trans*-acetate to give a new intermediate I. External acetate can then react with the symmetrical intermediate by inversion to give *trans*-diacetate. If water is present, it reacts preferentially at the carbonyl carbon atom of the intermediate to give *cis*-diol monoacetate.

The conversion of *trans*-2-aminocyclohexanol to the cis isomer illustrates the utility of neighboring group reactions.

An oxazoline

PROBLEMS

1. Outline reasonable laboratory syntheses of the following:

(a) $CH_3-CO-CH_3 \rightarrow (CH_3)_2\overset{\underset{\displaystyle OH}{|}}{C}-CH_2CH_2-\overset{\underset{\displaystyle OH}{|}}{C}(CH_3)_2$

(b) $Ph-CH_2Cl \rightarrow Ph-CH_2CH_2COOH$

(c) $CH_3COCH_2COOC_2H_5 \rightarrow CH_3COCHCH_2CH_2CH_3$ with CH_3 substituent

(d) $CH_3CH_2-\overset{\underset{\displaystyle OH}{|}}{\overset{\displaystyle CH_3}{C}}-CH_2CH_3$ from ethanol and acetic acid

(e) $CH_3CH_2CH_2CH-CH_2OH$ with CH_3 substituent   from *n*-propyl alcohol

(f) $N\equiv C-CH_2CH_2CH_2NO_2$ from compounds containing not more than three carbons.

(g) $HOOC-CH_2CHCH_2-COOH$ from benzaldehyde
            |
            Ph

(h) 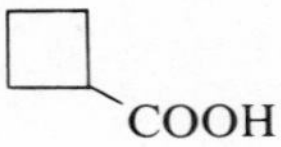 COOH

(i) 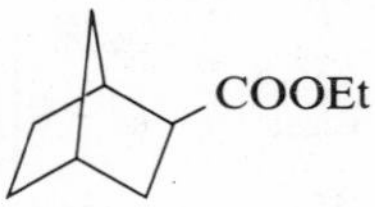 COOEt

(j) 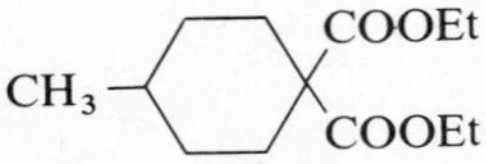 CH_3 COOEt / COOEt

(k) 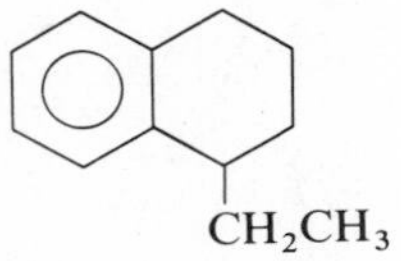 CH_2CH_3

(l) 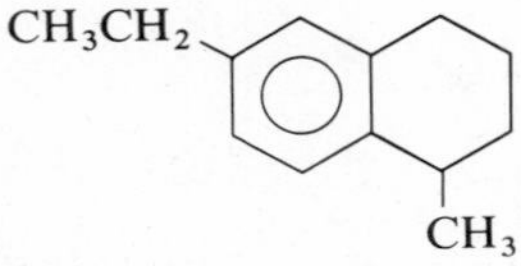 CH_3CH_2 CH_3

(m) 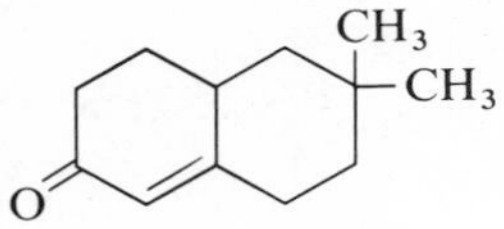 CH_3 / CH_3

(n) 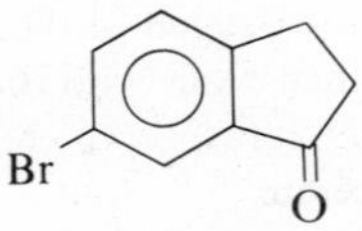 Br / O

(o) CH_3

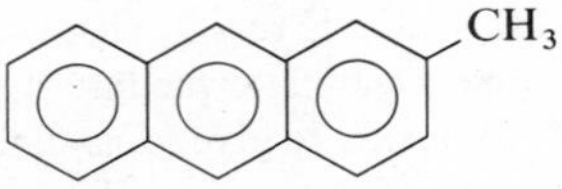

(p) 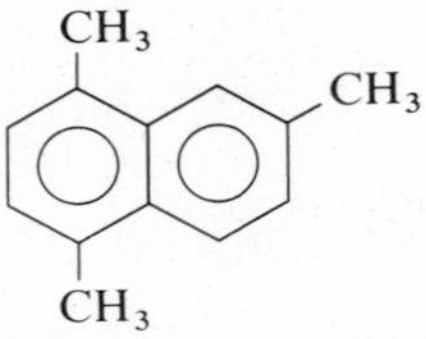 CH_3 / CH_3 / CH_3

2. Which of the following reactions is considered to be stereospecific? Provide a specific example of each.

(a) Addition of HOBr to an alkene.

(b) Reduction of a ketone with sodium borohydride.

(c) Hydroboration-oxidation of an alkene.

(d) The S_N2 reaction of a secondary halide and CH_3C (O / O$^-$) Na^+

(e) The reaction of an epoxide with ammonia.

(f) The Diels–Alder reaction.

(g) Reduction of an alkyne with sodium in ammonia.

(h) Epoxidation of alkenes with peracids.

(i) The reaction of a ketone with a phosphonium ylide.

(j) The Hofmann degradation of amides to amines.

(k) Decarboxylation of a disubstituted malonic acid.

(l) The addition of a Grignard reagent to a ketone.

3. Predict the structure and stereochemistry of the products of the following reactions:

(a) 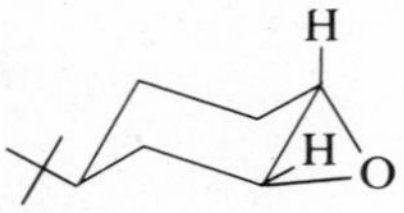 + $LiAlH_4 \rightarrow$

(b) 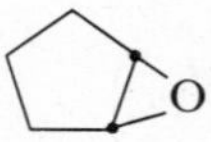 + $NH_3 \xrightarrow{heat}$

(c) 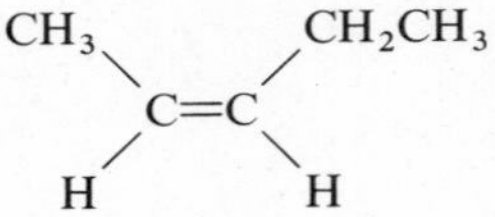 CH_3 / CH_2CH_3 C=C / H / H + $Br_2 \rightarrow$

(d)

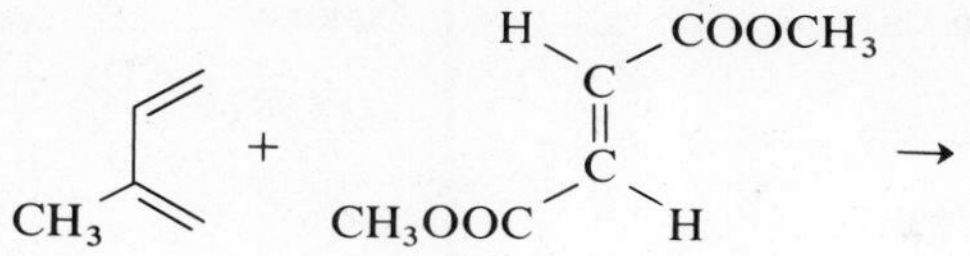

(e)

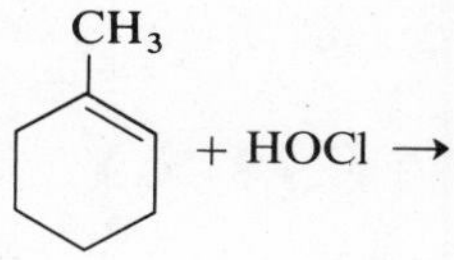

+ HOCl →

4.   Outline a stereospecific synthesis of

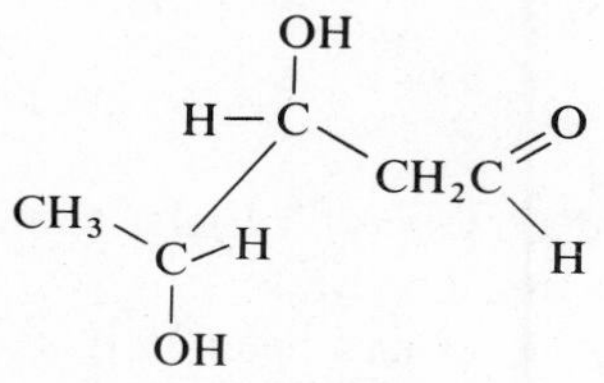

from readily available starting materials.

Optional Problems

1.   Outline a synthesis of 5,5-dimethylcyclooctanone from $(CH_3)_2C(CH_2COOH)_2$ and other readily available reagents.

2.   Cyclododecylamine is relatively inexpensive to purchase. Suggest a probable synthesis from readily available materials.

3.   Suggest a synthesis of cyclooctane-1,2,3,4-tetracarboxylic acid from the available 1,3-cyclooctadiene (*Hint*: See Example 9, Section 34.2).

4.   The following compound can be made in three steps from cyclooctene. Suggest the method.

CHAPTER 35

INDUSTRIAL ORGANIC CHEMISTRY

35.1   Introduction

About 100 years ago, in 1876, two organic chemists named Graebe and Liebermann synthesized the dyestuff alizarin from readily available starting materials. For years, this dye had been an important article of commerce in France. It had been extracted from the roots of the madder plant which was grown by farmers of a certain geographic area. It was possible to synthesize the dye at much smaller cost than was required for its isolation from natural sources, and within five years the French madder farmers were wiped out—a result that was catastrophic for that region and seriously detrimental to the French economy as a whole. Since that time a century ago, the organic chemist has been making progressively greater impact upon the economies of the various nations of the world.

Now that the gross national product of the United States is approaching one trillion dollars, it is instructive to attempt to assess the importance of the chemical industry. Chemical and allied products in 1969 amounted to $49.5 billion, of which the major elements were: industrial organic chemicals, $8.2 billion; inorganic chemicals, $6.4 billion; pharmaceutical preparations, $6.1 billion; plastic materials and resins, $4.1 billion; paints and related products, $3.8 billion; and soaps and detergents, $2.8 billion. In addition, the value of petroleum refinery shipments in 1969 came to $21.7 billion, rubber and allied plastic products were $16 billion, and man-made fibers were $2.9 billion. The food industry accounted for $82.8 billion in annual sales. These figures demonstrate that the chemical industry plays a major role in our economy, and that organic chemistry is a leader in the chemical industry.

Major sources of organic starting materials for industry are the fossil fuels, materials resulting from the decay and transformation of plant and animal remains. Prehistoric forests that turned to swamp gave rise to marsh gas (methane), which when trapped in the ground became our natural gas. By processes involving heat and pressure, these carbonaceous materials were converted first to petroleum and then to coal. Historically, the first organic starting materials were obtained by heating coal in the absence of oxygen, forming coke and volatile by-products called coal tar. From coal tar, various aromatic organic chemicals were isolated, including benzene, toluene, xylenes, ethylbenzene, naphthalene, pyridine bases, and creosote oil. These aromatic compounds were well suited to provide starting materials for chemical transformations that ultimately led to synthetic dyes, and thus the dye industry was one of the first major organic chemical industries. Other industries based on coal, inorganic salts, and the atmosphere developed rapidly in Europe, and these were supplemented by the fermentation industry and by the processing of animal and vegetable fats and oils. World War I demonstrated that the United States was quite dependent on Europe for strategic chemicals, and this recognition provided the initial impetus for growth of the U.S. chemical industry.

The vast oil deposits in the United States coupled with the blossoming automobile industry, resulted in the development of a chemical industry based largely on petroleum. The role of the petroleum industry has changed markedly over the past 50 years from that of a supplier of raw materials to that of a major partner with the traditional chemical industry. For example, most coal tar-derived aromatic chemicals are now synthesized by the petroleum industry.

To illustrate this point, the U.S. Tariff Commission's preliminary report on the production of synthetic organic chemicals in 1969 revealed that petrochemical benzene production was 1061 million gallons, as compared to 93 million gallons from coal-tar operations; and "petronaphthalene" production was 353 million pounds, whereas only 45 million pounds were obtained from coal.

Emphasis is placed in this chapter on large-volume, synthetic organic chemicals of commerce. While these are mainly petrochemicals, it is clear that other important bulk chemicals are produced by processes based on fats and oils, cotton, wood, sugar, starch, and other natural products. At the end of the chapter, some of the major and typical segments of the industry will be discussed briefly. For detailed information, the industrially oriented chemist is referred to the volume by Kirk-Othmer entitled *Encyclopedia of Chemical Technology* (Wiley-Interscience, New York, 1969). Petrochemical technology is set forth in an outstanding book called *Chemicals from Petroleum*, by A. L. Waddams (Chemical Publishing Company, 1969).

Industrial organic chemistry differs from laboratory chemistry in some important respects. Since laboratory operations are carried out on a small scale, the cost of the chemicals necessary for an experiment is usually small compared to the value of the chemist's time, so that reactions are carried out in such a way as to conserve the chemist's time rather than money. In large-scale industrial operations, the reverse is true. Thus, while in a laboratory a chemist may reduce a ketone to an alcohol with lithium aluminum hydride, which is expensive, the corresponding industrial operation is more likely to involve the use of a cheap nickel catalyst and hydrogen gas.

As a perusal of this chapter will show, the favorite industrial reactions are those which can be carried out at room temperature or thereabouts (since heat is expensive in large amounts), and which involve starting materials that are both available in very large quantities and very cheap. The reagents used are also chosen to be inexpensive (for example, air is often used as an oxidizing agent).

Another important difference between industrial chemistry and laboratory chemistry is that almost invariably in the laboratory a pure compound is desired. In industrial work, many solvents, fluids, and even products are mixtures of similar compounds. Thus, reactions which yield mixtures are often quite suitable for industrial syntheses, but not for laboratory work. Finally, it may be that a reaction mixture can profitably be separated on an industrial scale with very large continuous separation devices such as fractionating columns, while in the laboratory such processes might be too time consuming, and so a more expensive but quicker route would be used.

A beginning student usually has trouble in understanding the difference between an industrial process and the laboratory process. We have tried in this book not to confuse the two and have made a point of the fact that industrial processes are often unsuited to laboratory work. Industrial processes which have been mentioned in passing up to this point have been clearly labeled as such.

35.2 Chemical Raw Materials from Petroleum

As pointed out in Section 3.2, crude petroleum is a mixture of hydrocarbons which are primarily alkanes, but it also contains variable amounts of naphthenes (cycloalkanes) and aromatic compounds. These may be separated by distillation into series of fractions according to boiling points; the higher boiling the fraction, the greater the number of carbon atoms. A common or trade definition of the fractions is as follows: gas and liquefied gas, C_1–C_4 (methane up to the butanes); petroleum ether and ligroin (light naphtha), C_5–C_7; straight-run gasoline, C_6–C_{12}; kerosene, C_9–C_{15}; heating and fuel oils, C_{14}–C_{18}; lubricating oils and greases, C_{18} and up; and, finally, asphalt.

In terms of petroleum feedstock for conversion to useful starting materials for organic synthesis, the three major categories are natural gas, refinery gas, and liquid hydrocarbon fractions. Natural gas is methane or methane plus quantities of ethane. Refinery gas includes hydrogen and alkanes and alkenes through the butanes and butenes. The liquid hydrocarbon fractions range up to C_{10} or so.

Originally, refinery gases for chemical manufacture were produced exclusively by thermal cracking methods (Section 23.4). New processes have been developed over the years to improve the yields, diversify the products, and, of course, improve gasoline quality. The major operations relating to the production of raw materials for chemical conversion are *crude oil distillation, catalytic cracking* (and *hydrocracking*), and *catalytic reforming*. Catalytic cracking uses a gas/oil feedstock to produce a higher octane gasoline and a mixture of low molecular weight alkanes and alkenes. For this process, a fluid-bed catalyst of finely powdered alumina and silica is used. A more recent development is to use cracking catalysts of the molecular-sieve type, such as aluminum silicates with polyvalent metal cations. An important modification is hydrocracking, which is a combination of catalytic cracking and hydrogenation to produce gasoline and gaseous alkanes such as propane and the butanes. The various processes increase the efficiency of the refinery operation and permit the production of both the desired grades of gasoline as well as preferred raw materials for chemical conversion. Distillation of crude oil produces a heavy gasoline fraction, rich in naphthenes, which is subjected to catalytic reforming using a platinum-type catalyst. The naphthenes are isomerized (Section 23.3) and dehydrogenated (Section 23.6) to produce aromatic hydrocarbons. Catalytic reforming may be illustrated by one of many possible equations. Ideally, fractions

containing the proper number of carbon atoms can be catalytically reformed and dehydrogenated to yield the desired aromatic hydrocarbon.

From a chemical raw material point of view, refinery gases are most important as a source of the lower alkenes, ethylene and propylene. Separation and recycle operations are complex, and rigid process controls are required to maintain a balanced and proper output. Ethylene output may be increased by separate catalytic or pyrolytic cracking in which an ethane–propane mixture is recycled. A C_3 fraction containing propylene and propane may be used to convert the propylene to isopropanol, for example, which allows recycling of the propane. The following simplified equations illustrate the reactions which take place:

$$C_3H_8 \rightarrow CH_3CH{=}CH_2 + H_2$$
$$C_3H_8 \rightarrow CH_2{=}CH_2 + CH_4$$
$$C_nH_{2n+2} \rightarrow C_2H_4 + C_3H_6 + C_4H_8 + C_nH_{2n} + H_2 + CH_4 + \text{other}$$

Naphtha cracking utilizes liquid hydrocarbons at high temperatures (750 to 900°C), usually in combination with steam to reduce coking. The straight-chain alkanes yield alkenes and hydrogen, and the isoalkanes give much methane. Naphthenes do not crack readily, but give a good yield of butadiene, probably via cyclohexene. The aromatic hydrocarbons are relatively stable and are isolated in a liquid fraction. The cracking of paraffin wax gives largely a liquid fraction of alkenes (C_5 to C_{20}), which may be used as feed in the oxo process, for secondary alkyl sulfate detergents, or for alkylbenzene sulfonate detergents.

35.3   Unsaturated Hydrocarbons

The dominant role of the lower alkenes as chemical raw materials is apparent from their consumption figures. The consumption of ethylene in 1969 was estimated as 12 billion pounds and the consumption of propylene at about 8 billion pounds. The percentage use distribution of these two alkenes for the production of other chemicals was estimated to be approximately as follows:

Ethylene		*Propylene*	
Polyethylene	40%	Polypropylene	15%
Ethylene oxide	20%	Propylene oxide	10%
Ethanol	10%	Isopropyl Alcohol	20%
Ethylbenzene and styrene	10%	Cumene	8%
Halogen compounds	15%	Acrylonitrile	12%
Other	5%	Heptene	10%
		Trimer and tetramer	10%
		Other[a]	15%

[a] Butyraldehyde, glycerol, epichlorohydrin, isoprene, acrylic acid, rubbers.

Besides ethylene and propylene, acetylene, butylene, isobutylene, and butadiene are other important lower alkene raw materials.

Acetylene has traditionally been prepared by the hydrolysis of calcium carbide, which in turn is produced by heating lime and coke at 2000°C.

$$CaO + 3C \xrightarrow{\text{heat}} CaC_2 + CO$$

$$CaC_2 + H_2O \longrightarrow CaO + HC{\equiv}CH$$

This process is still used, but the trend today is to prepare acetylene from petroleum sources. These are high energy input, complex processes requiring careful control and will not be discussed here. A second trend is to replace acetylene by the much cheaper ethylene as a starting material, notably for the production of vinyl chloride, vinyl acetate, and the chlorinated ethylenes such as trichloroethylene (Triclene) and perchloroethylene (Perclene) (see Section 7.9). However, annual U.S. acetylene production is still about a billion pounds. Of this, approximately 25% is used for the manufacture of vinyl chloride, 22% for neoprene, 15% for vinyl acetate, 10% for acrylonitrile, 16% for the chloroethylenes, and 12% is consumed for nonchemical uses.

Indicative of the corollary impact of production trends on petrochemicals is the proportion of *ethylene* converted to polyethylene: In 1950 it was less than 5%, whereas in 1969 it was estimated at 40%. The increased usage is attributed, in part, to the improvement in the properties (high density, linear structure) of the polymer achieved by low-pressure polymerization employing a Ziegler–Natta catalyst (Section 25.4).

Since 1960, the manufacture of polypropylene has grown rapidly, and further growth is predicted. Here, as well, the use of Ziegler–Natta catalysts for polymerization of *propylene* (Section 25.4) has made polypropylene of varying properties available to the fabricator.

Copolymerization (Section 25.3) of *isobutylene* with a small amount of a diene (e.g., isoprene) gives a vulcanizable product known as *butyl rubber*.

Most *butadiene* is copolymerized with other monomers to form synthetic rubber for automobile tires; SBR (styrene/butadiene rubber) represents over half of the use (Section 25.3). Butadiene also is a component of the ABS resins (acrylonitrile-butadiene-styrene) for surface coatings and other uses.

A recent development is *cis*-polyisoprene rubber, a product very similar to natural rubber. *Isoprene* monomer is prepared by two routes. In the first, C_5 alkenes are dehydrogenated. In the second, propylene is dimerized with tripropylaluminum to give 2-methyl-1-pentene. This is then isomerized to the 2-alkene, which is thermally demethylated in the presence of steam and hydrogen bromide to generate isoprene.

$$2\,CH_3CH{=}CH_2 \rightarrow CH_2{=}\overset{\underset{\displaystyle |}{CH_3}}{C}{-}C_3H_7 \rightarrow CH_3{-}\overset{\underset{\displaystyle |}{CH_3}}{C}{=}CHC_2H_5$$

$$\xrightarrow[\Delta,\ \text{steam, HBr}]{-CH_4} CH_2{=}\overset{\underset{\displaystyle |}{CH_3}}{C}{-}CH{=}CH_2 \xrightarrow[\text{Li dispersion}]{\text{Ziegler–Natta catalyst or}} cis\text{-Polymer}$$

35.4   Halogenated Hydrocarbons

Halogen-containing organic compounds are prepared industrially from saturated and unsaturated hydrocarbons by substitution (Chapter 23) or addition (Chapter 15) reactions, respectively. A number of the compounds find direct uses, but the greater proportion of the output is converted to other intermediates.

The largest tonnage chlorine-containing product is *vinyl chloride*, the principal component of polyvinyl resins (Section 25.3). The original production process is based on the vapor-phase addition of hydrogen chloride to acetylene over a catalyst such as mercuric chloride on charcoal. However, vinyl chloride is also produced from ethylene by the following sequence of reactions, and this process now predominates.

$$CH_2{=}CH_2 \xrightarrow[\text{low temp}]{Cl_2} ClCH_2CH_2Cl \xrightarrow{500°C} CH_2{=}CHCl + HCl$$

The use of chlorine in the manufacture of vinyl chloride by way of ethylene dichloride, as well as for many other processes, was handicapped over the years because the by-product, hydrogen chloride, accounted for half the chlorine value. The development of a practical "oxychlorination" technique, whereby hydrogen chloride is oxidized catalytically to chlorine with air or oxygen, has had a marked effect on the economics of chlorination processes. For example:

$$CH_2{=}CH_2 + 2HCl + \tfrac{1}{2}O_2 \rightarrow CH_2ClCH_2Cl + H_2O$$

The catalyst is cuprous chloride plus an alkali metal halide supported on a bed of inert material such as silica or alumina.

Vinylidene chloride, copolymerized with vinyl chloride for Saran (Section 25.3), can be produced from vinyl chloride as follows:

$$CH_2{=}CHCl \xrightarrow{Cl_2} ClCH_2CHCl_2 \xrightarrow{NaOH} CH_2{=}CCl_2$$

Carbon tetrachloride used to be prepared from carbon disulfide and chlorine. The by-product of the first step, sulfur dichloride, is further converted to carbon tetrachloride by reaction with more carbon disulfide. This process, although not much used these days, produces high-purity carbon tetrachloride.

$$CS_2 + 3Cl_2 \xrightarrow{Fe^{+3}} CCl_4 + S_2Cl_2$$

$$CS_2 + 2S_2Cl_2 \longrightarrow 6S + CCl_4$$

The starting carbon disulfide is prepared today largely from methane and sulfur at about 700° over clay or alumina catalysts. The reaction may be represented as follows:

$$CH_4 + 2S_2 \xrightarrow[200°]{Al_2O_3} CS_2 + 2H_2S$$

The principal use of carbon disulfide in the United States is for viscose rayon and cellophane manufacture (70%) and about 20% is converted to carbon tetrachloride. Direct chlorination of methane (natural gas) is a major current source of carbon tetrachloride, as well as other chloromethanes.

Chloroform is made by the reduction of carbon tetrachloride and by the direct chlorination of methane; 21.7 million pounds was produced in 1969. The principal use today for both carbon tetrachloride and chloroform is as starting materials for fluorocarbon refrigerants, propellants, and plastics. Trichlorofluoromethane (Freon-11) and dichlorodifluoromethane (Freon-12) are examples. Chlorodifluoromethane, when pyrolyzed at 250°C, is converted to tetrafluoroethylene, the source of the popular, solvent-resistant and thermally stable polymer, *Teflon*.

$$2 \, CHClF_2 \xrightarrow[250°C]{} CF_2{=}CF_2 + 2 \, HCl$$

Chlorotrifluoroethylene produces a similar polymer known as *Kel-F*.

Methyl chloride is produced by the thermal chlorination of methane at 350–450° using a large excess of methane (Section 23.7). The compound is also produced by action of hydrogen chloride on methanol at 350°C over a catalyst. Production in 1969 was 390 million pounds with major applications for silicone resins (60%), tetramethyllead (15%), butyl rubber (10%), and methyl cellulose.

Methylene chloride is prepared by the chlorination of methane or methyl chloride (Section 23.7). Some 360 million pounds was produced in 1969 for paint removers, degreasing, extraction, plastics processing, coatings, and as an aerosol component.

Ethyl chloride is prepared by the ionic (catalytic) addition of hydrogen chloride to ethylene (Section 15.3). Most of the ethyl chloride (90%) is used for tetraethyllead. Tetraethyllead consumption was 550 million pounds in 1967.

The addition of hydrogen chloride to vinylidene chloride gives 1,1,1-trichloroethane, also known as *methyl chloroform*. This is the least toxic of the halogenated hydrocarbons, and its use for degreasing, drain cleaners, and solvents is increasing. Two important chlorinated alkenes, *trichloro- and perchloroethylene*, are used for degreasing and dry cleaning solvents, respectively. (See Section 35.3.) Production in 1969 was 573 and 624 million pounds, respectively.

Neoprene, a highly solvent-resistant rubber, is a polymer of *chloroprene* which is prepared from acetylene as follows:

$$2 \ HC{\equiv}CH \xrightarrow{\text{cat.}} H_2C{=}CH{-}C{\equiv}CH \xrightarrow{\text{HCl}} \underset{\underset{}{}}{CH_2{=}\overset{\overset{Cl}{|}}{C}{-}CH{=}CH_2}$$

Acetylene is dimerized to vinylacetylene in an aqueous solution of cuprous and ammonium chlorides at 70°C. Vinylacetylene adds hydrogen chloride readily in an aqueous solution of cupric chloride.

A recent process for chloroprene is based on butadiene, which is chlorinated in the vapor phase to mixed dichlorides. These are isomerized catalytically with cuprous chloride to 3, 4-dichloro-1-butene; elimination of 1 mole of hydrogen chloride gives chloroprene.

$$CH_2{=}CH{-}CH{=}CH_2 \xrightarrow{\text{2 steps}} \underset{\underset{Cl \quad Cl}{|\quad\;\;|}}{CH_2{-}CH{-}CH{=}CH_2} \xrightarrow{\text{heat}} \underset{}{CH_2{=}\overset{\overset{Cl}{|}}{C}{-}CH{=}CH_2}$$

The low-temperature chlorination of butadiene yields largely *1,4-dichloro-2-butene*. Treatment of the dichloroalkene with sodium cyanide gives the alkenic dinitrile. Hydrogenation in the vapor phase over palladium reduces only the double bond to give adiponitrile, which can be further hydrogenated to hexamethylenediamine (for nylon 6,6) at elevated temperature and pressure using a cobalt catalyst.

$$\underset{\text{1,4-Dichloro-2-butene}}{ClCH_2CH{=}CHCH_2Cl} \xrightarrow{\text{NaCN}} NCCH_2CH{=}CHCH_2CN \xrightarrow{\frac{H_2}{Pd}} NC(CH_2)_4CN$$

$$\underset{\text{Adiponitrile}}{H_2N(CH_2)_6NH_2} \xleftarrow{\text{H}_2,\text{ cat.}}$$

35.5   Aliphatic Alcohols

"Lower" aliphatic alcohols are usually classified as those containing up to five carbon atoms, and the higher alcohols are those containing six or more carbon atoms. Alcohols in all categories are large-volume chemicals, and they are produced by a number of processes. Methanol is formed from carbon monoxide and hydrogen, and other lower alcohols may be produced by an extension of this approach known as the *oxo process*, which involves hydroformylation of alkenes. Other procedures utilize the aldol condensation of aldehydes (Section 19.14), followed by dehydration and hydrogenation. The polymerization of ethylene with triethylaluminum (Ziegler catalyst) and the reduction of glycerides are most often used for higher alcohols. These methods will be described briefly.

A mixture of carbon monoxide and hydrogen called "synthesis gas" is used for the synthesis of ammonia, methanol, and derived compounds. The production of synthesis gas from coke was of great importance to the early European chemical industry. The basic reaction is as follows:

$$C + H_2O \rightarrow CO + H_2$$

In a subsequent equilibrium reaction, the carbon monoxide and water are converted to hydrogen and carbon dioxide.

$$CO + H_2O \rightleftharpoons CO_2 + H_2$$

In the early 1930s, a process was developed which produced from natural gas a mixture richer in hydrogen

$$CH_4 + H_2O \rightarrow CO + 3H_2$$

While the subsequent equilibrium reaction still occurs, it can be held at minimum because carbon dioxide is undesirable. Partial oxidation of methane is another major source of synthesis gas.

Methanol is formed from synthesis gas using catalysts at elevated temperatures (300°C) and pressures (300 atm). The principal reactions are as follows:

$$CO + 2H_2 \xrightarrow[\Delta, \text{ pressure}]{ZnO \cdot Cr_2O_3} CH_3OH$$

$$CO_2 + 3H_2 \rightarrow CH_3OH + H_2O$$

Some methanol is also produced by the oxidation of methane and a little (1 %) is still obtained from the destructive distillation of wood.

The production of methanol in the United States in 1969 was 4.1 billion pounds. Roughly 45 % is converted to formaldehyde for phenolic resins. The balance is distributed among such uses as solvents, methacrylates, polyformaldehyde, methylamines, dimethyl terephthalate, methyl halides, ethylene glycol, antifreeze, and aircraft fuel injection.

Ethyl alcohol is made both from the fermentation of molasses, grain, and starch, and synthetically by the hydration of ethylene (Section 15.3). The acid-catalyzed hydration process involves passing ethylene into 96 % sulfuric acid, and hydrolyzing the resulting monoethyl and diethyl sulfates with steam.

$$H_2C{=}CH_2 \xrightarrow{96\% \text{ H}_2\text{SO}_4} CH_3CH_2OSO_2OH + (C_2H_5O)_2SO_2$$

$$C_2H_5OH + H_2SO_4 \xleftarrow{\text{steam}}$$

The more recent vapor-phase process for ethanol involves passage of ethylene and steam under pressure (60–70 atm) over a supported phosphoric acid catalyst at 300°. However, the equilibrium formation of ethanol is low and recycling is necessary.

The principal uses of ethanol are for acetaldehyde production (45 %), solvents (30 %), and miscellaneous chemical processes. Ethyl acetate is produced to the extent of 100 million pounds annually as a fast-drying solvent for nitrocellulose, ethyl cellulose, shellac, rubbers, and vinyl resins.

Propylene is hydrated to *isopropyl alcohol* using 80 % sulfuric acid below 40°C; under the same conditions 1-butene and 2-butene give *sec-butyl alcohol*. Isobutylene requires only 60% sulfuric acid for hydration to give *t-butyl alcohol* (Section 15.3). Isopropyl alcohol production is some 1.6 billion pounds annually, and over one-half is converted to acetone. *n-Propyl alcohol* is available in the United States by the oxidation of propane-butane mixtures and by the reduction of propylene-derived acrolein.

1-Butanol is produced by the fermentation of blackstrap molasses, a source which is declining in significance. The two major synthetic processes are by the oxo reaction and the aldol condensation of acetaldehyde.

The *oxo process* has broad utility for primary alcohols. In the conventional form of the process, alkenes are converted to aldehydes by hydroformylation with an equimolar mixture of carbon monoxide and hydrogen. The active catalyst is cobalt octacarbonyl, which is formed in situ from cobalt salts and carbon monoxide. An example is cobalt naphthenate, which is soluble in organic media. With propylene, the reaction takes place in the liquid phase at about 200 atm.

$$CH_3CH{=}CH_2 + CO + H_2 \xrightarrow[\text{200 atm}]{Co_2(CO)_8} CH_3CH_2CH_2\overset{\displaystyle O}{\overset{\|}{C}}{-}H$$

The butyraldehyde is separated and reduced to 1-butanol with hydrogen at 150°C and 1500 psig in the presence of a nickel catalyst. Some isobutyraldehyde is formed, usually 20% or less. In fact, the economic utility of the oxo reaction demands keeping branched-chain by-products at a minimum.

A recent modification of the oxo process uses low pressure (30 atm) and cobalt carbonyl complexed with tributylphosphine as the catalyst. This will produce 1-butanol directly, and 2 moles of hydrogen per mole of carbon monoxide are employed.

Perhaps 40% of the supply of 1-butanol is made by the base-catalyzed aldol condensation of acetaldehyde (Section 19.14).

$$2\,CH_3CHO \xrightarrow[\text{dilute}]{NaOH} CH_3CHOHCH_2CHO \xrightarrow[(-H_2O)]{H^+} CH_3CH{=}CHCHO$$

$$\xrightarrow[\text{180°C, 30 psig}]{H_2,\ Ni{-}Cr} CH_3CH_2CH_2CH_2OH$$

The combined production of all butanols is close to 1 billion pounds annually. Butyl esters are lacquer solvents; the butanols themselves have a wide range of uses, including plasticizer intermediates.

Other "lower" alcohols include the various amyl alcohols and their esters for use as flotation agents, pharmaceuticals, plasticizers, and as solvents for paints and lacquers. Amyl acetate notably is an extractant in penicillin production.

Higher alcohols (C_6 up, including "fatty alcohols") range through a variety of structures—straight and branched chain with the hydroxyl group primary, secondary, or tertiary. Many of the commercial products are mixtures. Principal major applications are for surface-active agents, synthetic detergents, and plasticizers for vinyl resins. All of these uses involve the alcohols as intermediates for further conversion.

Fatty alcohols are those derived from the natural fats and oils (and waxes), principally coconut oil and tallows, which are triglycerides. Coconut oil contains mainly C_{12} and C_{14} acids, and tallow contains mainly C_{16} and C_{18} acids. The esters may be hydrogenated directly to the corresponding alcohols and glycerin, or they may be converted to other esters prior to reduction. A typical process operates at 300°C and 200 atm utilizing cupric oxide and copper chromite catalysts (Section 20.8). Lauryl alcohol, one of the most important fatty alcohols, is used as a surfactant (as the sulfate) and as a plasticizer, e.g., in di-*n*-dodecyl phthalate.

These natural-source fatty alcohols compete with synthetic products produced by the oxo process from alkenes and by the polymerization of ethylene using Ziegler catalysts. In the Ziegler method (Section 25.4), ethylene and triethylaluminum (TEA) are allowed to react at 50–100 atm at temperatures below 130°C. The resulting long-chain alkylaluminums are oxidized with dry air to yield the aluminum alkoxides, which are hydrolyzed with concentrated sulfuric acid to afford straight-chain primary alcohols in the C_{12} to C_{18} range.

$$AlEt_3 \xrightarrow{nC_2H_4} Al[(C_2H_4)_nEt]_3 \xrightarrow{\frac{3}{2}O_2} Al[O(C_2H_4)_nEt]_3$$

$$\xrightarrow{H_2SO_4} HO(CH_2CH_2)_nC_2H_5 + Al_2(SO_4)_3$$

Alternatively, the intermediate trialkylaluminums can be heated in the presence of ethylene at elevated temperatures (300°C) under pressure. The higher alkyl side chains are displaced to give straight-chain "α-olefins" and TEA. These alkenes are also useful, but more costly, for conversion to biodegradable detergent intermediates by application of the oxo process to yield primary alcohols or by alkylation of benzene to yield "detergent alkylate."

Perhaps the most widely used higher alcohol is *2-ethyl-1-hexanol*, which is produced to the extent of over 200 million pounds annually. The alcohol is produced from propylene by an oxo process which has been modified to include an aldol dimerization (Section 19.14) of the intermediate product *n*-butyraldehyde. Reduction of the eight-carbon unsaturated aldehyde gives 2-ethyl-1-hexanol directly. A multiple aldol process involving acetaldehyde is also employed and some 20% of the U.S. acetaldehyde production is converted to this alcohol. The largest single use is for DOP, di(2-ethylhexyl) phthalate (dioctyl phthalate), a major vinyl resin plasticizer.

35.6   Aliphatic Aldehydes and Ketones

About 4.2 million pounds of *formaldehyde* (37% aqueous solution) was produced in 1969, largely from methanol by catalytic vapor-phase oxidation or dehydrogenation. A supported silver or copper catalyst is used at 400–600°C, although other metal oxides are claimed to be useful at lower temperatures. The two reactions are as follows:

$$CH_3OH + \tfrac{1}{2}O_2 \xrightarrow{Fe_2O_3, MoO_3} CH_2O + H_2O$$

$$CH_3OH \xrightarrow[635°C]{Ag} CH_2O + H_2$$

Approximately 15% of formaldehyde production is by the vapor-phase oxidation of propane or butane with air or oxygen, or by the liquid-phase oxidation of butane with a cobalt or manganese acetate catalyst. Mixtures which include carboxylic acids, alcohols, and ketones are obtained.

Acetaldehyde was originally produced by the hydration of acetylene in the liquid phase using a mercury salt catalyst (Section 15.16). At present most acetaldehyde is obtained from ethyl alcohol by oxidation or dehydrogenation (Section 18.7) in a manner similar to the preparation of formaldehyde. Air and ethanol are passed over a silver gauze catalyst at 450°C, and the heat of reaction supports a parallel endothermic dehydrogenation reaction. Dehydrogenation alone may be employed using metallic oxide-promoted copper catalysts at 250–300°C, generating hydrogen as a by-product. Recently, the direct oxidation of ethylene to acetaldehyde using a palladium catalyst has become important (Wacker process).

$$CH_2{=}CH_2 + PdCl_2 + H_2O \rightarrow CH_3\overset{\displaystyle O}{\overset{\|}{C}}{-}H + Pd + 2HCl$$

$$2CuCl_2 + Pd \rightarrow 2CuCl + PdCl_2$$

$$\tfrac{1}{2}O_2 + 2CuCl + 2HCl \rightarrow 2CuCl_2 + H_2O$$

$$\overline{CH_2{=}CH_2 + \tfrac{1}{2}O_2 \rightarrow CH_3\underset{\displaystyle O}{\underset{\|}{C}}{-}H} \qquad \text{[net overall reaction]}$$

Cuprous chloride promotes the oxidation of Pd back to $PdCl_2$.

Acetaldehyde production is about 1.5 billion pounds annually. Of this, over 40% is converted to acetic acid and acetic anhydride, 20% goes to 1-butanol by the aldol process, and 20% is converted via the aldol process to 2-ethyl-1-hexanol. The balance is converted to vinyl acetate, peracetic acid, pentaerythritol, chloral, 1,3-butylene glycol, and other products.

Acrolein is prepared by the oxidation of propylene over a supported copper oxide catalyst in the presence of steam at 350°C. As described later, acrolein is used in glycerin processes and can be oxidized to acrylic acid.

$$O_2 + H_2C{=}CH{-}CH_3 \xrightarrow[325°C]{Cu_2O} H_2C{=}CH{-}\overset{\overset{\displaystyle O}{\|}}{C}{-}H + H_2O$$

Acetone is a product of major industrial importance. U.S. production in 1969 was 1.4 billion pounds. The important uses of acetone are for conversion to methyl isobutyl ketone, methylisobutylcarbinol, methyl methacrylate, and Bisphenol A. Solvent applications include paints, lacquers, and cellulose acetate. Acetone is largely produced by the vapor-phase catalytic dehydrogenation of 2-propanol (Section 18.7). Various catalysts are claimed, including copper, Raney nickel, and zinc oxide, at temperatures ranging from 150° to 500°C. Oxidation with air or oxygen is also feasible, incorporating a combination of oxidation and dehydrogenation over a silver or copper catalyst, but without the production of hydrogen. By-product acetone arises from the cumene process for phenol (Section 23.1) and the new Shell glycerin process, and acetone is a co-product from the oxidation of propane/butane mixtures.

An example of an integrated multiproduct operation is the production of *methyl isobutyl ketone*, of which 175 million pounds is used annually as a solvent for paints and lacquers. Acetone may be dimerized with soda lime in the cold to diacetone alcohol, which is dehydrated with sulfuric acid to mesityl oxide (Section 19.14). Hydrogenation with Raney nickel catalyst gives the ketone. Further hydrogenation yields methylisobutylcarbinol, and hydrogenation of diacetone alcohol will yield hexylene glycol, 2-methyl-2,4-pentanediol.

Hydrogen for the operation can be made available from a parallel dehydrogenation of isopropanol to produce the starting acetone.

Methyl ethyl ketone is prepared by dehydrogenation of *sec*-butyl alcohol over zinc oxide or brass catalyst at 350–400°C in a manner similar to the 2-propanol dehydrogenation. About 70% of the 300,000 pounds produced annually is used as solvent for surface coating and lacquers in competition with ethyl acetate.

Cyclohexanone, both an excellent solvent and a key caprolactam intermediate, is produced by the catalytic (nickel) hydrogenation of phenol to yield cyclohexanol (Section 16.10) which is then dehydrogenated in the vapor phase over a zinc-iron catalyst.

35.7 Aliphatic Acids and Anhydrides

Acetic acid production in the United States is estimated at 1.5 billion pounds annually, largely by processes involving the oxidation of acetaldehyde (Section 19.16). The production of *acetic anhydride*, most of which is used for cellulose acetate, was quoted at 1.75

billion pounds in 1969. Over 40% of acetic acid goes into cellulose acetate and acetic anhydride, about 30% goes into vinyl acetate, 10% or so goes into other esters, and 5% is converted to monochloroacetic acid.

The complex interrelationships of raw materials in industry are illustrated by the facts that over 40% of the ethanol produced is converted into acetaldehyde and that 40% of the acetaldehyde (from all sources) is converted to acetic acid and acetic anhydride. Acetaldehyde may be oxidized with air or oxygen in the liquid phase with cobalt or manganous acetate at moderate temperature and pressure. Acetic anhydride is a co-product by the following reaction from the peracetic acid intermediate under anhydrous conditions.

$$CH_3CO_3H + CH_3CHO \rightarrow (CH_3\overset{\overset{\displaystyle O}{\|}}{C})_2O + H_2O$$

The liquid-phase oxidation of butane with air or oxygen and a cobalt or manganese catalyst yields acetic acid as the major product, together with other oxygenated by-products. The product distribution depends upon the temperature (150–200°C), the pressure (50–75 atm), and perhaps the reaction solvents employed. A petroleum feed-stock of paraffins (C_4–C_8) can also be used to obtain acetic acid, together with formic acid and other products.

Carbonylation of methanol is catalyzed by cobalt octacarbonyl, and this provides another commercial reaction for the preparation of acetic acid.

$$CH_3OH + CO \xrightarrow[\text{210°C, 7500 psig}]{[Co(CO)_4]_2} CH_3\overset{\overset{\displaystyle O}{\|}}{C}-OH$$

An interesting new liquid-phase catalytic process uses 1-butene and acetic acid (recycled) to form sec-butyl acetate, which is oxidized and cracked with air at 50–60 atm and 200°C to yield 3 moles of acetic acid.

$$C_2H_5CH=CH_2 \xrightarrow{HOAc} \underset{\underset{\displaystyle OAc}{|}}{C_2H_5CHCH_3} \xrightarrow[\text{Heat}]{O_2} 3\ CH_3CO_2H$$

Early commercial acetic anhydride methods are those still used in the laboratory today for anhydrides, for example, heating the sodium salt of acetic acid with phosphorus oxychloride or thionyl chloride, and variations thereof. One major process now in use in the United States has been discussed, namely, the oxidation of acetaldehyde to yield both the acid and the anhydride. In another process, acetic acid is pyrolyzed at 700°C in the presence of triethyl phosphate to yield ketene. The ketene is then reacted with acetic acid to yield the anhydride (Section 20.5). Acetone may also be pyrolyzed at 650–700°C to yield ketene and methane.

$$CH_3CO_2H \xrightarrow{-H_2O} CH_2=C=O \xrightarrow{HOAc} (CH_3\overset{\overset{\displaystyle O}{\|}}{C})_2O$$

Acetylene and acetic acid react in the presence of a mercury catalyst to yield ethylidene diacetate in a manner similar to the production of vinyl acetate (Section 15.16). Distillation in the presence of zinc chloride or sodium pyrophosphate yields both acetic anhydride and acetaldehyde.

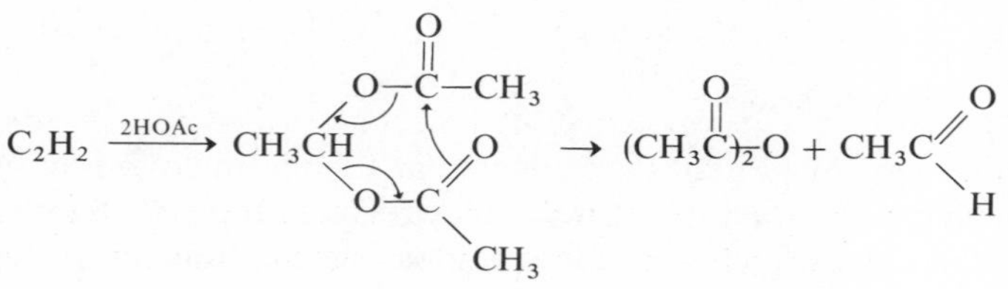

$$C_2H_2 \xrightarrow{2HOAc} CH_3\overset{\overset{\displaystyle O-\overset{\overset{\displaystyle O}{\|}}{C}-CH_3}{}}{\underset{\underset{\displaystyle O-\overset{}{C}\diagdown CH_3}{}}{CH}} \rightarrow (CH_3\overset{\overset{\displaystyle O}{\|}}{C})_2O + CH_3\overset{\diagup O}{\underset{\diagdown H}{C}}$$

Vinyl acetate may be regarded as a derivative of acetic acid. Traditionally vinyl acetate has been prepared by addition of acetic acid to acetylene in the vapor phase at 200°C over a zinc or cadmium acetate catalyst (Section 15.16). An ethylene-based technology has appeared recently to challenge the production of vinyl acetate from acetylene. For example, in a process similar to the Wacker acetaldehyde process described earlier (palladium catalyst), acetic acid replaces water. Some sodium acetate is also required.

Polyvinyl acetate may be hydrolyzed to *polyvinyl alcohol*, which competes with starch as a textile size. Treatment of polyvinyl alcohol with butyraldehyde yields *polyvinylbutyrol*, which is used as an inner layer in safety glass.

Formic acid is prepared from carbon monoxide and caustic soda.

$$CO + NaOH \rightarrow HCO_2Na \xrightarrow{H_2SO_4} HCO_2H$$

Propionic acid is prepared by either the oxidation of propionaldehyde or by a modification of the oxo process with ethylene. In the latter reaction water replaces the hydrogen, for example, and a hydrolytic cleavage of the transition metal carbonyl occurs instead of a reductive cleavage (which would give aldehyde).

35.8 Alkene Oxides and Glycols

In 1969, 3.2 billion pounds of ethylene oxide and 1.1 billion pounds of propylene oxide were produced. These versatile intermediates are obtained from the parent alkenes, and they yield a variety of important chemical products.

Early production of both of these alkene oxides was based on the well-known chlorohydrin process, that is, the Markovnikov addition of HOCl to alkenes (Section 15.5), illustrated for propylene as follows:

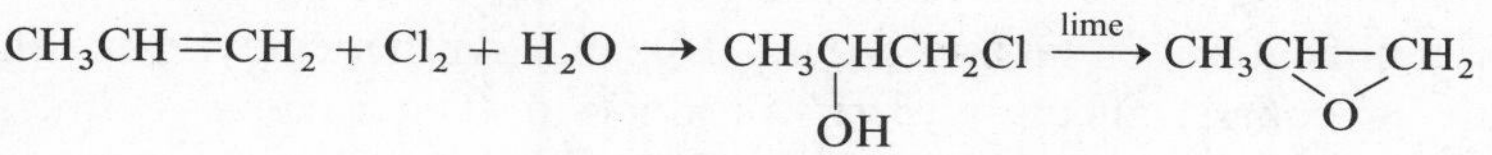

$$CH_3CH{=}CH_2 + Cl_2 + H_2O \rightarrow CH_3\underset{\underset{OH}{|}}{CH}CH_2Cl \xrightarrow{lime} CH_3CH{-}CH_2$$
$$\underset{O}{\diagdown\diagup}$$

Direct oxidation processes for *ethylene oxide* were developed after extensive research and they now replace the older process.

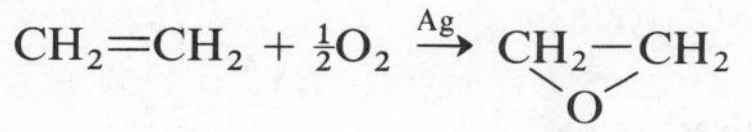

$$CH_2{=}CH_2 + \tfrac{1}{2}O_2 \xrightarrow{Ag} CH_2{-}CH_2$$
$$\underset{O}{\diagdown\diagup}$$

The procedure uses either air or oxygen and a silver catalyst, usually silver gauze. The temperature range is 200–300°C and the pressure is varied from 1 to 30 atm. Close control is required to avoid overoxidation to carbon dioxide. Perhaps 60% of the ethylene oxide is converted to ethylene glycol (antifreeze) and 10% goes for nonionic surfactants. The remaining 30% is used for glycol ethers, polyglycols, and ethanolamines, prepared as illustrated by the following generalized equations (see Section 18.9):

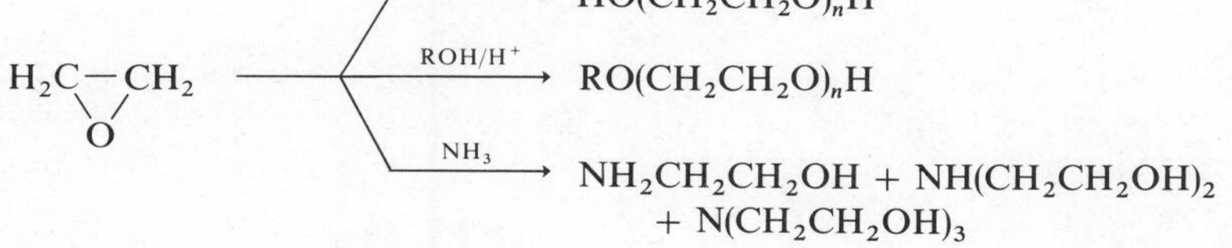

$$H_2C{-}CH_2 \quad\begin{cases} \xrightarrow{H_2O/H^+} & HO(CH_2CH_2O)_nH \\ \xrightarrow{ROH/H^+} & RO(CH_2CH_2O)_nH \\ \xrightarrow{NH_3} & NH_2CH_2CH_2OH + NH(CH_2CH_2OH)_2 \\ & \quad + N(CH_2CH_2OH)_3 \end{cases}$$

With excess water or alcohol, $n = 1$ in the two top equations. The value of n is highly dependent on the proportion of ethylene oxide and ROH employed.

The ethanolamines, for example, were produced to the extent of 258 million pounds in 1969.

Propylene oxide was prepared largely by the chlorohydrin process as illustrated above, inasmuch as direct oxidation methods did not prove feasible. Indirect processes have appeared which utilize hydrocarbon peroxides as intermediates. The hydroperoxides, such as that from isobutane (*t*-butyl hydroperoxide), for example, oxidize propylene to propylene oxide and yield *t*-butyl alcohol or the dehydration product, isobutylene, as a co-product.

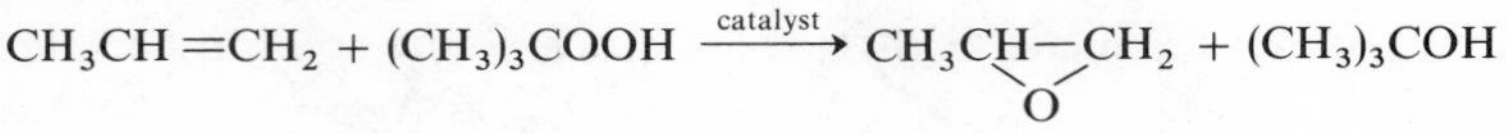
$CH_3CH=CH_2$ + $(CH_3)_3COOH$
catalyst
$CH_3CH—CH_2$
O
+ $(CH_3)_3COH$

Peracetic acid, generated *in situ* can be employed (Section 15.10). Treatment of a mixture of acetaldehyde and propylene in the liquid phase with air (oxygen) and a cobalt catalyst will generate propylene oxide with acetic acid as a co-product.

The chemical reactions of propylene oxide are similar to those of ethylene oxide (see Section 18.9). About 30% is converted to propylene glycol for polyester fibers, diester vinyl plasticizers, brake fluids, and for use in cellophane and as a humectant. Forty percent of the propylene oxide is reacted with polyhydric alcohols (mainly) to yield polypropoxy ethers (polyols) of high molecular weight, 15% goes to polypropylene glycols, perhaps 5% to dipropylene glycol, and the balance to other derivatives.

35.9 Other Polyhydric Alcohols

Glycerin and the alkene oxide-derived diols are the most important polyhydric alcohols. Glycerin is a versatile compound which goes into literally hundreds of products as a humectant in the food, tobacco, cosmetic, and drug industries. It is also used as a lubricant, plasticizer, thickening agent, and as a component of alkyl resins (glyptals).

The trinitrate ester of glycerin is the explosive nitroglycerin. Because it is extremely sensitive to shock, nitroglycerin is diluted with siliceous earth or sawdust to produce the powerful, high explosive dynamite.

Over the years glycerin production has been fairly evenly divided between natural glycerin (from the saponification of fats, Section 20.6) and synthetic glycerin. The declining use of soap, of course, affects glycerin production. The various synthetic processes developed over the years are summarized in Scheme 35.1; all of the steps are based on standard reactions.

Scheme 35.1
Synthetic Production of Glycerin

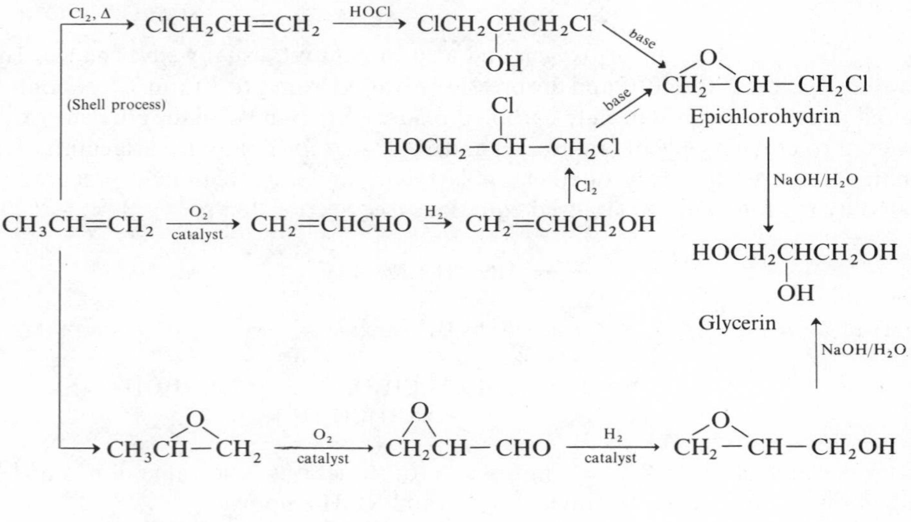
Cl_2, Δ
$ClCH_2CH=CH_2$
HOCl
$ClCH_2CHCH_2Cl$
OH
base
(Shell process)
Cl
$HOCH_2—CH—CH_2Cl$
base
$CH_2—CH—CH_2Cl$
Epichlorohydrin
Cl_2
NaOH/H_2O
$CH_3CH=CH_2$
O_2
catalyst
$CH_2=CHCHO$
H_2
$CH_2=CHCH_2OH$
$HOCH_2CHCH_2OH$
OH
Glycerin
NaOH/H_2O
$CH_3CH—CH_2$
O_2
catalyst
$CH_2CH—CHO$
H_2
catalyst
$CH_2—CH—CH_2OH$

Epichlorohydrin is a useful intermediate, which can be isolated from glycerin synthesis. Epichlorohydrin (in excess) and bisphenol are condensed in the presence of alkali to yield a linear polymer used for adhesives and surface coatings (Section 25.3).

Pentaerythritol is an important polyol used in resins, plastics, and drying oils. Over 90 million pounds was produced in 1969. It is prepared by a base-catalyzed aldol process with acetaldehyde and aqueous formaldehyde (Section 19.14). The tetranitrate (PETN) is an explosive.

35.10   Acrylonitrile and the Acrylates

Acrylonitrile, about 1.2 billion pounds in 1969, is consumed in the production of synthetic fibers (Orlon, Acrilan) (60%), ABS and SAN resins (20%), and nitrile rubber (10%).

In the early production process (Union Carbide) ethylene oxide was condensed with hydrogen cyanide to form the β-hydroxynitrile, which was dehydrated to acrylonitrile.

$$CH_2\!\!-\!\!CH_2 \xrightarrow{\text{HCN}} HOCH_2CH_2CN \xrightarrow{\text{catalyst}} CH_2\!\!=\!\!CHCN + H_2O$$
$$\underset{O}{\diagdown\diagup}$$

Acrylonitrile may be produced in one step by the cuprous chloride-catalyzed addition of hydrogen cyanide to acetylene. A third process (du Pont) uses propylene and nitric oxide which are reacted in the vapor phase at 700°C over a silver catalyst.

$$4\,CH_3CH\!\!=\!\!CH_2 \xrightarrow[\text{catalyst}]{\text{6NO}} 4\,CH_2\!\!=\!\!CHCN + 6\,H_2O + N_2$$

A current important process (Sohio) is the vapor-phase ammoxidation of propylene over a suitable catalyst:

$$CH_3CH\!\!=\!\!CH_2 + NH_3 + \tfrac{3}{2}O_2 \rightarrow CH_2\!\!=\!\!CH\!\!-\!\!CN + 3H_2O$$

Acrylic acid is prepared from propylene by successive oxidation to acrolein (as described) and then to the acid. A process based on acetylene is also used; it involves reacting carbon monoxide, water, and a nickel bromide catalyst under high pressure in THF solvent.

$$HC\!\!\equiv\!\!CH + CO + H_2O \xrightarrow{\text{NiBr}} H_2C\!\!=\!\!CH\!\!-\!\!CO_2H$$

Hydrolysis of ethylene cyanohydrin is another route and methanolysis will yield methyl acrylate directly.

$$HOCH_2CH_2CN + CH_3OH \xrightarrow{\text{H}_2\text{SO}_4} H_2C\!\!=\!\!CHCO_2CH_3$$

The concentrated sulfuric both causes the elimination of water and catalyzes the esterification reaction.

Ketene (from acetone cracking) and formaldehyde in the presence of zinc chloride or aluminum chloride give the highly versatile β-propiolactone. The base-catalyzed addition of methanol in the cold yields methyl hydracrylate which is dehydrated to methyl acrylate.

$$H_2C\!\!=\!\!C\!\!=\!\!O \xrightarrow[\text{ZnCl}_2]{\text{H}_2\text{CO}} \underset{\underset{O\!-\!\!-\!\!C=O}{|\qquad|}}{CH_2\!-\!CH_2} \xrightarrow{\text{CH}_3\text{OH}} HOCH_2CH_2CO_2CH_3$$

$$\xrightarrow{\text{catalyst}} H_2C\!\!=\!\!CH\!\!-\!\!CO_2CH_3 + H_2O$$

See Section 25.3, which describes acrylic polymers.

35.11   Amines and Miscellaneous Chemicals

Among the acyclic amines, in addition to the ethanolamines, the three *methylamines* are the most important. Production in 1969 was close to 110 million pounds. About 50% of monomethylamine went into the α-naphthol-derived carbamate insecticide, Carbaryl (Sevin), and 28% into surfactants. The major use for dimethylamine was for dimethylformamide (DMF) and dimethylacetamide, and most of the trimethylamine went into choline chloride, a major animal and poultry feed additive. The methylamines are produced from methanol and ammonia, which can be made to condense over an alumina catalyst at 450°C and 200 psig:

$$CH_3OH + NH_3 \xrightarrow[450°C, \, 200 \text{ psig}]{Al_2O_3} CH_3NH_2 + (CH_3)_2NH + (CH_3)_3N$$

Other acyclic amines of commercial interest include diethylamine, *n*-butylamine, hydrogenated tallow oil amine, coconut oil amine, and hexadecylamines.

Pyridine is derived both from coal-tar sources and by synthetic processes. About 2% of the U.S. acetaldehyde production is reported to go into synthetic pyridine, probably by ammonolysis of acetaldehyde/formaldehyde mixtures. Tetrahydrofurfuryl alcohol and ammonia over a molybdenum-alumina catalyst at 500°C will yield pyridine, in another example of a vapor-phase ammonolysis reaction.

Urea is a high tonnage chemical. Major uses are for fertilizers and the low-cost urea-formaldehyde thermosetting resins. Urea is produced from carbon dioxide and ammonia at elevated temperature and pressure, and also by the partial hydrolysis of cyanamide.

Only a few ethers are produced in large quantities commercially. *Diethyl ether*, the most important, is prepared by the action of concentrated sulfuric acid on ethanol at about 140° (Section 18.6). Cyclic ethers have some importance as solvents or intermediates. *Dioxane* is produced by acid-catalyzed dimerization of ethylene oxide (Section 18.6).

Tetrahydrofuran (THF) is made from farm wastes. These are first converted to furfuraldehyde and then decarbonylation is carried out over zinc chromite catalyst to give furan (Section 28.2), which in turn is hydrogenated to THF. Furfuraldehyde is useful as a resin component, while furan and THF are used mainly as solvents. Acid-catalyzed hydration of THF gives 1,4-butanediol.

35.12   Use Patterns of Major Aromatic Raw Materials

The consumption of benzene in the United States was about 1.2 billion gallons in 1969, with less than 10% of this from coal. Its estimated major uses are for the preparation of ethylbenzene (for styrene), 40%; cyclohexane (nylon intermediate), 30%; and phenol, 20%. The balance is distributed among detergent alkylates, aniline, maleic anhydride,

DDT, and other products. It may be noted that benzene is the aromatic in highest demand, although it is the minor component (10 % or so) from catalytic reforming.

Toluene production has increased severalfold in the past decade. In 1969, close to 800 million gallons were produced in the United States. In 1970, the U.S. production was approximately 850 million gallons, about 2 % coming from coal. Half of the total toluene production is hydrodealkylated to benzene to satisfy the demand for the latter. About half of the balance of 425 million gallons is used in auto gasoline and aviation fuel, with future changes forecast as leaded fuels decline. The chemical use pattern for the remaining 200 million gallons or so is distributed among solvents (30 %), toluene isocyanates (10 %), TNT (10 %), phenol, sulfonates, benzoic acid, aspirin, and exports.

Xylene production in 1969 was 450 million gallons, and it will soon be of the order of 550 million gallons, with very little (about 1 %) derived from coal. The complex processes of obtaining the individual isomers will not be discussed here. The C-8 stream from catalytic refining contains roughly 40 % *m*-xylene and 20 % each of the ortho and para isomers, as well as ethylbenzene; but new processes will affect these ratios. New uses are sought for the meta isomer, and isophthalic acid production is growing. *o*-Xylene (0.85 billion pounds in 1969) serves as an alternative source (with naphthalene) for phthalic anhydride, and *p*-xylene (1.6 billion pounds in 1969) goes to terephthalic acid for polyester fibers (Dacron, Terylene). Ethylbenzene is dehydrogenated to styrene, and the petroleum-reforming source supplements the synthetic product obtained by the alkylation of benzene with ethylene.

Naphthalene production in 1969 was about 700 million pounds from both coal and petroleum; about 75 % of it is oxidized to phthalic anhydride.

In addition, 215 million pounds of *cresylics* may be mentioned; the synthetic products exceed those from coal tar. The term includes the three cresol isomers and cresolic acid, which is primarily ortho but contains both meta and para isomers. These products are used for phenolic resins and phosphate esters, for example, tricresyl phosphate plasticizers and hydraulic fluids.

35.13 Products Derived from Benzene

Styrene is one of the largest volume products of the petroleum industry—4.6 billion pounds in 1969. The monomer is used for polystyrene (Section 25.3). Other major uses are styrene-butadiene elastomers and resins, rubber-modified styrene, and ABS resins (acrylonitrile-butadiene-styrene).

Most processes for the production of styrene are based on the alkylation of benzene with ethylene in the liquid phase using aluminum chloride at 90°C and at moderate pressure (Section 16.5).

$$C_6H_6 + C_2H_4 \xrightarrow{\text{AlCl}_3} C_6H_5CH_2CH_3 \xrightarrow[\text{catalyst}]{600°C} C_6H_5CH{=}CH_2 + H_2$$

Excess benzene is used to avoid polyalkylation. A vapor-phase process over a phosphoric acid or silica-alumina catalyst at higher temperature and pressure is also claimed. Ethylbenzene is dehydrogenated to styrene at 600°C or higher, in the presence of steam over metallic oxide catalysts. The reaction mixture is purified by distillation at reduced pressure in the presence of polymerization inhibitors.

Cyclohexane is produced in large quantity (2.2 billion pounds in 1969) by the hydrogenation of benzene (Section 16.10). It mainly winds up in nylon 6,6 production. Oxidation by air or oxygen yields a mixture of cyclohexanone and cyclohexanol, and these are oxidized further to adipic acid.

Current technology appears to favor a two-stage air oxidation of cyclohexane to adipic acid. Cyclohexane is first oxidized with air using a conventional cobalt acetate catalyst. In the second stage, acetic acid serves as solvent, with a copper or manganese catalyst. Cyclohexanol and cyclohexanone mixtures are intermediates, and the second stage replaces the older nitric acid oxidation step. Hexamethylenediamine, the second component for nylon 6,6 (Section 25.2), may be prepared from adipic acid. The equations are as follows:

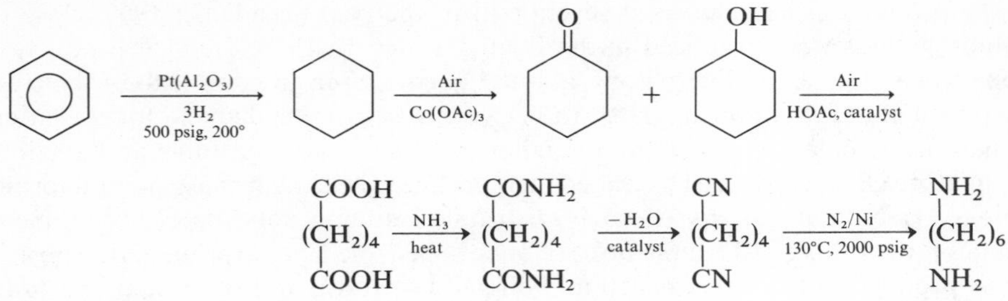

Caprolactam is a related polymer intermediate (Section 22.3) which can be prepared from cyclohexane by oxidation to cyclohexanone and cyclohexanol and then conversion to the oxime with hydroxylamine sulfate. Many producers utilize phenol to obtain cyclohexanol, which is dehydrogenated to the ketone over a zinc-iron catalyst at 450°C. Cyclohexanone oxime can be made to undergo a Beckmann rearrangement with a sulfuric acid catalyst to give the seven-membered cyclic amide, caprolactam (see Section 22.3). This cyclic amide can be polymerized to give the textile fiber nylon 6, which is produced in about one-fourth the quantity of nylon 6,6 in the United States. The sulfuric acid (oleum) is neutralized with ammonia to yield up to 5 pounds of ammonium sulfate (fertilizer) per pound of caprolactam. To avoid this, a Japanese process treats cyclohexane with nitrosyl chloride and hydrogen chloride photochemically to obtain the oxime. While sulfuric acid (oleum) is required still for the rearrangement to caprolactam, the amount is reduced by about 50% and the hydrogen chloride is recycled.

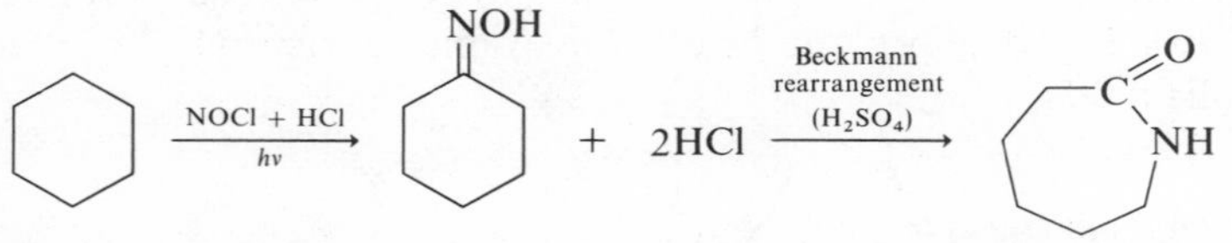

ε-Caprolactam

Another process (Union Carbide) for caprolactam is based on the oxidation of cyclohexanone with peracetic acid to yield caprolactone (Baeyer–Villiger reaction, Section 19.16). Treatment of the lactone with ammonia and water at 300–400°C and 300–400 atm yields the lactam.

Phenol is the third major chemical produced from benzene. The traditional methods involving caustic fusion of sodium benzenesulfonate and the hydrolysis of chlorobenzene (page 464) are being replaced by newer methods. In addition to the benzoic acid route, a process which starts with toluene, the most economical route is reputed to be via cumene hydroperoxide. Benzene is alkylated with propylene to yield cumene, which is oxidized with air to the hydroperoxide. The latter is decomposed with acid catalysis to yield phenol and by-product acetone (detailed in Section 23.1).

The approximate distribution of the 1.7 billion pounds of phenol produced in 1969 was phenolic resins, 50%, caprolactam, 20%; and Bisphenol A, 10%; the remainder went into adipic acid, 2,4-D, surface-active agents (nonylphenol), other alkylphenols, *p*-nitrophenol for the malathion insecticides, and other uses.

Benzene can be oxidized in the presence of vanadium pentoxide at 400°C to give *maleic anhydride*. Hydrogenation of maleic acid disodium salt over Raney nickel catalyst gives *succinic acid* as the salt.

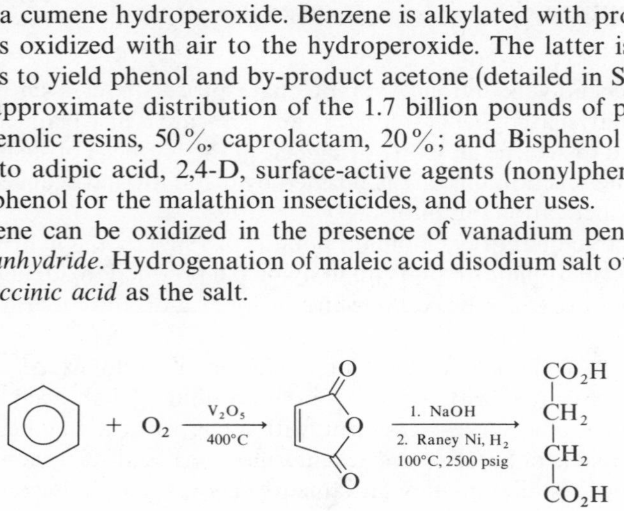

Maleic anhydride is easily the more important of the two products. Two hundred million pounds were produced in 1969, primarily for use in polyester resins to provide unsaturation for cross-linking. Succinic acid can be dehydrated to the cyclic succinic anhydride. Fumaric acid, which does not form a cyclic anhydride, is prepared from maleic anhydride to the extent of 500 million pounds annually. About 35% is used as food acidulant, 25% for hard resins, and the balance for paper size resins, surface coatings and plasticizers.

Chlorobenzene, 610 million pounds in 1969, is used for the preparation of DDT, phenol, aniline, and other derivatives. Chlorination of excess benzene at 40°C in the presence of iron yields predominantly monochlorobenzene (Section 16.2). At 40–60°, with complete utilization of the benzene, 10–20% of a mixture of *o*- and *p*-dichlorobenzenes is formed.

Aniline is a chemical old in the art; production in 1969 was 331 million pounds. It is used for rubber chemicals, dyes, isocyanates, and for various other products. Aniline may be produced by the reduction of nitrobenzene with iron and hydrochloric acid, or by catalytic hydrogenation (Section 22.1).

Another process is based on chlorobenzene and ammonia with a cuprous oxide catalyst. Cuprous chloride is the active catalyst and is formed from the reaction of the oxide with the ammonium chloride.

$$C_6H_5Cl \xrightarrow[Cu_2O]{2NH_3(aq.)} C_6H_5NH_2 + NH_4Cl$$

N,N-Dimethylaniline, an important dye intermediate, is prepared from aniline, methanol, and concentrated sulfuric acid at 230°C under pressure. Acetanilide, an analgesic and antipyretic, is another important derivative of aniline. These two derivatives account for 15–20 million pounds of aniline annually.

35.14 Products Derived from Toluene

Much of the toluene produced in the United States is converted to benzene, and the largest other use is as a solvent for synthetic resins, surface coatings, adhesives, and related items. As a chemical intermediate, the major traditional use, still important, is for the high explosive, TNT. Toluene is treated with a mixture of sulfuric acid and nitric acid, usually in three steps, to produce successively the mono, di, and finally 2,4,6-trinitrotoluene. The activating effect of the methyl group makes the process practical.

Toluene production has been stimulated by the rapid growth in importance of urethane polymers (Section 25.2). The most important commercial diisocyanate is toluene diisocyanate (TDI), prepared from 2,4-dinitrotoluene which has been reduced to the diamine. Treatment with phosgene generates the dicarbonyl chloride which is treated with hot air at 115°C to form the diisocyanate and liberate hydrogen chloride (Section 21.1).

The phosgene is prepared by the addition of chlorine to carbon monoxide at 200–250° in a carbon bed. Seventy percent of the annual production of 350 million pounds of phosgene goes into isocyanates; the rest goes into herbicides (carbamates) (15%), carbonyl insecticides (10%), and polycarbonates (5%).

Toluene was, and still is, chlorinated in stages to benzyl chloride, benzal chloride, and benzotrichloride. These can be hydrolyzed to benzyl alcohol, benzaldehyde, and benzoic acid, respectively. More than 80 million pounds of benzyl chloride was produced in 1969, with 60% going to benzyl phthalate plasticizers for vinyl floor tile. Eight million pounds of benzyl alcohol was manufactured; one increasing use is as a solvent-assist agent for nylon textile dyeing.

The liquid-phase air oxidation of toluene to benzoic acid takes place at 150–175°C and uses cobalt and manganese naphthenates as catalysts. The crude benzoic acid containing various impurities may be reacted with benzotrichloride in the presence of zinc chloride or other catalysts to form benzoyl chloride, which can be purified by distillation.

Benzoic acid itself can be purified by distillation and crystallization, and the direct purification of the crude acid from air oxidation is becoming more important.

Benzaldehyde free of chlorine is best obtained by vapor-phase, catalytic air oxidation of toluene, rather than from the hydrolysis of benzal chloride.

Benzoyl chloride is used for the preparation of benzoate esters of various polyols and benzoyl peroxide.

35.15   Products Derived from the Xylenes and Naphthalene

o-Xylene, separable by distillation from the mixed xylenes, is converted almost exclusively to phthalic anhydride and accounts for about 25% of the output of the latter. The oxidation process takes place at 550°C over vanadium pentoxide in a fixed-bed reactor. Naphthalene, the traditional raw material (75%), reacts in a similar process but either a fluid-bed or fixed-bed reaction can be employed (Section 16.9).

m-Xylene, unfortunately the predominant equilibrium isomer in catalytic reforming, has had a slow use development. Separation of m-xylene from the xylenes and ethylbenzene mixture is difficult, and techniques for this have included selective sulfonation (Chevron), clathrate formation, and possibly combined fractionation and crystallization. Oxidation to isophthalic acid presumably uses sulfur and ammonium polysulfide to yield the diamide. About 75 million pounds are produced annually, primarily for unsaturated polyester resins and alkyl resins.

p-Xylene, separated from mixed xylenes by a freezing/crystallization technique, is converted to terephthalic acid for the production of polyester fibers such as Dacron and Terylene (Section 25.2). The production of terephthalic acid involved much research and development. A two-step operation utilizes conventional air oxidation of p-xylene to form p-toluic acid, which is esterified and oxidized to the half-ester. A more recent one-step air-oxidation process uses acetic acid as solvent with a modified (bromine) cobalt salt catalyst at 200°C.

Two alternative processes for terephthalic acid are based on benzoic acid and on toluene. In the Raecke process, used abroad, 2 moles of potassium benzoate are heated to 400°C under carbon dioxide, and disproportionation to potassium terephthalate and benzene occurs. In the second process, toluene is chloromethylated and hydrolyzed to *p*-methylbenzyl alcohol, which is more amenable to oxidation than is *p*-xylene.

35.16 Plastics and Resins, Rubbers, and Fibers

Inasmuch as plastics and resins, rubbers, and fibers, all broadly classified as synthetic polymers, consume a quarter or more of the industrial organic chemicals, a separate chapter (Chapter 25) is devoted to such products. A few remarks are appropriate at this point, however.

The U.S. Department of Commerce places the value of shipments of plastic materials and resins in 1969 at $4.1 billion for 17.2 billion pounds. A $6 billion industry is predicted by 1975. The Tariff Commission reports that in the same year 5.7 billion pounds of rubbers were consumed, of which about 75% were synthetic. Synthetic rubber shipments in 1969 were valued at $1.2 billion, two-thirds of which go to tires and tire products. Synthetic fibers, for example, man-made noncellulosics, were valued at $2.6 billion in 1969; the cellulosics (rayon and acetate) were valued at $750 million, as estimated from data through 1967.

Production figures for selected polymer intermediates are equally impressive. Following is a list of monomers in billions of pounds annually for 1969, with the percentage application to polymers, where known, indicated: phthalic anhydride, 7.7; ethylene, 12 (40%); styrene, 4.6; butadiene, 3.1; vinyl chloride, 3.7; propylene, 8 (15%); acrylonitrile, 1.2; vinyl acetate, 1.7; phenol, 1.7 (50% to phenolics).

The relative importance of plastic and resins as end products of larger tonnage chemicals may be gauged from the September 1969 U.S. monthly production figures (U.S. Tariff Commission). Polyethylene (density below 0.94) was first, followed by polyvinyl chloride and styrene resins, all in excess of 200,000 pounds. Following in order were high-density polyethylene, polypropylene, phenolic resins, urea and melamine resins, polyester resins, ABS and SAN resins, alkyd resins, polyvinyl acetate, coumarone-indene and petroleum resins, and epoxy resins (13,000 pounds). The alkyd, phenolic, polyester, urea and melamine, and epoxy resins are classified as thermosetting; the others are thermoplastic resins.

About 25% of the 5.7 billion pounds of rubber was natural rubber; 50% was SBR (styrene-butadiene rubber); 10%, polybutadiene; and nearly 10%, neoprene. Rubbers produced in lesser amounts included *cis*-polyisoprene (3%), ethylene-propylene rubber (EPDM), silicone rubber, nitrile rubber (acrylonitrile-butadiene copolymer), urethane rubbers, polysulfide elastomers, Hypalon (chlorosulfonated polyethylene), and several others. SBR is the workhorse of the rubber industry, and about two-thirds goes into tires. A 20% growth for all rubbers in the next 5 years is forecast.

Rubber chemicals include accelerators, activators, vulcanization agents, antioxidants, antiozonants, stabilizers, blowing agents, and various other processing agents for natural and synthetic rubbers. These total some 280 million pounds annually. The Tariff Commission includes the vulcanizing agents, tetramethylthiuram disulfides (methyl tuads), as a key index of activity in the area; some 11 million pounds were produced in 1969.

Synthetic fibers are classified as man-made noncellulosics. U.S. production for 1969 is estimated at 2.5 billion pounds. The value of shipments is estimated at $2.6 billion. Nylon is still the largest at perhaps 45% of the total, followed by the polyesters (30%) such as Dacron and Terylene, and the acrylics (20%) such as Orlon and Acrilan. Major uses are for carpets, rugs, tire cord, and tire cord fabric. The other category of man-made fibers is the cellulosics, of which the most important is rayon (69%). The cellulosics have an estimated value of $750 million annually. In 1967 domestic consumption of man-made fibers passed that of the natural products cotton and wool. The trend continued to an estimated 57/43 ratio in 1969.

Rayon is an established designation for cellulosic fibers. Much of the rayon is cellulose regenerated by various processes, such as viscose rayon, prepared from chemical cotton.

Cellulose triacetate, as a fiber, is also a rayon and is called acetate rayon or acetate. Cellulose acetate is also used in plastics and films and for cigarette filters. Other forms of man-made cellulosics include cellulose acetate butyrate, cellulose propionate, and cellulose nitrate, the oldest. The latter is used in lacquers, flexible coatings for paper, foil, plastic films, and in printing inks. Other forms of cellulose include methyl and ethylcellulose, hydroxyethylcellulose (a latex paint thickener), and carboxymethyl-cellulose, variously used in detergents and as a thickening agent for drilling muds.

The textile mill industry generates some $21 billion in consumer products (fabrics) in the processing of various natural and synthetic fibers and blends of both.

35.17   Drugs and Pharmaceuticals

Consideration of a few highlights of this important industry is instructive. According to the Department of Commerce, industry shipments were valued at $6.1 billion in 1969, double that of 1960. Rising income dollars and increased health care were major growth factors.

Over 50% of the industry sales are in ethical drugs, which are dispensed by the health professions. *Brand name* drugs are proprietary items resulting from research by the pharmaceutical firm, and *generic drugs* are those dispensed under their common name.

The U.S. Tariff Commission lists the production of medicinal chemicals. Recent figures are not available, except for the key index chemicals, as follows (millions of pounds, 1969): aspirin, 38; choline chloride, 42; ascorbic acid, 7.4; and niacin and niacinamide, 29. Penicillin salts are listed as 2.9 million of billion international units (BIU) in 1969 vs. 0.43 million BIU 10 years ago; the 1969 figure corresponds to roughly 4 million pounds of penicillin and its salts.

The major tariff classifications in bulk medicinals are (a) cyclic/benzoid, (b) alicyclic and heterocyclic, and (c) acyclic. Products under (a) include, in part, aspirin, salicylic acid, sulfa drugs, phenylephrine hydrochloride, and p-aminobenzoic acid and derivatives (procaine hydrochloride). Category (b) accounts for over 88% of the dollar value and includes antibiotics as the most important (60%), followed by vitamins (except ascorbic and pantothenic acid), hormones (acyclic), barbiturates, tranquilizers, and many others. Products under (c) include choline chloride, ascorbic and pantothenic acid, certain tranquilizers, and amino acids. Ascorbic acid is by far the most important vitamin both in production and in sales. The synthetic product sells for about $3.50/kilogram.

Some bulk medicinals are isolated from natural sources, and in some cases the primary drugs are then modified chemically to produce analogs having the desired specific activities. Others are entirely synthetic in origin; the chemical reactions employed are more closely allied to standard laboratory methods than are those processes described in earlier sections of this chapter. A few typical manufacturing methods will be cited.

Aspirin is prepared by heating sodium phenoxide and carbon dioxide under pressure (Kolbe reaction, Section 20.17). Acidification generates salicylic acid which is acetylated with acetic anhydride. Esterification of salicylic acid with methanol and acid forms methyl salicylate, synthetic oil of wintergreen.

Methyl salicylate   Salicylic acid   Aspirin
                                               (Acetylsalicylic acid)

Penicillin is commercially produced by isolation from cultures of mutant strains of the mold *Penicillium chrysogenum*. There are a variety of active penicillins, all having the general structure shown below. The *P. chrysogenum* mold generates penicillin G (benzylpenicillin, $R = C_6H_5CH_2$), which is still the largest volume penicillin.

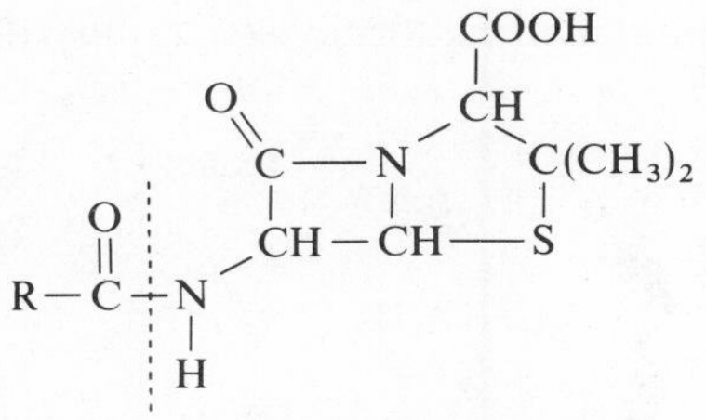

Penicillins

Penicillin G	$R = C_6H_5CH_2-$ (natural)
Penicillin F	$R = CH_3CH_2CH=CHCH_2-$ (natural)
Penicillin V	$R = C_6H_5OCH_2-$ (biosynthetic)
Phenoxyethylpenicillin	$R = C_6H_5OCH-$ (semisynthetic)
	$\quad\quad\quad\quad\quad CH_3$

Penicillin is administered as a salt of the carboxylic acid group, such as the sodium or potassium or procaine (an amine, see below) salt. By using other *Penicillium* strains, or by spiking the growth medium with side-chain precursors, other penicillins can be obtained. One important example of a "biosynthetic" penicillin is penicillin V ($R = C_6H_5OCH_2-$), generated by fermentation in the presence of phenoxyacetic acid. Significantly, known and new penicillins are now produced from 6-aminopenicillanic acid (structure above with RCO replaced by H), which can also be isolated from molds, but is best obtained by enzymic cleavage of penicillin G. By condensing this compound with the appropriate acid anhydride or by reacting it with an acid in the presence of dicyclohexylcarbodiimide, the desired penicillin is made. One such "semisynthetic" penicillin is phenoxyethylpenicillin ($R = C_6H_5OCHCH_3$). The biosynthetic production method has become important because of the necessity of generating new antibiotics that will attack natural-penicillin-resistant bacteria, of which there are many.

A majority of the sulfa drugs are prepared from *p*-acetamidobenzenesulfonyl chloride, which is obtained by reacting acetanilide with chlorosulfonic acid.

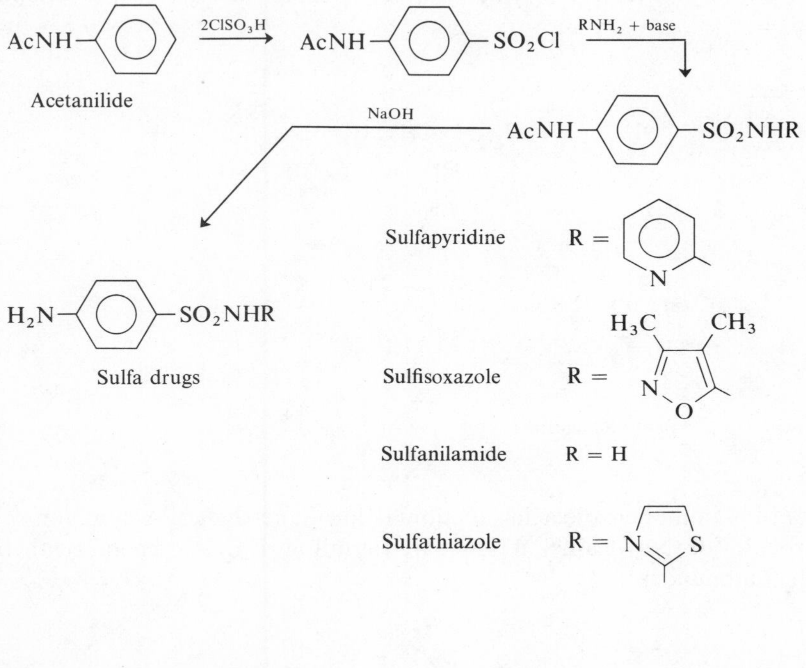

Sulfa drug production has pretty much levelled off since antibiotics have become available.

Phenylephrine hydrochloride (Neosynephrine) is one of many sympathomimetic drugs—other common ones are amphetamine (Benzedrine, 1-phenyl-2-propylamine) and epinephrine (adrenalin). The chemical name for phenylephrine hydrochloride is $(-)$-*m*-hydroxy-α-(methylaminomethyl)benzyl alcohol hydrochloride. It is usually manufactured as follows:

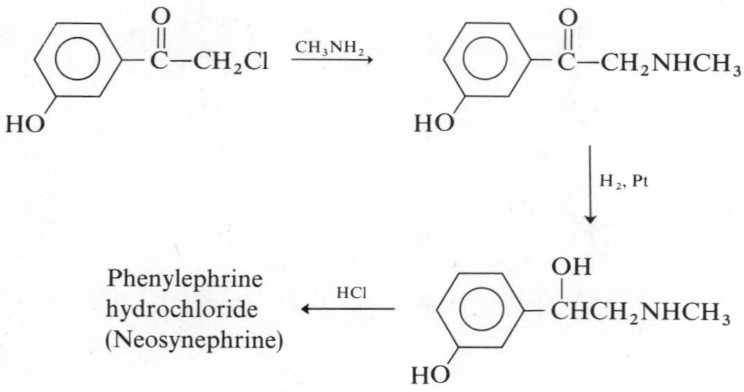

Several water-soluble "factors" appear to be quite important in animal and plant metabolism. Three of these are choline chloride, *p*-aminobenzoic acid, and pantothenic acid. Their importance in human nutrition is questionable, but they serve as normal constituents of all cells and they play important roles in cellular metabolism. In the human body they are synthesized by bacterial flora in the intestines, and they are present in many food sources. These compounds are produced commercially for use as animal (especially poultry) growth supplements. *p*-Aminobenzoic acid is manufactured by the oxidation of *p*-nitrotoluene with potassium dichromate (or potassium permanganate) in sulfuric acid to give *p*-nitrobenzoic acid. This is then reduced with iron or tin and hydrochloric acid to *p*-aminobenzoic acid hydrochloride. Choline, trimethyl-β-hydroxyethylammonium hydroxide, is usually made by reacting ethylene oxide with aqueous trimethylamine, and it can be converted to a variety of salts by neutralization with the appropriate acid (e.g., with hydrochloric acid for choline chloride). Acetylation of the hydroxyl group of choline chloride with acetic anhydride gives acetylcholine chloride.

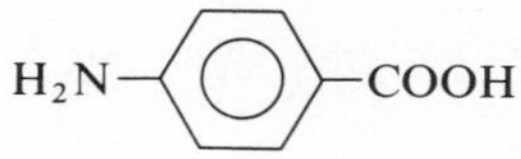

p-Aminobenzoic acid   Choline

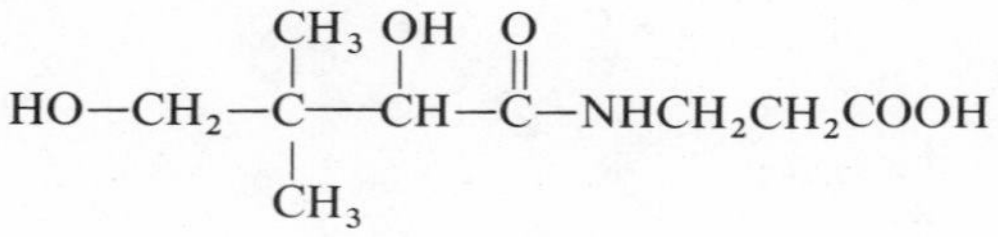

Pantothenic acid

Certain esters of *p*-aminobenzoic acid function as local anesthetics. A common one is procaine hydrochloride (Novocaine); it is prepared as follows (this is a general synthetic scheme for such compounds):

$$O_2N-\text{C}_6H_4-\underset{\underset{Cl}{|}}{\overset{\overset{O}{||}}{C}} + HOCH_2CH_2N(C_2H_5)_2 \xrightarrow{\text{base}}$$

$$O_2N-\text{C}_6H_4-\overset{\overset{O}{||}}{C}-OCH_2CH_2N(C_2H_5)_2$$

$$\Big\downarrow \text{Fe, HCl}$$

$$H_2N-\text{C}_6H_4-\overset{\overset{O}{||}}{C}-OCH_2CH_2\overset{+}{N}H(C_2H_5)_2 \quad Cl^-$$

Procaine hydrochloride
(Novocaine)

Finally, the syntheses of ascorbic acid (Vitamin C), nicotinic acid, and nicotinamide (Vitamin B family) may be outlined, as examples of the preparation of the large volume vitamins of commerce.

D-Glucose $\xrightarrow[\text{CuCrO}_2]{H_2}$ D-Sorbitol $\xrightarrow{\text{A. suboxydans}}$ L-Sorbose

$\xrightarrow[H^\oplus]{(CH_3)_2C=O}$ $\xrightarrow[\text{2. }H^\oplus]{\text{1. KMnO}_4}$ 2-Keto-L-gulonic acid

$\Big\downarrow$ 1. $CH_3OH + HCl$ 2. base

L-Ascorbic acid $\xleftarrow[\substack{\text{H}_2\text{O}}]{\text{powdered metals,}}$

Note especially the microbiological oxidation used in the second step.

For production of nicotinic acid and nicotinamide, the starting materials are coal-tar or synthetic quinoline and β-picoline (Sections 28.6, 28.7). Oxidation with permanganate generates nicotinic acid, which is converted to the amide via the methyl ester.

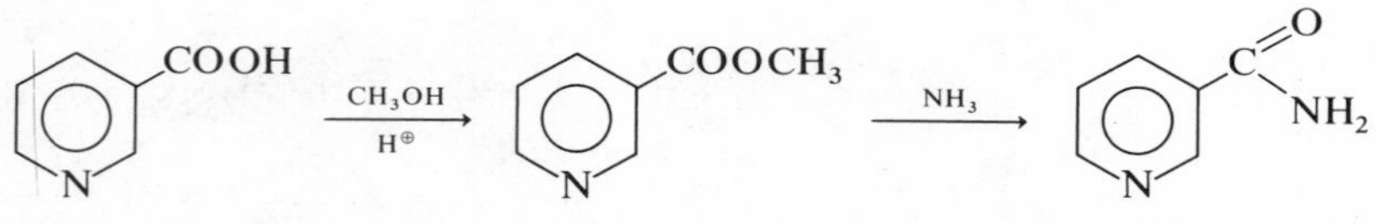

Nicotinic acid
(Niacin)

Nicotinamide
(Niacinamide)

35.18   Food Additives

Food additives are a small but important segment of the chemical industry and one that will be under increased surveillance in the 1970s. Some 840 million pounds of additives valued at 365 million dollars are forecast for 1970 for the United States. The food industry, as a whole, is a multibillion dollar industry.

The food additives, with examples, are classified as follows: emulsifiers; mono and diglycerides and polyborates; acidulants: citric, fumaric, adipic, and phosphoric acids; stabilizers and thickeners: gum arabic, agar gum, carboxymethylcellulose, methylcellulose, and calcium silicate; flavor agents and enhancers: ethyl acetate and butyrate, monosodium glutamate; leavening agents: calcium phosphates; preservatives and antioxidants: sodium nitrite, propionate, and benzoate; sweeteners: saccharin; and others, including vitamins. The Food and Drug Administration lists acceptable products as GRAS (generally regarded as safe) with concentration use limits. Many of the products are under reevaluation and in 1969 the cyclamate sweeteners were banned on the basis of cancer formation in animals. Saccharin is currently (1970) under attack and monosodium glutamate, the meat flavor enhancer, is under suspicion.

The cyclamates are salts of cyclamic acid (cyclohexanesulfamic acid). In commercial production excess cyclohexylamine is sulfonated with various agents such as sulfur trioxide and sulfamic acid (NH_2SO_3H). Both sodium and calcium cyclamates were commonly used as sweeteners before the 1969 ban.

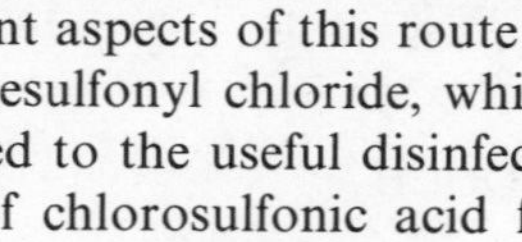

Sodium cyclamate

The commercial synthesis of saccharin also represents classical synthetic organic chemistry adapted to a commercial scale. The sequence is shown below. There are two important aspects of this route that are worthy of further mention: (1) the by-product p-toluenesulfonyl chloride, which is separated from the desired ortho isomer, can be converted to the useful disinfectant Chloramine-T; and (2) one should note the great utility of chlorosulfonic acid for aromatic substitution reactions (see discussion of sulfa drugs in the preceding section).

Monosodium glutamate has long been used as a flavor enhancer for a variety of food products. Although a synthetic route is available, isolation from natural sources is still the most economically feasible approach. Vegetable proteins (from flour, corn, soybean, beet) are hydrolyzed; and, after a complicated purification scheme, the product can be isolated. A fermentation method has also been developed. Interestingly, Japan is both the major producer (about 50%) and also the major user (~40%) of L-monosodium glutamate.

35.19   Insecticides, Herbicides, and Fungicides

Of importance to man and his ecology are the chemicals broadly classified as pesticides and categorized generally according to function as insecticides, herbicides, and fungicides. To these categories can be added such classes as fumigants, larvicides, miticides, insect repellents, sex attractants, sterilants, rodenticides, plant growth regulators, and defoliants. The growth of the pesticide industry has been spectacular, increasing in the past 5 years, 1964–1969, from a manufacturing value of about 0.5 billion dollars to an estimated 1.2 billion dollars (*Chemical Week,* April, 1969), including exports. The major growth has been in herbicides, and the 1.2 billion dollar market (1.9 billion dollars at consumer prices) is distributed as 30% insecticides, 65% herbicides, and 5% fungicides. About one-sixth of this represents the household market.

Historically, the highly chlorinated insecticides have been predominant and the most important and classical example is undoubtedly DDT, 2,2-di(*p*-chlorophenyl)-1,1,1-trichloroethane, which is prepared by the condensation of chlorobenzene with chloral (trichloroacetaldehyde) in the presence of sulfuric acid (Section 16.5). The product is actually a crude mixture containing 65–85% of this isomer, and the ortho, para isomer is a major by-product.

$$Cl_3CCHO + 2\ C_6H_5Cl \xrightarrow{H_2SO_4} Cl_3CCH(C_6H_4Cl)_2 + H_2O$$

DDT is a hard insecticide, one which is stable to environmental destructive forces and exists for months to years, not only in the soil and water systems, but in plant and animal life as well. If anisole (methoxybenzene) is used in the condensation instead of chlorobenzene, the less toxic Methoxychlor, 2,2-di(*p*-methoxyphenyl)-1,1,1-trichloroethane, is produced.

Other hard insecticides are derived by Diels–Alder reactions with hexachlorocyclopentadiene (hex). Hex is produced in a two-stage chlorination of pentanes. The first involves photochlorination with a 9:1 ratio of chlorine to pentane, and the second involves a catalytic chlorination, isomerization, dehydrochlorination reaction which finally results in the thermodynamically stable hexachlorocyclopentadiene. *Aldrin* is the adduct of hex with bicyclo[2.2.1]heptadiene, and *Dieldrin* is the monoepoxide of Aldrin. *Chlordane* is formed by adding chlorine across the reactive double bond of the

Aldrin   Dieldrin

Diels–Alder adduct formed between hex and cyclopentadiene. Photochlorination of benzene produces a gross mixture of products, in which the isomers of 1,2,3,4,5,6-hexachlorocyclohexane predominate. The active γ isomer, comprising 10–18 % of the mixture, is the hard insecticide *Lindane*.

γ-Lindane
(aaaeee)

Although highly efficient in the control of disease-transmitting insects and crop predators, the use of hard insecticides will be severely restricted because of the hazard to other life, including man.

A second major class of insecticides is formed by the organophosphates, represented by malathion and the parathions, notably methyl parathion. Such compounds are prepared by reaction of a phosphorylating agent of the general structure

with a nucleophile, for example, with sodium *p*-nitrophenoxide for the parathions. Such a general scheme allows for tremendous diversity in the formation of O—P or S—P toxicants. These compounds are less persistent, for example, they are subject to

$$(CH_3O)_2\overset{\displaystyle S}{\overset{\|}{P}}-S-\underset{\displaystyle CH_2CO_2C_2H_5}{\overset{\displaystyle |}{CH}}CO_2C_2H_5$$

Malathion

$$(RO)_2\overset{\displaystyle O}{\overset{\|}{P}}-O-\!\!\left\langle\bigcirc\right\rangle\!\!-NO_2$$

R = CH$_3$ and C$_2$H$_5$
Methyl and ethyl parathion

more rapid destruction by hydrolysis and oxidation. The organophosphates are also referred to as anticholinesterases, since they function by blocking the active site of acetylcholinesterase, an enzyme common to both mammals and insects. Some are highly toxic to man.

A third major class of insecticides is comprised of the carbamates, of which Carbaryl (Sevin) is the most important example. The synthesis is based on α-naphthol, which is condensed with phosgene to form the chlorocarbonate. Treatment with methylamine yields the carbamate.

Carbaryl

The production figures for 1969 include the following (in millions of pounds): DDT, 87 (vs. 105 for 1964) and methyl parathion, 48. Though figures are not available, Carbaryl production is perhaps 100 million pounds and Malathion 10 million pounds or more.

The pesticides emerged as weapons to control disease in man and animals caused by insect vectors (malaria, typhus, yellow fever, plague), plant diseases transmitted by insects, and the ravaging of crops by insects (boll weevil, corn earworm), weeds, and fungi. But toxicity levels among living species are without firm definition and the problem before us in the 1970s is to unravel the complex interplay of environmental factors resulting from the application of pesticides. New approaches to insect control are sought, and progress is being made in the areas of sex attractants and insect sterilization, for example.

Among the herbicides, 2,4-D, 2,4-dichlorophenoxyacetic acid, accounts for 40% of the market at 44 million pounds. It is classified as a post-emergence corn and wheat herbicide, and it is made by reaction of chloroacetic acid with sodium phenoxide. Some 15% of the market is taken by two triazines, *Atrazine* and *Simazine*, which are pre-emergence corn and grass-wheat control herbicides. Atrazine is 2-chloro-4-ethylamino-6-isopropylamino-*s*-triazine; Simazine is identical except that it bears a 6-ethylamino group. Other herbicides are substituted benzoic acids (Amiben) and 2,4,5-T, an old standby used for brush control on ranges and right-of-ways.

Fungicides are highly diverse in structure and function. These include the historical "Bordeaux mixture" made up on the farm from lime and copper sulfate, organics of the thiocarbamate class, and mercury and tin compounds, as well as many others.

35.20   Synthetic Detergents

In the United States today synthetic detergents outsell soap by about 7 to 1. The volume "as sold" to the consumer, including inerts and additives, is over 2 billion pounds. Alkylbenzenes form the backbone of the synthetic detergent industry and this situation will probably remain in the 1970s. In 1969, U.S. production of dodecylbenzene (straight chain, including C_{11} to C_{13} in the alkyl moiety) was about 520 million pounds. Dodecylbenzene is sulfonated (Section 16.4) and neutralized to form the linear alkylate sulfonate (LAS) of commerce. The latter is formulated by detergent producers (Proctor and Gamble, Colgate–Palmolive, Lever Bros.) with phosphates and other additives to meet various consumer requirements. The LAS products are categorized as "soft" inasmuch as the "linear" alkyl side chain renders the products relatively biodegradable and therefore less prone to foaming in sewage disposal plants. U.S. consumption is said to be exclusively in this category, and "hard" detergent alkylate production is exported.

The ABS (alkylbenzene sulfonate) detergents are those in which the alkyl group is highly branched and hence relatively resistant to biodegradation, for example, the "hard" detergents. The free world consumption of alkylbenzenes for soft and hard detergents was roughly 1.3 billion and 600 million pounds, respectively, in 1969.

Over the years, the source of the starting alkylbenzenes has varied. Originally, in the 1940s, a suitable kerosene fraction containing 11 to 14 carbon atoms was mono-chlorinated photochemically and the resulting keryl chloride was used to alkylate benzene with aluminum chloride catalyst (Section 16.5). The process became obsolete

$$C_{12}H_{26} \xrightarrow[h\nu]{Cl_2} C_{12}H_{25}Cl \xrightarrow[AlCl_3]{C_6H_6}$$

Detergent alkylate

when low-cost propylene tetramer became available. Alkylation of benzene with this C_{12} alkene at moderate temperatures with hydrogen fluoride catalyst gave the highly branched dodecylbenzene or "hard" alkylate. With the development of molecular sieves, n-paraffins became available from petroleum fractions as a source of LAS detergent alkylate, and the older keryl chloride Friedel–Crafts alkylation process was revived. Alternatively, the conventional hydrogen fluoride alkylation process and equipment may be used by prior dehydrohalogenation of the monochlorides, usually catalytically at elevated temperatures, to yield monoalkenes. Linear alkenes are also available from cracking of kerosene fractions and by the polymerization of ethylene (Ziegler), and these may make inroads in the future.

Competition with alkylbenzenes comes from synthetic primary alcohols in the C_{12}–C_{18} range, as described elsewhere. These are sulfated and neutralized with sodium hydroxide, forming products with the formula $ROSO_3Na$. Lauryl sulfate is an important example, but the sulfates are sold to the extent of perhaps one-fifth of the LAS products.

All of the above detergents and surfactants are classified as anionic. When the long-chain portion bears a cation, such as cetylpyridinium chloride, the detergent is called cationic. Nonionic surfactants bear no charge. One important product is made by the addition of 8 to 16 moles of ethylene oxide to nonylphenol to yield $RC_6H_4O(CH_2CH_2O)_nH$. Other examples utilize fatty acids, fatty alcohols, fatty amides, and alkylmercaptans to which alkene oxides in various proportions are added.

In addition to the problem of biodegradability, the current high phosphate content (up to 50% or so) of many of the formulated consumer products has drawn strong criticism. The phosphates enhance the cleaning efficiency. However, discharge of such detergents into the rivers and lakes from community sewage systems increases the nutrient content of the water. In the process known as *eutrophication*, an excess of nutrients causes the growth of algae and weeds, which in turn depletes the water of available oxygen. Other sources of phosphate nutrients include agricultural fertilizer and human waste.

The replacement of all or part of the phosphates with other builders will have a major impact on the detergent industry and segments of the chemical industry. At this writing, the course of possible action is uncertain; sodium nitrilotriacetate $[N(CH_2CO_2Na)_3]$ is claimed to be an effective replacement for phosphate builders.

Alternatively, phosphates can be removed at water treatment plants by the addition of lime or ferric chloride (from the pickling of steel) to form insoluble calcium or iron phosphate salts.

CHAPTER 36

A BRIEF HISTORY OF ORGANIC CHEMISTRY

In Chapter 2, an introduction to some of the very early history of organic chemistry was given, and historical footnotes have been included in various places throughout the text. The events important in the history of organic chemistry cannot be appreciated very well unless one first appreciates organic chemistry itself, and can then understand just why certain events were in fact significant at the time they occurred.

In this very brief chapter, we would like to tie together some of the events in the history of organic chemistry which are important for scientific, human interest, or other reasons.

To help the reader coordinate the history of organic chemistry with other historical events that are perhaps more familiar, we have summarized some of the high points of both aspects of history in Table 36.1.

Although traditional chemical procedures such as soap making, dyeing, fermentation, and sugar refining had been known and carried out on a large scale for many centuries, very few pure organic compounds were known as short a time ago as 1800. The isolation of relatively pure alcohol was recorded in the eleventh century and the production of ether from alcohol and sulfuric acid was discovered in the sixteenth century. The earliest known carboxylic acids were formic acid from the dry distillation of ants and acetic acid from the distillation of vinegar. Benzoic acid could be sublimed from gum benzoin and succinic acid could be produced by sublimation from amber. However, most of the literature of organic chemistry 200 years ago was largely descriptive, with emphasis on the plant or animal sources and the medicinal value of the various preparations.

The association of organic chemistry and organic compounds with animal products such as blood, urine, saliva, skin, and with plant products such as gums, sugar, and resins, led to the view held by many of the chemists of the day that these materials were produced by a vital force associated with an organized, living system, a force that would be destroyed when the system was taken apart. However, in 1828, Wöhler accidentally synthesized urea from silver cyanate and ammonium chloride, and recognized the product as being identical to the naturally occurring material which he had previously synthesized from organic compounds. In fact, in 1811, Humphrey Davy's younger brother John had also synthesized urea, but had not recognized it. Thus, 1828 is generally recorded as the year of the beginning of the downfall of the vital-force theory of organic chemistry.

The discovery of pure organic compounds by chemical or physical manipulation of natural substances was a slow and painful process at the beginning of the nineteenth century. Scheele was clearly the pioneer and master. He isolated many carboxylic acids directly from their natural sources by salt formation followed by regeneration with sulfuric acid. He also isolated many acids by chemical degradation of natural products, his favorite method being oxidation. Methane (under the name of *marsh gas*) and ethylene (under the name of *olefiant gas*) were known before 1800. Joseph Louis Proust, who formulated the law of definite proportions, also opened the field of carbohydrate chemistry by isolating and identifying glucose, fructose, sucrose, and mannitol.

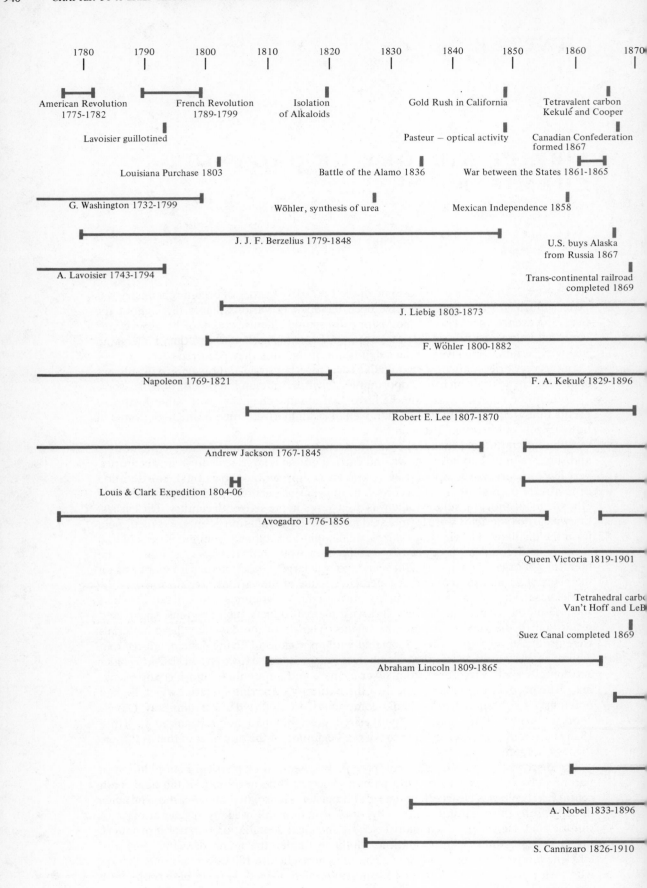

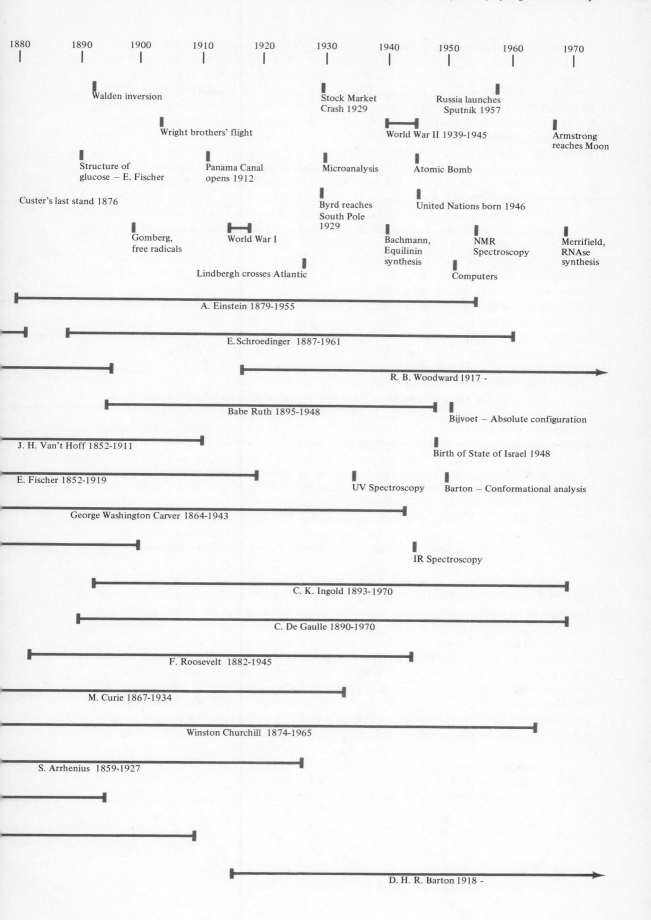

Crystalline morphine was isolated in 1805, but alkaloids as a group were not recognized until about 1820, when strychnine, brucine, and quinine were isolated and described. During the next fifteen years, about 25 more alkaloids were added to the group.

M. E. Chevreul† was the organic chemist who pioneered the investigation of the isolation of relatively pure organic compounds from fats. He recognized that the process for the production of soap from fat gave glycerol in addition to a soapy material, which he correctly identified as a salt of the fatty acid and not the fatty acid itself, as had been previously believed. As sometimes happens, this discovery, strictly academic at the time it was made, soon had great industrial importance. Whereas soap making involved the salts of fatty acids, candle making involved the fatty acids themselves. Candle making and candle burning was an untidy business in those days because the candles were soft and burned with a smoky flame that had a bad odor. As the candle became warm, it dripped profusely and softened. Only after the organic reactions necessary had been recognized could the candle-making industry do more than empirically search for better conditions. Using the data and results of the investigation of Chevreul, the industry was able to change to the higher melting stearic acid from the softer melting tallow that had been used previously.

Chevreul also recognized and introduced the concept of melting points as a criterion of purity, and clearly stated that a compound was pure only after several recrystallizations did not raise the melting point.

At about this time in the development in organic chemistry, Berzelius introduced the concept of *isomerism* to distinguish between compounds of identical elementary composition. He also introduced the term *polymerism*, which he applied to those compounds with the same elements in the same proportions but which had molecular weights which were multiples of each other.

Although Lavoisier had made the first serious attempt at quantitative analysis of organic compounds and had been followed by most of the famous chemists of the time, who also experimented with apparatus for quantitative analysis, it was Liebig who finally satisfied the need felt by all of these men to have accurate analyses. Using the work of the previous investigators, he completed the final development of a combustion train which is still used today with small modifications.

After attempts by many chemists to determine carbon, hydrogen, and nitrogen quantitatively with the same experiment, Liebig concluded that nitrogen determinations must be made upon a separate sample and Dumas soon introduced a satisfactory procedure.

The rapid increase in knowledge concerning experimental organic chemistry led to the synthesis of more and more pure compounds. Wöhler's synthesis provided further stimulus to organic research, as it suggested that there was not an unbridgeable gulf between mineral chemistry and the mysteries of organic compounds. The next key step, one that really launched systematic organic research, was the development of the idea of radicals as the organic equivalents of atoms. The most significant early research was probably that of Liebig and Wöhler on the benzoyl radical. It encouraged others to discover new radicals by systematic transformations of organic substances. This synthesis effort, coupled with the ever-increasing rate of isolation and purification of pure organic compounds from natural sources, led to a period of utter chaos and confusion. Because atomic weights could not be determined accurately and differences between atomic weights and equivalent weights were not clearly understood, the size of individual molecules remained a mystery.

For example, the following table shows the difference in formulation of alcohol and ether by three of the senior organic chemists of their time:

	Berzelius	*Liebig*	*Dumas*
Alcohol	$C_2H_5O \cdot H$	$C_2H_3O \cdot 3H$	$C_4H_4 \cdot H_2O$
Ether	$C_4H_{10} \cdot H_2O$	$C_4H_6O \cdot 6H$	$2C_2H_4 \cdot H_2O$

† Michel E. Chevreul. 1786–1889. Born Angers, France. University of Paris.

The differences in formulation arose in part from the differences in atomic weights that were in common use at the time, as shown in the following table:

	Berzelius	*Liebig*	*Dumas*
C	12	6	6
H	1	1	1
O	16	8	16

The work of Hofmann with amines, Williamson with ethers, and Wurtz with hydrocarbons resulted in the isolation of many new synthetic organic chemicals, the formulations of which clearly led to the concept of valence. With alkyl iodides and ammonia, Hofmann was able to prepare and isolate primary, secondary, and tertiary aliphatic amines. With alkyl iodides and alcoholates, Williamson was able to prepare ethers and, using the same alkyl halides and sodium, Wurtz was able to prepare hydrocarbons. The formulations written by these men to describe their many new compounds have many similarities to our stick-bond formulations of today, and they allowed Franklin and Kolbe to develop the concept of valence for each atom in organic compounds. Very shortly thereafter, Kekulé and Couper made the significant contribution of recognizing that the carbon atom was tetravalent (1857) and that carbon atoms had the capacity to link or bond together one with another (1858). Even with these ideas, organic chemistry was in an incredible state of confusion, and the interpretation of experimental results published in the literature of the time required a knowledge of the specific meaning of the formulations of a specific chemist and his school. The situation was not unlike that even today, in which the interpretation of the literature on so-called nonclassical ions requires a knowledge of the meaning of the dotted-line formulations of a particular chemist or school.

The confusion became so bad that a congress was convened in Karlsruhe in 1860, to which 140 of the most prominent chemists were invited. The goal was to attempt to find answers to the questions involving atoms, molecules, radicals, and equivalents. The Italian chemist Cannizzaro† must surely be voted the most valuable player in that game, because it was he who cleared the way for progress by proposing that a unified explanation was possible for the previously mentioned questions if the chemists would accept the hypothesis of Avogadro (available for 50 years) and determine experimentally the size of molecules by the weight of their vapors. During the emotion-packed convention, Cannizzaro failed to sway the audience to his position, but the cold logic and the usefulness of his proposal rapidly became apparent after the members of the audience returned to their chemical laboratories.

Although Kekulé introduced the concept of the chemical bond, he did not represent it symbolically by dot or line. It was Couper in 1858 who introduced the stick bond, and Hofmann in 1865 who used models constructed of sticks and croquet balls to represent organic compounds.

The problem of formulation of benzene and aromatic structures was a particularly difficult one, and it was Kekulé who in 1865 made the most significant contribution to its solution by assigning a ring structure of alternating single and double bonds to represent benzene. To quote from the *Kekulé Memorial Lecture* by R. Japp:

According to his own version, the idea came to him during a dream; "I was sitting, writing at my text-book; but the work did not progress, my thoughts were elsewhere. I turned my chair to the fire and dozed. Again the atoms were gambolling before my eyes. This time the smaller groups kept modestly in the background. My mental eye, rendered more acute by repeated visions of the kind, could now distinguish larger structures, of manifold conformation: long rows, sometimes more closely fitted together; all twining and twisting in snake-like motion. But look! What was that? One of the snakes had seized hold of its own tail, and the form whirled mockingly before my eyes. As if by a flash of lightning I awoke; and this time also I spent the rest of the night in working out the consequences of the hypothesis.

† Stanislao Cannizzaro. 1826–1910. Born Palermo, Italy. Universities of Genoa, Palermo, and Rome.

"Let us learn to dream, gentlemen," adds Kekulé, "then perhaps we shall find the truth . . . but let us beware of publishing our dreams before they have been put to the proof by the waking understanding.

Ladenburg pointed out that Kekulé's formula for benzene predicted the existence of two *ortho* isomers and Kekulé dealt with this problem by proposing that the atoms in the benzene molecule oscillate around a mean position. Although many chemists interpreted Kekulé's suggestion as indicating a rapid alternation between double and single bond, his concept was more complicated than this.

One of the most fundamental discoveries in organic chemistry was made by Louis Pasteur† in 1848 during his investigation of dissymmetry and optical activity of salts of tartaric acid, a constituent of grapes. The normal form of tartaric acid was dextrorotatory, but another form had been discovered and was named *racemic acid*.

Although Biot had shown that racemic acid and its salts did not rotate polarized light, Pasteur discovered that when the sodium ammonium tartrate was crystallized below 28°C, a tetrahydrate crystallized in which half of the crystals had their hemihedral faces oriented to the right and half the crystals had their faces oriented to the left. Pasteur hand-sorted these crystals under a magnifying glass and showed that one was the previously known dextro form, whereas the other was the previously unknown levorotatory acid. The unusual nature of the discovery is evident from the fact that since that time unsymmetrical crystals large enough to be hand-sorted using a magnifying glass and tweezers have been reported in only about ten cases.

Although the discovery of Pasteur clearly required asymmetry in the molecular structure of these molecules, Pasteur could only speculate on the possibility of the molecules being right-handed and left-handed helices. It was not until 1874 that van't Hoff and LeBel independently suggested the asymmetrical carbon atom. The publication of this concept brought the noted chemist H. Kolbe†† to a rage, and in 1877 he published in one of the top chemical journals of the time the following:

In a recently published paper with the same title [*Signs of the Times*], I pointed out that one of the causes of the present-day retrogression of chemical research in Germany is the lack of general and, at the same time, fundamental chemical knowledge; under this lack no small number of our professors of chemistry are laboring, with great harm to the science. A consequence of this is the spread of the weed of the apparently scholarly and clever, but actually trivial and stupid natural philosophy, which was displaced fifty years ago by exact natural science, but which is now brought forth again, out of the storeroom harboring the errors of the human mind, by pseudoscientists who try to smuggle it, like a fashionably dressed and freshly rouged prostitute, into good society, where it does not belong.

Anyone to whom this concern seems exaggerated may read, if he is able to, the book by Messrs. van't Hoff and Herrmann on *The Arrangement of Atoms in Space*, which has recently appeared and which overflows with fantastic foolishness. I would ignore this book, as [I have] many others, if a reputable chemist had not taken it under his protection and warmly recommended it as an excellent accomplishment.

A Dr. J. H. van't Hoff, of the Veterinary School at Utrecht, has no liking, it seems, for exact chemical investigation. He has considered it more convenient to mount Pegasus (apparently borrowed from the Veterinary School) and to proclaim in his *La chimie dans l'espace* how the atoms appear to him to be arranged in space, when he is on the chemical Mt. Parnassus which he has reached by bold flight.

Other senior chemists of the time also criticized van't Hoff's proposals, but the ideas gradually gained acceptance. In 1874, van't Hoff also investigated geometric isomerism and indicated that double bonds prevent free rotation and lead to the type of isomerism illustrated by maleic and fumaric acids. In 1896, keto and enol forms of a keto ester were isolated to confirm a type of isomerism that had been recognized and named *tautomerism* as early as 1885.

---

† Louis Pasteur. 1822–1895. Born Dole, France. Universities of Dijon, Strasbourg, Lille, and Sorbonne.
†† Herman Kolbe. 1818–1884. Born Germany. Universities of Marburg and Leipzig.

The stage was now set for rapid progress in organic chemistry. In addition to the known conversions of alcohols to halides and the Williamson synthesis of ethers, Wurtz and Fittig had introduced methods to prepare hydrocarbons, both aliphatic and aromatic in nature. The Friedel-Crafts reaction using anhydrous aluminum chloride was introduced about 1877. Claisen and Perkin developed condensation reactions and in 1901, Francois Auguste Victor Grignard† defended a doctoral thesis on a subject suggested to him by his professor, Barbier, on the subject of magnesium organic halides. After this thesis, he continued to work in this area and developed the very powerful synthetic tool now known as the Grignard reagent.

Hofmann reported the degradation of amides to amines in 1882, and Curtius, Beckmann, and Gabriel were investigating nitrogen chemistry and publishing synthetic methods for nitrogen compounds at the time.

In 1893, Paul Walden found the sequence of reactions now known as the *Walden inversion*, which provided a synthetic method for the conversion of an optically active substance to its enantiomer. The previous method involved racemization and then separation of the 50–50 mixture.

In 1875, Emil Fischer discovered the reagent phenylhydrazine and used it in an attack upon the structures and chemical reactions of carbohydrates. After a tremendous amount of chemistry, in 1891 Fischer could assign a configuration to glucose and some of the other sugars.

In addition to his brilliant investigations in carbohydrate chemistry, Emil Fischer also conducted important investigations on purines and proteins. His study of purines was initiated in 1881 and continued until 1914. In the area of proteins, Fischer investigated the amino acid linkage and concentrated on the preparation of peptides. By 1907, he and his colleagues had synthesized a polypeptide containing 18 amino acids. He showed that such polypeptides behaved in a similar manner to intermediates produced from the hydrolysis of natural proteins.

An account of the work by Gomberg on free radicals has been given earlier (page 268).

Alfred Nobel was an extremely influential industrial chemist of the nineteenth century. He was born in 1833 in Sweden and during his youth was too sickly to attend school regularly. At the age of nine he left Sweden, and by 1855 he had the opportunity to work with Professor Zinin at the University of St. Petersberg in Russia. Previously, a young Italian scientist, Ancanio Sobrero, had discovered the oily liquid, nitroglycerin, but had considered the compound too dangerous for commerce. Professor Zinin suggested that Alfred Nobel experiment with nitroglycerin as an explosive. In 1863 Nobel filed in the Swedish Patent Office his first patent involving the use of nitroglycerin as an explosive. Although nitroglycerin was many times more powerful than any other explosive, the unpredictable detonation characteristic of it was tragically demonstrated by an explosion in 1864 that completely destroyed his factory and killed one of his brothers.

Projects such as the building of the Suez Canal, the building of railroads across America, and the development of the mining and oil industries created a fantastic demand and market for nitroglycerin. However, after a series of large, serious, and inexplicable explosions in all parts of the world, many nitroglycerin factories were closed and many governments passed laws banning the manufacture or sale of nitroglycerin. At this point, Nobel discovered that nitroglycerin, when absorbed in sawdust or diatomaceous earth, would not explode until detonated. He called the product *dynamite*, patented it in many countries, and shortly became one of the wealthiest men in the world.

Although the military had used nitroglycerin since the earliest years regardless of the danger, Nobel considered himself a humanist and a contributor to the progress of mankind by his investigations in the area of explosives. It was a deep shock to him when a newspaper, upon the death of his brother, inadvertently printed his own obituary and convinced him that the world saw him as the "Merchant of Death." In the latter years

† Victor Grignard, 1871–1935. Born Cherbourg, France. Universities of Nancy, Lyon. Nobel Prize, 1912.

of his life he devoted much time and energy to public causes involving science, medicine, and in particular disarmament and peace. He was noted to remark after an especially unproductive Peace Congress that he supported. "Perhaps my dynamite factories will put an end to war even sooner than your congresses. On the day when two army camps may mutually annihilate each other in a second, all civilized nations will probably recoil with horror and disband their troops."

In 1895 he resolved to leave his entire fortune to a fund the income from which would be used as an annual award to honor leaders of science, literature, and those who have done the most to promote world peace. After several contestations of the will, Nobel Prizes were established in physics, chemistry, medicine, and literature, and they are awarded in Sweden. The Nobel Peace Prize was established and awarded in Norway, as specified under the terms of the will.

Alfred Nobel remained a bachelor of complex personality. He was a pacifist, but invented the most powerful explosive known in his time. He was a millionaire, but supported socialism. He was an atheist, but gave liberally to the church. He received little formal chemical education and earned no formal degree in chemistry, but he personally directed some 15 chemical research laboratories; and in his later years most of his personal mansions contained well-equipped chemical laboratories.

In the 1900s organic chemistry was dominated by the Germans, who continued their domination through World War I. During the war, many countries found themselves cut off from dyes, drugs, solvents, and many other chemicals. These countries then encouraged their own individual chemical industries by protection from foreign competition and by encouragement for expansion. Thereafter, leadership in organic chemistry began to shift to Switzerland, Britain, and the United States. The main source of organic chemicals initially was coal tar, and thus aromatic chemistry was the main area of investigation. With the advent of the internal combustion engine, petroleum gained importance as a source of raw material for organic materials and, coupled with natural gas and fermentation products, provided the source for the development of aliphatic chemistry. In addition to the interest in the synthesis of organic compounds with the variety of properties associated with the various structures, investigations were undertaken in the early part of this century into the mechanism of individual reactions, especially by Lapworth† and later by Ingold. Sir Robert Robinson and Sir Christopher Ingold developed the idea of the importance of the electronic theory in understanding reaction mechanisms, and Linus Pauling contributed to the understanding of the importance of quantum mechanics in organic chemistry.

The British carbohydrate chemist, Haworth, introduced the term *conformation*, and D. H. R. Barton made a significant contribution to structural chemistry by his analysis and predictions of chemical properties and reactions based on conformations.

With the development of instruments and techniques designed to follow the course of an organic reaction run on small scale, multistep syntheses have progressed at a rapid rate, from the total synthesis of equilenin by W. E. Bachman, W. Cole, and A. L. Wilds in 1940 to the total synthesis of an active enzyme RNAse in 1969 by R. B. Merrifield.

If one realizes that probably 90% of the organic chemists who ever inhabited the earth are alive and working today, one begins to get a perspective on the historical development of organic chemistry and sees that organic chemistry may have really just begun.

---

† Arthur Lapworth. 1872–1941. Born, Galashiels, Scotland. University of Manchester.

APPENDIX

Table 1   NMR Absorptions of Protons in Various Structural Environments

δ Value and Range†

Structural Type

16 15 14 13 12 11 10 9 8 7 6 5 4 3 2 1 0

1 TMS
2 —CH₂—, cyclopropane
3 CH₄
4 ROH, monomer, very dilute solution
5 CH₃—C— (saturated)
6 R₂NH‡, 0.1–0.9 mole fraction in an inert solvent
7 CH₃—C—C—X (X = Cl, Br, I, OH, OR, C = O, N)
8 —CH₂— (saturated)
9 RSH‡
10 RNH₂‡, 0.1–0.9 mole fraction in an inert solvent
11 —C—H (saturated)
12 CH₃—C—X (X = F, Cl, Br, I, OH, OR, OAr, N)
13 CH₃—C=C
14 CH₃—C=O
15 CH₃Ar
16 CH₃—S—
17 CH₃—N
18 H—C≡C—, nonconjugated
19 H—C≡C—, conjugated
20 ArSH‡
21 CH₃—O—
22 ArNH₂‡, ArNHR‡, and Ar₂NH‡
23 ROH‡, 0.1–0.9 mole fraction in an inert solvent
24 CH₂=C, nonconjugated
25 H₂C=C, acyclic, nonconjugated
26 H₂C=C, cyclic, nonconjugated
27 CH₂=C, conjugated
28 ArOH‡, polymeric association
29 H₂C=C, conjugated
30 H₂C=C, acyclic, conjugated
31 H—N—C=O
32 ArH, benzenoid
33 ArH, nonbenzenoid
34 RNH₃⁺, R₂NH₂⁺, and R₃NH⁺ (trifluoroacetic acid solution)
35 H—C(=O)(N)
36 H—C(=O)(O—)
37 ArNH₃⁺, ArRNH₂⁺, and ArR₂NH⁺ (trifluoroacetic acid solution)
38 C=N—OH ‡
39 RCHO, aliphatic, α,β-unsaturated
40 RCHO, aliphatic
41 ArCHO
42 ArOH, intramolecularly bonded
43 —SO₃H
44 RCO₂H, dimer, in nonpolar solvents
45 Enols

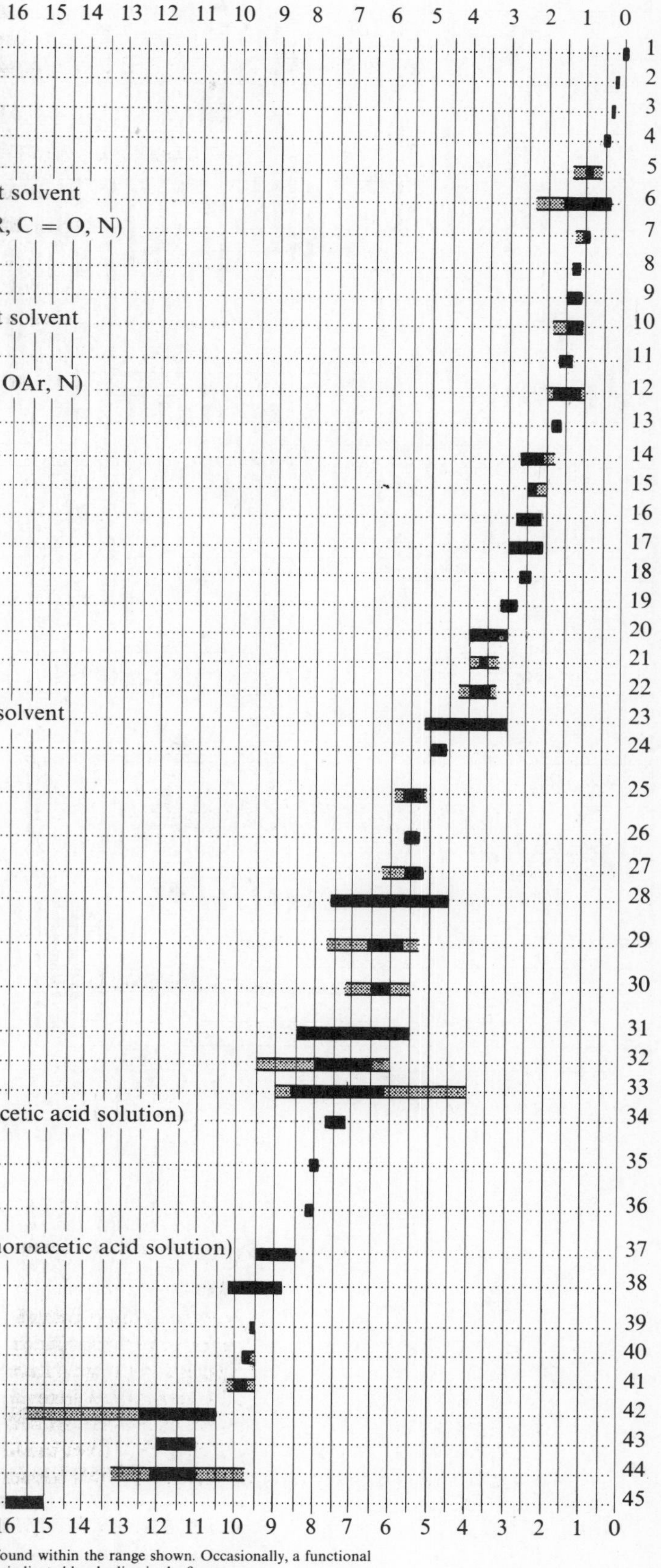

16 15 14 13 12 11 10 9 8 7 6 5 4 3 2 1 0

† Normally, absorptions for the functional groups indicated will be found within the range shown. Occasionally, a functional
group will absorb outside this range. Approximate limits for this are indicated by shading in the figure.
‡ The absorption positions of these groups are concentration-dependent and are shifted to lower δ values in more dilute solutions.

Table 2 Spectra-Structure Correlations

Probable Positions of Characteristic Infrared Absorption Bands

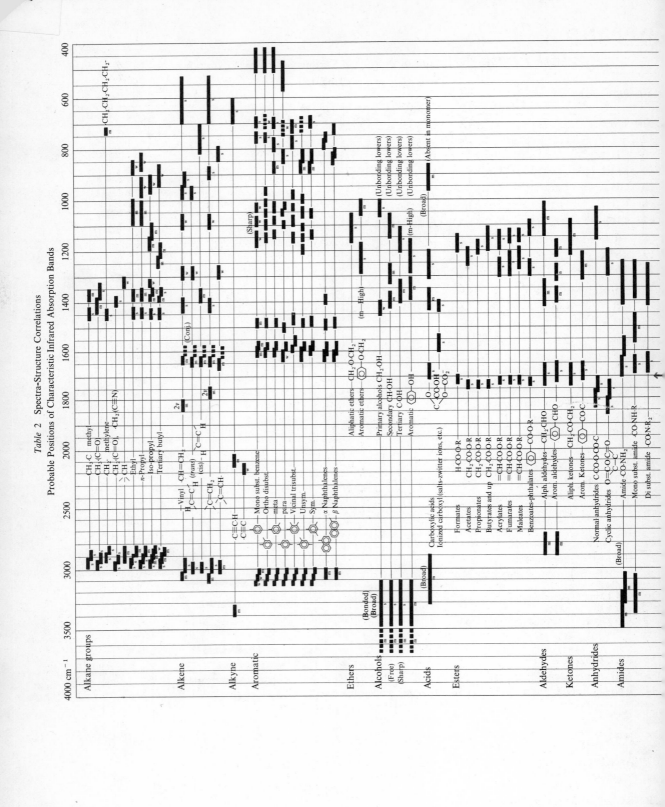

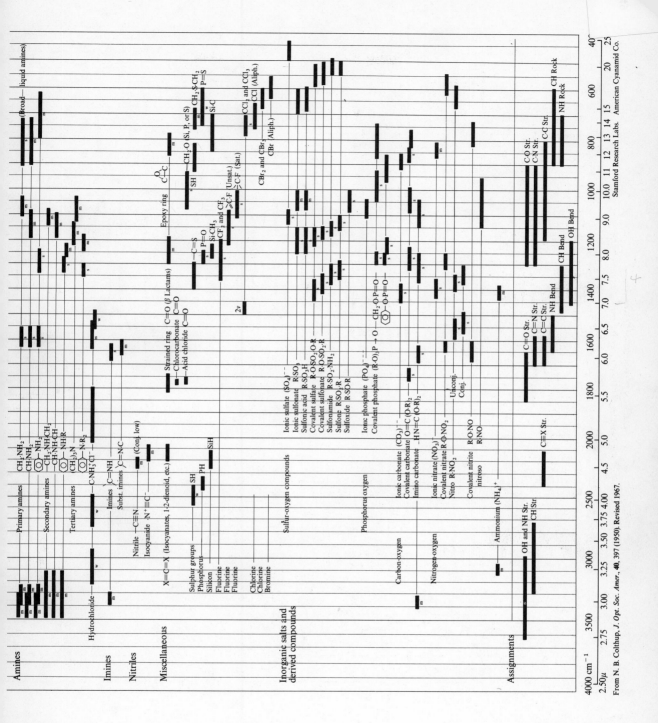

From N. B. Colthup, J. Opt. Soc. Amer., 40, 397 (1950). Revised 1967.

SELECTED ANSWERS TO EXERCISES

CHAPTER 2

2.1 Unhybridized case: $2 \times E_s + 5 \times E_p$, sp^3 case: $\frac{7}{4}E_s + \frac{21}{4}E_p$.

CHAPTER 3

3.1 (a) 3-Methylheptane   (b) 2,4-Dimethylheptane.

3.3 Very much like Figure 3.3, except that all maxima are the same height, about 3.0 kcal/mole.

3.4

3.6

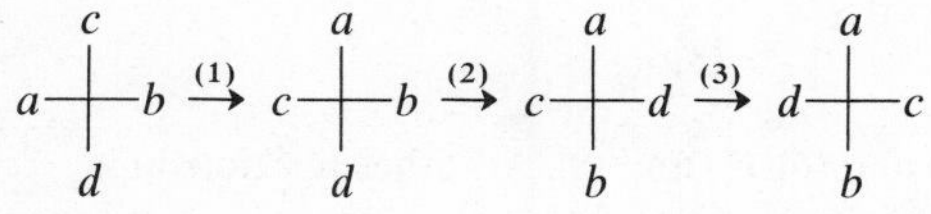

CHAPTER 4

4.1 (a) 5-Bromo-3-ethyl-6-methyl-1-heptanol   (b) 5-Methyl-1,2,4-heptanetriol

4.2 (a) 5-Methyl-2-n-propoxyhexane or 2-(5-methylhexyl) propyl ether
(b) 4-Methoxy-2-methyl-2-butanol

4.3 The smaller the value of pK_a, the stronger the acid and the weaker the conjugate base. Methylamine is a stronger base than ammonia by $10^{1.4}$ times. Inductive donation of electrons by the methyl group accounts for some of the difference.

4.4 The first is the more important. The hydroxyl proton is more acidic and the nitrogen lone pair is more basic.

CHAPTER 5

5.1 $200 \div 60 = \delta\ 3.33$.

5.2 $-O-CH_2-O-\ \delta\ 4.2–4.5$; the downfield position is due to deshielding by the two adjacent electronegative oxygens.

5.3 See Figure 5.10.

5.4 H_b will appear as a quintet with relative areas of $1:4:6:4:1$.

5.5 $(CH_3^aCH_2^b)_3C-Br$ $(CH_3^a)_2CH^bCH_2^cCH_2^dBr$ $(BrCH_2^dCH_2^c)_2CH^bCH_3^a$

CHAPTER 6

6.1

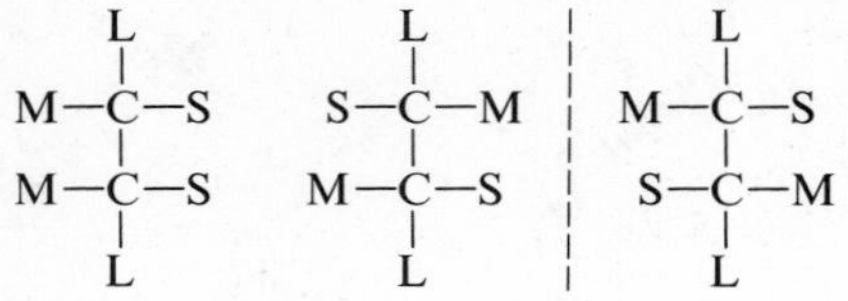

meso   dl

6.2

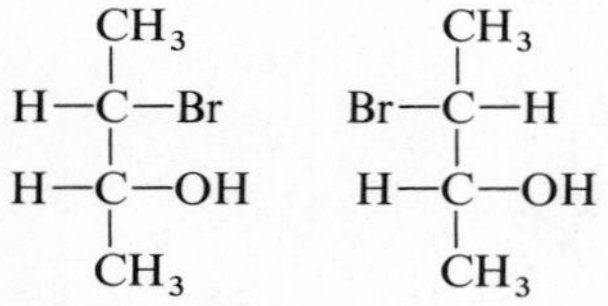

XIa, *erythro*   XIIa, *threo*

6.3

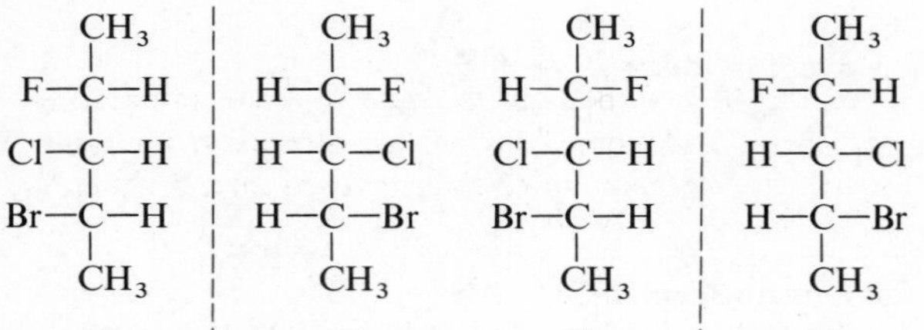

(1)   (2)   (3)   (4)

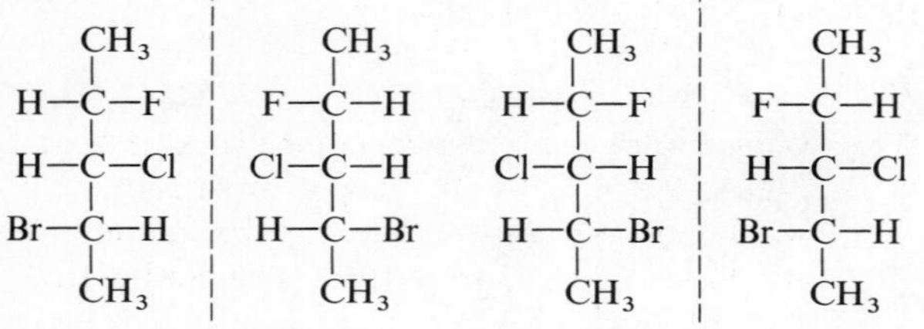

(5)   (6)   (7)   (8)

Enantiomers are (1) and (2), (3) and (4), (5) and (6), (7) and (8). All other relationships are diastereomeric.

6.4

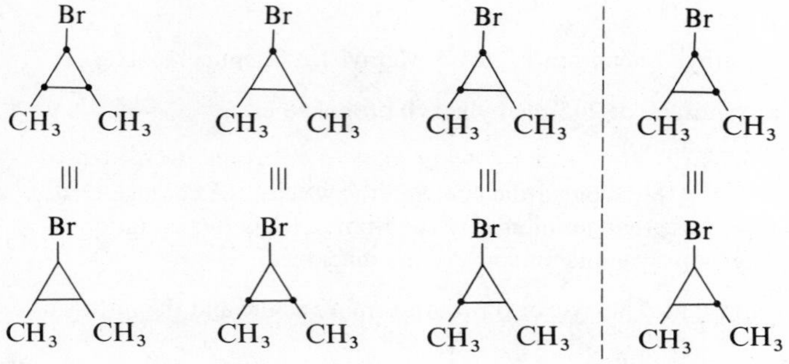

6.5

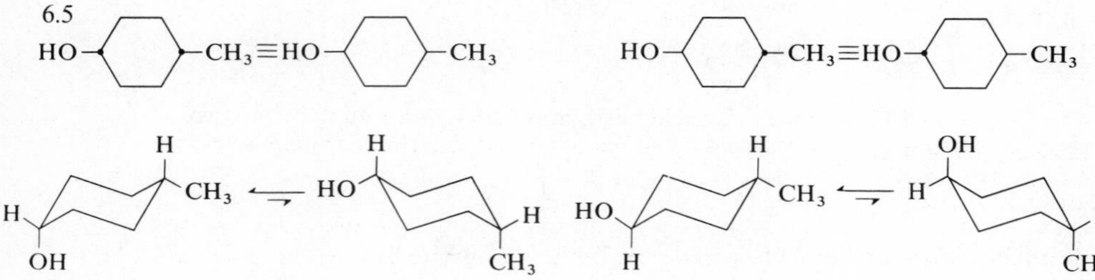

cis, meso   trans, meso

Actually there are four stereoisomers: all have a plane of symmetry and all are meso. However, the two cis diastereomers are conformational isomers rapidly interconverting. The same for the two trans diastereomers. Thus at normal temperatures, it is reasonable to speak only of one cis-meso and one trans-meso.

6.7   There would be 2^n total stereoisomers, or 1.26×10^{30}.

CHAPTER 7

7.2   Stereoisomers: (a) one; (b) one; (c) two. Proton types: (a) 6; (b) 4; (c) 5.

7.3   (a) 5-Methyl-2-hexene   (b) 3-Methylcyclohexene
       (c) *trans*-4,4-Dichlorocyclodecene   (d) 3-Methylenecyclopentene

7.4
       1.97 D   1.71 D

The trans isomer has the higher dipole moment because the methyl (electron-donating) and the chlorine (electron-withdrawing) have moments which are directed in the same direction, whereas the cis isomer has the moments somewhat opposed to each other.

7.7

7.8

I is the most important due to the covalent bond energy consideration (Rule 2a). II is important due to the electron-attracting power of F (2b). IV is important because it gives each atom a full octet, even though it places a positive charge on the fluorine nucleus. III is of negligible importance since it is the higher-energy counterpart of II.

7.10   Three sites.

7.11   One site. Some possibilities are

, etc.

CHAPTER 8

8.1   May be pictured as involving an sp^2-hybridized oxygen, one sp^2 orbital from oxygen used for the σ bond and the two lone pairs each in an sp^2 orbital.

8.2   The form with the negative charge on the electronegative oxygen atom (a) is more important.

8.3   All atoms with the exception of the hydrogens of the methyl must be in the same plane; the four p orbitals overlap as in butadiene.

8.4   Two *equivalent* resonance forms exist for the carboxylate ion.

8.5 $R-\underset{\underset{-O}{|}}{C}=CH_2$, because the negative charge is on the electronegative oxygen atom.

8.6   The enol form contains an internal hydrogen bond that reduces intermolecular association.

8.7   The aldehydic hydrogen lies in the plane of the C=O group, a strongly deshielding environment. It is not an acidic proton because the conjugate base has no resonance stabilization.

8.8 Figure 8.3,

$\overset{a}{C}H_3-\overset{b}{C}HO$ H_a, δ 2.40, 3H; doublet, split by H_b
                  H_b, δ 9.80, 1H, quartet, split by $3H_a$

$\overset{c}{C}H_3CO\overset{b}{C}H_2\overset{a}{C}H_3$ H_a, δ 1.05, 3H, triplet, split by $2H_b$
                     H_b, δ 2.47, 2H, quartet, split by $3H_a$
                     H_c, δ 2.13, 3H, singlet

8.9 (a) Hexanal   (b) 5-Methyl-2-hexanone   (c) *cis*-2-Undecen-6-one

8.11

The first form is more important because of the greater tendency of a ketone to enolize than an ester.

8.12 For methyl propionate there should be a methyl singlet at δ 3.7, a methylene quartet at δ 2.15, and a methyl triplet at δ 1.2.

8.13 The nitrogen atom in succinimide is very weakly basic (Section 8.13), but the hydrogen attached to the nitrogen is acidic (pK_a 9.6), as is typical of 1,3-dicarbonyl compounds.

8.14 $(\overset{a}{C}H_3)_3C\overset{b}{C}H_2\overset{||}{\underset{}{C}}-O\overset{c}{C}H_2\overset{d}{C}H_3$

    (a) Singlet at δ 1.05   (b) Singlet at δ 2.12
    (c) Quartet at δ 4.08   (d) Triplet at δ 1.25

CHAPTER 9

9.1 $\lambda = 1/v = 1/2900\ \text{cm}^{-1} = 3.45 \times 10^{-4}\ \text{cm} = 3.45\ \mu\text{m}$; $E = hv = 8.3\ \text{kcal/mole}$

9.2 Cyclopentane,

9.3 $vC-H = \sqrt{2}vC-D$; $vC-D = 2900/1.414 = 2060\ \text{cm}^{-1}$

9.4 The vibration is across a center of symmetry in 2-butyne, not in 1-butyne.

9.5 Resonance in crotonaldehyde may be pictured as follows:

$$CH_3CH=CH-\underset{\underset{H}{|}}{C}=O \quad \leftrightarrow \quad CH_3\overset{+}{C}H-CH=\underset{\underset{H}{|}}{C}-O^-$$

The effect of resonance is to lower both the frequency of the carbonyl group absorption (more single C—O bond character) and of the carbon–carbon double bond absorption (more single carbon–carbon bond character).

CHAPTER 10

10.1 Structure (b) would require the nitrogen atom to be *sp*-hybridized and the lone pair would reside in a *p* orbital, which is unfavorable. Isomerization about the C=N bond in oximes is in fact relatively slow, and syn,anti isomers of oximes can be isolated. In the case of acetone oxime (a), nmr shows *two different methyl groups*, one syn to the OH and the other anti.

10.2 Yes; the enol is a *dl* pair with the allene-type stereochemistry.

10.3 Yes, because the nitrogen atoms are sp^2-hybridized. Azo compounds have cis and trans forms. As with simple alkenes, the trans isomers are usually more stable.

10.4

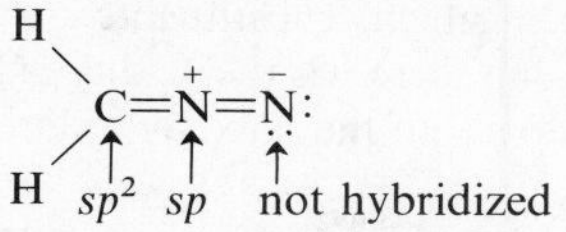

$$H-C-H = 120°$$
$$H-C-N = 120°$$
$$C-N-N = 180°$$

sp^2 sp not hybridized

10.5 There must be two pairs of nonequivalent fluorine atoms. This is best accommodated by a trigonal bipyramid structure (dsp^3 hybridization at S), with two fluorine nuclei and an electron pair in the equatorial positions, and two fluorines axial:

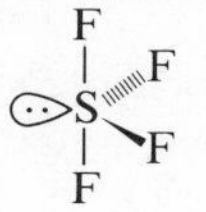

10.6

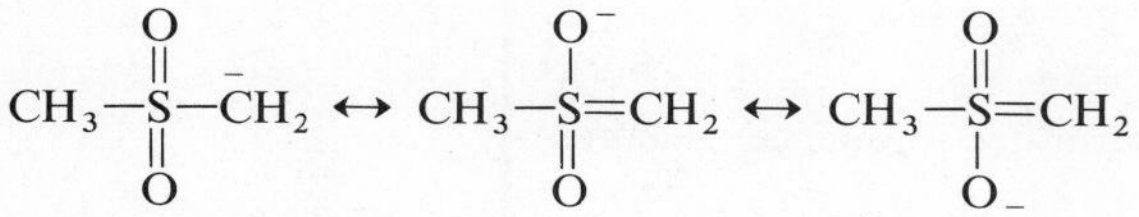

10.7 (a) Only structural isomers; For example, CH_3SCH_3 and CH_3S-OCH_3. Enols of the

type $CH_2=\overset{O}{\underset{OH}{\overset{\|}{S}}}-CH_3$ do not occur.   (b) The sulfoxide group is configurationally stable,

and enantiomers are possible if the two groups on sulfur are different.

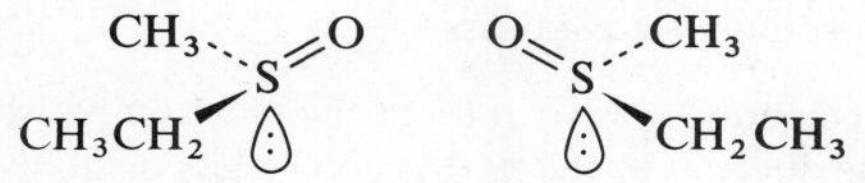

dl pair

(c) Diastereomers (geometrical isomers) are possible:

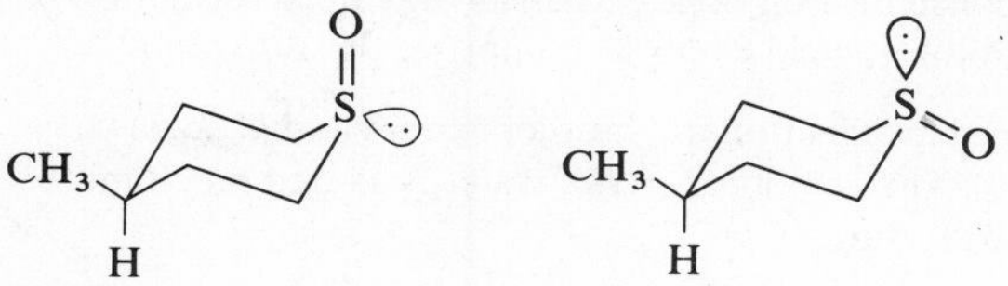

CHAPTER 11

11.1

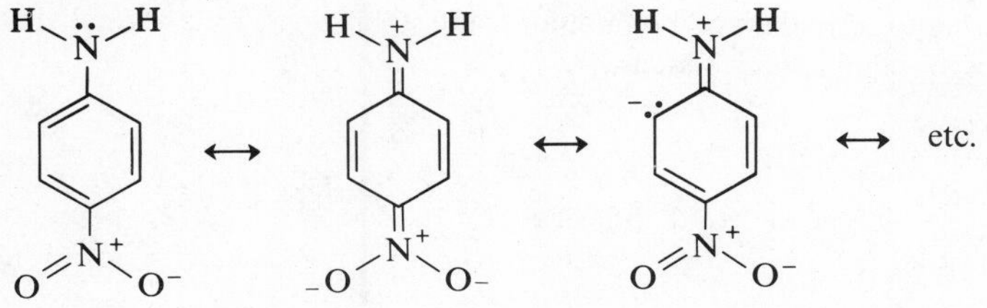

etc.

11.2 The definite upfield shift can be ascribed to the inductive donation of electrons of the methyl group to the benzene ring which causes increased shielding.

11.3 A, B, and C in order are ortho, para, and meta.

11.4 The 9,10 bond should be shortest because it shows double bond character in all but one of the five Kekulé structures.

CHAPTER 12

12.1 Six forms. H^+ $CH_2=\overset{}{\underset{H}{\overset{}{C}}}-CH_3$, etc.

12.2   The differences are attributable to the presence of electron-delocalizing substituents which tend to stabilize the conjugate base. Since a *p*-nitro group increases the acidity of phenol by 2.5 powers of 10 (Table 11.1, Page 236), it should do about the same for aniline, so estimate pK_a about 22 for *p*-nitroaniline.

12.3   Five forms, same as for the radical (page 271) with a negative charge in place of the odd electron.

12.4

To the extent that this resonance form is an important contributor, the seven-membered ring can be treated as aromatic (like the tropylium cation, six π electrons).

12.5   If we were to write the charge separated resonance structure,

each ring would have $(4n + 2)$ π electrons, and exhibit aromaticity according to Hückel's rule.

CHAPTER 14

14.1   (a) The rate expression does not contain B. No conclusions can be drawn regarding A.
(b) The reaction is autocatalytic, that is, the product is a catalyst.

14.2   (a) $\Delta G^{\ddagger} = \Delta H^{\ddagger} - T\Delta S^{\ddagger}$. By decreasing the temperature we can favor the reaction which yields B. At lower temperatures the $T\Delta S^{\ddagger}$ contribution to the $\Delta G^{\ddagger}$ becomes less positive for the reaction A → C.   (b) Formation of B can be favored by employing solvents which support ion formation, for example, solvents of higher polarity.   (c) Favor the formation of B by increasing the concentration of [Z], whereas the rate of formation of C should not be affected.   (d) Employ an acid catalyst to improve the B/C ratio.

14.3   The magnitude of isotope effects is dependent on the ratio of masses and k_H/k_D (1/2) is much smaller than $k_{O^{16}}/k_{O^{18}}$ (16/18). Thus any property of water is altered much more by D substitution than by O^{18} substitution.

CHAPTER 15

15.1 $^-OSO_3H$; Br^-; Cl^-; CF_3COOH (or CF_3COO^-); H_2O; CH_3COOH (or CH_3COO^-)

15.2   Both will be converted to secondary carbonium ions; the stabilizing effects of methyl and ethyl groups on a carbonium ion are similar.

15.3 $CF_3CH_2CH_2Cl$

15.4

15.5 $CH_2{=}CHCH_2Br + Br\cdot \rightarrow BrCH_2\dot{C}HCH_2Br \xrightarrow{HBr} BrCH_2CH_2CH_2Br + Br\cdot$
(most stable radical)

$CH_2{=}CHCl + Br\cdot \rightarrow BrCH_2\dot{C}HCl \xrightarrow{HBr} BrCH_2CH_2Cl + Br\cdot$
(Cl stabilizes
α radical)

15.6

15.7 $R_2C=CR_2 > R_2C=CHR > R_2C=CH_2 > RCH=CHR > RCH=CH_2$

15.9   The first step is proton addition, and the proton will add only to the terminal carbon atoms of the conjugated diene system because the intermediate carbonium ion will be allylic (most stable).

15.10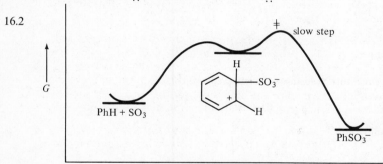

15.11 $CH_3C\equiv CH \xrightarrow[H^+]{Hg^{2+}}$

15.12   No. The linear acetylene will not allow the two ends of vinylacetylene to come close enough together.

CHAPTER 16

16.1 $:\overset{..}{O}=\overset{+}{N}=\overset{..}{O}: \leftrightarrow :\overset{..}{\overset{.}{O}}-\overset{+}{N}=\overset{..}{O}: \leftrightarrow :\overset{..}{O}=\overset{+}{N}-\overset{..}{\overset{.}{O}}:$

16.2

16.3 $2\,HOSO_2Cl \rightleftharpoons H_2^+O-SO_2Cl + SO_3 + Cl^- \rightleftharpoons {}^+SO_2Cl + \underline{HCl} + HSO_4^-$

16.4 $Cl_3CCHO + H^+ \rightarrow Cl_3C\overset{+}{C}HOH$

↓

$\underline{DDT} + H^+$

16.5

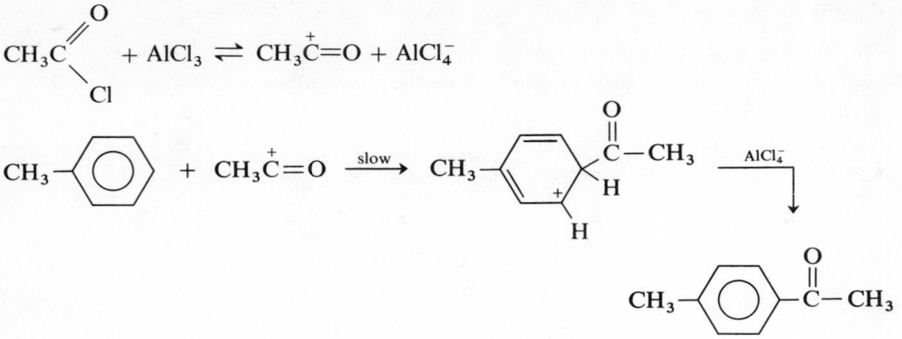

$$CH_3C\overset{O}{\underset{Cl}{}} + AlCl_3 \rightleftharpoons CH_3\overset{+}{C}{=}O + AlCl_4^-$$

16.6 $-CF_3$, deactivating, between PhCl and PhCOOH. , deactivating, between PhCl and PhCOOH.

16.7   An amine is more basic than an amide; the electron pair on nitrogen can be delocalized more into the ring in the amine, whereas with the amide delocalization of the type

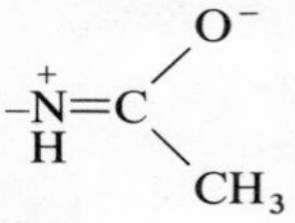

competes.

16.8

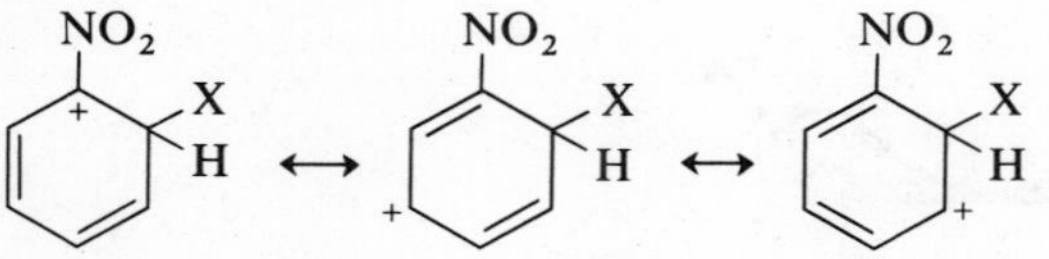

Very much like para substitution, form on the left very unfavorable.

16.9

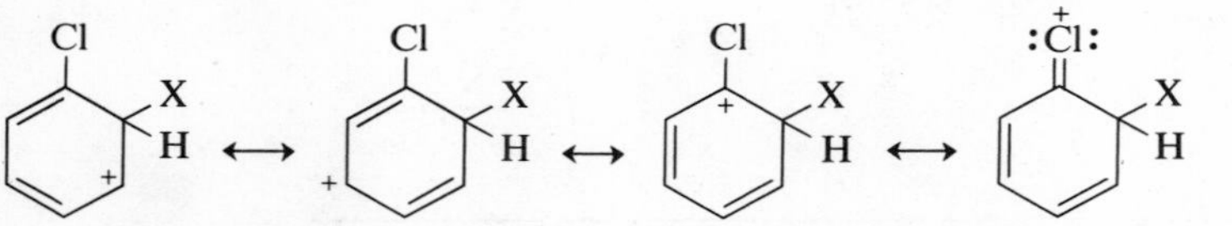

The latter form is especially good; all atoms have complete octets.

16.10

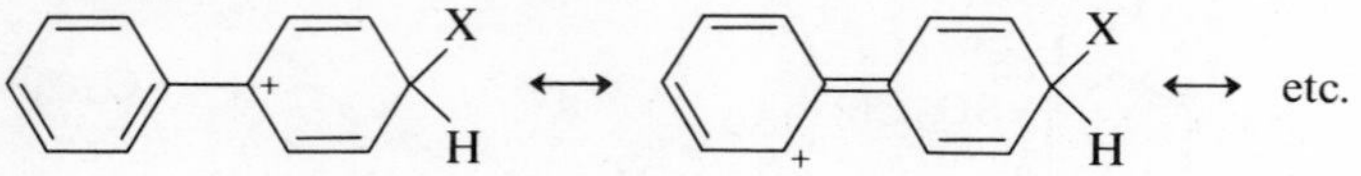

$^+NH_3$ is a *meta* director because of its powerful electron-withdrawing *inductive* effect.

16.11

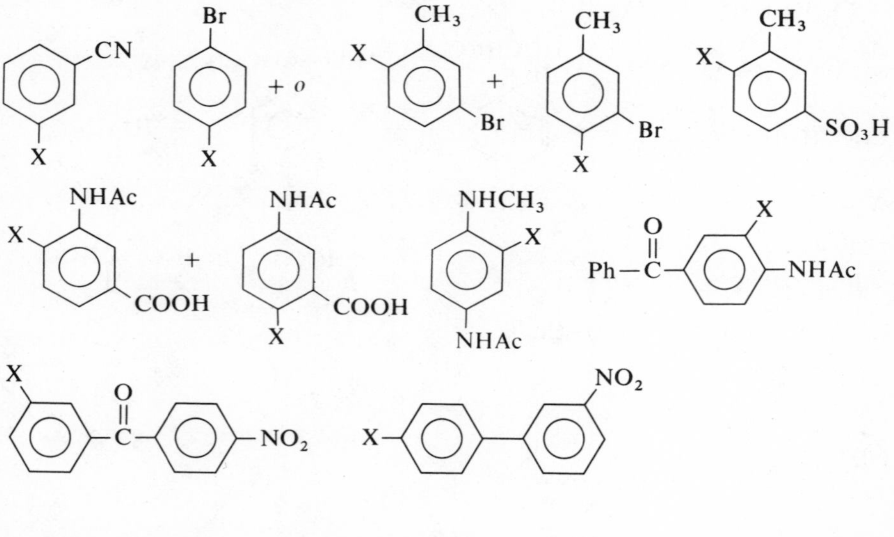

16.12 At 50°C the α isomer; at 170°C the β isomer. The β isomer is less sterically hindered (by the *peri*-hydrogen atom) than is the α compound, and is more stable.

16.13

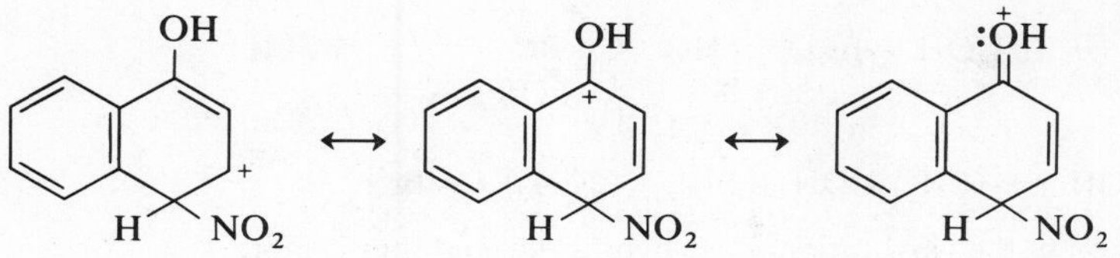

16.14

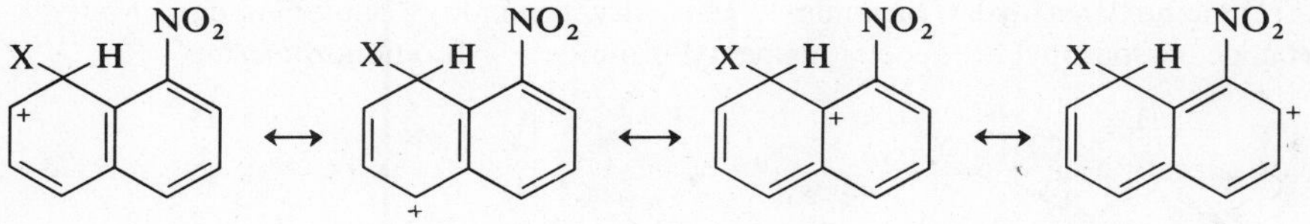

16.15

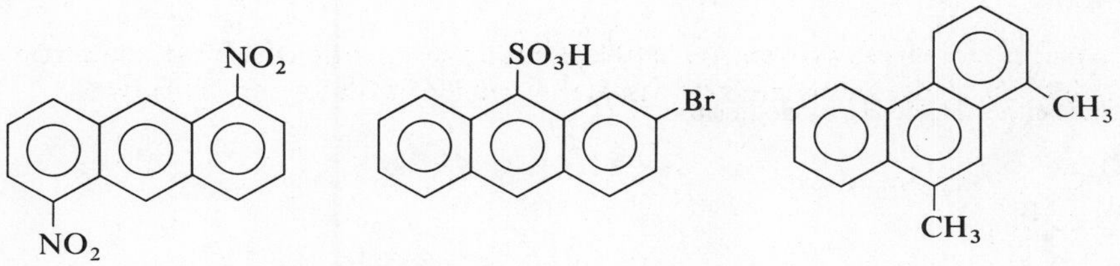

16.16 (a) 35.1 − 1.8 (from Table 7.4) = 33.3 kcal/mole lost (b) 59.4 − 51.0 (conjugation energy of styrene) = 8.4 kcal/mole lost (c) 89.7 − 68.7 (c.e. of biphenyl) = 21.0 kcal/mole lost (d) 81.3 − 2 × 35.1 (c.e. of benzene) = 11.1 kcal/mole lost.

16.17 Alizarin is more stable; the nmr shows six aromatic protons.

16.18

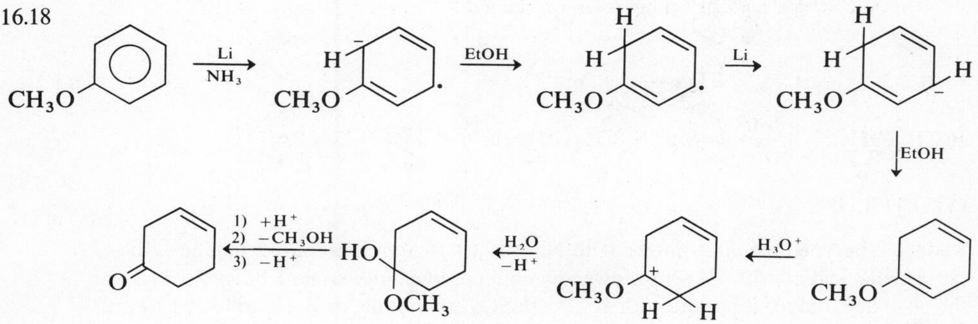

CHAPTER 17

17.1 (a) $CH_3CH_2CH_2Br + CH_3O^-Na^+$ or $CH_3I + CH_3CH_2CH_2O^-Na^+$
(b) $(CH_3)_2CHCH_2CH_2Br + (CH_3)_2CHCH_2COO^-Na^+$
(c) $2\,(CH_3)_2CH{-}Br + K^{+-}OOCCH_2CH_2COO^-K^+$

17.2 The negative charge is localized on a polarizable sulfur atom in RS^-.

17.3 (a) $CH_3CH_2CH_2CH_2S^-Na^+$ (b) $PhCH_2{-}\overset{+}{P}Ph_3$ Br^- (c) $CH_3COOCH_2CH_3$

17.4 ICH_3Cl and C_2H_6OBr

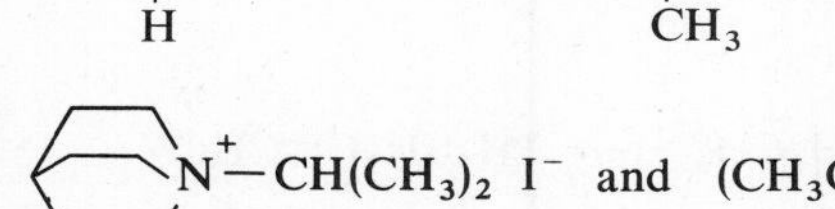

17.5

and $(CH_3CH_2)_3\overset{+}{N}CH(CH_3)_2$ I^-

17.7   Charge is being destroyed, so polar solvents stabilize the starting materials and raise the activation energy.

17.8 $CH_3Br + {}^-OH \rightarrow CH_3OH + Br^-$,

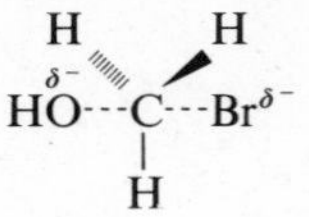

$(CH_3)_3CBr + {}^-OH \rightarrow (CH_3)_3COH + Br^-$, $(CH_3)_3\overset{\delta+}{C}\cdots Br^{\delta-}$

17.9   The positive carbon in the vinyl cation is sp^2-hybridized, and thus is more electronegative than sp^3 carbon.

17.10 *p,p'*-Dimethoxybenzhydryl bromide > benzhydryl bromide > *t*-butyl iodide > *t*-butyl bromide > isopropyl bromide > neopentyl bromide > 1-bromonorbornane

17.11

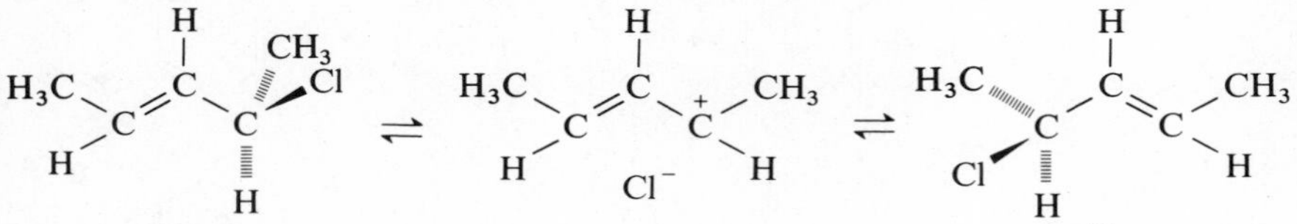

17.14 Replace either H_a or H_b by deuterium.

17.15

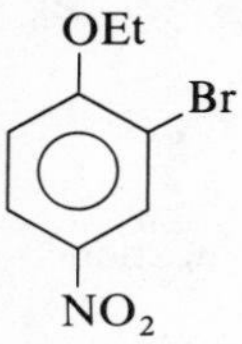

17.16

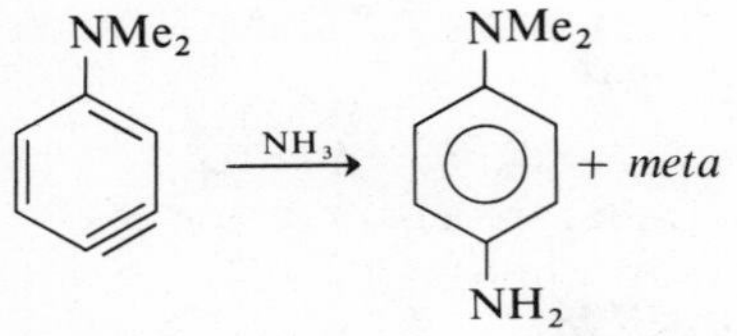

17.17 $BrCH_2CH_2CH_2Br \overset{Mg}{\rightarrow} Br\overset{+}{Mg}CH_2CH_2\overset{-}{CH_2}\frown Br \rightarrow \triangleright + MgBr_2$

CHAPTER 18

18.1   Reduce 2-butyne to *trans*-2-butene with $Na/NH_3(l)$. Reaction of *trans*-2-butene with perbenzoic acid or with HOBr followed by cold base will give *trans*-2-butene oxide. For the *cis*-oxide, reduce 2-butyne with H_2,$Pd/BaSO_4$, quinoline, or B_2H_6 followed by acetic acid and then carry out the same reactions as described for the *trans*-alkene.

18.2

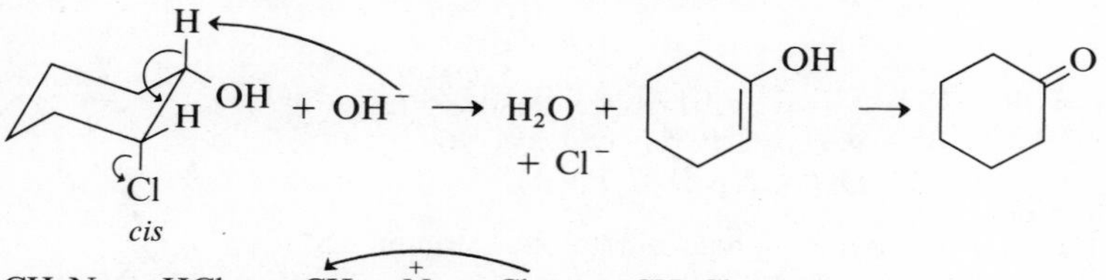

18.3 $CH_2N_2 + HCl \rightarrow CH_3 - \overset{+}{N_2} + Cl^- \rightarrow CH_3Cl + N_2$

18.4   Mostly with inversion; S_N2-type mechanism.

18.5

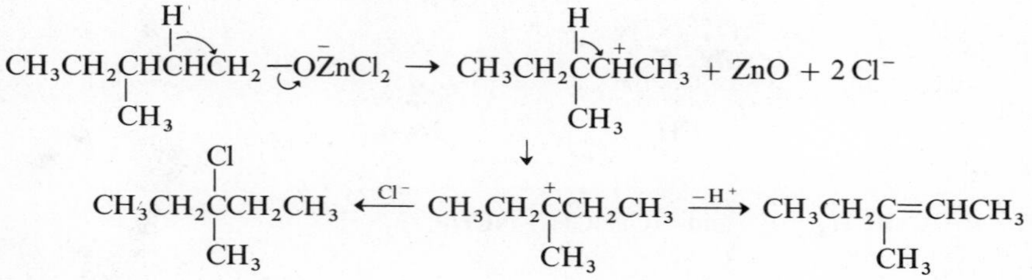

18.6   (CH$_3$)$_2$C—CH(CH$_3$)$_2$
                |
                Br

18.7   RCH$_2$OH + PCl$_5$ → R—CH$_2$—O—PCl$_3$ → RCH$_2$Cl + POCl$_3$ + HCl
                                   Cl$^-$ Cl
                                                 |
                                                 Cl

18.8

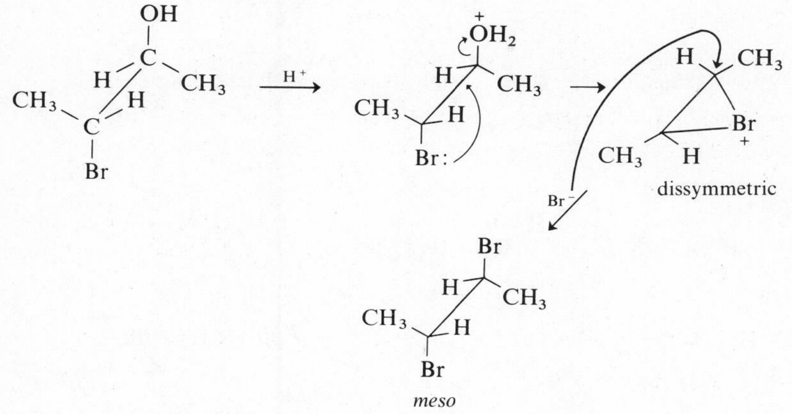

meso

18.9   (a) R—C—C—R   (b) RCH—CHR′   (c) R$_2$C—CH$_2$OH   (d)
              | | | | |
              R′ R′   OH   OH   OH
              (OH OH above a and R,C)

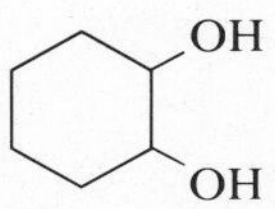

18.10   H$_2$C——CH$_2$ + H$^+$ → H$_2$C——CH$_2$ $\xrightarrow[\text{slow}]{\text{H}_2\ddot{\text{O}}}$ HOCH$_2$CH$_2$OH$_2^+$
              \ /   \ /
               O   O
                                    |
                                   +H
                                          $\xrightarrow{-\text{H}^+}$ HOCH$_2$CH$_2$OH

18.11   The strain energy of ethylene oxide is greater; thus protonated ethylene oxide is at a
        higher energy level than protonated ethyl ether and the $\Delta G^{\ddagger}$ is lower.

CHAPTER 19

19.1   Because of the polarization, $>$C$=$O ↔ $>\overset{+}{\text{C}}$—O$^-$, the carbonyl carbon is electrophilic
        and the nucleophile will attack at carbon. The intermediate B$\geqslant$C—O$^-$ is more stable
        than $>$C̄—O—B (negative charge on the more electronegative atom), which explains
        the thermodynamics.

19.2   Delocalization of an unshared pair of electrons on oxygen (resonance):

        R$_2\overset{+}{\text{C}}$—ÖR′ ↔ R$_2$C$=\overset{+}{\ddot{\text{O}}}$—R′

19.3   A new ring is formed in the final step and this is favored by entropy (Section 13.1).

19.4

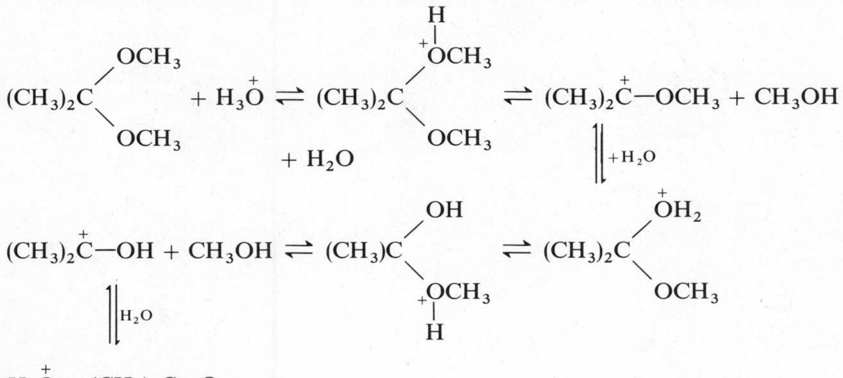

19.5 $CH_2=O + H^+ \rightleftharpoons CH_2=\overset{+}{O}H + CH_2=\ddot{O} \rightarrow CH_2=\overset{+}{O}-CH_2-OH$

$$\xleftarrow{\text{etc.}} CH_2=\overset{+}{O}-CH_2OCH_2OH \quad \xleftarrow{CH_2=\ddot{O}:}$$

19.6   Because the intermediate, $Ph-\overset{\overset{O^-}{|}}{\underset{\underset{OCH_2CH_3}{|}}{C}}-H$, is not sufficiently acidic to be converted to

$Ph-\overset{\overset{OH}{|}}{\underset{\underset{OCH_2CH_3}{|}}{C^-}}$

19.7   (a) $(CH_3)_2CHCH_2OH + PBr_3 \rightarrow (CH_3)_2CHCH_2Br \xrightarrow[Et_2O]{Mg}$

$CH_3\overset{\overset{OH}{|}}{C}HCH_2CH_3 \xrightarrow{K_2Cr_2O_7/H^+} CH_3\overset{\overset{O}{||}}{C}CH_2CH_3 \qquad (CH_3)_2CHCH_2MgBr$

$\xrightarrow{\text{then } NH_4Cl}$ Product

(b) ⬡ + $CH_3COCl \xrightarrow{AlCl_3}$ ⬡ $\overset{\overset{O}{||}}{C}-CH_3 \xrightarrow[NH_4Cl]{\text{then}}$ Product

$CH_3CH_2Br \xrightarrow[\text{ether}]{Mg} CH_3CH_2MgBr$

(c) $CH_2=CH_2 \xrightarrow{HBr} CH_3CH_2Br \xrightarrow[\text{ether}]{Mg} CH_3CH_2MgBr \xrightarrow[H_3O^+]{\text{then}}$ Product

$\xrightarrow{HOBr} \underset{\underset{Br}{|}}{CH_2}-CH_2OH \xrightarrow{\text{base}} H_2C\overset{}{\underset{O}{\diagdown\diagup}}CH_2$

(d) Prepare 1-butanol as in (c), convert it to *n*-butyl bromide with HBr. Make the Grignard reagent and react this with acetophenone (b).

19.8   These Grignard reagents do not have a β-hydrogen atom available.

19.9   (a) $PhCCH_3 + CH_2=PPh_3$ (from CH_3I and Ph_3P)   (b) $(CH_3CH_2)_2C=O +$
$\quad\quad\quad\;\;\overset{||}{O}$

$CH_3CH=PPh_3$ (c) 2 ⬡ $=O + Ph_3P=CH(CH_2)_4CH=PPh_3$ (from

$2\,Ph_3P + Br(CH_2)_6Br)$

19.10   (a) H_2, Pd/C, 25°C, 15 psi   (b) $NaBH_4$, MeOH, or $LiAlH_4$, ether; then hydrolysis
(c) (a) then (b) or *vice versa*; *or* H_2, Ni, 50°C, 1000 psi

19.11   (a) NH_2NH_2, KOH, diethylene glycol, 200°C   (b) Zn–Hg, HCl   (c) EtSH, H^+,
then Raney Ni   (d) H_2, Pd–C, 25°, H^+ (e) $NaBH_4$, then dehydrate with acid,
followed by H_2, Pd, 25°C, 15 psi

19.12   (a) ⬡ + $CH_3Cl \xrightarrow{AlCl_3}$ ⬡$-CH_3 \xrightarrow[Fe]{Br_2} Br-$⬡$-CH_3$

$\xrightarrow{KMnO_4}$

$Br-$⬡$-COOH$

(b) $CH_3MgI + CH_3CHO \xrightarrow[\text{H}_3\text{O}^+]{\text{then}} CH_3\overset{\overset{\displaystyle OH}{|}}{C}HCH_3 \xrightarrow{\text{HBr}} CH_3\overset{\overset{\displaystyle Br}{|}}{C}HCH_3$

$\downarrow$ Mg/ether

$(CH_3)_2CHCOOH \xleftarrow[\text{H}_3\text{O}^+]{\text{CO}_2,\text{ then}} (CH_3)_2CHMgBr$

(c) $2\,CH_3CHO \rightarrow CH_3\overset{\overset{\displaystyle OH}{|}}{C}HCH_2CHO \xrightarrow{\text{H}^+} CH_3CH{=}CHCHO \xrightarrow[\text{25°C, 1000 psi}]{\text{H}_2,\text{ Ni}}$

$\xleftarrow[\text{ether}]{\text{CH}_3\text{CHO}} \xleftarrow{\text{Mg}} CH_3CH_2CH_2CH_2Br \xleftarrow{\text{HBr}} CH_3CH_2CH_2CH_2OH$

$\xrightarrow[\text{H}_3\text{O}^+]{} CH_3CH_2CH_2CH_2\overset{\overset{\displaystyle OH}{|}}{C}HCH_3$

19.13 Using data in Table 13.1, the heat of combustion of the aldol dimer is calculated to be 20.7 kcal/mole lower than the other dimer. The first reaction would be more favorable.

19.14 The equilibrium between acetone and diacetone alcohol favors acetone. In the presence of acid, dehydration of diacetone alcohol to mesityl oxide occurs, forcing the overall equilibrium to the right.

19.15 $CH_3CHO + \bar{O}H \rightleftharpoons \bar{C}H_2CHO \xrightarrow{\text{CH}_2{=}\text{O}} \bar{O}CH_2CH_2CHO$

$\downarrow \text{H}_2\text{O}$

$(HOCH_2)_3CCHO \xleftarrow[\text{3 times}]{\text{repeat}} HOCH_2CH_2CHO$

$CH_2{=}O + \bar{O}H \rightleftharpoons \underset{HO}{\overset{O^-}{\underset{\quad H}{C}}}{}H \; + \; O{=}\overset{}{C}{-}C(CH_2OH)_3$

$\downarrow$

$HCOO^- + (HOCH_2)_4C \leftarrow HCOOH + \bar{O}CH_2C(CH_2OH)_3$

19.16 The enolate on the left is stabilized because the double bond is most highly substituted.

19.17 (structures)

19.18 (a) (b) $Ph{-}\overset{\overset{\displaystyle O}{\|}}{C}{-}O{-}\bigcirc{-}OCH_3$ (c)

19.19 $(CH_3)_2C{=}O$ (via a retroaldol reaction)

19.20 (a) $Ph{-}\overset{\overset{\displaystyle O}{}}{\underset{\displaystyle O}{C}}{-}CH_2CH_2N(CH_3)_2$ (b)   (c) $Ph{-}CH{-}CH_2$

19.21 (a) $CH_3CH_2NO_2 + Et_3N \rightleftharpoons Et_3\overset{+}{N}H + CH_3\overset{-}{C}HNO_2$

$\downarrow$ $CH_2{=}CH{-}\overset{\overset{\displaystyle O}{\|}}{C}{-}CH_3$

$CH_3\underset{NO_2}{\overset{}{C}}HCH_2CH_2\overset{\overset{\displaystyle O}{\|}}{C}CH_3 \xleftarrow{Et_3\overset{+}{N}H} CH_3\underset{NO_2}{\overset{}{C}}HCH_2CH{=}\overset{\overset{\displaystyle O^-}{|}}{C}CH_3$

(b) Similar mechanism: add $^-CH(CO_2CH_3)_2$ in a Michael reaction

(c) Michael addition to give

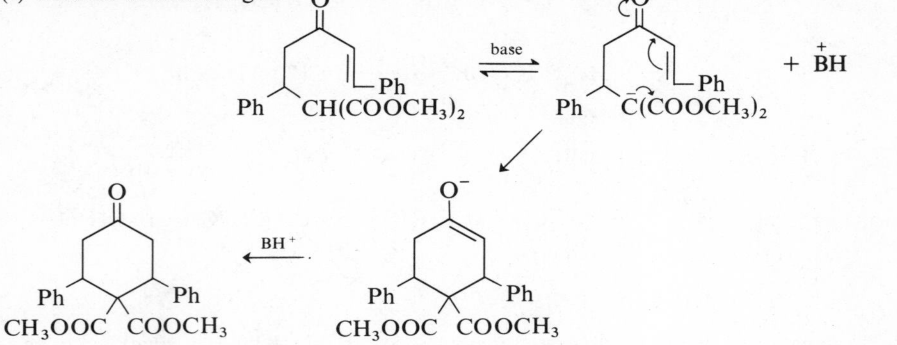

(d)

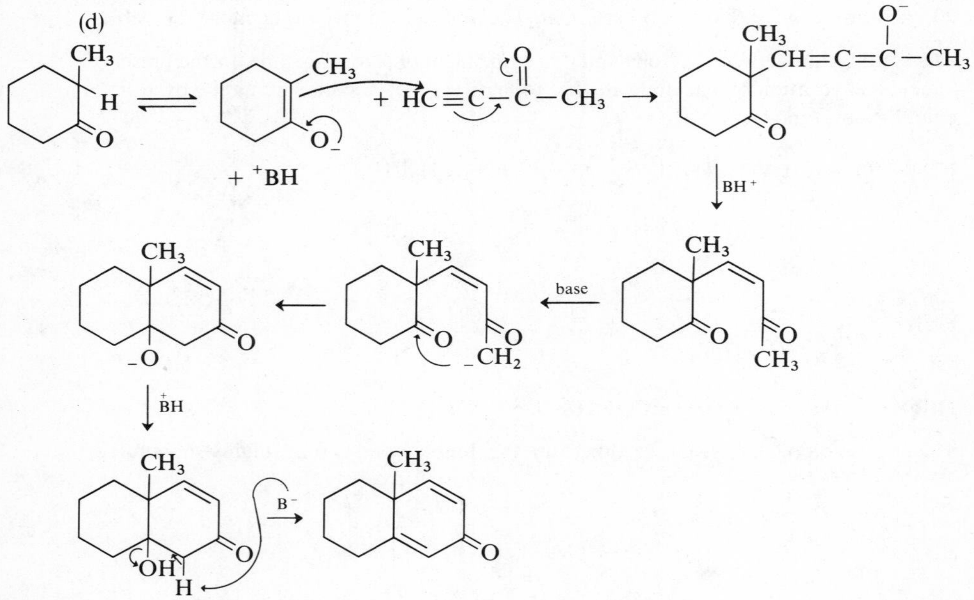

(e) Michael reaction between

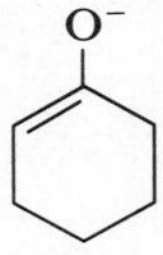

and

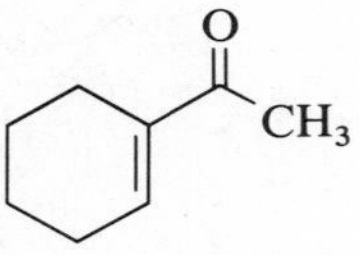

to give

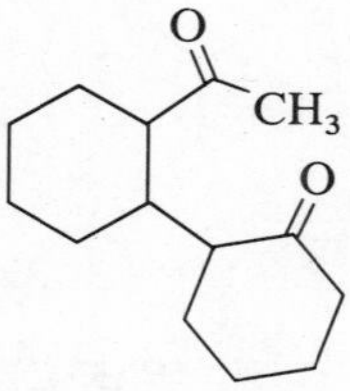

and intramolecular aldol condensation to the product

CHAPTER 20

20.1 $CH_3CHCOOH > CH_3CHClCOOH > O_2NCH_2CH_2COOH > CH_3CH_2COOH$
        $\quad\quad |$
        $\quad\ NO_2$

20.2 $CH_3\overset{O}{\overset{\|}{C}}OH + PCl_5 \rightarrow CH_3\overset{O}{\overset{\|}{C}}-O-PCl_3 + H^+Cl^- \rightarrow CH_3\overset{O}{\overset{\|}{C}}-Cl + POCl_3 + HCl$
        $\quad\quad\quad\quad\quad\quad\quad\quad\quad |$
        $\quad\quad\quad\quad\quad\quad\quad\quad\ Cl$

20.3

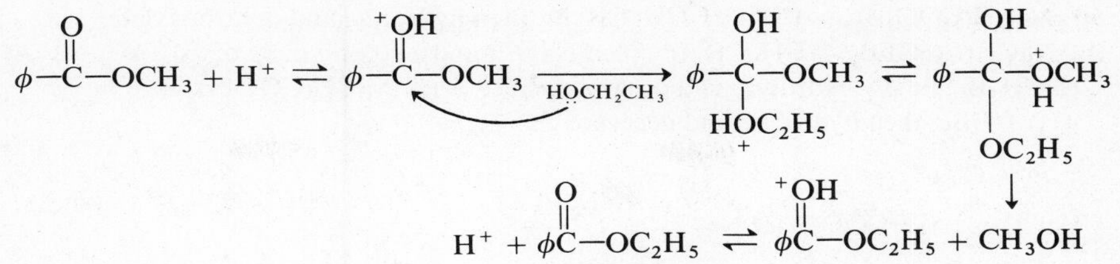

$$\phi-\overset{O}{\underset{}{C}}-OCH_3 + H^+ \rightleftharpoons \phi-\overset{+OH}{\underset{}{C}}-OCH_3 \xrightarrow[HOCH_2CH_3]{} \phi-\overset{OH}{\underset{\underset{+}{HOC_2H_5}}{C}}-OCH_3 \rightleftharpoons \phi-\overset{OH}{\underset{OC_2H_5}{\overset{|}{\underset{|}{C}}}}-\overset{+}{\underset{H}{OCH_3}}$$

$$H^+ + \phi\overset{O}{\underset{}{C}}-OC_2H_5 \rightleftharpoons \phi\overset{+OH}{\underset{}{C}}-OC_2H_5 + CH_3OH$$

20.4

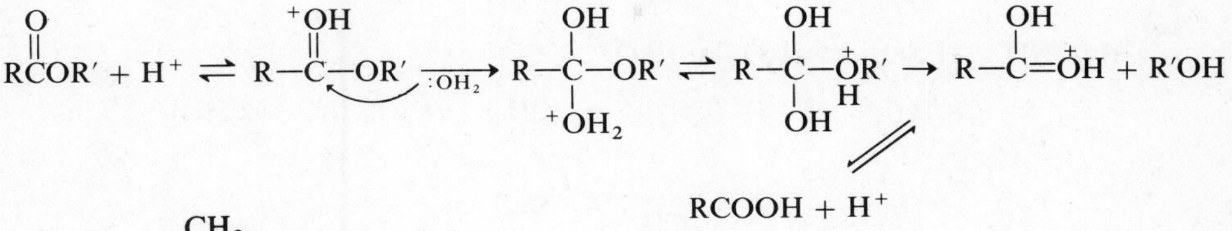

$$R\overset{O}{\underset{}{C}}OR' + H^+ \rightleftharpoons R-\overset{+OH}{\underset{}{C}}-OR' \xrightarrow{:OH_2} R-\overset{OH}{\underset{\overset{+}{OH_2}}{\overset{|}{\underset{|}{C}}}}-OR' \rightleftharpoons R-\overset{OH}{\underset{OH}{\overset{|}{\underset{|}{C}}}}-\overset{+}{\underset{H}{OR'}} \rightarrow R-\overset{OH}{\underset{}{C}}=\overset{+}{O}H + R'OH$$

$$RCOOH + H^+$$

20.5

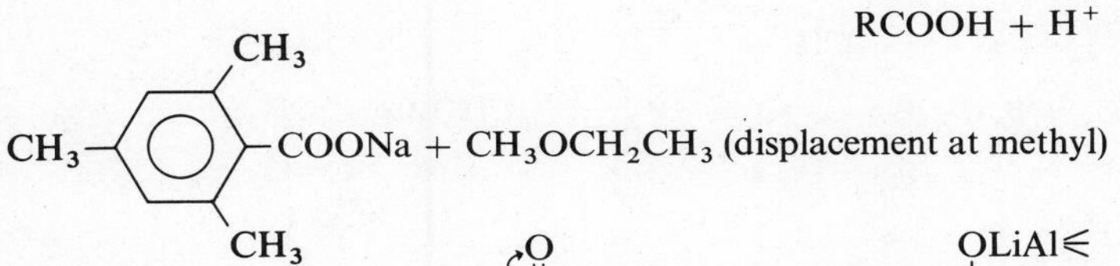

$CH_3- \bigcirc (2,4,6-(CH_3)_3) -COONa + CH_3OCH_2CH_3$ (displacement at methyl)

20.6 $CH_3COOH + LiAlH_4 \rightarrow CH_3\overset{O}{\underset{}{C}}-OLiAlH_3 \xrightarrow{H^-} CH_3-\overset{OLiAl\leqslant}{\underset{H}{\overset{|}{\underset{|}{C}}}}-OLiAl\leqslant$

$$Al(OH)_3 + Li^+ + CH_3CH_2OH \xleftarrow{H_3O^+} CH_3\overset{OLiAl\leqslant}{\underset{H}{\overset{|}{\underset{|}{C}}}}-H \xleftarrow{H^-} CH_3\overset{O}{\underset{}{C}}-H + LiAlOH$$

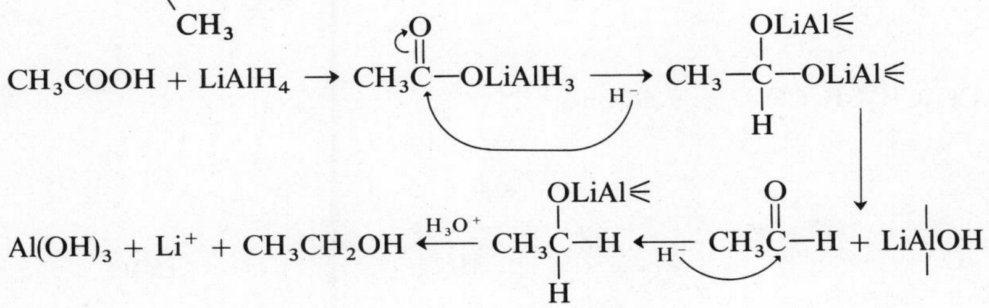

20.7 $R_3C-OMgX \xrightarrow[H_2O]{NH_4Cl} R_3COH$ (a 3° alcohol)

20.8 $R_2CH-OMgX \xrightarrow{H_3O^+} R_2CHOH$ (a 2° alcohol)

20.9

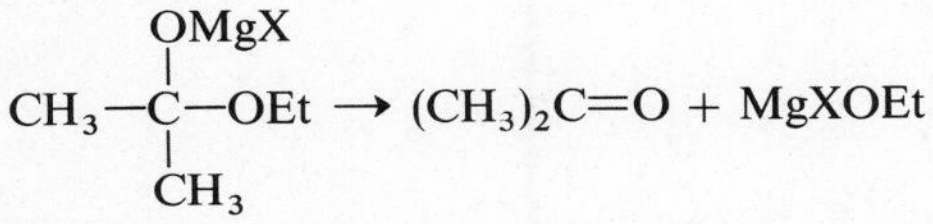

$$CH_3-\overset{OMgX}{\underset{CH_3}{\overset{|}{\underset{|}{C}}}}-OEt \rightarrow (CH_3)_2C=O + MgXOEt$$

Since ketones are more reactive than esters, the actual reaction products are $\frac{1}{2}$ mole $(CH_3)_3COH + \frac{1}{2}$ mole starting ester.

20.10

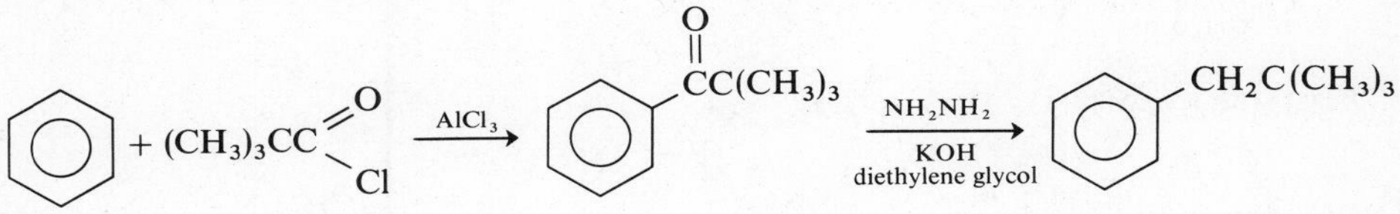

20.11

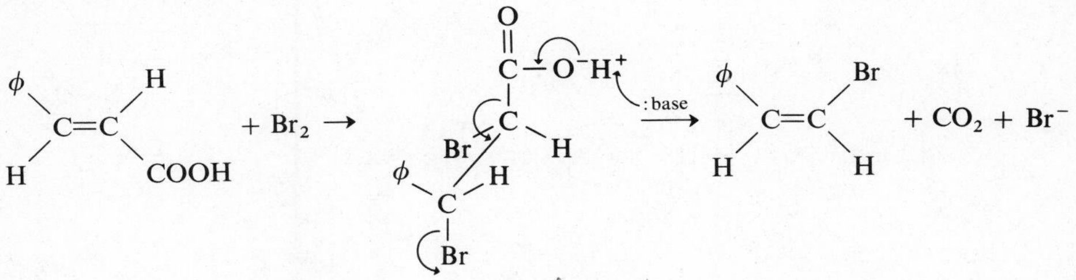

20.12 $CH_3CH_2COOH \xrightarrow{Br_2, P} CH_3\overset{}{\underset{Br}{CH}}COOH \xrightarrow[\Delta]{xsNH_3} CH_3\overset{}{\underset{NH_2}{CH}}COOH + NH_4Br$

20.13 $R-Br \xrightarrow{Mg} RMgBr \xrightarrow[CH_2-CH_2 (O)]{} RCH_2CH_2OMgBr \xrightarrow{H_3O^+} RCH_2CH_2OH$

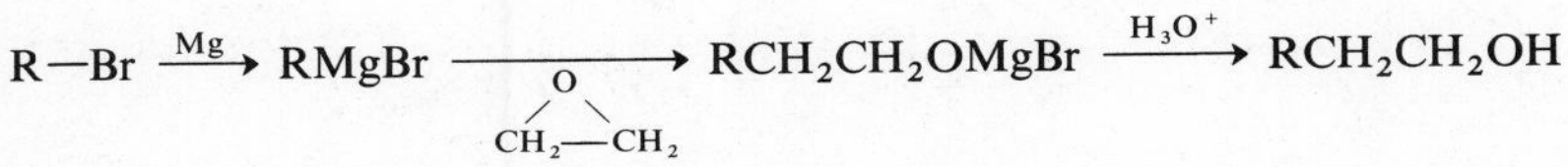

20.14 (a) NaCH(COOEt)$_2$ + CH$_3$CH$_2$CH$_2$CH$_2$Br, then hydrolyze and decarboxylate.
(b) NaCH(COOEt)$_2$ + CH$_3$CH$_2$Br; then NaOEt and a second mole of
CH$_3$CH$_2$Br; finally hydrolyze and decarboxylate.   (c) NaCH(COOEt)$_2$ +
(CH$_3$)$_2$CHBr; then hydrolyze and decarboxylate.

20.15

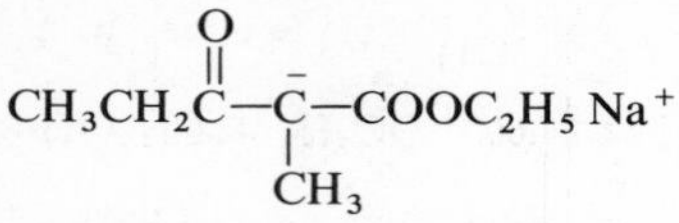

$$CH_3CH_2\overset{\overset{\displaystyle O}{\|}}{C}-\overset{\overset{\displaystyle -}{\underset{\underset{\displaystyle CH_3}{|}}{C}}}{}-COOC_2H_5 \; Na^+$$

20.16 HCOOH + H$_2$SO$_4$ $\rightleftharpoons$ H$_3$O$^+$ + HSO$_4^-$ + CO

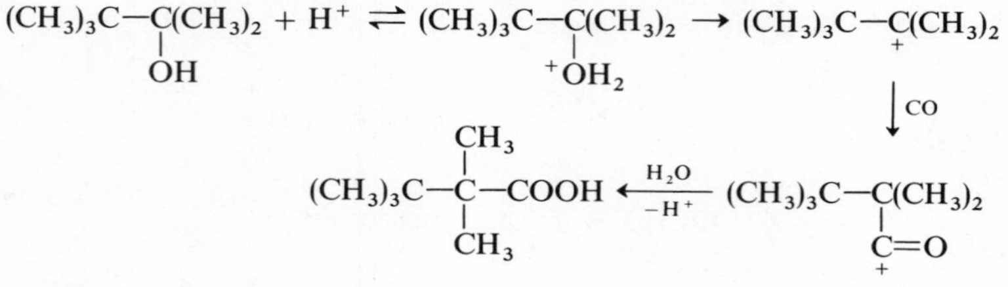

$$(CH_3)_3C-\underset{\underset{\displaystyle OH}{|}}{C}(CH_3)_2 + H^+ \rightleftharpoons (CH_3)_3C-\underset{\underset{\displaystyle ^+OH_2}{|}}{C}(CH_3)_2 \rightarrow (CH_3)_3C-\overset{+}{C}(CH_3)_2$$

$$\downarrow CO$$

$$(CH_3)_3C-\underset{\underset{\displaystyle CH_3}{|}}{\overset{\overset{\displaystyle CH_3}{|}}{C}}-COOH \xleftarrow[-H^+]{H_2O} (CH_3)_3C-\underset{\underset{\displaystyle \overset{+}{C}=O}{|}}{C}(CH_3)_2$$

20.17

$$\text{(OCH}_2\text{CH}_2\text{CH}_2\text{CH}_2\text{CH}_2\overset{\overset{\displaystyle O}{\|}}{\text{C}})_n, \text{ a polymer}$$

20.19

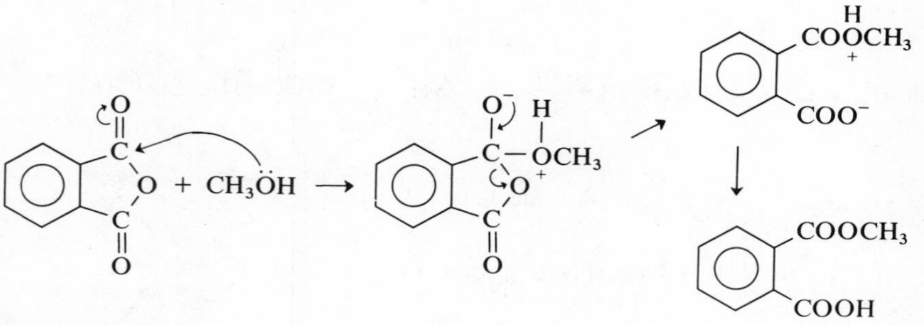

CHAPTER 21

21.1

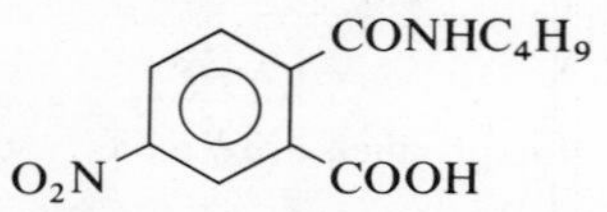

The most electron deficient carbonyl group of the anhydride is attacked (that para to the
nitro group).

21.2 2 HNO$_2$ $\rightleftharpoons$ $\overset{+}{N}$O + H$_2$O + $\overset{-}{N}$O$_2$

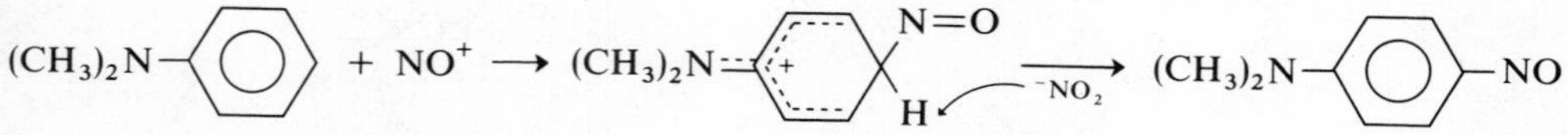

21.3

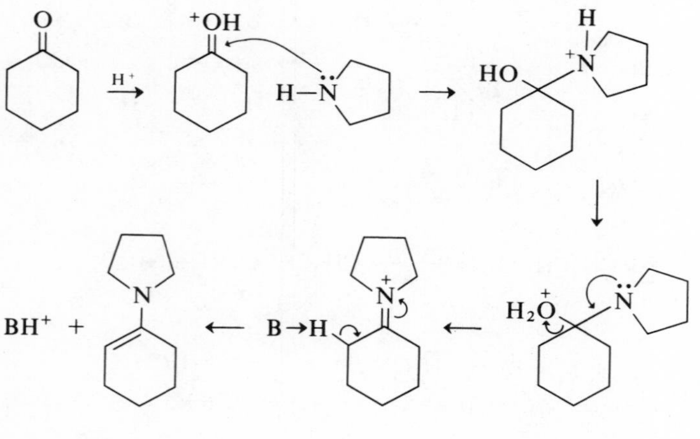

21.4   (a) $\phi—CN + H^+ \rightleftharpoons \phi\overset{+}{C}=NH \xrightarrow{H_2O} \phi\underset{\overset{|}{+}{OH_2}}{C}=N \underset{\overset{|}{OH}}{\overset{-H^+}{\rightleftharpoons}} \phi—\underset{OH}{C}=NH \rightleftharpoons \phi\underset{O}{\overset{\|}{C}}NH_2$

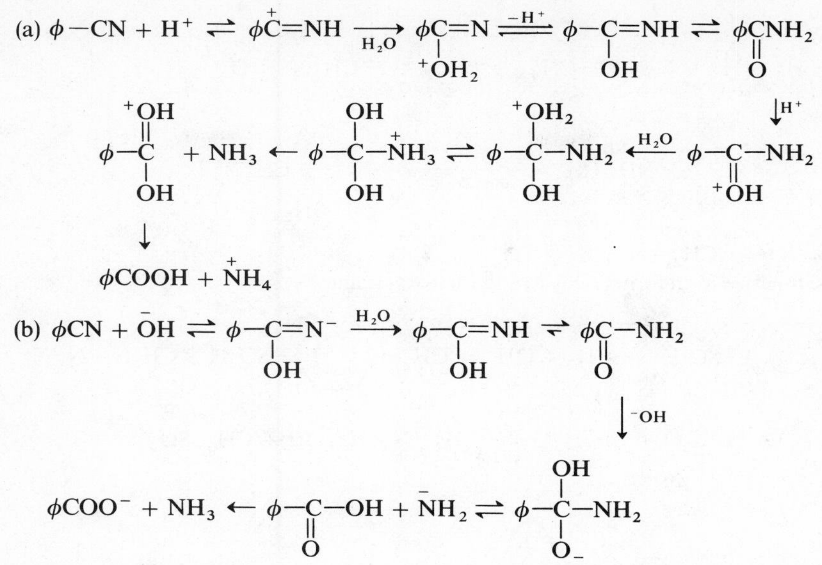

$\phi—\underset{OH}{\overset{+OH}{\overset{\|}{C}}} + NH_3 \leftarrow \phi—\underset{OH}{\overset{OH}{\underset{|}{C}}}—\overset{+}{N}H_3 \rightleftharpoons \phi—\underset{OH}{\overset{+OH_2}{\underset{|}{C}}}—NH_2 \xleftarrow{H_2O} \phi—\underset{+OH}{\overset{OH}{\underset{\|}{C}}}—NH_2 \downarrow{H^+}$

$\downarrow$

$\phi COOH + \overset{+}{N}H_4$

(b) $\phi CN + \overset{-}{O}H \rightleftharpoons \phi—\underset{OH}{C}=N^- \xrightarrow{H_2O} \phi—\underset{OH}{C}=NH \rightleftharpoons \phi\underset{O}{\overset{\|}{C}}—NH_2$

$\downarrow^{-OH}$

$\phi COO^- + NH_3 \leftarrow \phi—\underset{O}{\overset{\|}{C}}—OH + \overset{-}{N}H_2 \rightleftharpoons \phi—\underset{O_-}{\overset{OH}{\underset{|}{C}}}—NH_2$

21.5 $\underset{\text{COOEt}}{\overset{\text{CH}_2\text{COOEt}}{(CH_2)_n}} + NaOEt \rightleftharpoons \underset{\underset{O}{\overset{\|}{C}}—OEt}{\overset{\overset{-}{C}HCO_2Et}{(CH_2)_n}} \rightleftharpoons \underset{C=O}{\overset{CHCO_2Et}{(CH_2)_n}|}$

$\downarrow^{-OEt}$

$EtOH + \underset{C=O}{\overset{C=CO_2Et}{(CH_2)_n}|}$

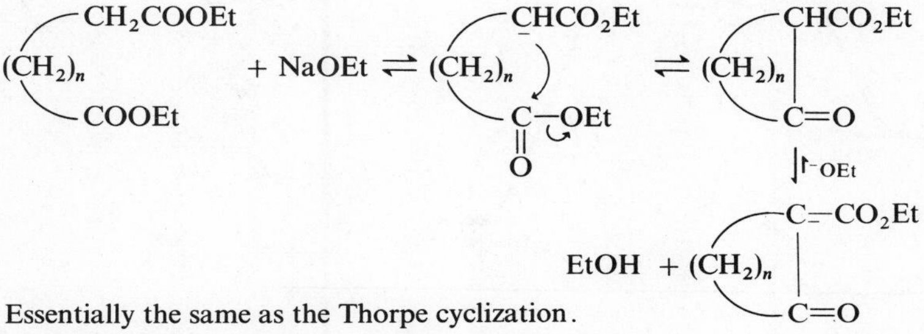

Essentially the same as the Thorpe cyclization.

21.6   No; because one could not alkylate potassium phthalimide with $(CH_3)_3C—X$ (dehydrohalogenation to isobutylene will occur).

21.7   Alkyl cations will rearrange to more stable cations; acylium ions will not rearrange; for example, $(CH_3)_3C\overset{+}{C}H_2 \rightarrow (CH_3)_2\overset{+}{C}CH_2CH_3$. However, acyl carbonium ions *do not* rearrange, $(CH_3)_3C\overset{+}{C}=O$.

21.8

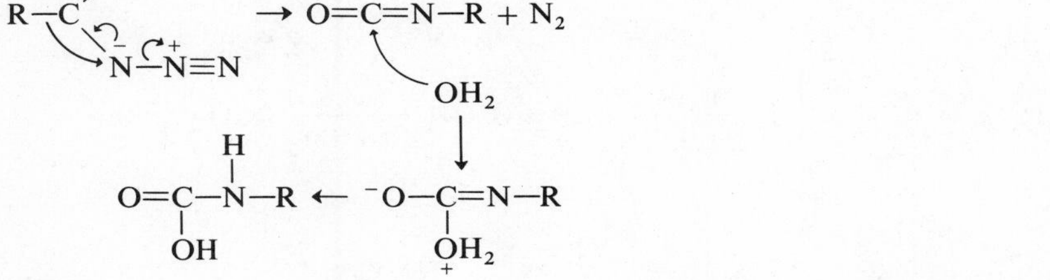

21.9

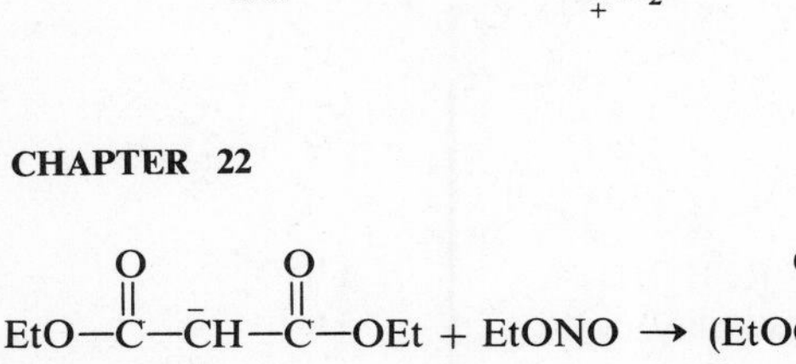

CHAPTER 22

22.1 $\underset{}{\overset{O}{\overset{\|}{EtO—C}}}—\overset{-}{C}H—\underset{}{\overset{O}{\overset{\|}{C}}}—OEt + EtONO \rightarrow (Et\overset{O}{\overset{\|}{OC}})_2CH—NO \rightarrow (Et\overset{O}{\overset{\|}{OC}})_2C=NOH$

22.2

$$\phi-\underset{\underset{\|}{N-OH}}{C}-CH_3 + H^+ \rightleftharpoons \phi-\underset{\underset{\|}{N-\overset{+}{O}H_2}}{C}-CH_3 \rightarrow \phi-\overset{+}{N}=C-CH_3 + H_2O$$

$$\phi NH\underset{\underset{\|}{O}}{C}CH_3 \xleftarrow[\text{tautomerize}]{-H^+} \phi-N=\underset{\underset{+}{OH_2}}{C}-CH_3$$

22.3 $CH_3-N=O \rightarrow CH_2=N-OH$
Would synthesize from formaldehyde and hydroxylamine.

22.4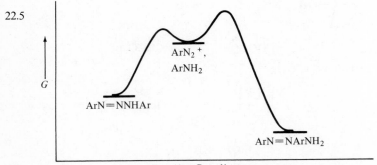

22.5

Reaction Coordinate ⟶

22.6 $H_2N-\langle\bigcirc\rangle-SO_3H \xrightarrow{HNO_2} {}^-O_3S-\langle\bigcirc\rangle-\overset{+}{N_2} + $ naphthol $\xrightarrow[\text{dil } {}^-OH]{}$ **Orange II**

$$\text{naphthalene} \xrightarrow[160°C]{H_2SO_4} \text{naphthalene-SO}_3H \xrightarrow[\substack{\text{fuse} \\ \text{with} \\ \text{NaOH}}]{}$$

22.7   The two amino groups are protonated, thus removing them from the conjugated system.

22.8   (a) α-Diazoacetophenone   (b) Methyl *p*-bromobenzoate
(c) Methyl *m*-methoxybenzoate

22.9 $RCH_2OH + ArSO_2Cl \xrightarrow{\text{pyridine}} RCH_2OSO_2Ar \xrightarrow{NaCN} RCH_2CN$

$$\downarrow HBr$$

$$RCH_2Br \xrightarrow{Mg} RCH_2MgBr \xrightarrow[\text{then } H_3O^+]{CH_2=O} RCH_2CH_2OH \xleftarrow[\text{then } H_3O^+]{LiAlH_4} RCH_2COOEt$$

with $\downarrow \begin{smallmatrix} EtOH \\ H_2O \end{smallmatrix}$ on right side

22.10 $RCH_2Br + $ (phthalimide-N⁻K⁺) $\longrightarrow$ (N-CH₂R phthalimide)

$$\downarrow {}^-OH$$

$$RCH_2NH_2$$
(Gabriel synthesis)

CHAPTER 23

23.1 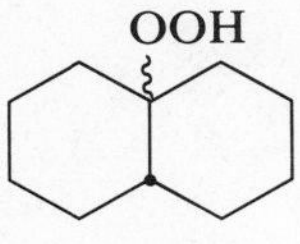 Both trans and cis isomers present.

23.2 In the ground state, the highest occupied molecular orbitals are the degenerate pair of $2p\pi^*$ orbitals, into which must be placed two electrons. According to Hund's rule these electrons must be placed one each in the two orbitals with the spins parallel. A higher energy state is therefore having both electrons, spin-paired, in the same molecular orbital.

23.3

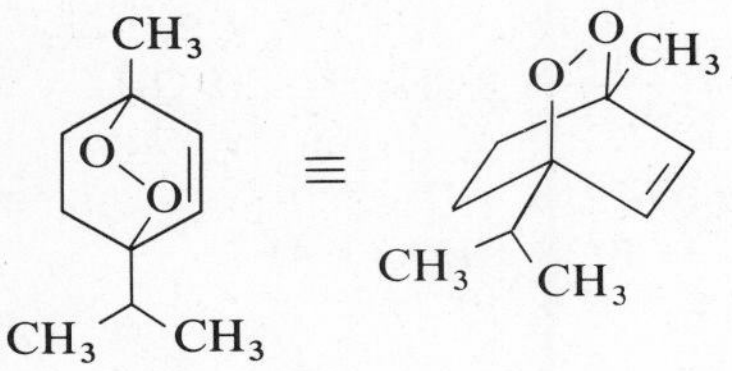

23.4 Trace alkene + $HAlCl_4 \rightleftharpoons R^+ + \bar{A}lCl_4$

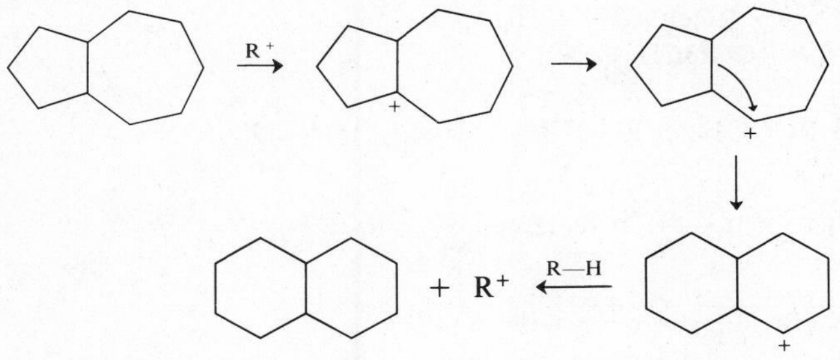

The driving force is the greater thermodynamic stability of decalin.

23.5 The entropy change *for dehydrogenation* is positive. At higher temperatures the $-T\Delta S°$ term (which is overall negative) becomes important, making $\Delta G°$ for dehydrogenation a negative value (favored).

23.6

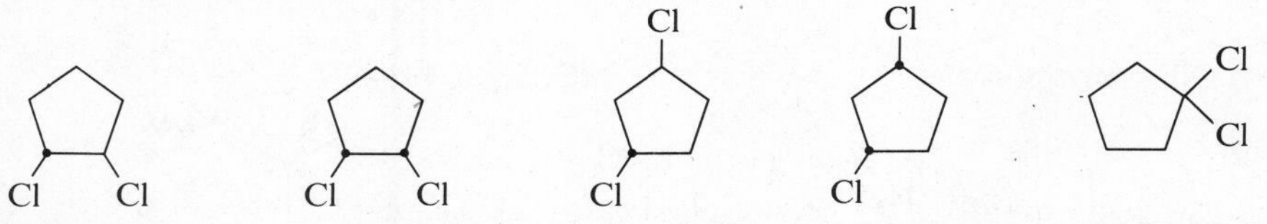

trans-1,2 (dl)	cis-1,2 (meso)	trans-1,3 (dl)	cis-1,3 (meso)	1,1 (inactive)

23.7 tertiary : primary $= \dfrac{1}{\frac{1}{9}} \times \dfrac{1}{2} = \dfrac{9}{2} = 4.5 : 1$

23.8

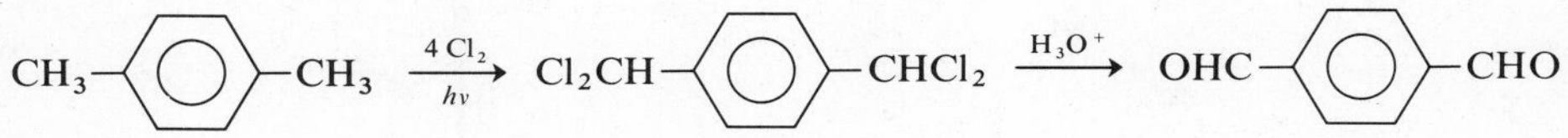

$+ 4\,HCl$

23.9 Ethylcyclobutane will react at lower temperature because it has a much higher internal energy (strain energy) than cyclohexane.

CHAPTER 24

24.1 (a) H_2NNH_2, KOH, diethylene glycol, heat; *or* Zn-Hg, HCl; *or* EtSH, H^+ then Raney Ni.

(b) $HOCH_2CH_2OH$, H^+, remove water as azeotrope.

(c) $RCH_2OH \xrightarrow{HBr} RCH_2Br \xrightarrow{Mg} RCH_2MgBr \xrightarrow{CH_2=O} RCH_2CH_2OMgBr$

$RCH_2Br \xrightarrow{NaCN} RCH_2CN$

$RCH_2CH_2OMgBr \xrightarrow[]{H_3O^+} RCH_2CH_2OH$

$RCH_2CN \xrightarrow[H_2O]{EtOH,} RCH_2COOEt \xrightarrow{LiAlH_4} (RCH_2CH_2O)_4\bar{Al} \xrightarrow{H_3O^+}$ (to RCH_2CH_2OH)

(d) $RCOOH \xrightarrow[SOCl_2]{PCl_5 \text{ or}} RCOCl \xrightarrow{xs\ CH_2N_2} RCOCHN_2 \xrightarrow[H_2O]{Ag^\circ} RCH_2COOH$

(e) $RCH_2OH \xrightarrow{HBr} RCH_2Br \xrightarrow{Mg} RCH_2MgBr \xrightarrow[\text{then } H_3O^+]{CH_2-CH_2 \text{ (epoxide)}} RCH_2CH_2CH_2OH$

$RCH_2Br \xrightarrow{NaCH(COOEt)_2} RCH_2CH(CO_2Et)_2 \xrightarrow[(-CO_2)]{H_3O^+} RCH_2CH_2COOH \xrightarrow[\text{then } H_3O^+]{LiAlH_4,} RCH_2CH_2CH_2OH$

(f) $RNH_2 + HCHO \xrightarrow{HCOOH} RN(CH_3)_2$

(g) $RCOOH + CH_3OH \xrightarrow{H^+} RCOOCH_3 + H_2O;\ or$
$RCOOH + CH_2N_2 \rightarrow RCOOCH_3 + N_2$

(h) $RCONH_2 \xrightarrow[or\ H_3O^+]{^-OH/H_2O} RCOOH;\ or\ RCONH_2 + HNO_2 \rightarrow RCOOH$

(i) $RCOOH \xrightarrow[or\ PCl_3]{SOCl_2} RCOCl \xrightarrow{NH_3} RCONH_2 \xrightarrow{SOCl_2} RC\equiv N$

(j) $RCON(CH_3)_2 + R'MgBr \xrightarrow[temp]{low} \xrightarrow{H_3O^+} R-\underset{O}{\underset{\|}{C}}-R'$

(k) $R-C\equiv C^-Na^+ \xrightarrow{R'Br} R-C\equiv C-R'$

24.3 (a) $(CH_3)_2CHCHO + H_2NOH \cdot HCl \xrightarrow{NaOAc} (CH_3)_2CHCH=NOH$

$(CH_3)_2CHCH=NOH \xrightarrow[\substack{or\ Na,\ ROH \\ or\ H_2,\ Pd}]{LiAlH_4} (CH_3)_2CHCH_2NH_2$

Other ways possible

(b)

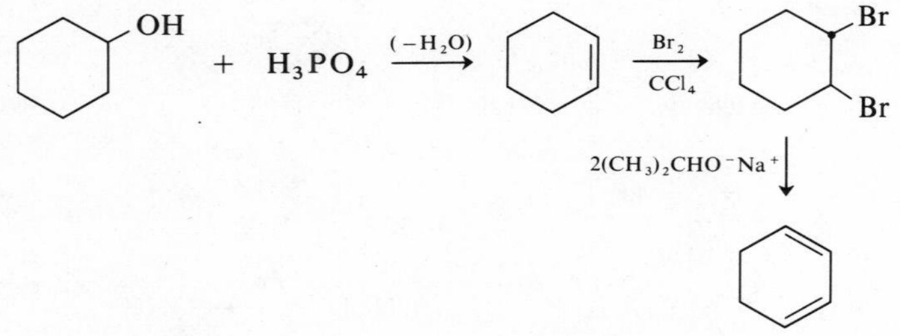

$2(CH_3)_2CHO^-Na^+$

(c)

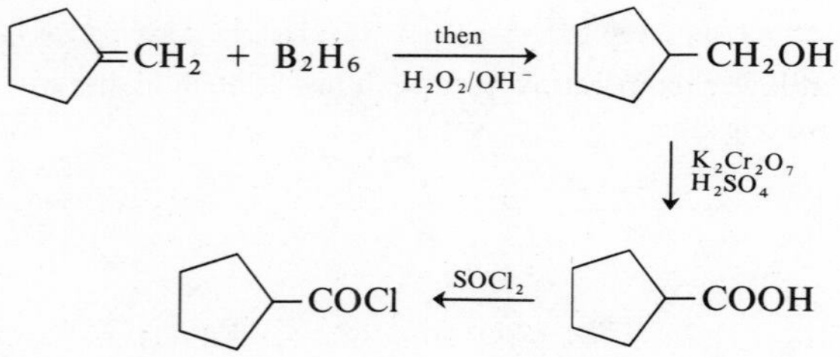

24.4 (a) $\phi CH_2OH \xrightarrow{MnO_2} \phi CHO \xrightarrow[H_2O,\ H^+]{NaCN} \phi \underset{OH}{CHCN} \xrightarrow{H_3O^+} \phi \underset{OH}{CHCOOH}$

(b) $(CH_3)_2CHOH \xrightarrow{PBr_3} (CH_3)_2CHBr \xrightarrow{Mg} (CH_3)_2CHMgBr \xrightarrow[\substack{\text{then} \\ H_3O^+}]{CO_2}$

$$(CH_3)_2CHCOOH$$

(c)

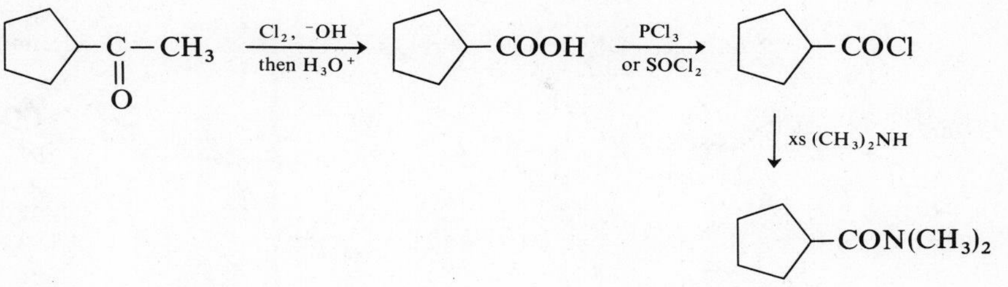

24.5 (a)

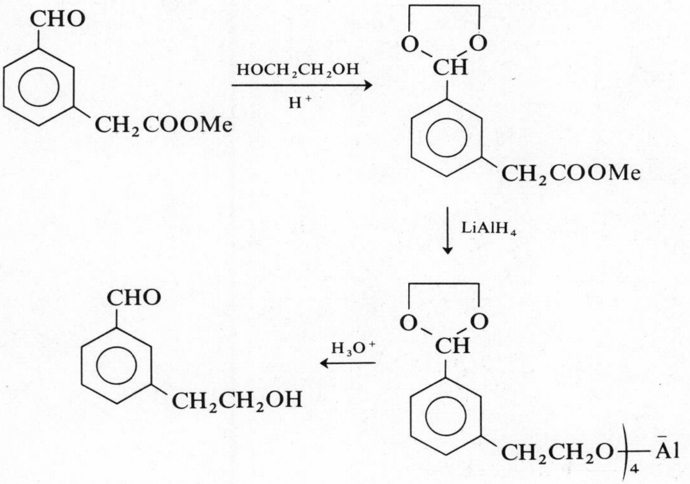

(b)

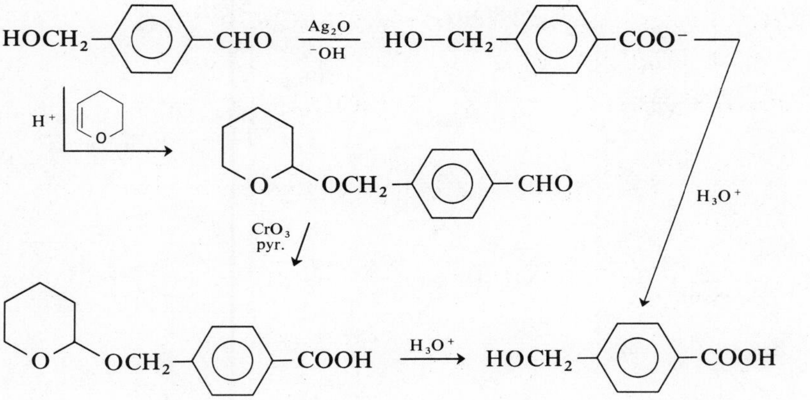

(c) Protect aldehyde via ethylene ketal, oxidize $-CH_2OH$ to $-COOH$ with $KMnO_4$, ^-OH, and remove protecting group with H_3O^+.

(d)

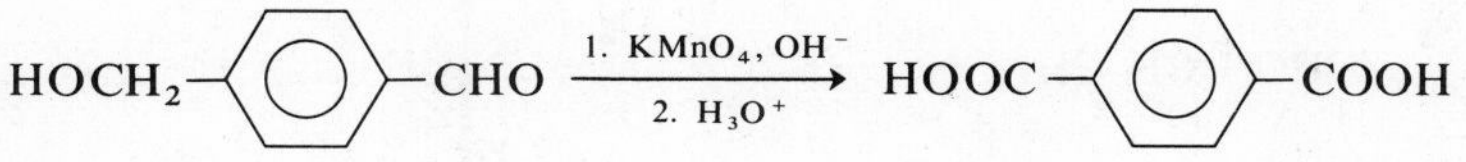

24.6 (a)

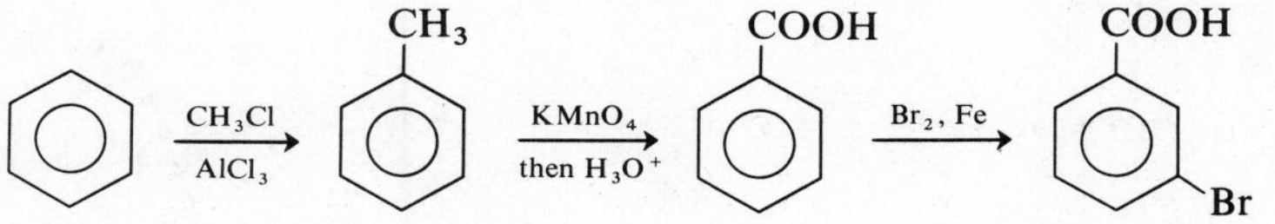

(b)

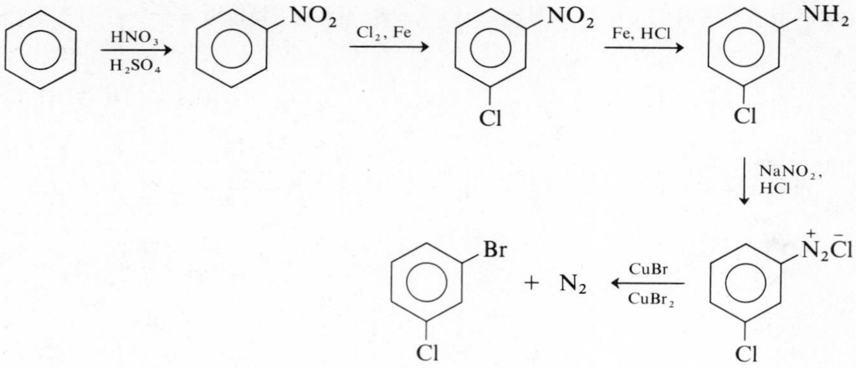

HNO₃
H₂SO₄
NO₂
Cl₂, Fe
NO₂
Cl
Fe, HCl
NH₂
Cl
NaNO₂,
HCl
N₂Cl
Cl
CuBr
CuBr₂
+ N₂
Br
Cl

(c)

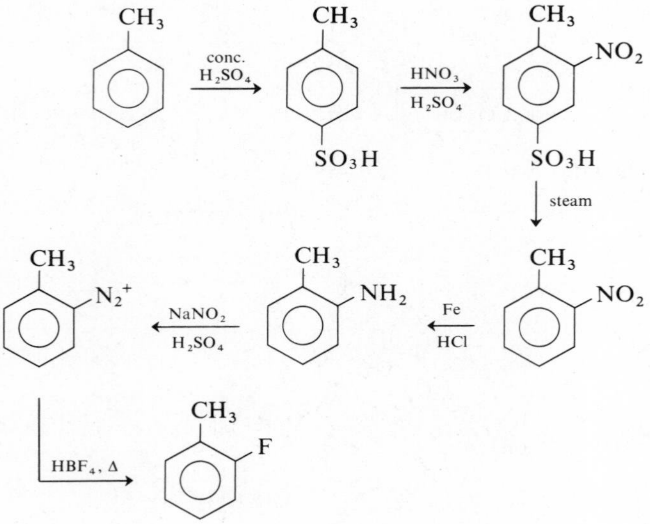

CH₃
conc.
H₂SO₄
CH₃
SO₃H
HNO₃
H₂SO₄
CH₃
NO₂
SO₃H
steam
CH₃
NO₂
Fe
HCl
CH₃
NH₂
NaNO₂
H₂SO₄
CH₃
N₂⁺
HBF₄, Δ
CH₃
F

(d)

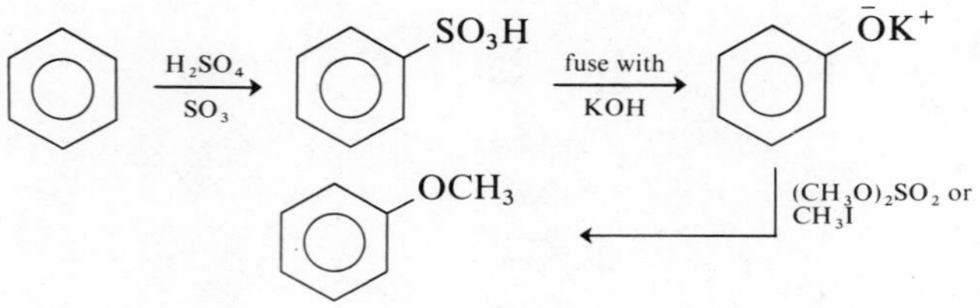

H₂SO₄
SO₃
SO₃H
fuse with
KOH
OK⁺
(CH₃O)₂SO₂ or
CH₃I
OCH₃

(e)

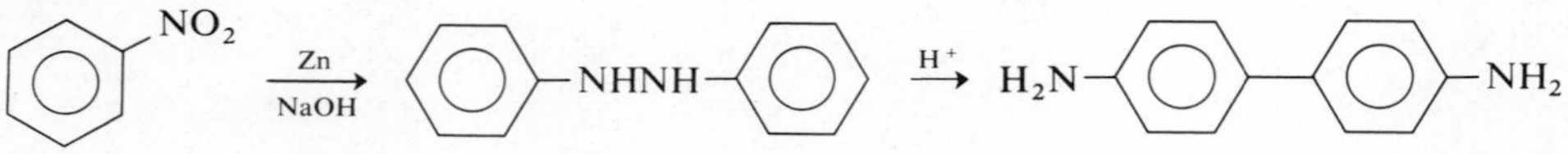

NO₂
Zn
NaOH
NHNH
H⁺
H₂N
NH₂

(f)

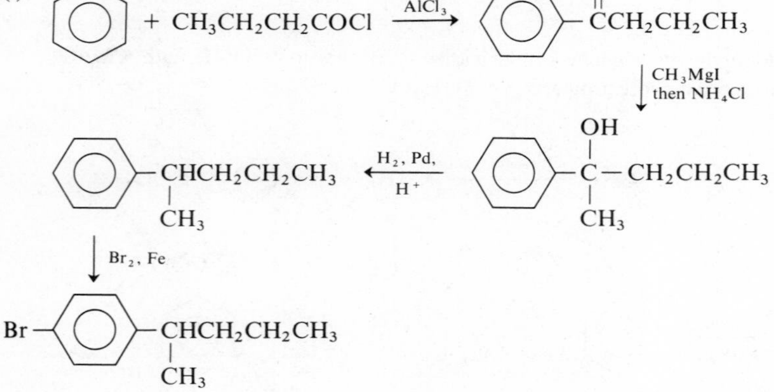

+ CH₃CH₂CH₂COCl
AlCl₃
O
CCH₂CH₂CH₃
CH₃MgI
then NH₄Cl
OH
C − CH₂CH₂CH₃
CH₃
H₂, Pd,
H⁺
CHCH₂CH₂CH₃
CH₃
Br₂, Fe
Br
CHCH₂CH₂CH₃
CH₃

24.7 (a) $\phi CH_3 \xrightarrow{Br_2,\ h\nu} \phi CH_2Br + HC\equiv CNa \rightarrow \phi CH_2C\equiv CH \xrightarrow{NaNH_2} \phi CH_2C\equiv CNa$

$$\downarrow CH_3Br$$

$$\phi CH_2C\equiv CCH_3$$

$CH_3OH \xrightarrow{HBr} CH_3Br$

(b) $CH_2(COOEt)_2 \xrightarrow{NaOEt} NaCH(COOEt)_2 \xrightarrow{(CH_3)_2CHCH_2Br}$

$(CH_3)_2CHCH_2\underset{\underset{CH_3}{|}}{C}(CO_2Et)_2 \xleftarrow[\text{2. } CH_3I]{\text{1. NaOEt}} (CH_3)_2CHCH_2CH(COOEt)_2$

$$\xrightarrow[\text{2. } H_3O^+]{\text{1. } H_2O,\ OH^-} (CH_3)_2CHCH_2\underset{\underset{CH_3}{|}}{C}HCOOH$$

24.7 (c) $CH_3\overset{\overset{O}{\|}}{C}CH_2CO_2Et \xrightarrow{NaOEt} CH_3\overset{\overset{O}{\|}}{C}CHNaCOOEt \longrightarrow$

$(CH_3)_2CHCH_2\overset{\overset{O}{\|}}{C}CH_3 \xleftarrow[\text{2. } H_3O^+]{\text{1. dil }^-OH} CH_3\overset{\overset{O}{\|}}{C}-\underset{\underset{CH(CH_3)_2}{|}}{C}HCOOEt$ $\quad \xleftarrow{(CH_3)_2CHBr}$

CHAPTER 26

26.1 (a) $CH_3SH + \phi\overset{\overset{O}{\|}}{C}\diagdown_{Cl} \rightarrow CH_3\overset{+}{\underset{\underset{H}{|}}{S}}-\overset{\overset{O}{\|}}{C}-\phi Cl^- \xrightarrow{base} CH_3S\overset{\overset{O}{\|}}{C}\phi$

(b) $(CH_3)_2C=O + H^+ \rightleftharpoons (CH_3)_2C=\overset{+}{O}H \xrightarrow{EtSH} (CH_3)_2\underset{\underset{+}{\underset{HSEt}{|}}}{C}-OH$

$$\Updownarrow$$

$\xrightarrow{EtSH} (CH_3)_2\overset{+}{C}-SEt + H_2O \leftarrow (CH_3)_2\underset{\underset{SEt}{|}}{C}-\overset{+}{O}H_2$

$(CH_3)_2\underset{\underset{+}{\underset{HSEt}{|}}}{C}-SEt \xrightarrow{-H^+} (CH_3)_2C(SEt)_2$

(c) $\phi CH_2SH + NaOH \rightarrow \phi CH_2S^-Na^+ \xrightarrow{CH_3-I} \phi CH_2SCH_3$
$\qquad\qquad\qquad\qquad\qquad + H_2O$

26.2 $R-\ddot{S}-H + I \frown I \rightarrow R-\underset{\underset{H}{|}}{\overset{+}{S}}-I + I^- \rightarrow R-S \frown I \cdot \xrightarrow{R-\ddot{S}H} R-S-S-R + HI$
$\qquad\qquad\qquad\qquad\qquad\qquad\qquad\qquad + HI$

26.3

$CH_2=\!\!\bigcirc\!\!-OH \xrightarrow[\text{pyridine}]{ArSO_2Cl} CH_2=\!\!\bigcirc\!\!-OSO_2Ar$

$$\downarrow CH_3S^-Na^+$$

$$CH_2=\!\!\bigcirc\!\!-SCH_3 + ArSO_3^-Na^+$$

26.4 $(CH_3)_3CCH{=}CH_2 + CH_3COSH \xrightarrow{h\nu} (CH_3)_3CCH_2CH_2SCCH_3$

$\underset{O}{\overset{\|}{}}$

$\downarrow$ 1. NaOH
2. H_3O^+
3. CH_2O, H^+

$[(CH_3)_3CCH_2CH_2S]_2CH_2$

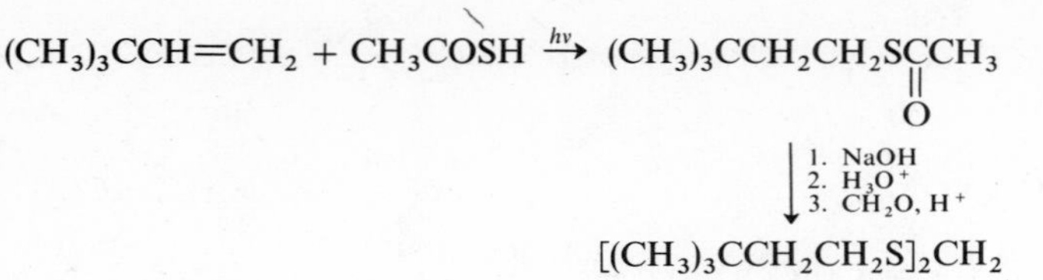

CHAPTER 27

27.1

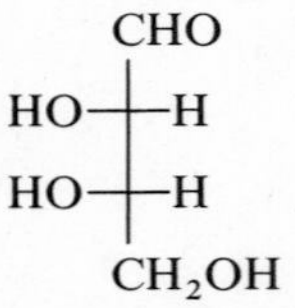

CHO
HO—H
HO—H
CH₂OH

L-Erythrose

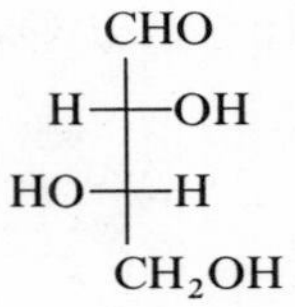

CHO
H—OH
HO—H
CH₂OH

L-Threose

27.2

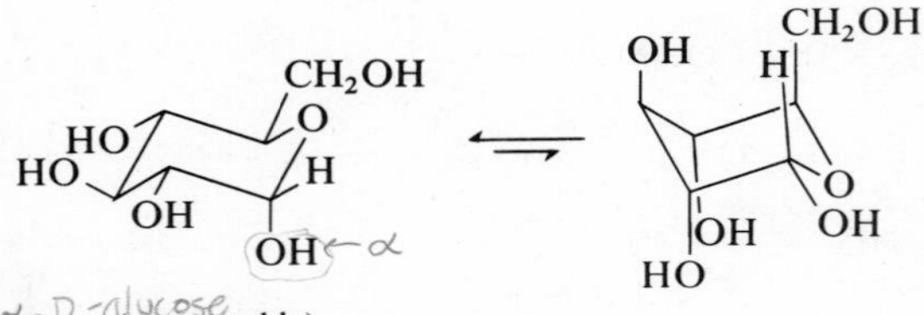

α-D-glucose (most stable)

27.3 (a)

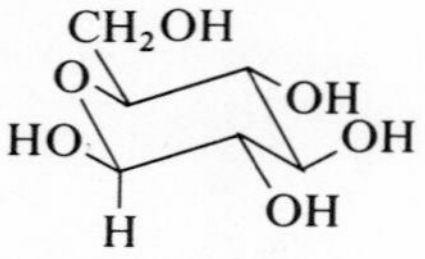

β-L-Glucopyranose

(b)

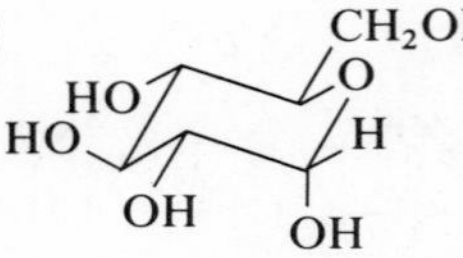

α-D-Glucopyranose

(c)

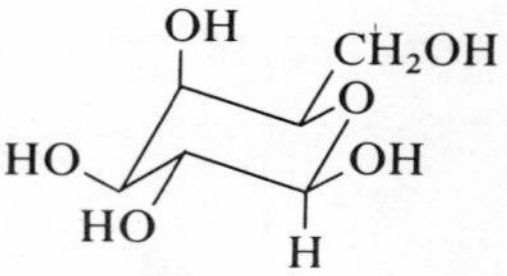

β-D-Galactopyranose

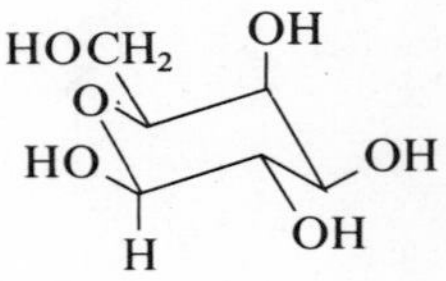

27.4 The ketal of the carbohydrate is cyclic and the entropy for the reaction proceeding to the right is positive. See also Exercises 19.3.

27.5 (a) No formic acid, no formaldehyde   (b) One mole of formic acid, no formaldehyde

27.6 Allose,   CHO , would give a *meso* (optically inactive) glycitol,   CH₂OH

H—OH
H—OH
H—OH
H—OH
CH₂OH

H—OH
H—OH
H—OH
H—OH
CH₂OH

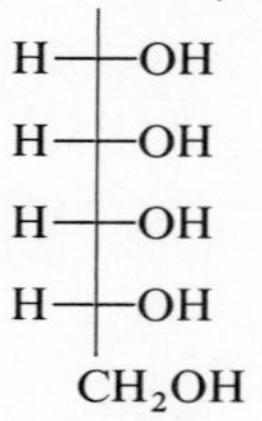

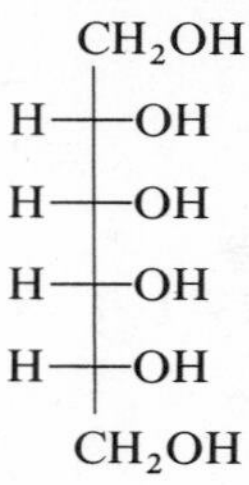

and galactose,   CHO , also gives a *meso* glycitol,   CH₂OH

H—OH
HO—H
HO—H
H—OH
CH₂OH

H—OH
HO—H
HO—H
H—OH
CH₂OH

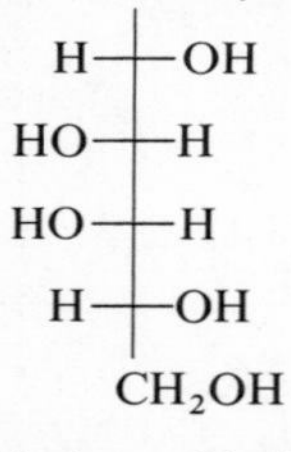

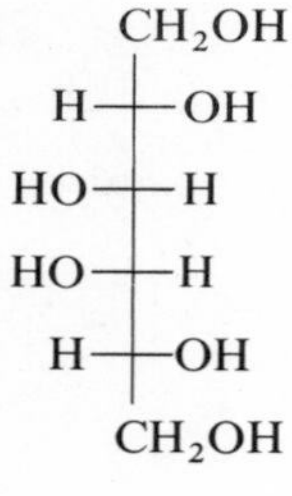

The other sorbitols would all be optically active.

CHAPTER 28

28.1

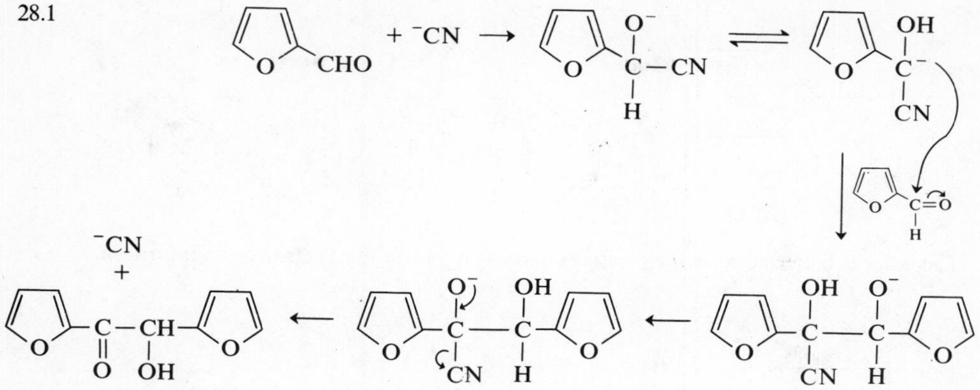

28.2

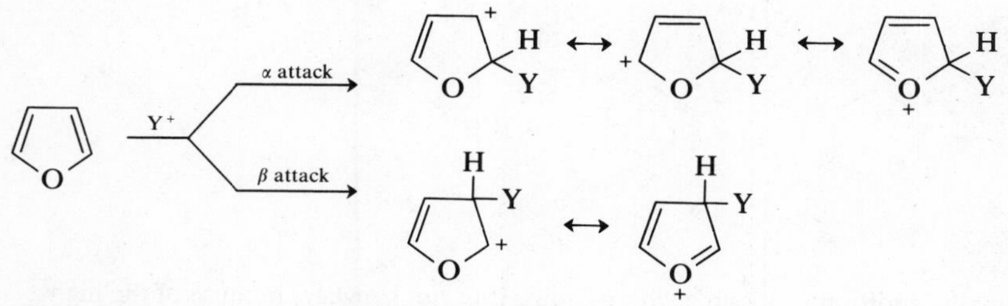

There is better delocalization from α attack.

28.3

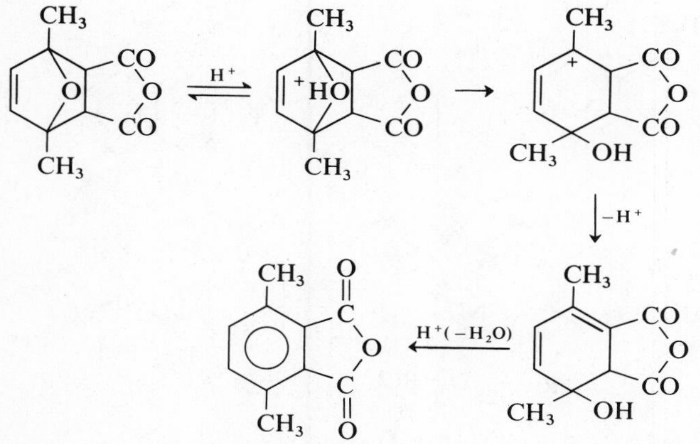

28.4 Nmr—the minor component has three low-field (C=C—H) protons and one O—H proton—the major component shows two C=C—H protons and two relatively high field protons (–CH₂–).

28.5

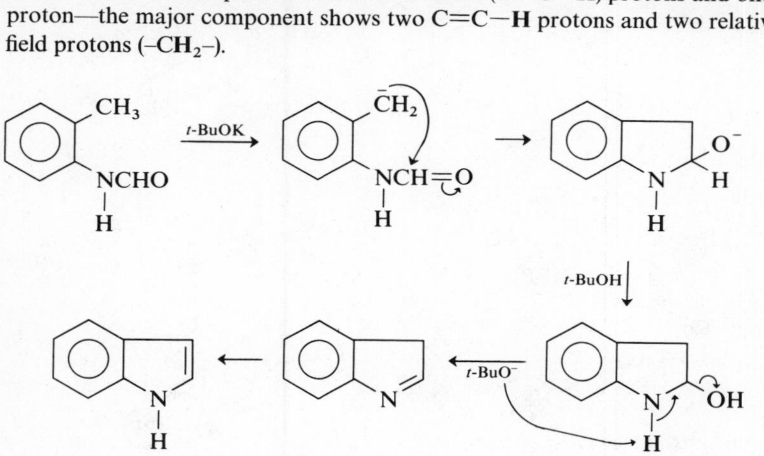

28.6

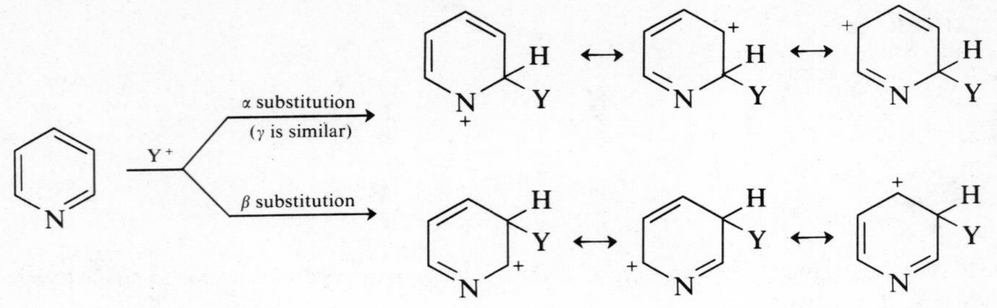

The latter is better because the positive charge is never on the electronegative nitrogen.

28.7

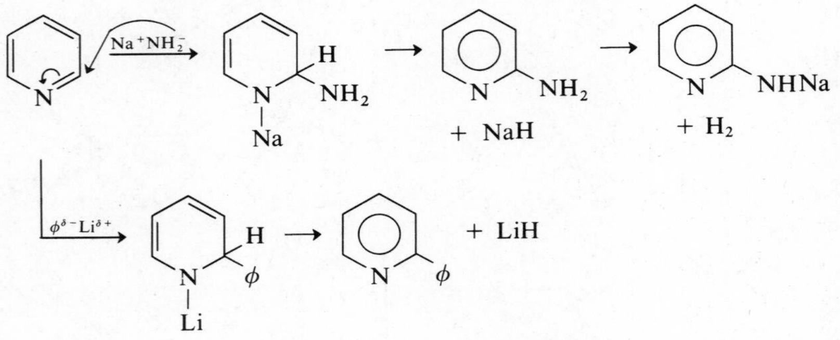

Nucleophilic addition is possible with pyridine (but not benzene) because of the high electronegativity of sp^2 nitrogen.

28.8   (a)   (b) CH$_3$ (c)

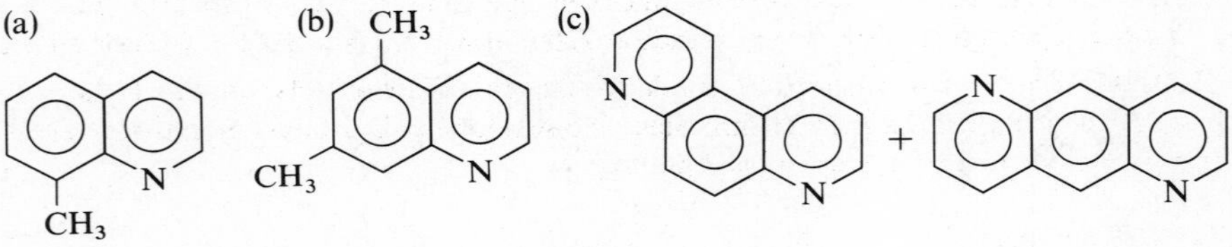

28.9

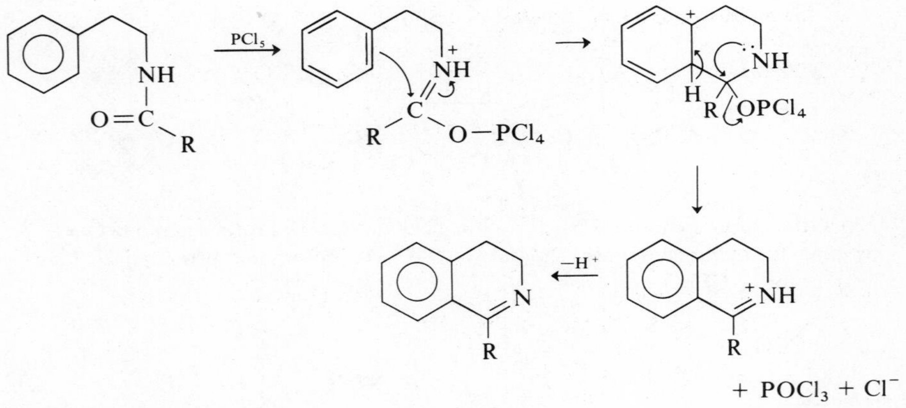

CHAPTER 30

30.1

Geranyl pyrophosphate
(page 785)

(PP)—OH +   Linalool

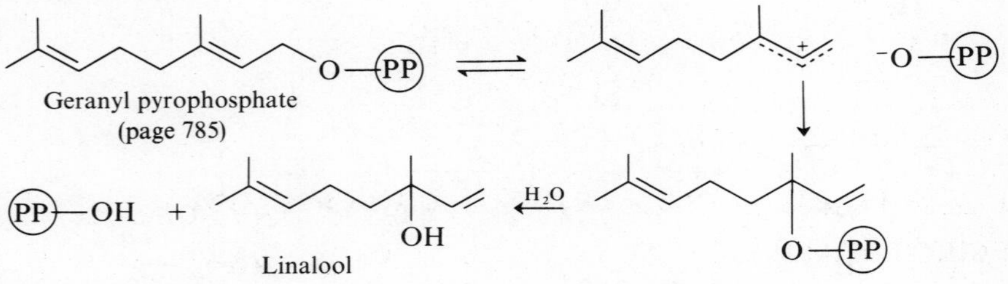

30.2

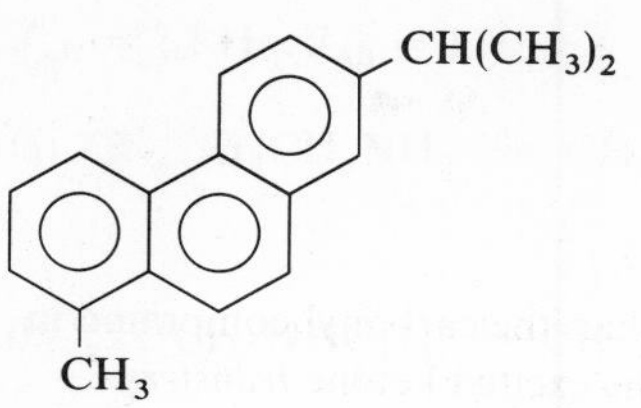

Note that the angular methyl group and the carboxylic acid group of abietic acid are *lost* upon dehydrogenation.

30.3   2 moles of $CH_3C(CH_2)_3C$———C—CHO, 4 CH_3C—CHO, 4 OHC—CHO

30.4

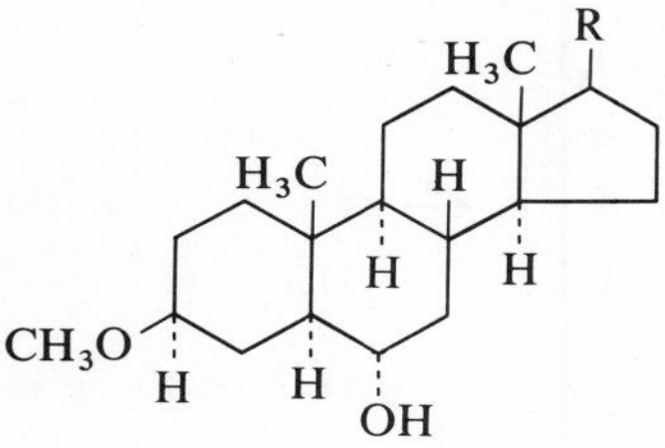

CHAPTER 31

31.2   Azobenzene, ϕ—$\ddot{N}$=$\ddot{N}$—ϕ (trans and cis) has the –$\ddot{N}$=$\ddot{N}$– chromophore conjugated to both aromatic rings. The long-wavelength absorption is $n \rightarrow \pi*$ at 440 nm ($\varepsilon \sim 500$) giving rise to the color, and $\pi \rightarrow \pi*$ bands at 320 and 230 nm ($\varepsilon > 10^4$). Hydrazobenzene, $\phi\ddot{N}H\ddot{N}H\phi$, should have a spectrum similar to that of aniline ($\phi\ddot{N}H_2$) for which the longest-wavelength band is at 280 nm, since the two lone-pair orbitals on nitrogen are approximately at right angles to one another.

31.3   217 nm (base)
         20 nm (four alkyl groups)
          5 nm (exocyclic double bond)
        _____
    λ_{max}^{calcd} 242 nm

31.4   215 nm (base)
                12 nm (one β-alkyl group)

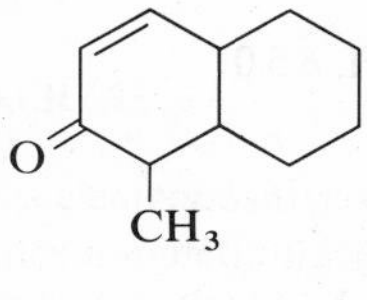

    (A) =   _____

       λ_{max}^{calcd} 227 nm ; λ_{max}^{obs} 225 nm

    If the compound had been 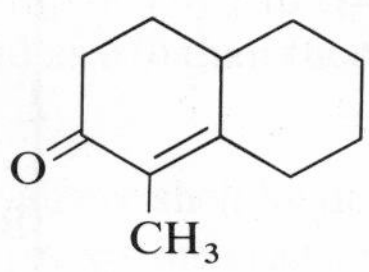   , $\lambda_{max}^{calcd} = 254$ nm

31.5   (a)

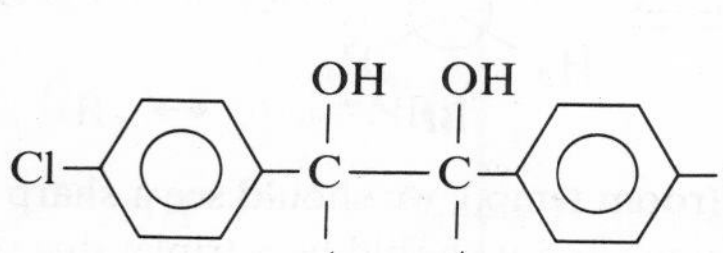

        threo + *erythro*

    (b) △ + CO + CH_2=C=O + CH_2=CH_2 + CH_2=$CHCH_2CHO$

    (c) CH_3CH=$CH(CH_2)_3CHO$

33.4 $(CH_3CH_2O)_3P + CH_3CH_2Br \rightarrow$

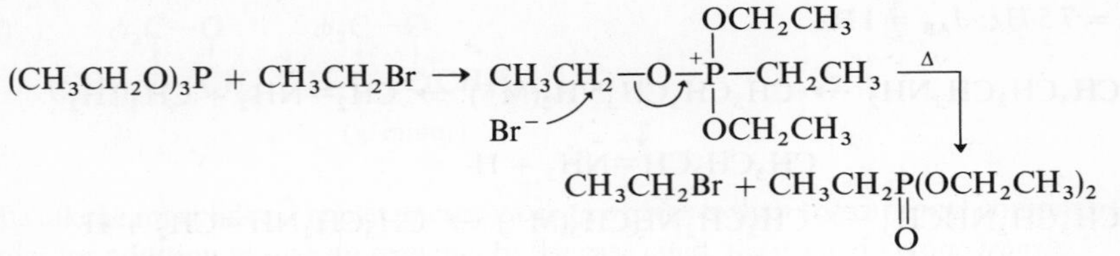

The overall reaction is an isomerization.

33.5 $(EtO)_3P + BrCH_2CH_2Br \rightarrow$

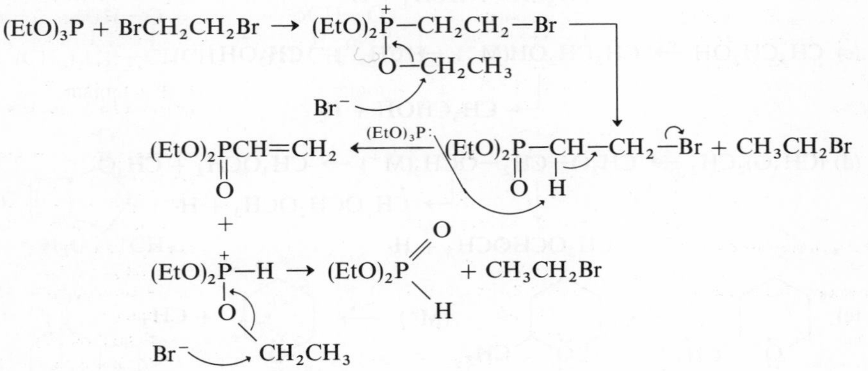

33.6   (S)-2-Bromobutane

CHAPTER 34

34.1   (a) and $CH_2(COOEt)_2$

(b) and $C_6H_5CH(COOEt)_2$

(c) $C_6H_5CH=C(COOEt)_2 + {}^-CN$; then hydrolysis and decarboxylation accompanies hydrolysis of the –CN group to –COOH

34.2

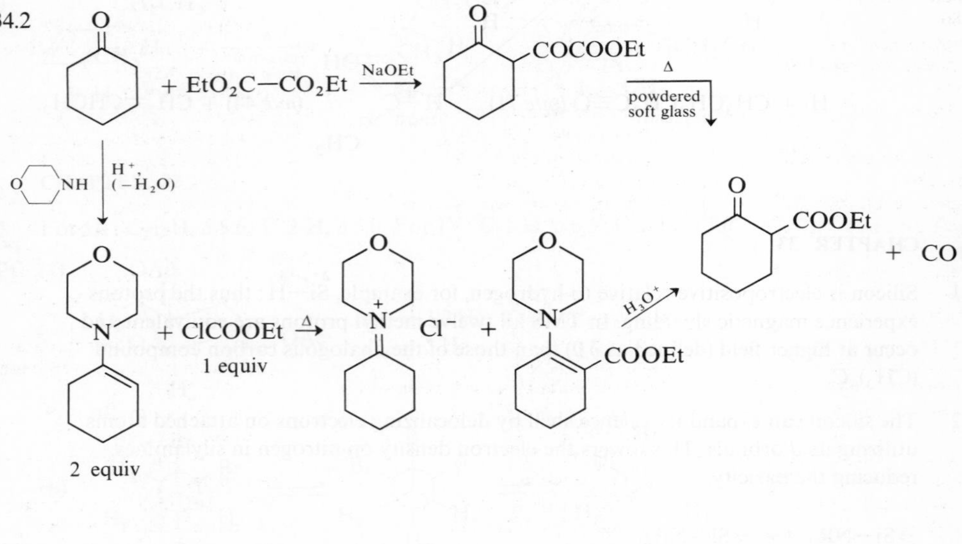

INDEX